FAST REACTOR TECHNOLOGY:
Plant Design

FAST REACTOR TECHNOLOGY:
Plant Design

John G. Yevick, Editor

A. Amorosi, Associate Editor

Prepared under the auspices of the
United States Atomic Energy Commission
Division of Technical Information

THE M.I.T. PRESS
Massachusetts Institute of Technology
Cambridge, Massachusetts and London, England

Foreword

The significance of fast reactors was recognized very early in the development of nuclear energy. Concerned with the long-range availability of naturally-occurring fissionable fuel, Fermi and Zinn, in the spring of 1944, had discussed the possibility of building a fast-neutron breeder reactor. The twenty-two years of slow but determined development of the fast breeder laid the foundation for the present intensive effort. The increasing demands upon the world's uranium resources, brought about by increasing world-wide acceptance of nuclear reactors, provide compelling reasons for this intensive development of economical, safe, and reliable fast reactors. The rapid evolution of this reactor type requires an increasing engineering knowledge, based on work done to date.

I think it indeed fortunate that this book, which records a considerable degree of accumulated knowledge, is being published at this time to provide the necessary guideposts during the present period of accelerating fast reactor research and development.

Glenn T. Seaborg

Chairman
U.S. Atomic Energy Commission

Preface

The development of atomic energy in the little over two decades between the discovery of fission in 1939 and the application of this discovery in the production of competitive electrical energy is an example of the compression in time possible today to develop an entirely new technology. This acceleration is a tribute to man's ability to apply accumulated technological resources to rapid program development. These resources are now needed to develop advanced means of utilizing atomic fission to meet long-term objectives.

Considering the immediate and near-future problem of insufficient demand for uranium to absorb the world's uranium output, it is difficult to realize that the tremendous energy demands of the future will require effective use of this world resource to avoid early depletion of economic ore bodies. An increasing world effort to develop fast reactor technology is needed as one means of increasing uranium utilization. It is to further aid this development that the United States Atomic Energy Commisssion requested the Atomic Power Development Associates to prepare this book to bring together, in one place, the technology of not only the Enrico Fermi Atomic Power Plant designed by APDA but also the United States experimental projects Clementine, EBR-I, EBR-II, LAMPRE-I, the Russian reactor BR-5, and the British fast reactor at Dounreay. The technology of the French reactor Rapsodie, now under construction, and other proposed U. S. plants is also included.

As is true for any technical area having such intensive and worldwide interest, the technology of fast reactors rapidly changes as a result of increasing development effort. A book written during this developmental period is not complete and current because of new developments. It is necessary, though, to consolidate the available information obtained over a 15-year period for use in the immediate crucial phase of fast reactor design. The book should be valuable to all interested in the design of fast reactors since it forms a base of common understanding and knowledge necessary for further development.

The primary audience for which this book was prepared is the fast reactor designer. It was recognized, however, that much of the information is not unique to fast reactors; thus the student of nuclear engineering or other reactor designers will find considerable information in this book applicable to other reactors.

The plan of the book is to discuss completely in each chapter one specific aspect of fast reactor design. Basic considerations are presented together with appropriate examples. By this means it was possible for each chapter to be written by an expert in the particular subject matter of the chapter, and the reader need study only the particular chapter of interest to obtain information. The decision to omit reactor fuel and core design, including materials and physics aspects, was made because an adequate discussion of fuel and core design would require a separate book.

The assistance and cooperation of a large number of people made this book possible. The authors are listed at the head of each chapter, and to each I express my appreciation for his work. My gratitude goes also to those many contributors who assisted the authors. They are listed by chapter in the front of the book. A. Amorosi, Technical Director of Atomic Power Development Associates and the Associate Editor of this book, was a constant source of inspiration and was instrumental in developing the book into its present form. It is not possible to list all individuals who aided in this work, particularly the USAEC reviewers who have remained anonymous but whose constructive criticisms have made the book more effective.

The editorial services of Marian C. Fox, Editorial Branch, Division of Technical Information Extension, USAEC, Oak Ridge, are gratefully acknowledged. Wert J. Pearson and the staff of the Scientific Illustration Section, DTI Extension, Oak Ridge, provided finished art, which makes the reading material more understandable. The services of W. O. Wright, formerly of APDA, in preparing the draft artwork and the editorial services of Peter Helmers of the Detroit Edison Company and of Anne C. Mansfield of APDA are also acknowledged.

This book could not have been possible without the patience and the understanding help given by James D. Cape and his aides of the USAEC Division of Technical Information and by Glen W. Wensch of the USAEC Division of Reactor Development and Technology.

Above all, the services of Josephine Stemelo, my factotum, and her staff were invaluable in the preparation of the book. Josephine's unfailing patience through many trying periods and her tireless attention to the myriad of details contributed greatly to the finished product.

J. G. Yevick

March 1966
Washington, D. C.

vii

List of Contributors*

Chapter 1—Introduction to Fast Reactors

A. Amorosi
  Atomic Power Development Associates, Inc.
  Detroit, Michigan
J. R. Dietrich
  Combustion Engineering
  Windsor, Connecticut
J. De Felice
  Nuclear Technology Corporation
  White Plains, New York
Anne C. Mansfield
  Atomic Power Development Associates, Inc.
  Detroit, Michigan
J. B. Nims
  Atomic Power Development Associates, Inc.
  Detroit, Michigan
R. G. Palmer
  United Kingdom Atomic Energy Authority
A. A. Shoudy
  Atomic Power Development Associates, Inc.
  Detroit, Michigan
W. H. Zinn
  Combustion Engineering
  Windsor, Connecticut

Chapter 2—Coolant Properties, Heat Transfer, and Fluid Flow of Liquid Metals

F. R. Beyer
  Atomics International, Canoga Park, California
  Formerly with Atomic Power Development Associates, Inc.
  Detroit, Michigan
C. F. Bonilla
  Columbia University
  New York, New York
J. S. Busch
  Kaiser Engineers, Oakland, California
  Formerly with Atomic Power Development Associates, Inc.
  Detroit, Michigan
W. L. Chase
  Atomic Power Development Associates, Inc.
  Detroit, Michigan

Evalene Di Giorgio
  Formerly with Atomic Power Development Associates, Inc.
  Detroit, Michigan
J. J. Edwards
  Atomic Power Development Associates, Inc.
  Detroit, Michigan
D. M. Green
  Atomic Power Development Associates, Inc.
  Detroit, Michigan
B. F. Hernady
  Atomic Power Development Associates, Inc.
  Detroit, Michigan
E. F. Hill
  Atomic Power Development Associates, Inc.
  Detroit, Michigan
P. R. Huebotter
  Atomic Power Development Associates, Inc.
  Detroit, Michigan
L. R. Kovac
  Atomic Power Development Associates, Inc.
  Detroit, Michigan
E. C. Kovacic
  Atomic Power Development Associates, Inc.
  Detroit, Michigan
C. R. Moore
  Nuclear Fuel Services, Inc., Washington, D. C.
  Formerly with Atomic Power Development Associates, Inc.
  Detroit, Michigan
J. Morelle
  Belgonucleaire, Brussels, Belgium
R. E. Mueller
  Atomic Power Development Associates, Inc.
  Detroit, Michigan
G. O'Neil
  General Electric Company
  San Jose, California

Chapter 3—Structural Analysis

F. R. Beyer
  Atomics International, Canoga Park, California
  Formerly with Atomic Power Development Associates, Inc.
  Detroit, Michigan

---

*Other than authors.

ix

W. Pollington
  Allstates Design and Development Company, Inc.
  Cincinnati, Ohio
  Formerly with Atomic Power Development Associates, Inc.
  Detroit, Michigan

Chapter 4—Heat-transport Systems

J. Bucki
  Atomic Power Development Associates, Inc.
  Detroit, Michigan
R. Balsbaugh
  Wisconsin Electric Power Company
  Milwaukee, Wisconsin
G. Freund
  Western Nuclear Corporation
  Idaho Falls, Idaho
G. Goldberg
  The Budd Company, Detroit, Michigan
  Formerly with Atomic Power Development Associates, Inc.
  Detroit, Michigan
P. S. Lindsey
  Atomic Power Development Associates, Inc.
  Detroit, Michigan
J. J. Morabito
  United States Atomic Energy Commission, Washington, D. C.
  Formerly with Atomic Power Development Associates, Inc.
  Detroit, Michigan
H. O. Muenchow
  Atomic Power Development Associates, Inc.
  Detroit, Michigan
T. P. Ross
  Atomic Power Development Associates, Inc.
  Detroit, Michigan
R. B. Shumaker
  Cleveland Electric Illuminating Company
  Cleveland, Ohio
R. C. Williams
  Bechtel Corporation, Washington, D. C.
  Formerly with Atomic Power Development Associates, Inc.
  Detroit, Michigan

Chapter 6—Plant Structures, Containment Design, and Site Criteria

W. B. Murray
  The Cincinnati Gas and Electric Company
  Cincinnati, Ohio

Chapter 7—Fuel Handling

J. W. Hess
  Atomic Power Development Associates, Inc.
  Detroit, Michigan
C. R. Nash
  Commonwealth Associates, Inc.
  Jackson, Michigan
R. Palazzolo
  NuTec Engineering Corporation
  Detroit, Michigan

S. Tjepkema
  Commonwealth Associates, Inc.
  Jackson, Michigan

Chapter 8—Shielding

J. Adamson
  United Kingdom Atomic Energy Authority
R. J. Beaudry
  Atomic Power Development Associates, Inc.
  Detroit, Michigan
E. P. Blizard (deceased)
  Oak Ridge National Laboratory, Oak Ridge
  Tennessee
W. F. Chaltron
  Niagara Mohawk Power Corporation, Buffalo
  New York
  Formerly with Atomic Power Development Associates, Inc.
  Detroit, Michigan
M. Grotenhuis
  Argonne National Laboratory
  Argonne, Illinois
R. F. Mantey
  Philadelphia Electric Company
  Philadelphia, Pennsylvania
R. E. Mueller
  Atomic Power Development Associates, Inc.
  Detroit, Michigan
S. K. Penny
  Oak Ridge National Laboratory, Oak Ridge
  Tennessee
D. Smith
  United Kingdom Atomic Energy Authority
K. Spinney (deceased)
  United Kingdom Atomic Energy Authority
S. Wolfson
  Wayne State University
  Detroit, Michigan

Chapter 9—Plant Instrumentation and Control

K. W. Barker
  Allison Division, General Motors
  Indianapolis, Indiana
C. H. Clarridge
  Rochester Instrument Systems
  Rochester, New York
M. Egleme
  Belgonucleaire, Brussels, Belgium
J. Levine
  The Detroit Edison Company
  Detroit, Michigan
H. D. Phillips
  Niagara Mohawk Power Corporation
  Buffalo, New York
G. H. Reicks
  Atomic Power Development Associates, Inc.
  Detroit, Michigan
H. E. Rokeberg
  Atomic Power Development Associates, Inc.
  Detroit, Michigan
R. A. Thomas
  Southern Services, Inc.
  Birmingham, Alabama

Chapter 10—Economics

C. W. Bary
  Consultant; formerly with Philadelphia Electric
    Company
  Philadelphia, Pennsylvania
R. F. Brower
  Retired; formerly with Consolidated Edison
    Company
  New York, New York
D. E. Hart
  The Detroit Edison Company
  Detroit, Michigan
W. B. Lewis
  Atomic Energy of Canada Limited
  Chalk River, Ontario, Canada

V. Lomuller
  Atomic Power Development Associates, Inc.
  Detroit, Michigan
E. W. Morehouse
  Consultant; formerly with General Public Util-
    ities Corporation
  New York, New York

Chapter 11—Description of Fast Reactors

L. P. Vautrey
  Commissariat a l'Energie Atomique
  France
C. P. Zaleski
  Commissariat a l'Energie Atomique
  France

Contents

Chapter 8   Shielding
By H. Eugene Hungerford

CHAPTER 1

Introduction to Fast Reactors

GLEN W. WENSCH
Division of Reactor Development
U. S. Atomic Energy Commission
Germantown, Maryland

Contents

The discovery of the fission process and the accompanying release of a large amount of energy resulted from the work of many investigators. Early investigators realized that, when fission occured, some neutrons were lost through extraneous absorption and leakage while others were used to sustain the chain reaction. They soon recognized the necessity of having sufficient neutrons for converting fertile atoms into fuel, preferably to the extent of making up for the fuel destroyed. This process is known as breeding.

The breeding process is important because U^{235}, which is the only nuclear fuel found in nature, is relatively scarce in its economically minable form; it is only slightly more abundant than fossil fuels. The processes of fission and absorption and, hence, breeding are influenced by the velocity or energy of the neutrons. It is important therefore to understand what type of reactor and what operating conditions give the best chance for achieving breeding. The fast-neutron energy reactor has a greater potential for breeding than the thermal (slow-neutron energy) reactor, particularly for the U^{238} cycle. For this reason the fast reactor has attracted interest, especially with respect to the long-range utilization of nuclear fuels.

So that the reader will have a perspective from which to view the fast reactor, this chapter contains a brief history of its development to date. It reviews some of the chief characteristics of this type of reactor and the reasons for the high breeding-ratio potential of the fast reactor. Also presented are a general discussion of safety considerations, a review of fuel-element design, and a brief summary of heat-transport problems with special reference to coolant-handling problems.

1.1 History of Fast Reactor Development

1.1.1 UNDERSTANDING THE NUCLEUS: 1803 to 1939

From a practical viewpoint, the history of nuclear reactors of any type began in January 1939 when the Danish scientist Niels Bohr arrived in the United States with news of the discovery of the nuclear fission of uranium. As is true of all of today's nuclear technology, however, nuclear power reactors have resulted from many discoveries by many scientists over a period of many years, some of which are reviewed briefly.

Dalton's enunciation of the atomic theory in 1803 is a good starting point although the idea in a philosophical form goes back to Greek philosophy. Samuel Glasstone [1] summarizes Dalton's role in this way: ". . . John Dalton made the theory quantitative . . . He introduced a feeling of reality into a purely abstract idea . . . It [the theory] provided an explanation or, at least, an interpretation of many chemical facts and, of greater consequence, is acted as a guide to further experimentation and investigation."

Research in chemistry and physics continued throughout the 1800's, and in 1869 Mendeleev classified the elements according to his periodic law. In 1895, almost a century after Dalton introduced his atomic theory, Roentgen observed the effect of X rays. This was followed, in 1896, by Becquerel's finding that uranium was radioactive, by Thomson's discovery of the electron in 1897, and by Pierre and Marie Curie's isolation of polonium and radium from uranium in 1898.

The beginning of the 20th century brought more developments. In 1902 came Rutherford and Soddy's theory of radioactive decay, followed in 1905 by Einstein's special theory of relativity—the equivalence of mass and energy—expressed by the equation $E = mc^2$. Other contributions in the early 1900's included Rutherford's theory of the atomic nucleus and Wilson's invention of the cloud chamber, both announced in 1911; Soddy's theory of the isotopes of elements in 1912; the formulation in 1913 of the atomic structure theory by Bohr and by Rutherford; and Einstein's general theory of relativity in 1915.

In 1919 Rutherford achieved the first nuclear reaction—the transmutation of nitrogen into oxygen—and in 1920 he discovered the proton. In 1928 the theory of alpha-particle emission was enunciated by Condon in the United States, Gurney in England, and Gamow in Russia.

In 1932 Chadwick discovered the neutron, perhaps one of the most important discoveries in nuclear physics next to that of fission itself. The existence of the neutron had been postulated as early as 1920, but no one had been successful in identifying it. In 1930, however, Bothe and Becker conducted several series of experiments in which they observed unusually penetrating radiation resulting from the exposure of beryllium, boron, or lithium to alpha particles from polonium. Considered at first to be gamma radiation, this phenomenon was studied by Irene Curie and her husband Frederic Joliot, who found in 1932 that this unknown radiation caused the ejection of protons of very high energy from hydrogen-containing compounds such as paraffin. Later in the year Chadwick performed a series of experiments showing that this phenomenon could not be gamma radiation. Suggesting that this new radiation consisted of uncharged particles (neutrons) of approximately the mass of the proton, he then verified his theory by experimentation.

Other events of 1932 included Cockcroft and Walton's transformation of lithium nuclei by artificially accelerated protons; Anderson's discovery of the positron; and the discovery of deuterium by Urey, Brickwedde, and Murphy.

These achievements were followed in early 1934 by Curie and Joliot's discovery of artificial radioactivity. This prompted Enrico Fermi to try to produce artificial radioactivity by bombarding the elements of the periodic table with neutrons rather than alpha particles. His attempts were successful in most cases. Fermi's work on neutron bombardment of uranium produced some unusual results (see Sec. 1.1.2). Although they were not interpreted correctly for several years, the results stimulated research in Fermi's laboratories and elsewhere.

Other events of the mid- and late-1930's were Dempster's discovery in 1935 of a third isotope of uranium, U^{235}, and the development of the cyclotron by Lawrence and the electrostatic high-voltage atom smasher by Van de Graaff and Herb.

Thus the stage was set. In retrospect, the discovery of nuclear fission of uranium seems an inevitable culmination of the steady march of the scientific events of the 1920's and 1930's. Certainly the pace quickened with the discovery of the proton, the neutron, and artificial radioactivity; the isolation of U^{235}; and the work of Fermi and his colleagues on neutron bombardment of uranium. In fact at the time the discovery of fission was announced, Philip H. Abelson, Ph.D. candidate at the University of California (Berkeley), was investigating the behavior of the uranium nucleus, a line of endeavor that almost certainly would have led him in a few weeks to the discovery of nuclear fission [2, 3].

1.1.2 FISSION

In Fermi's work on artificial radioactivity mentioned above, experiments with uranium produced what appeared to be a new element of atomic weight 93. This created quite a bit of controversy and aroused interest throughout the scientific world. One of the problems posed by Fermi's work was the fact that the quantities of the artificial radioactive elements resulting from neutron bombardment were so small that they could not be separated and analyzed by conventional methods. Intrigued by this problem, three scientists at the Kaiser Wilhelm Institute for Chemistry in Berlin, Otto Hahn, head of the radiochemistry department, a fellow chemist, Fritz Strassmann, and Lise Meitner, head of the nuclear physics department, attempted to develop special techniques for separation and chemical analysis of elements in question. Late in 1938 Hahn and Strassmann discovered a radioactive barium isotope among the products resulting from the neutron bombardment of uranium. They communicated their findings to Fräulein Meitner, who had been forced to flee Germany and had taken refuge in Sweden. Upon receiving Hahn's news, she concluded that the Hahn–Strassmann findings meant that a new type of nuclear reaction had taken place; Fräulein Meitner called it "fission." She immediately went to Denmark, where she was met by her nephew, Otto Frisch. The two scientists hurried to Niels Bohr's laboratories in Copenhagen to tell him of the theory that the uranium nucleus had split under neutron bombardment and outlined an experiment for verification.

Bohr left for the United States the day he met with Meitner and Frisch, who then began experiments to verify the fission theory at Bohr's laboratories. When Bohr arrived in the United States to spend a few months at the Institute for Advanced Studies at Princeton, he received word that Meitner and Frisch had completed their experiment and had obtained results in agreement with their theory [4]. Briefly stated, the Meitner–Frisch hypothesis was that when the uranium nucleus splits into two pieces under neutron bombardment, i.e., when fission occurs, an enormous amount of nuclear energy is released and the two fragments fly apart with tremendous speed. Word of the discovery spread quickly among American physicists, and in a very short time the fission process was confirmed experimentally at Columbia University; the Carnegie Institution in Washington, D. C.; Johns Hopkins University; and the University of California.

On January 26, 1939 a conference on theoretical physics was held in Washington, D. C. Enrico Fermi, now a professor at Columbia, and Bohr led off the conference with a discussion of fission. During the discussion Fermi suggested that neutrons might be emitted during the fission process. Fermi's suggestion at that time was a guess, but it gave strong implications of the possibility of a chain reaction. The implications were quickly recognized and many investigations of the various phenomena of fission were started in laboratories all over the country [5].

1.1.3 THE WAR YEARS: 1939 to 1945

Originally, in working toward the chain reaction, scientists considered such a reaction primarily as a source of neutrons for various scientific tools, and lastly as a weapon [3]. As the situation in Europe worsened and the entry of the United States into World War II drew nearer, however, the military applications became the prime consideration.

The military implications of a chain reaction were brought to the attention of the United States government as early as March 1939, and in October 1939 President Roosevelt appointed the Advisory Committee on Uranium to follow the work being done on the various aspects of uranium fission. In June 1940 this group became a subcommittee of the National Defense Research Committee. By this time, almost all work on the chain reaction was being done at Columbia. George B. Pegram, a physicist and dean of the graduate faculties, was administrator. Fermi and Leo Szilard were in immediate charge of the project, assisted by Herbert L. Anderson and Walter H. Zinn. Late in 1941 the responsibility for uranium research effort was transferred to the Office of Scientific Research and Development. The fundamental physical studies of the chain reaction and the measurement of nuclear properties, with special reference to the explosive chain reaction, were being carried out under the direction of A. H. Compton at Columbia and at the University of Chicago. Fermi's group was transferred early in 1942 from Columbia to the Metallurgical Laboratory at the University of Chicago [5].

By mid-1942 responsibility for the development of the atomic bomb was transferred to the United States Army Corps of Engineers. The Manhattan District of the Corps of Engineers was officially established in August of 1942. On Sept. 17, 1942, Brig. Gen. L. R. Groves assumed complete charge of all Army activities related to the DSM Project (Development of Substitute Materials), a code name used along with Metallurgical Laboratory and Manhattan District for security purposes [3].

On Dec. 2, 1942, Fermi and his associates were successful in producing a controlled self-sustaining chain reaction in a uranium graphite pile, known as CP-1 (Chicago Pile 1). This confirmation of the scientists' theory led, of course, to the eventual development of the atomic bomb. It also led in time to what the scientists chiefly hoped for—a source of neutrons for research and a source of power.

Because of the war effort, ideas concerning nuclear energy for civilian purposes had to be put aside. Nevertheless, much of the work done during this period was directly applicable to, and indeed necessary to, the peaceful uses of nuclear energy. As early as 1939 it was observed that some of the neutrons emitted in the fission process were not ejected immediately but were given off in decreasing quantity over a period of time. Additional measurements performed in 1942 verified this observation of the delayed-neutron phenomenon, in which approximately 0.75% of the neutrons emitted in the fission of U^{235} are delayed, some by as much as a minute. These findings, indicating that a chain reaction could be controlled, were substantiated by CP-1.

Fermi and his colleagues demonstrated that a chain reaction produced by slow neutrons (i.e., in a "moderated," or "thermal," reactor) was controllable, a fact that was further demonstrated by the production piles operated during the war. With respect to fast unmoderated reactors, it was assumed and later verified that delayed neutrons have essentially the same controlling effect as in the thermal reactors. Because the delayed neutrons determine the neutron-generation time of both thermal and fast reactors as long as the systems are close to critical, controlling a fast reactor was not expected to present problems any different from those encountered in thermal reactors. Thus, there was early recognition that chain reactions could be controlled over a wide range of neutron energies.

Two other developments of the early- to mid-1940's aroused interest in the range of neutron energies of unmoderated reactors. One was the discovery that U^{238} will fission when exposed to fast neutrons but will not fission when subjected to slow neutrons. The second was the measurement of the nuclear constants of the fissile isotopes U^{235} and Pu^{239}, the results of which showed that the η value for plutonium (the number of neutrons emitted per neutron absorbed) is more favorable in a fast-neutron spectrum than in a slow-neutron (thermal) spectrum. The combination of these developments raised the possibility that a chain reaction in a fast reactor would produce more fissile material than it consumed. Realization of the significance of these discoveries in relation to the potential of breeding plutonium from the relatively abundant uranium isotope U^{238} and the favorable behavior of Pu^{239} in a fast-neutron spectrum, both outgrowths of the war effort, gave considerable impetus to the eventual development of the fast breeder reactor.

Because of the original concept of nuclear energy as a source of power, it was not unusual that Fermi and his associates often speculated upon reactors of the future. One of their concerns was the long-range availability of U^{235} and Pu^{239}. Fermi and Zinn, especially, became intrigued with this idea of breeding plutonium from U^{238}, and as early as the spring of 1944 they discussed the possibility of building a fast-neutron breeder reactor to demonstrate the feasibility of the breeding concept.

In the summer of 1944 Fermi moved to Los Alamos, and Zinn took over his duties at the Metallurgical Laboratory. Later in 1944, encouraged by Fermi's interest in a breeder reactor, Zinn started to explore the concept of CP-4 (which he nicknamed "Jumbo, Jr."), later to be known as EBR-I (Experimental Breeder Reactor I). Fermi's enthusiasm for the breeder concept continued, and others at Los Alamos also became interested in the breeder concept. Eventually this interest resulted in the development of a fast reactor at Los Alamos. This reactor was called "Clementine."

1.1.4 WAR'S END: THE FIRST FAST REACTORS

1.1.4.1 EBR-I

By the fall of 1945 the EBR-I concept was fairly well advanced [6], and early in 1946 a formal proposal was made to the Manhattan Engineer

District to design and build a fast breeder reactor to prove the feasibility of breeding and to establish the engineering feasibility of liquid-metal coolants [7]. The fuel, U^{235}, was to be surrounded by a blanket of U^{238}, and the reactor cooled by sodium-potassium alloy (NaK). Development started in 1947, construction began in 1949, and the reactor went critical in August 1951. On Dec. 20, 1951, it produced the first usable amounts of electricity to be generated from a nuclear power reactor.

Of necessity, this is an oversimplified account of the remarkable achievement that is EBR-I. In the words of Norman Hilberry, former Director of the Argonne National Laboratory: [7] "It must be remembered that little was known of neutron properties in this area. There were practically no facilities available for making the physical measurements which today we would consider essential for the design. The use of liquid metals as a coolant was a virgin field. To all intents and purposes the technology for their use had to be developed from scratch. Despite these facts, the task was undertaken by Zinn and his small group of associates and the basic investigations and designs were started."

According to Walter Zinn, who was made Director of the Argonne National Laboratory in 1946, his biggest problem was persuading the government to allocate some 50 kg of fully enriched uranium, a very scarce weapons material, for an experiment.

1.1.4.2 Clementine

As the war drew to a close, the physicists at Los Alamos also looked to the future. Intrigued by the concept of a fast breeder reactor and sparked by Fermi's enthusiasm for the project, Philip Morrison and his colleagues started to work on a plutonium-fueled mercury-cooled fast reactor designed to operate at 25 kw. This low-power experiment was designed to demonstrate the feasibility of operating with plutonium fuel and fast neutrons and to serve as an experimental fast-neutron facility.

Approval to build the reactor, known as Clementine, was received from the Manhattan Engineer District in December 1945 and work started immediately. Actual construction of the reactor was started in September 1946. The first critical assembly of the reactor was made at an incomplete stage of construction on Nov. 21, 1946, and nuclear measurements were performed at a power level of approximately 1 watt without further construction until February 1947. During this period the reactor was used as a critical assembly, and measurements were made concerning the critical mass vs. core configuration, effectiveness of reactor control, temperature coefficient of the reactor, and spectrum of the neutrons. Work of this nature generally continued until January 1949, when the reactor was prepared for final assembly. In March 1949 the reactor was brought to full power.

Of the 3 1/2 years spent in assembly of the reactor, approximately 21 months were spent on low-power critical experiments. In December 1952 it became evident that a plutonium fuel rod had ruptured, thereby releasing plutonium into the mercury coolant. Inasmuch as the primary objectives of the experiment had been realized, it was decided to dismantle the reactor and this was completed by June 1953.

1.1.5 FAST BREEDER REACTORS: 1950-1963

1.1.5.1 Private Industry Participation in the United States

In 1950, as the AEC's reactor program encompassing several reactor types began to take form, private industry showed interest in participating in an atomic power program. As a result the Commission issued in January 1951 an invitation to industry to conduct studies of reactors for producing plutonium for military use and power for civilian use [8]. Four groups responded to the invitation and a year later made their initial report, expressing what the Commission termed "a cautious optimism that the difficult technical and cost factors involved will be solved eventually." At that time a significant milestone in fast reactor development was reached. Two of the four groups indicated interest in a fast reactor, and one group, made up of the Detroit Edison Company and the Dow Chemical Company, asked permission to pursue the development of a fast breeder reactor in a program to be financed jointly by the group and the Commission. Approved in the spring of 1952, this project grew steadily over the next few years, the number of industrial participants increasing until over 40 companies were involved. Dow Chemical Company withdrew in 1954, limiting its activities to the field of chemical reactors.

The next significant development with regard to commercial atomic energy programs occurred in 1955, when the AEC invited industry to submit proposals for constructing, with Commission assistance, power reactors in a program called the Power Reactor Demonstration Program. Three responses were received by April 1955, one of which concerned a fast breeder reactor. The Detroit group, now known as Atomic Power Development Associates, Inc. (APDA), proposed to build near Detroit a 100,000-kw(e) liquid-metal-cooled fast breeder reactor. The proposal was approved and a second nonprofit organization, Power Reactor Development Company, was formed to act as the prime construction contractor for the project while APDA carried out the design and development work. The reactor was named the Enrico Fermi Atomic Power Plant in recognition of Fermi's many contributions to the development and control of nuclear energy and his early interest in fast breeder reactors. The Fermi reactor went critical on August 23, 1963.

1.1.5.2 U.S. Atomic Energy Commission Program

Concurrently the AEC continued to develop various types of reactors, and in 1954, encouraged by the experience with EBR-I, decided to construct an advanced version of EBR-I at the Argonne National Laboratory facility in Idaho. The new breeder reactor, EBR-II, includes a complete fuel-processing and -fabrication facility in addition to the reactor, heat-transfer system, and steam-electric plant. Construction of the reactor began in 1958. Dry criticality was achieved in the late fall of 1961, and wet criticality, on Nov. 11, 1963, slightly less than three months after the Enrico Fermi plant went critical.

Interest in developing plutonium fuels for fast breeder applications continued at the Los Alamos Scientific Laboratory following the dismantling of Clementine in 1953. The concept of using molten plutonium as fuel for a fast breeder system evolved from investigations carried out at LASL. This work pointed up the need for information about the behavior of container and fuel materials as well as operating problems that might be unique to the fluid nature of the fuel. The decision was made to build a reactor fueled with a molten plutonium in which the fuel would be contained in cylindrical capsules with sodium coolant flowing outside. Development of LAMPRE-I began in the mid-1950's, and installation of the reactor at the Los Alamos site was made in 1959. The reactor went dry critical early in 1961 and reached its designed power level of 1 Mw a short time later. A second core loading was installed in April 1962. Since that time the reactor has been used primarily as a testing facility for materials intended to contain the highly corrosive fuel alloy and as a basic physics test unit for exploring the feasibility of using a molten-plutonium fuel.

1.1.5.3 Programs Abroad

Since the early 1950's, much work on fast breeders has been done abroad as well as in the United States, especially in the United Kingdom, the USSR, and France. More recently other European countries and Japan have shown interest in fast reactor programs.

Construction of the United Kingdom's Dounreay Fast Reactor was started in 1955. This NaK-cooled reactor, presently fueled with U–Mo, is designed for a maximum power of 72 Mw(t) and 15 Mw(e). The reactor went critical for the first time in November 1959 and operated at zero power until April 1960, when it was shut down for the installation of a second core, which reached a power level of 11 Mw in late 1961. A third fuel loading, made in mid-1962, reached criticality on July 26, 1962, and attained a power level of 30 Mw(t) shortly thereafter. A fourth loading completed in June 1963 has been operated at levels as high as 60 Mw(t).

The first fast reactor built in the USSR, BR-I, was built in 1955 as a zero-energy assembly for fast reactor physics investigations. The BR-I reactor was followed in 1956 by BR-2, a plutonium-fueled mercury-cooled reactor, which was operated to 100 kw(t). The successor to BR-2, BR-5, was completed in 1958 and became operational by the summer of 1959. This reactor is sodium cooled, is fueled with plutonium oxide, and has a maximum power of 5 Mw(t); it has been used for experimental purposes during the last few years.

In France, the Commissariat a l'Energie Atomique is building an experimental fast breeder reactor (Rapsodie) designed for a maximum power of 20 Mw(t). Planning began in 1958 and completion is scheduled for mid-1966. It is hoped that criticality will be achieved in 1967. Rapsodie will employ sodium as the coolant and a mixed oxide (PuO_2–UO_2) as the initial fuel loading.

1.1.6 FUTURE OF FAST BREEDER REACTORS

Water-cooled thermal reactors have demonstrated their feasibility. Some are close to achieving power at prices competitive to coal. The story of the fast breeder is yet to be told, but the importance of this story is clearly shown in the AEC's report to the President, dated Nov. 20, 1962: [9] "While the Commission has been proceeding on a considered course in general accord with its 10-year civilian power program adopted in 1958, that program is now on the threshold of attaining its primary objective of competitive nuclear power in high-fuel-cost areas by 1968. However, it became evident with the passage of time that our attention had probably with for too long remained focused narrowly on short-term objectives. This restudy made it apparent that, for the long-term benefit of the country, and indeed of the whole world, it was time we placed relatively more emphasis on the longer-range and more difficult problem of breeder reactors, which can make use of nearly all of our uranium and thorium reserves, instead of the less than 1% of the uranium and very little of the thorium utilized in the present types of reactors. Only by the use of breeders would we really solve the problem of adequate energy supply for future generations."

1.2 Breeding

1.2.1 ADVANTAGES OF OPERATING WITH HIGH-ENERGY NEUTRONS

The outstanding advantage that results from designing a reactor to operate on high-energy neutrons is the high breeding ratio achievable and the resulting potential for high utilization of U^{238} and possibly Th^{232}. Secondary advantages result from such features as a greater ability of the reactor to tolerate use of standard structural materials and the possibility of achieving an internal breeding ratio of unity. The latter makes possible the design of cores with longtime operation between shutdowns for fuel reloading. The major nuclear reactions involved in breeding in U^{238} and Th^{232} are shown in Figs. 1.1 and 1.2. The shaded areas are those of greatest interest.

1.2.2 BREEDING POTENTIAL

The breeding potential, or ratio, is commonly defined as the number of fissile nuclei created per fissile nucleus destroyed. This, however, is a general definition since several equations can be written in terms of capture and fission cross sections of the various isotopes that may be present.

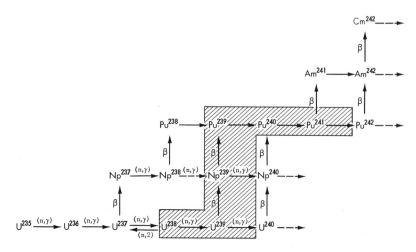

FIG. 1.1—Heavy-isotope buildup in natural uranium [10].

A simplified relation for the breeding ratio of a reactor including its blanket is

$$BR = \frac{\nu - 1 - a - A - L + F(\nu' - 1)}{1 + a} \quad (1.1)$$

where ν = number of neutrons produced per fission of primary fissile isotope

A = number of neutrons captured (nonfissile and nonfertile materials) in parasitic absorbers per fission of primary fissile isotope

L = number of neutrons leaking from blanket per fission of primary fissile isotope

F = number of fertile atoms fissioned per fission of primary fissile isotope

a = ratio of capture to fission cross section of fissile isotope

ν' = number of neutrons produced per fission of fertile isotope

In a comparison of the merits of various reactors from a breeding-potential standpoint, η is often used, i.e., the ratio of neutrons produced per neutron absorbed in the fissile isotope. The value of $\eta - 1$ is shown in Table 1.1. The relation between ν and η is given by

$$\eta = \nu \ \sigma_f/(\sigma_f + \sigma_c) \ = \nu/(1 + a)$$

The five factors that affect breeding potential, some of which contribute to the higher breeding ratio of fast reactors compared to thermal reactors, are ν, a, F, A, and L, as defined in Eq. 1.1 above. A brief discussion of these factors is given below:

(1) Number of neutrons produced per fission: This factor, ν, is not drastically different for a typical fast reactor spectrum than for a typical thermal reactor spectrum, as shown in Table 1.1. However, the fact that ν value for plutonium fuels is around 3 as compared to a value of 2.5 for uranium fuels is significant. Breeding is much easier to achieve with the U^{238} fertile-material cycle than with the Th^{232} fertile-material cycle.

(2) Ratio of capture cross section to fission cross section: This quantity, $a = \sigma_c/\sigma_f$, for the fissile isotopes is another important factor with respect to the breeding process. As shown in Eq. 1.1, a adversely affects breeding ratio because it appears as a negative term in the numerator and as a positive term in the denominator. The effect of a is little different for thermal and fast reactors as far as uranium fuels are concerned, but, where plutonium fuels are concerned, the α value is poor in thermal reactors.

The higher isotopes formed from the absorption of neutrons in plutonium have better breeding characteristics than the lower ones. An example of the improvement in breeding ratio that can be obtained

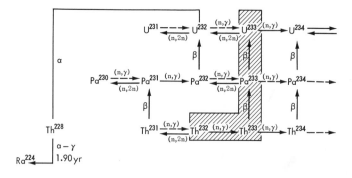

FIG. 1.2—Heavy-isotope buildup in thorium [10,11].

Table 1.1—Fast and Thermal Reactor Nuclear Data [12-14]

	Pu^{239}		Pu^{241}		U^{233}		U^{235}	
	Thermal	Fast	Thermal	Fast	Thermal	Fast	Thermal	Fast
ν	2.90	2.96	2.98	3.04	2.50	2.57	2.42	2.50
σ_f*	740	1.91	1000	2.54	530	2.69	580	1.78
σ_c*	270	0.438	400	0.290	50	0.290	100	0.435
$\alpha = \sigma_c/\sigma_f$	0.365	0.231	0.400	0.114	0.0943	0.108	0.172	0.244
$\eta - 1$	1.12	1.40	1.13	1.73	1.28	1.32	1.06	1.01

*σ_c, σ_f are microscopic cross sections for capture and fission, respectively, for the fissile isotopes.

from the formation of the higher isotopes of plutonium is given in Table 1.2. The calculated breeding ratios are for ideal conditions and do not represent real systems.

Table 1.2—Computed Breeding Ratios for Various Fast Reactor Fuels [12]

Fuel type	Composition of plutonium fuel, %				Breeding ratio
	239	240	241	242	
1	100	0	0	0	1.8
2	74.7	10.2	12.4	2.7	1.9
3	40	10	25	25	2.1

(3) Number of fertile atoms fissioned per fission of the primary fissile isotope: This ratio, denoted F and sometimes called the "fast fission effect," is strongly affected by the reactor spectrum. The threshold at which fast fission occurs is 1.4 Mev for both U^{238} and Th^{232}, as shown in Table 1.3. It is not surprising that this factor is as low as 0.02 to 0.06 for thermal reactors and ranges between 0.15 and 0.30 in fast reactors. (Note: The values of F for typical thermal and fast reactors, the Yankee and the Fermi reactors, respectively, are given in Table 1.5.)

Table 1.3—Fertile Material Data [15]
(800-liter Metal-fueled Fast Reactor)

	U^{238}	Th^{232}	Pu^{240}
Fission threshold, Mev	1.4	1.4	0.6
σ_f*	0.048	0.010	0.408
σ_c*	0.202	0.240	0.354
ν†	2.7	2.54	3.17

* Average over entire energy spectrum.
† Average above threshold.

Fast fission data for the naturally occurring and reactor-produced fertile materials are shown in Table 1.3. As indicated in Table 1.2, Pu^{240} can reach an equilibrium concentration of approximately 10% in recycled fuel and, because of the lower fission threshold of P^{240} and its transmutation to Pu^{241}, the breeding ratio of a fast reactor fueled with "dirty" plutonium is higher than that of a pure-plutonium-fueled core.

(4) Number of neutrons captured in nonfissile and nonfertile materials per fission of the primary fissile isotope: This factor, A, is expressed by the ratio (Σ_c) nonfuel / (Σ_f) fuel, where Σ_c is the macroscopic absorption cross section of the structural material and Σ_f is the macroscopic fission cross section of the fuel. The A factor directly reduces the breeding ratio as indicated in Eq. 1.1. As indicated in Table 1.4, the ratio of microscopic cross sections, σ_c/σ_f,* is not always lower in a fast reactor than in a thermal reactor. However, the fraction of neutrons lost by capture in nonfuel materials tends to be less in fast reactors because the relative number of fuel nuclei per unit volume is much higher. A comparison of the absorption cross sections of various coolant and structural materials is given in Table 1.4. The values of thermal reactor cross sections are based on the Yankee pressurized-water reactor, a thermal reactor. The values of the 800-liter plutonium-metal-fueled fast reactor are averaged over the entire fast reactor system. For any given material the value of A in Eq. 1.1 can be obtained by multiplying the value of σ_c/Σ_f in Table 1.4 by the average number of atoms per cubic centimeter of that material in the smeared core mixture. Table 1.4 indicates that there is greater freedom of choice of structural materials in fast reactors. The seriousness of the effect of absorption in structural material on the breeding ratio in a thermal reactor is shown in Table 1.5.

(5) Neutron leakage from blanket: the leakage factor, L, is dependent upon reactor size and the effectiveness of the blanket. The fraction of neutrons that would leak from a large core is less than the leakage from a small core because the surface-to-volume ratio is smaller in the larger core. Naturally it is easier to keep leakage from a thermal reactor core low because it is relatively large compared with that of a fast reactor. For a thermal reactor, L can be as low as 0.06 whereas leakage from the core of a fast reactor is large. Customarily a blanket is used to minimize net leakage. Reflectors can also be used. The thickness of the blanket reaches an economic limit where the cost of the incremental increase in the blanket thickness is less than the revenue from the additional fuel and heat [17]. Safety considerations may also affect blanket design, as discussed in Sec. 1.3.2 of this chapter.

The factors that affect breeding ratio and the breeding ratios of representative reactors are tabulated in Table 1.5.

The comparison in Table 1.5 between the Fermi reactor, which has a breeding ratio of 1.2, and the Yankee reactor, which has a breeding ratio of 0.53, is representative of the difference in

---

*σ_c is the microscopic absorption cross section of the structural material; σ_f is the microscopic fission cross section of the fuel.

Table 1.4—Material Absorption Cross Sections for Thermal and Fast Reactors [12, 15, 16]

Material	Thermal (Yankee)			Fast (800-liter Pu metal)		
	σ_c, barns	σ_c/σ_f	σ_c/Σ_f, 10^{-24} cm^3/atom	σ_c, barns	σ_c/σ_f	σ_c/Σ_f, 10^{-24} cm^3/atom
Fe	2.52	0.0043	15	0.008	0.0044	4
Cr	2.90	0.0050	17	0.01	0.0055	5
Ni	4.6	0.0079	27	0.011	0.0061	5
Zr	0.18	0.0003	1	0.006	0.0033	3
Mo	2.5	0.0043	15	0.073	0.040	35
Ta	21.3	0.036	126	0.322	0.18	155
Na	0.515	0.0009	3	0.0002	0.0001	0.1
K	1.97	0.0034	12	0.013	0.0072	6
Li	71	0.12	420	0.025	0.014	12
B (natural)	775	1.3	4500	0.27	0.15	130
Fission products	40	0.069	236	0.25	0.14	120

pressurized-light-water systems and sodium-cooled fast systems operating on enriched U^{235} fuel. Breeding ratios between 1.2 to 1.6 can be expected in plutonium-fueled fast reactors with considerable flexibility, depending on the relative emphasis placed upon breeding and on economics. The fast reactor operated on U^{233} is expected to have a breeding ratio about halfway between those operating on U^{235} and plutonium. In comparison, thermal systems are expected to be able to achieve a breeding ratio above 1.0 with U^{233} fuel [21, 22].

The breeding ratio obtained from Eq. 1.1 does not include fuel losses outside the reactor. The amount of fuel lost or not reclaimed during fabrication and reprocessing has not been well established for recycle systems but could be several percent of the total fuel handled per cycle.

Table 1.5—Comparison of the Breeding Ratio for Typical Thermal and Fast Reactors

	Future Pu-fueled fast reactor[18]	U^{235} Fermi (fast)[19]	U^{235} Yankee (thermal)[20]
$\nu - 1$	1.95	1.55	1.47
α	0.24	0.20	0.19
A	0.23	0.16	0.69
F	0.30	0.165	0.06
$\nu' - 1$	1.80	1.70	1.70
L	0.06	0.02 (0.4)*	0.06
Breeding ratio	1.60	1.20	0.53

* Leakage from core to blanket.

1.2.3 DOUBLING TIME

One measure of the merit or effectiveness of a reactor in increasing the quantity of fissile nuclei is the doubling time. This is the time, usually expressed in years, required for the fissile material in a given system, both internal and external to the core, to create excess material equivalent to that at the start. It is generally thought that doubling time should be less than 20 years for presently projected power demands.

The doubling time (t_D) for values of a breeding ratio greater than 1.0 is given by

$$t_D = \left(\frac{1000}{365 \, P.F.}\right)\left(\frac{I_R}{P}\right)\left(\frac{1}{(B.R.\text{-}1)(1 + a)(1 - f)}\right) \quad (1.2)$$

where t_D = doubling time, years
     P = specific power of reactor, Mw(t)/kg fuel
     I_R = the fuel-cycle inventory to core inventory ratio
     f = fraction of fissions in fertile material*
     a = σ_c/σ_f for fissile isotope
     $P.F.$ = yearly plant factor
     $B.R.$ = overall cycle breeding ratio

The importance of the factors that influence doubling time are illustrated by the two cases reviewed in Table 1.6.

Table 1.6—Doubling Time Data [15]

	Case I[18]	Case II[18]
Power, Mw (e)	300	300
Fuel	PuO$_2$-UO$_2$	PuO$_2$ in U-Mo cermet
Core dimensions:		
Diameter, ft	5	4
Height, ft	3	3
Critical mass, kg	674	735
U : Pu ratio	3	9
Specific power (P), Mw(t)/kg Pu	1.15	0.94
Cycle to core inventory (I_R)	2.23	1.92
Breeding ratio ($B.R.$)	1.3	1.5
Capture to fission (a)	0.27	0.21
Plant factor ($P.F.$)	0.8	0.8
Fraction of fissions in fertile material (f)	0.176	0.249
Doubling time (t_D), years	21.2	15.4

The values used in Table 1.6 for P (specific power), an important variable, are not as large as could be desired; the next generation of reactors, however, may have values of P even lower than those given here as detailed designs progress. It is obvious that doubling time increases rapidly as the breeding ratio decreases toward 1.0.

---

*As distinct from F, Eq. (1.1), where F is the ratio of fertile-atom fissions to primary fissile-atom fissions.

(Note: Table 1.6 does not include the fuel-cycle losses, which would increase the doubling time.)

For the cycle to core inventory to be kept low, it is important to have a high burnup fuel and minimum decay, reprocessing, and fabrication times. With the development of high burnup fuels, a lifetime of 1 to 3 years is expected. The out-of-pile inventory time should be reduced to about 1/2 year as facilities become available to reprocess and refabricate fuel on a demand basis. The value of l_R in Table 1.6 is based on present conditions.

Although a short doubling time is important in the long run for high utilization of fertile material, it is likely that in the near future more emphasis will be placed on economics than on short doubling time.

1.3 Safety Considerations in Fast Reactor Design

1.3.1 DIFFERENCES BETWEEN FAST AND THERMAL REACTORS

One essential area in the design of a reactor is physics, of which safety is an integral part. The following discussion presents general safety problems posed by fast reactors that may affect plant design.

In analyzing the safety of fast reactors, one must consider two features by which they differ from thermal reactors, the short prompt-neutron lifetime and the greater ease with which a supercritical condition is achieved by rearranging the fuel into a more-compact geometry.

First, the prompt-neutron lieftime is much shorter in a fast reactor, about 10^{-7} sec as compared to a prompt-neutron lifetime of 10^{-3} to 10^{-4} sec in a thermal reactor. The power level of a fast reactor can rise with a shorter period than that of a thermal reactor if the excess reactivity should exceed prompt criticality. In connection with the concept of prompt criticality, it is important to point out that the delayed-neutron fraction in a $Pu-U^{238}$ reactor is much smaller than that in a $U^{235}-U^{238}$ reactor, about 0.004 and 0.007, respectively. The consequent reduction in excess reactivity needed to achieve prompt criticality may result in more stringent control requirements.

The second important difference is the sensitivity of the reactivity of a fast core to fuel concentration. A supercritical condition can be achieved by fuel rearrangement. The most commonly assumed causes of such a rearrangement are meltdown accidents in which it can be hypothesized that some operating abnormality triggers a degree of fuel failure permitting the movement of fuel into a more reactive configuration. The consequence of this is a destructive burst of nuclear energy.

A fast reactor can be designed to prevent the introduction of more than 1 dollar of reactivity (1 dollar is defined as an amount of reactivity equal to the delayed-neutron fraction which, when added to a critical reactor, would cause the reactor to become prompt critical). For instance, the control system of a fast reactor can be designed so that any fast-acting regulating rod has a reactivity worth of less than 1 dollar. In such a system, the reactor could not become prompt critical by the inadvertent removal of the fast-acting regulating rod. The reactor should be designed so that gross core meltdown is rendered virtually impossible. For example, the sodium coolant system should be designed to prevent loss of core coolant.

1.3.2 REACTOR STABILITY

Safe operation requires that a reactor not behave in an autocatalytic manner or have any resonance instabilities at any power level of interest. It is important that the feedback transfer function and the range of uncertainty of this function be established. In any investigation of reactor stability, the fundamental properties of greatest interest are the power or reactivity coefficients of the core. The temperature coefficient is defined as the change in reactivity per unit of temperature rise of the material being considered.

There are five power or temperature coefficients of major importance in fast reactors. They are the axial fuel expansion coefficient, the sodium temperature coefficient, the Doppler coefficient, the fuel-element bowing coefficient, and the coefficient due to radial expansion of the core. Each of these is treated below.

(1) Axial fuel expansion coefficient: In metal-fueled fast reactors, this coefficient is of particular importance because of the very rapid expansion of fuel in response to any increase in power level. For a small or intermediate-sized reactor this coefficient is on the order of -5×10^{-6} $\Delta k/k/°C$.

For ceramic cores some question arises concerning axial fuel expansion because the fuel is likely to be in the form of pellets within a tube. Even if a longitudinally continuous fuel element were fabricated, it might crack into many pieces under irradiation. Thermal expansion in a definitely predictable manner cannot be depended upon in fuel that is segmented in this manner. Thus in a ceramic core greater dependence will have to be placed on the other negative temperature coefficients discussed below.

(2) Sodium coefficient: Until a few years ago, the sodium coefficient was thought to be negative. However, Nims and Zweifel [27] have pointed out that in some large reactor designs it is possible to obtain a positive sodium coefficient. This situation is caused by the fact that the sodium coefficient can be considered to consist primarily of two parts* : (1) leakage effect, which is always negative because a decrease in sodium density permits more neutrons to leak from the core and thus lowers reactivity and (2) a spectral hardening effect, which is generally positive. The neutron spectrum is hardened because the moderating effect of the sodium is lost when sodium is removed. The harder spectrum results in more fast fissions in U^{238}, fewer captures in U^{238}, and, generally, an increase in the number of fission neutrons emitted per absorption in Pu^{239}. These effects tend to increase reactivity.

In small- or medium-sized fast reactors, the leakage effect predominates, and the sodium coefficient is negative. In large fast reactors, the spectral hardening effect can predominate and thus

---

*A third effect, absorption, is negligible in comparison to the other two.

produce a positive sodium coefficient. However, even in a large fast reactor it might be possible to make, by appropriate core design, the sodium coefficient negative. Possible ways include increasing leakage by using a "pancake" design, i.e., a small height-to-diameter ratio [28, 29], or by having an internal blanket. Another approach consists of placing a sodium reflector directly above the core so that the positive sodium effect within the core is counteracted by the negative effect of the reduced density of the sodium reflector.

It should be noted that with the present state of knowledge many uncertainties exist in the calculating of the sodium reactivity coefficient. It is also important to note that the positive spectral hardening effect predominates over the negative leakage effect at the center of the core. Thus expulsion of sodium from the center of the core without expulsion of the blanket above the core would result in a positive coefficient even with a zero or slightly negative overall sodium coefficient.

(3) Doppler coefficient: The neutron-fission and capture cross sections are functions of the relative velocity of the neutron and the target nucleus. In the resonance region the effective cross sections are increased by the thermal agitation of the fuel nuclei because of the decrease in the height and increase in the width of the resonances. This is called Doppler broadening of resonances. The Doppler temperature coefficient is defined as the change in reactivity, due to Doppler broadening, per unit change in the fuel temperature.

Doppler broadening of fission resonances in U^{235}, Pu^{239}, or U^{233} increases reactivity whereas broadening of capture resonances in both fissile and fertile material decreases reactivity. The overall Doppler coefficient is the sum of these effects. In a fast reactor having a high ratio of fissile to fertile material therefore the coefficient would be slightly positive although in a moderately enriched reactor the coefficient is negative. As the ratio of fissile material to fertile material is decreased and the size of the core is increased, the Doppler coefficient may go from small positive through zero to small negative, and, in very large fast reactors, it can go to significantly large negative values.

In small highly enriched reactors like EBR-I, present calculations give a small positive Doppler coefficient (about 10^{-7} $\Delta k/k/°C$); in the intermediate-sized 25% enriched Enrico Fermi fast breeder reactor, the value is about -1×10^{-6}; and in a core with small fissile-to-fertile material ratio, it is expected to be about -5×10^{-6}. In a large oxide-fueled fast reactor, the Doppler effect may be sufficient to terminate accidental excursions in the absence of a dependable large negative axial fuel expansion coefficient.

An accurate theoretical evaluation of the Doppler coefficient requires detailed knowledge of the spectrum in the region below 10 kev and reliable statistics on the distribution of resonances.

(4) Fuel-element bowing: By differential thermal expansion, the thermal gradients across the reactor core can cause bowing of subassembly wrappers and can also cause bowing of thick fuel pins.

If a normal radial power distribution exists, i.e., maximum at the center and decreasing radially outward, a pin supported at its ends could bow inward and give a positive reactivity effect. Minimization or control of bowing so as to produce a negative reactivity is possible by suitable engineering design.

(5) Radial core expansion: Radial expansion of the core due to structural expansion produces a large negative temperature coefficient. However, this temperature coefficient has a large time constant since it is related to the structural material. The contribution of this coefficient to the total feedback is not sufficient to be effective against fast transients because the time constant is large. However, it is important to the total feedback during normal operation.

Generally, it is desirable not to have any significant positive reactivity coefficients. However, by choosing design parameters that result in a large negative Doppler coefficient, the designer may be able to maintain a safe design in a large fast reactor that has a positive sodium coefficient. Here the negative reactivity feedback of the Doppler coefficient for the condition of the reduced sodium density might counteract the positive feedback effect of the sodium. The complete stability of such a situation must also take into account the time constants of the feedback effects. An appropriate method that can be applied effectively has been developed by Bethe [23].

In addition to positive sodium feedback, long-delayed negative reactivity effects should be examined to determine whether they cause any instability either within or beyond the normal operating power range. The observed resonance instability of the Mark II core of EBR-I [24-26] demonstrated the need for attention to the resonance instability effect. The conclusions regarding the Mark II instability are presented in Ref. 26, a portion of which is quoted below:

> The instability of Mark II may be directly attributed to the combination of two undesirable features, both of which are easily eliminated through elementary changes in mechanical design. The lack of radial coupling between fuel rods was detrimental in two respects: rod bowing was permitted and the normally strong prompt negative feedback from radial fuel expansion was greatly weakened. The consequence was an over-all prompt positive power coefficient of reactivity. The other important feature was, of course, the shield plate system which was responsible for the delayed negative power coefficient. The combination of the two effects resulted in a feedback which permitted constructive interference of periodic reactivity insertions.

The operation of the subsequent Mark III core of EBR-I showed that proper design could remove the previous instability. Successful operation of the Mark III core and the operation of the Dounreay fast reactor have shown that fast reactors can be built to operate in a safe and stable manner.

1.3.3 REACTOR-ACCIDENT ANALYSIS

As assurance that a reactor can be operated safely, investigations should be made to ascertain that the following criteria are satisfied: (1) the reactor design and operating characteristics should be such that gross fuel-element failure and meltdown cannot result from credible accident conditions; (2) under postulated maximum hypothetical accident conditions, suitable containment should be provided to ensure that public safety is not endangered; and (3) the reactor should not respond autocatalytically, or in a divergent oscillatory fashion, to the random reactivity variations that occur during normal operation.

For the purpose of accident analysis, a credible accident is defined as one in which a sequence of events can happen from a postulated failure; an incredible or hypothetical accident is a hypothesized situation which may have no relation to reality. Hypothetical accidents are usually easy to calculate and are normally chosen as worse than any credible accident.

In general, a nuclear excursion could be caused by the rapid insertion of reactivity or the rapid reassembly of poorly supported fuel. The former can be the result of credible accidents; the latter usually is the result of hypothetical accidents.

1.3.3.1 Credible Accidents

Plausible incidents involving rapid insertions of reactivity from external and internal sources can be postulated. Generally these insertions can be minimized by design. Some of these design features are discussed below.

(1) Excess reactivity: Limiting the amount of excess reactivity to less than 1 dollar may be impractical in advanced designs. However, the rate of reactivity insertion can be controlled by limiting the drive speeds so that, on withdrawal of a control rod, the reactivity feedback effects will prevent excessive power levels. In addition, it may be possible to limit the amount of reactivity in a fast rod so that the power excursion, if the rod is withdrawn completely, could not cause the fuel and coolant temperatures to rise above the melting and boiling temperatures, respectively.

(2) Shutdown reactivity: The total shutdown reactivity should be distributed among several safety rods for greatest reliability. The safety rods should have a total negative worth of several dollars and a worth several times that of replaceable core components to ensure that the subcriticality of the reactor is always greater than any positive reactivity effect resulting from improper management of any replaceable core component. The reactivity insertion rate during safety-rod withdrawal should be limited to a rate for which the feedback mechanisms can easily compensate.

(3) Loading adjustments: Loading changes should be made with all safety rods inserted. Components should be inserted singly and at a speed equivalent to a very low reactivity insertion rate.

(4) Moderator materials: The insertion of a relatively small amount of hydrogenous material in a fast reactor core can produce a reactivity change, usually an increase. This type of accident can be prevented by provisions for excluding hydrogen-bearing compounds from the primary system. Outside the primary system, where there is a possibility of leakage, hydrogenous compounds should be permitted only if multiple barriers (seals and catchpans) are installed between the reservoir and primary system. Otherwise, nonhydrogenous materials should be used.

1.3.3.2 Maximum Hypothetical Accidents Involving Rearrangement of Fuel During a Meltdown

With extraneous reactivity additions eliminated or minimized, attention can be focused on the most serious and most difficult part of fast reactor safety evaluation—core collapse or meltdown. Gross meltdown accidents can be subdivided for convenience into two categories: (1) meltdown when sodium is present, and (2) meltdown following loss of sodium.

1.3.3.2.1 MELTDOWN WITH SODIUM. Meltdown with sodium present could result from a reactivity insertion which, although insufficient to cause an explosive excursion itself, raises the power level and causes coolant boiling. Because sodium-cooled reactors are unpressurized, the boiling point of sodium marks the transition between good and poor cooling. If the boiling point is exceeded even locally, then the entire channel may be rapidly voided because of the low density of the vapor. The heat-removal capability may be drastically reduced thereby causing a rapid increase in the fuel temperatures and subsequent fuel melting. In meltdowns with sodium present, the boiling sodium may tend to disperse fuel and prevent reassembly. The pressure caused by boiling of sodium will be highest near the center of the power distribution, which is also near the center of the reactivity distribution. Accordingly, the forces resulting from boiling should act predominately to drive fuel toward less reactive positions. In some out-of-pile experiments designed to investigate this effect [30], it was found that the melting of uranium in a liquid metal may not lead to the formation of a supercritical mass and that the vaporization of the coolant may be a mechanism for shutdown. However, as mentioned above, the sodium void may cause a positive reactivity effect. The combined reactivity effect should be evaluated.

Examples of other circumstances that should be examined to determine whether or not the sodium boiling point might be exceeded are loss of primary flow and loss of heat-dumping ability. Design features that minimize or eliminate problems in this category are auxiliary motors on the primary pumps which can be operated by emergency electrical power supplies, multiple primary and secondary loops, provisions for natural circulation, and an emergency feedwater supply. Nevertheless, studies of accident situations should be made to establish that no credible accident can lead to a gross meltdown with sodium present.

1.3.3.2.2 MELTDOWN WITHOUT SODIUM. Meltdown of fast reactor cores when sodium is not present may be a more serious situation than melt-down in the presence of sodium. If the sodium could drain away very rapidly, then the core would melt as a result of fission-product decay heating. It may be assumed that the core melts instanta-neously and reassembles under the influence of gravity. Even on this pessimistic basis, the energy release may be found to be containable with only minor expense. This accident can be considerably less severe for several reasons. The coolant probably would not drain instantaneously, but at a fairly slow rate. As fuel material became un-covered, it would melt and fall to lower elevations. The reassembly rate, at the time the configuration goes prompt critical, is an important factor in determining the energy release. This rate is much less than that obtained in a gravitational collapse for any reasonable leak rates, and the energy release would be correspondingly reduced. The fuel material and corresponding melting rates may never reach a super-prompt-critical condition; the fuel material may remelt as the secondary accumulation of fuel material approaches critical dimensions and then disperses into the lower re-gions. The design could incorporate such things as large channels, which would allow the molten material to drop to lower regions of the vessel where provisions could be made to accommodate this material in a dispersed arrangement, thereby preventing a secondary criticality problem.

Positive design steps should always be taken to make a loss-of-coolant accident virtually im-possible. These steps include the installation of secondary containers around the primary system and, if necessary, reserve sodium supplies to ensure that the core is not uncovered if a leak does occur. The design should also include con-sideration of natural-circulation loops to ensure an adequate heat loss.

1.3.3.3 Autocatalytic Behavior

A stability analysis should be performed during the reactor design to ensure that a reactor will not respond autocatalytically to either small inten-tional reactivity changes or to random reactivity variations that occur during normal operation. The method outlined in Ref. 23 can be used to determine the reactor behavior during forced oscil-lation. Such a determination requires a knowledge of the character of the feedback reactivity, which is based on the magnitudes of all of the power coefficients, along with the necessary time con-stants and time delays. This analysis could be confirmed during zero-power operation of the reac-tor.

1.3.4 EFFECT OF SAFETY CONSIDERA-TIONS ON PLANT DESIGN

All systems of the plant should be reviewed from the standpoint of their behavior with regard to public safety. The criteria for the design of the various systems include: (1) the given system should be designed for maximum normal operating conditions and for all credible maloperations, (2)

simple failure of a given system to perform its basic function should not create a safety probelm directly or give rise to safety problems in other systems, (3) for each system normally containing radioactive material, the effects of an uncontrolled release of this material should be analyzed and, based on the degree of hazard involved, measures should be taken to prevent such a release or to control it should it occur, and (4) systems connected to or passing through the reactor building should not compromise the containment aspects of the building.

1.4 Fuel-Element Design

This section presents a brief discussion of fuel elements and their design for use in fast reactors.

1.4.1 FUEL-ELEMENT SHAPE

The fuel elements are usually made in a pin form instead of plate or radiator form because pins can be more easily supported to accommodate the differential thermal expansion caused by the large temperature rise. Secondary reasons for the choice of a pin element are (1) the more uniform and symmetrical temperature distribution with a rod shape, which more easily accommodates ther-mal stresses; (2) the better shape for accommo-dating fission-product gas pressure and irradiation growth provided by a pin; and (3) simpler fabri-cation, which is particularly important in the fab-rication of radioactive fuel.

1.4.2 FUEL-ELEMENT DIAMETER

The diameter of a fast reactor fuel element is considerably smaller than that of a thermal power reactor fuel element for the following reasons: (1) the high specific power per unit of fissionable material, which is desired to minimize fuel-inven-tory charges, and (2) the absence of a diluent moderator or a large amount of fertile-material diluent within the pin. The ratio of fertile to fissile material ranges between 3:1 and 10:1, as dictated by criticality and safety considerations. Fortunately, hot spots caused by local thermaliza-tion and local heating are not a problem with fast reactors. For high-energy neutrons, the mean free path for fission or absorption is quite large, and this type of hot spot is not encountered. The diameters of pins range from about 1/8 in. in EBR-II and Fermi to 1/4 in. in some of the advanced designs of larger reactors.

1.4.3 SUBASSEMBLY SIZE

The size of a subassembly may vary between 2 to 4 in. across the flats of the wrapper can, as dictated or controlled by one of the following considerations: (1) reactivity worth, which it is desirable to limit to several dollars at the center of the core; (2) decay-heat removal considerations;

(3) weight considerations in handling the subassembly in fabrication or in reactor loading operations; and (4) criticality of individual subassemblies if inadvertently flooded with water in handling.

1.4.4 FUEL AND CLADDING MATERIALS

Fast reactor fuel elements should have high burnup to minimize fuel-cycle cost. A burnup of about 15×10^{20} fissions/cm or about 4 at.% for a metallic system and about 70,000 Mwd/ton for ceramic elements is desirable. High fuel density is desired to limit critical mass or core size. High density becomes less significant as the size of the reactor increases. A reproducible fuel expansion is desirable for nuclear safety; this is readily achievable with metallic fuel but not with ceramic fuels.

Cladding should provide adequate containment for fuel and fission products and should have dimensional changes limited to about 10% of the diameter of the fuel pin to avoid coolant blockage. At a reactor outlet coolant temperature of 1200°F, cladding should have reasonable tensile and creep properties for 1300°F operation. Tensile strength should be on the order of 40,000 psi, and creep strengths should be 5000 to 10,000 psi for 1% creep in 10,000 hr. Cladding should be resistant to fast-neutron damage, should remain ductile throughout its lifetime, and should be able to withstand high thermal stresses and strain cycling. Cladding should not react chemically with coolant or fuel. Provision should be made to avoid formation of low melting eutectics between the cladding and the fuel. Nuclearwise, cladding should have a low absorption cross section. Tungsten and tantalum may not be desirable from this standpoint.

These requirements for fuel elements depart sufficiently from conventional engineering undertakings that no standard approach to resolve them has evolved. The requirements may not be mutually compatible; changes may be required as experience is gained. It is interesting that for some fuel designs, such as ceramic elements, the structural demands are placed entirely on the cladding whereas in others, metallic or cermet, the fuel itself can serve as the structural member. In the former case, destruction of the fuel may be of little consequence. In the latter case, the fuel may be required to maintain its integrity.

1.4.4.1 Fuel Materials

Three basic fuel materials can be considered, each with its advantages and weaknesses. Each is reasonably corrosion resistant in sodium.

(1) Ceramic: The high melting point of this material allows a high temperature differential across the fuel. Because the cladding is the structural member and destruction of fuel structure is accepted, this material has good burnup potential but does not have reproducible fuel-expansion characteristics. The oxide has low uranium density and low conductivity. The carbide has higher values for both these properties.

(2) Metal: The uranium-base alloys have good thermal conductivity and high uranium density, ranging up to 18.9 g/cm³ when unalloyed. No satisfactory method of suppressing phase transformation of the uranium alloys has been found; and alloy pins therefore have a high swelling-to-burnup ratio. It may be necessary to restrain growth, as for ceramic elements, and to limit metal fuel to low-temperature systems. The uranium–plutonium alloys also have low melting points, again indicating low operating temperatures or low allowable coolant-to-fuel temperature differences.

The thorium metal system may be better in many respects. Thorium metal melts at 3100°F, has no transformation to 1650°F, has good conductivity, and has a density of 12.0 g/cm³. Furthermore, uranium has a limited solubility of about 2% in thorium. Above 2% the uranium is in the form of a dispersion. This is believed to be one of the reasons for the high burnup capabilities of about 4 at.% obtained for a limited number of samples [31]. The uranium–thorium system has a minor transformation at 1200°F. Thorium creep strength is low, being less than 1000 psi for 1% creep in 10,000 hr at 1000°F.

(3) Cermet: The concept of the cermet element is to disperse the ceramic fuel in a metallic matrix. The fuel particles take the destruction that occurs with burnup. The chemical composition of the dispersed phase and its density are chosen to assure localization of fuel and fission products. The metallic matrix material provides good thermal conductivity and some restraint to swelling or fuel growth. The matrix material also provides the basic integrity of the structure, although some of the stresses formed by the dispersed phase can be transferred to the cladding by the matrix. The matrix must be capable of operating at reasonably high temperatures. For central-station application where high internal breeding ratio is desired, it is preferable to make the matrix a fertile material. A U^{238} matrix will have about 15% of the fissions of the fertile dispersal phase whereas the fissions in a thorium matrix are quite small, as indicated by Table 1.3.

1.4.4.2 Cladding Materials

High-temperature application requires appropriate cladding. The status of cladding materials is briefly reviewed. Stainless steel has only fair mechanical properties at 1300°F. It forms a eutectic with uranium alloys around 1300°F and can be carburized at elevated temperatures. The zirconium alloys have rather poor mechanical properties at high temperature, do not have eutectic-formation problems, but can be hydrided or oxidized in impure sodium. The niobium alloys have somewhat better mechanical properties than zirconium but have a high absorption cross section. Molybdenum, if ductile throughout its handling and operation range, could be of interest. Tungsten and tantalum, because of their high absorption cross sections, should be used sparingly. Bimetallic claddings may have to be developed to meet all the requirements.

1.5 Heat Transport and Plant Design

Liquid-metal coolants are attractive because they provide a means of achieving high temperature and therefore high cycle efficiency [32]. Since more electricity is produced per unit of heat generated, a high cycle efficiency tends to result in low fuel and low capital costs.

Most liquid-metal-cooled plants employ sodium for its excellent heat-transfer properties, compatibility with structural materials, and reasonable cost. An intermediate link between the reactor and the steam generators is generally used to prevent the release of radioactive sodium in the event of a steam-generator tube rupture. Although the intermediate system represents added capital investment, the total flow of the primary plus intermediate coolant is generally no greater than the flow in the primary portion of a pressurized-water system. The total heat-transfer surface for the intermediate heat exchangers and the steam generators is about the same as that for the steam generators in a pressurized-water reactor because a higher temperature differential across the heat exchanger is possible with the liquid-metal systems and the heat-transfer coefficients are higher owing to better heat-transfer characteristics of liquid metals. The resultant cost of the combined systems is no greater than for a high-pressure primary system.

The coolant temperature rise, temperature drop across the heat exchangers, and other system temperatures are discussed in the following chapters. Present sodium-cooled reactors have relatively low operating temperatures, up to 1000°F maximum sodium temperature. The primary systems have been made from 300-series stainless steel, and the intermediate systems of low chrome alloy, e.g., 2.5 wt.% Cr–1.25 wt.% Mo steel. Carbon steel has been used in some auxiliary systems for operation up to 700°F. Present data indicate that type 316 stainless steel can be operated in high-purity sodium up to 1200 or 1250°F for extended periods of time without serious corrosion or mass transport. A number of central-station sodium plants now being studied use a primary-system sodium outlet temperature of 1200°F. Further development in fuel cladding and steam-generator material will be required if a primary-system temperature higher than 1200°F is to be used.

Several characteristics of sodium-cooled fast reactors strongly influence the plant layout:

1. Concern that the core might melt and reform into a supercritical mass leads to the practice of assuring high integrity of the primary system and double containment of the primary system.
2. The high operating temperature leads to differential expansion problems that influence piping layout and neutron streaming.
3. Concern over activation of the primary-system equipment by scattering of the high-energy neutrons down the pipe ducts favors an extended system layout in which the reactor is in a compartment separated from the rest of the primary system.
4. The problem of loading and unloading the fuel elements of a compact core while adequately taking care of decay heat and avoiding sodium–air reaction problems makes fuel-handling systems complicated.

It is of interest that a basic feature of the EBR-II is the large-pot concept of the primary system, satisfying item 1 above. The Fermi plant has a loose-coupled primary system to accommodate items 2 and 3.

Because sodium reacts with air, maintenance of sodium-cooled reactors is difficult. Care should be exercised to prevent air from entering the primary system during maintenance. Components should be cleaned before repairs are made, using cleaning materials such as alcohol, ammonia, or steam. These work either on the basis of dissolution of sodium or reaction with it. The preferred method is generally one that gives the least danger of creating an excessive temperature or pressure. Individual experience plays a major role in the choice of the cleaning procedure.

1.6 Conclusions

Some of the factors which should be considered in the design of a fast reactor have been reviewed briefly, including characteristics and safety of fast reactors; fuel technology; and some aspects of heat transport system design. It does appear that the requirements can be met at a relatively low cost and that the potential of the fast reactor, particularly its breeding capabilities, outweighs its problems. The designers of sodium-cooled fast reactors face a number of problems that are more difficult to handle than those encountered in reactors with other coolants, but they appear to be problems that can be resolved. When solution of these problems is found, the rather obvious advantages of the fast reactor will lead to its rapid advancement.

References

1. S. Glasstone, Sourcebook on Atomic Energy, D. Van Nostrand Company, Inc., New York, 1950.
2. P. Abelson, Cleavage of the Uranium Nucleus, Phys. Rev., 55(4):418(Feb. 15, 1939).
3. H. D. Smyth, Atomic Energy for Military Purposes, Princeton University Press, Princeton, N. J., 1945.
4. L. Fermi, Atoms in the Family, The University of Chicago Press, Chicago, 1954.
5. R. G. Hewlett and O. E. Anderson, Jr., History of the USAEC, The New World 1939/1946, Vol. 1, The Pennsylvania State University Press, University Park, Pa., 1962.
6. W. H. Zinn, personal interview by A. C. Mansfield, Atomic Power Development Associates, Inc., Sept. 19, 1963.
7. The Argonne News, Vol. 11 (Special Issue), Dec. 21, 1961.
8. Atoms for Power: United States Policy in Atomic Energy Development, The American Assembly, Columbia University, New York, December 1957.
9. Civilian Nuclear Power. . .a Report to the President–1962, U.S. Atomic Energy Commission, 1962.
10. S. Glasstone, Principles of Nuclear Reactor Engineering, 1st ed., pp. 373–374, D. Van Nostrand Company, Inc., New York, July 1955.
11. E. D. Arnold, Radiation Limitation on Recycle of Power Reactor Fuels, Proceedings of the Second United Nations Inter-

national Conference on the Peaceful Uses of Atomic Energy, Geneva, 1958, Vol. 13, p. 237, United Nations, New York, 1958.

12. S. Yiftah and D. Okrent, Some Physics Calculations on the Performance of Large Fast Breeder Power Reactors, USAEC Report ANL-6212, Argonne National Laboratory, December 1960.

13. S. Yiftah, D. Okrent, and P. A. Moldauer, Fast Reactor Cross Sections, pp. 29-34, Pergamon Press, New York, 1960.

14. D. T. Goldman and J. R. Stehn, Chart of the Nuclides, 6th ed., General Electric Company, revised December 1961.

15. D. Okrent and W. Loewenstein, The Physics of Fast Power Reactors, Proceedings of the Second United Nations International Conference on the Peaceful Uses of Atomic Energy, Geneva, 1958, Vol. 12, p. 16, United Nations, New York, 1958.

16. D. J. Hughes, B. A. Magurno, and M. K. Brussel, Neutron Cross Sections, USAEC Report BNL-325 (2nd Ed.) (Suppl. 1), Brookhaven National Laboratory, Jan. 1, 1960.

17. Design and Economic Evaluation of Fixed Blankets for Fast Reactor, USAEC Report APDA-156, Atomic Power Development Associates, Inc., Aug. 30, 1963.

18. A Plutonium-Fueled Fast Breeder Atomic Power Plant, Report APDA-129, Atomic Power Development Associates, Inc., Apr. 2, 1959.

19. Enrico Fermi Atomic Power Plant, Report APDA-124, Atomic Power Development Associates, Inc., January 1959.

20. Directory of Nuclear Reactors, International Atomic Energy Agency, Vienna, 1958.

21. J. Chernick, Breeding Potential of Thermal Reactors, in USAEC Report ANL-6122, Argonne National Laboratory, August 1960.

22. F. G. Dawson (Comp.), Plutonium as a Fuel for Thermal Power Reactors, in USAEC Report HW-75007, Hanford Laboratories, December 1962.

23. H. A. Bethe, Reactor Safety and Oscillator Tests, Report APDA-117, Atomic Development Associates, Inc., Oct. 15, 1956.

24. R. O. Brittan, Analysis of the EBR-1 Core Meltdown (F,S), Proceedings of the Second United Nations International Conference on the Peaceful Uses of Atomic Energy, Geneva, 1958, Vol. 12, p. 242, United Nations, New York, 1958.

25. F. W. Thalgott et al., Stability Studies on EBR-I(F,S), Proceedings of the Second United Nations International Conference on the Peaceful Uses of Atomic Energy, Geneva, 1958, Vol. 12, p. 242, United Nations, New York, 1958.

26. R. R. Smith et al., A Mechanism Explaining the Instability of ERB-I Mark-II, USAEC Report ANL-6266, Argonne National Laboratory, 1960.

27. J. B. Nims and P. F. Zweifel, Preliminary Report on Sodium Temperature Coefficients in Large Fast Reactors, USAEC Report APDA-135, Atomic Power Development Associates, Inc.; also Sodium Temperature Coefficients in Fast Reactors, Trans. Amer. Nucl. Soc., 2(2):172,(1959).

28. K. Cohen and B. Wolfe, Development of the Fast Ceramic Reactor, Nuclear News, 6(2):11 (February 1963).

29. K. M. Horst and B. A. Hutchins, Comparative Study of PuC-UC and PuO_2UO_2 As Fast Reactor Fuel, Part 1 - Technical Considerations, USAEC Report GEAP-3880, General Electric Atomic Power Equipment Department, Feb. 15, 1962.

30. J. O. Smith, C. J. Shuttleworth, and G. C. Kaercher, Model Studies of Reactor Coolant and Fuel Pin Behaviour Under Conditions of Coolant Boiling and Overheating of the Fuel Elements, Detroit Edison Company Report 59D65, Nov. 20, 1961.

31. ANL Metallurgy Division Annual Report for 1961, USAEC Report ANL-6516, Argonne National Laboratory, 1962.

32. L. J. Koch and H. C. Paxton, Fast Reactors, Ann. Rev. Nucl. Sci., 9:460 (1959).

CHAPTER 2

Coolant Properties, Heat Transfer, and Fluid Flow of Liquid Metals

AARON J. FRIEDLAND
Atomic Power Development Associates, Inc.
Detroit, Michigan

Contents

A fundamental requirement in fast reactor design is the avoidance of excessive moderation of the neutron flux. Therefore chemical elements of low atomic weight, particularly hydrogen, should be avoided in the core. Water and organic compounds are also ruled out as primary coolants. High power density is desirable to minimize fuel inventory. Liquid metals therefore become the prime candidates for fast reactor coolants. Fortunately they also offer many other advantages in this application, particularly in heat transfer and stability.

2.1 Coolants

2.1.1 GENERAL REQUIREMENTS

The choice of the specific coolant for a fast reactor is governed by such factors as

1. Heat-transfer and -transport properties: The coolant should yield high heat-transfer coefficients and should possess a reasonably high heat capacity.

2. Boiling point: Except for a boiling reactor, the normal boiling point of the coolant should be well above its range of operating temperatures. This will preserve the liquid coolant properties without the need for high pressures and the penalty of increased container wall thicknesses. As a corollary, coolants of high boiling point can be operated at high temperature to produce steam of high pressure and/or superheat.

3. Corrosion and chemical activity: The coolant should have low chemical affinity for the container walls, fuel cladding, and all solid surfaces that it contacts. Insoluble compounds or reaction products that might cause plugging should be kept to a minimum. Also, compatibility with the secondary working fluid is desirable in case of leaks.

4. Decomposition: The coolant should be stable in its temperature and radiation environment.

5. Melting point: Small, simple systems can be sufficiently preheated to accept melting points up to about 600°F. For filling complicated or large systems, a much lower melting point is preferred.

6. Radioactivity: Ideally a coolant should develop no gamma activities from environmental radiation. If it does, these activities should preferably have short half-lives and low energies. Alpha and beta activities can easily be shielded, but must be contained.

7. Nuclear properties: Since coolant normally occupies more than 30% of the volume of the core, its nuclear properties are very important. Its moderating power should be low, which eliminates liquid hydrogenous coolants (Table 2.15). It is desirable that the temperature coefficient of reactivity be negative. The coolant should have low cross sections of absorption and scattering.

8. Cost: Except for the metals that have a low cost per unit volume, such as sodium, the inventory cost of liquid-metal coolant can be substantial; generally, however, it is only a small fraction of the total plant investment.

The choice of a coolant will usually depend on a compromise since no known coolant excels in all criteria. Factors 1 through 4 and 7 make liquid metals the foremost choice as primary coolants. However, other coolants may be feasible if the requirements are relaxed. For example, if the power density is sufficiently low, gas cooling may be a possible alternate to liquid-metal cooling.

2.1.2 COMPARISONS

Table 2.1 lists pertinent properties at 1000°F, unless otherwise specified, of fifteen potential fast reactor coolants. The values are from Ref. 1 and from Sec. 2.1.3. Featured in the table are three "evaluation parameters," useful in the selection of a coolant.

1. The pumping power required for heat removal is an important economic consideration. For a given coolant temperature rise, the pumping power is proportional to the following grouping, assuming the heat output, geometry, and temperature differential are the same in all cases:

$$\mu^{0.2}/(\rho^2 c_p^{2.8}) \qquad (2.1)$$

where μ = viscosity, lb/ft/hr
ρ = density, lb/cu ft
c_p = specific heat, Btu/lb/°F

A low value for this grouping indicates a low pumping requirement [2].

2. The buildup of induced activity in the primary coolant is of major importance since it affects the amount of shielding required. The specific activity in curies per gram is given by

$$S = \frac{1}{K} \sum_{ij} f_i \frac{N_0 \varphi_j \sigma_{ij}}{A_w} \frac{\tau_r}{\tau_0} (1 - e^{-0.693\,\theta/\theta_i}) \quad (2.2)$$

where S = specific activity, curies/g
f_i = atomic fraction of ith isotope in coolant
N_0 = Avogadro's number (atoms/gram mole of coolant) = 0.60248×10^{24}
φ_j = neutron flux in jth energy interval, neutrons/cm^2/sec
σ_{ij} = microscopic reaction cross section for ith isotope and jth energy interval, cm^2/nucleus
A_w = atomic weight (grams/gram mole) of coolant
τ_r = coolant residence time in neutron flux during one cycle, sec
τ_0 = cycle time for coolant, sec
θ = irradiation time, sec
θ_i = half-life of ith isotope, sec
K = constant = 3.7×10^{10} dis/curie/sec

In Table 2.1 the specific activity is estimated in curies per gram of coolant for a 1000-Mw(t) reactor. Exact values depend on reactor design details. For coolants having little or no induced (gamma) activity, e.g., lead and lithium, activation of the contained impurities takes on added importance.

3. A measure of the useful temperature range of the liquid coolant is given by the expression

$$\frac{T_b - T_m}{T_w} \qquad (2.3)$$

where T_b, T_m, and T_w are the absolute temperatures (°R) at the coolant boiling point, melting point, and the reactor outlet, respectively. High values of this ratio are desirable.

2.1.3 PHYSICAL PROPERTIES

2.1.3.1 Introduction

Physical-property data are presented for six liquid-metal coolants: lead, lithium, mercury, potassium, sodium, and NaK. Where available, data

on the vapor, including thermodynamic-property diagrams, have also been included. Vapor pressures can be obtained from the thermodynamic diagrams. The graphs apply to the liquid state unless otherwise noted. Broken lines represent estimated values or extrapolated data.

Much of the data in this section was originally tabulated in Ref. 4. The literature from 1952 to 1963 was surveyed to update the compilation.

Sections 2.1.3.2 to 2.1.3.7 present liquid metals and their applicable physical properties. Graphs of each physical property except melting point, latent heat of fusion, boiling point, latent heat of vaporization, and volume change in fusion, which are point properties, are given in this section; references are given for the point properties. The Prandtl numbers were calculated from the given values of specific heat, absolute viscosity, and thermal conductivity. The values of thermal diffusivity were calculated from given values of thermal conductivity, specific heat, and density. The properties are presented in engineering units. Conversion factors to cgs units are provided in Table 2.2.

2.1.3.2 Lead

Data on melting point, latent heat of fusion, boiling point, latent heat of vaporization, and volume change on fusion are given in Ref. 4. Graphs of surface tension, density, specific heat, viscosity, thermal conductivity, Prandtl number, thermal diffusivity, electrical resistivity, and vapor pressure are given in Figs. 2.1 to 2.10, respectively.

2.1.3.3 Lithium

Reference 6 gives the melting point (triple point) and the latent heat of fusion (triple point). The boiling point and latent heat of vaporization, calculated from the data of Ref. 8, are given in Ref. 7. The volume change on fusion can be found in Ref. 4. Surface tension, density, specific heat, viscosity, thermal conductivity, Prandtl number, thermal diffusivity, electrical resistivity, and thermodynamic diagram are given in Figs. 2.11 to 2.22, respectively.

2.1.3.4 Mercury

Data on the melting point, latent heat of fusion, boiling point, latent heat of vaporization, and volume change on fusion are given in Ref. 4. Surface tension, density, specific heat, viscosity, thermal conductivity, Prandtl number, thermal diffusivity, electrical resistivity, and thermodynamic diagram are given in Figs. 2.23 to 2.34, respectively.

2.1.3.5 Potassium

Reference 8 gives the melting point (triple point). The latent heat of fusion is given in Ref. 8; a value 0.9% higher is reported in Ref. 9. The boiling point was taken from Ref. 10, which is

Table 2.1—Properties of

	Bismuth	Gallium	Lead	Lithium (nat.)	Mercury	Potassium
General physical properties:						
Atomic number	83	31	82	3	80	19
Atomic weight	209	69.72	207.21	6.94	200.61	39.100
Density, lb/cu ft	608	359	650	29.9	826 (a)	44.6
Viscosity, lb/ft/hr	2.664	1.836	4.1	0.82	2.76 (a)	0.41
Surface tension, lb/ft	0.0247	NA	0.0293	0.0238	0.0307 (a)	0.0057 (a)
Electrical resistivity, μohm/cm	142.78	NA	104	36	108.3 (a)	48
Vapor pressure, mm Hg	Neg.	Neg.	Neg.	Neg.	9300	62 (c)
Thermal properties:						
Melting point, °F	520	85.86	621	357	−37.97	146
Boiling point, °F	2691	3601	3159	2428	675	1402
Specific heat, Btu/lb/°F	0.0369	0.082	0.0346	0.996	0.0326 (a)	0.182
Thermal conductivity, Btu/hr/ft/°F	8.95	18.0	8.84/9.01 (d)	27.6	5.8 (a)	21.2
Heat of fusion, Btu/lb	21.6	34.49	10.60	185.9	5.0	25.5
Heat of vaporization, Btu/lb	367.74	1825	368.3	8349	125.	853
Prandtl number ($c_p \mu/k$)	0.011	0.0083 (b)	0.016	0.0295	0.0154 (a)	0.0035
Change of volume on fusion, % solid volume	−3.32	−3.1	3.6	1.5	3.6	2.41
Nuclear properties:						
Fast activation cross section, mb	0.6	28.0	3.1	0.03	89.0	0.59
Nonelastic scattering cross section at 2 Mev, barns	0.53	NA	0.64	<1	2	4 (3.7 Mev)
$n,\ \gamma$ daughter half-life	None	14.1 hr	None	None	48 days	12.4 hr
$n,\ \gamma$ daughter activity, Mev	None	0.84, 0.60, 3.35	None	None	0.28	0.32, 1.51
ξ, average log energy decrement	0.0096	0.0287	0.0097	0.2643	0.0100	0.0507
General properties:						
Cost/lb (as of 1960)	$2.25	$675	$0.12	$11 (h)	$2.82	$3.66
Container material	Cr-Mo steel	Graphite	Carbon steel	Cb-Zr	Ferrous metals	304 SS
Reactions with uranium	Soluble	Soluble	Sl. soluble	Slight	Soluble	Slight (i)
Reaction with plutonium	Soluble	Soluble	Sl. soluble	Slight	Soluble	Slight (i)
Toxicity	Slight	Slight	High	Moderate	High	High
Fire or explosion hazard	Slight	None	Moderate as dust	High	None	High
Evaluation parameters:						
$\mu^{0.2}/(\rho^2 c_p^{2.8})$, pumping power criterion	0.034	0.009	0.039	0.00109	0.0261	0.050
S (specific activity), curies/g for 1,000-Mw(t) reactor	0.17	2.3	(j)	(k)	0.28	0.11
$(T_b\text{-}T_m)/T_w$, temperature range ratio	1.49	2.41	1.74	1.40	0.94	0.86

* All properties are for a temperature of 1000°F unless otherwise specified.

† Notes:

NA = Not available.
(a) At 300°F.
(b) Computed from data.
(c) See Ref. 3.
(d) See Refs. 4 and 5.
(e) Effective $\sigma_{n,p}$ over energy spectrum
(f) (n,p) reaction

(g) Computed from lead and bismuth.
(h) 99.99% Li[7], $54.50 per lb.
(i) Due to impurities.
(j) No gamma activity; beta activity is 0.090 curie/g.
(k) No gamma activity; beta activity from Li[8] is about 0.03 curie/g.
(m) No gamma activity; beta activity is about 1.5 curie/g.

close to that given in Ref. 11. Reference 12 reports a value of 1389°F; Ref. 13, which treats the data in the same manner, reports a value of 1396°F. The correlation in Ref. 14 yields a value of 1400°F. The value of 1466°F given in Ref. 15 differs considerably from the values from other observers. The value for latent heat of vaporization is from Ref. 11, and it is close to that given in Ref. 16. Other values reported in the literature are 835 Btu/lb (Ref. 17), 869 and 871 Btu/lb (p. 51, Ref. 4), 893 Btu/lb (Ref. 4), and 894 Btu/lb (Ref. 18 from data in Ref. 12). Volume change on fusion is given in Ref. 4.

Surface tension, density, specific heat, viscosity, thermal conductivity, Prandtl number, thermal diffusivity, electrical resistivity, and thermodynamic diagram are given in Figs. 2.35 to 2.46.

2.1.3.6 Sodium

Reference 8 gives the melting point (triple point) and latent heat of fusion (triple point). The boiling-point value from the correlation in Ref. 14 is in good agreement with the more recent experimental values in Refs. 12 and 19. Reference 20 gives the value for the latent heat of vaporization. Reference 21 gives a value of 1673 Btu/lb, calculated from the correlation of Ref. 14, and Ref. 22 gives a value of 1614 Btu/lb. Reference 4 gives the volume change on fusion.

Surface tension, density, specific heat, viscosity, thermal conductivity, Prandtl number, thermal diffusivity, electrical resistivity, and thermodynamic diagram are given in Figs. 2.47 to 2.59, respectively.

Liquid Metals[*][†]

Rubidium	Sodium	Tin	Zinc	Na (56%) K (44%)	Na (22%) K (78%)	Pb (44.5%) Bi (55.5%)	Sulfur	Phosphorus
37	11	50	30				16	15
85.48	22.997	118.70	65.38	30.082	35.557	208.2	32.066	31
84.4	51.4	421	428	47.4	46.3	625.5	102.5 (732°F)	84.9 (436°F)
0.415	0.55	2.736	6.192	0.47	0.43	2.88	680 (732°F)	<1
0.0022 (b)	0.0101	0.0347	0.0535	0.0071 (a)	0.0078 (a)	NA	0.00294	NA
60 (b)	29	55.54	35.22	61	71	129.85	173 (732°F)	NA
139 (c)	9 (c)	Neg.	Neg.	26 (b,c)	45 (b,c)	Neg.	310.2 (732°F)	227.5 (436°F)
102	208.1	449	787	66.2	12	257	246	111.5
1270	1618	4118	1663	1518	1443	3038	832	536
0.0877	0.301	0.0639	0.1165	0.2485	0.209	0.035	0.248 (732°F)	NA
13.2	37	19.0	33.2	16.4	15.05	8.05	0.0952	NA
11.0	48.7	26.1	43.92	NA	NA	NA	25.8 (15°C)	9.06 (15°C)
363	1718	1031	755.1	NA	NA	NA	121.2	254 (15°C)
0.00276 (b)	0.0044	0.0095	0.022	0.0071	0.0060	0.0125	1771	<1
2.5	2.5	2.6	6.9	2.5	2.5	0.0	NA	NA
46.0	0.87	14.0	13.0	0.80	0.64	3.5	1.4 (e,f)	3 (e,f)
NA	<1	1	1	NA	NA	0.58 (g)	NA	NA
19 days	15 hr	112 days	None	See K, Na	See K, Na	None	None	None
1.1	2.775, 1.368	0.39	None	NA	NA	None	None	None
0.0234	0.0852	0.0169	0.0305	NA	NA	NA	0.0616	0.0637
$390	$0.17	$1.00	$0.13	$0.60	$0.80	See Pb, Bi	$0.08	$0.09
304 SS	304 SS	Quartz	Graphite	304 SS	304 SS	Cr-Mo steel	Graphite	NA
Slight (i)	Slight (i)	Sl. soluble	Sl. soluble	Slight	Slight	Sl. soluble	Reacts	Reacts
Slight (i)	Slight (i)	Alloys	NA	Slight	Slight	Sl. soluble	Reacts	Reacts
Moderate	High	None	None	High	High	High	Slight	Moderate
High	High	Slight as dust	Moderate	High	High	Moderate as dust	Slight	High
0.107	0.0097	0.015	0.003	0.0189	0.0316	0.024	0.0174	NA
2.6	0.20	0.95	1.17	0.16	0.11	0.09	0.80	(m)
0.80	0.97	2.51	0.60	0.99	0.98	1.91	0.90	0.47

Table 2.2—Factors for Conversion from Engineering Units to CGS Units

Temperature	$°C = \frac{5}{9}(°F - 32)$
Latent heat	1 Btu/lb (mass) = 0.5556 cal/g
Surface tension	1 lb (force)/ft = 1.459 × 10^4 dynes/cm
Density (ρ)	1 lb (mass)/cu ft = 0.01602 g/cm^3
Specific heat (c_p)	1 Btu/lb (mass)/°F = 1 cal/g/°C
Viscosity (μ)	1 lb (mass)/ft/hr = 4.134 × 10^{-3} g/cm/sec, or poise
Thermal conductivity (k)	1 Btu/hr/ft/°F = 4.134 × 10^{-3} cal/sec/cm/°C
Prandtl number	$N_{Pr} = c_p \mu/k$, dimensionless
Thermal diffusivity $k/(c_p \rho)$	1 sq ft/hr = 0.2581 cm^2/sec

2.1.3.7 Sodium–Potassium Alloys

Reference 4 gives the melting point and a phase diagram of the sodium–potassium system. Reference 4 also gives the boiling-point values (which agree well with those calculated from the

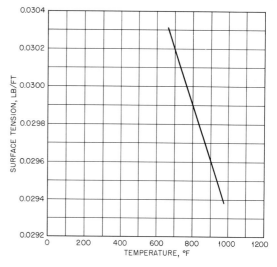

FIG. 2.1—Lead, surface tension [4, 23].

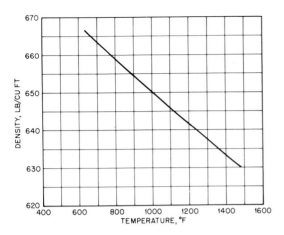

FIG. 2.2—Lead, density. The data are from Ref. 24; the values in Ref. 4 are 0.9% lower.

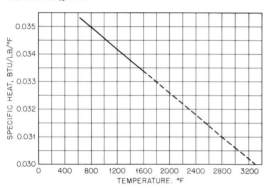

FIG. 2.3—Lead, specific heat. The values are from Ref. 25, and the extrapolation is from Ref. 7.

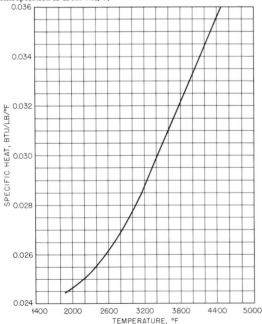

FIG. 2.4—Lead, specific heat of saturated vapor. The values for the ideal monatomic gas were calculated in Refs. 7 and 32.

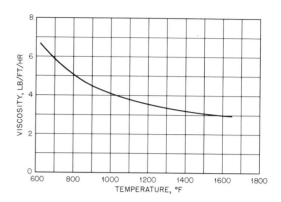

FIG. 2.5—Lead, viscosity. The values are from Ref. 26 and are close to those from Ref. 5. They are within 5% of the values from Refs. 4 and 27. The curves from Refs. 28 and 29 for temperatures below 825°F cross the curve from Ref. 26, that from Ref. 28 is 10% lower at 625°F, and that from Ref. 29 is 15% higher at 825°F.

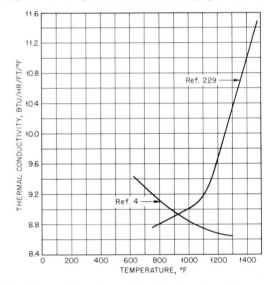

FIG. 2.6—Lead, thermal conductivity. The values from Refs. 4 and 229 are both shown.

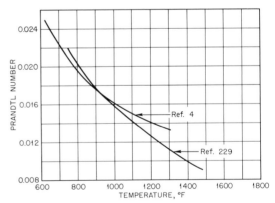

FIG. 2.7—Lead, Prandtl number. Based on thermal conductivity from Refs. 4 and 229.

vapor-pressure data of the pure metals using Raoult's law) and the volume change on fusion.

Surface tension, density, specific heat, viscosity, thermal conductivity, thermal diffusivity,

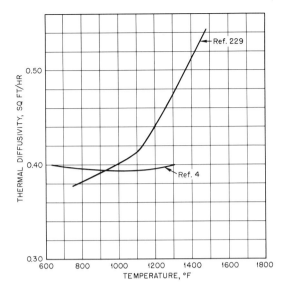

FIG. 2.8—Lead, thermal diffusivity. Based on thermal conductivity from Refs. 4 and 229.

Prandtl number, electrical resistivity, and vapor pressure are given in Figs. 2.60 to 2.68, respectively.

2.1.4 CHEMICAL PROPERTIES

2.1.4.1 Impurities

Many impurities are present in liquid metals as trace quantities only and are therefore of little consequence to the designer of the coolant system of a fast reactor. Nevertheless, the designer should include in his specification limitations on the allowable concentration of those impurities that may be deleterious to his system or that may affect the nuclear-control characteristics of the reactor. The impurities of primary concern are carbon, calcium, hydrogen, and uranium. The "normal" impurities found in liquid metals are listed in Table 2.3.

Minute amounts of many elements and compounds are soluble in liquid metals. Quantitative

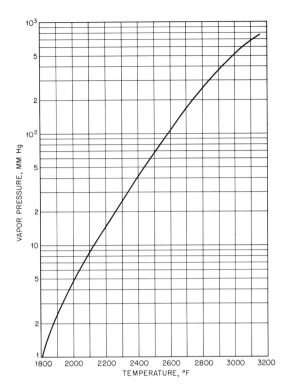

FIG. 2.10—Lead, vapor pressure [4].

analyses of these impurities require rather demanding analytical procedures. Because of the reactive nature of liquid metals, especially the alkali metals, extreme care should be exercised to avoid contamination during sampling, transport, and analysis. Small quantities of air admitted at any time during the cycle from initial sampling to analysis can render the results completely meaningless. Contamination from the walls of the sample container can have a similar effect.

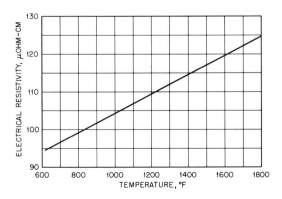

FIG. 2.9—Lead, electrical resistivity [4].

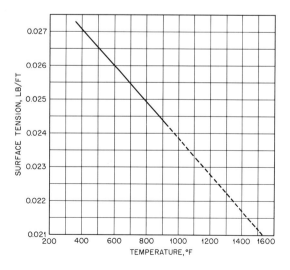

FIG. 2.11—Lithium, surface tension [30].

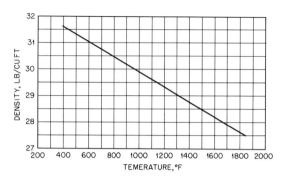

FIG. 2.12—Lithium, density [4].

Both physical and wet chemical methods are used for liquid-metals analysis. Spectrographic analysis, from which the impurity data for potassium and NaK given in Table 2.3 were obtained, is a common method. The various methods used in sodium and lithium analysis are listed in Tables 2.4 and 2.5, respectively (see p. 34).

2.1.4.2 Analysis of Oxygen in Sodium

2.1.4.2.1 MERCURY AMALGAMATION METHOD. This method was originally developed by

Pepkowitz and Judd [81]. The procedure involves the separation of sodium monoxide from free sodium by extraction of the latter with mercury.

The precision reported in the original work was ± 0.01% for a series of samples. Further modifications in the procedure resulted in an improvement in precision to ± 0.0016% oxygen

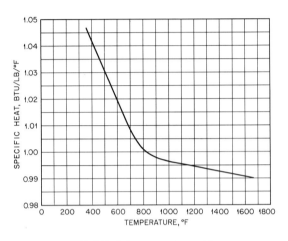

FIG. 2.13—Lithium, specific heat[6].

Table 2.3—Normal Impurities (in parts per million) in Liquid Metals [73-77]

| Impurity | Liquid metal | | | | Impurity | Liquid metal | | | |
	Na (Ref. 73)	NaK (Ref. 74)	K (Ref. 74)	Li (Ref. 75)		Na (Ref. 73)	NaK (Ref. 74)	K (Ref. 74)	Li (Ref. 75)
Ag	<1	<1	<1		In	2[†]			
Al	7.7	4	2		K	100			100
Au					La				
B	<1*−4	<50	<20		Li	1*−17			
Ba	2				Mg	5	1	5	
Be	<1[†]	<5	<1		Mn	2	2	1	
Bi	<10[†]	<10			Mo	2[†]	5	1	
Br					Na				50−300
C	37				N				100
Ca	<5*−191	<50	1	100	Ni	0.5	10	2	
Cb					O				
Cd	<1	<50			P	10			
Ce	2				Pb	1.1	5	4	
Cl	10*−30				Pd	5			
Co	2	<10	5		S	5*−14			
Cr	<1	<5	<3		Sb				
Cs	<5				Si	0.5	5	10	
Cu	2	3	3		Sm				
F		<5			Sn	10[†]	10	1	
Fe	2.4	10	<1	10	Sr	5			
Ga					Ta				
Gd					Th				
Ge					Ti	10[†]	10	10	
H					U	3.5*			
Hf					V	5		2	
Hg	<4[†]				Zn	2[‡]	100		
I					Zr-Hf	2[‡]			

* Reference 76.

[†] None detected

[‡] Reference 77.

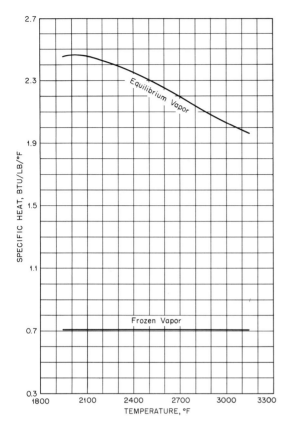

FIG. 2.14—Lithium, specific heat of saturated vapor. The values were calculated in Ref. 32.

[82]. Williams and Miller [83] made additional modifications to the procedure and apparatus and reported a precision of ± 0.0006% (6 ppm oxygen). For the same method, Ref. 84 reports a sensitivity of 100 μg of Na$_2$O with a coefficient of variation of ± 30%. The poor precision is attributed to sampling difficulties. The amalgamation method has also been used by the Russians

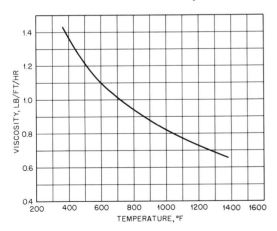

FIG. 2.15—Lithium, viscosity. The values are from Ref. 5; the values in Ref. 31 are 5% lower at 546°F and agree well at lower temperatures.

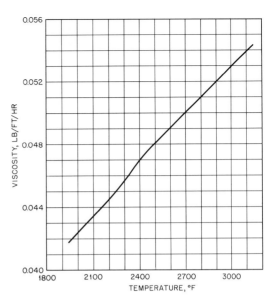

FIG. 2.16—Lithium, viscosity of saturated vapor. The values were calculated in Refs. 16 and 32.

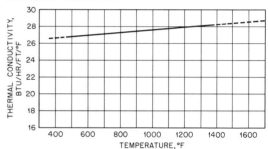

FIG. 2.17—Lithium, thermal conductivity. The values are from Ref. 5. The preliminary data in Ref. 33 are 10% lower at 542°F and 4% higher at 973°F. The values in Refs. 34 and 35 are in good agreement at low temperatures, but the values in Ref. 34 are 25% higher at 1400°F and 28% higher than the extrapolated value at 2000°F. The values in Ref. 35 are 36% lower at 1000°F.

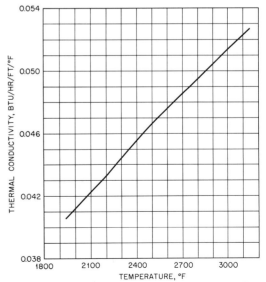

FIG. 2.18—Lithium, thermal conductivity of saturated vapor. The values were estimated in Ref. 32.

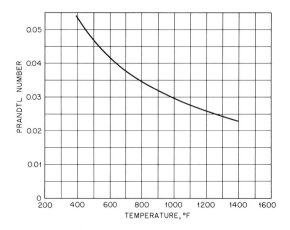

FIG. 2.19—Lithium, Prandtl number.

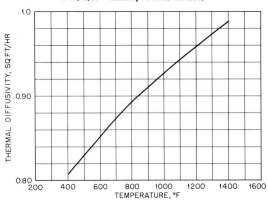

FIG. 2.20—Lithium, thermal diffusivity.

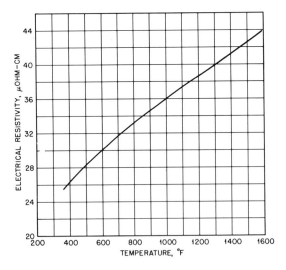

FIG. 2.21—Lithium, electrical resistivity. The values are from Ref. 36; the values in Ref. 37 are 4% lower over the range 392 to 1022°F.

[85] with a reported sensitivity of 0.001% and an accuracy of 10%.

The subsequent analysis of the residue after amalgamation is critical as Na_2O_2, NaO_2, $NaOH$,

Na_2CO_3, NaH, and sodium carbides could also be separated from free sodium by the amalgamation process. Dissolution of the residue in water should not be performed without considering the possibility of the presence of these other impurities. Epstein [86] suggested that provision be made for collection of any effluent gases resulting from aqueous dissolution of the residue. These gases could then be analyzed by gas chromatography. Standard acid could then be added to react with any carbonates or carbides that are resistant to decomposition by water and the effluent gases could again be collected and analyzed. Finally, the sodium oxide would be determined by titration or flame photometry with appropriate correction for the presence of other impurities as indicated by gas evolution.

Steinmetz and Minushkin [87] made significant modifications to the amalgamation method. These modifications eliminate the effect of some of the interfering elements and extend the sensitivity to less than 10 ppm. After the amalgamation step, the residue is dissolved in alcohol and reacted with an organic acid which converts sodium oxide into an equivalent amount of water. This water is then titrated with Karl Fischer reagent. The method had the advantage of not requiring a complete separation of sodium from sodium oxide. The method was checked with samples containing known amounts of oxygen. The analysis of a series of zirconium-gettered sodium samples gave a mean value of 3 ppm of oxygen with a standard deviation of ± 1.5 ppm.

2.1.4.2.2 ALKYL HALIDE METHOD. White, Ross, and Rowan [88] developed the butyl bromide method for the determination of sodium monoxide. The method depends upon the reaction between sodium and excess n-butyl bromide (1-bromobutane) in hexane solution. Sodium monoxide does not react with the reagent and can be determined, after the addition of water, by titration. The method requires only the simplest equipment and is easily adapted to the analysis of large numbers of samples. The standard deviation is 0.003 to 0.005%. The method has been applied to sodium that has been sampled in glass and in metallic containers. The method is believed to be applicable in the range 0 to 0.02%, (0 to 200 ppm) if large samples are used. This method has been applied by Silverman and Shideler [89] to analysis of oxygen in sodium and NaK and by Kirtchik and Riechmann [90] to analysis of oxygen in potassium.

DeBruin [91] has reported work on the development of a method with an accuracy and a reproducibility that exceed those of the conventional alkyl halide method. Improved procedures to a lower limit of 20 ppm with an accuracy to ± 20% are detailed. A Wurtz reaction, employing n-amyl chloride, is followed by infrared analysis of the solid reaction products containing the oxygen impurity. Again, Epstein [86] points out that, since the Wurtz reaction eliminates only the sodium, the residue should be analyzed with the assumption that the same interfering compounds are present that are present in the amalgamation method.

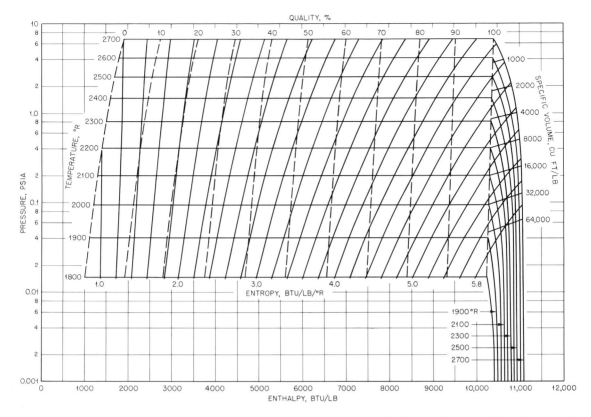

FIG. 2.22—Lithium, pressure-enthalpy diagram. The pressure-enthalpy diagram based on 1954 National Bureau of Standards data is from Ref. 11. Reference 32 gives a Mollier diagram based on Ref. 16.

2.1.4.2.3 VACUUM-DISTILLATION METHOD. Humphreys [92] developed a method for the analysis of oxygen in sodium using vacuum distillation to accomplish the separation of sodium and sodium oxide. Peaks [93] reports his experience with the distillation method for the analysis of sodium oxide in NaK. He claims that, although the method lacks precision, it is recommended as a convenient means for analysis of oxide in liquid-metal systems. Epstein [86] reports that the vacuum-distillation technique is in routine use at Dounreay with a reproducibility of ± 2 ppm of oxygen.

Frost [94] comments that the presence of other sodium compounds could cause errors, depending upon how the residue is analyzed. Errors could also result if elements capable of reducing Na_2O are present.

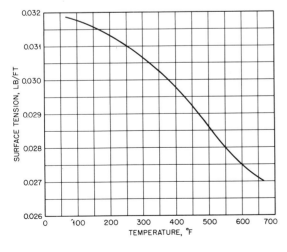

FIG. 2.23—Mercury, surface tension [4].

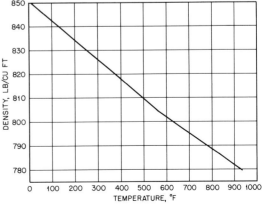

FIG. 2.24—Mercury, density [4, 5].

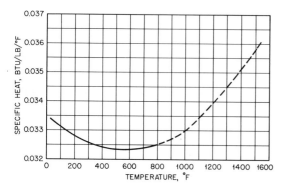

FIG. 2.25—Mercury, specific heat. The values are from Ref. 38, and the extrapolation is from Ref. 16.

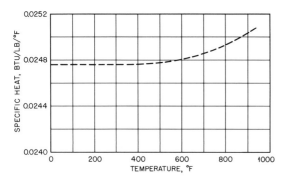

FIG. 2.26—Mercury vapor, specific heat. The values were calculated in Ref. 38.

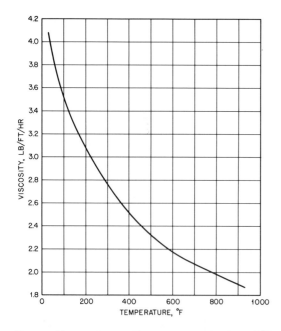

FIG. 2.27—Mercury, viscosity. The values are from Ref. 5. At 650°F, they are 6% higher than the values in Ref. 4 and 5% lower than the values in Ref. 39. At 570°F, they are 11% lower than the values in Ref. 40. At low temperatures, the agreement is good.

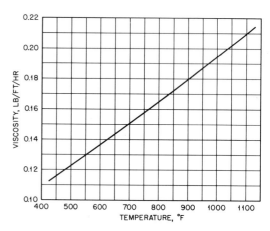

FIG. 2.28—Mercury vapor, viscosity. The values are from an equation in Ref. 41 that was fitted to the experimental data in Refs. 42 and 43.

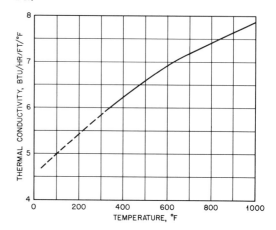

FIG. 2.29—Mercury, thermal conductivity. The values are from Ref. 44. The values from Ref. 5 are almost identical above 650°F and are up to 4% lower at lower temperatures. The values from Ref. 45 are 6% higher than the recommended curve at 160°F and are closer at higher and lower temperatures.

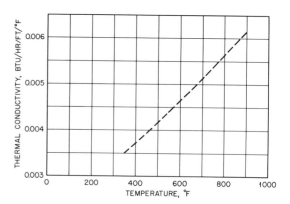

FIG. 2.30—Mercury vapor, thermal conductivity. The values were estimated from the specific heat and viscosity assuming a constant Prandtl number of 0.73.

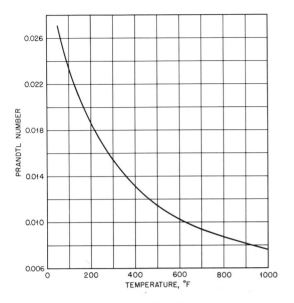

FIG. 2.31—Mercury, Prandtl number.

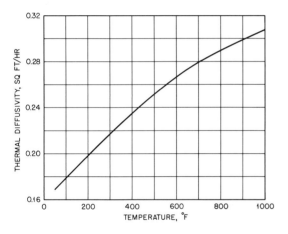

FIG. 2.32—Mercury, thermal diffusivity.

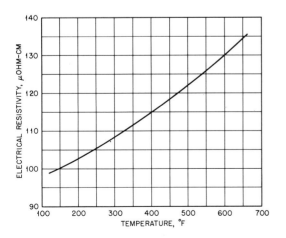

FIG. 2.33—Mercury, electrical resistivity [4].

2.1.4.2.4 OTHER METHODS. Several other possible methods for oxygen analysis in sodium have been analytically and experimentally reviewed at Battelle Memorial Institute [95]. An excellent review of all methods is given by Smith [96].

2.1.4.3 Analysis of Elemental Carbon in Sodium

Carbon appears to occur in sodium in a variety of forms. Some of the compounds that may be present are carbides, formates, oxylates, suboxides, carbonates, "amorphous" carbon, and graphitic carbon. Some of these materials appear to be present in true solution; others appear as suspended particles. Some may be present in both forms.

One way to develop some knowledge about the nature of carbon contained in a specific sample is to treat the sample as follows:

1. Add an amount of water to react with all the sodium present in an accurately weighed sample plus an excess of four to five times this amount. The sample should be contained in a leak-free gas-collecting system and not a flow-through apparatus. If any carbon-containing materials of the carbide type are present, methane or acetylene will be evolved. These gases can be measured directly by gas chromographic techniques, or they can be oxidized to CO_2 and measured in that form. Although it has been assumed that sodium carbides should evolve acetylene upon hydrolysis, carbides having an aluminum carbide structure evolve methane, as described by W. A. Weyl in Pennsylvania State College Bulletin No. 57, p. 85, 1951. This type of structure cannot be ruled out for sodium carbide in sodium. Another source of methane is the possible reaction of elemental carbon or organic compounds with water under the reducing condition of the sodium—water reaction to form hydrocarbons.

2. If the alkaline solution formed by the above treatment is now treated with an excess of acid, an additional amount of carbon-containing gas is evolved, mainly carbon monoxide and carbon dioxide in varying ratios; the relative amount will depend in part upon the time–temperature history of the sample. The gas can also be collected and measured by an appropriate method to allow a quantitative estimate of the proportion of carbon of this type. The most likely sources of these gases are sodium carbonate, sodium formate, sodium oxylate, sodium salts of C_3O_2, and other carbon compounds that are unstable in an acid solution.

3. The carbon remaining in the aqueous solution of the sample after the above two treatments is generally considered to be elemental carbon and is the type generally reported as carbon when the Van Slyke method of carbon oxidation, modified by Pepkowitz and Porter [97], is used. The acidified solution is treated with a strong oxidizing agent in this method, and the evolved carbon dioxide is measured. Much confusion has been caused by this method. It should be realized that the method was never intended to measure any type of carbon except elemental carbon when this method is used.

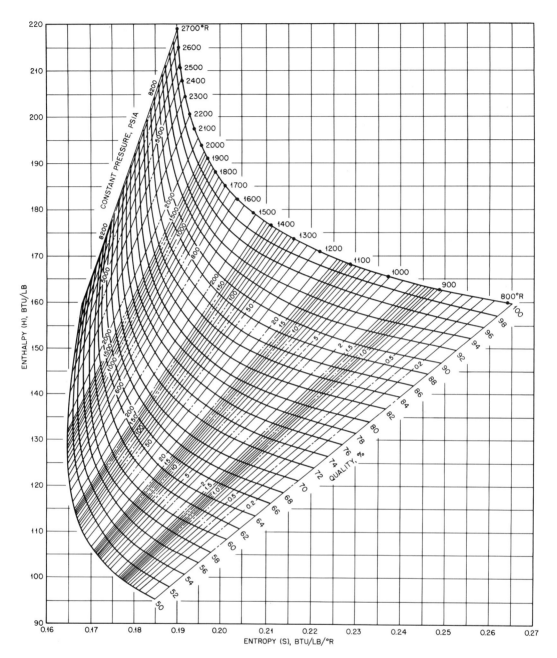

FIG. 2.34—Mercury, thermodynamic diagram. Reference point: enthalpy at 0°R:0, entropy at 0°R:0. Redrawn from copy furnished by Flight Propulsion Department, General Electric Company. Superheat region deleted because no dimerization was included in its calculation. Data sources: Refs. 32 and 46. Properties: liquid specific heat, melting point, liquid molecular weight, enthalpy and free-energy functions, and specific heat of monatomic vapor.

A further difficulty is the large reproducible blank of the Van Slyke reagent, which raises serious doubts that the reported accuracy and precision can be achieved. However, various laboratories have reported [79, 84, 87] that this method is in use.

A more direct method of analyzing for total carbon in sodium is by the use of direct combustion with oxygen so that the sample is converted to a mixture of sodium carbonate and sodium oxide. Stoffer and Phillips [99] reported on the use of this method for the determination of carbon in a sodium—potassium alloy. After the sample has been oxidized, the mixture of sodium carbonate and sodium oxide should be thermally decomposed at a sufficiently high temperature to drive out all the CO_2. This appears [98] to require a temperature of 1100°C.

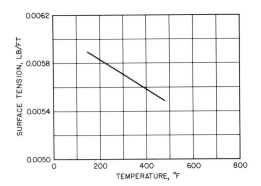

FIG. 2.35—Potassium, surface tension. The values are preliminary Naval Research Laboratory data quoted in Ref. 4 and are close to those given in Ref. 47.

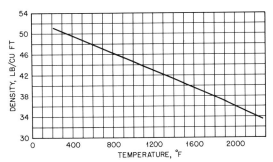

FIG. 2.36—Potassium, density [4, 48].

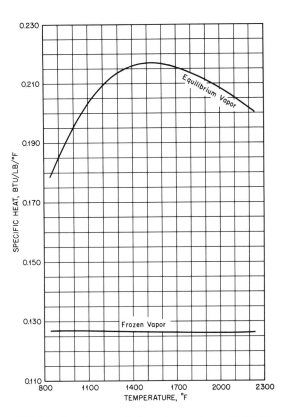

FIG. 2.38—Potassium, specific heat of saturated vapor [16, 32]. The values were calculated in Ref. 16.

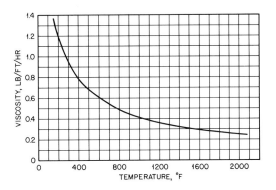

FIG. 2.39—Potassium, viscosity. The values are from Ref. 50. The values in Ref. 5 agree well at 150 and 1330°F and are up to 5% higher in the region between. The agreement with Refs. 51 and 52 is good. The values of Ref. 53 are 6% lower at 160°F and cross over at 460°F. The values of Refs. 54 and 55 for temperatures up to 660°F are about 10% lower.

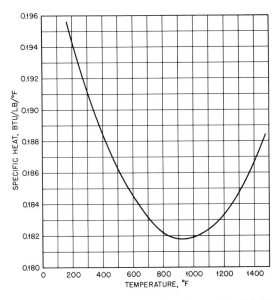

FIG. 2.37—Potassium, specific heat. The values are from Ref. 49. The data in Ref. 9 are given by $c_p = 0.2004 - 0.8777 \times 10^{-4}t + 1.0970 \times 10^{-7}t^2$ (t in °C) in the range 146 to 2102°F. They are within 1% of the values in Ref. 49 below 900°F and are 6.4% higher at 1472°F.

2.1.4.4 Analysis of Carbonate in Sodium

A method for the determination of carbon in the form of carbonate in sodium is given in Ref. 84. A minimum of 50 μg of carbon can be detected. A negative bias of 5% is reported with a coefficient of variation of $\pm 6.5\%$ at the 500-μg level.

2.1.4.5 Analysis of Hydrogen in Sodium

2.1.4.5.1 ISOTOPIC-DILUTION METHOD. Holt [100] reports a method for the analysis of hydrogen in sodium using isotopic dilution. Spikes equivalent

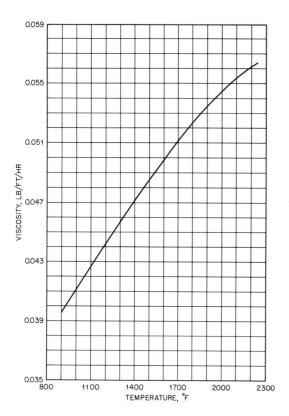

FIG. 2.40—Potassium, viscosity of saturated vapor. The values were calculated in Ref. 32.

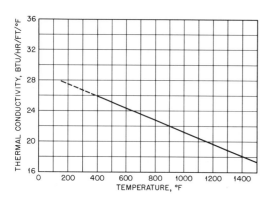

FIG. 2.41—Potassium, thermal conductivity. The values are from Ref. 56 below 1100°F and from Ref. 10 above 1100°F. The values from Ref. 10 are 14% higher at 300°F and are in good agreement above 800°F. The values from Ref. 5 are in good agreement below 800°F and are 14% lower at 1300°F.

to 5 to 250 ppm of hydrogen were recovered in 2-g samples with a standard deviation of ± 2 ppm.

2.1.4.5.2 DIFFUSION METHOD. Pepkowitz and Proud [80] give a method for the determination of hydrogen in sodium. The basis of the method is the evolution of hydrogen from the sample contained in a sealed iron capsule and the subsequent diffusion of the liberated hydrogen through the walls of the capsule into a simple vacuum system. The reported average deviation is 10 ppm of hydrogen. A hydrogen

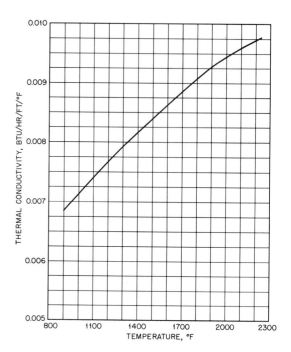

FIG. 2.42—Potassium, thermal conductivity of saturated vapor. The values were estimated in Ref. 32.

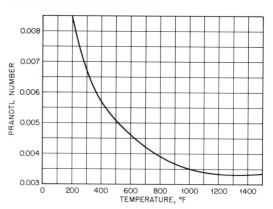

FIG. 2.43—Potassium, Prandtl number.

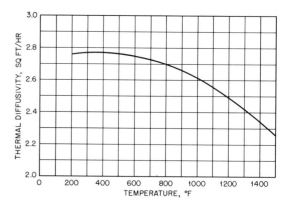

FIG. 2.44—Potassium, thermal diffusivity.

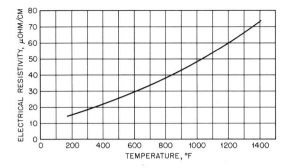

FIG. 2.45—Potassium, electrical resistivity. The values are from Ref. 57. The agreement with the values in Refs. 4 and 10 is very good.

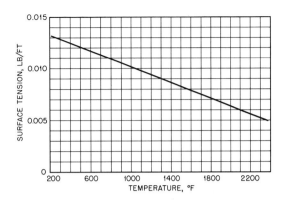

FIG. 2.47—Sodium, surface tension. The values are from Ref. 58. An equation given in Ref. 22, based on the experimental data of Refs. 59 and 60 from the melting point to 842°F, was used to extrapolate to higher temperatures.

monitor for continuous indication is reported in Ref. 101.

2.1.4.6 Solubility of Oxygen in Lithium

The solubility of oxygen in lithium is shown in Fig. 2.69. The curve was prepared from tests conducted at four temperatures; a minimum of seven samples was taken at each temperature. The results are not consistent with the reported ineffectiveness of cold-trapping techniques for reducing oxygen content in lithium. However, the inconsistency may be due to the different analytical techniques employed.

2.1.4.7 Solubility of Materials in Sodium

Oxygen impurity normally is present as sodium monoxide, sodium hydroxide, and sodium carbonate. Hydrogen impurity normally is present as sodium

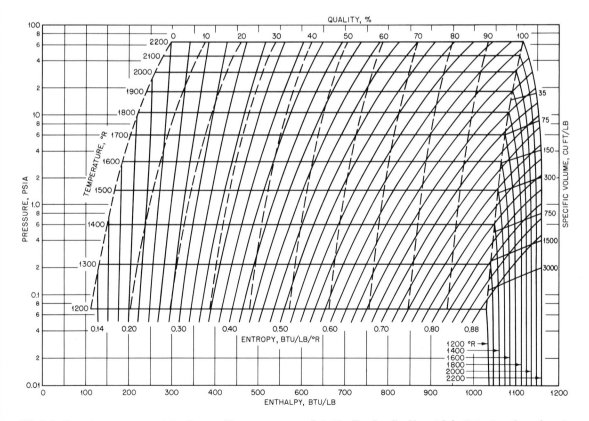

FIG. 2.46—Potassium, pressure–enthalpy diagram. The pressure–enthalpy diagram based on 1954 National Bureau of Standards data is from Ref. 11. Reference 32 gives a Mollier diagram based on Ref. 16. The Battelle Memorial Institute gives thermodynamic data in Ref. 17 and is in the process of preparing a Mollier diagram.

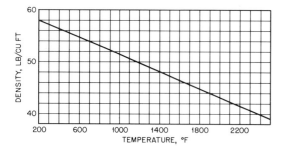

FIG. 2.48—Sodium, density. The values are from Ref. 58. An equation given in Ref. 22, which is based on the experimental data of Refs. 61 to 63, is used from the melting point to 1184°F and extended linearly to join the high-temperature preliminary data of Ref. 64.

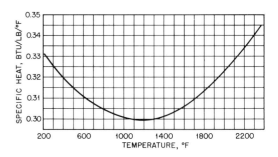

FIG. 2.50—Sodium, specific heat. The values are from Ref. 58. An equation given in Ref. 22, based on the experimental data of Ref. 65 from the melting point to 1647°F, was used to extrapolate to higher temperatures.

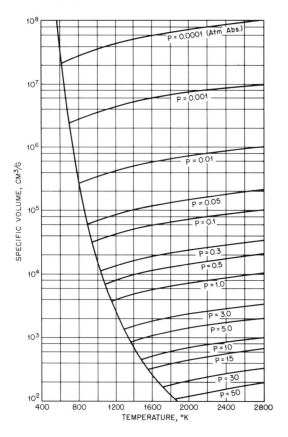

FIG. 2.49—Sodium, specific volume vapor. The specific volume (reciprocal density) values were calculated in Ref. 20.

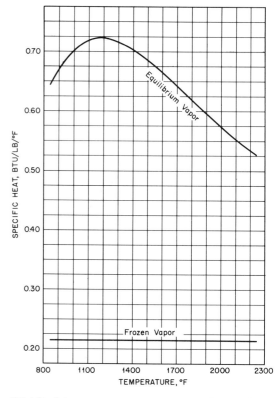

FIG. 2.51—Sodium, specific heat of saturated vapor [16, 32, 66]. The values were calculated in Ref. 16. The values for the frozen vapor are close to those given in Ref. 66.

hydride and sodium hydroxide. Carbon impurity may be present as elemental carbon and sodium carbonate.

2.1.4.7.1 SODIUM MONOXIDE. The solubility of sodium monoxide in sodium has been investigated and discussed by a number of workers [102-112]. The available data over the temperature range 250 to 1000°F are shown in Fig. 2.70. The scatter in the data appears to correlate as a straight line on a log—log plot although considerable scatter exists. The line shown in Fig.

2.70 was taken from KAPL studies [102] and appears to be as good a line as can be drawn through the data points generated by the other investigators.

A detailed review and critique of the solubility experiments and data given in Refs. 102 through 105 appears in Ref. 107.

2.1.4.7.2 CARBON. The solubility of carbon in liquid sodium [113] is shown in Fig. 2.71. These data tend to indicate that carbon solubility is oxygen dependent. Additional information is needed to definitely establish this dependency.

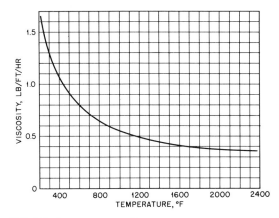

FIG. 2.52—Sodium, viscosity. The values are from Ref. 22 and are based on the experimental data of Refs. 54, 62, and 67 from the melting point to 1615°F. The extrapolation is from Ref. 58. The values from Ref. 5 are 5% higher at 212°F, 10% lower at 1472°F, and are close at intermediate temperatures.

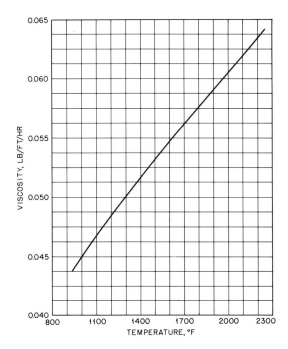

FIG. 2.53—Sodium, viscosity of saturated vapor. The values given were calculated in Ref. 32. They are up to twice as large as the values given in Ref. 58.

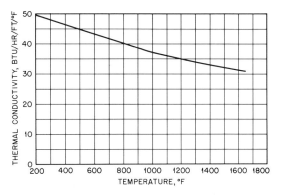

FIG. 2.54—Sodium, thermal conductivity (Refs. 5, 22, 32, 34, 56, 58, 68). The values are based on the experimental data of Refs. 56 and 68 and of the General Electric Company as given in Refs. 22 and 34. The values in Ref. 5 are in very good agreement at the ends of the range and are 3% lower at intermediate temperatures.

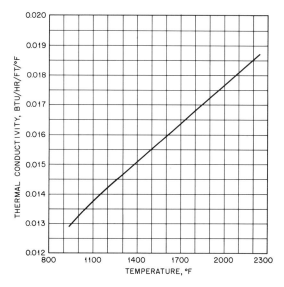

FIG. 2.55—Sodium, thermal conductivity of saturated vapor. The values were estimated in Ref. 32 and are lower than the values given in Ref. 58 by up to a factor of 2.

2.1.4.7.6 URANIUM. The solubility of uranium in sodium is not well known. Reference 115 gives a value of 0.007 wt.% at 97.8°C (208°F) but points out that this may not be precise owing to several possible errors.

2.1.4.7.7 XENON. A study of the solubility of xenon in sodium has been made [116], and the results are shown in Fig. 2.74. These data were obtained using a xenon pressure of 1 atm over the sodium. With only a partial atmosphere of xenon, which is generally the case, applicable relations, such as Henry's law, can be used to estimate the solubility.

2.1.4.7.8 ARGON. The solubility of argon in liquid sodium has been calculated in Ref. 117 and is shown in Fig. 2.75. The curve applies to a sodium–argon system in which the partial pressure of argon is 1 atm.

2.1.4.7.3 SODIUM HYDROXIDE. The solubility of sodium hydroxide in sodium [18] is shown in Fig. 2.72.

2.1.4.7.4 SODIUM HYDRIDE. The solubility of sodium hydride in sodium [114] is shown in Fig. 2.73. It should be noted that sodium hydride is unstable and decomposes as a function of temperature.

2.1.4.7.5 SODIUM CARBONATE. The solubility of sodium carbonate in liquid sodium [114] is shown in Fig. 2.73.

Table 2.4—Standard Methods of Sodium-impurity Analysis

Impurity	Method [78,79]	Accuracy, *ppm
Aluminum	8-Hydroxy-quinoline	±1
Boron	Curcumin	±0.10
Cadmium	Dithizone	±0.02
Calcium	8-Hydroxy-quinoline and murexide	±2
	Hydroxide-cyanide and calcain (titrate with standard EDTA solution) [79]	N.A.
Carbon	Van-Slyke solution and titration (silver nitrate) (Refs. 78, 79, 84, 87)	±10
	Combustion process [99]	±50
Chlorides	Turbidimetric	±5
Hafnium	Sodium alizarin sulfonate	±1
Hydrogen	Diffusion through iron membrane [80]	N.A.
Iron	Hydrazine [79]	N.A.
Lanthanides	Sodium alizarin sulfonate	±1
Lead	Coprecipitate with Fe^{3+} and polarograph	±0.5
Lithium	HCl gas and Thoron	±0.05
	Flame photometry [79]	N.A.
Nickel	Dimethylglyoxime reagent [79]	N.A.
Oxygen	Extraction with mercury and titration (KAPL method) [78, 79]	±10
	Same with Karl Fischer method [87]	±1.5
	Alkyl halide, (Refs. 86, 88, 89, 90, and 91)	±4
	Vacuum distillation, (Refs. 86, 92, 93, and 94)	±2
Phosphorus	Coprecipitation with Fe^{3+} and molybdenum blue	±0.5
Potassium	HCl gas and sodium tetraphenyl boron	±15
	Flame photometry [79]	N.A.
Silver	Dithizone	±1
Sulfur	$BaCl_2$ turbidimetric	±5
Tin	Coprecipitate with Fe^{3+} and polarograph	±0.5
Tungsten	Thiocyanate and stannous chloride	±1
Zinc	Dithizone	±1
Zirconium	Alizarin reagent [79]	N.A.

*N.A., not available.

2.1.4.7.9 HELIUM. According to Ref. 18, the solubility of helium in liquid sodium is 1.63×10^{-14} mole fraction at 450°F and 1.48×10^{-10} mole fraction at 900°F.

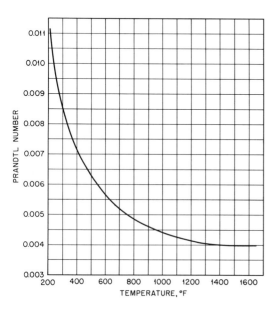

FIG. 2.56—Sodium, Prandtl number.

Table 2.5—Standard Methods of Lithium Impurity Analysis

Impurity	Method [75]
Calcium	Ammonium oxalate
Iron	Colorimetric (orthophenanthroline monohydrate)
Nitrogen	Colorimetry
Potassium	Flame photometry
Sodium	Flame photometry

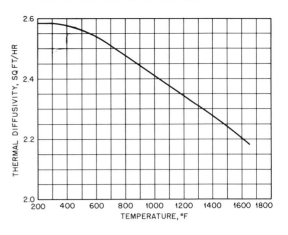

FIG. 2.57—Sodium, thermal diffusivity.

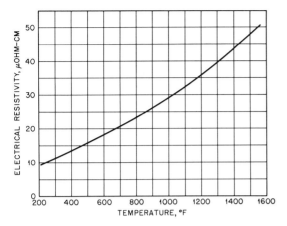

FIG. 2.58—Sodium, electrical resistivity. The values are from Ref. 57. The values from Ref. 37 for temperatures up to 1112°F are 4% lower, and the values given in Ref. 22, based on earlier experimental data, are 7% lower at 662°F and approach the values from Ref. 57 at lower temperatures.

2.1.4.7.10 CALCIUM. An equation, given in Ref. 18, yields the curve shown in Fig. 2.76 for the solubility of calcium in liquid sodium.

2.1.4.8 Reactions with Gases

In general, the alkali metals react chemically with oxygen, air, carbon dioxide, carbon monoxide, and hydrogen. Each of these reactions is presented below.

2.1.4.8.1 OXYGEN. (See Ref. 118 for thermodynamic data.)

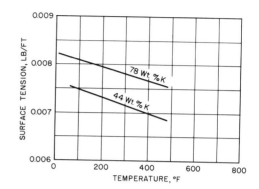

FIG. 2.60—NaK, surface tension [4].

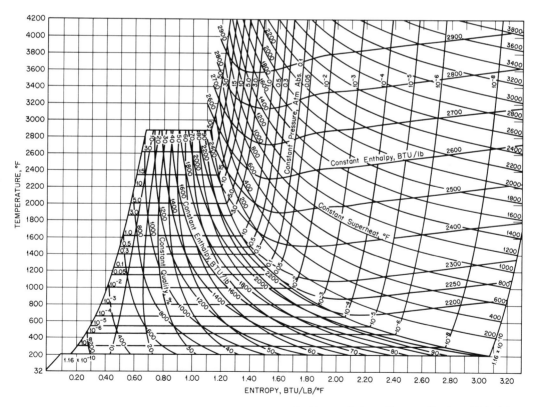

FIG. 2.59—Sodium, thermodynamic diagram. The temperature-entropy diagram is from Ref. 20. The highest vapor pressure data available for the diagram were those of Ref. 69, which go to 6.5 atm. More recent experimental vapor pressure data (Ref. 70) agree closely with those of Ref. 69 but extend the range to 120 atm. The data were fitted by the following relations: $\log_{10} P_{atm} = 4.5772 - 5286.1/T_k$ from 1.99 to 34.8 atm and $\log_{10} P_{atm} = 4.4837 -$ $5129.7/T_k$ from 34.8 to 120.4 atm. The data of Ref. 19 from 1 to 25 atm agree at low temperatures but are about 40 psi lower than the values in Ref. 70 at the upper end of the temperature range, 2580°F. A pressure–enthalpy diagram is given in Ref. 11; Mollier diagrams are given in Refs. 58, 32, and 21, and a temperature–entropy diagram is given in Ref. 21.

$$2Na + \tfrac{1}{2}O_2 \longrightarrow Na_2O$$

$$\Delta H^{\circ}_{298} = -99.4 \text{ kcal/mole} \qquad (2.4)$$

$$\Delta F^{\circ}_{298} = -89.9 \text{ kcal/mole}$$

$$2Na + O_2 \longrightarrow Na_2O_2$$

$$\Delta H^{\circ}_{298} = -122.2 \text{ kcal/mole} \qquad (2.5)$$

$$\Delta F^{\circ}_{298} = -107.1 \text{ kcal/mole}$$

$$Na(s) + O_2 \longrightarrow NaO_2$$

$$\Delta H^{\circ}_{298} = -62 \text{ kcal/mole} \qquad (2.6)$$

$$\Delta F^{\circ}_{298} = -52 \text{ kcal/mole}$$

Na K + O_2 preferentially forms Na_2O according to Eq. 2.4 plus potassium.

$$2Li + \tfrac{1}{2}O_2 \longrightarrow Li_2O \text{ (above } 100^{\circ}C)$$

$$\Delta H^{\circ}_{298} = -142.57 \text{ kcal/mole} \qquad (2.7)$$

$$\Delta F^{\circ}_{298} = -133.8 \text{ kcal/mole}$$

$$2Li + O_2 \longrightarrow Li_2O_2$$

$$\Delta H^{\circ}_{298} = -151.9 \text{ kcal/mole} \qquad (2.8)$$

$$\Delta F^{\circ}_{298} = -138.1 \text{ kcal/mole}$$

Burning sodium or potassium in excess oxygen produces the superoxide. Burning lithium in excess oxygen produces the monoxide.

2.1.4.8.2 AIR. Sodium and sodium–potassium alloy (NaK) react only with the oxygen in air to produce the oxides shown above. Lithium reacts with both oxygen (as above) and nitrogen.

$$3Li + \tfrac{1}{2}N_2 \longrightarrow Li_3N \qquad (2.9)$$

$$\Delta H^{\circ}_{298} = -47.45 \text{ kcal/mole} \quad (\text{Ref. 119})$$

$$\Delta F^{\circ}_{298} = -37.33 \text{ kcal/mole} \quad (\text{Ref. 119})$$

2.1.4.8.3 CARBON DIOXIDE.

$$4Na + 3CO_2 \longrightarrow 2Na_2CO_3 + C \qquad (2.10)$$

$$\Delta H^{\circ}_{298} \text{ (calculated)} = -256.76 \text{ kcal/mole}$$

$$\Delta F^{\circ}_{298} \text{ (calculated)} = -216.32 \text{ kcal/mole}$$

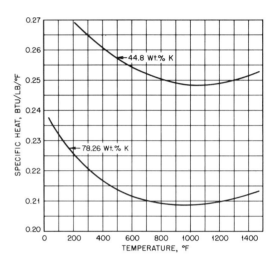

FIG. 2.62—NaK, specific heat. The values are from Ref. 18 and agree well with those calculated from the relation $c = W_{Na} c_{Na} + W_K c_K$, where c is specific heat and W is weight fraction.

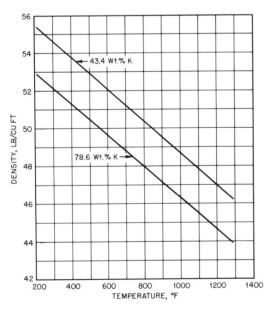

FIG. 2.61—NaK, density. The values are from Ref. 18 and agree well with those calculated from the relation $V = M_K v_K + M_{Na} v_{Na}$, where v is specific volume and M is mole fraction.

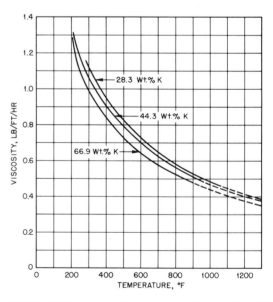

FIG. 2.63—NaK, viscosity. The values in Ref. 5 for the 75 wt.% K alloy are slightly lower than those from Ref. 55 for the 44.3 wt.% K alloy.

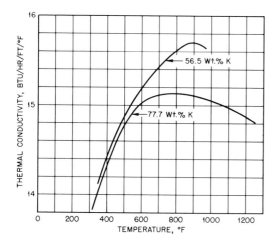

FIG. 2.64—NaK, thermal conductivity. The values are from Ref. 18 from the experimental data in Ref. 44.

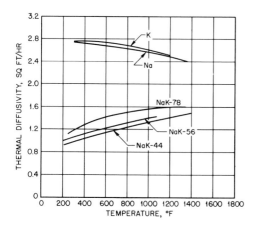

FIG. 2.65—Sodium, potassium, and NaK, thermal diffusivity. The curves are from Ref. 18.

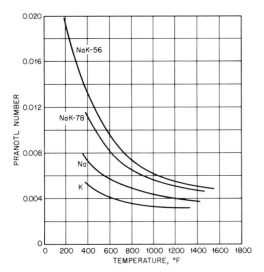

FIG. 2.66—Sodium, potassium, and NaK, Prandtl number. The curves are from Ref. 18.

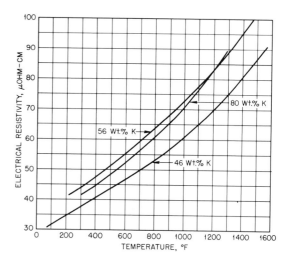

FIG. 2.67—NaK, electrical resistivity. The values for 46 wt.% K are from Ref. 36 and agree well with those in Refs. 71 and 4. The values for 56 wt.% K and 80 wt.% K are from Ref. 18 from the experimental data in Refs. 72 and 71, respectively.

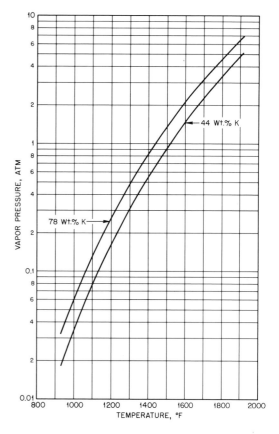

FIG. 2.68—NaK, vapor pressure. The values are calculated from vapor-pressure equations in Ref. 3 using Raoult's law: $P = M_{Na} P_{Na} + M_K P_K$, where P is vapor pressure and M is mole fraction. Agreement with Raoult's law was noted in Ref. 3 for 30.6 wt.% K alloy.

$$4Li + 3CO_2 \longrightarrow 2Li_2CO_3 + C \qquad (2.11)$$

$$\Delta H_{298}^\circ \text{ (calculated)} = -148.6 \text{ kcal/mole}$$

$$\Delta F_{298}^\circ \text{ (calculated)} = -128.4 \text{ kcal/mole}$$

2.1.4.8.4 CARBON MONOXIDE.

$$2Na + 3CO \longrightarrow Na_2CO_3 + 2C \qquad (2.12)$$

$$\Delta H_{298}^\circ \text{ (calculated)} = -190.2 \text{ kcal/mole}$$

$$\Delta F_{298}^\circ \text{ (calculated)} = -151.13 \text{ kcal/mole}$$

$$2Li + 3CO \longrightarrow Li_2CO_3 + 2C \qquad (2.13)$$

$$\Delta H_{298}^\circ \text{ (calculated)} = -210.45 \text{ kcal/mole}$$

$$\Delta F_{298}^\circ \text{ (calculated)} = -171.38 \text{ kcal/mole}$$

2.1.4.8.5 HYDROGEN.

$$Na + \tfrac{1}{2}H_2 \longrightarrow NaH \qquad (2.14)$$

$$\Delta H_{298}^\circ = -14 \text{ kcal/mole (Ref.119)}$$

$$\Delta F_{298}^\circ = -9.30 \text{ kcal/mole (Ref. 119)}$$

$$Li + \tfrac{1}{2}H_2 \longrightarrow LiH \qquad (2.15)$$

$$\Delta H_{298}^\circ = -22.9 \text{ kcal/mole (Ref. 119)}$$

$$\Delta F_{298}^\circ = -16.72 \text{ kcal/mole (Ref. 4)}$$

2.1.4.9 Reactions with Liquids

2.1.4.9.1 WATER. (See Refs. 120 through 129). The following chemical reactions between sodium and water are possible under proper conditions:

$$Na(liq) + H_2O(liq) \longrightarrow NaOH(solid) + \tfrac{1}{2}H_2(gas)$$
$$\Delta H_{298}^\circ = -35.2 \text{ kcal/mole} \qquad (2.16)$$

$$Na(liq) + H_2O(gas) \longrightarrow NaOH(solid) + \tfrac{1}{2}H_2(gas)$$
$$\Delta H_{298}^\circ = -45.7 \text{ kcal/mole} \qquad (2.17)$$

$$Na(solid) + H_2O(gas) \longrightarrow NaOH(solid) + \tfrac{1}{2}H_2(gas) \quad (2.18)$$

$$Na(liq) + NaOH(liq) \longrightarrow Na_2O(solid) + \tfrac{1}{2}H_2(gas) \quad (2.19)$$

$$\Delta H_{298}^\circ = -1.59 \text{ kcal/mole}$$

$$Na(liq) + \tfrac{1}{2}H_2 \longrightarrow NaH(solid) \qquad (2.20)$$

$$\Delta H_{298}^\circ = -13.7 \text{ kcal/mole}$$

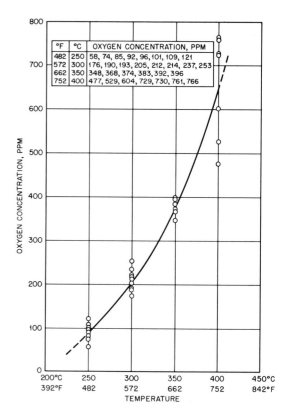

°F	°C	OXYGEN CONCENTRATION, PPM
482	250	58, 74, 85, 92, 96, 101, 109, 121
572	300	176, 190, 193, 205, 212, 214, 237, 253
662	350	348, 368, 374, 383, 392, 396
752	400	477, 529, 604, 729, 730, 761, 766

FIG. 2.69—Solubility of oxygen in lithium [133].

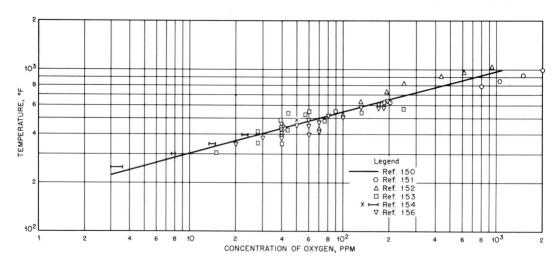

FIG. 2.70—Solubility of Na$_2$O in liquid sodium from 250 to 1000°F [102].

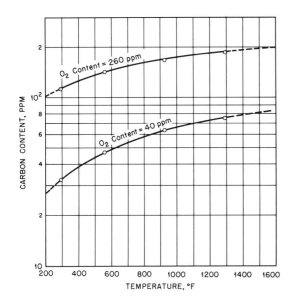

FIG. 2.71—Solubility of carbon in liquid sodium[113].

$$2Na\,(liq) \;+\; \tfrac{1}{2}O_2\,(gas) \;\longrightarrow\; Na_2O\,(solid)$$
$$\Delta H^\circ_{298} \;=\; -100.7 \text{ kcal/mole} \tag{2.21}$$

$$H_2\,(gas) \;+\; \tfrac{1}{2}O_2\,(gas) \;\longrightarrow\; H_2O\,(liq)$$
$$\Delta H^\circ_{298} \;=\; -68.4 \text{ kcal/mole} \tag{2.22}$$

Equations 2.16 to 2.18 occur in the presence of excess water or steam or equimolar quantities of sodium and water. Equation 2.19 occurs in the presence of excess sodium if the temperature is above the melting point of sodium hydroxide (600°F). Report GEAP 3208 by S. C. Furman, The Kinetics of Metal—Water Reactions, July 31, 1959, indicates that in vacuum or low partial pressures of H_2 (<10mm) Eq. 2.18 is unstable in the presence of excess sodium at temperatures above 400°F. Equation 2.20 may occur with excess sodium if the temperature is below the decomposition temperature of sodium hydride (700°F). Potassium and NaK react similarly.

In the solid state alkali metals react briskly, sometimes explosively, with water although the usual cause of destruction from this reaction is either the accumulation of hydrogen pressure or the detonation and combustion of the hydrogen in air. The reaction of liquid alkali metals with water is generally more violent. The metals are usually

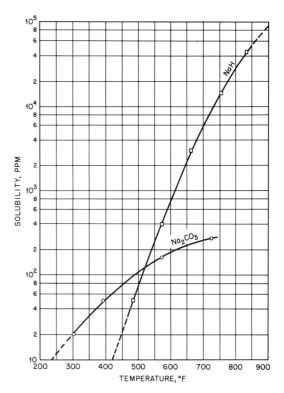

FIG. 2.73—Solubility of sodium hydride and sodium carbonate in liquid sodium[112, 114].

heated to their ignition temperature by this reaction. The disposal of sodium or NaK is often accomplished by burning, which is initiated by a light water spray.

In a system where sodium can come into contact with water, provisions should be made for pressure relief and the prevention of hydrogen ignition. King [124-128] has reported on a number of sodium—water reaction tests. A study of the reaction based on hydrogen generated in a rigid container indicates that the peak adiabatic pressures and temperatures occur when equimolar

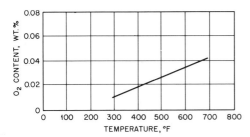

FIG. 2.72—Solubility of sodium hydroxide in liquid sodium[18].

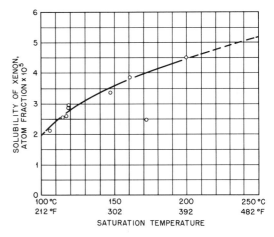

FIG. 2.74—Solubility of xenon in liquid sodium[116].

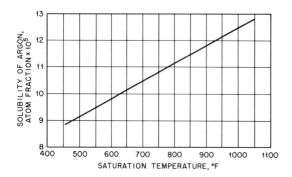

FIG. 2.75—Solubility of argon in liquid sodium [117].

quantities of sodium and water react and that an excess of either reactant greatly lowers the temperature pulse. Some of the experiments by King indicated that mixing of the reactants is erratic and is slower than expected because of separation by reaction products after initial contact. Other experiments have shown that a smooth relief of gas through a relief valve can be accomplished if the initial reaction temperature is above 600°F. If the initial temperature is below 600°F, the heat of reaction causes a temperature rise, and reaction 2.18 takes place as the sodium hydroxide melts. The large instantaneous release of hydrogen increases the hazard of pressure pulses. King reports that little hazard exists in the reaction of NaK and superheated steam.

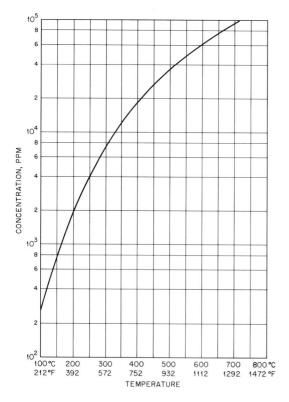

FIG. 2.76—Solubility of calcium in liquid sodium [18].

The reaction between water and sodium, followed by reaction of the liberated hydrogen with air in a closed vessel, has been treated as a thermodynamic problem at constant volume. The pressure resulting from the reaction of stoichiometric amounts of sodium and water was found to follow the equation [120]:

$$P = 3.44 + 45.64R - 7.97R^2 \qquad (2.23)$$

where P is the final pressure in psig and R is the ratio of sodium (in hundreds of cubic feet at 350°F) to void volume (in millions of cubic feet at 77°F).

2.1.4.9.2 ORGANICS. 2.1.4.9.2.1 Hydrocarbons. Hydrocarbons react with sodium at a rate dependent upon the temperature of the sodium. Assuming the hydrocarbon to be chemically pure, the reaction is characterized by the following effects: (1) thermal decomposition of the hydrocarbon, (2) formation of an insoluble (in sodium) carbonaceous mass, (3) formation of a soluble (in liquid sodium) hydride by reaction of sodium with hydrogen atoms from the compound, and (4) liberation of gaseous vapors. The gaseous reaction products are mainly hydrocarbon vapors and free hydrogen. In an oxygen atmosphere these vapors may burn readily (depending on temperature), and the combustion products themselves may be reactive.

The rate of reaction is more rapid at elevated temperature but is generally not of explosive intensity because thermal decomposition must occur before the sodium can react chemically with the decomposition products.

The reaction with carbon tetrachloride is perhaps the most violent reaction that alkali metals are known to undergo [114]. The reaction is apparently a true detonation. Under no circumstances should carbon tetrachloride or other polyhalogenated hydrocarbons be permitted near alkali metals. The reaction is erratic, and cases are on record of people who have degreased sodium systems with carbon tetracholoride for years without incident, only to have the system explode violently with no apparent change in the washing techniques. The reaction is so violent that any experimental effort to produce the reaction should be conducted on a very small scale and with careful shielding.

Commerically refined hydrocarboneous compounds, such as kerosene, gasoline, lubricating oils, and greases, may also contain impurities that react with sodium. These impurities may be water, sulfur, lime, talc (hydrated magnesium silicate), and chlorinated organic compounds.

2.1.4.9.2.2 Kerosene. Kerosenes vary in chemical composition and therefore exhibit different behaviors toward sodium and heat [130]. Certain possible constituents of kerosene form air-reactive compounds with sodium. These constituents have not as yet been identified but are believed to be of the C_nH_{2n-6} and C_nH_{2n-8} classes. The concentration of these ingredients is found to be very small in one type of kerosene and larger in another. Thermal stability of paraffins appears to be higher for branched than for straight-chain structures.

In order to arrive at a specification for a safe type of kerosene to use in the intended application, one would have to establish the chemical composition of kerosenes in greater detail.

2.1.4.9.2.3 Tetralin. Simplified, nonequilibrium experiments designed to qualitatively study the behavior of tetralin in the presence of sodium have been performed at temperatures up to 950°F [131]. It was found that tetralin decomposes rapidly in the presence of hot liquid sodium. The ultimate decomposition products are hydrogen, carbon, and low-molecular-weight aliphatic compounds. The hydrogen is rapidly absorbed by the hot sodium up to approximately 750°F. At higher temperatures sodium tends to release hydrogen.

2.1.4.9.2.4 Alcohols. Sodium reacts with low-molecular-weight alcohols, the rate of reaction decreasing with increasing molecular weight of the alcohol. Branch-chain alcohols are less reactive than straight-chain alcohols. Methyl alcohol reacts vigorously with solid sodium whereas the reaction with isobutanol is very mild. Small additions of water to alcohol greatly increase the rate of reaction with sodium; the higher molecular weight alcohols, with the controlled addition of water, are often used for cleaning sodium-covered components.

The reaction of sodium with excess alcohol involves the displacement of hydrogen from the hydroxyl group with the formation of gaseous hydrogen and sodium alcoholate. The reaction with methyl and ethyl alcohol is strongly exothermic. The chemical equation for the reaction with methyl alcohol is typical of the reaction with the straight-chain alcohols

$$CH_3OH(liq) + Na(solid) \longrightarrow NaOCH_3 (in\ CH_3OH) + \frac{1}{2}H_2(gas) \tag{2.24}$$

$$\Delta H_{293} = -48.1\ kcal/mole\ (Ref.\ 4) \tag{2.25}$$

The use of alcohol for the removal of sodium from piping and components is common in industry [18, 77] despite certain disadvantages, such as its flammability, the evolution of hydrogen, incomplete reaction of the sodium owing to the protective action of the semi-gelatinous alcoholate reaction product, and the production of a sooty by-product owing to carburization of the alcohol. Because of the flammability of the alcohol and the by-product hydrogen, alcohol cleaning should be carried out in vented, closed systems with an inert cover gas. For complete reaction of the sodium, the gelatinous alcoholate film must be broken up either by flushing or by mechanical action. A hot-water flush or steaming is needed for complete removal of the gelatinous film and traces of sodium. Steaming is preferable to flushing because pools of sodium that are protected by the gelatinous film react explosively with water whereas the reaction with steam is controlled.

Because of the hazards associated with the use of alcohol, its use for cleaning reactor components and systems has been limited. The use of steam to react sodium, followed by a water rinse, is the method used most frequently in the reactor industry for removal of sodium.

2.1.4.9.2.5 Fluorolubes [132]. The fluorolubes are linear polymers of trifluoro-vinyl chloride built of the following recurring unit:

$$\begin{array}{c} F\quad F \\ |\quad | \\ -C-C- \\ |\quad | \\ F\quad Cl \end{array}$$

Terminal groups on each end of a chain of these units are derived from the polymerization catalyst and/or the solvent. The resultant polymer has high chemical stability and extreme resistance to oxidation and is an oily fluid having lubricating properties. Fluorolubes are used in sodium-cooled reactors to lubricate moving parts in high-temperature sodium vapor. Having a low surface tension, the polymers wet metallic surfaces readily. They are essentially noncorrosive to metals and bearing alloys and are thermally stable to about 570°F, at which temperature rupture occurs at the C—C linkage. Compatibility tests have shown that a reaction occurs at temperatures above 300°F between liquid sodium and MO-10, a fluorolube manufactured by the Hooker Chemical Company.

There appears to be no danger other than carbon buildup for slow dripping leaks of MO-10 into hot sodium. The ability to tolerate the carbon buildup, pressure rise, and temperature rise resulting from sudden slug leakages into hot sodium will depend upon heat capacities, clearances, expansion volumes, and other design details.

2.1.4.9.2.6 Silicones. The reaction of silicones with liquid sodium has not been determined. Silicones (water repellants, resins, oils, rubber, and greases) are synthetically constructed molecules consisting of alternating silicon and oxygen atoms. Silicones probably thermally decompose if any reaction occurs.

2.1.4.10 Reaction with Solids

2.1.4.10.1 METALS. The interaction of solids and liquid metals can be one of direct chemical attack, dissolution, or chemical reaction with liquid-metal impurities, such as oxygen. Direct chemical reaction is rare. Dissolution is pertinent and can usually be detected only in a nonisothermal system. Impurities are important in corrosion of metals; so test results should be carefully evaluated.

Figure 2.77 is a condensed summary of the resistance of ferrous and nonferrous metals to various liquid metals at 300, 600, and 800°C (572, 1112, and 1472°F). The following sections discuss the reaction of liquid lithium, sodium, sodium-potassium, and mercury with metals.

2.1.4.10.1.1 Metals vs. Lithium [133-135]. Tests indicate that lithium is more aggressive in its corrosive attack on most metals than either sodium or sodium-potassium alloys although the questionable purity of the lithium used in most

Liquid Metal	Na,K, NaK	Li	Mg	Zn	Cd	Hg	Al	Ga	In	Ti	Sn	Pb	Pb-Bi	Pb-Bi-Sn	Sb	Bi
Melting Point, °F	-9.86 to 208.9	366.8	1203.8	787.1	609.8	-37.48	1220	85.6	313.5	577.4	449.4	620.6	257	206.6	1166.9	520.3
Melting Point, °C	-12.3 to 98.3	186	651	419.5	321	-38.6	660	29.8	156.4	303	231.9	327	125	97	630.5	271.3

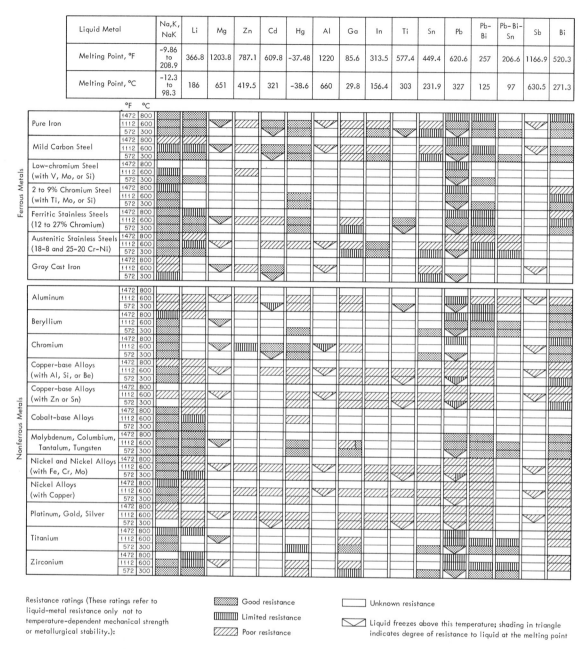

FIG. 2.77—Resistance of materials to liquid metals at 300, 600, and 800°C [4].

tests may make the results somewhat misleading. Among the contaminants commonly dissolved in lithium, or mechanically dispersed in it as lithium compounds, are nitrogen, oxygen, chlorine, hydrogen, calcium, aluminum, iron, silicon, sodium, and carbon. Little data exist on corrosion as a function of the amount of contamination of lithium by these impurities.

Lithium nitride, which is readily formed by the reaction of nitrogen with liquid or solid lithium, is a very reactive compound. No metal or ceramic material has been found to be resistant to the molten nitride although it has been tested with all

the common metals and with their oxides, nitrides, and silicides as well as with porcelain.

Oxygen is more often present in solid lithium as a hydroxide than as an oxide. Molten lithium hydroxide is very corrosive and, again, no refractory or metal has been found suitable for its containment. When heated above its melting point, 455°C (851°F), the hydroxide tends to decompose to form the oxide.

Lithium hydroxide or oxide can combine with or flux many refractories and in this way can either remove protective oxide films from metals or, in some cases, add to the thickness of the films. The hydroxide also attacks metals, including those which form acidic ions, such as iron and platinum. Molten lithium chloride attacks iron and copper. This compound is rather generally found in commercial lithium although some lighium is chloride free. Lithium hydride, which is likely to be present in molten lithium that has been exposed to moisture or to hydrogen, is reactive with metals and ceramics at high temperatures.

Most of the reported corrosion tests have used commercial lithium of questionable, and certainly not consistent, purity. Many of these tests have been made in containers of a dissimilar metal, and mass-transfer effects have obscured the results. In some cases the lithium was first freed from oil by treatment with petroleum ether and then passed through a sintered stainless-steel filter. In other cases no attempt was made to free the lithium from inorganic contaminants or from traces of protective oil. Efforts to obtain lithium of high purity using both filtration and distillation have been successful at the Knolls Atomic Power Laboratory.

Oak Ridge National Laboratory has conducted experiments in the purification of lithium by means of filtration, vacuum distillation, and gettering with active metals, such as titanium, zirconium, and yttrium [133]. Filtration through 10μ stainless-steel filters at 482°F (250°C) did not reduce the nitrogen or oxygen content of lithium. Vacuum distillation at 1202°F (650°C) and 10^{-4}mm Hg was also ineffective in removing nitrogen or oxygen. Titanium and zirconium were very effective in removing nitrogen from lithium at 1500°F (816°C) but were not effective in removing oxygen. Titanium gettering was used in test batches to produce lithium with an oxygen content of less than 10 ppm. Preliminary studies of yttrium in lithium at 1500°F (816°C) show the yttrium is more effective than titanium or zirconium in reducing the oxygen content of lithium. Tests with yttrium turnings in lithium at 1500°F (816°C) resulted in lithium with less than 100 ppm each of oxygen and nitrogen.

Attempts to melt most commercial lithium in quartz result in almost immediate failure of the container. Quartz appears to have good resistance to pure lithium at temperatures up to 285°C (545°F), Fig. 2.78, but not to lithium oxide or nitride. At higher temperatures the materials react to form lithium silicide. Glass has no resistance to attack by commercial lithium at 150°C (302°F) although lithium has been vacuum distilled in glass containers under carefully controlled conditions.

Porcelain and other silicates are attacked by liquid lithium. Molten lithium penetrates magnesia but does not otherwise attack it whereas molten lithium attacks most other oxides of structural

RESISTANCE OF MATERIALS TO ATTACK BY LITHIUM

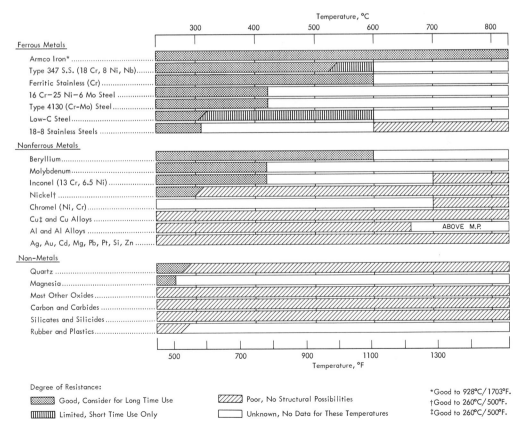

FIG. 2.78—Resistance of materials to attack by lithium [4].

metals and also attacks carbides, silicides, rubber, and plastics. Near its melting point, lithium does not attack Dow-Corning silicone D. C. 550.

Figures 2.78, 2.79, and Table 2.6 give data on the corrosion resistance of various materials to liquid lithium as a function of both time and temperature.

2.1.4.10.1.2 Metals vs. Sodium, Potassium, and Sodium–Potassium Alloy [136–140]. When its initial carbon content is low, sodium decarburizes carbon steel by a diffusion mechanism. On the other hand, stainless steel carburizes when the carbon present in the sodium exceeds an equilibrium value. The equilibrium value for uncarburized 304 stainless steel at 1200°F is reported to be 15 to 18 ppm of carbon in sodium.

Mass transfer occurs in a flowing nonisothermal liquid-metal system at a rate dependent upon the maximum temperature and the temperature difference. The mass transfer of common structural materials in sodium or NaK systems is probably solution rate limited rather than diffusion limited. The limiting process has not been qualitatively or quantitatively confirmed for Inconel–sodium or Inconel–NaK systems. Oxygen and water vapor form oxides, which increase mass transfer, although mass transfer in reasonably clean systems with less than 50 ppm of oxygen does not usually

Table 2.6—Attack and Concentration Data for Type 347 Stainless Steel in Lithium

Element	Attack rate* (removal of source metal) in lithium, $\mu g/(cm^2)(month)$		
	825°C	625°C	425°C
Iron	1922	5.8	1.0
Nickel	70	6.0	0.07
Manganese	62	2.3	0.09
Cobalt	4.1	0.1	0.002
Tantalum	0.24	0.007	0.006
Zinc	0.24		
Silver	0.17	0.0028	7×10^{-4}
Tin	8×10^{-3}	6.0×10^{-4}	$<3 \times 10^{-5}$

Element	Equilibrium concentration in lithium, $\mu g/g$ of lithium		
	825°C	625°C	425°C
Iron	0.31	0.037	0.15
Nickel	20		0.071
Manganese	56	3.1	0.094
Cobalt	6.9×10^{-3}	1.5×10^{-4}	1.6×10^{-4}
Tantalum	0.61	5.8×10^{-3}	0.027
Zinc	0.99	6.0×10^{-4}	0.026
Silver	0.69	0.012	2.6×10^{-3}
Tin	0.017	1.2×10^{-3}	1.2×10^{-4}

* Thirty-day isothermal exposures; metal removal determined by radiotracers.

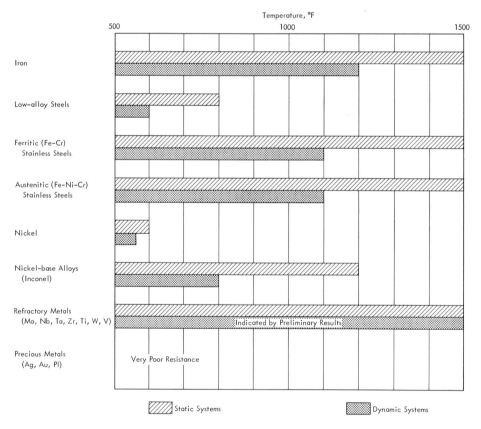

FIG. 2.79—Corrosion resistance of various metals and alloys in lithium [133]. Bars indicate approximate temperatures below which a system might be operated for 1000 hr with less than 0.005 in. of attack or container surface removal. Data from Oak Ridge National Laboratory.

become important until the coolant temperature rises above 1100 to 1200°F.

Table 2.7 lists materials suitable for use in sodium or NaK. Figure 2.80 is a bar diagram indicating the resistance of various materials to sodium and NaK. Table 2.8 presents some recent test data for various materials in sodium and NaK environments. In general, ferrous-metal welds are not attacked preferentially by sodium and NaK.

2.1.4.10.1.3 Metals vs. Mercury [139, 141-148]. Mercury can attack materials by chemical combination, by alloy formation, and by dissolution. The resistance of the material to wetting by mercury is a factor in its resistance to degradation by the above-mentioned modes of attack; if the material is not wetted by mercury, it will not be affected by the mercury.

The rates and degrees of all three modes of attack by mercury are temperature dependent. In dynamic systems where mercury contacts its containment material at a high temperature and then is transported to and cooled in another section of the system, mass transport and precipitation of the containment material in the cooler portion of the system can be appreciable even with low (few parts per million) solubility of the containment material in mercury.

Some of the pioneering work on the determination of the resistance of engineering materials to mercury at elevated temperatures was performed by A. J. Nerad and associates in connection with the development of the mercury-vapor turbine by the General Electric Company [141]. During the past decade investigations of mercury corrosion of numerous metals, alloys, and nonmetals have been and are now being made by a number of national laboratories and by private research organizations under federal government contracts.

Figure 2.81 and Tables 2.9 and 2.10 present a compilation of the resistance of various materials to mercury corrosion and a tabulation of current test work in this area with comments.

In some short-term corrosion tests [139] performed in mercury at 900°F, Ta, W, TiC, WC, and Mo + 0.5 wt.% Ti showed no measurable attacks, and low-carbon steels and 400 series stainless steels showed very slight attack, about 2 on a scale using 100 as a maximum attack rating. The 300 series stainless steels (310 not tested) showed about 7 for the severity of corrosion as did the low-carbon steels; nickel alloys (Ni > 20%) and Nichrome had about three times as great a corrosion attack, with a rating of about 45, as did the 300 stainless steels. The metals showing the poorest resistance to mercury corrosion of all the metals tested, with a corrosion attack rating of about 88, were titanium, platinum, manganese, magnesium, aluminum, and zirconium. It has been found [139] that low-alloy steels containing 4 to 6 wt.% chro-

Table 2.7—Materials Usable in Sodium or NaK [135]

At least up to 900°C (1652°F)	Up to 500°C (932°F)	Up to 200°C (392°F)
Armco iron	Carbon steel	Gray cast iron ‡
300 and 400 series	SAE 52100	2S and 3S aluminum
stainless steel	2 to 9 wt.% Cr—0.5 to	MgO
Nickel	1 wt.% Mo steels*	Darkoid
Inconel	Worthite*	Asbestos
Nichrome	18 wt.% W—4 wt.% Cr, IV	Hycar rubber
Hastelloys A, B, C	(tool steel)*	Brass (40 wt.% Zn)‡
Columbium	Invar*	
Molybdenum	28 wt.% Ni—18 wt.% Co*	
Tantalum	Alnico 5*	
Tungsten	Hadfields Mn steel†	
Chromium	80 wt.% Fe—20 wt.% P brazing alloy*	
Cobalt and high-cobalt	Monel†	
alloys	Copper (OFHC and P deox.)	
	Aluminum bronze*	
	Beryllium bronze*	
	Cupro nickel†	
	Titanium†	
	Vanadium	
	Zirconium	
	Beryllium†	
	Al_2O_3 (sapphire or Alundum)	
	BeO*	
	Graphite‡	
	Tungsten carbide cemented with nickel or copper	
	Titanium carbide cemented with nickel or copper	
	Chromium carbide cemented with nickel or copper	

* Temperature limitation due to lack of data; may be good for much higher temperature.

† Good only for limited use above 600°C (1112°F).

‡ Good only in sodium; not good in potassium or NaK at any temperature. (See also Sec. 2.1.4.10.4.1.)

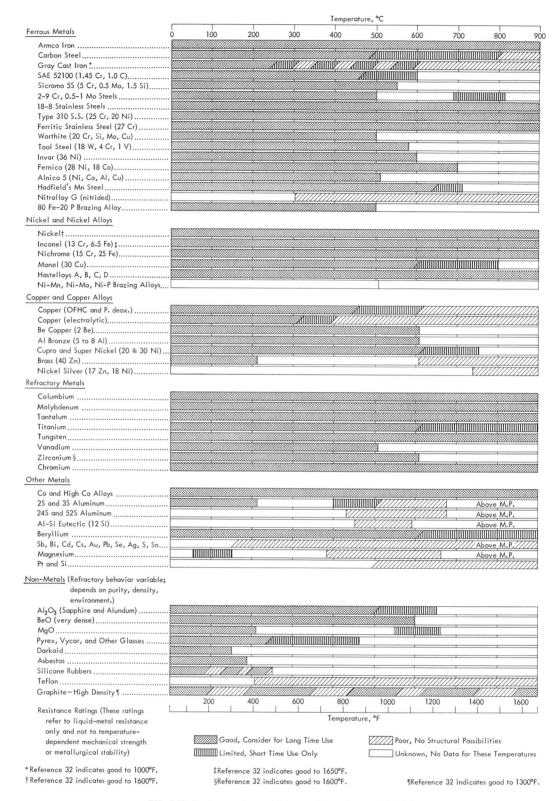

FIG. 2.80—Resistance of materials to attack by sodium and NaK [4].

Table 2.8—Summary of Materials Tests in Sodium, Potassium, and NaK [139]

Site*	Liquid metal	Type of test	Test conditions	Observation
AI	NaK (Snap)	Compatibility	347 ss and Hastelloy N in contact with Be in 1200 and 1300°F NaK	Intermetallics at interface
BMI	NaK	Tilting-furnace, screening	Hot end 1600°F; cold end terminated 1200°F; 5000 cycles in 110 hr; 61 materials	Materials suffering less than 1 mil penetration: Mo, Nb, Re, Ta, V, W, Zr, Hastelloy B, Inconel S, Kanthal, Stellite 6, Thermenol, cermets based on WC, TiC, Cr_3C_2, Mo_2C, dense ceramics TiC, WC, NbC, and BeO
BMI	NaK	Pumping loop, corrosion	1500°F peak; $T = 360°F$; $v = 15$ ft/sec; 500 hr; 316 ss	Some voids in hot zone to 2-mil depth; surface roughening; some mass transfer (nickel) in cold zone
MSA	NaK	Na-heated loops	1450°F; 30 days; Inconel X, 316 ss, Hastelloy X loops; $O_2 < 0.005$ wt. %; irradiated heat exchanger	Mass transfer and corrosion (1 mil); max. activity deposited at heat-exchanger outlet
GE-FPLD	Na, K	Capsule tests	F-48 and Mo—0.5 wt. % Zr sheet specimens in Nb cup inside stainless capsule; 300 hr at 1700°F	Weight and hardness changes slight; ductility OK; some pitting on one edge of one F-48 specimen
MSA	Na	Thermal harps	1000°F hot side; 800°F cold side; irradiated tabs; 1 wt. % inhibitors added	Order of mass-transfer inhibitor effectiveness: Ba, Ca, Mg, K, Be, and Zn
BMI	Na	Pumping loop corrosion and creep	Tantalum at 700 to 1200°F; 65 to 400 hr; loops of 316 ss	Na has no effect on creep strength of Ta; slight corrosion depending on oxygen content of Na
MSA	Na	Oscillating-flow isothermal	925°F; 0.003, 0.005, and 0.010 wt. % oxygen; 347 ss	Leaching of Fe, Co, Ta, and Mn depends on oxygen level
MSA	Na	Nitriding studies	To 1300°F; N_2 cover gas	Be nitrided slightly; 1% Ca increased nitriding; 2.0% oxygen produced massive nitriding and interface corrosion
AI	NaK (Snap)	Thermal-convection loops	1200°F and 1400°F for 1000, 2000, 2500, and 3500 hr; materials 304, 316, 347 ss, Hastelloys C, N, and R-235, Haynes 25, Inconel X, Mo, Nb, and Rene 41	Hastelloy N very good; Mo unattacked; other materials showed varying evidences of corrosion
NASA	Na, K	Two-phase thermal-convection loops	1600 to 2500°F; circular loop; 14 in. dia., preheat, boiling, superheat, condensing; vacuum chamber for oxidizable materials	Inconel loop failed by dissolution at liquid-vapor interface; severe intergranular penetration
NASA	Na, K	Elastomer seal tests in alkali metals	250 and 300°F; 100 to 250 hr	K much harder on elastomers than Na; best for Na: Buna-N and Kel-F; best for K: Buna S.
ORNL	K	Refluxing capsule	1500 and 1600°F boiling; 316 ss, Inconel, and Haynes 25; 500 and 1000 hr	Inconel has less corrosion resistance than 316 ss or Haynes 25
ORNL	K	Boiling loop	Test 1: 316 ss, 200 hr; 1600°F boiling; 65 gal/min in ½-in. pipe	No attack metallographically; slight weight losses in hot regions; slight weight gains in cold regions
			Test 2: 316 ss; 3000 hr; 1600°F boiling; 50 ft/sec	Same as Test 1; 2 mils max. attack in hot zone; 3-mil deposits in cold zone; no effect on mechanical properties; mass transfer analyzed as C and $Cr_{23}C_6$

*AI, Atomics International
 BMI, Battelle Memorial Institute
 MSA, Mine Safety Appliance

GE-FPLD, General Electric Flight Propulsion Laboratory
NASA, National Aeronautics and Space Administration
ORNL, Oak Ridge National Laboratory.

mium, 0.5 wt.% molybdenum, and 1 to 2 wt.% silicon had better resistance to attack by mercury than did the low-carbon steels.

This suggests the possibilities of using duplex materials consisting of a low-carbon or low-alloy steel layer (for the contacting surface) metallurgically bonded to an austenitic stainless steel or a nickel-base alloy to provide the elevated tempera-

ture strength or mercury service up to 650°C (1202°F).*

In thermal-convection loop tests it was found that the corrosion of ferrous-base alloys by

*L. R. Kovac, private conversation with Brookhaven National Laboratory personnel at AEC Corrosion Symposium, May 1962.

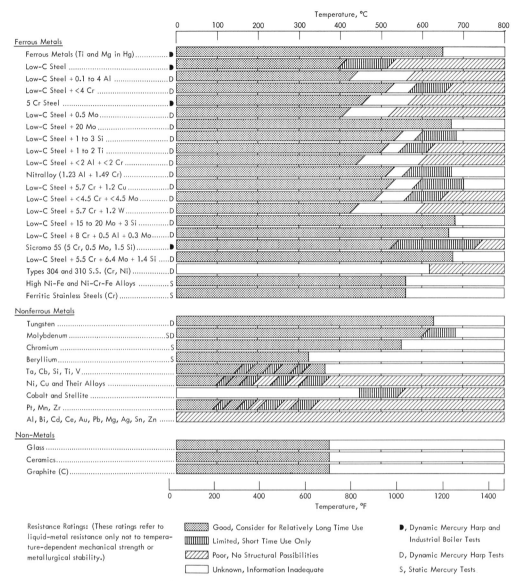

FIG. 2.81—Resistance of materials to liquid mercury [4].

mercury could be significantly reduced by dissolving small amounts of titanium in the mercury.* The explanation of the corrosion-inhibition mechanism was that the titanium reacted with the nitrogen and carbon in the ferrous materials and formed a thin film of TiC and TiN on the surface which served as a barrier between the mercury and the container material.†

Much work has been done on the resistance of engineering materials to attack by mercury. Considerable work is in progress, but much more has

to be performed, particularly on the effect of impurities in mercury on its corrosion of materials and on the purposeful addition of certain impurities to mercury to inhibit its corrosion of its containment material.

2.1.4.10.2 BRAZING MATERIALS. Brazing materials [149, 150] are of particular interest in joining fuel plates and in fabricating fuel-pin support grids. Many of the brazing alloys investigated possess excellent resistance to sodium corrosion and oxidation. Alloy systems of the Ni–Si–B, Ni–Cr–Si–B, and Ni–Cr–Si types are compatible with liquid sodium. Precious-metal alloys, in general, are severely attacked by sodium, as are many of the silicon-free, chromium-free, phosphorus-bearing alloys. Alloys containing manganese, tin, or copper exhibit poor resistance to

*J. R. Weeks (Ed.), Proceedings of the Eleventh Annual AEC Corrosion Symposium, USAEC Report BNL–728, May 1962.
†J. R. Weeks and C. J. Klamut, Liquid Metal Corrosion Mechanisms, Corrosion of Reactor Materials, Vol. 1, Proceedings of the Conference on Corrosion of Reactor Materials, IAEA, June 1962.

Table 2.9—Dynamic Harp Tests on Ferrous Alloys in Mercury [4]

Material	Major alloying elements, wt.%	Time of test, hr	Maximum harp temp., °C	Rate of attack (weight change data)	
				Mg/cm²/month	Mils/year
Low-C steel	0.2 C	*	482	− 7	4
(mild steel)		*	538	−15	9
		*	593	−37	22
			649	−88	53
Low-C steel	0.1 Al[†]	162	625	−28	17
(+ Al)	0.2 Al[†]	48	650	−18	11
	0.5 Al[†]	257	625	−64	40
	1 Al[†]	95	620	−52	32
	4 Al[†]	113	630	−69	43
	4 Al[†]	48	650	− 7	4
Low-C steel	0.2 Cr[†]	46	650	−13	8
(+ Cr)	0.5 Cr[†]	138	615	− 7	4
	4 Cr[†]	138	625	−23	14
5 wt. % Cr steel	5 Cr	*	482	− 3	2
		*	538	− 7	4
		*	593	−17	10
		*	649	−42	25
Low-C steel	0.5 Mo[†]	161	670	−86	53
(+ Mo)	20 Mo[†]	64	650	<− 0.5	< 0.3
Low-C steel	1 Si[†]	67	640	− 7	4
(+ Si)	2 Si[†]	107	640	−11	7
	3 Si[†]	67	640	− 7	4
Low-C steel	1 Ti[†]	329	620	− 9	6
(+ Ti)	1 Ti[†]	329	675	−39	24
	2 Ti[†]	329	625	− 7	4
	2 Ti[†]	329	640	−15	9
Low-C steel	0.1 Al, 0.1 Cr[†]	136	625	−46	29
(+ Al + Cr)	0.5 Al, 0.5 Cr[†]	137	630	−37	23
	2 Al, 2 Cr[†]	48	620	−44	27
	2 Al, 2 Cr[†]	142	650	−13	8
Nitralloy	1.23 Al, 1.49 Cr	165	650	− 7	4
(not nitrided)		2	615	6	4
Low-C steel	5.7 Cr, 1.2 Cu[†]	161	670	− 8	5
(+ Cr + Cu)					
Low-C steel	0.5 Cr, 0.5 Mo[†]	140	650	− 6	4
(+ Cr + Mo)	4.5 Cr, 4.5 Mo[†]	140	640	− 6	4
	4.9 Cr, 0.5 Mo	161	670	−86	53
Low-C steel	5.7 Cr, 1.2 W	100	660	−26	16
(+ Cr + W)					
Low-C steel	15 Mo, 3 Si[†]	89	655	− 1	0.6
(+ Mo + Si)	20 Mo, 3 Si[†]	88	655	<− 0.5	< 0.3
Low-C steel	0.5 Al, 8 Cr				
(+ Al + Cr + Mo)	0.3 Mo[†]	140	650	− 1	0.6
Low-C steel	4.6 Cr, 0.5 Mo, 1.23 Si[†]	140	640	− 6	4
(+ Cr + Mo + Si)	4.6 Cr, 0.45-0.65 Mo,				
	1-2 Si	*	482	− 0.3	0.2
	(Sicromo 5S or				
	Croloy 5 Si)	*	538	− 0.80	0.5
		*	593	− 1.8	1.1
		*	649	− 4	2.5
	5.5 Cr, 6.4 Mo,				
	1.4 Si[†]	280	588	− 0.7	0.4
		982	620	− 0.8	0.5
		111	650	− 0.8	0.5
Low-C steel	0.8 Al, 5 Cr, 0.5 Mo,				
(+ Al + Cr + Mo + Si)	0.9 Si[†]	450	650	−64	38
Type 304 SS	18 Cr, 8 Ni	460	652	−32	20
Type 310 SS	25 Cr, 20 Ni	400-500	650	−77	47

*Average of a large number of laboratory tests as well as samples from large-scale boiler operations; exposures of up to 10,000 hr.

†Alloys made in General Electric laboratory by melting portions of a single low-carbon steel billet and adding desired alloying elements.

oxidation at 1500°F. In most cases, oxidation is more pronounced at 1700°F. Tables 2.11 to 2.13 list results of static tests of brazing alloys in sodium.

2.1.4.10.3 RUBBER AND CLOTH. Data on the compatibility of selected cloth and rubber materials to hot sodium have been obtained by Atomic Power Development Associates [151]. Two types of tests were performed. In the first series, the samples were placed in an open pan and hot sodium was

poured on them. A thermocouple was placed on each sample at the spot where the hot sodium stream was poured onto the material. When the temperature dropped to the freezing point, the sodium was scraped off the sample. In the second test series, the samples were soaked in 550°F sodium for 5 min.

From the appearance of the samples, as summarized in Table 2.14, it was apparent that the silicon rubber and the impregnated asbestos cloth

Table 2.10—Summary of Material Tests in Mercury [139]

Site*	Liquid metal	Type of test	Test conditions	Status	Observations
AGN	Hg (SNAP VIII)	Heat-transfer loop; component tests; corrosion tests	Boil at 1075°F; superheat to 1200°F; condense at 700°F; cool to 560°F	Construction begun	
AGN	Hg (SNAP VIII)	Capsule	Long-time effects of Hg in Haynes 25; Nb as backup material	Just starting	
BNL	Hg (SNAP)	Capsule screening	Quartz capsules, designed for boiling at 1050°F superheating to 1300°F; minimum test 1000 hr	Shakedown runs; results in perhaps 6 weeks	
BNL	Hg (SNAP)	Natural-convection loops	Two loops, liquid at 1000 to 600°F; carbon steel, clad with 1.25 wt. % Cr - 0.5 wt. % Mo ; one loop contains Ti and Mg inhibitors; two loops boiling and condensing at 1000°F, superheat to 1150°F, cool to 600°F	In operation	No corrosion or mass transfer detected by radiography after 1500 hr
BNL	Hg (SNAP)	Natural-convection loops	Carbon steel clad with Inconel; Ti and Zr inhibitors; Cb–1 wt. % Zr loops also; boiling at 1100°F, superheat to 1400°F	Facility built	
BNL	Hg (SNAP)	Natural-convection loop	v_{vapor} = 100 ft/sec, v_{liquid} = 2 ft/sec, 1000°F boiler, 1200°F superheater; test specimens in various portions of loop	Loop designed	
BNL	Hg (SNAP)	Pumped loop	Gas-bearing pump; boiling and condensing at 1100°F, superheat to 1400°F; v_{vapor} = 200 ft/sec v_{liq} = 6 ft/sec	British pump under test	Pump working OK
BNL	Hg (SNAP)	Solubility studies	Fe, Cr, Ti, Zr in Hg at 500 to 1400°F; Cb, Ta, Mo, V, W, and Co at 750°F	Planning stage	
BNL	Hg (SNAP)	Surface-reaction studies	Carbon steel, low Cr steels, Cb, and Fe in Hg containing Ti and Mg at 700 to 800°C; long time	Planning stage	
TRW	Hg (SNAP II)	Refluxing capsules	Tab specimen in pool and sometimes in vapor; 700 to 1100°F; mostly 12-day tests	Over 500 tests completed	Order of corrosion resistance at 900°F: (1) Ta, W, TiC, WC, Mo–0.5 wt. % Ti; (2) C steels, 400 series ss; (3) 300 series ss, except 310; (4) High-nickel alloys (>20 wt.%); (5) Ti, Pt, Mn, Mg, Al, and Zr
TRW	Hg	Two-phase natural-convection loops	0.5-in. - OD tubing; 76 in. high, 14½ in. wide; 700 to 1000°F in boiling section; Ti and other additives as corrosion inhibitors	Continuing	

* AGN, Aerojet - General Nucleonics.
  BNL, Brookhaven National Laboratory.
  TRW, Thompson - Ramo Wooldridge.

stand up very well against attack by hot sodium. The wire-reinforced asbestos impregnated with Silastic 131 has both mechanical strength and good compatibility with hot sodium. The silicone rubber does not have the mechanical strength of the wire-reinforced asbestos, but it is much more flexible. Plain asbestos is badly damaged by hot sodium.

2.1.4.10.4 SHIELDING MATERIALS. None of the bulk shielding materials discussed below are completely impervious to attack by molten liquid metals. Each, however, has distinct attributes that may suggest its use in a specific environment. Chapter 8 should be referred to for further information on shielding materials.

2.1.4.10.4.1 Graphite [152-154]. Protection of fabricated graphite blocks from direct contact with molten sodium under reactor operating conditions is essential. Sodium in the temperature range of 600 to 1000°F is initially nonwetting to graphite; but, in a matter of minutes, this condition changes, and the sodium attacks the graphite. The result is a gross dilation and, in some cases, decrepitation and disintegration of the graphite. Linear expansion on the order of 1% has been observed in 100 hr at 1000°F. The initial attack is grain-boundary penetration and pore filling, probably accompanied by inter-lamellar compound formation.

Vacuum deposition, electroplating, electro-forming, flame spraying, and vapor decomposition

Table 2.11—Results of Static Tests of Brazing Alloys on "A" Nickel T-joints
in Sodium at 1500°F for 100 Hours [149]

Brazing-alloys* composition	Weight change[†]		Metallographic notes
	Grams	%	
General Electric No. 81	+0.0001	+0.005	No attack on braze fillet
Coast Metals No. 52	−0.0019	−0.068	0.5-mil surface attack along fillet edge
80 wt. % Ni−10 wt. % P−10 wt. % Cr	−0.0017	−0.061	1-mil nonuniform attack along fillet
Nicrobraz	−0.0022	−0.082	1.5-mil layer of small subsurface voids along fillet edge
75 wt. % Ni−25 wt. % Ge	0.0	0.0	2-mil nonuniform attack along surface of braze fillet
50 wt. % Ni−25 wt. % Mo−25 wt. % Ge	−0.0009	−0.036	2.5-mil attack along surface of fillet
65 wt. % Ni−25 wt. % Ge−10 wt. % Cr	−0.0024	−0.085	3-mil uniform surface attack along fillet
40 wt. % Ni−60 wt. % Mn	−0.0020	−0.079	9-mil uniform attack along entire fillet
35 wt. % Ni−55 wt. % Mn−10 wt. % Cr	−0.0005	−0.020	13 mils of small voids in from surface of fillet
68 wt. % Ni−32 wt. % Sn	−0.0171	−0.540	Complete attack of whole fillet

* Brazing alloys listed in order of decreasing corrosion resistance to sodium.
[†] Weight-change data for brazing alloys and base material of joint.

of a metal halide have been used for deposition of chromium, nickel, zirconium, zirconium carbide, tungsten carbide, silicon carbide, silicon nitride, and molybdenum disilicide on graphite test specimens. Although these coatings do protect the graphite from sodium attack, failure occurs owing to pinholes in the coating. Even if a pore-free coating were attainable on small laboratory specimens, it is doubtful that the same technique would result in a pore-free structure on a graphite block of large dimensions.

Corrosion (i.e., weight loss) of graphite by

Table 2.12—Results of Static Tests of Brazing Alloys Developed by Wall Colmonoy Corporation
on Types 304 and 310 Stainless Steels in Sodium at 1500°F for 100 Hours [149]

Brazing-alloy* composition	Base material	Weight change[†]		Metallographic notes
		Grams	%	
Alloy F-11 (73 wt.%Ni−9 wt.%Si−18 wt.%Cr)	304 ss	0.0	0.0	No attack along surface of braze fillet
Alloy B-13 (88 wt.%Ni−3 wt.%P−9 wt.%Si)	310 ss	0.0	0.0	No attack along surface of fillet; several cracks were observed in fillet
Alloy P-11 (82 wt.%Ni−10 wt.%Si−8 wt.%Mn)	310 ss	−0.0002	−0.018	No attack along fillet; several cracks in fillet
Alloy P-10 (78 wt.%Ni−16 wt.%Si−6 wt.%Mn)	310 ss	+0.0004	+0.043	No evidence of attack; however, several large cracks appeared throughout fillet
Alloy E-11 (87 wt.%Ni−13 wt.%Si)	304 ss	−0.0007	−0.068	Surface of braze fillet unattacked
Alloy C-29 (77 wt.%Ni−10 wt.%P−13 wt.%Cr)	304 ss	+0.0004	+0.054	Less than 0.5 mils of small subsurface voids
Alloy P-14 (64 wt.%Ni−6 wt.%Si−30 wt.%Mn)	310 ss	−0.0002	−0.022	1-mil erratic surface attack with large cracks throughout fillet
Alloy G-20 (80 wt.%Ni−9 wt.%P−11 wt.%W)	310 ss	−0.0002	−0.019	2.5-mil uniform attack along surface of braze fillet
Alloy S-10 (54 wt.%NI−10 wt.%Si−14 wt.%Cr−19 wt.%Fe−3 wt.%Mo)	310 ss	0.0	0.0	Subsurface voids to a depth of 3 mils along fillet
Alloy B-15 (89 wt.%Ni−5 wt.%P−6 wt.%Si)	310 ss	0.0	0.0	Maximum attack of 4 mil along surface of fillet
Alloy B-11 (80 wt.%Ni−11 wt.%P−9 wt.%Si)	304 ss	0.0	0.0	Subsurface voids to a depth of 4 mils along fillet
Alloy B-17 (89 wt.%Ni−8 wt.%P−3 wt.%Si)	310 ss	−0.0012	−0.14	Maximum attack of 4 mils along surface of braze fillet
Alloy L-20 (38 wt.%Ni−57 wt.%Mn−5 wt.%Cr)	310 ss	−0.0004	−0.043	Attack in the form of stringers to a maximum depth of 5 mils; not uniform

* Brazing alloys listed in order of decreasing corrosion resistance to sodium.
[†] Weight-change data for brazing alloys and braze material of joint.

Table 2.13—Brazing Alloys on Inconel T-joints Seesaw Tested in Sodium
for 100 Hours at Hot-zone Temperature of 1500°F [149]

Brazing-alloy* composition	Weight change[†]		Metallographic notes
	Grams	%	
Coast Metals No. 52	−0.0011	−0.073	No attack along surface of braze fillet
Coast Metals No. 53	−0.0009	−0.071	1-mil erratic attack along surface of braze fillet
Low-melting Nicrobraz	−0.0007	−0.051	Subsurface voids to a maximum depth of 1.5 mils along surface of braze fillet
Coast Metals No. 50	−0.0012	−0.077	1.5-mil very erratic surface attack along fillet
70 wt.% Ni—13 wt.% Ge—11 wt.% Cr—6 wt.% Si	−0.0023	−0.139	Nonuniform attack along surface of braze fillet to a depth of 2.5 mils
Coast Metals NP	−0.0069	−0.622	2.5-mil uniform attack along surface of braze fillet
General Electric No. 81	−0.0018	−0.163	3-mil uniform surface attack along braze fillet
Nicrobraz	0.0	0.0	Very erratic stringer attack to a maximum depth of 4 mils along surface of braze fillet
65 wt.% Ni—25 wt.% Ge—10 wt.% Cr	−0.0019	−0.113	Intermittent surface attack to a maximum depth of 4 mils along braze fillet

* Brazing alloys listed in order of decreasing corrosion resistance to sodium.
[†] Weight-change data for brazing alloys and base material of joint.

Table 2.14—Compatibility of Various Rubbers and Cloths with Hot Sodium [151]

Test series*	Sample	Temp., °F	Effect
1	Silicone rubber	510	One indentation in material approximately 1/8-in. in diameter
1	Wire-reinforced asbestos	555	Three small burn spots on surface of material
1	Wire-reinforced asbestos impregnated with Silastic 131	600	Brown stain on surface
1	Wire-reinforced asbestos impregnated with Dow-Corning 1109	580	Slight brown stain on surface
1	Wire-reinforced asbestos impregnated with 10% Dow-Corning 1109	495	A few small burn spots on surface
1	Plain asbestos	585	Material burned completely away where contacted with sodium
1	Plain asbestos impregnated with Silastic 131	435	Brown stain on surface
1	Plain asbestos impregnated with Dow-Corning 1109	665	Three small holes burned through material
1	Plain asbestos impregnated with 10% Dow-Corning 1109	555	Several holes burned through material
2	Silicone rubber	550	Discolored slightly; no apparent bad effects
2	Wire-reinforced asbestos	550	Discolored (brown), otherwise no change
2	Wire-reinforced asbestos impregnated with Silastic 131	550	No apparent effect
2	Wire-reinforced asbestos impregnated with Dow-Corning 1109	550	No apparent effect
2	Wire-reinforced asbestos impregnated with 10% Dow-Corning 1109	550	No apparent effect
2	Plain asbestos	550	Badly discolored and withered
2	Plain asbestos impregnated with Silastic 131	550	Discolored brown
2	Plain asbestos impregnated with Dow-Corning 1109	550	No apparent effect
2	Plain asbestos impregnated with 10% Dow-Corning 1109	550	Discolored, withered

* See text for description of tests.

liquid sodium occurs at significant rates only when a "sink" is available to remove the carbon that enters the sodium. In circulating sodium in contact with graphite, mass-transfer effects have been observed that result in carbon removal from the hot regions and deposition in the colder regions. Appreciable graphite corrosion rates have also been observed in isothermal systems where carburization of the container material occurred. At sufficiently high temperatures, carbon enters the sodium and produces carburization of stainless steel and zirconium surfaces without physical contact between these metals and the graphite. In experiments where nickel was the container material and the only metal present, negligible corrosion of the graphite occurred. Since nickel does not carburize, no "sink" was provided for removal of the carbon. The equilibrium carbon content of the sodium contained in these nickel capsules proved to be a function of operating temperature; it was approximately 2000 ppm after operation at 750°C (1382°F) and nil after operation at 525°C (955°F).

The mechanism by which carbon enters the sodium has not been firmly established. Suggested mechanisms are (1) the true solution of carbon in sodium and (2) the formation of Na_2C_2, which decomposes at lower temperatures. However, no Na_2C_2 was observed in any of the capsule tests.

Carburization of stainless steel was not observed below 550°C (1022°F) but was noticeable at 600°C (1112°F) and increased with higher temperatures. Zirconium also showed carburization at 750°C (1382°F) but not at 600°C (1112°F) or below.

Tests have shown that corrosion and dimensional stability of irradiated graphite in liquid sodium are significantly werse than unirradiated graphite under similar conditions.

Hot graphite immersed into cooler liquid sodium may be fractured by thermal shock. It appears that wetting, in addition to a sufficient temperature difference between the solid and the liquid, is a necessary condition for this type of failure.

2.1.4.10.4.2 Concrete. Only sketchy information is available on the effect of liquid metals on concrete. Preliminary results from dropwise or spray tests indicate a spalling or random surface granulation of a limited depth. Reported accidents involving a large amount of hot (800°F) sodium and a small amount of exposed concrete surface, however, resulted in gross granulation and bulk

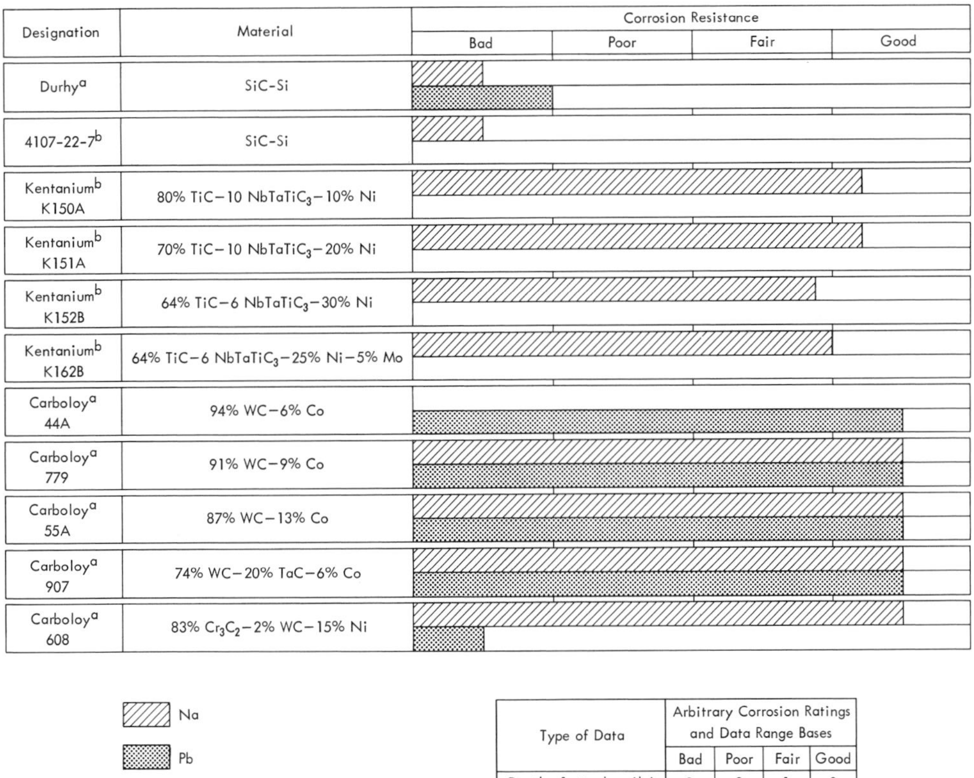

Designation	Material	Corrosion Resistance			
		Bad	Poor	Fair	Good
Durhy[a]	SiC-Si				
4107-22-7[b]	SiC-Si				
Kentanium[b] K150A	80% TiC–10 NbTaTiC$_3$–10% Ni				
Kentanium[b] K151A	70% TiC–10 NbTaTiC$_3$–20% Ni				
Kentanium[b] K152B	64% TiC–6 NbTaTiC$_3$–30% Ni				
Kentanium[b] K162B	64% TiC–6 NbTaTiC$_3$–25% Ni–5% Mo				
Carboloy[a] 44A	94% WC–6% Co				
Carboloy[a] 779	91% WC–9% Co				
Carboloy[a] 55A	87% WC–13% Co				
Carboloy[a] 907	74% WC–20% TaC–6% Co				
Carboloy[a] 608	83% Cr$_3$C$_2$–2% WC–15% Ni				

 Na

Pb

[a]Static Test
[b]Seesaw Test
Hot Zone: 1500°F
Cold Zone: 1150°F

Type of Data	Arbitrary Corrosion Ratings and Data Range Bases			
	Bad	Poor	Fair	Good
Depth of attack, mils*	3	2	1	0
Weight change, %†	6	4	2	0
Dimensional change, %	3	2	1	0

* Measured in metallographic examinations.
† Determined by direct measurement and/or by calculations based on the material(s) found in the test medium by chemical analyses.

FIG. 2.82—Corrosion resistance of cermets to sodium and lead[156].

failure of the concrete member. In the latter cases the water of hydration apparently reacted with the liquid metal involved.

2.1.4.10.4.3 Serpentine. Serpentine is an asbestos mineral, i.e., a hydrous magnesium silicate, with the formula $3MgO \cdot 2SiO_2 \cdot 2H_2O$. The water of hydration in serpentine amounts to about 13.5 wt.%. A remarkable characteristic of this substance is that it has the ability to retain its bound water to a much higher temperature than is normally the case with hydrated molecules. The rock has a lump density of between 2.55 and 2.65 g/cm^3 (160 to 165 lb/cu ft). It can be piled loosely to a density of from 80 to 110 lb/cu ft. It can be easily crushed and tamped as a fine powder to a density of about 130 lb/cu ft. Little is known of the effect of liquid metals on serpentine.

2.1.4.10.5 INSULATING MATERIALS [155]. In general, insulating materials do not hold up well in a liquid-metal environment. Most reported test data show attack in varying degrees. Many specimens which cured at 1000°F with no color change showed drastic changes at 950°F due to the action of sodium. The materials that showed the least disintegration and the greatest preservation of

mechanical properties were Superex paste and Eagle-Pitcher mineral wool. The uncured Superex Block did not hold up as well as Superex paste, presumably because of the presence of water of crystallization. After the blocks were cured, their behavior was similar to that of the paste. The refractory clays show the greatest degree of destruction. The time element is of vital importance since a long period of contact with liquid sodium presumably results in complete destruction of every specimen tested.

2.1.4.10.6 CERAMICS AND CERMETS [156, 157]. Cermets and ceramics show generally good resistance to corrosion by liquid metals. The ceramics, essentially inert to chemical reaction, show good corrosion resistance to mercury, sodium, and NaK, with less resistance to lithium. Figures 2.82 and 2.83 give an indication of the corrosion resistance of various cermets and ceramics to liquid metals.

2.1.4.11 Phase Diagrams

Phase diagrams for four binary-alloy systems of particular interest for fast reactor application are presented in Figs. 2.84 to 2.87. These are

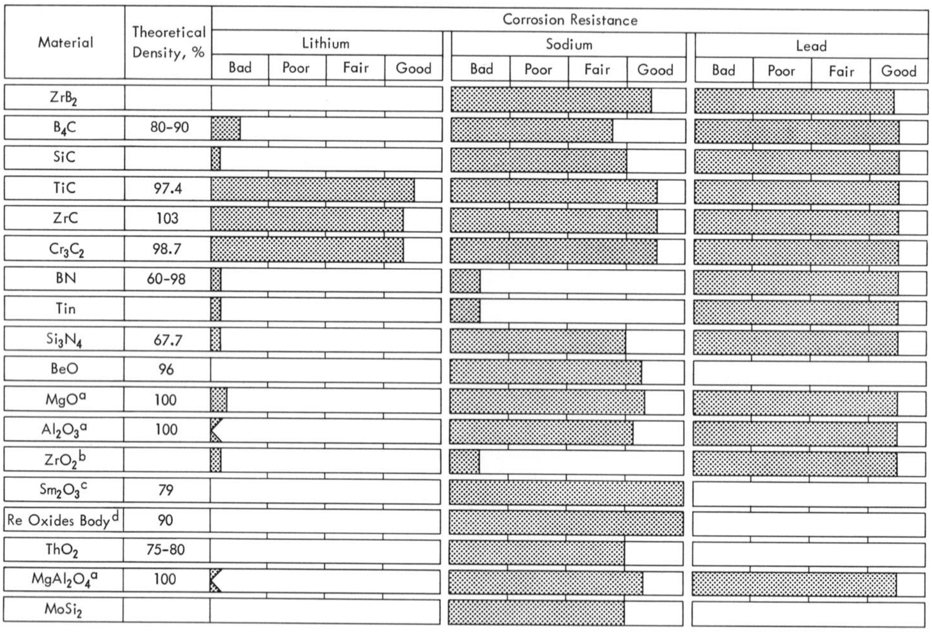

Material	Theoretical Density, %
ZrB$_2$	
B$_4$C	80–90
SiC	
TiC	97.4
ZrC	103
Cr$_3$C$_2$	98.7
BN	60–98
Tin	
Si$_3$N$_4$	67.7
BeO	96
MgO^a	100
Al$_2$O$_3$^{a}	100
ZrO$_2$^{b}	
Sm$_2$O$_3$^{c}	79
Re Oxides Body^d	90
ThO$_2$	75–80
MgAl$_2$O$_4$^{a}	100
MoSi$_2$	

Significance of Shortest Bars:

▨ Pieces of the Tested Specimen Remained

◪ There Was No Visible Trace of the Tested Specimen

[a]Specimen from a single crystal.
[b]CaO-stabilized.
[c]A 1000-hr test.
[d]A 500-hr test. Body composition: 45.0 to 49.5% Sm$_2$O$_3$–22.5 to 27% Gd$_2$O$_3$–balance primarily other rare-earth oxides.

Type of Date	Arbitrary Corrosion Ratings and Data Range Bases			
	Bad	Poor	Fair	Good
Depth of attack, mils*	3	2	1	0
Weight change, %†	6	4	2	0
Dimensional change, %	3	2	1	0

* Measured in metallographic examinations.
† Determined by direct measurements and/or by calculations based on the material(s) found in the test medium by chemical analyses.

FIG. 2.83—Corrosion resistance of ceramics to liquid metals [157].

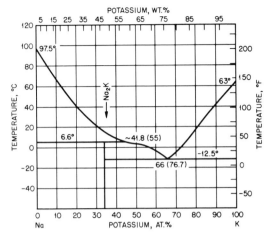

FIG. 2.84—Potassium–sodium constitution diagram. (From M. Hansen, Constitution of Binary Alloys, 2nd ed., p. 876, McGraw-Hill Book Company, Inc., New York, 1958.)

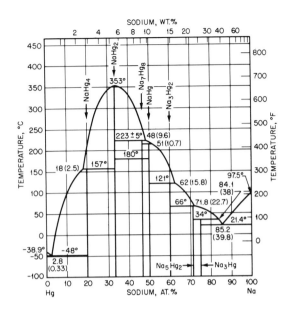

FIG. 2.86—Mercury-sodium constitution diagram. (From M. Hansen, Constitution of Binary Alloys, 2nd ed., p. 827, McGraw-Hill Book Company, Inc., New York, 1958.)

potassium–sodium (Fig. 2.84), bismuth–lead (Fig. 2.85), mercury–sodium (Fig. 2.86), and lead–mercury (Fig. 2.87). References 158 to 164 cover the bismuth–lead system; Refs. 165 to 186 apply to the sodium–potassium alloys; Refs. 187 to 205 pertain to sodium–mercury; and Refs. 206 and 207 are general. For the sodium–potassium alloys the following concentrations are given for the peritectic points: 40.05 (Ref. 165), 42 (Ref. 166), 40-42 (Ref. 168) at.% K; and for the eutectic points: 66.6 (Ref. 165), 66.6 (Ref. 166), and 66 (Ref. 168) at.% K. The seven liquidus points at atmospheric pressure for the NaK alloy agree with the thermal results of Ref. 168.

2.1.5 NUCLEAR PROPERTIES

The coolant in a fast reactor occupies a large fraction of the core volume. For neutron economy and other reasons, it is a prime nuclear prerequisite for the coolant to be a rela-

tively poor moderator. Liquid metals are poor moderators and thus are well suited for use as fast reactor coolants. Some moderation occurs, however, because elastic and inelastic neutron collisions with coolant, structural, and fuel atoms degrade the energy of the neutrons. The amount of moderation caused by a particular coolant depends upon the coolant volume, the macroscopic elastic and inelastic scattering cross section, Σ_{el} and Σ_{in}, and the value of the average logarithmic energy loss per elastic collision, ξ.

2.1.5.1 Neutron Cross Sections

Table 2.15 gives values of ξ, Σ_{el}, $\xi\Sigma_{el}$, Σ_{in}, and the macroscopic capture cross section, Σ_c, of some liquid–metal coolants for fast reactors.

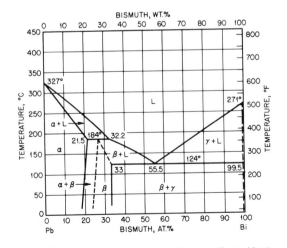

FIG. 2.85—Bismuth–lead constitution diagram. (From Metals Handbook, p. 1179, American Society for Metals, 1948.)

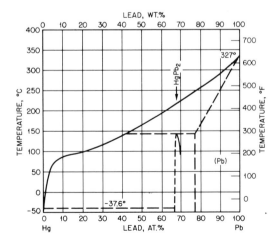

FIG. 2.87—Lead–mercury constitution diagram. (From M. Hansen, Constitution of Binary Alloys, 2nd ed., p. 830, McGraw-Hill Book Company, Inc., New York, 1958.)

Table 2.15—Nuclear Properties of Liquid-Metal Coolants for Fast Reactors*

Metal	Approximate atomic weight	ξ	Σ_{el},† cm^{-1}	Moderating power ($\xi\Sigma_{el}$)	Σ_{in}, cm^{-1}	Σ_c, cm^{-1}	Induced activity
Sodium	23	0.0845	0.0672	0.00568	0.0056	0.000013	Na^{24} 14.8 hr; 1.38 to 2.76-Mev gamma Na^{22} 2.9 Mev gamma; 1.3-Mev gamma
Potassium	39	0.0504	0.0246	0.00124	0.0037	0.000040	K^{38} 7.7 min; 2.2 Mev-gamma K^{42} 12.4 hr; 1.5 Mev-gamma
NaK (22 wt.%Na and 78 wt.%K)		0.0645	0.0318	0.00205	0.0039	0.000033	Na^{24}, Na^{22} (as above), K^{38}, K^{42}(as above)
Natural lithium (7.5 wt.%Li^6 and 92.5 wt.%Li^7)	7	0.268	0.0645	0.01729	0.0086	0.0022	Li^8 0.88 sec; bremsstrahlung from 12-Mev beta
Separated lithium (100 wt.%Li^7)	7	0.268	0.0645	0.01729	0.0086	0.0000014	
Lead	207	0.0096	0.1860	0.00179	0.0062	0.00031	Pb^{205} 51.5 days; 0.28-Mev gamma
Mercury	200	0.0099	0.1800	0.00178	0.0360	0.0035	Hg^{199} 43 min; 0.53-Mev gamma

* Cross section values are those for the natural form of the element. Energy range is 0.80 to 1.3 Mev.
† The metal densities which the macroscopic cross sections are based upon are the densities at the melting points.

Lithium is the strongest moderator among the liquid metals. Its inelastic and elastic slowing-down effects are appreciable. It should probably not be used where neutron economy is important. Sodium is the next strongest moderator, followed by mercury, which has a large inelastic cross section for slowing down fast neutrons. There is little difference between NaK and potassium since both have similar moderating ability. Lead is the weakest moderator among the liquid metals. Its inelastic scattering cross section, though relatively large, has a high threshold energy compared to the other liquid metals.

2.1.5.2 Coolant Reactivity Coefficient

The influence of the coolant on critical mass and reactor stability is determined from the coolant reactivity coefficient. This coefficient consists of three components resulting from the effect of the coolant on neutron leakage, spectrum, and absorption.

The coolant scatters neutrons and reduces leakage from the core. This component, the leakage component, of the coolant reactivity coefficient is positive. Its importance decreases with core size. In small reactors it is often the dominant effect. Of the liquid-metal coolants, the leakage component is most important for lead and mercury because of their large scattering cross sections.

The spectral component of the coolant reactivity coefficient arises because elastic and inelastic neutron collisions with coolant atoms soften the spectrum and affect reactivity through a change in the effective probability of fission absorption. This component can be either positive or negative depending upon the reactor composition, i.e., the type and amount of fissile, fertile, and structural material in the core. The spectral component is more important for lithium, sodium, and mercury than for the other liquid-metal coolants.

Neutron absorption, a negative reactivity effect, is very small for sodium, potassium, NaK, and lead, but it becomes quite important for lithium and mercury, both of which have relatively large capture cross sections for fast neutrons.

The value (sign and magnitude) of the coolant reactivity coefficient depends upon the importance of each component and is a strong function of reactor design as well as the choice of coolant.

2.1.5.3 Effect of Coolant on Critical Mass

With the exception of lithium, the liquid-metal coolants contribute relatively little to the total reactivity. In reactors such as Fermi and EBR-II, both of which are sodium-cooled fast reactors, the coolant worth is positive and approximately equal to 5% in reactivity. This is equivalent to a 6 to 10% reduction in critical mass. On the other hand, a reactor whose coolant has a negative reactivity coefficient requires an increase in critical mass to compensate for the coolant. In a large mercury-cooled fast reactor under investigation [208], the coolant reactivity coefficient is negative, and thus a 2% increase in critical mass is required. Compared to other liquid metals, lithium has an appreciable effect on critical mass because of its strong absorption and neutron-energy-degrading properties.

2.1.5.4 Effect of Coolant on the Temperature Coefficient

In considering the coolant temperature coefficient, the leakage effect tends to make the coefficient negative, the absorption term tends to be positive, and the spectral term either positive or negative depending upon the reactor spectrum and composition. Lead, sodium, potassium, and NaK are less likely to give rise to positive coolant temperature coefficients of reactivity than the other liquid-metal coolants because of their smaller effect on the spectrum and their small capture cross sections. For these coolants, the negative leakage component is most likely to be dominant in all but the largest reactors.

All sodium-cooled fast reactors that have been built to date have negative coolant temperature coefficients of reactivity. In these reactors the positive absorption component is insignificant compared to the spectral and leakage components, both of which are negative. However, the tendency in advanced fast reactor design is toward larger cores, increased concentrations of fertile (threshold fission) material, and the use of Pu^{239} rather than U^{235} as the fuel. These factors tend to make the leakage term less important and the spectral term more positive [209]. The net result is that the spectral component may be positive and larger in absolute magnitude than the negative leakage term, and thus a positive sodium temperature coefficient will exist.

Natural lithium has very strong absorption for fast neutrons. Consequently the absorption component of its temperature coefficient is strongly positive, and the sign of its net temperature coefficient depends upon the sign and magnitude of its spectral component since its leakage term is comparatively small. The strong positive absorption component of lithium can be eliminated by using lithium from which the Li^6 isotope has been removed since its absorption cross section is almost entirely due to the (n,a) reaction in this isotope.

Mercury also has very strong neutron-absorption and energy-degrading properties. However, its energy degradation is mainly by inelastic scattering at high energies, and this tends to make the spectral component of the coolant temperature coefficient positive in reactors that have a significant amount of threshold fission or fertile material in the core. In a fast breeder mercury-cooled reactor sized for central-station use, the coolant temperature coefficient of reactivity will probably be positive no matter what fissile material is used.

2.1.5.5 Coolant Activation

Although liquid metals have relatively small capture cross sections for fast neutrons, some of them can nevertheless become highly activated when used as the primary coolant in a high-flux power reactor. Consequently, if the coolant is circulated outside the primary shield area, additional shielding is required for piping, pumps, and heat exchangers, and maintenance problems are increased. The activation of the reactor coolant depends upon its cross section as a function of energy, the reactor flux level, flux spectrum, coolant cycle time, and the half-life of the isotope formed.

The liquid-metal coolants can be divided into two basic categories of induced activity: the high-activity coolants, sodium, potassium, and NaK, and the low-activity coolants, lithium, lead, and mercury.

Liquid sodium, potassium, and NaK are nearly identical in regard to their induced activities and shield requirements in fast reactors. Table 2.15 shows that all three coolants have comparable capture cross sections for fast neutrons. The radioisotopes formed, Na^{24} and K^{42}, both have about the same half-life and both emit gamma-ray photons of fairly high energy. In addition, all three of these coolants undergo $(n,2n)$ reactions with fast neutrons to form either Na^{22} or K^{38}. Although the cross section for the $(n,2n)$ reaction is small compared to the capture cross section, it can be an important consideration in the case of sodium.

Here, the longer lived Na^{22} isotope becomes the principal activity after long decay periods, and therefore it is important for maintenance consideration.

Lithium is classified as a low-activity coolant because its activation cross section (Li^7) is small and because its activity consists entirely of beta particles from decay of the Li^8 radioisotope. Beta particles are easily stopped by all materials, and the only problem is the bremsstrahlung X-radiation which results when the 12-Mev betas are absorbed. A coolant shield, utilizing materials of low atomic number, would greatly minimize the bremsstrahlung problem.

Although both lead and mercury have relatively high capture cross sections (Table 2.15), they have low activity. Most of the captures occur in the Pb^{208} and Hg^{199} isotopes to produce Pb^{209}, a weak beta emitter, and Hg^{200}, a nonradioactive isotope. The macroscopic capture cross sections (in the fast spectrum) are relatively small for Pb^{204} and Hg^{198}, and even these captures are not extremely troublesome since the radioactive products, Pb^{205} and Hg^{199}, have relatively low induced activities and emit gammas of low energy.

An additional advantage is that external shielding requirements for lead and mercury are reduced because both metals have high densities and afford considerable gamma shielding.

2.2 Heat Transfer

2.2.1 INTRODUCTION

Liquid metals used as fast reactor coolants have relatively high thermal conductivities (Table 2.1) and produce high heat-transfer coefficients. The specific heats are also reasonably high and thus permit large rates of heat removal without excessive coolant flow or temperature rise.

2.2.2 CONDUCTION

Conductive heat-transfer rates (Btu/hr/sq ft) can be calculated by Fourier's equation

$$\frac{q}{A} = -k \frac{dt}{dx} \tag{2.26}$$

where q = rate of heat transfer, Btu/hr
A = area, sq ft
k = thermal conductivity, Btu/hr/ft/°F
t = temperature, °F
x = distance measured in direction of heat flow, ft

Several measurements of the contact resistance between liquid metals and metallic surfaces have been performed. When the liquid wets the solid surface, the contact resistance is small and difficult to measure, and the results vary widely depending on metal cleanliness, presence of gas, filling technique, time, temperature, and other variables. Experimental results yield contact heat-transfer coefficients, varying from 20,000 Btu/hr/sq ft/°F for a mercury–chromium interface [210] to 100,000 to 300,000 Btu/hr/sq ft/°F for a sodium–stainless steel interface [211, 212].

2.2.3 CONVECTION

The heat generated in a heterogeneous reactor is removed by a fluid flowing past the fuel elements. Heat transfer between a solid surface and a fluid requires a temperature difference between the wall and the coolant. The rate (Btu/hr/sq ft) of heat transfer (q) per unit area (A) is given by

$$\frac{q}{A} = h(t_w - \bar{t}_c) \tag{2.27}$$

where h = surface heat-transfer coefficient, Btu/hr/sq ft/°F
t_w = wall temperature, °F
$\bar{t}_c$ = bulk coolant temperature, °F

The heat-transfer properties of fluids are related to their Prandtl number (N_{Pr}), a dimensionless ratio containing the heat capacity (c_p), the viscosity (μ), and the thermal conductivity (k)

$$N_{Pr} = \frac{c_p \mu}{k} \tag{2.28}$$

The Prandtl number may be defined as the ratio of the molecular diffusivities of momentum and of heat. Gaseous and nonmetallic fluids have Prandtl numbers close to, or larger than, unity. Owing to their high thermal conductivities, liquid metals have Prandtl numbers in the range of 0.001 to 0.1. The main consequence of the low Prandtl number is that heat from a solid surface is propagated by conduction much farther into the stream of coolant than it is in a fluid with a higher Prandtl number. Thus turbulence is less necessary to achieve good heat transfer into the stream, and heat-transfer coefficients are less dependent on circulation rate, whether in forced or free convection.

To calculate the temperature drop $t_w - \bar{t}_c$ by Eq. 2.27 or to determine the heat flux q/A to be expected with a given value of $t_w - \bar{t}_c$, one must determine or predict the heat-transfer coefficient h. Analytical equations and dimensionless correlations of experimental results that yield h as a function of flow conditions in commonly encountered geometries are available.

In subsequent sections equations and correlations are given for the heat-transfer situations that most frequently arise in fast reactors. For other, more specialized cases, standard references should be consulted (Refs. 2, 4, 5, 18, 119, 212, 214, and 215).

2.2.3.1 Forced Convection

For forced-convection heat transfer, the most common form of correlation is the relation between the Nusselt number

$$N_{Nu} = \frac{hD}{k} \tag{2.29}$$

the Prandtl number (Eq. 2.28), and the Reynolds number

$$N_{Re} = \frac{vD\rho}{\mu} = \frac{vD}{\nu} \tag{2.30}$$

N_{Pr} and N_{Re} frequently are employed for the geometry in question only as their product, which is abbreviated as the Peclet number

$$N_{Pe} = N_{Re} \times N_{Pr} \tag{2.31}$$

The variables are:
v = velocity of the fluid, ft/hr
k = thermal conductivity of the fluid, Btu/hr/ft/°F
ρ = density of the fluid, lb/cu ft
ν = kinematic viscosity of the fluid, sq ft/hr
μ = absolute viscosity of the fluid, lb(mass)/ft/hr
h = heat transfer coefficient, Btu/hr/sq ft/°F
D = characteristic length for the flow, ft

The Reynolds number is the ratio of inertia forces to viscous forces, and the Peclet number is a ratio of heat transfer by convection to heat transfer by conduction.

Theoretically, the correlations would be affected by the temperature variations caused by the heat transfer itself. Considering any local condition, the thermal properties of liquid metals do not vary greatly with temperature, and, in addition, liquid metals yield high values of h (consequently low values of $t_w - \bar{t}_c$); thus the effect on the heat transfer is small. Correlations of N_{Nu} vs. N_{Pe} are therefore adequately precise when obtained using the average properties of the liquid metal at any location. The coolant temperature generally varies by several hundred degrees axially across a fast reactor core, however; so it is not usually acceptable to use overall average fluid temperature or thermal properties for correlating or predicting heat transfer-coefficients at specific locations.

2.2.3.1.1 TURBULENT FLOW. Since the turbulent or eddy viscosity and, correspondingly, the velocity profile exhibit almost no temperature dependence, the Nusselt number is primarily a function only of the Prandtl number and of the Reynolds number, as stated above. Figure 2.88 shows the effect of Prandtl number on the radial temperature profile for turbulent heat transfer in smooth circular tubes at $N_{Re} = 10,000$. It is seen that fluids of Prandtl number close to 1 have a fractional temperature change that almost coincides with the fractional velocity change. For liquid metals (i.e., low Prandtl number), the temperature variation extends over the entire tube radius; considerably higher Reynolds numbers are required before the turbulent-eddy conductivity substantially takes over the heat-transfer function from the molecular conductivity.

Values of the heat-transfer coefficient for various coolants flowing in a 0.2-in. channel at typical reactor conditions are given in Table 2.16. Gases and organic liquids are seen to have low heat-transfer coefficients; liquid metals, large coefficients; and water, intermediate coefficients.

Figure 2.89 shows the dependence of the Nusselt number upon the Peclet number for forced convection of liquid metals inside pipes, as found in a

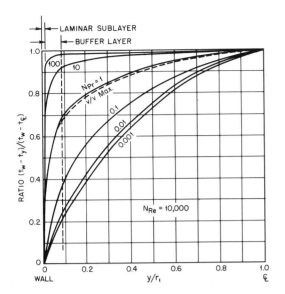

FIG. 2.88—Effect of Prandtl number on heat-transfer effectiveness for fixed Reynolds number in a smooth tube. [From R. C. Martinelli, Heat Transfer to Molten Metals, Trans. Am. Soc. Mech. Engrs., 69: 947(1947).]

Table 2.16—Typical Forced-convection Heat-transfer Coefficients

Coolant	Temp., °F	Velocity, ft/sec	h, Btu/hr/sq ft/°F
Na	700	20	18,000
H_2O	400*	20	8,000
$(C_6H_5)_2$ (biphenyl)	500	20	1,700
He	1500†	150	150

* 2000 psia.
† 200 psig.

number of tests. In general, experimental data for liquid metals exhibit considerable scatter because of the difficulty of measuring the very small temperature differences accurately. The oxide content of the fluid has an appreciable effect on the heat-transfer coefficient, and experiments performed in high-purity liquid metal show the best heat transfer [217-219].

Table 2.17 lists the principal theoretical and experimental heat-transfer correlations for liquid metals in fully established turbulent flow in various geometries. It can be noted from Table 2.17 that most correlations yield a limiting value of the Nusselt number when the Prandtl number, and hence the Peclet number, tend to zero. This limiting

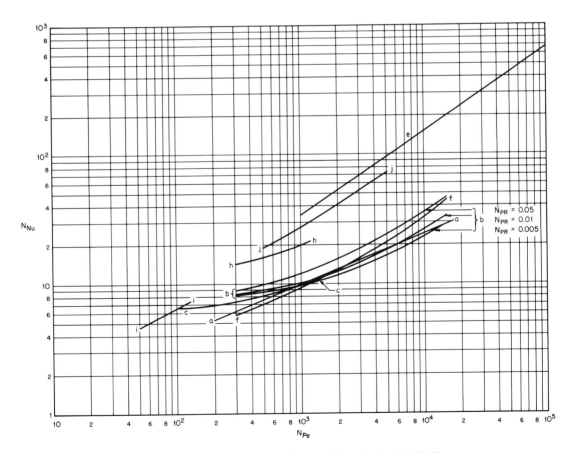

FIG. 2.89—Nusselt number vs. Peclet number in turbulent flow (see Table 2.17).

Table 2.17—Turbulent-flow Heat Transfer for Liquid Metals
(See Fig. 2.89)

Designation	Ref.	Case	Limitations	Correlations*
a	221	In long tube	Constant q/A: $200 < N_{Pe} < 20,000$	$N_{Nu} = 0.625\, N_{Pe}^{0.4}$
b	222	In long tube	Constant q/A: $N_{Pr} < 0.1$; $N_{Pe} < 15,000$	$N_{Nu} = 7 + 0.05\, N_{Pr}^{0.25}\, N_{Pe}^{0.77}$
c	5	In long tube	Constant t_w: $100 < N_{Pe} < 1,400$	$N_{Nu} = 4.8 + 0.014\, N_{Pe}^{0.8}$
d	223	Along an unbaffled bundle	$800 < N_{Pe} < 5,000$; triangular pitch/diameter = 1.75	$N_{Nu} = 0.409\, N_{Pe}^{0.53}$
e	229	Along a plate	Constant t_w; $10^3 < N_{Pe} < 10^5$	$\bar{N}_{Nu}† = 0.38\, N_{Pe}^{0.65}$
f	224	Narrow concentric annulus, wide rectangular channels $(d_2/d_1 \cong 1)$	Constant q/A through one wall	$N_{Nu} = 7.0 + 0.025\, N_{Pe}^{0.8}$
g	224, 225	Concentric annulus $(d_2/d_1 > 1)$	Constant q/A at d_2	$N_{Nu} = 0.75 \left(\dfrac{d_2}{d_1}\right)^{0.3} \left(7 + 0.025\, N_{Pe}^{0.8}\right)$
h	213, 224	Narrow concentric annulus, wide rectangular channels $(d_2/d_1 \cong 1)$	Constant q/A through both walls	$N_{Nu} = 10.5 + 0.036\, N_{Pe}^{0.8}$
i	226	Single tube in cross flow	$50 < N_{Pe} < 125$	$\bar{N}_{Nu}‡ = 0.65\, N_{Pe}^{0.5}$
j	227	Cross flow of Hg in tube bank in triangular array	$500 < N_{Pe} < 5,000$	$\bar{N}_{Nu}§ = 4.03 + 0.228\, N_{Pe}^{0.67}$
k	212, 228	Cross flow of NaK in tube bank in triangular array	$20 < N_{Pe} < 600$	$N_{Nu}§ = 1.17\,(N_{Pe})^{0.8}\, N_{Pr}^{1/3}$
m	220	Shell side of heat exchangers		$N_{Nu} = 0.313 + 0.2\, N_{Pe}^{0.613}$

* Reynolds and Nusselt numbers are based on equivalent diameter, except when otherwise indicated.
† Nusselt and Reynolds numbers based on plate length.
‡ Nusselt and Reynolds numbers based on tube diameter.
§ Nusselt and Reynolds numbers based on tube diameter with the minimum flow area used to calculate the velocity in the Reynolds number.

value is predictable by theory and corresponds to the case where the contribution of turbulence to the heat transfer disappears. The following notes apply to Table 2.17:

1. Equation a is an empirical curve that correlates many experimental data within approximately 25%.
2. Equation b is obtained on theoretical grounds and is in fair agreement with experimental data.
3. Equation c is recommended for high-purity sodium. Equations d to k have been confirmed by experiments.
4. Equation m is the best estimate of the heat-transfer coefficient on the shell side of heat exchangers. However, few experimental data are available for liquid-metal heat transfer in this case. This equation is based upon recommended values for nonmetallic fluids and was adapted to liquid metals using experimental data [220] in which a specific heat exchanger was operated with liquid metals and nonmetals.

Correlations for water, gases, and other nonmetallic fluids in these and other geometries can be found in Refs. 212 and 220.

Equations a through h in Table 2.17 apply to fully established hydraulic and thermal conditions, namely, long tubes. For liquid metals the effect of the entrance region upon the heat-transfer coefficient is not very pronounced and disappears in about 10 diameters downstream. Long-tube equations can be corrected [229] to give the short-tube local N_{Nu} by multiplying the right-hand side by the

correction factor $[1.72\,(D/L)^{0.16}]$. Since the long-tube h must always be lower than the short-tube h, the long-tube equations can safely be used in a conservative design.

2.2.3.1.2 LAMINAR FLOW. The heat-transfer coefficient for laminar flow can be calculated for any specified conditions [229, 230]. For any fluid flowing in a long tube, the Nusselt number rapidly approaches a constant value of 4.36 for constant heat flux when the wall temperature increase is linear and 3.65 when the wall temperature is uniform.

For laminar flow along a plate at constant temperature, the average heat-transfer coefficient between the leading edge of the plate and a distance L downstream is

$$\bar{N}_{Nu} \approx 1.1 \left[\left(1 - N_{Pr}^{1/3}\right) N_{Pe}\right]^{1/2} \qquad (2.32)$$

where the Peclet and Nusselt numbers are based on the distance L from the origin [229].

2.2.3.2 Free Convection

Free convection (also called natural, thermal, or gravity convection) is caused by density changes in the fluid due to thermal expansion from the application of heat or temperature difference to the fluid.

The Grashof number normally is used to describe the intensity of free convection:

$$N_{Gr} = \frac{L^3 \rho^2 g \beta \Delta T}{\mu^2} \qquad (2.33)$$

Other applicable dimensionless ratios are the Rayleigh number, N_{Ra},

$$N_{Ra} = N_{Gr} N_{Pr} = \frac{L^3 \rho^2 c_p g \beta \, \Delta T}{\mu k} \qquad (2.34)$$

and, for liquid metals,

$$N_{Gr} N_{Pr}^2 = \frac{L^3 \rho^2 c_p^2 g \beta \, \Delta T}{k^2} \qquad (2.35)$$

where L = characteristic length, ft
ρ = density, lb/cu ft
g = acceleration of gravity, $4.17 \times 10^8 \text{ft/hr}^2$
β = coefficient of thermal expansion, $1/°F$
μ = absolute viscosity, lb(mass)/hr/ft
ΔT = difference between the coolant temperature at the wall and far from the wall, $°F$

2.2.3.2.1 EXTERNAL FREE CONVECTION.
External free convection takes place when a large body of the fluid surrounds the heated or cooled surfaces.

For a vertical plate of height L, the average heat-transfer coefficient over this height is given by [229]

$$\overline{N}_{Nu} = 0.67 \left(\frac{N_{Gr} N_{Pr}^2}{1 + N_{Pr}} \right)^{1/4} \quad \text{(for } 10^2 < N_{Gr} < 10^8) \quad (2.36)$$

$$\overline{N}_{Nu} = 0.16 \left(\frac{N_{Gr} N_{Pr}^2}{1 + N_{Pr}} \right)^{1/3} \quad \text{(for } N_{Gr} > 10^8) \quad (2.37)$$

In nuclear reactors ΔT is not generally constant; the heat flux q/A, however, is constant or at least fixed. Therefore the thermally critical locations are generally local positions near the exit of a channel or, in the case of a surface cooled by free convection, near the top of the surface. Local h is more significant and more useful than average h over the whole surface. It is readily shown by differentiating equations of the type of Eqs. 2.36 and 2.37 that the local h (or N_{Nu}) equals the average value $\overline{h}$ (or $\overline{N}_{Nu}$) multiplied by the total exponent of L. Thus, for the conditions of Eq. 2.36

$$N_{Nu} = 0.75 \, \overline{N}_{Nu} \qquad (2.38)$$

Similarly, for the conditions of Eq. 2.38 there is no difference between h and $\overline{h}$, and for Eq. 2.32 $N_{Nu} = 0.5 \overline{N}_{Nu}$.

Equation 2.36 also describes the heat transfer from a horizontal tube [5, 212, 231] when D is used for the characteristic length in N_{Nu} and N_{Gr} and the coefficient is changed from 0.67 to 0.53.

For the heating of a cold plate of diameter D facing down on the top of a large pool (or the cooling of a hot plate on the bottom facing up), the following equation is applicable [232] over the range $4.8 \times 10^6 < N_{Ra} < 4 \times 10^7$:

$$N_{Nu} = 0.0785 \, N_{Ra}^{0.32} \qquad (2.39)$$

The diameter of the cold spot is the characteristic length.*

---

* For a more general equation see Ref. 233.

2.2.3.2.2 INTERNAL FREE CONVECTION.
In this case the heating and cooling surfaces substantially surround the liquid pool.

For horizontal layers heated from below [234], having a layer width-to-thickness ratio of more than 2, Eq. 2.40 is applicable in the range $10^5 < N_{Ra} < 10^9$

$$N_{Nu} = 0.104 \, N_{Ra}^{0.305} \, N_{Pr}^{0.084} \qquad (2.40)$$

The thickness of the layer is the length used in the Nusselt and Rayleigh numbers.

For narrow vertical annuli or slots heated from below and cooled from above, the following approximate equation is applicable [235]:

$$N_{Nu} = 0.00347 \, N_{Ra} \qquad (2.41)$$

The width of the annulus or slot is the characteristic length.

For heat transfer through a horizontal pipe heated at one end and cooled at the other, the heat-transfer rate can be approximately calculated [236] from

$$\frac{q(\text{conv})}{q(\text{cond})} = 0.44 \left[\frac{N_{Gr} N_{Pr}^2 \, (L/D)^2}{N + (L/D) \, 0.37 \, N_{Re}^{-0.2} + 0.28} \right]^{1/2} \qquad (2.42)$$

where $q(\text{conv})$ = heat transferred by convection, Btu/hr
$q(\text{conv})$ = heat transferred by conduction, Btu/hr
L/D = length-to-diameter ratio of pipe
N_{Gr} = Grashof number based on pipe diameter and axial temperature difference
N = number of velocity heads lost in bends and angles

The Reynolds number in the expression is calculated from

$$N_{Re} = 0.89 \left[\frac{N_{Gr}}{N + (L/D) \left(0.37 \, N_{Re}^{-0.2} + 0.28 \right)} \right]^{1/2} \qquad (2.43)$$

2.2.3.2.3 THERMAL CIRCULATION IN A LOOP.
The flow rates and temperatures for thermal circulation in a loop can be calculated from the density difference in the various parts of the loop, the hydraulic resistance, and the forced-convection Nusselt numbers pertinent to the geometry of the loop [2].

2.2.3.3 Boiling

One of the characteristics of liquid metals is their high saturation temperatures at atmospheric pressure. They are of potential interest in boiling reactors because high temperatures can be reached without high pressures. Operation at low pressure, however, results in a large specific volume of the vapor. Hence the vaporization of a small fraction of the volume of liquid can yield a very large volume of vapor and lead to significant changes in the flow behavior of the fluid. Limited experience with boiling mercury flowing in tubes [229] has shown that boiling-mercury void fractions and pressure drops can be calculated with the methods developed for water, despite the fact that the flow patterns are quite different for the two fluids.

Boiling on a heated surface can occur in different ways: (1) according to whether or not the coolant temperature exceeds the saturation temperature (saturated or subcooled boiling), (2) according to the magnitude of the temperature difference between the heated wall and the liquid (nucleate, mixed, or film boiling), and (3) according to the method of circulation of the fluid (pool, natural-circulation or forced-convection boiling) [2,212]. Whereas almost all combinations of the above conditions have been investigated for water, much less information is available for liquid metals. All data available at present pertain to experiments performed with the coolant at saturation temperature. Most tests have been run under pool boiling conditions, and only a few in natural convection or in forced circulation.

The experimental temperature differences between a heated wall and a saturated liquid metal cover the range from nucleate boiling to film boiling. In nucleate boiling the temperature of the wall only slightly exceeds the fluid temperature; bubbles grow on the surface and cause an intense local agitation of the coolant which promotes the transfer of heat and yields high heat-transfer coefficients. When the temperature difference becomes larger, a point is reached where the surface is almost covered with bubbles, and a maximum heat flux (critical heat flux) is obtained. At this point the liquid cannot reach the surface as easily, and the heat-transfer coefficient decreases with further increases in temperature driving force (mixed or unstable film boiling). Further increase in temperature difference causes a complete vapor layer to form at the surface, which becomes physically isolated from the bulk liquid (film boiling). The transfer of heat does not occur by direct contact with the liquid but by conduction and radiation through the vapor layer. Since this layer has a low thermal conductivity, the heat-transfer coefficient drops considerably in film boiling. In liquid metals the contact between the liquid and the wall can be lost not only by the presence of a vapor film but also by poor wetting conditions which decrease or prevent actual contact between the liquid and the wall. Thus, film boiling and the corresponding low values of heat-transfer coefficient can also be found at low temperature differences if the liquid does not wet the wall. Wetting has been shown [229] to have little effect on pressure drop, but the wetting characteristics of the coolant must be determined before boiling heat-transfer coefficients can be predicted. Improving the wetting characteristics of the fluid [e.g., addition of sodium (0.1%), or magnesium (0.02%) and titanium (0.0001%), to mercury] increases the heat-transfer coefficient by a large factor [237].

2.2.3.3.1 SATURATED POOL BOILING. Figure 2.90 shows experimental values of boiling heat-transfer coefficients for pool boiling of liquid metals. The conditions are listed in Table 2.18. When wetting occurs, the heat-transfer coefficient can be approximated by an expression of the type

$$h = B(q/A)^n \quad \text{Btu/hr/sq ft/°F} \qquad (2.44)$$

where n, a constant, is equal to about 0.6 to 0.7 and B, a constant, is about 1.5 to 3.5. In the absence of wetting, much lower coefficients are obtained, as shown by curves g, h, and i of Fig. 2.90.

Pool-boiling heat-transfer coefficients of liquid metals are comparable to those for water (curve w of Fig. 2.90). The effect of tube diameter on nucleate boiling of a metal is negligible [229], at least for diameters up to 1.6 in. The effect of pressure is to increase the heat-transfer coefficient as the 0.2 to 0.4 power of the absolute pressure, as shown by Eq. 2.45 for the pool boiling of mercury-titanium-magnesium amalgam on a horizontal plate at 83 to 800 mm Hg [Ref. 237 (particularly Fig. 9) and curves l, m, n of Fig. 2.90]:

$$h = 4.5(q/A)^{0.56} P^{0.29} \quad \text{Btu/hr/sq ft/°F} \qquad (2.45)$$

where q/A is in Btu per hour per square foot and P is in pounds per square inch absolute.

Large local fluctuations in the surface temperature are noticed [238] even below the critical heat flux and when the wetting conditions are thought to be satisfactory. Critical heat fluxes were not reached for pool-boiling mercury-titanium-magnesium amalgams (curves l, m, and n of Fig. 2.90). They were reached, however, for mercury-sodium amalgam (curve d, Fig. 2.90) and for mercury-magnesium amalgam (curve k). Figure 2.91 shows how the critical heat flux varies with magnesium content for the mercury-magnesium amalgam. In general, the limited data available do not, as yet, allow the critical heat flux to be predicted with accuracy [240] although Noyes [241] presents a correlation for critical heat flux for sodium at a horizontal cylinder.

2.2.3.3.2 SATURATED BOILING INSIDE TUBES. Heat transfer for saturated boiling flow inside tubes has received little attention. For mercury with wetting additives, the heat-transfer coefficient is reported to be substantially the same function of the pressure gradient whether the mercury is below the boiling point, at boiling, or superheated vapor [212]. The boiling heat-transfer coefficient could thus be approximated from a relation for liquid metals or from a standard correlation for gases in tubes.

A specific equation reported in Ref. 239 is

$$h = 6100(\Delta P/\Delta L)^{0.445} (D)^{1/3} \quad \text{Btu/hr/sq ft/°F} \quad (2.46)$$

where D is in inches, ΔP is in pounds per square inch, and ΔL is in feet.

Heat fluxes in excess of 600,000 Btu/hr/sq ft/°F have been reached without exceeding the critical heat flux [242]. Mercury boiler tubes have been operated at large void vapor fraction (98%) and low quality (12%) with a large factor of safety [243].

The heat-transfer coefficient for mercury-magnesium amalgam boiling in a vertical tube under natural circulation is shown as curve j of Fig. 2.90. There is little difference between boiling outside and inside vertical tubes, as seen by comparing curves j and k of Fig. 2.90. (A similar behavior if observed with nonmetals.)

The boiling of mercury-magnesium amalgam inside horizontal tubes [229] yields flow stratification

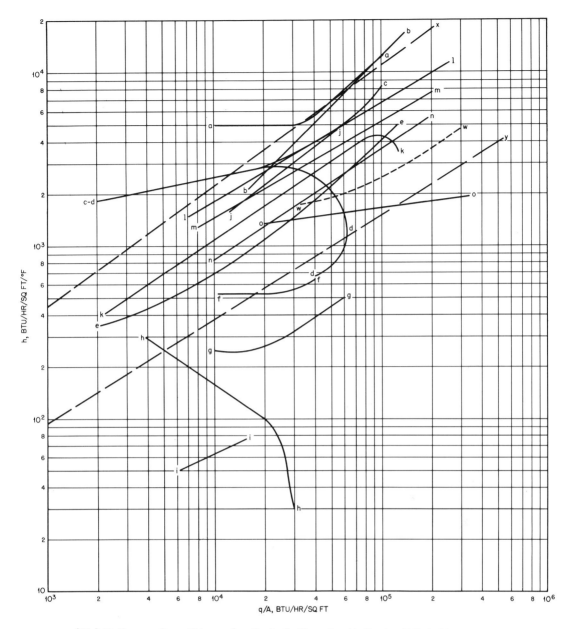

FIG. 2.90—Heat-transfer coefficient vs. heat flux for liquid-metal pool boiling (see Table 2.18 for conditions).

below a limiting value of the liquid velocity which can be approximated by

$$v_l \approx 0.085 (q/A)^{0.42} D^{0.76} \qquad (2.47)$$

where v_l = limiting liquid velocity, ft/sec
$\quad q/A$ = heat flux, Btu/hr/sq ft
$\quad D$ = inside diameter, ft

Below v_l the coolant flows predominantly at the bottom of the tube, and poor heat transfer occurs in the upper portion. Above this velocity the heat-transfer coefficient is uniform around the tube and is given by

$$h = 0.258 (q/A)^{0.67} v_g^{0.3} D^{-0.45} \qquad (2.48)$$

where h = heat-transfer coefficient, Btu/hr/sq ft/°F
$\quad q/A$ = heat flux, Btu/hr/sq ft
$\quad v_g$ = gas-phase velocity, ft/sec
$\quad D$ = inside diameter, ft

This expression is applicable to pressures of from 1 to 12 atm and covers the following range of variables:

$$1840 < q/A < 35,800 \text{ Btu/hr/sq ft}$$

$$3.28 < v_g < 62 \text{ ft/sec}$$

$$0.043 < D < 0.131 \text{ ft}$$

The velocities for Eqs. 2.47 and 2.48 assume that the phase covers the entire cross sectional area.

Table 2.18—Test Conditions Referred to in Figure 2.90

Designation and Ref.	Description	Range
a (239)	NaK on 316 stainless steel	$12,800 < q/A < 129,000$
b (239)	Na on 316 stainless steel	$15,300 < q/A < 128,000$
c (239)	Hg + 0.02 wt.% Mg + 0.0001 wt.% Ti on stainless steel	$2,000 < q/A < 100,300$
d (239)	Hg + 0.1 wt.% Na on Ti stainless steel	$2,100 < q/A < 57,400$
e (239)	Water	
f (239)	Hg on Cu	$12,000 < q/A < 61,500$
g (239)	Hg on Cr	$10,000 < q/A < 84,000$
h (239)	Hg on stainless steel	$4,140 < q/A < 30,000$
i (239)	Cd on stainless steel	$6,380 < q/A < 12,800$
j (5)	Hg–Mg amalgam inside vertical tube	$12,000 < q/A < 55,000$
k (5)	Hg–Mg amalgam outside a vertical tube	$2,000 < q/A < 10,000$
l (237)	Hg–Ti–Mg amalgam on horizontal low-carbon steel plate, 800 mm Hg pressure	$7,000 < q/A < 180,000$
m (237)	Same at 287 mm Hg pressure	$11,000 < q/A < 160,000$
n (237)	Same at 83 mm Hg pressure	$10,000 < q/A < 160,000$
o (238)	NaK on horizontal plate	$30,000 < q/A < 90,000$
w (5)	Water on horizontal tube, 1 atm	$30,000 < q/A < 350,000$
x, y	Upper and lower limits of Eq. 2.44	

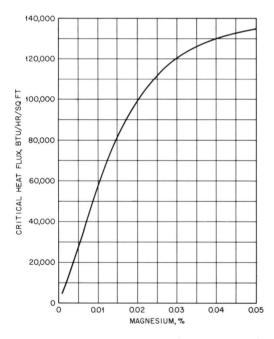

FIG. 2.91—Effect of magnesium content of a mercury–magnesium amalgam on the critical heat flux in pool boiling.

Experiments of boiling mercury in unwetted vertical and inclined tubes yield coefficients about 10% of those under wetting conditions. Flow velocity and tube diameter have a significant effect, but pressure has little [5].

2.2.3.4 Condensation

When a vapor is in contact with a surface which is below the saturation temperature, it will condense on that surface to form either a thin film or droplets. The heat-transfer coefficient in laminar film condensation ($4\Gamma/\mu < 10^4$) on a vertical surface is given by Nusselt's theory for any fluid. The average heat-transfer coefficient at a distance L down the plate is [212]

$$\bar{h}_L = 0.943 \left(\frac{\lambda g \rho^2 k^3}{\mu L \, \Delta T} \right)^{1/4} = 0.925 \left(\frac{k^3 g \rho^2}{\mu^2} \right)^{1/3} \left(\frac{\Gamma}{\mu} \right)^{-1/3}$$

(2.49)

where $\bar{h}_L$ = average heat-transfer coefficient from 0 to L, Btu/hr/sq ft/°F

k = conductivity of the condensate, Btu/hr/ft/°F

ρ = density of the condensate, lb/cu ft

μ = viscosity of the condensate, lb(mass)/hr/ft

λ = latent heat of vaporization, Btu/lb

Γ = mass flow rate of condensate per unit width at the distance L down the plate, lb/hr/ft

ΔT = temperature difference between the liquid–vapor interface and the wall, °F

g = acceleration due to gravity, 4.18×10^8 ft/hr^2

For film condensation on n horizontal tubes of diameter D in a vertical bank [212], the average heat-transfer coefficient is

$$\bar{h} = 0.724 \left(\frac{\lambda g \rho^2 k^3}{\mu n D \, \Delta T} \right)^{1/4} = 0.76 \left(\frac{k^3 g \rho^2}{\mu^2} \right)^{1/3} \left(\frac{\Gamma}{\mu} \right)^{-1/3}$$

(2.50)

According to these expressions the heat-transfer coefficient in laminar filmwise condensation is inversely proportional to the 0.25 power of the temperature difference. The temperature dependency is small. In dropwise condensation, the heat-transfer coefficient can be shown to be inversely proportional to the square root of the temperature difference.

As described in connection with Eq. 2.38, local h is generally more useful than the average, $\bar{h}$. With equations explicit for h, such as 2.49 and 2.50 $\bar{h}$ should be multiplied by unity for the total exponent of L. Thus for both these equations

$$h = 0.75\bar{h} \qquad (2.51)$$

Although the above theoretical derivations can be shown to hold reasonably well for nonmetallic vapors, wide discrepancies are encountered when they are applied to metals. Experiments with mercury [229] indicate that the heat-transfer coefficient drops rapidly with temperature, as shown in Fig. 2.92 for dropwise condensation of mercury on tubes. The results of tests run over the pressure range from 1.5 to 17.8 psia with temperature drops from 2 to 160°F and vapor mass flow rates from 0.6 to 9.2 lb/sq ft/sec were correlated by

$$q/A = 0.181 \times 10^5 \sqrt[3]{P} \left(1 + 1.694 \sqrt[3]{\rho_g v_g}\right) \text{ Btu/hr/sq ft} \qquad (2.52)$$

where P = pressure of the vapor, psia
ρ_g = density of the vapor, lb/cu ft
v_g = velocity of the vapor, ft/sec

The condensation of mercury is almost independent of the orientation of the tube.

The heat-transfer coefficient in Fig. 2.92 is almost inversely proportional to the temperature difference whereas available theories indicate less temperature dependence. The heat flux in dropwise condensation of mercury is thus suggested to be almost independent of the temperature difference. This is an improbable situation and seems to sug-

gest that the tests were, in effect, limited to definite values of heating rate. The same situation has been observed in the condensation of potassium and rubidium vapors in vertical tubes [244].

For sodium the heat-transfer coefficient can be conservatively estimated [212] from Eqs. 2.49 and 2.50 for low values of ΔT. The following empirical relation [245] can also be used whenever it yields a smaller value of h than those obtained from Eqs. 2.49 and 2.50:

$$h = 22,000 - \frac{36,000}{\Delta T} \text{ Btu/hr/sq ft/°F} \qquad (2.53)$$

where ΔT is the temperature difference in °F.

2.3 Fluid Flow

2.3.1 METHODS OF ANALYSIS

In most of the subsequent sections, results of fluid-flow experiments will be analyzed, interpreted, and correlated to put them in a useful form for reactor design. For cases in which such results are not available, it is frequently necessary to predict them. Such a prediction could be used as a guide for an experiment for an important case or an adequate solution of a less important or less doubtful one. These predictions are, of course, also very valuable for comparison and evaluation of any subsequent test results.

There are three general methods for predicting flow characteristics and phenomena: (1) analytical solutions, (2) electrical analogs, and (3) hydraulic models.

2.3.1.1 Analytical

The mathematical basis of the science of fluid flow is the group of differential equations known as the Navier—Stokes equations [246].

In dealing with an incompressible fluid in laminar flow, assuming that the temperature is relatively constant or at least that temperature effects on density and viscosity are small, the Navier—Stokes equations take on the following form in Cartesian coordinates:

$$\rho \left(\frac{\partial u}{\partial \theta} + u \frac{\partial u}{\partial x} + v \frac{\partial u}{\partial y} + w \frac{\partial u}{\partial z} \right) =$$
$$X - \frac{\partial P}{\partial x} + \mu \left(\frac{\partial^2 u}{\partial x^2} + \frac{\partial^2 u}{\partial y^2} + \frac{\partial^2 u}{\partial z^2} \right) \qquad (2.54)$$

$$\rho \left(\frac{\partial v}{\partial \theta} + u \frac{\partial v}{\partial x} + v \frac{\partial v}{\partial y} + w \frac{\partial v}{\partial z} \right) =$$
$$Y - \frac{\partial P}{\partial y} + \mu \left(\frac{\partial^2 v}{\partial x^2} + \frac{\partial^2 v}{\partial y^2} + \frac{\partial^2 v}{\partial z^2} \right) \qquad (2.55)$$

$$\rho \left(\frac{\partial w}{\partial \theta} + u \frac{\partial w}{\partial x} + v \frac{\partial w}{\partial y} + w \frac{\partial w}{\partial z} \right) =$$
$$Z - \frac{\partial P}{\partial z} + \mu \left(\frac{\partial^2 w}{\partial x^2} + \frac{\partial^2 w}{\partial y^2} + \frac{\partial^2 w}{\partial z^2} \right) \qquad (2.56)$$

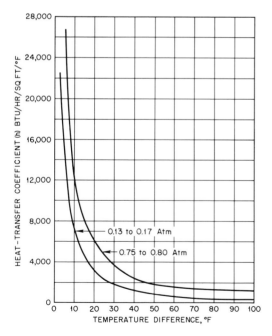

FIG. 2.92—Heat-transfer coefficient vs. temperature drop for mercury vapor condensing on a vertical tube. [From S. S. Kutateladze, V. M. Borishanskii, I. I. Novikov, and O. S. Fedynskii, At. Energ. Supplement 2 (1958).]

$$\frac{\partial u}{\partial x} + \frac{\partial v}{\partial y} + \frac{\partial w}{\partial z} = 0 \qquad (2.57)$$

where ρ = fluid density
   μ = fluid viscosity
   θ = time
   P = pressure
u,v,w = velocity components
X,Y,Z = body forces
x,y,z = coordinates

With known body forces, there are four equations for the four unknowns u, v, w, P.

The solutions of the above equations become fully determined physically when the boundary and initial conditions are specified. In the case of viscous fluids, the conditions of no slip on solid boundaries must be satisfied, i.e., on a wall both the normal and tangential component of the velocity must vanish, $v = 0$ and $v_t = 0$ on solid walls.

The mathematical difficulties encountered when solving the Navier—Stokes equations have thus far prevented a single solution in which the convective terms interact in a general way with the friction terms. The general validity of the Navier—Stokes equations has, however, been proved by experimental verification of known solutions, such as laminar flow through a circular pipe (Sec. 2.3.2.1.1).

2.3.1.2 Analogs

The electrical analog has proven useful as a tool for analyzing certain types of heat-transfer problems and has also, with less frequency, been applied to fluid flow. The analogy between these three types of systems is summarized as follows:

	Electrical	Thermal	Hydraulic
Driving force	Voltage	Temperature	Pressure
Flow	Current	Heat	Mass
Resistance	Electrical	Thermal	Hydraulic

In short, all three systems obey the general equation

$$\text{Flow} = \frac{\text{Driving force}}{\text{Resistance}} \qquad (2.58)$$

In an electrical circuit

$$I = \frac{E}{R_e} \text{ amp} \qquad (2.59)$$

In a thermal system

$$q = \frac{\Delta t}{R_t} \text{ Btu/hr} \qquad (2.60)$$

In a hydraulic system (nonturbulent)

$$Q = \frac{\Delta P}{R_h} \text{ cu ft/sec} \qquad (2.61)$$

A convenient type of "passive" analog is a two-dimensional model of the system cut from a sheet of material with controlled electrical conductance. The most common product for such use is Teledeltos* paper, which is available in two conduc-

---

* The conductivity of Teledeltos paper can be locally decreased, when desired, by punching a grid of holes through it with the appropriate spacing in diameters [2]. In addition, it can be locally increased (to the reciprocal of the decrease) by circles of silver paint of the same diameter-to-spacing ratio.

tivities [247]. Du Pont No. 4817 silver paint is applied to the models where required to stimulate lines or zones of constant pressure. Current from a dry cell is forced through the model in the direction that would be taken by the flowing fluid. Voltages are probed at various locations within the model, and lines of constant-velocity potential are thus established. The passive analog lends itself rather well to such applications as evaluating the flow patterns around an obstruction in the stream since the obstruction can be easily represented by an appropriately sized hole in the paper model. Several such applications have been described [248]. The method's shortcomings lie in the fact that it can analyze only laminar or potential (nonviscous) steady-state two-dimensional fluid-flow problems where the boundary conditions can be realistically mocked up. Although it is not a tool widely used by nuclear reactor fluid-flow analysts, they have sometimes been able, by using ingenuity, to construct a representative model of a local area of interest and gain valuable knowledge of the flow characteristics. This method can be employed to give conservative estimates of coolant maldistribution. In laminar flow the distribution among parallel channels is less uniform than in turbulent flow.

The electronic analog, or differential analyzer, is a computer capable of solving differential equations. It can solve most reactor problems that can be expressed mathematically. Although this device has not been extensively used to solve the type of fluid-flow problem that usually confronts the reactor designer, its applications are increasing.

2.3.1.3 Hydraulic Models and Similitude

Physical phenomena may frequently be predicted conveniently by studying the phenomenon in a scale model or in a different but similar system. If a phenomenon is to be reproduced in a model, similarity requires that all the independent dimensionless ratios of the physical qualities for the model be equal to the same ratios for the prototype. Geometric similarity can usually be achieved since any convenient scale meets this requirement. However, since other dimensionless ratios involve the fluid properties, it is frequently not practical to satisfy more than one of these. Models are generally operated to satisfy the most significant parameter; corrections are made for lesser effects.

Because of the difficulties associated with the analytical and analog methods, hydraulic testing is the most common approach to determining flow characteristics in complex geometries such as those with which the core designer is usually confronted.

In hydraulic testing it is advantageous to work with a noncorrosive, chemically inert, nontoxic, inexpensive transparent fluid as a substitute for the actual liquid-metal coolant, which probably possesses none of these qualities. As discussed in Sec. 2.3.2.2, liquid metals exhibit the same flow characteristics as the common liquids; so hydraulic experimentation can be carried out using water, which is generally much more convenient to use.

The most straightforward approach in conducting hydraulic tests is to duplicate full scale the geometry and the fluid velocity and to choose a test temperature such that

$$\left(\frac{\mu}{\rho}\right) \text{ of the liquid metal}$$
$$= \left(\frac{\mu}{\rho}\right) \text{ of the water sq ft/sec} \tag{2.62}$$

Thus, N_{Re} liquid metal = N_{Re} water, and, in addition, the velocity heads and Froude numbers* can be duplicated in the model. Table 2.19 gives the temperatures at which the kinematic viscosity (μ/ρ) of water equals that for several liquid metals over a range of operating temperatures. With a geometrically exact full-scale model, N_{Re} can be duplicated by proper selection of the velocity; i.e., if the prototype velocity is not exactly obtained or obtainable, a compensating change in μ/ρ is generally adequate.

It is often inconvenient or prohibitively expensive to conduct a test using a full-scale model. Miniaturization is sometimes indicated, as in a hydraulic mock-up of a complete reactor core. Oversize modeling is often required for the study of small regions and the minimization of perturbations caused by dye-injection hardware, pitot tubes, and other auxiliary apparatus. The planning and analysis of tests employing other than full-scale models require more extensive use of the principles of dynamic similarity [2].

---

*Froude number, $N_{Fr} = v_o^2/(gD_e)$, can be defined as the ratio of inertial to gravitational forces.

2.3.2 LIQUID-METAL APPLICATIONS

The relations which govern the flow behavior of common fluids, such as water, are also valid for liquid metals. Similarly, the methods by which frictional losses and form (or shock) losses are calculated for common fluids can be used with liquid metals. The data developed for predicting frictional losses as a function of Reynolds number and roughness form losses as a function of velocity, and velocity profiles in ducts (primarily round ducts) as a function of Reynolds numbers are useful to the fast reactor designer.

The bulk of all information in the field of fluid flow has been developed for isothermal flow. In nonisothermal flow the changes in physical properties along the flow path may be significant. This is not difficult to handle when the fluid temperature is uniform throughout any given cross section of the duct but becomes awkward when large temperature differences exist at a given cross section of the coolant stream. In applied fast reactor engineering, the error introduced by assuming that planes perpendicular to the flow axis are isothermal is generally of little consequence.

2.3.2.1 Types of Flow

The Reynolds number (N_{Re}) is a measure of the degree of turbulence of a flowing fluid (Sec. 2.2.3). Consistent units must be used in the evaluation of Reynolds number so that the dimensionless value is computed. The Reynolds number describes the character of the flow. In round tubes:

1. For $N_{Re} < 1900$ to 2000, all the flow filaments are parallel to the flow axis, and the flow is laminar.

Table 2.19—Conditions of Equal Kinematic Viscosity
Between Water and Some Liquid Metals

Liquid metal	Temp., °C	Temp., °F	Kinematic viscosity (μ/ρ), sq ft/sec	Temperature at which saturated water has this μ/ρ, °F
Hg	−20	4	1.46×10^{-6}	500
Hg	20	68	1.34×10^{-6}	
Hg	100	212	1.25×10^{-6}	
Hg	200	392	0.993×10^{-6}	
Hg	300	572	0.844×10^{-6}	
K	200	392	3.93×10^{-6}	177
K	250	482	3.55×10^{-6}	196
K	400	752	2.75×10^{-6}	235
K	600	1112	2.31×10^{-6}	286
K	700	1292	2.17×10^{-6}	302
Na (56 wt.%) K (44 wt.%)	100	212	6.35×10^{-6}	116
Na (56 wt.%) K (44 wt.%)	250	482	3.70×10^{-6}	186
Na (56 wt.%) K (44 wt.%)	400	752	2.85×10^{-6}	235
Na (56 wt.%) K (44 wt.%)	500	932	2.52×10^{-6}	260
Na (56 wt.%) K (44 wt.%)	700	1292	2.24×10^{-6}	290
Na (22 wt.%) K (78 wt.%)	100	212	6.04×10^{-6}	122
Na (22 wt.%) K (78 wt.%)	250	482	4.00×10^{-6}	175
Na (22 wt.%) K (78 wt.%)	400	752	3.04×10^{-6}	220
Na (22 wt.%) K (78 wt.%)	500	932	2.58×10^{-6}	255
Na (22 wt.%) K (78 wt.%)	700	1292	2.34×10^{-6}	280
Na	100	212	8.23×10^{-6}	90
Na	200	392	5.84×10^{-6}	132
Na	300	572	4.44×10^{-6}	160
Na	400	752	3.78×10^{-6}	180
Na	500	932	3.40×10^{-6}	200
Na	600	1112	3.17×10^{-6}	212

2. For $N_{Re} > 4000$, the flow filaments present no constant pattern with respect to time and the walls of the duct, and the flow is turbulent.

3. For $2000 < N_{Re} < 4000$, the flow is in the critical zone with either laminar or turbulent conditions, depending on the absence or presence, respectively, of irregularities in the duct, vibrations, prior turbulence, and other factors.

2.3.2.1.1 LAMINAR FLOW. Generally speaking if the body forces acting on a flowing fluid can be defined, point velocities in a flowing stream can be calculated using the Navier–Stokes equations (Sec. 2.3.1.1). These equations reduce to the following simple forms for incompressible one-dimensional steady-state flow:

$$\frac{g_c \, dP}{\mu dx} = \left(\frac{\partial^2 v}{\partial y^2} + \frac{\partial^2 v}{\partial z^2} \right) \text{ in rectangular coordinates} \quad (2.63)$$

$$\frac{g_c \, dP}{\mu dx} = \left(\frac{1}{r} \frac{\partial v}{\partial r} + \frac{\partial^2 v}{\partial r^2} \right) \text{ in cylindrical coordinates} \quad (2.64)$$

where g_c = conversion factor, 32.2 lb(mass)ft/lb (force)/sec^2

$\frac{dP}{dx}$ = pressure gradient in the direction parallel to flow, psf/ft

r = distance from the center line of the tube, ft

By integrating Eq. 2.64 one obtains the point velocity in feet per second

$$v = \frac{g_c}{4\mu} \frac{dP}{dx} (r_1^2 - r^2) \quad (2.65)$$

where r_1 is the radius of the tube. The maximum velocity, v_{max}, is evidently located at the axis, and

$$v_{max.} = \frac{g_c r_1^2}{4\mu} \frac{dP}{dx} \quad (2.66)$$

Integrating over the cross section of the stream results in

$$\bar{v} = \frac{v_{max.}}{2} = \frac{g_c r_1^2}{8\mu} \frac{dP}{dx} \quad (2.67)$$

2.3.2.1.2 TURBULENT FLOW. The Navier–Stokes equations cannot be generally solved for the case of turbulent flow. However, several empirical velocity-profile equations have been developed for isothermal turbulent flow in tubes. The Prandtl velocity distribution equation [210] is

$$v = v_{max.} + 2.5 \left[\frac{dP}{dx} \left(\frac{r_1}{2} \right) \frac{g_c}{\rho} \right]^{1/2} \left(\ln \frac{r_1 - r}{r_1} \right) \quad (2.68)$$

Several other investigations have developed general velocity-distribution equations for isothermal turbulent flow in both smooth and rough tubes [2, 210, 246] which are useful for predicting pressure drop and heat transfer in unusual channels, etc.

2.3.2.2 Liquid-metal Flow Characteristics

Liquid-metal flow is no different than that of nonmetals. Isakoff and Drew [249] for 4×10^4 $< N_{Re} < 4 \times 10^5$, and Brown et al. [250] for 2.5×10^5 $< N_{Re} < 7.3 \times 10^5$ observed liquid-metal velocity profiles that compared within 5 to 10% with generalized velocity-distribution diagrams for isothermal flow. Fluid pressure drop for smooth tubes and for slightly rough tubes was also found to agree with relations developed with common fluids [249-251]. Evidently all the generalized correlations developed for liquids, such as loss factors, can be applied directly to liquid-metal flow problems.

When the temperature of the coolant changes slowly as the coolant flows through the duct so that the coolant is substantially isothermal in planes normal to the axis of the flow duct, changes in coolant physical properties with temperature are easy to accommodate. For instance, total pressure drop is obtainable by summing pressure drops calculated over successive short sections of duct length using average physical-property values for each section.

However, when physical properties, particularly viscosity, change substantially with temperature in the same cross section, there is a redistribution of the velocity profile. However, the effect is small with liquid metals. The Prandtl number (Eq. 2.28) is an index of the degree of departure of the velocity profile under nonisothermal conditions from that of isothermal conditions; as N_{Pr} approaches zero, the velocity profile approaches that for isothermal conditions. Isakoff and Drew [249] reported, for the conditions of their test, that the velocity profiles were identical for isothermal and nonisothermal flow. Thus, even at high values of heat flux no substantial local effect on flow or heat transfer need be expected in liquid metals.

2.3.2.3 Pressure-drop Formulas

Since the flow characteristics of liquid metals and nonmetals are similar, conventional formulas and techniques of calculation can be used in the design of liquid-metal piping systems. Common pressure-drop calculations are given in the following sections. More extensive pressure-drop correlations and methods of analysis are given in Refs. 2 and 252.

2.3.2.3.1 PIPES. In round pipes the inside diameter of the conduit is the length in the Reynolds number (Eq. 2.30). The dimensionless Weisbach friction factor, f, a function* of Reynolds number and relative roughness, ϵ/D, can be obtained from Fig. 2.93. When surface roughness, ϵ, is not known, the relative roughness can be approximated with sufficient accuracy from Fig. 2.94. The frictional pressure drop across a straight length of conduit can then be calculated by

$$\Delta P = \frac{fL\rho}{D} \frac{\bar{v}^2}{2g_c} \text{ psf} \quad (2.69)$$

where L = length of conduit, ft

g_c = conversion factor, 32.2 lb(mass)ft/lb (force)/sec^2

---

*The Weisbach f should not be confused with the Fanning f, which is only one-fourth as large. If a correlation or equation is employed which yields the Fanning f, the 2 in Eq. 2.69 should be moved to the numerator.

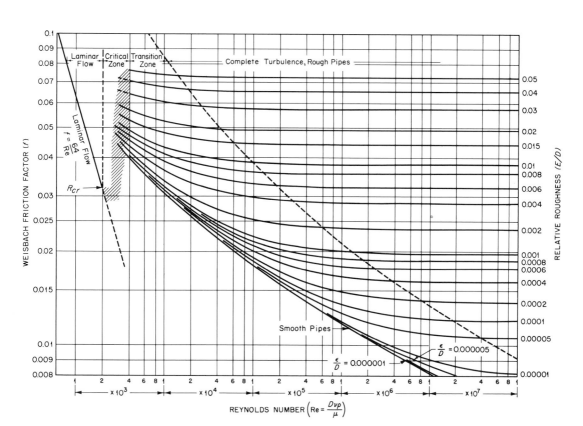

FIG. 2.93—Friction factor as a function of Reynolds number with relative roughness as a parameter. [From L. F. Moody, Trans. Am. Soc. Mech. Engrs., 66:671 (1944).]

D = inside pipe diameter, ft
ρ = fluid density, lb/cu ft
$\bar{v}$ = fluid velocity (averaged over cross section), ft/sec

Pressure losses due to fittings, valves, bends, contractions, and expansions are called form losses. These objects cause the flowing fluid to lose energy owing to a sudden change of cross section or change of direction. Such a loss in energy is proportional to $\bar{v}^2$ and, unlike wall friction, has little if any dependence upon Reynolds number and relative roughness.

In general, the effects of fittings and valves cannot be presumed reliably calculable because of interdependence between adjacent fittings (unless they are widely separated) and because of differences between the products of the various commercial fabricators. Nevertheless, the designer frequently must produce a reasonable estimate of the head loss in a loop. It has been shown [252] that fairly reliable estimates can be made by the simple process of summing the losses for each fitting by itself; increases and decreases due to proximity of fittings tend to cancel each other.

The preferred basis for loss estimates is the velocity head-loss coefficient K. Table 2.20 gives, for typical pipe fittings and other changes, the values of K for the turbulent regime [2]. The pressure loss is computed from

$$\Delta P = \frac{K \rho \bar{v}^2}{2 g_c} \qquad (2.70)$$

where $\bar{v}$ is the average velocity in the smaller cross section if there is a change in cross section in the fitting involved. Since Eq. 2.70 only includes energy losses, Bernoulli pressure changes due to differences in velocity (kinetic energy) across the fitting are not included. If there is a change in flow cross section, the additional acceleration ΔP of $\rho \Delta (v)^2 / 2 g_c$ should be added to the lost ΔP by Eq. 2.70 to yield the total net ΔP.

In laminar flow the frictional pressure drop is independent of the surface condition of the conduit, and

$$f = 64/N_{Re} \qquad (2.71)$$

Therefore in the laminar regime frictional pressure drop can be calculated from Poiseuille's equation, which combines Eqs. 2.69 and 2.71.

$$\Delta P = \frac{32 L \bar{v} \mu}{g_c D^2} \qquad (2.72)$$

The Reynolds number in a sodium or NaK system for a particular combination of the three parameters (velocity, pipe size, and temperature) can be found directly from Fig. 2.95.

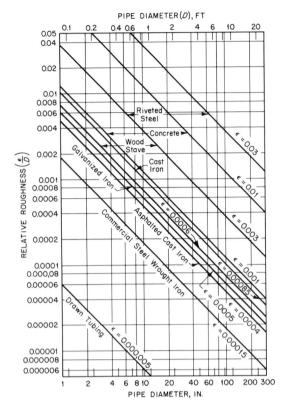

PIPE DIAMETER(D), FT

RELATIVE ROUGHNESS$\left(\frac{\epsilon}{D}\right)$

PIPE DIAMETER, IN.

FIG. 2.94—Relative roughness as a function of pipe diameter for various materials. [From L. F. Moody, Trans. Am. Soc. Mech. Engrs., 66: 671 (1944).]

Table 2.20—Velocity Head-loss Coefficient in Typical Pipe Fittings, etc., in Turbulent Flow [2]

	K^*
Fitting:	
One average-velocity head	1
Pipe fittings:	
Elbow, 45° standard	0.35
Elbow, 45° long radius	0.2
Elbow, 90° standard	0.82
Elbow, 90° long radius	0.53
Elbow, 90° square	1.3
Return bend, 180° close	2.0
Return bend, 180° medium	1.2
Tee, 0° through	0.4
Tee, 90° side outlet	1.3
Tee, 90° side inlet	1.5
Coupling, union, 0° through	0.04
Valves:	
Valve, open, 0° gate	0.16
Valve, open, 0° globe	6
Valve, open, 90° angle	3
Valve, open, 0° swing check	2
Pipe bends:	
Bend, 90°; $r/D = 0.5$	0.8
Bend, 90°; $r/D = 1$	0.35
Bend, 90°; $r/D = 4$	0.16
Bend, 90°; $r/D = 10$	0.16
Coil, each turn, 360°; $r/D = 1$	2.2
Coil, each turn, 360°; $r/D = 4$	0.55
Coil, each turn, 360°; $r/D = 10$	0.3
Contraction and expansion:	
Sudden contraction, $D_1/D_2 = 1.33$	0.19
Sudden contraction, $D_1/D_2 = 2$	0.33
Sudden contraction, $D_1/D_2 = 4$	0.42
Sudden expansion, $D_2/D_1 = 1.33$	0.19
Sudden expansion, $D_2/D_1 = 2$	0.56
Sudden expansion, $D_2/D_1 = 4$	0.92
Gradual conical expansion in pipe	0.2 - 0.5
Gradual conical convergence in pipe	0.06 - 0.15
Gradual conical converging inlet	0.13 - 0.14
Orifices and nozzles[†]	
Small square-edged orifice	0.05
Rounded nozzle	0.05
Excess in tube below nozzle	0.02
Short tube downstream of plate (L < 3D)	0.05
Long tube downstream of plate (L > 3D)	0.5
Short tube upstream of plate (L < 3D)	0.06
Long tube upstream of plate (L > 3D)	0.8

* Where there is a change in cross section, K applies to the velocity head in the smaller cross section.

† K does not include downstream losses, which can be calculated as for an expansion.

D = diameter of fitting or pipe; L = length; and r = radius of fitting or pipe.

The frictional pressure drop per foot of conduit in a sodium or NaK system can be conveniently determined from Fig. 2.96 if it falls within the ranges covered in this chart. Figure 2.96 assumes a smooth conduit, i.e., ϵ/D of the order 1×10^{-6}. The more general calculation involving Fig. 2.93 and Eq. 2.69 should otherwise be used.

2.3.2.3.2 NONCIRCULAR SECTION, EQUIVALENT DIAMETER. With conduits of noncircular cross section, the approach of Sec. 2.3.2.3.1 is generally valid, but the inside pipe diameter, D, is replaced with an equivalent diameter, D_e, customarily calculated as follows:

$$D_e = \frac{4A}{p} \text{ ft} \qquad (2.73)$$

where A is the flow area in square feet and p is the wetted perimeter in feet.

In narrow rectangular channels there is a markedly reduced velocity in the extremities of the channel [254]. The proper analysis of such geometries often requires special tests (Secs. 2.3.1.2 and 2.3.1.3).

2.3.2.3.3 EFFECTS OF STREAM DISCONTINUITIES. One of the most common geometries utilized in nuclear-fuel technology is the pin or rod bundle, where coolant flows parallel to the bundle axis. The spacing devices employed to avoid pin

vibration and local overheating from pin contact vary and can be considered in two categories: (1) spiral spacer wires wrapped around each individual pin and (2) transverse spacer grids of various types.

The overall pressure loss across these complicated geometries is predicted by adding three components

$$\Delta P_T = \Delta P_E + \Delta P_R + \Delta P_S \qquad (2.74)$$

where ΔP_T = the overall pressure loss, psf

ΔP_E = the pressure loss occurring at the bundle exit and entrance, psf

ΔP_R = the frictional pressure drop calculated for the rod bundle without spacer, psf

ΔP_S = the pressure loss due to spacing devices, psf

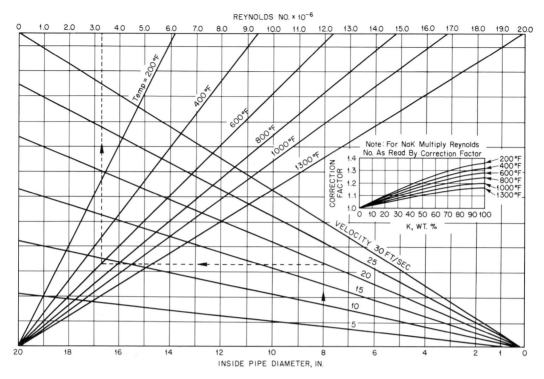

FIG. 2.95—Reynolds number chart for sodium and NaK alloys [18].

ΔP_E can be measured experimentally or predicted as follows: For an abrupt expansion, K in Eq. 2.70 is given by

$$K = \left(1 - \frac{A_1}{A_2}\right)^2 \qquad (2.75)$$

where A_1 and A_2 are the inlet and outlet areas, respectively. For an abrupt contraction, K is given by Fig. 2.97. In both cases, the velocity in Eq. 2.70 is that in the smaller cross section.

ΔP_R for the flow unit is calculated, as shown in Sec. 2.3.2.3.1, using the appropriate equivalent

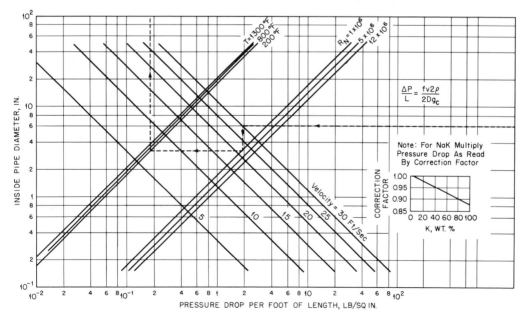

FIG. 2.96—Pressure-drop chart for sodium and NaK alloys [18].

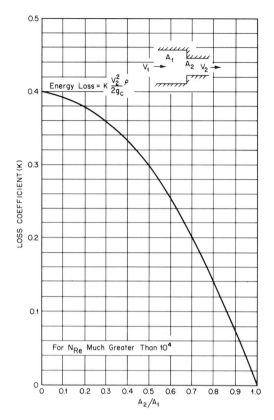

FIG. 2.97—Loss coefficient for sudden contraction. (From W. H. McAdams, Heat Transmission, 3rd ed., McGraw-Hill Book Company, Inc., New York, 1954.)

diameter (Sec. 2.3.2.3.2).

ΔP_S is most generally calculated from the successive contraction, friction, and expansion losses in the spacer system, using the same procedure for the friction in the spacing device as above for ΔP_E and ΔP_R for the rest of the flow path.

Although this method of predicting the spacer loss has given satisfactory results in specific cases of transverse spacer grids [255], it has given wide discrepancies in other cases [256, 257] presumably owing to shorter L/D ratios. Evidently it could not be applied to spiral spacer systems to predict the increase of pressure drop with a decreased longitudinal wire pitch. An alternative method based on experimentally determined drag coefficients [258] is summarized below.

The following expression for ΔP_S is obtained by using the force equilibrium conditions for the fluid across the spacer device

$$\Delta P_S = \frac{C_s \rho v_s^2 S}{2 g_c A} \qquad (2.76)$$

where C_s = the spacer drag coefficient
v_s = the velocity in the spacer region, ft/sec
A = the unrestricted flow area in the bundle (away from spacer), sq ft
S = the spacer projected frontal area, sq ft
g_c = 32.2 lb(mass) ft/lb(force)/sec^2

C_s is similar to classical drag coefficients for flow around a body in a fluid stream and can be correlated as a function of a Reynolds number employing the spacer frontal dimension and the velocity existing in the spacer region.

2.3.2.3.3.1 Spiral Wires. Table 2.21 gives the geometrical characteristics of 12 subassembly models hydraulically tested. The tests were conducted with water, generally over a wide range of Reynolds numbers. The drag coefficients, C_s, were calculated from Eqs. 2.74 and 2.76 and are plotted in Fig. 2.98 vs. Reynolds number.

It is seen that the calculated points for each model generally fall on a smooth curve pertinent to that model. However, the spread from model to model covers a relatively wide area. The causes for this variation can be (1) varying error in the friction factor for the ΔP_R calculation but a consistent error within any single model calculation, (2) influence of the spiral-wire pitch on the perturbed flow region, and (3) experimental error in ΔP_T determination. The curve shown in Fig. 2.98 is the arithmetic average of the points. The spread in the data covers about 40% of the value of the curve. Since the pressure loss due to the spacing device is on the order of 30 to 70 % of the total, calculations based on this correlation should yield accuracies of 10 to 30%, which is generally satisfactory for preliminary reactor design.

2.3.2.3.3.2 Grid Supports. The geometrical characteristics of 18 subassembly models employing transverse grid supports are given in Table 2.22. These models were hydraulically tested in a water loop, and the experimental values of C_s were thus obtained and correlated against Reynolds number (Fig. 2.99) for the three basic types of transverse supports tested, i.e., circular wires, lenticular wires, and honeycomb grids (Fig. 2.100). The values of C_s for circular wires were found to be independent of wire angle, and the values for lenticular wires were substantially lower than for circular wires because of better streamlining of the trailing edge. Again the curves represent arithmetic averaging of the points. The data spread about ±15%.

2.3.2.4 Two-phase Flow

Two-phase flow is of interest in boiling or evaporation-cooled liquid-metal reactors. It is also of interest in the boiler of binary-system plants. Two conditions are of particular interest. One is the case encountered in pool boiling where the liquid is substantially stagnant and the gas flow tends to follow Stokes' law behavior; the other is the case where both the liquid and gas phase are in motion.

2.3.2.4.1 STAGNANT LIQUID. Where the gas flows through a stagnant liquid, the following correlation can be used:

$$a = K \left(\frac{\rho_g}{\rho_l - \rho_g} \right)^{0.17} \left\{ \frac{[\sigma g_c / g (\rho_l - \rho_g)]^{1/2}}{d} \right\}^{0.1} \left\{ \frac{v}{[\sigma g_c g / (\rho_l - \rho_g)]^{1/4}} \right\}^{a} \qquad (2.77)$$

Table 2.21—Characteristics of Pin Bundles with Spiral Wire Spacers [258]

Model	Can shape	Pin array	Pin diameter, in.	Spacer diameter, in.	Spacer pitch, in.	Flow area, sq in.	Equivalent diameter, in.	Number of pins per can	Notes
APDA core model 1	Square	Square	0.158	0.044 × 0.020	6	3.01	0.124	144	(Rectangular spacer wires)
APDA core model 2	Square	Square	0.158	0.044 × 0.020	8	3.01	0.124	144	
APDA core model 1-a	Square	Square	0.158	0.038	6	2.68	0.108	144	
APDA core model 3	Square	Square	0.159	0.045	6	3.01	0.1185	144	
APDA 121 pin model	Square	Square	0.193	0.025	6	2.393	0.1032	121	
APDA 143 pin model	Square	Hexagon	0.159	0.045	6	2.506	0.0972	143	Fillers used to fit the hexagonal pin bundle inside square can
APDA blanket model	Square	Square	0.434	0.040	9	2.06	0.177	25	
Westinghouse CVTR models	Hexagon	Hexagon	0.500	0.100	4	2.75	0.247	19	
	Hexagon	Hexagon	0.500	0.100	8	2.75	0.247	19	
	Hexagon	Hexagon	0.500	0.100	12	2.75	0.247	19	
	Hexagon	Hexagon	0.500	0.100	15	2.75	0.247	19	
EBR-II core model	Hexagon	Hexagon	0.1725	0.050	6	1.91	0.107	91	

Table 2.22—Characteristics of Square-pitch Pin Bundles with Transverse Spacer Grids [258]

APDA model symbol	Pin pitch, in.	Number of pins per can	Pin diameter, sq in.	Grid type*	Wire dimension (d_s), in.	Grid spacing, in.	Total unrestricted flow area, sq in.	Total equivalent diameter, in.
Core model 4	0.189	144	0.158	A	0.031	2	2.61	0.1280
Core model 5	0.199	144	0.158	A	0.041	2	3.37	0.1648
Large-scale models, perpendicular circular wires	0.480	25	0.385	A	0.095	4.8	3.154	0.3060
	0.480	25	0.385	A	0.095	7.2	3.154	0.3060
	0.480	25	0.385	A	0.095	9.6	3.154	0.3060
Large-scale models 45° inclined circular wires	0.480	25	0.385	B	0.095	4.8	3.154	0.3060
	0.480	25	0.385	B	0.095	7.2	3.154	0.3060
	0.480	25	0.385	B	0.095	9.6	3.154	0.3060
Subassembly prototypes from fuel manufacturers	0.200	144	0.158	C	0.042	2	3.20	0.1575
Large-scale models perpendicular lenticular wires	0.480	25	0.385	D	0.095 × 0.600	4.8	3.154	0.3060
	0.480	25	0.385	D	0.095 × 0.600	7.2	3.154	0.3060
	0.480	25	0.385	D	0.095 × 0.600	9.8	3.154	0.3060
DEM-6	0.200	144	0.158	E	0.042 × 0.250	2	3.20	0.1575
DEM-7						4 in. between groups of 2 grids		
MARV-1	0.194	144	0.158	F	0.036 × 0.250	4	3.20	0.1575
HB-1	0.200	144	0.159	G	Strip thickness: 0.015 Dimple: 0.013 Length: 0.438	4.44	3.163	0.1548
HB-7	0.200	144	0.159	G	Strip thickness: 0.012 Dimple: 0.0145 Length: 0.5	3	3.163	0.1548
HB-8	0.200	144	0.159	H	Strip thickness: 0.012 Dimple: 0.0145 Length: 0.5	$1\frac{7}{8}$	3.163	0.1548
Westinghouse Yankee	0.425	93	0.335	I	Strip thickness: 1/32 Length: 1	14	9.67	0.335

*A, perpendicular circular wires, five and six wires per grid, alternately. B, 45° inclined circular wires, two wires per grid. C, 45° inclined circular wires, five and six wires per grid, alternately. D, perpendicular lenticular wires, two wires per grid. E, perpendicular lenticular wires, five and six wires per grid, alternately. F, perpendicular lenticular wires, 13 wires per grid. G, elastic honeycomb. H, nine elastic honeycomb grids and seven simple honeycomb grids. I, simple honeycomb grid.

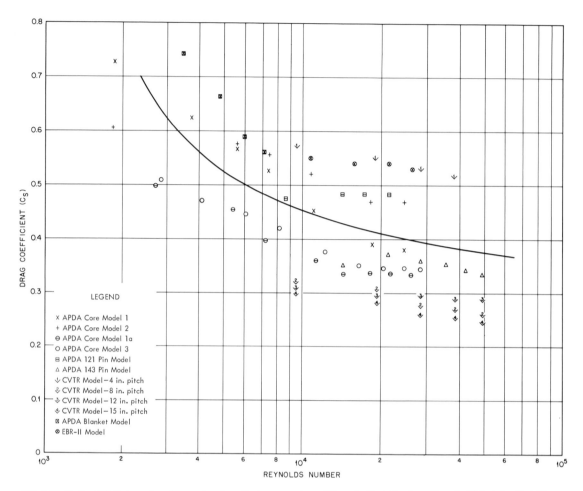

FIG. 2.98—Drag coefficient vs. Reynolds number for spiral spacer wires. [From A. N. de Stordeur, Drag Coefficients for Fuel Element Spacers, Nucleonics, 19(6):74-79 (June 1961).]

where

$$\frac{v}{[\sigma g_c g/(\rho_l - \rho_g)]^{1/4}} < 2 \quad K = 0.68 \quad a = 0.62$$

$$\frac{v}{[\sigma g_c g/(\rho_l - \rho_g)]^{1/4}} \geq 2 \quad K = 0.88 \quad a = 0.40$$

a = fraction of pool volume occupied by vapor
v = velocity of gas, ft/sec
σ = surface tension, lb(force)/ft
ρ_l = liquid density, lb/cu ft
ρ_g = gas density, lb/cu ft
d = vessel diameter, ft
g = acceleration due to gravity, 32.2 ft/sec^2
g_c = conversion factor, 32.2 lb(mass)ft/lb (force)/sec^2

This correlation was obtained by Wilson, Grenda, and Patterson [259] by bubbling steam through a column of saturated water in two test vessels, 4 in. and 19 in. in diameter. Both were approximately 12 ft high. So that uniform distribution would be obtained, the steam was made to enter the saturated water through holes in a perforated plate placed in the bottom of the vessel. The density of the mixture was measured with a manometer.

Correlation of all test data in terms of primary variables is shown in Fig. 2.101. The change in slope of the curve at a particular steam velocity confirms a portion of the work of Dementiev as reported by Yeh and Zuber [260] and indicates a possible change in flow regime.

2.3.2.4.2 BOTH PHASES FLOWING. For the case where both the liquid and gas phases are in motion, the following calculation procedure,* based on the data and methods of Refs. 261 and 262, is recommended by Elrod [263]. It applies to the case of horizontal or vertical flow in smooth pipe, with or without evaporation, when the liquid and vapor flow rates would separately produce turbulent flow in the pipe. Figure 2.102 is used to find the shear stress at the wall.

---

*More complete analyses of reactor-core boiling and boiling flow are available [2, 212, 264].

τ = wall shear stress in two-phase flow, psf

τ_l = wall shear stress that would exist if the pipe were carrying the quantity W_l of single-phase liquid water alone, psf

τ_g = corresponding wall shear stress with gas phase alone, psf

W_l = liquid-phase flow rate, lb(mass)/sec

W_g = gas-phase flow rate, lb(mass)/sec

τ_l and τ_g are to be computed from the usual formula, e.g.,

$$\tau_l = f\rho_l \frac{\left[W_l/(\rho_l A)\right]^2}{2g_c} \qquad (2.78)$$

where $f = 0.046 \, (N_{Re})^{-1/5}$ for $5000 \le N_{Re} \le 200,000$ (2.79)

and N_{Re} = pipe Reynolds number based on hydraulic diameter

ρ_l = liquid density, lb/cu ft

A = flow cross-sectional area, sq ft

g_c = conversion factor, 32.2 lb (mass) ft/lb (force)/sec^2

The same equation applies for τ_g, changing subscript l to subscript g.

The fraction of duct volume occupied by vapor, a, is found from whichever of the following two equations gives the smaller value of a:

$$a = 1 - \left(\frac{\tau}{\tau_l}\right)^{-5/9} \qquad (2.80)$$

$$\frac{1}{a} = 1 + \left(\frac{\rho_g}{\rho_l}\right)\left(\frac{W_l}{W_g}\right) \qquad (2.81)$$

The corresponding mixture density, ρ, is

$$\rho = \rho_l(1 - a) + \rho_g a \qquad (2.82)$$

The velocities of the individual phases in two-phase flow are

$$v_l = \frac{W_l}{\rho_l A(1 - a)} \qquad (2.83)$$

$$v_g = \frac{W_g}{\rho_g A a}$$

The pressure gradient, dP/dL, in the flow direction is

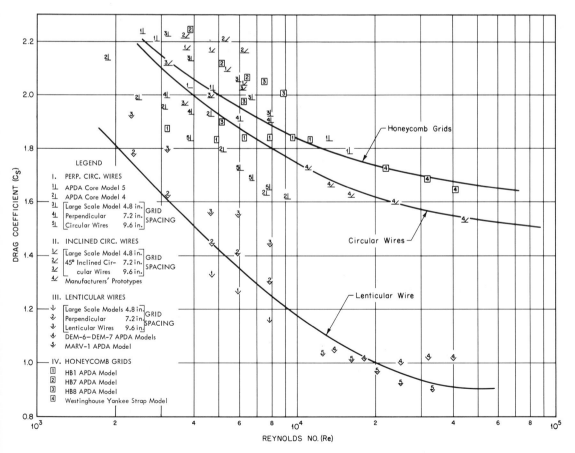

FIG. 2.99—Drag coefficient vs. Reynolds number for transverse spacer grids. [From A. N. de Stordeur, Drag Coefficients for Fuel Element Spacers, Nucleonics, 19(6):74-79 (June 1961).]

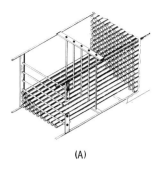

(A)

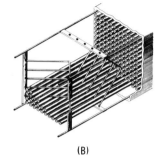

(B)

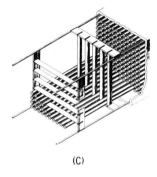

(C)

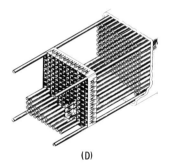

(D)

FIG. 2.100—Grid type spacers tested by APDA. (A) Circular wires perpendicular to flow direction. (B) Circular wires inclined to flow direction. (C) Lenticular wires perpendicular (MARV I) to flow direction. (D) Honeycomb grid.

$$\frac{-dP}{dL} = \frac{4\tau}{D_e} + \rho\left(\frac{dZ}{dL}\right) + \frac{1}{g_c A}\frac{d(W_l v_l)}{dL}$$
$$+ \frac{1}{g_c A}\frac{d(W_g v_g)}{dL} \quad \text{psf/ft}$$
(2.84)

where Z = elevation, ft
A = flow cross sectional area, sq ft
D_e = equivalent diameter of the flow section (Eq. 2.73), ft

This expression can be graphically integrated or averaged over L to give the total ΔP.

Static pressure changes across sudden enlargements or contractions in two-phase flow are found by computing the static pressure change that would occur if the actual liquid flow rate, W_l, occupied the entire flow section and multiplying this result by the following factor [263]:

$$\frac{1}{1-a}\left[1 + \left(\frac{\rho_l}{\rho_g}\right)\left(\frac{1-a}{a}\right)\left(\frac{W_g}{W_l}\right)^2\right]$$
(2.85)

The vapor volume fraction, a, in the above factor should be computed for the smaller of the two adjoining flow sections by means of Eq. 2.80 or 2.81.

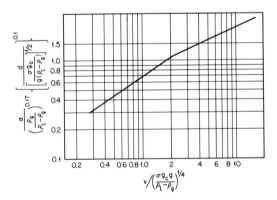

FIG. 2.101—Correlation of steam volume fraction data. [From J. F. Wilson, R. J. Grenda, and J. F. Patterson, Steam Volume Fraction in a Bubbling Two-phase Mixture, Trans. Am. Nucl. Soc., 4(2): 356 (1961).]

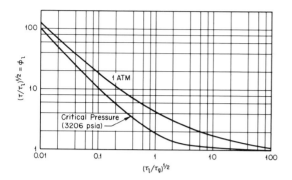

FIG. 2.102—Pressure-drop correlation for turbulent flow of water-steam mixtures [261-263].

Values of $(\tau/\tau_l)^{1/2} = \Phi_l$ may be found at an intermediate pressure P (in psia) by linear interpolation on Fig. 2.102

$$\frac{\Phi_{l, P}}{\Phi_{l, 1 \text{ atm}}} = \left(\frac{\Phi_{l, \text{crit}}}{\Phi_{l, 1 \text{ atm}}}\right)^{\frac{P-14.7}{3190}} \quad (2.86)$$

If used, the general reliability of Fig. 2.102 should be verified.

For cases where the liquid flow is viscous, tabulations corresponding to Fig. 2.102 are given in Ref. 212, Sec. 9.2.6.2.

The maximum two-phase flow rate in a pipe cannot exceed the sonic velocity, which is given [2] by

$$G_c = \rho \left(\frac{g_c \, dP}{d\rho}\right)_s^{1/2} \quad (2.87)$$

where G_c = maximum mass velocity, lb/sec/sq ft
ρ = mixture density, lb/cu ft
P = pressure, lb/sq ft
g_c = conversion factor, 32.2 lb(mass)ft/lb (force)/sec^2
s = constant entropy

Equation 2.87 assumes that equilibrium is established between the two phases ("fog flow"). Actually, equilibrium is not normally attained [2, 264].

If G_c is reached at all in a pipe, it must be at the discharge end, and further reduction of the outlet pressure will not then increase the flow rate.

For the case of vertical upward two-phase flow in a pipe, an empirical relation derived by Marchaterre and Hoglund [265] and given in Fig. 2.103 can be used to determine the relative velocities of the two phases more accurately. The correlation was determined with steam—water data and is in terms of the Froude number v_0^2/gD, the velocity ratio v_g/v_l, and the ratio of volumetric flow rates $[X/(1 - X)]\rho_l/\rho_g$, where X is vapor quality, i.e., weight fraction of gas in the flowing stream. The term v_0 in the Froude number is a superficial velocity based on the total flow being liquid. The term X is also called the weight flow rate ratio, i.e., gas phase to total flow rate. The volume fraction of vapor, a, is then obtained from the equation

$$\frac{v_g}{v_l} = \left(\frac{X}{1 - X}\right)\left(\frac{1 - a}{a}\right)\frac{\rho_l}{\rho_g} \quad (2.88)$$

For cases where the superficial velocity is low, the significant velocity is the relative velocity between the phases, and the correlation presented here is no longer valid. This correlation is not recommended for v_0 less than 0.8 ft/sec.

It appears from the available data that the channel-diameter effect decreases as the diameter increases and becomes negligible when the channel diameter is larger than the bubble or slug diameter. Therefore, it is recommended that D equal 3 in. be used for evaluating the Froude number where the channel diameter is greater than 3 in.

An additional group, the viscosity ratio μ_g/μ_l, could be included, but this effect is small; and, for liquids whose viscosities do not vary from water by more than a factor of 2 or 3, the correlation should still hold. This correlation holds only for the region beyond local boiling, which has been defined as the region in which the vapor volume fraction is no longer heat-flux dependent. Vapor volume fractions in the local boiling region may be estimated by the method proposed by Maurer [266].

2.3.2.5 Mixing

Mixing in the plenums of reactor and heat-exchanger vessels minimizes variations in the temperatures of their coolants and thereby reduces thermal stresses in structural components and improves heat-transfer characteristics. Mixing takes place under both steady-state and transient conditions. For example, across the core of the Fermi reactor at steady-state 300-Mw(t) power operation, the temperature of the outlet coolant ranges from more than 950°F at the center sub-assembly to about 700°F at the outer row. The outlet plenum pool provides mixing to produce a uniform coolant temperature at the vessel outlets.

2.3.2.5.1 MECHANISM OF MIXING. Mixing is primarily the result of turbulence and is strong at high Reynolds numbers. Even during gross steady-state flow, the secondary motions comprising turbulence fluctuate rapidly in a random manner not only from point to point but at any given point with time. The particles involved are not single molecules but small volumes of the fluid of varying size which continually agglomerate and disinte-

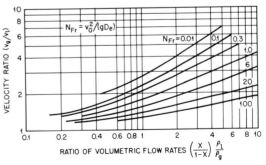

FIG. 2.103—Correlation of velocity ratios as a function of Froude number and the volumetric flow rate of each phase. [From J. F. Marchaterre and B. M. Hoglund, Nucleonics, 20(8): 142 (August 1962).]

grate. Their size depends on the geometry of the flow channel, as for example, the mesh of a screen or grid through which the flow passes or the fuel subassembly outlet configuration.

2.3.2.5.2 STEADY-STATE ANALYSIS.

Detailed mathematical analysis of turbulence is precluded by its random nature, but useful results have been achieved by making certain assumptions from careful experimental observations. Among the more fruitful are Prandtl's mixing-length hypothesis, G. I. Taylor's vorticity transfer theory, and von Karman's similarity hypothesis. Detailed discussion of these theories and their application can be found in Refs. 246 and 267 to 270.

Circulation in heat-exchanger loops involves the discharge of coolant into a plenum chamber from one or several pipes or from a number of heat-exchanger tubes or nuclear-fuel subassemblies. These cases are roughly approximated by Schlichting's [246] "free jet" and "jet boundary." A free jet involves discharge from a nozzle or an orifice into a stagnant pool. Turbulence causes the emerging jet to mix partially with the surrounding fluid. A jet boundary involves the interaction of two adjacent parallel streams moving at different speeds. This gives rise to a zone of turbulent mixing, which increases in the downstream direction.

The two-dimensional jet or the circular jet, depending on actual geometry, approximates the flow of a single jet into a plenum. If many closely spaced parallel jets are involved, as in the exit of coolant from a cluster of fuel subassemblies, the jet boundary applies to the interaction between the jets. The degree of mixing of the adjacent jets improves as the velocity differences increase. The gross effect is one of a large jet discharging into a stagnant pool.

The transfer of heat in steady turbulent flow has been shown to differ from that of momentum transfer. Measurements by A. Fage and V. M. Falkner [271], for example, show that, in the wake behind a row of heated bars, the temperature profile is wider than the velocity profile, the heat transfer being about twice as great as the momentum transfer. H. Reichardt [272] has derived the following relation between the temperature and velocity distributions:

$$\frac{\Delta T}{\Delta T_{\max.}} = \left(\frac{v}{v_{\max.}}\right)^{A_v/A_t} \tag{2.89}$$

where A_v and A_t are the coefficients for momentum transfer and heat transfer, respectively. Equation 2.89 was verified for a two-dimensional jet with $A_t = 2A_v$. Measurements of the temperature distribution in a heated circular turbulent jet have been made by Hinze and Zijnen [273] and by Corrsin and Uberoi [274].

2.3.2.5.3 TRANSIENT ANALYSIS.

Thermal transients arise in a fluid system during thermal start-up or shutdown or when changes are made in the coolant flow with constant heat generation. When these changes are rapid, the mixing of heat will be almost entirely due to turbulence; density differences and thermal conduction are second-order quantities. The mixing theory in advanced stages is also useful in predicting the stability of homogeneous reactors [275, 276].

Mixing will attenuate a thermal transient produced in the coolant flowing from the reactor core and discharging into the plenum. Mixing is perfect if each incoming increment of coolant mixes instantaneously and uniformly with all the coolant in the plenum. Mixing less than perfect can be treated by considering the incoming coolant to mix with only a fraction J of the volume of coolant in the plenum. Thus, J, the mixing coefficient, ranges from zero for no mixing to unity for perfect mixing.

The following expression is a heat balance, taken at time θ for a time increment $d\theta$, in a mixing plenum into which a liquid stream flows at one temperature and leaves at another:

$$Fc_p \rho t_i \, d\theta = Fc_p \rho t \, d\theta + d(JVc_p \rho t) \tag{2.90}$$

where F = volumetric flow rate of the stream, cu ft/sec
θ = time, sec
c_p = fluid heat capacity, Btu/lb/°F
ρ = fluid density, lb/cu ft
t_i = temperature of the stream entering the plenum, °F
t = temperature of the stream leaving the plenum, °F
J = mixing coefficient, dimensionless
V = volume of fluid in the plenum, cu ft

Assuming J, c_p, and ρ to be constant,

$$\frac{dt}{d\theta} + \frac{Q}{JV}(t - t_i) = 0 \tag{2.91}$$

If the temperature of the incoming coolant changes in a stepwise fashion, the outlet response is given by

$$\frac{t - t_1}{t_2 - t_1} = 1 - \exp(-\theta'/J\tau) \quad (\theta' \geq 0) \tag{2.92}$$

where $t_i = t_1$ for $\theta < 0 = t_2$ for $\theta \geq 0$
$\theta' = \theta - \theta_d \rho$ (θ_d = the time delay between the start of the transient at the plenum inlet and the start of its response at the outlet), sec
$\tau = V/Q$, the plenum transport time, that is, the time required to discharge one plenum volume, sec

The input temperature step and the plenum transport time being known, Eq. 2.92 gives the outlet temperature as a function of time and the mixing coefficient. The mixing coefficient depends on the geometry of the plenum, the rate of flow, and the size and geometry of the input stream. The coefficient is generally determined experimentally.

2.3.2.5.4 EXPERIMENTAL TECHNIQUES.

Experimental mixing studies generally depend on the measurement of changes in the concentration of a substance added to the main flow. These additives may be dissolved salts, gaseous tracers, or radioactive tracers. They may be injected into the main flow at a steady rate or in a time-dependent manner.

Steady-state mixing studies using SO_2 as a gaseous tracer in an air-flow model have been reported [277]. Gas samples were drawn off at various positions in the flow cross section and analyzed with a Titrilog recorder. The instrument scale had a range of 0 to 10 ppm of SO_2 and a sensitivity of about 0.1 ppm. It required about 10 sec to reach equilibrium after each measurement. Radioactive tracers [278] can be used in a similar way, the counting rate being used as a measure of the concentration. Neither of these methods is particularly suitable for transient-mixing studies.

The electrical conductivity of the solution has also been used to study transient mixing. Calibrated conductivity cells measured the conductivity of a small volume of fluid at a particular point. The time lag for the response of a conductivity cell is smaller than that of the common temperature-sensing devices, such as thermocouples. The output from the conductivity cells is, therefore, ideal for transient-mixing studies and can be recorded as a function of time using standard bridge circuits and recording instruments. Steady-state analyses can be made easily by moving a cell from place to place. Reference 279 describes a conductivity cell consisting of two No. 26 platinum wires 1 mm apart and extending about 1.2 mm out of a 5-mm sealed glass tube. Hydrochloric acid can be used as the electrolyte.

The mixing coefficient for the outlet plenum of the Fermi reactor was determined experimentally [280]. Commercially available flow type conductivity cells measured the concentration of dilute sodium hydroxide. A dilute solution was used; thus conductance is very nearly linear with concentration. Changes in temperature are analogous to changes in concentration.

The mixing coefficient was determined from tests [281] made with water on a one-quarter scale model of the outlet plenum and core hold-down mechanism. The inlet to the plenum simulated the core outlet flow. The inlet to the plenum model was provided with an electrolyte-injection apparatus that could approximate stepwise changes in electrolyte concentration with a nearly uniform front at the plenum inlet. Changes in concentration at the plenum inlet and at an outlet nozzle were recorded simultaneously as a function of time and for a range of Reynolds numbers.

The mixing coefficient can be obtained by fitting Eq. 2.92 as closely as possible to the experimental response curves of the outlet nozzles with a step input transient and determining J. Considerable difficulty is encountered with this method of analysis because the nature of the mixing process causes random fluctuations in concentration, and Eq. 2.92 at best only approximates the actual mixing. The following technique was devised to extract an appropriate mixing coefficient from the experimental data.

The initial slope of the response curve in °F per second is

$$\left[\frac{d(t - t_1)}{d\theta'}\right]_{\theta' = 1} = \frac{t_2 - t_1}{J\tau} \tag{2.93}$$

However, it is only slightly more satisfactory to guess the initial slope of the response curve than it is to guess the proper exponential. A further improvement in accuracy is obtained by estimating from the plotted data the value of θ' when $(t - t_1)$ has

reached $(1 - 1/e) = 63.2\%$ of its final value $(t_2 - t_1)$. The mixing coefficient is then obtained from

$$J = \frac{\theta' 0.632}{\tau} = \frac{0.632(t_2 - t_1)}{\tau \times \text{average slope}} \tag{2.94}$$

where the "average slope" is that of the line from the origin to the above point. For the Fermi reactor outlet plenum, it was found to increase with the Reynolds number, leveling off at about 0.75.

Reproducibility was checked by making 10 test runs at one of the flow rates. The ratio of the standard deviation to the mean response averaged about 0.04 for most of the curve. The ratio of the standard deviation to the mean mixing coefficient obtained from these runs was 0.135.

The time delay of the outlet response to an inlet transient is readily obtained from the test data. It is a function of the plenum transport time and the mixing coefficient and is an important consideration in system analysis.

2.3.2.5.4.1 Similitude in Mixing. Mixing is caused by turbulence due to the random inertia forces of the fluid particles. Viscous shear forces tend to maintain laminar flow, where little or no mixing occurs [282]. Thus, similarity in mixing results when the model and prototype are operated at the same ratio of these forces, namely, the same Reynolds number. Identical Reynolds numbers are even more vital to reproduce the critical regions where the transition from laminar to turbulent flow takes place.

Equal Reynolds numbers are also desirable for plenum flows because unstable vortices and oscillations may develop. However, if the flow rate is large enough to assure a high degree of turbulence throughout, as is usually the case in reactor plenums, mixing will be nearly independent of Reynolds number. This is borne out by the Fermi mixing tests [281] described above. The mixing coefficient increased to 0.75 and leveled off at a model flow rate of 80 gal/min for which the Reynolds number ratio of the model to prototype is about 0.25%. The absolute Reynolds number for the outlet nozzles of the model at this flow rate is about 8000, well above the critical value of 2000. Although the model flow was later increased to 430 gal/min, raising the outlet-nozzle Reynolds number above 50,000, no appreciable subsequent change in the mixing coefficient was observed. The Reynolds number for the outlet nozzle of the prototype is over 3,000,000. In the experimental study reported [277], the Reynolds number ratio was 1/67 with the model Reynolds number about 450,000. In general, the geometry of turbulence, jet shape and eddy formation, is nearly independent of the Reynolds number at values above 5000 except in boundary layers on surfaces [279].

2.3.2.5.4.2 Results of Transient Mixing Tests. An input step transient is attenuated by plenum mixing so that its mean rate at the outlet is

$$\text{Mean rate} = \frac{0.632(t_2 - t_1)}{J\tau} \tag{2.95}$$

This is Eq. 2.94 solved for the average slope. It is apparent that the attenuation depends on the plenum transport time in the same manner it does on the mixing coefficient. Large plenum volumes, low flow rates, and good mixing therefore will increase the attenuation of input transients. The amount of attenuation is not very sensitive to the mixing coefficient at its higher values. At $J = 0.67$, for example, the mean rate of the outlet transient is only 50% greater than for perfect mixing. It is generally sufficient to establish that the mixing coefficient is better than a certain minimum, say, 0.6 or 0.7.

Stress calculations for the Fermi reactor were based on 430-Mw(t) operation, for which the input bulk sodium transient is approximated by a step of about 300°F. For 75% mixing and the 18-sec plenum transport time, the mean rate of the outlet nozzle response is 14°F/sec. Table 2.23 shows the effect of a change in the mixing coefficient or in the plenum transport time, that is, in its volume or in the flow rate.

Table 2.23—Effect of Change in Mixing Coefficient or in Transport Time on Transient[280]

Mixing coefficient (J)	Transport time (τ), sec	Mean rate of outlet transient, °F/sec
1.0	18	10.5
0.75	18	14
0.5	18	21
0.75	18	14
0.75	13.5	18.7
0.75	9	28

2.3.2.6 Cavitation

Perturbations in a rapidly moving stream of liquid can create local regions of greatly reduced pressure. When, in such instances, the pressure is reduced to a value below the vapor pressure of the liquid, vapor bubbles are formed. As these bubbles move out of the low-pressure region, they collapse violently, creating a local shock known as cavitation. Since this can result in damage to, or at least reduced effective life of, system components, cavitation should be avoided whenever possible.

In a reactor there may be several places where the possibility of cavitation should be closely examined. Where the local pressure reduction cannot be satisfactorily calculated, hydraulic tests are indicated.

2.3.2.6.1 CAVITATION BEHIND QUICK-CLOSING VALVES. Upon closure of a valve in a system filled with flowing fluid, a negative pressure is developed on the downstream side of the valve. The mechanics of this and of the transmittal of pressure waves are discussed more fully in Sec. 2.3.2.7.

The pressure reduction ΔP in pounds per square foot due to sudden valve closure can be calculated as follows:

$$\Delta P = \frac{\rho a v_0}{g_c} \qquad (2.96)$$

where a = velocity of sound in the flowing medium, ft/sec
g_c = 32.2 lb(mass)ft/lb(force)/sec^2

v_0 = velocity at the time of valve closure, ft/sec
ρ = density of the fluid, lb/cu ft

Cavitation will occur when

$$P_0 - \Delta P \leq P_v \qquad (2.97)$$

where P_0 is the original pressure and P_v the vapor pressure of the fluid at the prevailing temperature, in pounds per square foot.

2.3.2.6.2 CAVITATION FROM SUBASSEMBLY ORIFICING. For more uniform coolant exit temperatures or fuel hot-spot temperatures, it is usually desirable to restrict coolant flow in certain reactor subassemblies by orificing. The best place to locate the orifice to prevent cavitation is in the inlet nozzle since it is here that the fluid pressure is normally highest. Even then cavitation may occur, depending upon the degree of flow reduction being attempted.

The pressure drop across a sharp-edged orifice is given by the expression

$$P_1 - P_2 = \frac{\rho v_0^2}{2K^2 g_c} \qquad (2.98)$$

where P_1 = inlet pressure, psf
P_2 = pressure at the vena contracta, psf
ρ = density of flowing fluid, lb/cu ft
v_0 = fluid velocity in the orifice, ft/sec
K = vena contracta flow coefficient
g_c = conversion factor, 32.2 lb(mass)ft/lb (force)/sec^2

The volumetric flow rate, Q, in cubic feet per second is given by

$$Q = \frac{v_0 \pi D_0^2}{4} \qquad (2.99)$$

where D_0 is the orifice diameter, in feet, and if it is remembered that cavitation occurs when $P_2 \cong P_v$, the expression for orifice cavitation, in pounds per square foot, can be written

$$P_1 = \frac{8\rho Q_c^2}{\pi^2 g_c K^2 D_0^4} + P_v \qquad (2.100)$$

where Q_c is the volumetric flow rate at the cavitation threshold, in cubic feet per second.

The recommended analytical test for cavitation by a single sharp-edged orifice is as follows:

Evaluate the ratio $1.25 (P_1 - P_2)/(P_1 - P_v)$, where the coefficient 1.25 is the recommended safety factor, based on work performed by APDA.

When the ratio is greater than or equal to 1.0, the design should not produce cavitation, but when the ratio is less than 1.0, cavitation may occur, and a design solution should be sought.

The Enrico Fermi Reactor inner radial blanket subassemblies presented a cavitation problem. These subassemblies are fed from a high-pressure plenum, but thermal optimization requires a flow rate of only 20% of that through a core subassembly. A single orifice of the necessary size would, at design flow rate, produce a pressure drop very close to the cavitation threshold. The solution was to use two orifices in series. A double orifice holder, which maintains a distance of 7 in. between orifices, was designed to slip into the nozzle section of the subassembly. Hydraulic tests showed that a 0.700-in. orifice in the downstream position and a 0.500-in. orifice in the upstream position have roughly the same effect on flow rate as a single 0.475-in. orifice and avoid the cavitation threshold by a safe margin.

2.3.2.7 Fluid Hammer

Fluid hammer is of concern in the design of multiloop liquid-metal-cooled reactors. In the reactor system the primary loops have a common point at the reactor. A shutdown of one pump with the other loops operating will produce a reverse flow in the shutdown loop. This reversal may be rapid enough to close the check valve in the shutdown loop with high accelerations. The result may be fluid hammer induced by the rapid changes in pressure.

The pressure induced by fluid hammer will, in general, act downstream from the check valve in the affected loop. Some pressure changes may occur upstream from the valve owing to reflections around the loop or to some mass movement on valve closure. The prediction of wave intensity, mechanism of wave travel, and effect on the pipe wall are covered below.

2.3.2.7.1 FUNDAMENTAL LAWS OF SURGE TRAVEL. The following discussion considers the portion of the system between the end of the pipe projecting into the "infinite" supply plenum (open end) and a valve located a distance L downstream from the open end. Friction losses are temporarily disregarded.

The maximum pressure increase ($\Delta P_{max.}$) resulting from valve closure is given by Eq. 2.96. At the instant of closure, a pressure wave of intensity $P_0 + \Delta P_{max.}$ travels along the pipe toward the open end with the velocity of sound a. The fluid between the valve and the wave front will be at rest, and that between the wave front and the open end will move at velocity v_0 toward the valve, as shown in Fig. 2.104.

When the wave front reaches the open end in a time $\theta = L/a$ after valve closure, the whole pipe is filled with fluid under a pressure of $P_0 + \Delta P_{max.}$, where P_0 is the pressure before valve closure. The $\Delta P_{max.}$ pressure difference at the open end causes the fluid to begin to flow toward the supply plenum, reducing the pressure to its original value. This reflected pressure wave, P_0, travels with velocity a back toward the valve, as shown in Fig. 2.104, arriving at time $\theta = 2L/a$. Since the valve is closed, no fluid is available at the valve to maintain the flow and a pressure wave $P_0 - \Delta P_{max.}$ develops. This pressure wave travels back toward the open end as shown in Fig. 2.104, arriving at $\theta = 3L/a$. At the instant the pressure wave arrives at the open end of the pipe, the fluid is at rest under a pressure $P_0 - \Delta P_{max.}$. At $\theta = 4L/a$, the pipe and fluid have returned to the initial conditions (Fig. 2.104). If

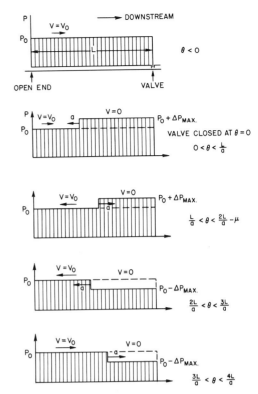

FIG. 2.104—Pressure-surge travel neglecting friction losses.

fluid friction is neglected, this entire process is repeated in periods of $4L/a$ sec.

These pressure waves traveling along the pipe result in a characteristic pressure history at each point. Figure 2.105 shows the pressure at $x = L$ and $x = L/4$ plotted against time, where the time axis is divided into increments of μ, where $\mu = 2L/a$.

2.3.2.7.2 INFLUENCE OF PIPE-WALL INERTIA. Any actual pipe wall is somewhat flexible and accommodates to the pressure waves described in Sec. 2.3.2.7.1. The sudden application of the increased pressure $\Delta P_{max.}$ at $\theta = 0$ and $x = L$ (i.e., at the valve) will cause the pipe to vibrate with an amplitude of Δr, as shown in Fig. 2.106. At the end of the half-period, μ, the pressure adjustment is from $P_0 + \Delta P_{max.}$ to $P_0 - \Delta P_{max.}$ and the resultant vibration has an approximate amplitude of $2\Delta r$, as

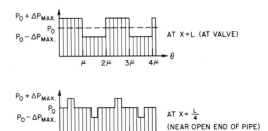

FIG. 2.105—Characteristic pressure fluctuations neglecting friction losses.

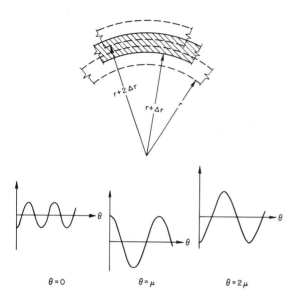

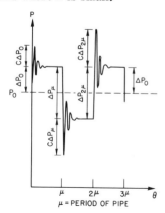

FIG. 2.106—Radial vibrations due to characteristic pressure fluctuations at x = L.

shown in Fig. 2.106. Consequently the pipe wall, at $\theta = \mu$, will be subjected to stresses roughly twice as high as that caused by the original pressure. Figure 2.106 pictures the vibrational effects of the instantaneous readjustment in pressure from $P_0 - \Delta P_{\max}$. to $P_0 + \Delta P_{\max}$. at $\theta = 2\mu$.

On the basis of sparse experimental data, a correction factor should be made:

$$P_{\text{wall}} = P_{0 \text{ fluid}} \ \pm (1 + C)\Delta P_{\text{fluid}} \ \text{psf} \quad (2.101)$$

where $C \sim 0.75$.

The frequency of these radial vibrations is several orders of magnitude higher than that of the longitudinal vibrations, and they tend to die out quickly, as shown in Fig. 2.107.

A resonant condition could occur wherein a longitudinal pressure wave expires at a time coincident with a half-period of the radial vibration and before the radial vibration has had a chance to die out. This would create an additional problem in systems where L is small.

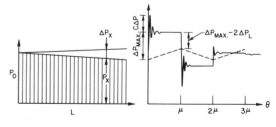

FIG. 2.107—Typical vibrational history at x = L.

2.3.2.7.3 INFLUENCE OF PIPE FRICTION.

The supernormal pressure waves would repeat themselves undiminished if there were no friction along the pipe. The influence of friction can be seen from Fig. 2.108. The pressure at any point x is diminished by the frictional pressure loss to that point

$$P_x = P_0 - \Delta P_x \quad (2.102)$$

where, as discussed in Sec. 2.3.2.3.1,

$$\Delta P_x = fx\rho \frac{v_0^2}{2g_c D} \quad (2.103)$$

Therefore, during the initial pressure wave,

$$P_{x\,\text{total}} = P_0 - \Delta P_x + \Delta P_{\max}. \quad (2.104)$$

The reflected wave is reduced by twice the value of the pressure drop to the given point, and the magnitude of the pressure wave at $x = L$, after a complete cycle 2μ, is reduced to

$$\Delta P = \Delta P_{\max}. \ - 4\Delta P_L \quad (2.105)$$

The number of cycles needed to completely eliminate the pressure wave is

$$n = \frac{\Delta P_{\max}.}{4 \Delta P_L} \quad (2.106)$$

2.3.2.7.4 CHECK-VALVE FLUID HAMMER

[283]. In nuclear power plants, fluid hammer surges up to 2500 psia have been reported. When one pump shuts down in a multiple-loop system and parallel pumps continue to operate, flow through the deenergized pump will reverse. The check valve disk cannot follow the fast coastdown and will allow some backflow to build up before seating. However, since the disk is moving with the reverse flow, there is almost instantaneous stopping of the reverse flow.

The magnitude of fluid hammer is determined by analyzing the coastdown flow and disk motion. After the coastdown characteristic is known, the disk-motion analysis can be made using the momentum equation.

$$w_D \, r \sin \varphi + I \frac{d^2\varphi}{d\theta^2} = f(\varphi)\left(\frac{W_\theta}{W_0}\right)^2 + C_1 \left(\frac{d\varphi}{d\theta}\right)^2$$

$$- (C_2 + C_3 \varphi) \quad (2.107)$$

here stated in absolute units. The terms are

$$w_D \, r \sin \varphi + I \frac{d^2\varphi}{d\theta^2} = \text{the simple pendulum expression, ft-lb}$$

FIG. 2.108—Graphical representation of the influence of pipe friction at x = L.

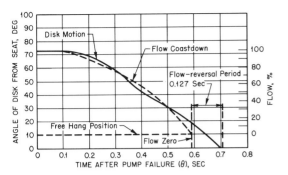

FIG. 2.109—Typical check-valve and flow-coastdown characteristics following a pump failure.

$$f(\varphi)\left(\frac{W_\theta}{W_0}\right)^2 = \text{the flow moment, ft-lb}$$

$$C_1\left(\frac{d\varphi}{d\theta}\right)^2 = \text{the damping moment, ft-lb}$$

$C_2 + C_3\varphi$ = the spring moment, ft-lb

w_D = the weight of the disk, lb

r = the radius of the disk's center of gravity, ft

φ = the angle of the disk with respect to the closed position, radians

I = the moment of inertia, slug-sq ft

$f(\varphi)$ = the form drag on the disk

W_0 = the initial flow rate, lb(mass)/sec

W_θ = the flow rate of time θ, lb(mass)/sec

The solution of the moment equation yields the time interval between the beginning of coastdown and the seating of the disk. Knowing this time interval, the maximum reversed-flow velocity and the resulting fluid hammer can be calculated. A typical result is shown in Fig. 2.109, where the dashed curve represents the flow coastdown characteristics and the solid curve represents the disk-motion characteristics. Whenever the latter curve dips into the coastdown curve, the disk is retarded and has to regain its velocity, thus losing valuable time and increasing the fluid hammer.

The same method can be used to calculate fluid hammer at pump start-up in multiloop systems. The results of calculations and tests show that no one type of valve can be universally applied for the elimination of fluid hammer. Optimization of disk weight and shape, pivot location, body configuration, and spring tensions will yield the best combined solution. Surge tanks of the proper size are also helpful.

Glossary

A	area, sq ft
A_v/A_t	ratio of the coefficients for momentum and heat transfer
A_w	atomic weight, grams/gram mole
a	velocity of sound in the flowing medium, ft/sec
B,C	constants, dimensionless
c_p	specific heat, Btu/lb/°F
C_s	spacer drag coefficient, dimensionless
D,d	diameter, ft
D_e	equivalent diameter, ft
E	electrical potential, volts
F	volumetric flow rate, cu ft/sec
f	friction factor, dimensionless
f_i	atomic fraction of ith isotope in coolant
g	acceleration due to gravity, usually taken as standard value of 32.2 ft/sec^2
g_c	conversion factor, 32.2 lb(mass)ft/lb(force)/sec^2 or 4.17×10^8 lb(mass)ft/lb(force)/hr^2
G_c	maximum mass velocity as limited by sonic phenomenon, lb/sec/sq ft
h	surface heat-transfer coefficient, Btu/hr/sq ft/°F
I	current, flow, amps; also moment of inertia, slugs-sq ft
J	mixing coefficient, dimensionless
K	a constant, 3.7×10^{10} dis/curie/sec; also velocity head loss coefficient, dimensionless; also vena contracta flow coefficient, dimensionless
k	thermal conductivity, Btu/hr/ft/°F
L	length, ft
M	mass, lb
N,n	characteristic number, dimensionless
N_{Fr}	Froude number v_0^2/gD_e, dimensionless
N_{Gr}	Grashof number, $gL^3\rho^2\beta\,\Delta T/\mu^2$, dimensionless
N_0	Avogadro's number, 0.60248×10^{24} atoms/gram mole
N_{Nu}	Nusselt number, hD/k, dimensionless
N_{Pe}	Peclet number, $(N_{Pr}N_{Re}) = c_pDv\rho/k$, dimensionless
N_{Pr}	Prandtl number, $c_p\mu/k$, dimensionless
N_{Ra}	Rayleigh number, $(N_{Pr}N_{Gr}) = L^3\rho^2 c_p\beta\,\Delta T/\mu k$
N_{Re}	Reynolds number, $vD\rho/\mu$, dimensionless
P	pressure, psia
ΔP	pressure drop, psi or psf
p	wetted perimeter, ft
P_0	initial pressure, psia or psfa
P_v	vapor pressure, psfa
Q	volumetric flow rate, cu ft/sec
Q_c	volumetric flow rate at the cavitation threshold, cu ft/sec
q	heat transfer rate, Btu/hr
q (cond)	heat transferred by conduction
q (conv)	heat transferred by convection
R	ratio of sodium (in hundreds of cubic feet at 350°F) to void volume (in millions of cubic feet at 77°F)
R_e,R_t,R_h	electrical, thermal, and hydraulic resistance
r	radial distance, ft
r_i	tube radius, ft
S	specific activity, curies/g; also spacer projected frontal area, sq ft
s	constant entropy
T_b	boiling temperature, °R
T_m	melting temperature, °R
T_w	reactor outlet temperature, °R
t	temperature, °F
t_w	wall temperature, °F
$\bar{t}_c$	bulk coolant temperature, °F

t_y	temperature at distance y from the wall, °F
$t_{\mathfrak{t}}$	center-line temperature, °F
u,v,w	velocity, ft/sec, ft/hr
V	volume, cu ft
v_g	gas-phase velocity, ft/sec, ft/hr
v_l	liquid-phase velocity, ft/sec, ft/hr
v_0	superficial velocity based on total flow rate being liquid; also initial velocity; also velocity in an orifice, ft/sec, ft/hr
v_s	velocity in spacer region, ft/sec
W	mass flow rate, lb/sec
W_l	liquid-phase mass flow rate, lb/sec
W_g	gas-phase mass flow rate, lb/sec
W_0	initial flow rate, lb/sec
w_D	weight of disk, lb
X,Y,Z	body forces (Sec. 2.3.1.1)
W_θ	flow rate at time θ, lb/sec
X	vapor quality, i.e., weight fraction vapor, dimensionless
Z	elevation above given reference, ft
a	fraction of volume occupied by vapor, dimensionless
β	volumetric coefficient of thermal expansion, °F^{-1}(cu ft/cu ft/°F)
Γ	mass flow rate of condensate per unit width, lb/hr/ft
ΔT	temperature difference, °F
θ	time, sec
θ_i	half-life of ith isotope, sec
λ	latent heat of vaporization, Btu/lb
μ	absolute viscosity, lb(mass)/ft/hr; half period of pipe (Sec. 2.3.2.7), sec
ν	kinematic viscosity, sq ft/hr
ξ	average logarithmic energy loss per elastic collision
ρ	density, lb/cu ft
ρ_g	gas density, lb/cu ft
ρ_l	liquid density, lb/cu ft
Σ_c	macroscopic capture cross section, cm^{-1}
Σ_{el}	macroscopic elastic scattering cross section, cm^{-1}
Σ_{in}	macroscopic inelastic scattering cross section, cm^{-1}
σ	surface tension, lb(force)/ft
σ_{ij}	microscopic reaction cross section for ith isotope and jth energy interval, cm^2/nucleus
φ_j	neutron flux in jth energy group, neutrons/cm^2/sec
Φ_l	$(\tau/\tau_l)^{1/2}$ square root of ratio of wall shear stress in two phase flow to wall shear stress of all liquid phase flow, dimensionless
τ	wall shear stress in two-phase flow, psf; transport time, sec
τ_g	wall shear stress due to all gas-phase flow, psf
τ_l	wall shear stress due to all liquid flow, psf
τ_0	coolant cycle time, sec
τ_r	coolant residence time in neutron flux during one cycle, sec
φ	angle of the check valve disk with respect to the closed position, radians
ϵ/D	relative roughness factor, dimensionless

References

1. L. Green, Table of Reactor Coolant Properties, USAEC Report BNL–661, Brookhaven National Laboratory, March 10, 1961.
2. C. F. Bonilla (Ed.), Nuclear Engineering, McGraw-Hill Book Company, Inc., New York, 1957.
3. C. F. Bonilla, D. L. Sawhrey, and M. M. Makansi, Am. Soc. Metals, Trans. Quart., 55:877 (1962).
4. R. N. Lyon (Ed.), Liquid-Metals Handbook, 2nd ed. (Report NAVEXOS P-733, Rev.), 1952.
5. M. A. Mikheev (Ed.), Problems of Heat Transfer, Academy of Sciences SSSR, Moscow, 1959, USAEC Report AEC–TR–4511, 1962.
6. T. B. Douglas, L. F. Epstein, J. L. Dever, and W. H. Howland, Lithium: Heat Content from 0 to 900°, Triple Point and Heat of Fusion and Thermodynamic Properties of the Solid and Liquid, J. Am. Chem. Soc., 77:2144 (1955).
7. D. R. Stull and G. C. Sinke, Thermodynamic Properties of the Elements, American Chemical Society, Washington, 1956.
8. W. H. Evans, R. Jacobson, T. R. Munson, and D. D. Wagman, Thermodynamic Properties of the Alkali Metals, J. Research Nat'l Bur. Standards, A, 55:83 (1955).
9. H. W. Deem, E. A. Eldridge, and C. F. Lucks, Report BATT–4673–T2, Battelle Memorial Institute, 1962.
10. A. W. Lemmon, Jr., Engineering Properties of Potassium, Quarterly Report No. 8, Battelle Memorial Institute, 1962.
11. L. G. Epel and J. R. Simmons, Thermodynamic Diagram for Lithium, Sodium and Potassium, USAEC Report ORNL-CF-59-11-67, Oak Ridge National Laboratory, Nov. 12, 1959.
12. M. M. Makansi, N. Madsen, W. A. Selke, and C. F. Bonilla, Vapor Pressure of Potassium, J. Phys. Chem., 60:128 (1956).
13. R. J. Thorn and G. H. Winslow, Pressure Equation by Use of the Second Virial Coefficient, J. Phys. Chem., 65:1297 (1961).
14. R. W. Ditchburn and J. C. Gilmour, The Vapor Pressure of Monatomic Vapor, Rev. Mod. Phys., 13:310 (1941).
15. N. S. Grachev and P. L. Kirillov, Report NASA-TT-F-66, National Aeronautics and Space Administration, translation from Inzhener.—Fiz. Zhur., Akad, Nauk Belorus, SSR, 3(6):62 (1960).
16. C. J. Meisl, Review by A. Shapiro, Report R6OFPD358-A, 2nd Review, Bendix Corporation, 1960.
17. A. W. Lemmon, Jr., Engineering Properties of Potassium, Quarterly Report No. 10, Battelle Memorial Institute, 1963.
18. C. R. Jackson (Ed.), Liquid-Metals Handbook, Sodium-NaK Supplement, USAEC Report TID-5277, July 1955.
19. C. T. Ewing, J. P. Stone, J. R. Spann, T. A. Kovacina, and R. R. Miller, High Temperature of Sodium and Potassium, Report NRL–5964, Naval Research Laboratory, May 20, 1963.
20. M. M. Makansi, W. A. Selke, and C. F. Bonilla, J. Chem. Eng. Data, 5:441 (1960).
21. C. T. Ewing, J. P. Stone, and R. R. Miller, Report NRL–1069, Naval Research Laboratory, 1960.
22. G. W. Thomson and E. Garelis, Physical and Thermodynamic Properties of Sodium, 2nd ed., Ethyl Corporation, 1955.
23. T. R. Hogness, J. Am. Chem. Soc., 43:1621 (1921).
24. S. W. Strauss, L. E. Richards, and B. F. Brown, Nucl. Sci. Eng., 7:442 (1960).
25. T. B. Douglas and J. L. Dever, Report NBS-2544, National Bureau of Standards, 1953.
26. E. Gebhardt, M. Becker, and H. Tragner, Z. Metallk., 46:90 (1955).
27. T. P. Yao and V. Kondic, The Viscosity of Molten Tin, Lead, Zinc, Aluminum, and Some of Their Alloys, J. Inst. Metals, 81:17 (1952).
28. H. J. Fisher and A. Phillips, Trans. Am. Soc. Mech. Engrs., 200:1060 (1954).
29. W. R. D. Jones and J. B. Davies, The Viscosity of Lead, Tin, and Their Alloys, J. Inst. Metals, 86:164 (1957).
30. J. W. Taylor, British Report AERE-M/R-1620, 1955.
31. E. N. da C. Andrade and E. R. Dobbs, The Viscosities of Liquid Lithium Rubidium and Caesium, Proc. Roy. Soc. London, 211:12 (1952).
32. W. D. Weatherford, Jr., J. C. Tyler, and P. M. Ku, Properties of Inorganic Energy-Conversion and Heat Transfer Fluids for Space Applications, Report WADD-TR-61-96, Wright Air Development Division, November 1961.
33. C. T. Ewing, The Electrical Resistivity of Lithium and Sodium Potassium Alloy, Report PWAC-349, Pratt and Whitney Aircraft Division, 1961.
34. I. I. Rudnev, V. S. Lyashenko, and M. D. Abramovich, Diffusivity of Sodium and Lithium, At. Energ., 11:230 (September 1961).
35. H. A. Webber, D. Goldstein, and R. C. Fellinger, Determination of the Thermal Conductivity of Molten Lithium, Trans. Am. Soc. Mech. Engrs., 77:97 (1955).
36. S. M. Kapelner, USAEC Report PWAC-349, Pratt and Whitney Aircraft Division, 1961.

37. J. F. Freedman and W. D. Robertson, J. Phys. Chem., 34:789 (1961).
38. T. B. Douglas, A. F. Ball, and D. C. Ginnings, Heat Capacity of Liquid Mercury Between 0° and 450°C; Calculation of Certain Thermodynamic Properties of the Saturated Liquid and Vapor, J. Research Nat'l Bur. Standards, A, 46:334 (1951).
39. Handbook of Chemistry and Physics, 44th ed., Chemical Rubber Publishing Company, 1962-63.
40. P. M. Kampmeyer, The Temperature Dependence of Viscosity for Water and Mercury, J. Appl. Phys., 23:99 (1952).
41. L. F. Epstein and M. D. Powers, USAEC Report AECU-1893, Knolls Atomic Power Laboratory.
42. W. Koenig, Bestimmung einiger Reibungscoefficienten und Versuche ueber den Einfluss der Magnetisirung und Electrisirung auf die Reibung der Fluessigkeiten, Ann. Physik, 25:618 (1885) and 32:1943 (1887).
43. H. Braune, R. Basch, and W. Wentzel, Ueber die innere Reibung einiger Gase und Daemfe, Z. physik. Chem. Leipzig, 137:176, 447 (1928).
44. C. T. Ewing, R. E. Seebold, J. A. Grand, and R. R. Miller, J. Phys. Chem., 59:524 (1955).
45. R. W. Powell and R. P. Type, International Developments in Heat Transfer, Proceedings of International Heat Transfer Conference, Boulder, Colo., and Westminster, England, 1961-1962, Vol. 4, p. 856, American Society of Mechanical Engineers, New York, 1963.
46. Paul D. Cohn, Heat Transfer and Thermodynamic Properties of Mercury, USAEC Report NAA-SR-Memo-4666, Atomics International, 1959.
47. L. A. Quarterman and W. L. Primak, The Capillary Rise, Contact Angle and Surface Tension of Potassium, J. Am. Chem. Soc., 72:3035 (1950).
48. C. T. Ewing, J. P. Stone, J. R. Spann, E. W. Steinkuller, T. A. Kovacina, and R. R. Miller, High Temperature Properties of Sodium and Potassium, Report NRL-5844, Naval Research Laboratory, Aug. 27, 1962.
49. T. B. Douglas, A. F. Ball, D. C. Ginnings, and W. D. Davis, Heat Capacity of Potassium and Three Potassium Sodium Alloys Between 0 and 800°; the Triple Point and Heat of Fusion of Potassium, J. Am. Chem. Soc., 74:2472 (1952).
50. E. H. Hall and J. M. Blocker, Jr., Report BATT-4673-T1, Battelle Memorial Institute, 1962.
51. K. Gering and F. Sauerwald, Z. Anorg. Allgem. Chem., 223:204 (1935).
52. F. Sauerwald, Z. Metallk., 26:259 (1954).
53. Y. S. Chiong, Viscosity of Liquid Sodium and Potassium, Proc. Roy. Soc. London, 157:264 (1963).
54. C. T. Ewing, J. A. Grand, and R. R. Miller, Viscosity of the Sodium-Potassium System, J. Am. Chem. Soc., 73:1168 (1951).
55. C. T. Ewing, J. A. Grand, and R. R. Miller, Viscosity of the Sodium-Potassium System, J. Phys. Chem., 58:1086 (1954).
56. C. T. Ewing, J. A. Grand, and R. R. Miller, Thermal Conductivity of Liquid Sodium and Potassium, J. Am. Chem. Soc., 74:11 (1952).
57. S. M. Kapelner and W. D. Bratton, USAEC Report PWAC-376, Pratt and Whitney Aircraft Division, 1962.
58. E. L. Dunning, Thermodynamic and Transport Properties of Sodium and Sodium Vapor, USAEC Report ANL-6246, Argonne National Laboratory, 1960.
59. J. W. Taylor, The Surface Tension of Sodium, J. Inst. Metals, 83:143 (1954).
60. C. C. Addison, D. H. Kerridge, and J. Lewis, J. Am. Chem. Soc., 76:2861 (1954).
61. C. T. Ewing, H. B. Atkinson, Jr., and T. K. Rice, Report NP-340, Naval Research Laboratory, 1948.
62. E. B. Hagen, Ueber die Warmeausdehnung des Natriums, des Kaliums, und deren Legierung im festen und im geschmotzenen Zustande, Ann. Physik, 19:436 (1883).
63. E. Rinck, Comptes rendus de l'academie des sciences, 189:39 (1929).
64. J. P. Stone, C. T. Ewing, J. R. Spann, E. W. Steinkuller, T. A. Kovacina, and R. R. Miller, Report NRL-Memo-1312, Naval Research Laboratory, 1962.
65. D. G. Ginnings, T. B. Douglas, and A. F. Ball, Heat Capacity of Sodium Between 0° and 900°C; The Triple Point and Heat of Fusion, J. Research Nat'l Bur. Standards, 45:23 (1950).
66. W. D. Weatherford, J. C. Tyler, and P. M. Ku, Report WADC-TR 59-598, Wright Air Development Center, 1959.
67. J. Godfrey, University of Cincinnati, Technical Report to General Electric Company, May 1952.
68. W. C. Hall, The Thermal Conductivities of Mercury, Sodium and Sodium Amalgams in the Liquid State, Phys. Rev., 53:1004 (1938).
69. M. M. Makansi, C. H. Muendel, and W. A. Selke, Determination of the Vapor Pressure of Sodium, J. Phys. Chem., 59:40 (1955).
70. K. Bowles and L. Rosenblum, Paper No. 27, 54th Annual Meeting, American Institute of Chemical Engineers, Dec. 5, 1961.
71. P. G. Drugas, I. R. Rehn, and W. D. Wilkinson, USAEC Report ANL-5115, Argonne National Laboratory, 1943.

72. R. Rahiser, R. Werner, and C. B. Jackson, Mine Safety Appliance Co. Technical Report 24, June 1953.
73. W. H. Bruggeman, Purity Control in Sodium-Cooled Systems, Am. Inst. Chem Engrs. J., 2:153-156 (June 1956).
74. NaK and Potassium, Technical Bulletin, Mine Safety Appliance Research Corporation, Callery, Penn., Jan. 4, 1960.
75. Technical Bulletin, Lithium Corporation of America, 500 Fifth Avenue, New York 36, N. Y.
76. J. P. Holis, From Analysis of Sodium Supplied to the Enrico Fermi Atomic Power Plant, E. I. du Pont de Nemours and Company, Inc., Wilmington, Delaware, private communication, 1959.
77. Dupont Electrochemicals Department Bulletin SP-23-758, E. I. du Pont de Nemours and Company, Inc., Wilmington, Delaware.
78. Sodium Analytical Data, communicated by E. I. du Pont de Nemours and Company, Inc. to Atomic Power Development Associates, Inc., 1960.
79. H. E. Perrine, Collected Methods for Analysis of Sodium Metal, GEAP-3273, General Electric Company, Oct. 15, 1959.
80. L. P. Pepkowitz and E. R. Proud, Determination of Hydrogen, Anal. Chem., 21(8):1000-1003 (August 1949).
81. L. P. Pepkowitz and W. C. Judd, Determination of Sodium Monoxide in Sodium, Anal. Chem., 22(10):1283-1286 (October 1950).
82. L. P. Pepkowitz, W. C. Judd, and R. J. Downer, Determination of Sodium Monoxide in Sodium, An Addendum, Anal. Chem., 26:246 (1954).
83. D. D. Williams and R. R. Miller, Modified Apparatus for Determination of Sodium Monoxide in Sodium, Anal. Chem., 23(12):1865-1866 (December 1951).
84. The Analysis of Sodium and Sodium-Potassium Alloy, (Collected Capenhurst Methods), British Report IGO-AM/CA-110, 1958.
85. Malikova and Turovtseva, V. K. Vernadskii, Determination of Oxygen in Alkali Metals and Their Alloys by Mercury Extraction, Tr. Lomis. Khim. Akad. Nauk SSSR, Inst. Geokhim. i Analit. Khim., 10:91-96 (1960).
86. L. F. Epstein, Notes on Liquid Metal Studies in France and Great Britain, Report GEST-2012, General Electric Company, Jan. 15, 1963.
87. H. Steinmetz and B. Minushkin, Experimental Determination of Contaminants in Sodium, USAEC Report NDA-2154-6, United Nuclear Corporation, Aug. 30, 1961.
88. J. C. White, W. J. Ross, and R. Rowan, Jr., Determination of Oxygen in Sodium, Anal. Chem., 26(1):210-213 (January 1954).
89. L. Silverman and M. Shideler, Determination of Oxygen in Sodium and in Sodium-Potassium Alloy by the Butyl Bromide Method, Anal. Chem., 27(10):1660-1662 (October 1955).
90. H. Kirtchik and G. Riechmann, Research on Analytical Methods for Oxygen in Liquid Alkali Metals, Report NASA-N62-11319, National Aeronautics and Space Administration, Apr. 3, 1961.
91. H. J. deBruin, Determination of Traces of Oxygen in Sodium Metal by Infrared Spectrophotometry, Anal. Chem., 32(3):360-362 (March 1960).
92. J. R. Humphreys, Sampling and Analysis for Impurities in Liquid Sodium Systems, American Institute of Chemical Engineers, Preprint 67, Nuclear Engineering and Science Congress, Dec. 12-16, 1955.
93. R. D. Peaks, Operation of the Distillation Method for the Determination of Sodium Oxide in NaK During the Calibration of a Plug Indicator, USAEC Report CF-57-4-115, Oak Ridge National Laboratory, Apr. 30, 1957.
94. B. R. T. Frost, Advances in Liquid Metal Technology, J. Nucl. Mater., 7(2):109-124 (1962).
95. D. R. Grieser, G. C. Cocks, E. H. Hall, W. M. Henry, and J. McCallum, Determination of Oxygen in Sodium at Concentrations Below 10 ppm, USAEC Report BMI-1538, Battelle Memorial Institute, Aug. 23, 1961.
96. C. R. F. Smith, The Determination of Oxygen in Sodium—A Critical Review of Analytical Methods, USAEC Report NAA-SR-Memo-2061, Atomics International, 1961.
97. L. P. Pepkowitz and J. T. Porter, Determination of Elemental Carbon in Sodium, Anal. Chem., 28(10):1606 (October 1955).
98. T. G. Mungall et al., Determination of Microgram Amounts of Carbon in Sodium Metal, 145th Meeting, American Chemical Society, 1963.
99. K. G. Stoffer and J. H. Phillips, Determination of Carbon in Sodium-Potassium Alloy, Anal. Chem., 27(5):773-776 (May 1955).
100. B. D. Holt, Determination of Hydrogen in Alkali Metals by Isotope Dilution Method, Anal. Chem., 31(1):51 (January 1959).
101. H. Strahl, A Device for Continuous Detection of Hydrogen in Sodium, USAEC Report NAA-SR-6986, Atomics International, December 1960.
102. O. N. Salmon and T. J. Cashman, Jr., Solubility of Sodium Monoxide in Liquid Sodium, USAEC Report KAPL-1653, Knolls Atomic Power Laboratory, Nov. 30, 1956.
103. S. L. Walters, The Effects of Adding Oxygen to Sodium Flowing in a Stainless Steel System, Technical Report VI, Mine Safety Appliance, Sept. 1, 1950.

104. A. D. Bogard and D. D. Williams, Solubility of Sodium Monoxide and of Sodium Hydroxide in Metallic Sodium, Report NRL-3865, Naval Research Laboratory, Sept. 26, 1951.

105. J. D. Noden and K. Q. Bagley, The Solubility of Oxygen in Sodium and Sodium-Potassium Alloy, British Report, R and DB(C)TN-80, Research and Development Branch, Culcheth Laboratory Industrial Group Headquarters, Risley, Warrington, Lancashire, July 20, 1954.

106. Dounreay Experimental Reactor Establishment, Fast Reactor Newsletter, November 1959.

107. C. R. F. Smith, The Determination of Oxygen in Sodium—A Critical Review of Analytical Methods, USAEC Report NAA-SR-Memo-2061, Atomics International, 1961.

108. I. L. Gray, R. L. Neal, and B. G. Voorhees, Control of Oxygen in Sodium Heat Transfer Systems, Liquid Metals Technology, Chemical Engineering Progress Symposium Series, Vol. 53, No. 20, American Institute of Chemical Engineers, New York, 1957.

109. S. Siegel and L. F. Epstein, The Diffusion of Na$_2$O in Sodium in the Range 900 - 1000°F, Report GEAP-3357, General Electric Company (in preparation).

110. G. Billuris, Experimental Investigations of the Removal of Sodium Oxide from Liquid Sodium, Report GEAP-3328, General Electric Company, Jan. 18, 1960.

111. C. E. Weber and L. F. Epstein, Problems in the Use of Molten Sodium as a Heat Transfer Fluid (extracts from Journal of Metallurgy and Ceramics), USAEC Report TID-2501 (Del.), p. 291.

112. W. B. Cottrell and L. A. Mann, Sodium Plumbing, USAEC Report ORNL-1688, Oak Ridge National Laboratory, Aug. 14, 1953.

113. J. G. Gratton, Solubility of Carbon in Sodium at Elevated Temperatures, USAEC Report KAPL-1807, Knolls Atomic Power Laboratory, June 30, 1957.

114. M. Sittig, Sodium, Its Manufacture and Uses, Reinhold Publishing Corporation, New York, 1956.

115. T. B. Douglas, A Cryoscopic Study of the Solubility of Uranium in Sodium at 97.8°C, USAEC Report AECD-3254, National Bureau of Standards, Mar. 12, 1951.

116. C. Mitra and C. F. Bonilla, The Solubility of Xenon in Liquid Metals, Columbia University, 1959.

117. C. F. Bonilla, private communication, July 30, 1961.

118. Alvin Glassner, The Thermochemical Properties of the Oxides, Fluorides, and Chlorides to 2500°K, USAEC Report ANL-5750, Argonne National Laboratory, 1957.

119. J. H. Perry (Ed.), Chemical Engineers' Handbook, 3rd ed., McGraw-Hill Book Company, Inc., New York, 1950.

120. W. S. Horton, Static Pressure Due to Sodium-Water Reactions in Closed Vessels, USAEC Report KAPL-722, Knolls Atomic Power Laboratory, Mar. 26, 1952.

121. J. W. Weber, Results of NaK Capsule Failures in Hot-Water Flow Tube, USAEC Report HW-56558, Hanford Atomic Products Operation, Sept. 12, 1958.

122. L. Corrsin, H. Steinmetz, and B. Marano, Sodium-Water Reaction Rate Studies, USAEC Report NDA-84-19, Nuclear Development Associates, May 15, 1959.

123. D. D. Adams, G. J. Barenborg, and W. W. Kendall, An Evaluation of the Sodium Water Reaction in Heat Transfer Systems, USAEC Report KAPL-P-1512, Knolls Atomic Power Laboratory, April 1956.

124. E. C. King, Reaction of NaK-H$_2$O, Report NP-3646, MSA-TR-XII, Mine Safety Appliance Co., January 1952.

125. E. C. King and C. A. Wedge, Jr., Reaction of NaK and Water, MSA-TR-III, Mine Safety Appliance Co., Feb. 1, 1950.

126. E. C. King, Reaction of NaK-H$_2$O, Report NP-1956, MSA-TR-VII, Mine Safety Appliance Co., November 1950.

127. E. C. King, Reaction of NaK-H$_2$O, Report NP-3334, MSA-TR-XI, Mine Safety Appliance Co., September 1951.

128. E. C. King et al., Third Fluid Tube Sheet Hazard, Report NP-5990, MSA-MR-101, Mine Safety Appliance Co., December 1955.

129. R. H. Jones, H. J. Williams, and J. A. Murphy, NaK-Water Reaction Tests, USAEC Report AECU-3193, Atomic Power Development Associates, Inc., December 1956.

130. G. M. Wolten and R. A. Meyer, The Compatability of Kerosene with Sodium in a Closed System to 1200°F, USAEC Report NAA-SR-5687, p. 15, Nov. 1, 1960.

131. R. L. McKisson and K. E. Horton, The Behavior of Tetralin in Liquid Sodium, USAEC Report NAA-SR-1771, p. 19, Atomics International, Feb. 1, 1957.

132. R. H. Jones, Compatibility of Fluorolube MO-10 with Sodium, APDA Test Memo No. 2, Atomic Power Development Associates, Inc., Feb. 6, 1958.

133. E. E. Hoffman, Corrosion of Materials by Lithium at Elevated Temperatures, (Thesis), USAEC Report ORNL-2924, p. 150, Oak Ridge National Laboratory, Oct. 27, 1960.

134. John J. Sand, Solubility of Iron in Liquid Lithium, Report OMCC-HEF-166, p. 1995, Syracuse University, May 1, 1959.

135. C. R. Tipton (Ed.), Reactor Handbook, 2nd ed., Vol. 1, Materials, Interscience Publishers, Inc., New York, 1960.

136. R. Carlander and E. E. Hoffman, Compatibility Tests of Various Materials in Molten Sodium, USAEC Report CR-57-3-126, p. 10, Oak Ridge National Laboratory, Mar. 25, 1957.

137. J. H. DeVan and J. B. West, A Brief Review of Thermal Gradient Mass Transfer in Sodium and NaK Systems, USAEC Report CF-57-2-146, p. 19, Oak Ridge National Laboratory, Feb. 11, 1957.

138. W. W. Kendall, Corrosion of Beryllium in Flowing Sodium, USAEC Report GEAP-3333, p. 30, General Electric Company, Jan. 15, 1960.

139. National Aeronautics and Space Administration—Atomic Energy Commission, Liquid-Metals Corrosion Meeting, December 7-8, 1960, Report NASA-TN-D769, February 1961.

140. W. J. Anderson and G. V. Sneesby, Carburization of Austenite Stainless Steel in Liquid Sodium, USAEC Report NAA-SR-5282, Atomics International, 1960.

141. J. F. Strachan and N. L. Harris, The Effect of Mercury on the Corrosion and Properties of Various Materials, Final Report, Part 3, A Survey of the Interactions of the Metallic Elements with Static Liquid Mercury at Room Temperature and 500°C, British Report AERE-X/R-1503, July 19, 1954.

142. J. F. Strachan and N. L. Harris, The Attack of Unstressed Metals by Liquid Mercury, J. Inst. Metals, 85:17-24 (1956-57).

143. Evaluation of Mercury-cooled Breeder Reactors, USAEC Report ATL-118, Appendix D, American-Standard, September 1959.

144. H. A. Saller and F. A. Rough, Compilation of U. S. and U. K. Uranium and Thorium Constitutional Diagrams, USAEC Report BMI-1000, Battelle Memorial Institute, July 1955.

145. A. S. Wilson, D. H. Ahmann, and R. R. Baldwin, unpublished work, October 1945.

146. B. R. T. Frost, The System Uranium-Mercury, J. Inst. Metals, 82(9):456-462 (1954).

147. R. E. Rundle and A. S. Wilson, The Structures of Some Metal Compounds, Acta Cryst., 2:148-150 (1949).

148. R. H. Armstrong et al., A Lunar Power Plant, USAEC Report ANL-6261, Argonne National Laboratory, December 1960.

149. G. M. Slaughter et al., Sodium Corrosion and Oxidation Resistance of High-Temperature Brazing Alloys, Welding J., Vol. XXXVI, 217s-225s(May 1957).

150. USAEC Report CF-56-4-130, Oak Ridge National Laboratory, Feb. 14, 1957.

151. R. Biggs and R. H. Jones, Compatibility of Asbestos and Silicone Cloth, APDA Test Memo No. 17, Atomic Power Development Associates, Inc., Feb. 2, 1960.

152. T. A. Coultas and R. Cygan, Compatibility of Sodium, Graphite and Stainless Steel, USAEC Report NAA-SR-258, Atomics International, Oct. 4, 1953.

153. J. J. Gill, Sodium-Graphite Interaction and Graphite Protective Coatings, USAEC Report NAA-SR-6094, Atomics International, May 1, 1961.

154. P. R. Huebotter, unpublished APDA test data, 1961.

155. M. Tarpinian, Effect of Molten Sodium on Thermal Insulation Specimens, USAEC Report NAA-SR-Memo-1171, p. 8, Atomics International, Nov. 19, 1954.

156. W. H. Cook, Corrosion Resistance of Various Ceramics and Cermets to Liquid Metals, USAEC Report ORNL-2391, Oak Ridge National Laboratory, July 15, 1960.

157. J. H. Stang, Corrosion by Liquid Metals and Fused Salts, Reactor Core Mater., 2(1):30 (February 1959).

158. W. E. Barlow, The Binary and Ternary Alloys of Cadmium, Bismuth, and Lead, J. Am. Chem. Soc., 32:1390 (1910).

159. D. Solomon and W. M. Jones, An X-Ray Investigation of the Lead-Bismuth and the Tin-Bismuth Alloys, Phil. Mag., 11:1090 (1910).

160. H. S. Strickler and H. Seitz, A Thermodynamic Study of the Lead-Bismuth System, J. Am. Chem. Soc., 58:2084 (1936).

161. H. von Hofe and H. Manemann, Z. Metallk., 32:112 (1940).

162. M. Hayasi, Nippon Kinzoku Gakkaishi, 3:123 (1939).

163. N. S. Kurnakov and V. A. Ageeva, Izv. Akad. Nauk SSSR Otd. Khem. Nauk., 735 (1937).

164. W. C. Smith, Cerro de Pasco Copper Corp., New York, data regarding the eutectic.

165. N. S. Kurnakov and N. A. Puschin, Z. Anorg. Allgem. Chem., 30:109-112 (1902).

166. G. L. C. M. van Rossen Koogendijk van Bleiswijk, Z. Anorg. Allgem. Chem., 74:152-156 (1912).

167. E. Janecke, Z. Metallk., 20:115 (1928).

168. E. Rinck, Diagrammes de Solidification des Alliages Formes par deux met aux Alcalins, Alliages Sodium-Potassium, Compt. Rend., 197:49-51 (1933).

169. E. Hagen, Ueber die Warmeausdehnung des Natriums, des Kaliums, und deren Legierung im festen und im geschmotzenen Zustande, Ann. Physik, 19:472 (1883).

170. G. Tammann, Zur Konstitution der Legierungen, Z. Physik. Chem. (Leipzig), 3:446 (1889).

171. C. T. Heycock and F. H. Neville, J. Chem. Soc., 55:674 (1889).

172. M. Rosenfeld, Notizen ueber Natrium, Ber. Deut. Keram. Ges., 24:1658 (1891).

173. K. Siebel, Ueber die Aenderung der Thermokraft und der Elektrischen Leitfaehigkeit einer Kalium-Natriumlegierung beim Uebergang vom festen in dem fluessigen Aggregatzustand, Ann. Physik, 60:260-278 (1919).

174. S. Walters and R. R. Miller, Ind. Eng. Chem. (Anal. Ed.), 18: 468-469 (1946).
175. C. T. Ewing, R. S. Hartmann, H. B. Atkinson, and R. R. Miller, Report NRL-C-3105, Naval Research Laboratory, April 1947.
176. E. Rinck, Diagramme de solidification des alliages calcium-sodium, Comptes rendus de l'academie des sciences, 192: 1378 (1931).
177. K. Bornemann, Metallurgie, 6:239 (1909).
178. B. Bohm and W. Klemm, Zur Kenntnis des Verhaltens der Alkalimetalle zueinander, Z. Anorg. Allgem. Chem., 243:69-85 (1939).
179. W. Hume-Rothery and G. V. Raynor, The Structure of Metals and Alloys, 3rd ed., The Institute of Metals, London, 1954.
180. F. Laves and H. J. Wallbaum, Z. Anorg. Allgem. Chem., 250:110-120 (1952).
181. C. H. Kean, The Pressure-Temperature Phase Diagram of NaK Alloys and the Effect of Pressure on the Resistance of the Liquid Phase, Phys. Rev., 55:750-754 (1939).
182. R. L. McKisson and L. A. Bromley, Heat of Formation of Sodium Potassium Alloys, J. Am. Chem. Soc., 73:314 (1951).
183. A. Joannis, Ann. Chim. Phys., [6] 12:358 (1887).
184. K. Banerjee, X-Ray Diffraction, Indian J. Phys., 3:339 (1929); see also C. W. Heaps, The Diffraction of X-Rays by Liquid NaK Alloy in a Magnetic Field, Phys. Rev., 48:491 (1935).
185. R. Kremann, M. Pestemer, and H. Schreiner, Die innere Reibung von kalium Natrium-Legierung im fluessigen Zustande, Rec. Trav. Chim., 51:557 (1932).
186. N. S. Gingrich and R. E. Kenderson, The Diffraction of X-Rays by Liquid Alloys of Sodium and Potassium, J. Chem. Phys., 20:1117-1120 (1952).
187. W. Kerp, Zur Kenntnis der Amalgame, Ann. Physik, 17:288-300 (1898).
188. W. Kerp, W. Bottger, and H. Winter, Zur Kenntnis der Amalgame, Ann. Physik, 25:7-16 (1900).
189. A. Guntz and J. Feree, Compt. Rend., 131:182-184 (1900).
190. E. Macy, Die Verbindungen des Li, Na, und K mit Hg, bestimmt aus ihrem spezifischen Volumen, Z. Physik. Chem., 29:129 (1899).
191. N. S. Kurnakov, Ueber die gegenseitigen Verbindunger der Metalle, Ann. Physik, 23:441-455 (1900).
192. Kraut and Pott, Ann. Chem., 159:188 (1871).
193. G. P. Grimaldi, Atti Accad. Nazl. Lincei Mem. Classe Sci. Fis. Mat. Nat. Sez. II, 4:32 (1887).
194. G. McPhail Smith and H. C. Bennett, Additional Notes on the Alkali and Alkali Earth Amalgams, J. Am. Chem. Soc., 32:622-626 (1910).
195. A. Schuller, Zur Kenntnis der Natriumamalgame, Ann. Physik, 40:385-399 (1904).
196. E. Vanstone, The Physico-Chemical Study of Mercury-Sodium Alloys on Sodium Amalgams, Trans. Faraday Soc., 7:42-63 (1911); Chemical News, 103:181-185, 198-200, 207-209 (1911).
197. G. Tammann, Zur Konstitution der Legierungen, Z. Physik. Chem. 3:443, 447 (1889).
198. C. T. Heycock and F. H. Neville, J. Am. Chem. Soc., 55:672 (1889).
199. N. C. Baenziger, J. W. Nielsen, and E. J. Duwell, USAEC Report COO-126, Iowa State University, 1953.
200. E. Janecke, Z. Metallk., 20:113-115 (1928).
201. E. Janecke, Ueber zwei chemische Verbindungen dreier Metalle unter sich (NaKHg$_2$ und NaCdHg), Z. Physik. Chem., 57:510 (1907).
202. E. Janecke and Carl Winter, Kurzgefasstes Handbuch aller Legierungen, pp. 263-265, Heidelberg, 1949.
203. R. C. Rodgers, Change of Resistance with Temperature of Various Sodium Amalgams, Phys. Rev., 8:259 (1916).
204. W. Klemm and B. Hauschulz, Magnetochemische Untersuchungen. XXXII Magnetische Messungen an Alkalimetall-Amalgamen, Z. Elektrochem., 45:346-353 (1939).
205. J. W. Nielsen and N. C. Baenziger, The Crystal Structures of NaHg$_2$, NaHg and Na$_3$Hg$_2$, Acta Cryst., 7:277-282 (1954).
206. Metals Handbook, p. 1179, American Society for Metals, 1948.
207. M. Hansen, Constitution of Binary Alloys, 2nd ed., pp. 827, 830, 876, McGraw-Hill Book Company, Inc., New York, 1958.
208. An Evaluation of Mercury Cooled Breeder Reactors, Report ATL-C42, Advanced Technology Laboratories, Oct. 31, 1959.
209. J. B. Nims and P. F. Zweifel, Preliminary Report on Sodium Temperature Coefficients in Large Fast Reactors, Report APDA-135, Atomic Power Development Associates, Inc., November 1959.
210. J. G. Knudsen and P. L. Katz, Fluid Dynamics and Heat Transfer, McGraw-Hill Book Company, Inc., New York, 1958.
211. E. Schmidt, Heat Transfer by Natural Convection, Lecture, International Developments in Heat Transfer, Proceedings of International Heat Transfer Conference, Boulder, Colo., and Westminster, England, 1961-1962, p. xxix, Am. Soc. Mech. Engrs., New York, 1963.
212. H. Etherington (Ed.), Nuclear Engineering Handbook, Sec. 9, McGraw-Hill Book Company, Inc., New York, 1958.
213. J. F. Hogerton and R. C. Grass (Eds.), Reactor Handbook, 1st ed., Vol. 2, Engineering, USAEC Report AECD-3646, 1955.

214. W. H. McAdams, Heat Transmission, 3rd ed., McGraw-Hill Book Company, Inc., New York, 1954.
215. M. M. El-Wakil, Nuclear Power Engineering, Chap. 11, McGraw-Hill Book Company, Inc., New York, 1962.
216. R. C. Martinelli, Heat Transfer to Molten Metals, Trans. Am. Soc. Mech. Engrs., 69:947 (1947).
217. S. S. Kutaleladze, V. J. Jobbotin, V. M. Borishanskii, and P. O. Kirillov, Heat Transfer for Liquid Metals Flowing in Pipes, Proceedings of the Second United Nations International Conference on the Peaceful Uses of Atomic Energy, Geneva, 1958, Vol. 7, pp. 132-138, United Nations, New York.
218. M. A. Mikheyev, V. A. Baum, K. D. Voskresensky, and O. S. Fedynsky, Heat Transfer of Molten Metals, Proceedings of the Second United Nations International Conference on the Peaceful Uses of Atomic Energy, Geneva, 1958, Vol. 9, pp. 285-289, United Nations, New York.
219. R. A. Baker and A. Sesonske, Heat Transfer in Sodium-Potassium Alloy, Trans. Am. Nucl. Soc., 3:468-469 (1960).
220. R. W. Schroeder and M. A. Chionchio, Description of Intermediate Heat Exchanger and Steam Generator Selections, USAEC Report TID-6881, Griscom-Russell Co., 1959.
221. B. Lubarsky and S. J. Kaufman, Review of Experimental Investigations of Liquid-Metal Heat Transfer, Report NACA-1270, National Advisory Committee for Aeronautics, 1956.
222. N. Z. Azer and B. T. Chao, A Mechanism of Turbulent Heat Transfer in Liquid Metals, Intern. J. Heat Mass Transfer, 1:121-138 (1960).
223. A. J. Friedland, O. E. Dwyer, W. Maresca, and C. F. Bonilla, Heat Transfer to Mercury in Parallel Flow Through Bundles of Circular Rods, International Developments in Heat Transfer, Proceedings of International Heat Transfer Conference, Boulder, Colo., and Westminster, England, 1961-1962, Vol. 3, pp. 526-534, American Society of Mechanical Engineers, New York, 1963.
224. E. M. Khabakhpasheva and Y. V. Il'in, Heat Transfer to a Sodium-Potassium Alloy in an Annulus, At. Energ., 9:494-496 (December 1960).
225. R. N. Lyon, Liquid Metal Heat Transfer Coefficient, Am. Inst. Chem. Engrs., J., 47:(2)75-79 (1951).
226. A. A. Andreevskii, Heat Transfer Between a Stream of Molten Sodium and a Single Cylinder Lying Across the Direction of Flow, J. Nucl. Energy, B, 1:263-264 (1961).
227. C. L. Rickard, O. E. Dwyer, and D. Dropkin, Heat Transfer Rates to Cross-Flowing Mercury in a Staggered Tube Bank, Trans. Am. Soc. Mech. Engrs., 80:646 (1958).
228. M. J. McGoff and J. W. Mausteller, Heat Transfer and Pressure Drop with NaK-56 Flowing Perpendicular to Vertical Tubes, Mine Safety Appliance Report 87, 1955.
229. S. S. Kutateladze, V. M. Borishanskii, I. I. Novikov, and O. S. Fedynskii, Liquid-Metal Heat Transfer Media, At. Energ., Supplement 2, 1958, translated by Consultants Bureau, Inc., New York, 1959.
230. W. H. Giedt, Principles of Engineering Heat Transfer, D. Van Nostrand Company, Inc., Princeton, N. J., 1957.
231. S. C. Hyman, C. F. Bonilla, and S. W. Ehrlich, Heat Transfer—Atlantic City, Chemical Engineering Progress Symposium Series, No. 5, p. 21 American Institute of Chemical Engineers, New York, 1953.
232. J. S. McDonald and T. J. Connolly, Investigation of Natural Convection Heat Transfer in Liquid Sodium, Nucl. Sci. Eng., 8:369-377 (1960).
233. S. Globe and D. Dropkin, Natural Convection Heat Transfer in Liquids Confined by Two Horizontal Plates and Heated from Below, J. Heat Transfer (Am. Soc. Mech. Engrs. Trans. Series C), 81(1):24(1959).
234. J. L. O'Toole and P. L. Silverston, Correlations of Convective Heat Transfer in Confined Horizontal Layers, Heat Transfer—Buffalo, Chemical Engineering Progress Symposium Series, No. 32, pp. 81-86, American Institute of Chemical Engineers, New York, 1961.
235. D. P. Timo, Free Convection in Narrow Vertical Sodium Annuli, USAEC Report KAPL-1082, Knolls Atomic Power Laboratory, Mar. 5, 1954.
236. J. P. Frazer and J. D. Oakley, Turbulent Free Convection Heat Transfer Rates in a Horizontal Pipe, USAEC Report KAPL-1494, Knolls Atomic Power Laboratory, 1957.
237. C. F. Bonilla, J. S. Busch, A. Stalder, N. S. Shaikhmanmu, and A. Ramachandran, Pool Boiling Heat Transfer with Mercury, USAEC Report TID-7529, Part 1, pp. 324-341, 1956.
238. Niels Madsen and C. F. Bonilla, Heat Transfer—Storrs, Chemical Engineering Progress Symposium Series, No. 3, pp. 251-259, American Institute of Chemical Engineers, New York, 1960.
239. A. J. Nerad and A. Howard, unpublished work, General Electric Company, 1936.
240. W. R. Gambill and H. W. Hoffman, Boiling Liquid-Metal Heat Transfer, preprint 1737-61, American Rocket Society, Space Nuclear Conference, May 3-5, 1961, Gatlinburg, Tenn.
241. R. C. Noyes, Experimental Study of Sodium Pool Boiling Heat Transfer, Paper 62-HT-24, American Society of Mechanical Engineers, New York, 1962.

242. F. E. Romie et al., Heat Transfer to Boiling Mercury, J. Heat Transfer (Am. Soc. Mech. Engrs. Trans. Series XC), 82(2): 287, (November 1960).
243. H. N. Hackett and D. Douglas, Modern Mercury-Unit Power Plant Design, Trans. Am. Soc. Mech. Engrs., 72:89 (1950).
244. J. C. Englebrecht, M. S. Thesis in Chemical Engineering, Columbia University, 1961; C. F. Bonilla, U. S. Air Force ASD Technical Report 61-697, Wright-Patterson Air Force Base, April 30, 1962.
245. B. Misra and C. F. Bonilla, Heat Transfer—Louisville, Chemical Engineering Progress Symposium Series, No. 18, p. 7, American Institute of Chemical Engineers, New York, 1956.
246. H. Schlichting, Boundary Layer Theory, translated by J. Kestin, Pergamon Press, New York, 1955.
247. G. Hotchkiss, Electrosensitive Recording Paper for Facsimile Telegraph Apparatus and Graphic Chart Instruments, Western Union Technical Rev., 3:6-16 (1949).
248. W. W. Soroka, Analog Methods in Computation and Simulation, McGraw-Hill Book Company, Inc., New York, 1945.
249. S. E. Isakoff and T. B. Drew, Heat and Momentum Transfer in Turbulent Flow of Mercury, USAEC Report AECU-1199, Columbia University, 1951.
250. H. E. Brown, B. A. Amstead, and B. E. Short, Temperature and Velocity Distribution and Transfer of Heat in a Liquid Metal, Trans. Am. Soc. Mech. Engrs., 79:279-285 (February 1957).
251. C. F. Bonilla et al., Mass Transfer in Molten Metal and Molten Salt Systems, Proceedings of the Second United Nations International Conference on the Peaceful Uses of Atomic Energy, Geneva, 1955, Vol. 9, pp. 331-340, United Nations, New York.
252. J. S. Busch, L. L. Lyon, and C. F. Bonilla, The Calculation of Pressure Drop and Flow Distribution Within a Reactor Vessel in a Pressurized Water Nuclear Reactor System, USAEC Report WAPD-217, Westinghouse Electric Corporation, August 1959.
253. L. F. Moody, Trans. Am. Soc. Mech. Engrs., 66:671 (1944).
254. J. P. Hartnett and T. F. Irvine, Nusselt Values for Estimating Turbulent Liquid Metal Heat Transfer in Noncircular Ducts, J. Am. Inst. Chem. Engrs., 3(3):313 (1957).
255. R. T. Berringer and A. A. Bishop, Model Study of the Pressure Drop Relationships in a Typical Fuel Rod Assembly, USAEC Report YAEC-75, Westinghouse Electric Corporation, February 1959.
256. O. E. Homeister, W. N. McDaniel, and R. A. Yagee, Model Studies of the Flow Characteristics of the Fuel Elements for the Enrico Fermi Reactor, paper presented at the Fourth Nuclear Engineering and Science Conference, Chicago, March 17-21, 1958.
257. A. C. Spengos, Tests on Models of Nuclear Reactor Elements - IV - Model Study of Fuel Element Supports, Report UMRI-2431-4-P, University of Michigan, July 1959.
258. A. N. de Stordeur, Drag Coefficients for Fuel Element Spacers, Nucleonics, 19(6):75-79 (June 1961).
259. J. F. Wilson, R. J. Grenda, and J. F. Patterson, Steam Volume Fraction in a Bubbling Two-Phase Mixture, Trans. Am. Nucl. Soc., 4(2):356 (1961).
260. G. C. Yeh and N. Zuber, On the Problem of Liquid Entrainment, USAEC Report ANL-6244, Ramo-Wooldridge, October 1960.
261. R. W. Lockhart and R. C. Martinelli, Proposed Correlation of Data for Isothermal Two-Phase, Two-Component Flow in Pipes, Chem. Eng. Prog., 45:39 (1949).
262. R. C. Martinelli and D. B. Nelson, Prediction of Pressure Drop During Forced-Circulation Boiling of Water, Trans. Am. Soc. Mech. Engrs., 70:695 (1948).
263. H. G. Elrod, Jr., Tentative Calculation Procedures for Pressure Drop and Volumetric Density in Two-Phase Flow, USAEC Report NDA-2131-7, Nuclear Development Associates, 1962.
264. H. Fauske, in Proceedings of the 1961 Heat Transfer and Fluid Mechanics Institute, Held at University of Southern California, June 19-21, 1961, Stanford University Press, 1961.
265. J. F. Marchaterre and B. M. Hoglund, Correlation for Two-Phase Flow, Nucleonics, 20(8):142 (August 1962).
266. G. W. Maurer, A Method for Predicting Steady-State Boiling Vapor Fractions in Reactor Coolant Channels, USAEC Report WAPD-BT-19, Westinghouse Electric Corporation, June 1960.
267. G. I. Taylor, The Transport of Vorticity and Heat Through Fluids in Turbulent Motion, Proc. Roy. Soc. London, 135A: 685 (1932).
268. T. Von Karman, Proceedings of the Third International Congress of Applied Mechanics, Stockholm, 1930, Vol. 1, Part 1, p. 85, Kungl. Boktryckeriet, P. A. Norstedt and Soener, Stockholm, 1931; also Report NACA-TN-611, National Advisory Committee for Aeronautics, 1931.
269. S. Goldstein, Modern Developments in Fluid Dynamics, Oxford University Press, New York, 1938.
270. H. Rouse, Advanced Mechanics of Fluids, John Wiley & Sons, Inc., New York, 1959.
271. A. Fage and V. M. Falkner, Note on Experiment on the Temperature and Velocity in Section of a Heated Cylindrical Obstacle, Proc. Roy. Soc. London, 135A:702-705 (1932).
272. H. Reichardt, Impuls und Warmeaustausch in freier Turbulenz, Z. Angew. Math. Mech., 24:268 (1944).
273. J. O. Hinze and B. G. van der Hegge Zijnen, Transfer of Heat and Matter in the Turbulent Mixing Zone of an Axially Symmetric Jet, Proceedings of the Seventh International Congress of Applied Mechanics, Part 1, Vol. 2, p. 286, Her Majesty's Stationery Office, 1948.
274. S. Corrsin and M. S. Uberoi, Further Experiments on the Flow and Heat Transfer in a Heated Turbulent Air Jet, Report NACA-TN-998, National Advisory Committee for Aeronautics, 1950.
275. C. G. Lawson et al., Trans. Am. Nucl. Soc. 4(2):315 (1961).
276. Homogeneous Reactor Program Quarterly Progress Report, USAEC Report ORNL-3004, p. 29, Oak Ridge National Laboratory, July 31, 1960.
277. H. R. Hazard and A. Rotkowitz, Studies of Mixing in the Lower Plenum of a Quarter-Scale Flow Model of the PWR Reactor, USAEC Report BMI-1172, Battelle Memorial Institute, 1957.
278. O. U. Anders, Accelerator Made Tracer Solves a Mixing Problem, Nucleonics, 18(12):77 (1960).
279. J. M. Prausnitz and R. H. Wilhelm, Turbulent Concentration Fluctuations Through Electrical Conductivity Measurements, Rev. Sci. Instr., 27(11):941 (1956).
280. M. P. Norin, An Electrolyte Method for Transient Mixing Measurements, J. Franklin Inst., 266(3):229 (1958).
281. F. R. Beyer and M. P. Norin, The Effect of Mixing in the Outlet Plenum of the Fermi Reactor, Trans. Am. Nucl. Soc., 3:186 (1960).
282. O. Reynolds, An Experimental Investigation of the Circumstances Which Determine Whether the Motion of Water Shall be Direct or Sinous and of the Law of Resistance in Parallel Channels, Phil. Trans. Roy. Soc., A, 174:935 (1883).
283. S. H. Esleeck and R. M. Rosser, Check Valve Water Hammer Characteristics, Trans. Am. Nucl. Soc., 2:180-181 (November 1959).

CHAPTER 3

Structural Analysis

KENNETH R. STEARNS
Franklin Institute Laboratories
Philadelphia, Pennsylvania

Contents

3.1 Introduction

This chapter is intended to serve as a guide and an aid in the design of load-bearing parts to be used in fast reactors for nuclear power systems. The intent is to alert the designer to special problems and to present means for their solution. Since the treatment is condensed, the principles of structural design are not presented; bibliographical references to them, however, are given. A few examples of analysis are given in Sec. 3.4.

3.2 Design Conditions

3.2.1 ENVIRONMENTAL FACTORS

The reactor design should include allowance for environmental factors not present in more conventional heat power components: (1) high temperature differences and transients, (2) liquid metals, and (3) radiation.

3.2.1.1 Temperature

A high reactor outlet temperature of the working fluid is desirable to optimize the efficiency of modern high-temperature turbogenerators. This introduces problems of lower strength of structural materials at high temperatures, high temperature gradients across structural parts, and high temperature transients during normal or abnormal system changes. Structural analysis deals with these problems, seeking the best solutions within the allowable limits set by the design conditions.

3.2.1.2 Liquid Metals

The high heat-transfer rates of liquid metals across the boundary layer between structural parts and the liquid metal are much better than those with water or gases because of their high thermal conductivity and film coefficients. The assumption that the surface of an element is at the temperature of the contiguous liquid metal is often used, and this assumption is a good first approximation even for rapid changes in the temperature of coolant. As a result, a temperature gradient along the normal to the surface is created whose steepness varies inversely with the conductivity of the material. If the coolant temperature should change rapidly, the intensity of the gradient would also depend on the heat capacity of the conducting material. The surface layer of the structure may be so constrained by the remaining mass that it cannot assume the expansion corresponding to its temperature, and as a result severe stresses caused by the temperature gradient may be set up in the surface. As pointed out in Chap. 2, internal heat generation is high in fast reactors; therefore the steady-state temperature gradients tend to be high. The large temperature rise of the coolant as it flows through the reactor may also result in large variations in coolant temperature during operating load changes. In the event of an accident or scram, these changes would be rapid.

The low vapor pressure of liquid metals results in low design pressures. The vessel walls therefore are thin, and the thermal stresses are low. Thermal baffles can be used effectively during thermal transients to protect structural members. Table 3.4 shows that a transient of 100°F per second induces a stress in a 0.5-in. plate equal to 82% of the stress in a 2-in. plate. The effectiveness of a multiple thermal baffle equal to 40% of the total thickness of wall plus baffle, the first baffle being equal to 10% of total thickness, is shown in Table 3.6. The maximum stress in the wall, for a 300°F change in 20 sec, is reduced from a maximum value of 91,400 psi for the unbaffled wall to 34,100 psi for the baffled wall.

3.2.1.3 Radiation

The effects of irradiation and consequent heating on the mechanical and chemical properties of the material should be evaluated. Shielding may be required to reduce neutron- and gamma-flux levels.

3.2.2 SPECIFICATION OF DESIGN CONDITIONS

As a fast reactor system progresses from the early concept toward the developmental stage, design conditions, both normal and emergency, should be specified. One key part of the specification is the definition of transients. Besides normal changes in power levels, including routine start-up and shutdown, account should be taken of the more drastic changes caused by such malfunctions as loss of pump power. After operating conditions have been specified, the next step is a determination, based on the material properties, of the allowable limits to be imposed on the structural materials. Finally the stresses and deflections of the structural members of each component should be determined by analysis for the specified loading conditions and allowable limits. The specifications for the component or system should include the loadings and an estimate of the loading cycles.

3.2.2.1 Design Loadings

Classifications of loading conditions that affect the design of structural components of fast reactor plants are: (1) pressure differences across walls, diaphragms, and supports; (2) weight of component and its internal components, static loads, superimposed weights or forces, including weights of piping contents and appendages, and component support reactions; (3) nozzle reactions caused by thermal expansion or contraction of piping and of the vessels or housings connected thereto; (4) steady-state thermal loadings; (5) differential expansions caused by heating joined dissimilar materials; (6) transient thermal loadings; (7) mechanical shock and vibration; (8) hydrodynamic forces; (9) seismic loadings; and (10) combinations of the foregoing loadings.

3.2.2.2 Loading Cycles

The number of mechanical loadings, as well as the thermal-strain inputs, are variable with time, even though some may assume steady-state conditions for protracted periods. In the combinations to be expected, these changing loads will subject virtually every part of all structural components of the reactor to a complex pattern of time-dependent stresses that may be thought of as fluctuations about a mean value. These stress fluctuations have various probable frequencies of occurrence and an intensity associated with each frequency; thus they may be roughly classified into a spectrum of cyclical stresses. This spectrum can be known only as precisely as past operating experience can be extended to the proposed power

system. Detailed integration of the damage done by each interval of frequency is generally unwarranted. Three categories of amplitude of alternating stress intensity should be adequate for the fatigue evaluation. These might be defined, for each loading, as follows:

Class 1   Small or slow temperature variations resulting from normal load changes, totaling 100,000 cycles
Class 2   Intermediate, 2500 cycles
Class 3   Scrams, start-ups, accidents, 500 cycles

3.2.2.3 Dimensional Integrity

A fast reactor poses a challenging problem to the designer of the structural members of fuel elements and core supports. Nuclear reactivity is extremely sensitive to dimensional variations in the core. Examples are distortion of fuel subassembly cans (containers for fuel elements) and dimensional changes in support plates brought about by variations in radial temperature gradients. If these thermal distortions are not carefully compensated, control of the reactor may be difficult. Good design is needed to avoid misalignment of safety- and control-rod guide tubes, which could lead to jamming and loss of control. The remotely operated fuel-handling devices may also require that certain dimensional changes remain small throughout the life of the reactor.

3.2.2.4 Miscellaneous Design Conditions

Due account should be taken of the compatibility of mating surfaces, discontinuities, fabrication procedures, surface finishes, heat treatments, and changes in materials induced by irradiation, and allowances should be made as required. Consideration also should be given to factors contributing to corrosion, such as oxide formation, mass transfer, carburization, decarburization, nitriding, hydriding, sensitization of parent metal or welds, stress, fatigue, and crevices.

3.3 Design Limits

3.3.1 INTRODUCTION

The structural design of components for a fast reactor is founded on the successful prediction of the resistance of materials to the loadings they will undergo. Their capacity for withstanding, at elevated temperatures, the plastic strain peculiar to creep and fatigue becomes critical.

It is not likely that a thoroughly rational basis for a quantitative prediction of the lifetime behavior of a new alloy under arbitrary loading and environment will be forthcoming soon. Yet effective design cannot ignore the physics of the solid state. The strength of metals arises altogether from interatomic forces that become nil at a distance of a few spacings of the crystal lattice. Intelligent use of materials in design is promoted by an awareness of the progress of investigations into the nature of the resistance of metallic alloys to strain, plastic loss of dimensions, and rupture.

The existing technology of the engineering properties of materials serves as the basis of the working ground rules for establishing the limits of loading of materials for structural use. Effort to lessen the lag of this technology behind the discoveries of science is in the interest of engineering design.

3.3.2 DEFORMATION AND FRACTURE OF STRUCTURAL MATERIALS

Solids can be classified as brittle or ductile according to the amount of plastic set they exhibit in a tensile stress—strain test to fracture. In general, if other desired engineering properties can be obtained, structural designers prefer ductile materials to carry working loads. Two compelling advantages of ductility are (1) the ability of the material to absorb large amounts of shock energy or strain input by plastic flow and (2) the relative insensitivity of the material to unfavorable geometry (stress raisers). Brittleness is temperature dependent. Paradoxically, for two important classes of structural loading, ductile materials apparently show brittle fractures although by microscopy profound irreversible displacements are discernible. Two classes are the moderate but protracted loadings at temperatures sufficiently elevated to cause eventual creep rupture and moderate loadings, alternating in direction, that can cause fatigue fracture. These important damage mechanisms may be cooperating during long-period cyclic loadings of heated structural components.

3.3.2.1 Plastic Flow

Plastic slip of a crystal at stress on the order of one thousandth of the elastic modulus was explained by Taylor in terms of a moving dislocation [1]. An imperfection, such as a row of lattice vacancies, permits a stress that would seem negligible in view of the atomic binding energy to slip successive lines of atoms through one atomic spacing with binding forces almost in equilibrium. As the laterally moving dislocation line sweeps through the lattice, it generates a surface, usually the (1 1 1) plane of body-centered cubic crystals, which has slipped in shear by one lattice pitch. Not only are lattice defects everywhere inherently dense in the growth process of metallic crystals, but Frank and Read [2] predicted that a blocked dislocation line could become a continuing source of closed dislocation loops expanding seriatim close on each other's heels or a close spiral if one end of the source were in a boundary. Thus the ratchet frequency would be adequate, coupled with the density of dislocation striae found in a single slip band, to explain the high rates of strain of metallic crystals which are observed. Wilsdorf [3] recorded by electron microscopy in strained polycrystalline stainless-steel foil successive stages in the life of a spontaneously formed Frank—Read source and the growth of a dislocation line spiraling within a trape-

zoidal boundary formed by the slip lines of other slip systems viewed relatively edge-on. Reference 4 is an introduction to modern theories of strength.

3.3.2.2 Creep

Cottrell [5] attributes the yield phenomenon in mild steel to the strong preferential diffusion of solute (interstitial) carbon and nitrogen atoms toward dislocations. The "atmosphere" of bound interstitials then greatly impedes movement of the dislocation; so creep is almost suppressed in a body-centered cubic lattice at moderate temperatures. The sharply defined yield stress of unyielded or strain-aged mild steel is exactly the force intensity needed to pull the dislocations free of their binding atmospheres; thus they are free to move and thereby generate plastic deformation. This yield-point phenomenon is suppressed at elevated temperatures because the increased thermal energy "evaporates" the interstitials throughout the crystal.

Work hardening may be interpreted as a sum of many effects. Two important ones are the growing number of mutual interferences of dislocations gliding on intersecting slip planes and the squeezing out (precipitation) of alloying interstitial atoms at dislocations, which tends to immobilize these dislocations and thus set up resistance to plastic flow or creep. Annealing is an inverse tendency; the subgrain boundaries formed by the interlocking slip bands tend to be annihilated as the crystal regrows and as precipitates diffuse throughout the lattice. There is much evidence to support the controversial statement that steady-state or second-stage creep is mainly an uneasy equilibrium between work hardening and time annealing, but it must be remembered that even at low strain rates in creep irreversible damage is accumulating. Intergranular slip at crystal corners and perhaps condensation of lattice vacancies may generate widening microscopic cracks and nucleate voids that would foretell eventual rupture if observed and correctly interpreted. Intergranular slip appears to depend primarily on the maximum principal stress and to be largely independent of the other two principal stresses. Creep rupture occurs at small total strains and with little direct warning. The most drastic annealing, short of destruction of a component, fails to cure completely creep damage that has passed an early stage. The austenitic stainless steels have good creep resistance at high temperatures but at these temperatures are prone to serious precipitation damage and the development of a brittle sigma phase. Tendencies toward embrittlement in weld deposits and in the weld heat-affected zones require special consideration. Temperature- and time-dependent metallurgical changes can be suppressed for years by additives and by heat treatment during manufacture; therefore it is dangerous to extrapolate short-time creep data for such complex, special alloys with short service histories [6-10].

3.3.2.3 Fatigue.

Metal fatigue is at once the most vital and the least understood of the problems in the structural design of fast breeder reactors. Thompson and Wadsworth [11] have reviewed, from the solid-state physicists' viewpoint, the advances in theory and the complementary experimental work and have indicated the complexity of the problem. Yen [12] has recently reviewed the engineering aspects of thermal fatigue.

A fatigue cycle has an elastic (energy recoverable) portion and an inelastic portion. In the latter the lost energy per unit volume is represented by the area of the stress—strain hysteresis loop and, if a mean stress is present or if temperature is cyclic, by a small permanent strain. In contrast to the widely distributed slip of monotonic strain, fatigue cycling causes a few intense slip bands that have been shown by electron microscopy and etching to become microcracks very early in the fatigue life of the specimen.

Reference 13 examines the role of small flaws as stress foci in fatigue. In 1933 Gough [14] speculated that strain hardening resulting from slip in the glide planes that respond to the maximum resolved shear stress [15] leads to cracking and fragmentation into crystallites, which, in turn, suffer reorientation. This theory was examined and expanded [16-22].

Head [23] stated that fatigue life is determined by the rate of crack growth. He devised a model consisting of elemental regions of high stress concentration just ahead of the crack which are work hardened and fractured successively. The theory of moving dislocations is the most satisfactory explanation of the rapidity with which large localized slip displacements form. Mott's model accounting for the extrusion of subgrain by a screw dislocation [24] from a Frank—Read source has had some corroboration [25-27]. Wood [28] described the role played by work hardening in fatigue in terms of lattice defects and dislocations, with experimental verification. Yokobori [29] conceived of dislocation pileups and of the obstacles, that pin these pileups, as submicroscopic notches responsible for the early stages of fatigue damage.

3.3.2.4 Cumulative Damage

In practical power-reactor component design, an arbitrary variation in the amplitude of successive strain cycles should be taken into account. Palmgren [30] in 1924 stated a linear damage-accumulation rule: "There is a uniform accumulation of damage $1/N_S$ corresponding to each cycle of alternating stress of amplitude S, if N_S denotes the number of cycles of that constant amplitude S that would cause failure." Later the linear rule was rephrased by Langer [31] and by Miner [32]. Although this is a simple and useful working hypothesis, its precision has been questioned by many experimenters. For example, Dolan and coworkers [33-36] showed that there is a marked increase in total damage when larger amplitudes precede rather than follow lesser amplitudes.

Henry [37] assumed previous fatigue damage to be equivalent to an increase in a stress concentration factor and derived a damage equation that includes an overstress ratio as well as the cycle ratio. Freudenthal and Heller [38] proposed a quasi-linear rule of cumulative damage based on factors of stress interaction. Their diagram of fictitious stress ratio vs. number of cycles produced by such interaction was confirmed by tests on aluminum and steel alloys. It is notable that most of the points for steel would have been included if Miner's sum of cycle ratios were taken as 0.1.

3.3.2.5 Low Cycle Fatigue

All schemes for the estimation of cumulative damage are predicated on complete knowledge of the left-hand end of the S—N curve relating alternating stress amplitude to number of cycles to failure. For normal temperatures and cycling frequencies, Weisman and Kaplan [39] and Finch [40] have supplied data on a number of low-alloy steels. In the log—log plot of the ratio of stress amplitude to ultimate stress against number of cycles to failure, the scatter band of the completely reversed axial push—pull specimens of Ref. 39 shows the now-familiar linear trend from unity at a quarter cycle to the endurance limit ratio in the neighborhood of 10^6 or 10^7 cycles. The notched axial specimens appear slightly stronger (triaxial condition at base of notch) in low-cycle fatigue, but their band crosses that of the smooth test pieces between 10^3 and 10^4 cycles and then rapidly sinks to the ratio expected from the notch sensitivity index in the unlimited endurance region. The distinctive behavior of (1) round specimens loaded as rotating beams, (2) beam specimens of rectangular cross section bent one way from their unloaded configurations about one of their principal axes, (3) rectangular beams in wholly reversed flexure about one of the principal axes of their cross sections, and (4) round specimens in one-way and reversed axial pull are clearly brought out in Ref. 39. Reference 39 shows that elastic theory cannot cope with plastic conditions. In bending, the low-cycle fatigue performance not only differs from that of axial specimens, but it becomes a function of the manner in which the area is distributed over the cross section. Such divergences forbid blind reliance on results of fatigue experiments in design work without careful attention to actual stress or true plastic strain. Finch [40] plots fatigue strength factors against number of cycles to failure, the two other parameters being material and the geometry of the notch. Petersen [41] has expressed the S—N curves below 10^6 cycles as follows:

(a) Completely alternating axial load, unnotched:

$$S_{ae} = S_u - \left(\frac{S_u - S_e}{6}\right) \log N \qquad (3.1)$$

(b) Notched:

$$S_{kae} = S_u - \left(\frac{S_u - \dfrac{S_e}{K_f}}{6}\right) \log N \qquad (3.2)$$

(c) Completely alternating bending, $10^3 < N < 10^6$, unnotched:

$$S_{ae} = \frac{S_u}{(N/1000)(1/3)\log(S_u/S_e)} \qquad (3.3)$$

(d) Notched:

$$S_{kae} = \frac{S_u}{(N/1000)(1/3)\log(K_f S_u/S_e)} \qquad (3.4)$$

where S_u = ultimate tensile strength

S_e = endurance limit, the maximum amplitude of completely reversed stress that will not cause failure of the specimen in 10^6 cycles (in Petersen's discussion)

S_{ae} = amplitude of completely reversed alternating stress that will cause failure for some $N < 10^6$

N = number of cycles to failure

K_f = fatigue notch factor, defined as $K_f = S_e/S_{ke}$

S_{ke} = notched endurance limit, the maximum amplitude of completely reversed alternating stress that will not cause failure of a specimen with a particular geometry of notch

S_{kae} = amplitude of completely reversed alternating stress that will cause failure at some $N < 10^6$ for a specimen having the notch geometry in question

The axially loaded and notched relation is unduly conservative in the 10^2 to 10^4 cycle interval by comparison with the other three.

As Langer [42] has shown, in the low-cycle thermal fatigue encountered in nuclear power reactors, the stress levels imposed by temperature gradients are incidental to the self-restraint of structural components. Clearly such thermal-expansion incompatibilities represent a strain input pattern that can frequently be predicted with fair assurance, but the resultant stress distribution will be affected by such temperature- and load-history-dependent phenomenas as work hardening, annealing, creep, and Bauschinger softening; therefore thermal-stress intensities tend to be less tangible. During low-cycle fatigue the stress amplitude may be well into the plastic range (beyond the yield stress). The concept of fictitious elastic stress, $Ea \Delta T$, offers little help in predicting fatigue damage in low-cycle fatigue service at elevated temperatures, where the stress–strain relation of the material in question may be undergoing continuing modifications by the service environment and loading. A truer measure of potential fatigue damage would be the sum of the absolute values of the plastic strain during the heating and cooling cycle. Coffin [43] has succeeded in monitoring this incremental plastic strain for type 347 stainless steel; the strain input to an axial specimen clamped in a rigid fixture was applied by electrical conduction heating followed by air cooling. He found that N is related to the plastic-strain change per half cycle $\Delta \epsilon_p$ by

$$N^k \Delta \epsilon_p = C$$

where the exponent k is very close to $1/2$ for a number of ductile metals; the constant C is associated with ductility. Coffin and coworkers had excellent correlation between the foregoing equation and results from tests of fully-reversed cyclic axial strain at uniform temperature [44]. At room temperature and cyclic strain ranging from 0.002 to 0.50, seven of eight different metals [45] showed the characteristic straight line of slope $-1/2$ in the region $10^5 > N \geq 1/4$ cycles in the log–log plot of $\Delta \epsilon_p$ vs. N. Usefully precise measurements of $\Delta \epsilon_p$ become difficult if N is large or the material is relatively brittle [46].

3.3.2.6 Combined Loadings

Reactor vessels are generally subjected to combinations of static and alternating load. Any asymmetry in a stress cycle can be attributed to such a combined loading. The simultaneous operation of creep-rupture mechanisms and fatigue damage should be considered in the design of components that will carry appreciable mechanical loading for several hundred thousand hours at elevated temperature and will be arbitrarily subjected to repeated, severe thermal transients. Vitovec [47] pointed out that the alternating component affects small regions of particular grains whereas the steady component causes creep in the entire matrix at elevated temperatures. He set up Maxwell nonlinear models to predict the behavior. Clauss and Freeman [48] measured the stress-rupture life of specimens that had been subjected to prior thermal fatigue. They found that S-816 steel suffers no significant loss of stress-rupture life at 1350°F and 40,000 psi regardless of how many times it had been cycled between 200 and 1350°F. Inconel 550 at first shows rapid loss of rupture life; this becomes slower with increased cycles of previous thermal fatigue between the foregoing temperature limits. Ross and Morrow [49] conducted relaxation tests on specimens during an alternating strain cycle fatigue test (cycle-dependent relaxation of mean stress). The mean stress decreases rapidly at first. The fatigue limit of A286 was lowered 30% at 80,000 psi initial mean tension stress and raised 15% at 60,000 psi initial mean compressive stress.

Reference 50 shows how cyclic heat flux in the wall of a pressurized vessel could cause progressive growth of the vessel and derives stress-ratio limits to avoid this thermal ratcheting. Coffin [51] showed the instability of 2S aluminum and of OFHC copper specimens that displayed massive migrations of material and large plastic strains at seemingly negligible mean stresses. He named this phenomenon cyclic-strain-induced creep.

3.3.2.7 Fatigue of Pressure Vessels

In 1948 the Pressure Vessel Research Committee (PVRC) started a program to make available to designers data on new high-strength alloys. The experimental work grew into a PVRC coordinated program including work at Lehigh University, University of Illinois, Ecole Polytechnic at Montreal, and Coffin's work at Knolls Atomic Power

Laboratory (KAPL), with the cooperation of the AEC, Bureau of Ships, and a number of fabricators. Dolan [52] interpreted the philosophy behind the design of fatigue-resistant vessels in 1954 and pointed out that it is essential to eliminate stress raisers to exploit the high-strength steels [53]. The University of Illinois work on plates subjected to repeated 2:1 biaxial strain is summarized in Ref. 54. Kooistra [55] reported the results of the program up to 1957 and provided an evaluation of testing methods and procedures to establish effective geometrical strain-concentration factors and conclusions toward setting up safe design limits. Hardenbergh [56] summarized the PVRC program to solve the problem of strain concentration at vessel nozzle penetrations. Largely through the joint work of Cooper, Langer, and Mershon, the Tentative Structural Design Basis for Reactor Pressure Vessels and Directly Associated Components (Pressurized Water Cooled Systems) [57] was developed. This Bureau of Ships vessel code takes account of thermal fatigue in a rational manner up to 700°F for thick-walled highly pressurized systems. It is an extension of Soderberg's 1930 rules [58] for working stress to suit a new generation of heat power systems. Reference 59 describes a recent PVRC fatigue program using a series of 3-ft-diameter pressure vessels having seven or eight nozzles of varied profile or location.

3.3.2.8 Component Geometry and Creep

The influence of notching on creep strength at elevated temperatures may be complicated by two phenomena, namely, (1) strength is time dependent (for the same rupture time, notch rupture strength is compared with a smooth specimen rupture strength) and (2) certain combinations of temperature and applied stress may result in property changes [60]. These structural instabilities may greatly affect the notch rupture strength ratio and both the smooth and notch ductility of the metal. Often stability is also a function of previous plastic deformation and heat-treatment history. The complex interaction of stress, temperature, and time on the factors that determine the creep–rupture notch sensitivity of Inconel-X in the 1 to 1000 hr to rupture interval is shown in Fig. 3.1. Low notch strength ratios may be associated with both high and low smooth ductilities. The notch rupture strength of a notch-ductile alloy (19-9 DL) increases with increasing notch depth whereas an increase in notch depth reduces the notch strength for a notch-sensitive material (K-42B) [61]. For a relatively unstable material (Waspalloy), the effect of notch sharpness depends on the test duration and temperature [62]. High normalizing temperature, high hardness, and large grain size tend to increase notch brittleness of a number of alloys, but these effects are attenuated at long rupture times. Sessler [63] reported rupture tests showing marked increase in notch sensitivity in weld-affected zones of AMS5616 and 17-22-A-S. Vacuum melting raises both the smooth- and notched-rupture strength of Waspalloy. Operating environment may cause embrittlement and increased notch sensitivity.

Although the designer will provide appropriate fillets and smooth finish, small surface cracks

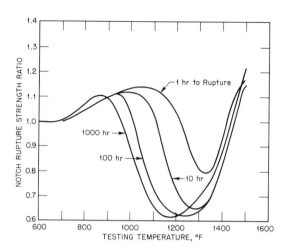

FIG. 3.1—Notch rupture strength ratio for Inconel-X. [From G. Sachs, J. G. Sessler, and W. F. Brown, Jr., Am. Soc. Testing Mater. Spec. Tech. Publ. No. 260, p. 33 (1959).]

may escape inspection, and cladding, plating, hard surfacing, screw threads, and contact pressures may introduce stress concentrations. Until more information is accumulated, respectful underexploitation of compositions and treatments suspected of introducing creep–rupture notch sensitivity under the working environment of a structure seems in order for power reactor applications.

3.3.2.9 Interaction of Creep and Fatigue

In reactor operation the temperature and loading of structural parts will vary with time. Manson and Brown [64] have surveyed the complex relations between steady and nonsteady creep. If load or temperature changes, it is difficult to separate the various strain-recovery effects, recrystallization, and precipitation processes involved even if the transient thermal stresses are known exactly. If load is removed or lessened, inelastic recovery, loss of strain hardening, and a Bauschinger transient softening is observed; in general, these effects are probably superimposed, which accounts for the complex and seemingly contradictory results of interrupted creep tests. Engineering alloys are frequently subject to structural changes during creep in their service-temperature range. Intermittent loading may cause precipitation hardening and may accelerate rupture. Many results of tests of intermittent heating are obscure because the effects of thermal-stress cycling were not monitored.

Various analytical methods of predicting or correlating intermittent creep have been developed and compared against tests of engineering materials with small success. Reference 64 discusses (1) the diffusion type parameter of Dorn [65] intended for pure metals under constant stress but arbitrary temperature, (2) the K factor method [66, 67] for bringing a family of isothermal creep curves for different stress levels into coincidence by scaling the time coordinate, and (3) methods based on fraction of life used, a counterpart of Miner's hypothesis for fatigue life. In the latter, it is assumed that each segment of creep is independent; thus a stress and a temperature acting for a time Δt will use $\Delta t / t_r$ of the rupture life t_r, and, if these fractions are summed over a complex load-temperature regime, an estimate of life for this regime will be obtained. Robinson [68] applied this method at constant stress but for various wave forms of cyclic temperature, using the Larson and Miller parameter [69]. For certain unstable alloys it appears that life estimated as time to rupture for steady creep at the peak stress and peak temperature of a particular operating cycle may not necessarily be conservative.

The current status of the problem of setting design limits for pressure-vessel materials has been summarized by Rastrelli [70]. The following six conclusions are quoted from his report:

1. The only existing hypothesis for predicting the behavior of a material when subjected to a varying amplitude load history of practical significance in the analyses of a pressure vessel is Miner's so modified as to yield conservative estimates of the number of cycles to failure.

2. Other materials hypotheses are based on more comprehensive equations for depicting the change (i.e., damage) in a material's characteristics as a result of some load experience, but in their final form, the very parameters that serve to distinguish these hypotheses from Miner's are removed. In those instances where it is possible to retain one of the parameters and thus compare theory with experimental evidence, one finds that all the uncertainties prevalent in Miner's hypotheses also exist in the other hypotheses, except in a different form. In essence, one term that is sensitive to the particular test history's characteristics is replaced with another term that is equally sensitive to the very same characteristics.

3. None of the equations for the hypotheses are conducive to being used successfully and meaningfully in the analysis of a pressure vessel, since even in their most general form, they reflect only the cyclic characteristics of the service history and exclude the very important aspects of sequence of load application.

4. The fact that the damage concept is an abstraction defeats the very purpose of the so-called damage theories—namely, to enable the designer to predict the behavior of a material in a complex load history on the basis of material information acquired in the simpler constant-amplitude tests. It seems quite improbable that the needs of the pressure vessel designer, which in the simplest sense requires the establishment of time-dependent design criteria and comparable design allowables, can be satisfied with an arbitrary term like "damage."

5. The controlled-strain fatigue studies currently available in the literature are more meaningful to the pressure vessel field if for no other reason than the fact that the histories involve a relatively few number of cycles to failure. However, the data generated thus far reflect the relationship between number of cycles to failure and some aspect of strain. As such, the manner in which these data can be used by the pressure vessel designer is again limited to that of comparing one material with another. In addition, it is necessary to convert the cyclic strain to some equivalent stress quantity so that both the experimental results obtained from the materials specimens and the computed quantities representing the pressure vessel are reduced to the same level of abstraction; and this conversion of strain to stress is usually accomplished by some arbitrary quantity such as an "equivalent" modulus of elasticity.

6. Aside from those creep and relaxation formulations dealing with an elevated steady-state temperature, and constant mechanically applied loads, there are no readily discernible trends to which the pressure vessel designer can turn to deal with the combined effects of time-dependent load and time-dependent temperature conditions. For the cyclic load with constant elevated temperature, there appear to be relationships between stress or strain and the number of cycles to failure that are similar in form to those suggested for room temperature. For those elevated temperature environments where the aspect of time is particularly conducive to the simultaneous existence of fatigue and creep, or where fatigue and creep are the result of fluctuations of both the mechanically applied and thermally induced load, there is little in the way of materials information that the designer can use for a guide beyond the familiar elevated temperature creep and fatigue information that is already incorporated in pressure vessel design procedures.

3.3.3 STRESS INTENSITY

Long before the dislocation theory was formulated, the observation of the orientations of slip lines in ductile tension specimens and of cracks formed during compression tests of brittle materials indicated that plastic flow and even rupture are shearing phenomena. Wire-drawing experiments led H. Tresca to announce that the criterion of deformation is the algebraic difference in principal stresses and that this deformation is shear along a plane making a 45° angle with the direction of these stresses. O. Mohr generalized the maximum-shear theorem to three dimensions and presented his well-known graphical representation. He spoke of the diameters of his principal-stress circles (the differences $S_1 - S_2$,

$S_2 - S_3$, and $S_1 - S_3$, which are double the maximum shear in their respective planes) as "equivalent stress intensities" for comparison with a uniaxial stress–strain test. Although this theory was the first to account for experimental work with equal magnitude but oppositely directed biaxial stress and equal triaxial stresses, it was found that yield seemed also to be a function of

$$S_2 - \frac{S_1 + S_3}{2} \quad \text{(when } S_1 > S_2 > S_3) \quad (3.5)$$

In a rectangular space plot against the three axes of principal stress at a point, the envelope of the flow criterion of the maximum-shear theory for an isotropic ductile material is a regular hexagonal prism whose elemental direction cosines are $1/\sqrt{3}$. This surface is not only intractable mathematically because of the discontinuities at the corners, but it is also intuitively unnatural. R. von Mises suggested replacing this prism by its circumscribed circular cylinder

$$(S_1 - S_2)^2 + (S_2 - S_3)^2$$
$$+ (S_3 - S_1)^2 = S_k^2 = \text{constant} \quad (3.6)$$

where S_k is yield shear stress in a simple uniaxial tension test. H. Hencky showed that the left hand member of this equation is directly proportional to the net energy of distortion, that is, equal to the total strain energy per unit volume existing at the stressed point, diminished by the work of dilation, all multiplied by 12 times the elastic shear modulus. The von Mises–Hencky distortion-energy theory gives the best experimental fit of any of the flow criteria, but it is more complicated for practical use than the maximum-shear theory, is less conservative, and, finally, it has not been proven applicable to material that has been damaged by creep or fatigue.

In 1930 Soderberg, in a paper [58] discussing the fundamentals on which working stresses in machine parts should be based, outlined a rational scheme for the logical interpretation and design evaluation of the interaction of steady and variable stresses. His method involves the superposition of the different possibilities to which the material is put to use using static and/or variable loadings. The resultant is used to determine the total utilization factor.

In the foregoing loading category for ductile material at normal temperature, Soderberg's proposal involved a number of principles that have reasonable experimental evidence:

1. Frequency of loading is not significant at normal temperature. Note that, when stated thus, heating effects caused by rapid cyclical inelastic or plastic strains, as well as creep damage during slow cycling at elevated temperature, are excluded.
2. The maximum-shear theory is an adequate criterion of failure for practical design.
3. Under steady stresses:
   (a) Failure is predicted by a material constant, the yield stress S_y, which can be said to be fully defined for ordinary steels.

(b) Failure is caused by the maximum shear stress and consists of unacceptably large dimensional changes stemming from permanent macroscopic shearing deformations along the surfaces of maximum shear.
   (c) Local concentrations of stress do not contribute appreciably to failure.
4. Under alternating stresses:
   (a) Failure can be predicted by a material constant, the endurance limit S_e of the material for 10^6 cycles. The constant S_e should be fully defined and measurable for practical purposes. It could be the highest completely reversed direct stress that a smooth bar of the material can endure for 10^6 cycles.
   (b) Failure is caused by the maximum alternating shear stress and consists in ruptures along surfaces of maximum shear.
   (c) Local concentrations of stress contribute to the failure.
   (d) The failure line or band of experiments in combined steady and variable stress is wholly included between the elliptical quadrant and the secant intercepting the endurance limit S_e and the ultimate tensile stress S_u in Fig. 3.2.

It has been shown since that the foregoing laws are conservative for compressive mean stress.

The general stress cycle may be interpreted as a steady component S_0 on which a variable component S_v is imposed, as shown in Fig. 3.3.

The variable stress S_v as determined by simple analysis is multiplied by the stress concentration factor k appropriate for the geometry of the region near the point in question. For the sake of simple superposition and conservative design, the failure line of Fig. 3.2 has been replaced in Fig. 3.4 by a straight line joining S_e and S_y since dimensional integrity will not admit a higher steady-stress component. The definition of factor of safety n as the ratio of stress to cause failure to the actual stress is extended to include pulsing stress, i.e.,

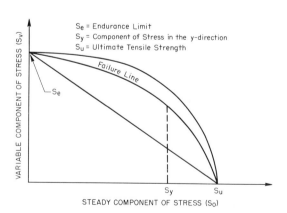

S_e = Endurance Limit
S_y = Component of Stress in the y-direction
S_u = Ultimate Tensile Strength

Failure Line

VARIABLE COMPONENT OF STRESS (S_v)

S_e

S_y S_u

STEADY COMPONENT OF STRESS (S_0)

FIG. 3.2—Experimental line of failure for combined variable and steady stress. [From C. R. Soderberg, Trans. Am. Soc. Mech. Engrs., 52 (Pt. I):20 (1930).]

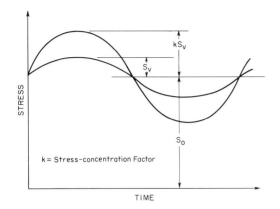

FIG. 3.3—General stress cycle for combined variable and steady stress. [From C. R. Soderberg, Trans. Am. Soc. Mech. Engrs., 52 (Pt. I):17 (1930).]

for a constant stress S_0, $n = S_y/S_0$, and, for variable stress kS_v, $n = S_e/(kS_v)$. All stress combinations on the line through the intercepts $S_v = S_e/n$ and $S_0 = S_y/n$ are characterized by the factor of safety n. In the intercept form the equation of this line is

$$1 = \frac{S_0}{S_y/n} + \frac{kS_v}{S_e/n} \tag{3.7}$$

or

$$\frac{1}{n} = \frac{S_0}{S_y} + \frac{kS_v}{S_e} = \frac{1}{n_0} + \frac{1}{n_v} \tag{3.8}$$

where $1/n$ is the total utilization fraction and $1/n_0$ and $1/n_v$ are utilization fractions of the steady and the variable components, respectively, if each is acting alone. For the general case where all three principal stresses S_1, S_2, and S_3 must be taken into account, any one of the three maximum shear planes may be the most dangerous. Assuming that it is the plane parallel to the axis of S_2, the shearing stress in this plane is

$$[S_{01} \pm k_1 S_{v1} - (S_{03} \pm k_3 S_{v3})]/2 \tag{3.9}$$

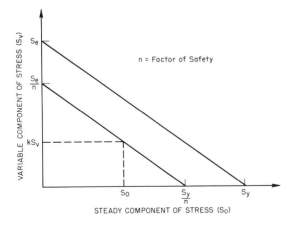

FIG. 3.4—Simplified line of failure for combined variable and steady stress. [From C. R. Soderberg, Trans. Am. Soc. Mech. Engrs., 52(Pt. I):20 (1930).]

with a constant component

$$\frac{(S_{01} - S_{03})}{2} \tag{3.10}$$

and a variable component

$$(\pm k_1 S_{v1} \pm k_3 S_{v3})/2 \tag{3.11}$$

thus the factor of utilization is

$$\frac{1}{n} = \frac{S_{01} - S_{03}}{S_y} + \frac{k_1 S_{v1} - k_3 S_{v3}}{S_e} \tag{3.12}$$

Professor Soderberg reviewed in 1956 the difficult problem of generalizing the behavior of structural materials when alternating stresses are superimposed upon a constant stress [71]. The linear superposition rule has been found consistent with experiments at moderate temperatures for alloy steels. The von Mises—Hencky theory gives reasonable correlation for crack initiation; for crack propagation the maximum stress normal to the crack has greater influence than the maximum energy of distortion or the maximum-shear theories would suggest. Reference 71 examines the implications of brittle fractures in large steel structures, such as welded ships and turbogenerator rotor forgings. E. Orowan's criterion for crack propagation (which may approach acoustic velocities in ordinarily ductile materials with low driving energy), the influence of the nil-ductility transition, the effect of time rate of strain on the ductility of steel, the embrittlement of steel by dissolved hydrogen, and creep damage at unsteady elevated-temperature loadings are noted as problems that fail to fit any unified failure theory. These are potential hazards to life and property that a designer should not ignore; intensive investigations are needed.

3.3.4 ASME BOILER AND PRESSURE VESSEL CODE

The ASME Boiler and Pressure Vessel Codes establish rules for the construction of stationary power boilers and certain other pressure vessels [72, 73]. The code stamp is generally required for such vessels by state laws and by insurance companies. However, the code does not cover deterioration resulting from radiation effects, material instability, mechanical shock, or vibration. The codes are a compilation of safety rules that place on the designer and fabricator the responsibility for considering and making provisions for such matters as deterioration of materials, concentrations of stress, cyclic thermal stresses not covered by the code, external reactions, material instability, fabrication defects, mechanical shock, and vibration [73, 74]. Service experience indicates that the vessels created under Secs. I and VIII of the code have been generally conservative for primary stresses induced by pressure loading. References 75 and 76 discuss some of the code limitations which should be considered in the design of high-temperature vessels.

Robinson [75] calls attention to the inordinate damage that may result from the uneven absorption of creep strain by the portions of a structure. The widespread necessity for matching creep strains in the adjacent members of high-temperature components is explained in Ref. 77. Hayes [76] points out that, although mechanical loading imposes a specific load on a structure so that in conventional design it is only necessary for the design engineer to be sure that the region of highest stress is strained elastically by this load, thermal strains induced as a result of the excellent heat-transfer characteristics of sodium are significantly larger than the strains resulting from mechanical loading. The differential expansion resulting from uneven heating produces displacements in a structure that can result in high strain. The designer would like to ensure that the smallest effective section is capable of absorbing the total displacement elastically. However, in the presence of notches or even in a uniform short section, the localized plastic strain can be very high. Localized plastic strain can be especially severe in liquid-metal fast reactors because of the high temperature rise of the coolant and the good thermal conductivity of the sodium boundary layer. Smooth structural members, large radii, gentle thickness transitions, and matched creep rates become important.

At temperatures above 700 to 750°F, creep becomes important. The phenomena involved in unsteady creep are entirely unlike those at work in fatigue at moderate temperature [64]. The meager evidence available now gives warning that much more must be known about the load spectrum, the exact temperatures, and the long-time behavior of the materials to achieve safe yet economical design in the future as the working temperatures are increased. Paralleling this warning, materials lose completely their accommodating ductile natures as their working temperatures fall toward the point of nil-ductility transition.

3.3.4.1 Code Interpretations for Nuclear Cases

The early nuclear code cases were annulled and their rulings were generally incorporated into consecutively numbered cases beginning with 1270 and designated by suffix N.

3.3.4.2 Section III of ASME Code [78]

Section III of the ASME Code supplants Secs. I and VIII and the Nuclear Code Cases for Class A, Class B, and Class C vessels defined in Sec. III of the Code as follows: Class A, essentially reactor vessels; Class B, essentially containment vessels with internal design pressures greater than 5 psig; and Class C, vessels previously within scope of Sec. VIII and connected to the reactor coolant system, such as heat exchangers or pump tanks.

Section III covers the following items inadequately covered in other sections: (1) nil-ductility material tests; (2) design limits for primary bending stress, local primary membrane stress, secondary stress, peak stress, and cyclic loads; (3) fatigue analysis and stress limits for bolts; (4) special stress limits, such as bearing stress, pure shear,

thermal-stress ratcheting, progressive distortion of nonintegral connections, stresses beyond yield, and triaxial stresses; (5) general design rules for stress analysis; (6) openings and their compensation; (7) penetrameters; (8) ultrasonic examination of welded joints; (9) magnetic particle testing; (10) liquid penetrant testing; (11) pressure-relief devices; (12) stress-analysis methods; (13) pressure stresses in openings; (14) experimental stress analysis; (15) basis for establishing stress intensity values; (16) nozzle configurations; (17) yield strengths for carbon and alloy steels; (18) coefficients of thermal expansion and moduli of elasticity for carbon and alloy steels, aluminum, and nickel-chrome-iron; and (19) curves of fatigue strength for some steels and nickel-chrome-iron alloy.

3.4 Analytical Techniques

3.4.1 INTRODUCTION

Section 3.3 discussed the design limits of structures (i.e., their ability to resist loadings in an operating environment that subjects them to creep, fatigue, and fracture), stress intensity, the combining of steady-state and alternating limits, cumulative loading effects, and code limits.

Section 3.4 covers analysis methods that determine whether or not the limit criteria discussed in Sec. 3.3 are being met. Several examples are discussed, particularly those predominant in reactor plant design. References are made to more-detailed information regarding analysis and formulas. References 79 and 80 contain applicable formulas and commonly used methods for structural analysis.

3.4.2 STEADY-STATE MECHANICAL LOADINGS

This section discusses stresses induced by mechanical loadings including edge loads on cylinders, bolt loading of a flange, perforated plates, pipe attachments, and bellows.

1. Edge loads on cylinders, influence coefficients: The following summarizes the effect of edge loads M_0 and H_0 uniformly distributed along the $x = 0$ edge of a long $(l > 2\pi/\beta)$ cylindrical shell (Fig. 3.5) [57].

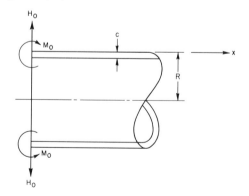

FIG. 3.5—Edge loading of cylinder.

The reciprocal attenuation length is defined as

$$\beta = \left[\frac{3(1 - \nu^2)}{a^2 c^2} \right]^{1/4} \tag{3.13}$$

and the flexural rigidity is defined as

$$D = \frac{Ec^3}{12(1 - \nu^2)} \tag{3.14}$$

The radial deflection is an exponentially decaying sinusoid:

$$\delta = \exp(-\beta x) \frac{[\beta M_0 (\sin \beta x - \cos \beta x) - H_0 \cos \beta x]}{2\beta^3 D} \tag{3.15}$$

Reference 79, p. 470, introduces the notation

$$\varphi(\beta x) = \exp(-\beta x)[(\cos \beta x + \sin \beta x)] \tag{3.16}$$

$$\Psi(\beta x) = \exp(-\beta x)[(\cos \beta x - \sin \beta x)] \tag{3.17}$$

$$\theta(\beta x) = \exp(-\beta x) \cos \beta x \tag{3.18}$$

$$\xi(\beta x) = \exp(-\beta x) \sin \beta x \tag{3.19}$$

The deflection and its derivatives can then be abbreviated

$$\delta = \frac{-[\beta M_0 \Psi + H_0 \theta]}{2\beta^3 D} \tag{3.20}$$

$$\delta' = \frac{[2\beta M_0 \theta + H_0 \varphi]}{2\beta^2 D} \tag{3.21}$$

$$\delta'' = \frac{-[2\beta M_0 \varphi + H_0 \xi]}{2\beta D} \tag{3.22}$$

$$\delta''' = \frac{[2\beta M_0 \xi - H_0 \Psi]}{D} \tag{3.23}$$

Functions of βx are tabulated in Table 3.1 for $0 \leq \beta x \leq 1.0$ from Ref. 79, where values to $\beta x = 7.0$ will be found.

Table 3.1—Functions of βx

βx	φ	Ψ	θ	ξ
0	1.0000	1.0000	1.0000	0.0000
0.1	0.9907	0.8100	0.9003	0.0903
0.2	0.9651	0.6398	0.8024	0.1627
0.3	0.9267	0.4888	0.7077	0.2189
0.4	0.8784	0.3564	0.6174	0.2610
0.5	0.8231	0.2415	0.5323	0.2908
0.6	0.7628	0.1431	0.4530	0.3099
0.7	0.6997	0.0599	0.3798	0.3185
0.8	0.6354	−0.0093	0.3131	0.3223
0.9	0.5712	−0.0657	0.2527	0.3185
1.0	0.5083	−0.1108	0.1988	0.3096

In Ref. 81 the eight coefficients of M_0 and H_0 needed to calculate the deflections and slopes at both ends of finite-length circular cylindrical shells caused by a uniformly distributed moment and/or shear applied at one end are tabulated for values of the dimensionless length $0.11 \leq \beta l \leq 7.00$ to six significant places for increments of the argument of 0.01. Equations 3.20 through 3.23 contain the four coefficients for a long cylinder.

If the continuities of deflection and slope across every cut are used in conjunction with the foregoing influence coefficients, the force, the moment, and thus the stress can be found at any axisymmetrical discontinuity of thickness, material, loading, or temperature in a cylindrical shell. Arbitrary axial temperature gradients in preliminary work can be approximated by a series of ramps with corresponding cuts in the shell.

Reference 81 gives means of calculating influence coefficients for rings (flanges) and heads and procedures for evaluating stresses at their junctions with shell.

2. Shell with conical hub and flange [82]: The ASME Power Boiler Code, Section III, Nuclear Vessels, presents rules for designing bolted-flange connections. Experience has shown that large diameters, high-temperature service, rapid temperature changes, and great dissimilarity in rigidity and mass of mating members all may make it difficult to maintain leak-tightness. References 83–88 provide details on flange design.

Figure 3.6 illustrates a shell with a conical hub and a flange bolted to a plate. The assembly is subject to an axial temperature distribution, $T(x)$. With the bolts removed, the temperature distribution would cause a calculable angular misalignment χ^* and radial misalignment δ^* between plate and flange.

If such misalignments are to be suppressed, moment and shear force reactions M and H whose magnitudes can be calculated must be developed at contacting surfaces of plate and flange. Whether or not these reactions do develop depends on the preload tension P of the bolts, which furnishes certain available moments and shear forces. If these quantities are larger than the calculated M and H, a tight joint results. If, however, the available moment drops below the required moment M, an angular gap, say γ^*, opens between plate and flange, as illustrated in Fig. 3.6. The gap, however, is not of the full magnitude χ^* since the available moment suppresses part of it and since some of the opening effort goes into extending and bending the bolt. If the available shear force is below the required H, slippage Σ^* occurs between plate and flange, as illustrated in Fig. 3.6. The slippage, however, is not of the full magnitude δ^* since the available moment suppresses part of it and since some of the displacement effort goes into bending and shearing the bolt. Dislocations (motion of flange relative to plate) are detrimental to the proper operation of the container. Dislocations may cause leaks, bolt fatigue, and even container

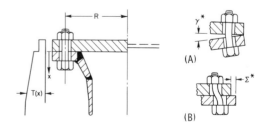

FIG. 3.6—Stress analysis of a shell with a conical hub and flange bolted to a plate. [From G. Horvay, Nucl. Eng., 1:232 (1956).]

or plate fatigue. The relative motion of plate and flange may cause, for some materials and media, fretting corrosion; in other instances the mating surfaces may seize, as is sometimes the case with stainless-steel surfaces in the presence of sodium. If such galling takes place in a grossly dislocated position (as shown in part B of Fig. 3.6), during, for example, a thermal transient, stresses of large magnitude may become locked up in the system. During subsequent normal operation of the system, the cycling of stresses of small amplitude, ordinarily regarded as harmless, may cause a fatigue failure when superimposed on the large residual stresses that are present.

The characteristics of such occurrences do not seem to be described in the literature. These have to be figured out, described, and interpreted to explain the implications of failure of this kind. There are ways of avoiding a redesign of the joint, e.g., by protecting the bolts by shear bushings, by incorporating rabbets in the mating parts, by using thermal baffling, and frequently by the simple expediency of applying greater preload to the bolts or by specifying heavier bolting. On other occasions it may be necessary to change the thermal programming of the container.

There are further problems in connection with the assembly shown in Fig. 3.6. The size of the unbolted plate is determined by its average temperature. The penetration of temperature into a slab of steel during a transient must be considered. Because of its greater heat capacity, the cover plate will come up to temperature during a start-up transient more slowly than the rest of the assembly, and during a shutdown it will return more slowly. The temperature distribution shown on the left of Fig. 3.6 is illustrative also of the start-up case. The thermal lags that develop during fast heating of the assembly cause stress problems quite similar to the one discussed earlier.

If the contemplated temperature variations of the above container are large, it may be advisable to do away with the weld at the junction of flange and conical hub and replace the section by a single forged piece, in spite of its greater expense. The weldment, frequently of higher yield strength than the parent material, introduces a discontinuity into the material properties of the structure in the region of highest stresses. This causes strain localization in the heat-affected region that adjoins the weld. The strength of a structure may thus be adversely affected by injudiciously located welds. The weld near the less exposed knuckle portion of the shell can undoubtedly be retained.

3. Perforated plates: Perforated plates with holes arranged according to an equilateral triangle pattern play an important role in heat-exchanger apparatus, and their behavior has been investigated under stretching (in-plane) loads and bending (transverse) loads in Refs. 89-100. Qualitatively it is simple enough to explain the behavior of a perforated plate. The presence of the holes renders the plate more flexible. In deformation the plate behaves like a solid plate of equal thickness but reduced stiffness. Photo-elastic photographs show that the photo-elastically determined stresses are in agreement with the theoretical predictions, even though the requirement of slow load variation, the

basic assumption of the analysis, is violated in the load-application regions.

The theory of perforated plates has been extended to two-layer plates in Ref. 90. The bar used for experimental checking had two layers of holes. The upper layer, reaching to a depth of about one-half plate thickness, had wide holes. In the lower half the holes were narrowed to about half the upper diameters. The tests confirmed the adequacy of theoretical single-layer and two-layer bending formulas.

4. Pipe attachments, bellows [82]: Pipes, by virtue of their thermal expansions and contractions, may apply very large forces or moments to a shell. Analysis is not yet sufficiently developed to account for the distorted circular opening of the shell (the intersection of two cylinders is not a plane figure, much less a circle), for the flare and taper of the pipe near the attachment, or for the local inhomogeneity and consequent strain concentrations introduced by a weld in the case of plastic loading. Model testing must still be used to a major extent [101-122].

Bellows have been considered in pipe lines to provide flexibility and thus reduce pipe reactions. Bellows of toroidal contour may be analyzed by methods of Refs. 123-125. Reference 126 predicts the performance of welded bellows with slightly arched convolutions. A computer routine is available for axisymmetric shells of arbitrary meridional shape, thickness variation, and manner of loading [127].

3.4.3 STEADY-STATE THERMAL STRESS

Following are nine examples of stresses induced by steady-state temperature effects including internal heat generation.

1. Constrained uniformly heated bar [128]: For a uniformly heated prismatical bar prevented from changing length, the axial stress is

$$S_x = -E\alpha\,\Delta T$$

2. Rectangular beam subjected to ΔT, ends fixed [128]: The stress in a constant rectangular-section beam, of vertical thickness c, maintained at $+\,\Delta T/2$ at the top face and $-\,\Delta T/2$ at the bottom face, with the ends prevented from rotating is

$$S = -\frac{E\alpha\,\Delta T}{2}\,\frac{2y}{c} \tag{3.24}$$

$$S_{\text{max.}} = -\frac{E\alpha\,\Delta T}{2} \tag{3.25}$$

where y is the variable vertical distance from the neutral axis and c is the vertical thickness of the beam.

3. Flat plate, constrained and heated to ΔT [128]: The stress in a flat plate constrained from expansion in both directions in its plane and uniformly heated to ΔT is

$$S_x = S_z = -\frac{E\alpha\,\Delta T}{1 - \nu} \tag{3.26}$$

4. Flat plate, no rotation at edges, ΔT across faces [128]: The stress in a flat plate of thickness c, maintained at $-\Delta T/2$ on one face and at $+\Delta T/2$ on other face, with the edges prevented from rotating is

$$S_x = S_z = -\frac{Ea\,\Delta T}{2(1-\nu)}\frac{2y}{c} \qquad (3.27)$$

$$S_{x\,\text{max.}} = S_{z\,\text{max.}} = -\frac{Ea\,\Delta T}{2(1-\nu)} \qquad (3.28)$$

where y is the variable distance from the neutral axis in the direction of the thickness.

5. Hollow circular cylinder, ΔT across wall [128]: In a hollow circular cylinder at steady state, with the outer surface $(r = R_2)$ held at $T = 0$ and the inner surface $(r = R_1)$ at ΔT, remote from the free end $(z = 0)$ where $z > \pi/\beta$ the compressive radial stress for ΔT positive is

$$S_r = \frac{Ea\,\Delta T}{2(1-\nu)\ln(R_2/R_1)}$$
$$-\frac{\ln(R_2/r) - R_1^2}{R_2^2 - R_1^2}\left(\frac{1 - R_2^2}{r^2}\right)\ln\left(\frac{R_2}{R_1}\right) \qquad (3.29)$$

The tangential stress is

$$S_\theta = \frac{Ea\,\Delta T}{2(1-\nu)\ln(R_2/R_1)}\left[1 - \ln\left(\frac{R_2}{r}\right)\right.$$
$$\left. -\frac{R_1^2}{R_2^2 - R_1^2}\left(1 + \frac{R_2^2}{r^2}\right)\ln\left(\frac{R_2}{R_1}\right)\right] \qquad (3.30)$$

The longitudinal stress is

$$S_z = \frac{Ea\,\Delta T}{2(1-\nu)\ln(R_2/R_1)}\left[1 - 2\ln\left(\frac{R_2}{r}\right)\right.$$
$$\left. -\frac{2R_1^2}{R_2^2 - R_1^2}\ln\left(\frac{R_2}{R_1}\right)\right] \qquad (3.31)$$

The extrema at surfaces are

$(S_\theta)_{r=R_1} = (S_z)_{r=R_1}$

$$= \frac{Ea\,\Delta T}{2(1-\nu)\ln(R_2/R_1)}\left[1 - \frac{2R_2^2}{R_2^2 - R_1^2}\ln\left(\frac{R_2}{R_1}\right)\right] \qquad (3.32)$$

$(S_\theta)_{r=R_2} = (S_z)_{r=R_2}$

$$= \frac{Ea\,\Delta T}{2(1-\nu)\ln(R_2/R_1)}\left[1 - \frac{2R_1^2}{R_2^2 - R_1^2}\ln\left(\frac{R_2}{R_1}\right)\right] \qquad (3.33)$$

If the thickness of the wall is small compared with the radius R_2, if $R_2/R_1 = 1 + m$ and $\ln(R_2/R_1) = m - (m^2/2) + (m^3/3) - \ldots$, and if m is considered a small quantity,

$$(S_\theta)_{r=R_1} = (S_z)_{r=R_1} = -\frac{Ea\,\Delta T}{2(1-\nu)}\frac{1+m}{3} \qquad (3.34)$$

$$(S_\theta)_{r=R_2} = (S_z)_{r=R_2} = \frac{Ea\,\Delta T}{2(1-\nu)}\frac{1-m}{3} \qquad (3.35)$$

At the free end $(z = 0)$, the maximum tangential stress for a thin-walled cylinder is

$$(S_\theta)_{\text{max.}} = \frac{Ea\,\Delta T}{2(1-\nu)}\left[(1-\nu^2)^{1/2}(3)^{-1/2} - \nu + 1\right] \qquad (3.36)$$

6. Hollow sphere, ΔT across wall [128]: In a hollow spherical shell, at steady state, with the outer $(r = R_2)$ surface held at $T = 0$ and the inner surface $(r = R_1)$ at ΔT, the radial stress is

$$S_r = \frac{Ea\,\Delta T\,R_1 R_2}{(1-\nu)(R_2^3 - R_1^3)}\left[R_1 + R_2\right.$$
$$\left. -\left(\frac{1}{r}\right)(R_1^2 + R_1 R_2 + R_2^2) + R_1^2 R_2^2\left(\frac{1}{r^3}\right)\right] \qquad (3.37)$$

The tangential stress is

$$S_\theta = \frac{Ea\,\Delta T\,R_1 R_2}{(1-\nu)(R_2^3 - R_1^3)}\left[R_1 + R_2\right.$$
$$\left. -\left(\frac{1}{2r}\right)(R_1^2 + R_1 R_2 + R_2^2) - R_1^2 R_2^2\left(\frac{1}{2r^3}\right)\right] \qquad (3.38)$$

At $r = R_1$:

$$S_\theta = \frac{-Ea\,\Delta T(R_1 R_2 + 2R_2^2)}{2(1-\nu)(R_1^2 + R_1 R_2 + R_2^2)} \qquad (3.39)$$

At $r = R_2$:

$$S_\theta = \frac{Ea\,\Delta T(R_1 R_2 + 2R_1^2)}{2(1-\nu)(R_1^2 + R_1 R_2 + R_2^2)} \qquad (3.40)$$

7. Long hollow cylinder, internal heat generation [129]: Given an axisymmetric internal heat generation $Q = Q_0 \exp[\mu(r - R_1)]$ in a long hollow cylinder, then, at a point remote from the ends, the resulting axial and tangential stresses are equal at both $r = R_1$ and $r = R_2$.

$$S_x = S_\theta = \frac{Ea\,Q_0\,\sigma}{(1-\nu)\mu^2 k} \qquad (3.41)$$

where Q_0 = heat produced by gamma rays in unit volume during unit time at inner (entrance) surface

μ = absorption coefficient, reciprocal of length

k = thermal conductivity
σ = dimensionless stress parameter

Case I: Inner wall surface held at T_0, outer surface insulated. Obtain σ from Fig. 3.7.

Case II: Surface temperatures maintained equal, read σ from Fig. 3.8 (see Ref. 129).

8. Thermal stresses due to internal heat generation in a rod [82, 130]: A parabolic temperature distribution $T = T_0(1 - r^2/R^2)$ may exist in a solid rod of length l with internal heat generation, where R is the radius of the rod, r is the variable radius, and T_0 is the temperature at $r = 0$. Slicing the cylinder into vertical 60° sectors (and still retaining the foregoing temperature distribution) may alleviate the thermal stresses. A rough approximation can be made of the stresses, which, guided by experience and judgment, can provide reasonable estimates in a short time.

In terms of the reference stress, $S = EaT_0/(1 - \nu)$, the cylinder stress away from the end faces reaches the maximum value $0.5S$ in both the axial direction (S_z) and the peripheral direction (S_θ). On the end faces $(z = 0,\ z = l)$, the peripheral stresses S_θ reach a magnitude of about $0.7S$. The inability of the cylinder to deform (the outer layers of the cylinder restrain the inner layers, and vice-versa, except near the end faces) is mainly responsible for the large stresses in the complete cylinder. Representative values for 347 stainless steel are $E = 28 \times 10^6$ psi, $\nu = 0.3$, $a = 10^{-5}$ in./in./°F, and a yield stress of 28,000 psi. A temperature

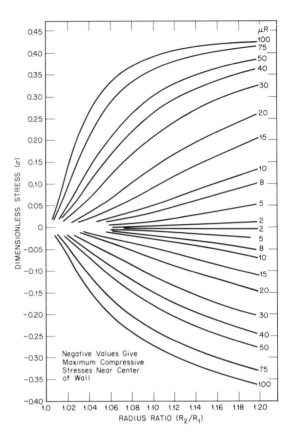

FIG. 3.8—Long hollow cylinder, internal heat generation, radius ratio of cylinder (R_2/R_1) vs. dimensionless stress, surface temperatures equal. (From G. Sonnemann and D. M. Davis, ASME Paper 57-A-256, 1957.)

rise of 140°F from surface to axis will initiate yielding.

When the cylinder is sliced into sectors, the sectors will bow with a radius of curvature $R/(1.24aT_0)$. This deformation alleviates thermal stresses. The maximum stress in the sector is about $0.24S$. The improvement in stresses obtained by slicing the cylinder into 60° sectors is about threefold.

9. Thin-wall cylinder, lower portion restrained and heated [82]: Thermal loads occur when part of a structure is heated, wants to expand, but is restrained by an adjoining structure. Such a case is illustrated in Fig. 3.9, where the lower portion of a thin-walled cylindrical container of average wall radius R is raised to temperature T from a temperature of 0°. The lower portion wants to increase its radius by $\delta = RaT$ (a, the coefficient of thermal expansion, is $10^{-5}/$°F for austenitic stainless steel), and the upper part of the shell, at temperature 0°, wants to maintain the original radius. The first effort is successful a distance about $2.5l$ below $x = 0$; the second, about $2.5l$ above $x = 0$, where $l = 0.778\sqrt{Rc}$ and the wall thickness c is small, less than $R/5$. In the in-between region, about $5l$ wide, a compromise develops since continuity in radial displacement δ and slope x must be maintained between upper and lower portions. The transition portion incurs stresses (sketched in Fig. 3.9) which

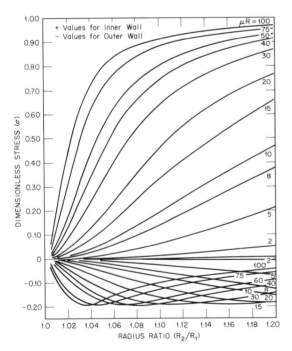

FIG. 3.7—Long hollow cylinder, internal heat generation, radius ratio (R_2/R_1) vs. dimensionless stress, outer surface insulated. (From G. Sonnemann and D. M. Davis, ASME Paper 57-A-256, 1957.)

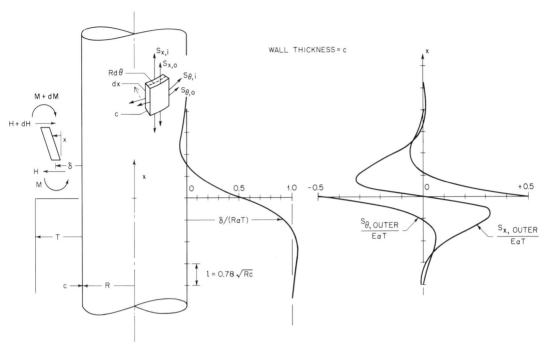

FIG. 3.9—Stress analysis of a thin-wall cylinder, lower portion restrained and heated. [From G. Horvay, Nucl. Eng., 1:231 (1956).]

may become inadmissibly severe when T is large. For brittle materials an excessive T may mean fracture under a single loading; for ductile materials the primary concern is with excessive plastic flow and cumulative fatigue damage under repeated loading. The above introduced characteristic length can be called the attenuation length because it represents the distance in which actions developing at discontinuities, such as $x = 0$, decay by a factor of e from their edge ($x = 0$) values.

If, instead of acquiring a uniform temperature T, the lower portion of the shell is subject to a linear axial temperature gradient T deg/in., then the lower portion would like to acquire a conical shape of slope equal to RaT. This conical shape again could be without stresses (linear temperature variations in a homogeneous isotropic body never cause stresses if the deformations are not suppressed) were it not for the restraint exercised by the upper shell portion. The requirement of continuity of displacement and slope between the two shell parts leads to a transition region where the slope has values intermediate to those of the slope of the lower section as it exists below $x < -2.5l$ (approximately) or the slope above level $x > 2.5l$ (approximately).

If the lower shell portion is subject to a nonlinear temperature variation, then stresses will arise not only near the juncture, owing to elimination of misalignments between upper and lower portions, but also in the entire lower portion. A nonlinear temperature distribution [one that is not of the form $(a + bx + cy + dz)$ would like to create deformations that cannot be accommodated by the volume elements $(cR \, d\theta \, dx)$, Fig. 3.9] of the shell

without interfering with the deformation of neighboring elements; it is this mutual interference which creates stresses. For very sharp temperature gradients, the hoop stress S_θ is the dominant stress; for milder temperature gradients, the meridional bending stress S_x is dominant.

3.4.4 STRESSES CAUSED BY THERMAL TRANSIENTS

A convenient method is presented here for the preliminary determination of temperature distributions and stresses in an infinite plate (or finite plate whose edges are restrained against rotation) caused by any arbitrary transient temperature change on one surface of the plate when the other surface is insulated. It is assumed that the temperature of the "washed" surface is equal to that of the coolant, i.e., the fluid film coefficient is infinite. For liquid metals, such as sodium, with a high film coefficient, this is a conservative but useful approximation. For cylinders, such as reactor vessels, where the radius of the vessel is large compared to the vessel thickness, the techniques presented are applicable.

Considerable time is required to design baffles to protect the vessel wall of liquid-metal reactors from excessive thermal stresses. These designs generally incorporate a number of steel thermal baffles of varying thickness, the intervening spaces being filled with liquid metal. Where the liquid metal in the annuli is stagnant, techniques are presented here for preliminary design.

A plate element whose edges are restrained from rotating and whose thickness is c is subjected to a ramp (temperature of washed face linear with time) temperature rise of ΔT_0 in time t at one face; the other face is perfectly insulated against heat flux. In Fig. 3.10 the temperature rise ratio $\Delta T/\Delta T_0$ is plotted against the ratio of depth x/c with the dimensionless ratio at/c^2 as the parameter (a = thermal diffusivity of wall material). The symbol x denotes distance from the insulated wall, and ΔT is the temperature rise at any x/c at the time when the heated face ($x/c = 1.0$) has just reached a rise of ΔT_0.

For a wall protected by any number of thermal baffles, providing that the intervening annuli of coolant are essentially stagnant, the entire array of baffles, coolant annuli, and wall can be treated as an equivalent solid slab, and to each annulus can be assigned an equivalent thickness obtained by multiplying its real thickness by the square root of the ratio of its thermal diffusivity to the basic thermal diffusivity of the equivalent slab. Each interface of baffles and liquid-metal annuli is then characterized by an x/c = constant vertical line in the chart.

Superimposed on the temperature-distribution network of Fig. 3.10 is a second network of curves emanating from the upper left-hand corner of the chart. These curves are labeled "stress parameter for 100% solid wall" in steps of 10% down to "10% wall" at the right; to the left, in steps of 10% down to "10% baffle" near the left edge of the chart. The

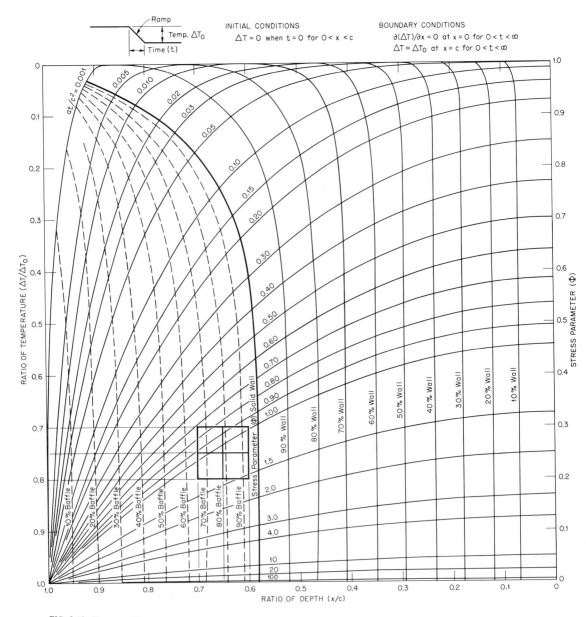

FIG. 3.10—Heat transfer and thermal stresses in an infinite slab of thickness c when subjected to any arbitrary ramp transient.

stress parameter is read at the intersection with the curve, interpolated if necessary, for the temperature distribution at the time t. This intersection is the centroid of the distribution of temperature change existing at time t in the wall (right-hand region) and in the innermost baffle (left-hand region). For elastic conditions, neglecting the temperature dependence of Young's modulus, this centroid is also the neutral layer for thermal stress; this fractional location Φ defines the thermal stress at the washed face

$$S = [EaT_0/(1 - \nu)]\Phi \qquad (3.42)$$

In the process of designing intermediate baffles, it is necessary to estimate the location of the centroid of the segment of the temperature-distribution curve lying between the baffle interfaces. Then the difference in the stress parameter at the centroid and at the face in question will determine the thermal stress. The procedure will be clearer in the following examples.

For more precise work, the computer results in tabular form are available from Atomic Power Development Associates (APDA). The tabular intervals are small enough to facilitate accurate interpolation. Data for Fig. 3.10 and the associated tables were taken from an unpublished work paper prepared by the Franklin Institute laboratories for APDA.

1. Ramp transient (100°F in 60 sec): Three-inch-thick wall of austenitic stainless steel (Fig. 3.11)

$$at/c^2 = 0.0075(60)/3^2 = 0.05$$

The temperature $T_{x/c}$ is determined from the $at/c^2 = 0.05$ curve on Fig. 3.10. The intersection of an x/c vertical line with the $at/c^2 = 0.05$ curve extended horizontal to the $\Delta T/\Delta T_0$ vertical scale will give the $\Delta T/\Delta T_0$ ratio that is to be multiplied by the ramp transient ΔT_0 to give the value of $\Delta T = T_{x/c}$ at $t = 60$ sec

$$T_{x/c} = 100°F (\Delta T/\Delta T_0)$$

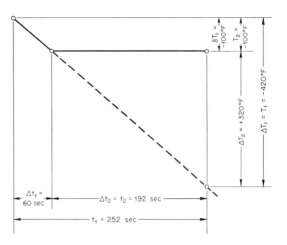

FIG. 3.12—Ramp transient followed by steady state.

The intersection of the $at/c^2 = 0.05$ line and the "stress parameter, solid wall" line gives $\Phi = 0.828$. Therefore at 60 sec stresses are

$$S = [Ea\,\Delta T/(1 - \nu)]\Phi$$

$$\approx 379(100) \begin{cases} 0.828 \\ 0.828-1.0 \end{cases} \begin{matrix} 31{,}400 \text{ psi at inner face} \\ -6{,}500 \text{ psi at outer face} \end{matrix} \qquad (3.43)$$

2. Same as 1 with inner-face temperature constant after 60 sec: If the inner-face temperature thereafter remains constant, what are the temperature and the stress 252 sec from the start of transient? (See Fig. 3.12.) This is solved as the difference between the initial ramp, which is overridden at $t = 60$ sec, and the second, and overriding, ramp which is equal rate but opposite sense. Table 3.2 tabulates parameters and presents results.

3. Three-inch slab, 100°F drop in 60 sec and 160°F rise in next 192 sec (Figs. 3.13 and 3.14): Table 3.3 lists parameters and results. From

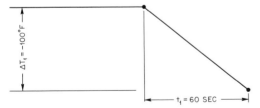

FIG. 3.11—Ramp transient.

Table 3.3—Ramp Transient Followed by Temperature Rise

Interval	t_i, sec	T_i, °F	at_i/c^2	Φ	$T_{x/c}$ for x/c 1.0	0.5	0
t_1	252	-420	0.21	0.655	-420	-104	-34
t_2	192	$+480$	0.16	0.700	$+480$	$+92$	$+21$
					$+60$	-12	-13

$$S = 379[420(0.655) - 480(0.700)] = 24{,}600 \text{ psi}$$

Table 3.2—Ramp Transient Followed by Steady State

Interval	t_i, sec	ΔT_i, °F	at_i/c^2	Φ	$\Delta T/\Delta T_0$ for x/c 1.0	0.5	0	$T_{x/c}$ for x/c 1.0	0.5	0
t_1	252	-420	0.21	0.655	1.0	0.248	0.080	-420	-104	-34
t_2	192	$+320$	0.16	0.700	1.0	0.192	0.032	$+320$	$+61$	$+14$
								$-100°F$	$-43°F$	$-20°F$

$$S = [E\alpha/(1 - \nu)][\Delta T_1\Phi_1 - \Delta T_2\Phi_2]$$

$$= 379[420(0.655) - 320(0.700)] = 379(51) = 19{,}300 \text{ psi}$$

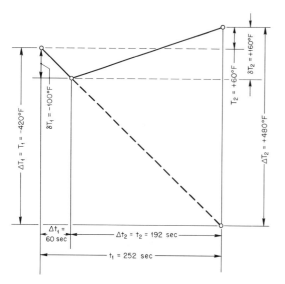

FIG. 3.13—Ramp transient followed by temperature rise.

Fig. 3.10, Table 3.4 has been evaluated to show the effect plate thickness has on induced stresses.

Table 3.4—Effect of Plate Thickness on Stresses Induced by Thermal Transients

Rate of transient, °F/sec	Plate thickness (c), in.	Ratio of thermal stress in plate thickness to thermal stress in 2-in. plate
100	2	1.000
	1	0.942
	0.5	0.816
	0.25	0.585
50	2	1.000
	1	0.915
	0.5	0.746
10	4	1.107
	2	1.000

Note that example 3 is solved in the same way as example 2. Any broken-line approximation of an arbitrary transient heating can be handled as a series of ramps, each superimposed on those preceding it at its particular starting time (see Fig. 3.15, which illustrates example 4). The ith

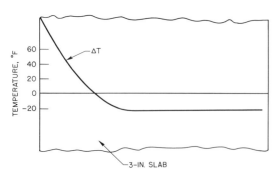

FIG. 3.14—Temperature distribution through slab subject to ramp transient.

segment of the heat pulse is characterized by a duration Δt_i during which the surface temperature changes by δT_i at a rate $\delta T_i / \Delta t_i$. The ith ramp corresponding to this segment begins at time

$$t = \sum_{j=1}^{i-1} \Delta t_j \qquad (3.44)$$

The total time from the beginning of the transient to the time at which the temperature distribution and stress are desired at the end of the nth ramp is

$$t_1 = \sum_{j=1}^{n} \Delta t_j \qquad (3.45)$$

The duration of influence of ith ramp is the interval

$$t_i = \sum_{j=i}^{n} \Delta t_j \qquad (3.46)$$

where the temperature distribution and stress are desired at the end of the nth ramp.

The starting temperature for the ith ramp is the algebraic sum $\sum_{j=1}^{i-1} \delta T_j$, and the projected temperature prediction during the ith segment becomes

$$T_i = t_i \frac{\delta T_i}{\Delta t_i} + \sum_{j=1}^{i-1} \delta T_j \qquad (3.47)$$

For a tabular calculation, as in example 4, numerical integration of time increments Δt_j starting at t_1 and proceeding backward in time (toward left) gives t_i directly, as in Table 3.5.

The "strength" of the ith ramp pulse at the disturbed surface, for calculating its contribution to temperature and stress, is $\Delta T_i = T_i - T_{i-1}$, where $T_0 = 0$ (see Fig. 3.15). Thus at t_1 the stress would be

$$S = \frac{Ea}{1 - \nu} \sum_{1}^{n} (\Delta T_i \, \Phi_i) \qquad (3.48)$$

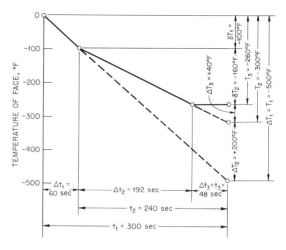

FIG. 3.15—Two ramp transients followed by steady state.

Table 3.5—Two Ramp Transients, Followed by Steady State

	Interval			
	t_1	t_2	t_3	
Temperature change (δT_i) during ith ramp, °F	−100	−160	0	
Duration of the ith ramp (Δt_i), sec	60	192	48	
Duration of influence of the ith ramp $\left(t_i = \sum_1^n \Delta t_j\right)$, sec	300	240	48	
at_i/c^2	0.25	0.20	0.04	
Temperature at start of ith ramp $\left(\sum_1^{i-1} \delta T_j\right)$, °F	0	−100	−260	
Rate of ith ramp ($\delta T_i/\Delta t_i$), °F/sec	−1.66	−0.833	0	
$t_i\,\delta T_i/\Delta t_i$, °F	−500	−200	0	
Projected temperature (T_i), °F	−500	−300	−260	
Strength of the ith ramp (ΔT_i), °F	−500	+200	+40	
Stress function (Φ)	0.625	0.663	0.848	$E\alpha/(1-\nu) = 379$
$\Phi\,\Delta T_i$	−312	+133	+34	$\sum \Phi\,\Delta T_i = 145$
$\Delta T_x/\Delta T_{x=c}$ $x/c = 1.0$	1.0	1.0	1.0	Stress* $= 55,000$ psi
$x/c = 0.5$	0.288	0.239	0.023	
$x/c = 0$	0.112	0.072	0	
				Net temperature[†]
$\left(\dfrac{\Delta T_x}{\Delta T_{x=c}}\right)\Delta T_i$ $x/c = 1.0$	−500	+200	+40	−260°F
$x/c = 0.5$	−144	+48	+1	−95°F
$x/c = 0$	−56	+14	0	−42°F

* At face of wall.

[†] Indicates that at the washed face the total transient is −260°F as indicated by the boundary conditions; −95°F at 1.5 in. at the end of 300 sec; −42°F at the insulated face at the end of 300 sec.

and the temperature at x/c for time t_1 would be

$$T_{x/c} = \sum_1^n \left(\frac{\Delta T_x}{\Delta T_{x=c}}\,\Delta T_i\right) \qquad (3.49)$$

4. Three-inch slab; 100°F drop in first 60 sec; 160°F drop in next 192 sec; constant for next 48 sec (Fig. 3.15): Results are presented in Table 3.5.

5. Stainless-steel bare and baffled wall + 300°F in 20 sec; constant thereafter: (a) Bare wall 1.5 in. thick. (b) Wall 1.5 in. thick with 1.0-in. baffle (60% wall, 40% baffle). (c) Wall 1.5 in. thick with multiple baffles totaling 1 in. = 40%, but first baffle 0.25 in. thick. Results are shown in Fig. 3.16 and Table 3.6.

6. Thermal transient, end problems [82, 97, 98]: Consider a long thin metal strip with one of the short edges attached to a very rigid, large mass of material. The heavy ring with thin spokes illustrated in Fig. 3.17 may be regarded as representative of such a structure. Suppose the surface temperature of the assembly, originally zero, is suddenly lowered (shocked) T degrees, such as would occur if the assembly were suddenly dumped into a large fluid bath at $-T$ temperature. The thin strip would acquire the temperature $-T$ almost instantaneously, but the thick mass would still be essentially at 0°. The strip height would shrink by $2c\alpha T$ through most of the length of the strip. On the other hand, the rigid connection between strip and mass prevents the edge $B'B$ of the strip from deforming; a short transition region connects the two portions, as illustrated in the figure. One can demonstrate that complete restraint of edge $B'B$ causes, according to elastic theory, infinite stresses at the corners B and B' (see the curve in Fig. 3.17).

Such problems as the stress determination of the structure in Fig. 3.17 are highly idealized prototypes of a large variety of practical occurrences; so their solutions should be of great practical value. Nevertheless there is no solution

Table 3.6—Effect of Thermal Baffling on Wall Stresses

Elapsed time (t_1), sec	$\Delta T_1 = T_1$, °F	ΔT_2, °F	Bare wall 1½ in. thick		Wall 1½ in. thick baffled by plates totaling 1 in.			
			at/c^2	Φ	at/c^2	Φ for 60% wall	Φ for 40% solid baffle	Φ for 10% 1st baffle
10	150		0.0333	0.861	0.012	0.000	0.790	0.387
20	300		0.0667	0.803	0.024	0.016	0.708	0.300
30	450	− 150	0.1	0.761	0.036	0.039	0.654	0.255
40	600	− 300	0.1333	0.725	0.048	0.063	0.605	0.226
60	900	− 600	0.2000	0.663	0.072	0.096	0.540	0.190
80	1200	− 900	0.2667	0.611	0.096	0.125	0.498	0.164
100	1500	− 1200	0.3333	0.568	0.120	0.149	0.466	0.148
120	1800	− 1500	0.4	0.526	0.144	0.161	0.446	0.133
140	2100	− 1800	0.4667	0.492	0.168	0.165	0.413	0.125

At 10 sec (ΔT_1 only)

$$S = [E\alpha/(1-\nu)]\Delta T\, \Phi = 379\,(150) \begin{pmatrix} 0.861 \\ 0.000 \\ 0.790 \\ 0.387 \end{pmatrix} = 379 \begin{pmatrix} 129 \\ 0 \\ 119 \\ 58 \end{pmatrix} = \begin{matrix} 48{,}900 \text{ psi bare} \\ 0 \text{ psi baffled} \\ 45{,}100 \text{ psi } 40\% \text{ baffle} \\ 22{,}000 \text{ psi } 10\% \text{ baffle} \end{matrix}$$

At 20 sec (ΔT_1 only)

$$S = 379\,(300) \begin{pmatrix} 0.803 \\ 0.016 \\ 0.708 \\ 0.300 \end{pmatrix} = 379 \begin{pmatrix} 241 \\ 5 \\ 212 \\ 90 \end{pmatrix} = \begin{matrix} 91{,}000 \text{ psi bare wall} \\ 1{,}900 \text{ psi baffled wall} \\ 80{,}300 \text{ psi } 40\% \text{ baffle} \\ 34{,}100 \text{ psi } 10\% \text{ baffle} \end{matrix}$$

At 30 sec the "second ramp" has been acting and $S = [E\alpha/(1-\nu)](\Delta T_1\,\Phi_1 + \Delta T_2\,\Phi_2)$

$$S = 379 \left[450 \begin{pmatrix} 0.761 \\ 0.039 \\ 0.654 \\ 0.255 \end{pmatrix} - 150 \begin{pmatrix} 0.861 \\ 0.000 \\ 0.790 \\ 0.387 \end{pmatrix} \right] = 379 \left[\begin{pmatrix} 342 \\ 18 \\ 294 \\ 115 \end{pmatrix} - \begin{pmatrix} 129 \\ 0 \\ 119 \\ 58 \end{pmatrix} \right] = \begin{matrix} 84{,}500 \text{ psi bare wall} \\ 6{,}800 \text{ psi baffled} \\ 66{,}400 \text{ psi } 40\% \text{ baffle} \\ 21{,}600 \text{ psi } 10\% \text{ baffle} \end{matrix}$$

At 40 sec

$$S = 379 \left[600 \begin{pmatrix} 0.725 \\ 0.063 \\ 0.605 \\ 0.226 \end{pmatrix} - 300 \begin{pmatrix} 0.803 \\ 0.016 \\ 0.708 \\ 0.300 \end{pmatrix} \right] = 379 \left[\begin{pmatrix} 435 \\ 38 \\ 363 \\ 136 \end{pmatrix} - \begin{pmatrix} 241 \\ 5 \\ 212 \\ 90 \end{pmatrix} \right] = \begin{matrix} 73{,}600 \text{ psi} \\ 12{,}500 \text{ psi} \\ 57{,}200 \text{ psi} \\ 17{,}400 \text{ psi} \end{matrix}$$

At 60 sec

$$S = 379 \left[900 \begin{pmatrix} 0.663 \\ 0.096 \\ 0.540 \\ 0.190 \end{pmatrix} - 600 \begin{pmatrix} 0.725 \\ 0.063 \\ 0.605 \\ 0.226 \end{pmatrix} \right] = 379 \left[\begin{pmatrix} 596 \\ 86 \\ 486 \\ 171 \end{pmatrix} - \begin{pmatrix} 435 \\ 38 \\ 363 \\ 136 \end{pmatrix} \right] = \begin{matrix} 61{,}000 \text{ psi} \\ 18{,}200 \text{ psi} \\ 46{,}500 \text{ psi} \\ 13{,}300 \text{ psi} \end{matrix}$$

At 80 sec

$$S = 379 \left[1200 \begin{pmatrix} 0.611 \\ 0.125 \\ 0.498 \\ 0.164 \end{pmatrix} - 900 \begin{pmatrix} 0.663 \\ 0.096 \\ 0.540 \\ 0.190 \end{pmatrix} \right] = 379 \left[\begin{pmatrix} 733 \\ 150 \\ 598 \\ 197 \end{pmatrix} - \begin{pmatrix} 596 \\ 86 \\ 486 \\ 171 \end{pmatrix} \right] = \begin{matrix} 51{,}900 \text{ psi} \\ 24{,}000 \text{ psi} \\ 42{,}800 \text{ psi} \\ 9{,}900 \text{ psi} \end{matrix}$$

At 100 sec

$$S = 379 \left[1500 \begin{pmatrix} 0.568 \\ 0.149 \\ 0.466 \\ 0.148 \end{pmatrix} - 1200 \begin{pmatrix} 0.611 \\ 0.125 \\ 0.498 \\ 0.164 \end{pmatrix} \right] = 379 \left[\begin{pmatrix} 853 \\ 224 \\ 700 \\ 222 \end{pmatrix} - \begin{pmatrix} 733 \\ 150 \\ 598 \\ 197 \end{pmatrix} \right] = \begin{matrix} 45{,}500 \text{ psi} \\ 28{,}100 \text{ psi} \\ 38{,}700 \text{ psi} \\ 9{,}500 \text{ psi} \end{matrix}$$

At 120 sec

$$S = 379 \left[1800 \begin{pmatrix} 0.526 \\ 0.161 \\ 0.446 \\ 0.133 \end{pmatrix} - 1500 \begin{pmatrix} 0.568 \\ 0.149 \\ 0.466 \\ 0.148 \end{pmatrix} \right] = 379 \left[\begin{pmatrix} 948 \\ 290 \\ 804 \\ 240 \end{pmatrix} - \begin{pmatrix} 853 \\ 224 \\ 700 \\ 222 \end{pmatrix} \right] = \begin{matrix} 36{,}000 \text{ psi} \\ 25{,}000 \text{ psi} \\ 39{,}400 \text{ psi} \\ 6{,}800 \text{ psi} \end{matrix}$$

At 140 sec

$$S = 379 \left[2100 \begin{pmatrix} 0.492 \\ 0.165 \\ 0.413 \\ 0.125 \end{pmatrix} - 1800 \begin{pmatrix} 0.526 \\ 0.161 \\ 0.446 \\ 0.133 \end{pmatrix} \right] = 379 \left[\begin{pmatrix} 1034 \\ 347 \\ 870 \\ 263 \end{pmatrix} - \begin{pmatrix} 948 \\ 290 \\ 804 \\ 240 \end{pmatrix} \right] = \begin{matrix} 32{,}600 \text{ psi} \\ 21{,}600 \text{ psi} \\ 25{,}000 \text{ psi} \\ 8{,}700 \text{ psi} \end{matrix}$$

available for these problems in the literature. They belong to a class of problems that may be referred to as "end problems," where the strip is not subjected to tractions anywhere, except along the short edge $B'B$. Here, however, the normal and shear tractions that act (and are of unknown magnitudes in the example of Fig. 3.17) form a self-equilibrating system, i.e., have no force and moment resultant. Such a system of stresses has only very localized effects, as predicted by St. Venant in 1855 and demonstrated approximately in Ref. 131. The stresses will be barely noticeable at a distance $x = 2c$ (approximately) from the vertical edge. Nevertheless, their high intensity in the vicinity of

$B'B$ may cause fracture if the piece is brittle or plastic strain and fatigue damage if the piece is ductile. A simple problem of this type is solved in Ref. 132. Solutions developed constitute merely a first step toward answering the many important questions that relate to a more realistic formulation of this class of problems, where the connection between strip and mass (as it concerns Fig. 3.17) is not infinitely rigid but merely very rigid and where, in the region of large stresses, plastic flow may take place. How many shocks of magnitude T can specified engineering materials sustain before cracking when they are supported, say, in semi-rigid fashion, as are the strips in Fig. 3.17? To

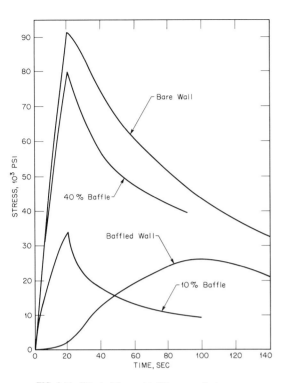

FIG. 3.16—Effect of thermal baffling on wall stresses.

what extent do fillets reduce the stresses in the corner? How is behavior affected by a weld nearby? Some are obviously tasks for the experimenter. All of them are of great concern because obviously solutions have to be provided or remedies offered for problems of similar nature day after day.

One of the current problems of particular concern is the problem of thermal shocking of holes. In contrast to the problems of Fig. 3.17, this one does not give rise to infinite stresses (not even in theory); so a purely elastic analysis is adequate for its treatment when the shocks are moderate. The surfaces are suddenly chilled by some liquid into which the plate is dumped from zero, say, to a temperature $-T$. Two cases are of interest:

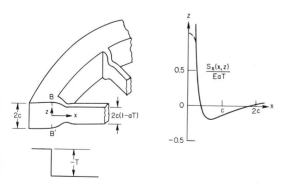

FIG. 3.17—Thermal transient end problem, heavy ring with thin spokes. [From G. Horvay, Nucl. Eng., 1:233 (1956).]

(1) the hole is plugged so that the internal surface of the hole is not subjected to a chill and (2) the hole surface is also exposed to the liquid. When chilled, the surface of the plate wants to contract, but the hot subsurface material keeps it extended; thus surface layers incur uniform biaxial tensile stresses

$$S_r = S_\theta = EaT/(1 - \nu) \qquad (3.50)$$

at some distance from the hole. The disturbance created by the presence of the hole increases the stresses in the vicinity of the hole to a maximum value of $EaT\ k(z)/(1 - \nu)$. What is the value of the concentration factor $k(z)$ when the stresses are elastic? What are the strains when part of the material in the vicinity of the hole incurs plastic flow? (Note: ν also varies in this case.) To what extent can the stress or strain concentration factors be reduced by suitable chamfering of the holes? Again, some of these questions may be treated analytically, some experimentally, still others both ways; but they all contain information that must be ferreted out to avoid excessive conservatism in design.

3.5 Experimental Techniques

3.5.1 INTRODUCTION

Examples of structural analysis and references to more comprehensive methods of analysis were given in Sec. 3.4. Analysis using applicable theories of elasticity and plasticity may solve many problems, but the state of the art is still quite empirical in many instances (pipe attachments, pipeline elbows, extent of stress reduction by corner fillets, rapid thermal shocks particularly of holes, fatigue correlation of intermittent creep to determine life, to name a few), and experimentation of different types is necessary (1) to complement analysis when loadings are not known exactly, (2) when the problem cannot be solved theoretically, (3) to establish a relation between theory and experiment, and (4) to build up a theory based on experimentation. Theory and experiment are supplementary.

The proof of adequacy of a structure is satisfactory performance in service. Adherence to established design codes and required strength tests give a high degree of confidence in relatively standard structures. The demands made on reactor vessels and system components, particularly in fast reactors, may differ from those made on conventional system components. The environment, operating procedures, and fuel-handling requirements of fast reactor systems result in more severe conditions than those for conventional plants. The consequences of reactor plant failure may be more severe. Therefore experimental testing of completed components or of scale models is extremely relevant.

3.5.2 STRUCTURAL TESTS OF REACTOR-SYSTEM COMPONENTS

Structural tests fall into three general categories:

1. Tests of full-scale plant components. These are proof tests to determine structural adequacy and the margin of safety.

2. Tests of prototypes or models to check the design and to determine how it can be improved.

3. Tests of structural features, such as penetrations and appendages. These produce general design information for possible adoption by codes or design standards after sufficient data have been evaluated and after subsequent successful service experience.

Few of the many tests of full-scale plant components (category 1) are reported in the literature because of the limited interest in them and their routine nature. Reference 133 describes strain-gauge and brittle lacquer tests of some British gas-cooled reactors. Strain-gauge tests of the Pressurized Water Reactor (PWR) vessel are described in Ref. 134. A brief summary of the results of a strain-gauge test of the Fermi vessel is given in Ref. 135. Early development of strain gauges and their use in testing pressure vessels is reported in Refs. 101 and 136 to 138.

Few category 2 tests appear in the literature, probably because each test applies to a very narrow and specific situation. The variety of problems and the various experimental techniques are illustrated in Refs. 139-144.

Because of their general interest, many tests of the category 3 tests are reported in the literature. They are characterized by precision and detail and employ proven test techniques and procedures. Several examples are given in Refs. 102 and 142 to 144. Much of the work in the three categories is sponsored by governmental agencies or technical societies, such as the Pressure Vessel Research Committee (PVRC) of the Welding Research Council; (Refs. 103 and 145 to 147 are examples).

3.5.3 TECHNIQUES FOR STRAIN MEASUREMENTS

The literature is replete with strain-measuring techniques and their applications. The Proceedings of the Society for Experimental Stress Analysis is the best source of up-to-date information. The Handbook of Experimental Stress Analysis [148] is also an excellent source. The experimental techniques that are currently most useful for strain measurements utilize photoelasticity, electrical-resistance strain gauges, and brittle coatings [149-151].

Each technique has its particular advantages and limitations. Photoelastic analysis is the only technique that can give internal stresses. It gives the peak stresses, i.e., the stress at a point rather than an average. It requires a model made from double-refracting material and is slow, involved, and costly, especially if the model is three-dimensional.

Electrical-resistance strain gauges can be used on models or on the actual structures. Only surface-strain components in the direction of the gauge filaments and averaged over their length are obtained. The technique is highly developed, reliable, and accurate into the range of 500 to 600°F. The gauges are relatively cheap and are easily and quickly installed.

Brittle coatings can be applied to models and to actual structures. The points of maximum surface strain, the directions of the principal strains, and, under favorable conditions, the approximate magnitudes of principal strains can be obtained. Rather narrow environmental conditions, such as temperature, must be maintained throughout a test. This technique is useful for determining the overall strain pattern; it can be followed by a strain-gauge test to obtain accurate magnitudes.

3.5.3.1 Photoelasticity

Photoelastic analysis is especially useful in obtaining detailed and accurate stress distributions throughout geometrically involved structural components. Extended treatment of the photoelastic method is presented in Ref. 152. Principles and methods of photoelastic analysis are discussed in Ref. 153. Chapter 17 of Ref. 148 discusses the theory and applications of both two- and three-dimensional photoelasticity and contains an extensive bibliography. Reference 149 has more details. Recent information on three-dimensional techniques will be found in Refs. 154 to 156. Specific applications to nuclear reactor components are given in Refs. 139 and 140.

Photostress is a related technique that has been developed recently. It holds some promise as a practical tool for experimental stress analysis [157-159]. A thin coating of special double-refracting plastic is cemented to the structure. A reflecting polariscope is used to determine the stresses. The method can be applied to actual structures and can provide a complete survey of its surface stresses.

3.5.3.2 Strain Gauges

Bonded electrical-resistance strain gauges are today the most widely used strain-measuring tools because they are the most convenivent and are available in great variety. The gauge elements are generally grids of wire approximately 0.001 in. in diameter or foil approximately 0.0001 in. thick. The elements come in lengths as small as 1/64 in. and are made of various alloys, such as constantan, nichrome, and Karma, the particular alloy depending on the application. Their resistance generally ranges between 50 and 1000 ohms. Several cements are available for gauge installation, including a pressure-sensitive cement which makes possible almost immediate use of installed gauges.

Although the strain gauge dates from about 1940, the fundamental principle, changes in electrical resistance accompany changes in strain, was stated over 100 years ago. The ratio of the unit resistance change to the strain change is known as the strain sensitivity or gauge factor. The factor for gauges on the market varies from about − 5.3 to 3.5.

Strain-gauge lead wires, circuitry, and instrumentation are also important in determining the accuracy of the strain measurements. References 148, 150, and 160 contain detailed information on strain gauges and their circuitry. The Proceedings of the Society for Experimental Stress Analysis and Strain Gauge Readings [161] are the best sources of information on current practice. Strain gauges are widely used as the sensing elements of transducers, such as pressure pickups, accelerometers, and force and torque dynamometers.

3.5.3.3 *High-temperature Strain Gauges*

As yet no commercially available strain gauge has been used successfully to measure static strains at temperatures on the order of 1000°F. Some of the efforts up to 1950 are described in Refs. 162 to 166. The state of the art in 1957 is set forth in Ref. 167. In the last few years interest in high-temperature strain gauges has been greatly spurred by the demands of space and nuclear technology. The National Bureau of Standards has undertaken the testing of selected strain gauges as they become commercially available [168]. Development of strain gauges for high-temperature static strain measurements continues. Some recent field installations are described in Refs. 134, 169, and 170.

High temperature in reference to strain gauges generally means temperatures in excess of 500°F. Above 500°F ceramic cements must be used. These are subject to bond failure because of differences in the coefficients of expansion of the cement and the structure. Ceramic cements are brittle and rather sensitive to thermal shock. Their electrical resistance becomes very low as temperatures are raised above 1000°F. Field installation is difficult and is in most cases impractical [134, 169]. One solution to the problem is to use premounted, precured, and precycled weldable strain gauges [170].

The most serious problems in the use of strain gauges at high temperatures are metallurgical in nature, e.g., the change of resistance of the gauge sensing element with temperature and time. One problem involves the temperature coefficient of resistance, which is the relative change in resistance per unit change in temperature. This coefficient changes with changes in temperature and produces changes in strain-gauge output. These changes are usually referred to as apparent strains. They can be large enough to completely mask the strains to be measured. Another problem is the result of the instability of the sensing elements at elevated temperatures, which results in a seemingly never-ending resistance change. A third problem is the metallurgical phase change which the sensing element alloy undergoes. For Nichrome this occurs around 1000°F and for Karma around 900°F. Some control over these variables has been achieved by varying the trace elements in the composition of these alloys by heat treatment and by cold working. To date only limited success has been attained. Other problems include changes in the temperature coefficient and in the gauge factor with changes in temperature. Attempts to eliminate these problems by using an unstrained compensating gauge in the bridge circuit have met with some success [134, 169, 170].

The lead wires present a problem. Thermocouple effect, lead-wire instability, lead-wire temperature coefficient, and desensitizing of the strain gauge by the external lead-wire resistance are some of the items to be considered.

Detailed information on high-temperature strain-gauge behavior is given in Refs. 167, 168, 171, and 172. Strain measurement in intense radiation fields is discussed in Ref. 173.

3.5.3.4 *Brittle Coatings*

An overall picture of the state of strain at the surface of any structure can be obtained by the brittle-coating technique. The coating known by the trade name Stresscoat is used extensively. Its properties and use are described in detail in Chap. 14 of Ref. 148, in Chap. 13 of Ref. 150 and in Refs. 151 and 174 to 178. Practical examples of the application of this technique to pressure vessels are given in Refs. 133, 141, and 142. The extension of the brittle-coating technique to temperatures up to 600°F is given in Refs. 167 and 179.

3.6 Computer Techniques

3.6.1 INTRODUCTION

The solution of many complex equations in structural analysis can be expedited by means of high-speed computers. Some computer techniques and their uses in determining stresses and deflections in reactor vessels and other structural components for both mechanical- and thermal-loading conditions are covered in this section for only the more generalized type of shell structures and piping systems. References are made to other more detailed information regarding numerical analysis and methods of solving these problems on computers.

3.6.2 COMPUTERS AND COMPUTER PROGRAMMING

The digital computer is used to obtain numerical solutions to finite problems. Since the computer can only add, subtract, multiply, divide, and compare, it is necessary to break the problem down into a series of arithmetical solutions that are properly interconnected to obtain a finite answer. The methods discussed here are for use in digital computers. Information on specific machines is available from the manufacturers of the equipment.

Methods of standard programming, such as Fortran (developed by International Business Machines Corp.), permit the use of symbolic notation rather than the absolute code of the computer and are widely used.

3.6.3 GENERAL SOLUTION OF SHELL TYPE STRUCTURES

Of most concern in shell type structures are membrane stresses and discontinuity stresses. The membrane stresses are usually quite simple to calculate. The calculations should satisfy the conditions and rules established in the ASME Boiler and Pressure Vessel Code. The discontinuity stresses and stresses caused by concentrated loads should be determined by either analytical or experimental methods. Stresses and loads on flanges and reinforcing rings and changes in shell thickness and cross section should be determined in this manner. High-speed digital computers can be used to produce results in a minimum of time.

The first step is to break the problem down into simple mathematical statements that can be solved numerically. Since most reactor vessels are shells having a form or a surface of revolution and since the shells are loaded more or less symmetrically with respect to their axes, the general solution of stresses and deflections can be solved with numerical methods based on the "theory of beams on an elastic foundation" [180]. This theory is applicable to any shell configuration where the shape of the meridian and the thickness of the shell can be specified analytically with a continuous function of a single scalar parameter, such as a cylinder, a cone, a sphere, and an ellipsoid. It is assumed that the beam is a meridional element of the shell and that the modulus of the elastic foundation is represented by the resilience of the hoop elements in the shell.

As a simplified example of the theory, consider a thin-walled cylindrical tube subjected to radial forces uniformly distributed along an arbitrary circle on the tube, Fig. 3.18. Because of the symmetry of the loading, every section normal to the tube axis will remain circular, and the radius R will change by $\Delta R = y$. This change in radius varies longitudinally away from the applied load and produces bending stresses in the longitudinal elements. The symmetry of the system requires that only one longitudinal element be considered. This element acts as a beam.

The radial displacement is accompanied by a circumferential compression of the tube equal to y/R, which, in turn, results in a compressive hoop stress $S_\theta = Ecy/R$ where E is the modulus of elasticity, c is the wall thickness, and R is the mean radius of cylinder. The resultant will have a radial direction with the value $P = S_\theta/R = Ecy/R^2$. Since the force P is proportional to the displacement, Ec/R^2, the proportionality factor is the spring rate or foundation modulus k of the shell.

For loads applied normal to the beam and/or meridional bending moments, displacements of the beam can be obtained by solving the general elastic line equation for the particular shell configuration. The slope, internal moment, and shearing force in the beam at any particular distance x from the applied load are determined by taking the consecutive derivatives of the elastic line equations and equating them to the proper constants of integration. Solutions to these equations as well as to equations for specific loading conditions for the more common shell configurations are given in Ref. 180.

Most vessels are analyzed by parts because of the continuous function requirement in deriving the elastic line equations. The usual procedure is to assume sections of the vessel with a continuous meridian as free bodies and to analyze each of these separately using the proper boundary conditions. The boundary conditions are applied shear forces, meridional bending moments, and axial loads at the ends of the free bodies that will satisfy the static equilibrium of the whole. There is only one set of reactions that will produce displacements at the junction of the free bodies such that compatibility is not disturbed. The end reactions, i.e., forces and moments applied to the adjacent free-body edges, are internal to the structure and are equal in magnitude and opposite in direction to the adjacent free body.

A nondimensional pressure vessel, Fig. 3.19, shows a general breakdown of this vessel into free bodies with the resulting redundant continuity forces. The primary loading considered in the diagram is internal pressure.

The elastic line is approximately sinusoidal in nature with a rapidly increasing amplitude; therefore the effect of the boundary conditions is local. The effective length of these conditions should be determined to limit the investigation to a realistic dimension. The flexural rigidity of the beam and the elasticity of the supporting medium are important factors influencing the shape of the elastic line. The characteristic of the system [180] is usually referred to by $\lambda = 4\sqrt{k/(4EI)}$ where k is the foundation modulus, E is the modulus of elasticity, and I is the moment of inertia. Since the dimension of the characteristic is the reciprocal of length, the term $1/\lambda$ is frequently referred to as the characteristic length, consequently, λx will be an absolute number. As may be seen from the table of constants of integration in Ref. 180, when $(\lambda x) > 1.5\pi$, the value of any of the four functions is under 0.01. This means that the applied loads have negligible effect on the beam in a distance of $x > 1.5\pi/\lambda$ from the point of application of the load. The characteristic length is also applicable to other loading conditions as long as they are radial forces or meridional bending moments uniformly distributed along an arbitrary circle on the shell.

Since the displacement, change in slope, and internal meridional moments and shear loads are proportional to the applied loads, the principle of superposition and the reciprocity theorem are directly applicable to the beams on an elastic foundation principle. It is then possible to include the effects of reinforcing rings, flanges, and/or the effects of differential temperatures in the

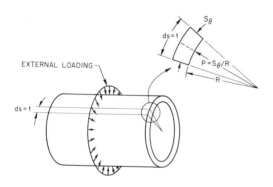

FIG. 3.18—Diagram of beam and foundation of a cylinder. (From M. Hetenyi, Beams on Elastic Foundation, p. 30, University of Michigan Press, 1955, copyrighted 1946.)

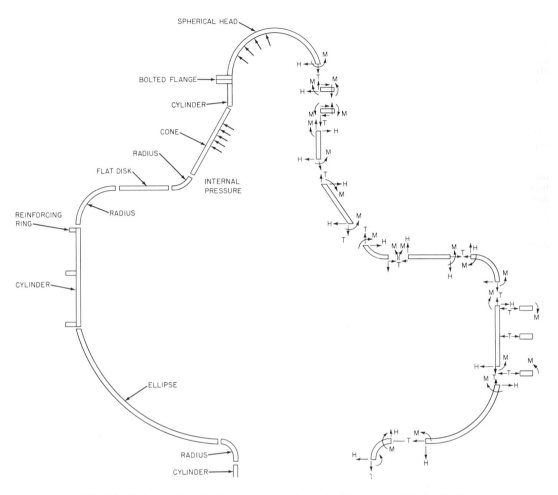

FIG. 3.19—Random nondimensional pressure vessel, showing breakdown of vessel into free bodies.

computer program with a minimum of effort. The effect of axial loads on a vessel is predominant at flanged connections and in areas of rapid change in vessel cross section.

Finite relative displacements at the edges of the free bodies are determined from the elastic line equations, and the redundant forces should satisfy the compatibility equations to maintain continuity between the free bodies. That is, the relative displacements between bodies are equal to zero and the relative slope of the edges are equal to each other. The equations of compatibility can be derived in a more formal manner by utilizing the principle of minimum complementary energy or the principle of least work. From the basic laws of statics, the redundant forces of adjacent free bodies are equal and opposite. Equations containing the redundant forces can now be formulated, i.e., radial forces and meridional moments, as well as equations for the unknown slope and deflection at the ends of the free bodies.

The set of equations of the unknown forces and deflections are solved simultaneously. There are several methods available for solving these equations on the larger high-speed computers using a single program. Two methods [181] that can be adapted to the solution of simultaneous linear equations are (1) Cholesky's scheme, a method consisting of a general systematic procedure for the elimination of the unknowns using a matrix solution (this method is the simplest and fastest among known elimination methods) and (2) Gauss–Seidel iteration method, which as the name implies, uses an iteration process. There are several other methods of numerical analysis that can be used in solving simultaneous equations; they are presented in the many textbooks covering this subject.

It is usually advantageous to use a unit load analysis for determining influence coefficients for each free body. These coefficients should be determined for each location of known applied loads and for the redundant end conditions. Changes in conditions can be made readily and with a minimum of effort, which is essential in the preliminary design of vessels. Programming for the smaller desk type computers requires that the problem be broken into several programs. The usual method is to write a program for each free body that will determine the slope and displacement for the ends considering all the applied loads for the free body and the influence coefficients for the redundants. Continuity equations using these coefficients can then be solved in a separate program for solving simultaneous equations. For extremely complicated vessels several free bodies can be joined with the simultaneous-equation program, and then these free bodies can be joined with the same program.

There are several programs available from the various laboratories and research and development organizations that were written primarily for pressure vessels. Of particular interest is a program available from the Franklin Institute entitled Computer Analysis of Axisymmetric Redundant Structures [127]. This is a program to determine the discontinuity stresses in pressure vessels. A system of compatibility equations for axisymmetric structures is derived on the basis of the principle of complementary energy. The program covers most of the usually encountered shell configurations as well as bolted flanges, arbitrarily shaped rings, and vessels with varying wall thickness in a meridional direction.

3.6.4 GENERAL SOLUTION FOR CIRCULAR PLATES

Circular plates and disks are often used in reactor vessels and for related structural purposes. These plates or disks are usually a part of a redundant structure. Generalized computer programs can be used to obtain the stresses and deflections for various loading and edge restraint conditions. There are two basic circular-plate problems: (1) symmetrical bending and (2) circular plates on an elastic foundation. Each requires a separate program.

Symmetrical bending will be considered first. If the load acting on the plate is symmetrically distributed about the axis perpendicular to the plate through its center, the deflection surface to which the plate is bent will also be symmetrical. The general equations for the principal curvatures and the corresponding bending moments for pure bending are [79]

$$M_r = -D\left[\left(\frac{d^2\delta}{dv^2}\right) + \left(\frac{\nu\,d\delta}{r\,dr}\right)\right] \quad (3.51)$$

$$M_t = -D\left(\frac{1}{r}\,\frac{d\delta}{dr} + \nu\,\frac{d^2\delta}{dr^2}\right) \quad (3.52)$$

where M_r = bending moments per unit length along circumferential sections of the plate
M_t = bending moments per unit length along a diametral section of the plate
D = flexural rigidity of the plate
r = radial distance to points on the plate
δ = deflection of the plate at a point
ν = Poisson's ratio

The effect on deflections of shearing stresses acting on normal sections of the plate perpendicular to meridians is neglected in these equations. This effect is negligible in plates where the thickness is small compared to the diameter.

Since the displacement and change in slope are proportional to the applied loads, a general solution of circular plates symmetrically loaded with respect to the center can be solved by the method of superposition for the case of uniformly distributed loads (total load P) along a concentric circle, Fig. 3.20. The deflection in the downward direction for any point r from the center is

$$\delta = \frac{P}{8\pi}\left\{\left[(b^2 + r^2)\log\left(\frac{b}{l}\right)\right] \right.$$

$$\left. + \left[(l - b^2)\,\frac{(3+\nu)l^2 - (1-\nu)r^2}{2(1+\nu)l^2}\right]\right\} \quad (3.53)$$

and the slope is the first derivative of this equation. The moments M_r and M_t are obtained by substitution of the first and second derivatives of the equation into the general bend equations. Effects of a circular hole at the center of the plate and/or various edge restraints are introduced into the problem by calculating the constants of integration for the particular boundary conditions. Any particular series of uniformly distributed loads can be superimposed on the original condition. The derivation of these equations and the boundary conditions for various loadings and plate configurations are presented in Ref. 79. Since solutions to the differential equations are readily available, programming of the circular-plate equations are straightforward. There are many standard methods of handling these equations numerically.

General equations for circular plates on an elastic foundation are given in Ref. 180. A complete analysis of this subject is provided along with final equations that can be solved numerically. The constants of integration for the less complicated loading conditions are also given. Programming techniques similar to those used for the symmetrical bending of circular plates are used.

3.6.5 THERMAL STRESSES

Thermal stresses occur in structural components whenever there is unequal heating of different sections of a body or when thermal expansion of a body is restrained by external means. In nuclear reactor components, thermal stresses are caused by both these conditions.

In many cases the maximum power level of a reactor is determined by the rate at which heat can be removed. This removal of heat requires coolants, which, in turn, introduces the problem of

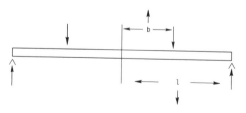

FIG. 3.20—Symmetrically loaded plate.

conducting heat through the structural components to a surface that will contact the coolant. Such a temperature distribution, e.g., the thermal gradient through a reactor vessel wall, causes thermal stresses. Before these stresses can be determined, the temperature distribution throughout the structure must be determined. Accuracy of the calculated thermal stresses is, then, a function of the accuracy of the calculated temperature distribution and the assumed boundary conditions. Sections 3.4.3 and 3.4.4 contain several simplified examples of thermal stresses caused by steady-state and transient conditions.

General equations for thermal stress are presented in the many texts on the theory of elasticity (see, for example, Ref. 128). Thermal stresses in most of the structures encountered in nuclear reactors can be obtained with a reasonable amount of accuracy by assuming a two-dimensional temperature distribution. General equations for two-dimensional thermal stresses for thin disks and long cylinders where the temperature varies across the thickness of the cylinder or radially on the disk and is constant over the length of the cylinder and for the thickness of the disk are presented in Ref. 182. Hoop stresses and radial stresses are determined for the disk, and hoop stresses and meridional bending stresses are determined for the cylinder for these equations.

Approximations for other shell configurations, such as cones, ellipsoids, and spherical sections, can be determined from these equations by using the radius of curvature in place of the cylindrical radius.

Other special types of thermal-stress problems include the effect of flanges, reinforcing rings, and step functions in the temperature distribution on shell type structures. These problems are too complicated to solve by the general thermal stress-strain equations and should be solved in parts or as free bodies as described in Sec. 3.6.3 for mechanical stresses in shell type structures.

Free bodies are established as in Fig. 3.19 except that additional free bodies will be assumed for each step function in the temperature distribution. The internal stresses, displacements, and changes in slope are determined for each body from the general thermal-stress program. For a three-dimensional temperature distribution, stresses, and deflections in shell type structures, the problem is broken down into two parts: (1) variation in temperature across the shell thickness for each element and (2) variation in temperature longitudinally using an average temperature. This method provides approximate values within the accuracy of the temperature distribution and the assumed thermal boundary conditions.

The equations from Ref. 182 assume that the temperature distribution in the cylinder varies only across the shell thickness and provides the maximum numerical stresses in the tangential and axial directions. These equations are not applicable when the temperature varies longitudinally over the length of the cylinder. This type of problem can best be solved by use of the theory of beams on an elastic foundation. Consider a cylinder with a nonlinear longitudinal temperature distribution. If the ends are free to expand and the temperature

across the thickness does not vary, the primary stresses will be from meridional bending and hoop tension or from compression and radial shear. If it is assumed that the shell is divided into unit ring elements, the freely expanded shape of the vessel can be determined where the change in radius is

$$\Delta R = \alpha R \, \Delta T \qquad (3.54)$$

Radial forces that will prevent this expansion are then determined

$$F = -\alpha E \, \Delta T \qquad (3.55)$$

where α = coefficient of thermal expansion
E = modulus of elasticity
ΔT = temperature change in axial direction per unit of length

A new shape with continuity of the rings is obtained by applying these forces to a longitudinal beam of unit width supported by the foundation modulus consisting of the resiliency of the rings. The induced bending moment at any point is derived from the general shell program, and the hoop loads are derived by multiplying the difference between the free expansion and that obtained from the general shell program by the foundation modulus k (see Sec. 3.6.3). The general shell program can be adapted to handle the longitudinal temperature distribution problem. It is only necessary to include the numerical evaluation of the thermal expansions of the ring elements and to convert the differential expansion into hoop loads. Once the slope and deflection at the ends of the free bodies have been obtained, the forces required to bring about continuity of the structure are determined by simultaneously solving the general shell equations. The resulting discontinuity stresses and thermal stresses are superimposed on the mechanical stresses for the maximum stresses of the system.

A one-dimensional analysis will usually suffice for most beam configurations when considering the effects of conduction, convection, or radiant heating. A two-dimensional analysis is required when considering nuclear heating. It may be advantageous to establish a special computer program for beams and beam type structures. General equations for this type problem and methods for solving them numerically are presented in Ref. 183. For transient conditions the temperature profile is determined for each time increment of interest, and then the stresses are determined as for the steady state.

High-speed computers can use numerical methods, such as iteration, finite differences, or a relaxation procedure, to solve these problems. The usual procedure is to solve for the displacements by one of the numerical methods for a network of nodes; from these the slope, bending moments, and radial or hoop stresses can be determined. Since all conditions considered are for circular shapes loaded symmetrically, a system using polar coordinates offers the most expeditious method for programming. Applications of the above numerical methods are given in many textbooks and published data. Of particular interest are Refs. 182-186.

Methods of determining the effect of local hot spots by rigorous analysis for shell structures are not available. The designer should have some means of evaluating them. Of primary concern are the additive thermal stresses to the overall stress network and the effect of local buckling with the resulting redistribution of loads within the system. Equations for determining the buckling stresses and deflections for flat plates and beams are given in Refs. 183 and 187. Variations of these methods can be used to some advantage in determining buckling characteristics in curved shells. A strip analysis will probably provide approximate answers that can be used as a guide for design purposes. The area of concern is divided into longitudinal strips of unit width that are rigidly fixed at the ends. Since the adjacent strips are realizing similar conditions and the local area is also growing circumferentially, the longitudinal edges are assumed to be free. The strips at the edges of the affected area are assumed to have edge restraint on one side only. The compressive stresses, including bending due to temperature differentials across the thickness, restraints of thermal expansion, and mechanical stresses, are compared to the allowable buckling stress of the strip. This analysis is in its simplest form and may be elaborated on to the degree of accuracy desired.

Once the temperature and stress profiles of a structure have been determined, they can be compared with the allowable stresses, considering plastic flow, creep, fatigue, and cumulative damage, as listed in the ASME Pressure Vessel Code for the applicable component or in the piping code or determined from other applicable design-limit criteria.

3.6.6 STRESSES DUE TO NOZZLE AND PIPE LOADS

Local stresses in shell structures resulting from nozzle and pipe loads are often controlling factors in shell thickness, location of transition sections, and other parameters. Actual stresses at the juncture of a nozzle and a shell can often be determined by tests. There also are methods of determining the stresses in the near vicinity of the attachment which provide reasonable accuracy for design purposes. These methods are presented in Refs. 101, 104, 106, 107, and 188. The equations for developing the curves in Refs. 104, 106, and 107 are presented in Refs. 105 and 120. Techniques for programming the referenced equations are basically the same as for the general shell and thermal-stress programs. Before accepting the methods in the referenced data, a thorough search should be made of the more recent data because a great deal of work is being done in this particular field. This work is providing new concepts and methods of analysis which may provide better programming techniques as well as information on the actual nozzles and/or pipe connections.

3.6.7 PIPE STRESSES AND DEFLECTIONS

Since nuclear reactors are primarily a source of thermal energy, a system of pipes is required for transferring this energy by means of a heat-transfer medium to a heat exchanger. The resulting thermal expansions induce very large loads on the piping system in addition to the already present static and dynamic loads. Also, the end reactions of the pipes are transmitted to the nozzles of the reactor vessel and heat exchangers, and these should also be analyzed. It is necessary to know the movement of the pipes so that the clearances required between components can be determined.

A piping system usually consists of attachments to a vessel through a nozzle and of straight sections of pipe, curved sections, bellows, valves, flanges, and external restraints at specific locations which are either spring mounted or rigid. In most cases the vessel will also move relative to the piping system owing to thermal expansions. The piping system is a redundant structure that is subjected to both internal and external loading conditions. The ends are usually considered to be fixed relative to slope and displacement from the induced loads.

For computer work the problem should first be broken down into components or free bodies that are of a continuous function and can be solved numerically. There are three redundant forces and three redundant moments required to maintain continuity between the free bodies in addition to the applied loads. The effects of internal pressure and pressure surges should also be considered as acting on the free body. An arbitrary piping system broken down into free bodies with their redundant forces is shown in Fig. 3.21. Each free body is subjected to membrane stresses, torsion, and bending in two planes.

There are several analytical methods for determining the slope and deflection at any point in a beam type structure. In a piping structure the pipes act as beams, and a numerical solution can be obtained. Castigliano's theorem is most widely used because it is well suited to statically indeterminate problems and can also be adapted to torsional deflections. This method and its applications to both straight and curved beams are presented in Ref. 189.

It should be noted that the rigidity of curved cylindrical beams is deduced from the general flexure theory. Since both the tensile forces at the convex side of the cylinder and the compressive forces at the concave side have resultants toward the neutral axis, the circular cross sections are flattened and become elliptical. This

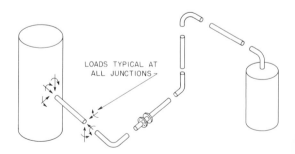

FIG. 3.21—Random nondimensional piping system, showing breakdown of piping system into free bodies and redundant forces.

flattening of the cross section affects the strain of the longitudinal fibers of the tube. These effects and a method for evaluating them are shown in Ref. 189.

The redundant forces and moments are solved simultaneously in conjunction with the compatibility equations, which include the boundary conditions for each free body. The computer program and method of programming are very similar to those of Sec. 3.6.3. The primary difference is in the solution of the redundant forces. Since the maximum stresses occur at either the applied loads or the areas of discontinuity, it is only necessary to investigate these locations. Discontinuity stresses at flanges or reinforcing rings are identical to those presented in Sec. 3.6.3 for shell structures and can be evaluated using the general shell program.

Glossary

a	thermal diffusivity; constant
b	length; constant
c	thickness of plate, wall of cylinder, wall of sphere, or beam; constant
d	constant
k	constant; thermal conductivity; foundation modulus; stress-concentration factor
k_1, k_3	stress-concentration factors applied to S_1 and S_3
$k(z)$	stress-concentration factor
l	length
m	constant
n	factor of safety; upper limit in $\overset{n}{\Sigma}$
n_0	factor of safety for steady component of stress
n_v	factor of safety for variable component of stress
r	variable radius
t	time
t_r	rupture life
Δt	element of time
x	variable
y	variable
z	variable
ds	element of arc
C	constant
D	flexural rigidity
E	modulus of elasticity
F	force
H	radial or horizontal shear force
H_0	radial or horizontal shear force at origin
I	moment of inertia
K_f	fatigue notch factor $= S_e/S_{ke}$
M_0	edge load at origin
N	number of cycles to failure
N_s	number of cycles of constant amplitude to cause failure
P	force; preload tension on bolt; load
Q	internal heat generation
Q_0	heat generation at surface $x = 0$
R, R_1, R_2	constant radius
S	stress
S_1, S_2, S_3	components of principal stress
S_0	steady-state component of stress
S_v	variable component of stress
S_{01}, S_{03}	steady-state component of principal stress
S_{v1}, S_{v3}	variable component of principal stress
S_{ae}	alternating stress that will cause failure
S_e	endurance limit
S_k	yield stress in shear for a simple uniaxial tension test
S_{ke}	notched endurance limit
S_{kae}	alternating stress that will cause failure for a notched geometry
S_r	radial stress
S_θ	tangential or hoop stress
S_u	ultimate tensile strength
S_x	component of stress in x direction
S_y	component of stress in y direction
S_z	component of stress in z direction
T	temperature
ΔT	change in temperature
T_0	initial temperature; temperature at origin
ΔT_i	strength of an ith ramp in a transient at the surface
δT_i	surface temperature change produced by the ith ramp
$T_{x/c}$	temperatre at point x/c
ΔT_x	change in temperature at point x
ΔT_0	initial temperature change at surface
T_x	temperature at point x
$T(x)$	axial temperature distribution
a	coefficient of thermal expansion
χ^*	angular misalignment
δ^*	radial misalignment
σ^*	slippage
γ^*	angular misalignment less than χ^*
ν	Poisson's ratio
$\Delta\epsilon_p$	plastic-strain change per half cycle
λ	characteristic constant
$\delta, \delta', \delta'', \delta'''$	displacement or deflection and its derivatives
μ	gamma-ray absorption coefficient, (length)$^{-1}$
$\theta(\beta x)$	function of βx
$\Psi(\beta x)$	function of βx
$\varphi(\beta x)$	function of βx
$\xi(\beta x)$	function of βx
$d\theta$	element of angle
β	reciprocal attenuation length
Σ^*	slippage less than σ^*
Φ	stress parameter

References

1. G. I. Taylor, The Mechanism of Plastic Deformation in Crystals, Part I. Theoretical, Proc. Roy. Soc. (London), [A] 145:362–387 (1934).
2. F. C. Frank and W. T. Read, Jr., Multiplication Processes for Slow Moving Dislocations, Phys. Rev., [2] 79:722–723 (1950).
3. H. G. F. Wilsdorf, On the Multiplication of Dislocations in Thin Foils, Proceedings of an International Conference on Structure and Properties of Thin Films at Bolton Landing, N. Y., John Wiley & Sons, Inc., New York, 1959.
4. N. F. Mott, Atomic Structure and the Strength of Metals, Page–Barbour Lectures at the University of Virginia, Pergamon Press, New York, 1956.
5. A. H. Cottrell, Dislocations and Plastic Flow in Crystals, Oxford Clarendon Press, London, 1953.
6. A. Nadai, Theory of Flow and Fracture of Solids, 2nd ed., McGraw-Hill Book Company, Inc., New York, 1950.
7. R. Hill, The Mathematical Theory of Plasticity, Oxford University Press, Fair Lawn, N. J., 1950.

8. I. Finnie and W. R. Heller, Creep of Engineering Materials, McGraw-Hill Book Company, Inc., New York, 1959.

9. R. M. Goldhoff, Some Observations on the Extrapolation of High Temperature Ferritic Steel Data, Trans. Am. Soc. Mech. Engrs., [D] 82:848-854 (December 1960).

10. K. D. Shimmin, Applicability of Present Creep Prediction Techniques For Extrapolating Very Long Time Creep Behavior, Report WADD-TR-60-523, October 1960.

11. N. Thomspon and N. J. Wadsworth, Metal Fatigue, Advan. Phys., 7:82 (Janaury 1958).

12. T. C. Yen, Thermal Fatigue, A Critical Review, Welding Research Council Bulletin No. 72 (October 1961).

13. R. V. Southwell and J. J. Gough, On the Concentration of Stress in the Neighborhood of a Small Flaw and on the Propagation of Fatigue Fractures in Statistically Isotropic Materials, British Report ARC-1003, p. 862, 1926.

14. H. J. Gough, Crystalline Structure in Relation to Fatigue of Metals Especially by Fatigue, Am. Soc. Testing Mater. Proc. 33(Pt. II):3 (1933).

15. E. Schmid, Neuere Untersuchungen an Metallkristallen, International Congress of Applied Mechanics, Delft, p. 342, 1924.

16. W. A. Wood, The Lower Limiting Crystalline Size and Internal Strains in Some Cold-Worked Metals, Proc. Roy. Soc. (London), [A] 174:310 (1939).

17. W. A. Wood and P. L. Thorpe, Behavior of the Crystalline Structure of Brass under Slow and Rapid Cyclic Stresses, Proc. Roy. Soc. (London), [A] 174:310 (1940).

18. W. L. Bragg, A Theory of the Strength of Metals, Nature, 49:511 (May 1942).

19. W. A. Wood and W. A. Rachinger, Crystallite Theory of Strength of Metals, J. Inst. Metals, 75:571 (March 1949).

20. P. J. E. Forsyth, Some Metallographic Observations on the Fatigue of Metals, J. Inst. Metals, 80:181 (December 1951).

21. P. J. E. Forsyth, British Report RAE-MET-70, December 1952. (Classified)

22. A. K. Head, The Propagation of Fatigue Cracks, J. Appl. Mech., 23:407 (September 1956).

23. A. K. Head, The Growth of Fatigue Cracks, Phil. Mag., [7] 44:925 (1953).

24. N. F. Mott, A Theory of the Origin of Fatigue Cracks, Acta Met., 6:195 (1958).

25. W. A. Wood, Formation of Fatigue Cracks, Phil. Mag., 3(31):692 (July 1958).

26. A. J. McEvily, Jr., and E. S. Machlin, in Fracture: Proceedings of an International Conference on the Atomic Mechanisms of Fracture, Swampscott, Mass., Apr. 12-16, 1959, p. 450, B. L. Averbach et al. (Eds.), Technology Press, Massachusetts Institute of Technology and John Wiley & Sons, Inc., New York.

27. W. A. Backofen, in Fracture: Proceedings of An International Conference on the Atomic Mechanisms of Fracture, Swampscott, Mass., Apr. 12-16, 1959, p. 435, B. L. Averbach et al. (Eds.), Technology Press, Massachusetts Institute of Technology and John Wiley & Sons, Inc., New York.

28. W. A. Wood, in Fracture: Proceedings of an International Conference on the Atomic Mechanisms of Fracture, Swampscott, Mass., Apr. 12-16, 1959, p. 412, B. L. Averbach et al. (Eds.), Technology Press, Massachusetts Institute of Technology and John Wiley & Sons, Inc., New York.

29. T. Yokobori, Stress Criterion for Fatigue Fracture of Steels, J. Mech. Phys. Solids, 8(2):81 (May 1960).

30. A. Palmgren, Die Lebensdauer von Kugellagern, VDI Zeits., 68(14):339 (1924).

31. B. F. Langer, Fatigue Failure from Stress Cycles of Varying Amplitude, J. Appl. Mech., 4:A160 (December 1937).

32. M. A. Miner, Cumulative Damage in Fatigue, J. Appl. Mech., 12:159 (September 1945).

33. T. J. Dolan, F. E. Richart, Jr., and C. E. Work, The Influence of Fluctuations in Stress Amplitude on the Fatigue of Metals, Am. Soc. Testing Mater. Proc., 48:767 (1948).

34. T. J. Dolan and H. F. Brown, Effect of Prior Repeated Stressing on the Fatigue Life of 75S-T Aluminum, Am. Soc. Testing Mater. Proc., 52:733 (1952).

35. G. M. Sinclair and T. J. Dolan, Use of a Recrystallization Method to Study the Nature of Damage in Fatigue of Metals, in Proceedings of the First U. S. National Congress of Applied Mechanics, pp. 647-651, American Society of Mechanical Engineers, 1952; also Effect of Stress Amplitude on Statistical Variability in Fatigue of 75S-T6 Aluminum Alloy, Trans. Am. Soc. Mech. Engrs., 75:867-870 (1953).

36. G. M. Sinclair, An Investigation of the Coaxing Effect in the Fatigue of Metals, Am. Soc. Testing Mater. Proc., 52:743 (1952).

37. D. L. Henry, A Theory of Fatigue Damage Accumulation in Steel, Trans. Am. Soc. Mech. Engrs., 77:913 (1955).

38. A. M. Freudenthal and R. A. Heller, On Stress Interaction in Fatigue and a Cumulative Damage Rule, J. Aerospace Sci., 26(7):431 (July 1959).

39. M. H. Weisman and M. H. Kaplan, The Fatigue Strength of Steel Through the Range from 1/2 to 30,000 Cycles of Stress, Am. Soc. Testing Mater. Proc., 50:649 (1950).

40. W. G. Finch, A Study of Steels in the Finite Region of the S-N Curve, Am. Soc. Testing Mater. Proc., 52:759 (1952).

41. R. E. Petersen, Brittle Fracture and Fatigue in Machinery, in Fatigue and Fracture of Metals, p. 74, W. M. Murray (Ed.), Technology Press, Massachusetts Institute of Technology and John Wiley & Sons, Inc., New York, 1952.

42. B. F. Langer, Working Stress Criteria for Nuclear Power Plants, Trans. Am. Soc. Mech. Engrs., 77(5):661 (July 1955); also, Design Values for Thermal Stress in Ductile Materials, Welding J. (N. Y.), 37:411-s to 417-s (September 1958).

43. L. F. Coffin, A Study of the Effects of Cyclic Thermal Stresses On Ductile Metals, Trans. Am. Soc. Mech. Engrs., 76:931-950 (1954).

44. L. F. Coffin, Jr., and J. F. Tavernelli, The Cyclic Straining and Fatigue of Metals, Trans. Am. Inst. Mech. Engrs., 215:794-807 (October 1959).

45. E. E. Baldwin, G. J. Sokol, and L. F. Coffin, Jr., Cyclic Strain Fatigue Studies on AISI Type 347 Stainless Steel, Am. Soc. Testing Mater. Proc., 57:567-581 and 581-586 (1957).

46. F. J. Mehringer and R. P. Felgar, Low-Cycle Fatigue of Two Nickel-Based Alloys by Thermal Stress Cycling, Trans. Am. Soc. Mech. Engrs., [D]82:661 (September 1960).

47. F. H. Vitovec, Effect of Relaxation on the Behavior of Materials Under Combined Alternating and Static Stress, Trans. Am. Soc. Mech. Engrs., [D]82:441 (June 1960).

48. F. J. Clauss and J. W. Freeman, Thermal Fatigue of Ductile Materials. II. Effect of Cyclic Thermal Stressing on the Stress-Rupture Life and Ductility of S-816 and Inconel 550, Report NACA-TN-4165, Lewis Flight Propulsion Laboratory, 1960.

49. A. S. Ross and J. D. Morrow, Cycle-Dependent Stress Relaxation of A-286 Alloy, Trans. Am. Soc. Mech. Engrs., [D]82(3):654 (September 1960).

50. D. R. Miller, Thermal-Stress Ratchet Mechanism in Pressure Vessels, Trans. Am. Soc. Mech. Engrs., [D]81:190 (1959).

51. L. F. Coffin, The Stability of Metals Under Cyclic Plastic Strain, Trans. Am. Soc. Mech. Engrs., [D]82(3):671 (September 1960).

52. T. J. Dolan, Fatigue as a Factor in Pressure Vessel Design, Welding J. (N. Y.), 33(6):265-s (June 1954).

53. T. J. Dolan, Significance of Fatigue Data in Design of Pressure Vessels, Welding J. (N. Y.), 35(5):255-s (May 1960).

54. C. E. Bowman and T. J. Dolan, Studies of Biaxial Fatigue Properties of Pressure Vessels, Welding J. (N. Y.), 34(1):51-s (January 1955).

55. L. F. Kooistra, Effect of Plastic Fatigue on Pressure Vessel Materials and Design, Welding J. (N. Y.), 36(3):120-s (March 1957).

56. D. E. Hardenbergh, Stresses in Contoured Nozzles when Subjected to External Loadings, USAEC Report NYO-7565, Sept. 15, 1959.

57. Tentative Structural Design Basis for Reactor Pressure Vessels and Directly Associated Components (Pressurized Water Cooled Systems) Bureau of Ships, U. S. Navy, Dec. 1, 1958.

58. C. R. Soderberg, Factor of Safety and Working Stresses, Trans. Am. Soc. Mech. Engrs., 52(Pt. 1):13-28 (1930).

59. L. F. Kooistra and M. M. Lemcoe, Low-Cycle Fatigue Research on Full-Size Pressure Vessels, Welding J. (N.Y.), 41(7):297-s-306-s (July 1962).

60. G. Sachs, S. J. G. Sessler, and W. F. Brown, Jr., Influence of Stress Concentrations at Elevated Temperatures, Am. Soc. Testing Mater. Spec. Tech. Publ. No. 260 (1959).

61. E. A. Davis and M. J. Manjoine, Effects of Notch Geometry on Rupture Strength at Elevated Temperatures, Am. Soc. Testing Mater. Spec. Tech. Publ. No. 128 (1956).

62. F. H. Vitovec and B. J. Lazan, Fatigue Creep and Rupture Properties of Heat Resistant Materials, WADC-TR-56-181, University of Minnesota, 1956.

63. J. Sessler, Stress Rupture Behavior of Weldmens and Brazed Joints, in Proceedings of the Third Sagamore Research Conference, 1956, pp. 592-594 and 594-600, Syracuse University, 1957.

64. S. S. Manson and W. F. Brown, Jr., A Survey of the Effects of Nonsteady Load and Temperature Conditions on the Creep of Metals, Am. Soc. Testing Mater. Spec. Tech. Publ. No. 260, pp. 63-104 (December 1959).

65. J. E. Dorn, Some Fundamental Experiments on High-Temperature Creep, J. Mech. Phys. Solids, 3:85 (1954).

66. H. J. Tapsell, P. G. Forrest, and G. R. Tremaine, Creep Due to Fluctuating Stresses at Elevated Temperatures, Engineering, 170:189 (1950).

67. L. A. Shepard, C. D. Starr, C. D. Wiseman, and J. E. Dorn, The Creep Properties of Metals Under Intermittent Stressing and Heating Conditions, Report WADC-TR-53-336, Part 3, University of California, July 1954.

68. E. L. Robinson, Effect of Temperature Variation on the Creep Strength of Steel, Trans. Am. Soc. Mech. Engrs., 60:253 (1938); also, Effect of Temperature Variation on the Long-Time Rupture Strength of Steels, Trans. Am. Soc. Mech. Engrs., 74:777 (1952).

69. F. R. Larson and J. Miller, A Time-Temperature Relationship for Rupture and Creep Stresses, Trans. Am. Soc. Mech. Engrs., 74:765 (1952).

70. L. U. Rastrelli, An Evaluation of Time-Dependent Materials Information for Purposes of Pressure Vessel Design and Analysis, USAEC Report NYO-9376, July 1960.

71. C. R. Soderberg, Mechanical Properties in Relation to Design Requirements, Met. Rev., 1(Pt. 1):31-63 (1956).

72. American Society of Mechanical Engineers, ASME Boiler and Pressure Vessel Codes, Section I. Power Boilers, Preamble.

73. American Society of Mechanical Engineers, ASME Boiler and Pressure Vessel Codes, Section VIII, Unfired Pressure Vessels.

74. Code Interpretation Case 1270N-4, General Requirements for Nuclear Vessels, Mech. Eng., 83:105 (November 1961).

75. E. L. Robinson, Safety Margins and Stress Levels in High Temperature Equipment, Trans. Am. Soc. Mech. Engrs., 73:89-99 (1951).

76. W. C. Hayes, Comments on the Application of ASME and ASA Boiler and Piping Codes to Sodium Systems, USAEC Report NAA-SR-4102, North American Aviation, 1959.

77. E. Orowan and C. R. Soderberg, Design and Performance of Gas-Turbine Power Plants, in High Speed Aerodynamics and Jet Propulsion, Vol. 11, W. R. Hawthorne and W. T. Olson (Eds.), Princeton University Press, Princeton, N. J., 1960.

78. American Society of Mechanical Engineers, ASME Boiler and Pressure Vessel Codes, Section III, Nuclear Vessels.

79. S. Timoshenko and S. Woinowsky-Krieger, Theory of Plates and Shells, 2nd ed., McGraw-Hill Book Company, Inc., New York, 1961.

80. R. J. Roark, Stresses in Long Thick-Walled Cylinders, 3rd ed., McGraw-Hill Book Company Inc., New York, 1954.

81. Z. Zudans, Tsi Chu Yen, and W. H. Steigelmann, Thermal Stress Techniques in the Nuclear Industry, American Elsevier Publishing Company, Inc., New York, 1965.

82. G. Horvay, Problems of Mechanical Analysis, Nucl. Eng., 1:231 (September 1956).

83. E. O. Waters, D. B. Wesstrom, D. B. Rossheim, and F. S. G. Williams, Formulas for Stresses in Bolted Connections, Trans. Am. Soc. Mech. Engrs., 59:161-169 (1937).

84. E. O. Waters, D. B. Wesstrom, D. B. Rossheim, and F. S. G. Williams, Development of General Formulas for Bolted Connections, Taylor Forge and Pipe Company, Chicago, Ill.

85. E. O. Waters, Modern Flange Design, Taylor Forge and Pipe Company, Chicago, Ill., 1938.

86. D. B. Wesstrom and S. E. Berge, Effect of Internal Pressure on Stresses and Strains in Bolted-Flanged Connections, Trans. Am. Soc. Mech. Engrs., 73:553-562; 562-568 (1951).

87. N. W. Murray and D. G. Stuart, Behavior of Large Taper-Hub Flanges, in Symposium on Pressure-Vessel Research Toward Better Design, Paper No. 9, Institution of Mechanical Engineers, London, January 1961.

88. G. Horvay and I. M. Clausen, Stresses and Deformations of Flanged Shells, J. Appl. Mech., 76:109 (1954).

89. G. Horvay, Thermal Stresses in Perforated Plates, in Proceedings of the First U. S. National Congress of Applied Mechanics, p. 247, American Society of Mechanical Engineers, 1952 (also available as USAEC Report KAPL-P-456, Knolls Atomic Power Laboratory, January 1951).

90. G. Horvay, The Plane Stress Problem of Perforated Plates, J. Appl. Mech., 19:355 (1952).

91. G. Horvay, Bending of Honeycombs and of Perforated Plates, J. Appl. Mech., 19:122 and 405 (1952).

92. V. L. Salerno and J. F. Mahoney, A Review, Comparison, and Modification of Present Deflection Theory for Flat Perforated Plates, Welding Research Council Bulletin No. 52 (July 1959).

93. L. Deagle, Correlation of Experimental Data with Theory for Perforated Plates with a Triangular Hole Array, Welding Research Council Bulletin No. 52 (July 1959).

94. D. Bynum, Jr., and M. M. Lemcoe, Stresses and Deflections in Laterally Loaded Perforated Plates, Welding Research Council Bulletin No. 80 (August 1962).

95. J. B. Mahoney, V. L. Salerno, and M. A. Goldberg, Analysis of a Perforated Circular Plate Containing a Rectangular Array of Holes, Welding Research Council Bulletin No. 80 (August 1962).

96. W. J. O'Donnell and B. F. Langer, Design of Perforated Plates, Trans. Am. Soc. Mech. Engrs., [B]84(3):307-320 (1962).

97. G. Horvay, Problems of Mechanical Analysis in Reactor Technology, Preprint No. 355, Nuclear Engineering and Science Congress, American Institute of Chemical Engineers and American Society of Mechanical Engineers, Cleveland, Ohio, Dec. 12-16, 1955.

98. G. Horvay, Problems of Stress Analysis of Perforated Plates, in Proceedings Summer Seminar in Thermal Mechanics, published by Continuing Education Service, Kellogg Center, Michigan State University, East Lansing, Mich., 1959.

99. W. J. O'Donnell, Effective Elastic Constants for Steam Generator Tube Sheets, Report WAPD-X (CE)-162, Westinghouse Electric Corporation, June 1960.

100. W. J. O'Donnell, An Analysis of Average Stress Intensities in Steam Generator Tube Sheets, Bettis Technical Review, Reactor Technology, Report WAPD-BT-21, Westinghouse Electric Corporation, November 1960.

101. G. J. Schoessow and L. F. Kooistra, Stresses in a Cylindrical Shell Due to Nozzle or Pipe Connection, J. Appl. Mech., 12(2):A107 (1945).

102. F. J. Mehringer and W. E. Cooper, Experimental Determinations of Stresses in the Vicinity of Pipe Appendages to a Cylindrical Shell, Proc. Soc. Exp. Stress Anal., 14(2):159 (1957).

103. E. T. Cranch, An Experimental Investigation of Stresses in the Neighborhood of Attachments to a Cylindrical Shell, Welding Research Council Bulletin 60 (1960).

104. P. P. Bijlaard, Stresses From Radial Loads in Cylindrical Pressure Vessels, Welding J. (N. Y.), 33(12):615s-623s (December 1954).

105. P. P. Bijlaard, Stresses From Local Loadings in Cylindrical Pressure Vessels, Trans. Am. Soc. Mech. Engrs., 77(6): 805-814 and 814-816 (August 1955).

106. P. P. Bijlaard, Stresses from Radial Loads and External Moments in Cylindrical Pressure Vessels, Welding J. (N. Y.), 34(12):608s-617s (December 1955).

107. P. P. Bijlaard, Local Stresses in Spherical Shells From Radial or Moment Loadings, Welding J. (N. Y.), 36(5):240s-243s (May 1957).

108. P. P. Bijlaard, Stresses in a Spherical Vessel From Radial Loads Acting on a Pipe, Welding Research Council Bulletin No. 49 (April 1959).

109. P. P. Bijlaard, Stresses in a Spherical Vessel From External Moments Acting on a Pipe, Welding Research Council Bulletin No. 49 (April 1959).

110. P. P. Bijlaard, Influence of a Reinforcing Pad on the Stresses in a Spherical Vessel Under Local Loading, Welding Research Council Bulletin No. 49 (April 1959).

111. P. P. Bijlaard, Stresses in Spherical Vessels From Local Loads Transferred By a Pipe, Welding Research Council Bulletin No. 50 (May 1959).

112. P. P. Bijlaard, Additional Data on Stresses in Cylindrical Shells Under Local Loading, Welding Research Council Bulletin No. 50 (May 1959).

113. D. H. Hardenbergh, Stresses in Contoured Openings of Pressure Vessels, ASME Paper No. 58-A-207, American Society of Mechanical Engineers, February 1959.

114. J. L. Mershon, PVRC Research on Reinforcement of Openings in Pressure Vessels, Welding Research Council Bulletin No. 77 (May 1962).

115. E. O. Waters, Theoretical Stresses Near a Circular Opening in a Flat Plate Reinforced with a Cylindrical Outlet, Welding Research Council Bulletin No. 51 (June 1959).

116. F. S. G. Williams and E. P. Auler, Unreinforced Openings in a Pressure Vessel, Welding Research Council Bulletin No. 51 (June 1959).

117. P. P. Bijlaard and E. T. Cranch, Interpretive Commentary on the Application of Theory to Experimental Results (for stresses near attachments to a cylindrical shell), Welding Research Council Bulletin No. 60 (May 1960).

118. J. W. Dally, An Experimental Investigation of the Stresses Produced in Spherical Vessels by External Loads Transferred by a Nozzle, Welding Research Council Bulletin No. 84 (January 1963).

119. G. D. Galletly, Bending of 2:1 and 3:1 Open-Crown Ellipsoidal Shells, Welding Research Council Bulletin No. 54 (October 1959).

120. P. P. Bijlaard, Computation of the Stresses From Local Loads in Spherical Pressure Vessels or Pressure Vessel Heads, Welding Research Council Bulletin No. 34 (March 1957).

121. R. Bailey and R. Hicks, Localized Loads Applied to Spherical Pressure Vessel Through Cylindrical Insert, J. Mech. Eng. Sci., 2(4):302-311 (December 1960).

122. R. Kitching and J. Perkins, Stress Analysis of Rim-Reinforced Openings in Pressure Vessels, J. Nucl. Energy, 6(63):334-338 (August 1961).

123. R. A. Clark, On The Theory of Thin Elastic Toroidal Shells, J. Math. Phys., 29:146-178 (1950).

124. C. E. Turner, Study of the Symmetrical Elastic Loading of Some Shells of Revolution With Special Reference To Toroidal Elements and Stress and Deflection Studies of Flat Plate and Toroidal Expansion Bellows, Subjected to Axial, Eccentric, or Internal Pressure Loading, J. Mech. Eng. Sci., 1(2):113-129 and 130-143 (September 1959).

125. G. D. Galletly, Edge Influence Coefficients for Toroidal Shells of Positive Gaussian Curvature and Edge Influence Coefficients for Toroidal Shells of Negative Gaussian Curvature, Trans. Am. Soc. Mech. Engrs., [B]82:60-68 and 69-75 (February 1960).

126. M. I. Hetenyi and R. J. Timms, Analysis of Axially Loaded Annular Shells with Applications to Welded Bellows, ASME Paper 59-A-175, American Socieity of Mechanical Engineers, 1959.

127. Zenons Zudans, Computer Analysis of Axisymmetric Redundant Structures, Franklin Institute Laboratores Brochure, April 1963.

128. S. Timoshenko and J. N. Goodier, Theory of Elasticity, 2nd ed., McGraw-Hill Book Company, Inc., New York, 1951.

129. G. Sonnemann and D. M. Davis, Stresses in Long Thick-Walled Cylinders Caused By Pressure and Temperature, ASME Paper 57-A-256, American Society of Mechanical Engineers, 1957.

130. G. Horvay, Stress Relief Obtainable in Sectioned Heat-Generating Cylinders, in Second Midwestern Conference on Solid Mechanics, Edward Brothers, Ann Arbor, Mich., 1955.

131. G. Horvay, The End Problem of Rectangular Strips, J. Appl. Mech., 20:87 and 576 (1953).

132. J. S. Born and G. Horvay, Thermal Stresses in Rectangular Strips. II, J. Appl. Mech., 22:401 (1955).

133. A. C. Dearden and T. F. Brock, in Proceedings of a Symposium on Nuclear Reactor Containment Buildings and Pressure Vessels, p. 496, Royal College of Science and Technology, Glasgow, Butterworth & Co., Ltd., 1960.

134. C. W. Lawton, Strain Gauge Test on Model Vessels for Nuclear Power Plant Designs, Proc. Soc. Exptl. Stress Anal., 17(1):149 (1959).

135. F. R. Beyer, Some Notes on the Strength of the Enrico Fermi Reactor Vessel Structure, Trans. Am. Soc. Mech. Engrs., 81:66-72 (1959).

136. L. P. Zick and C. E. Carlson, Strain Gauge Survey Around the Supports of a 48-Foot Diameter Hortonsphere, Proc. Soc. Exptl. Stress Anal., 6(2):41 (1949).

137. G. J. Schoessow and S. A. Brooks, Analysis of Experimental Data Regarding Certain Design Features of Pressure Vessels, Trans. Am. Soc. Mech. Engrs., 72(5):567 (1950).

138. L. F. Kooistra and R. U. Blaser, Experimental Technique in Pressure Vessel Testing, Trans. Am. Soc. Mech. Engrs., 72(5):579 (1950).

139. B. F. Langer, Experimental Mechanics of Nuclear Power Reactors, Proc. Soc. Exptl. Stress Anal., 17(2):97 (1960).

140. M. M. Leven and R. C. Sampson, Photoelastic Stress and Deformation Analysis of Nuclear Reactor Components, Proc. Soc. Exptl. Stress Anal., 17(1):161 (1959).

141. J. W. Dally and A. J. Durelli, Stress Analysis of a Reactor Head Closure, Proc. Soc. Exptl. Stress Anal., 17(2):71 (1960).

142. A. J. Durelli, J. W. Dally, and S. Morse, Experimental Study of Large Diameter Thin-Wall Pressure Vessels, Proc. Soc. Exptl. Stress Anal., 18(1):33 (1961).

143. D. E. Hardenbergh, Stresses at Nozzle Connections of Pressure Vessels, Proc. Soc. Exptl. Stress Anal., 18(1):152 (1961).

144. A. S. Tooth, in Proceedings of a Symposium on Nuclear Reactor Containment Buildings and Pressure Vessels, p. 298, Royal College of Science and Technology, Glasgow, Butterworth & Co., Ltd., 1960.

145. J. Dubac and C. Welter, Investigation of Static and Fatigue Resistance of Model Pressure Vessels, Welding J. (N. Y.), 35(7):329s (1956).

146. L. F. Kooistra, Effect of Plastic Fatigue on Pressure Vessel Materials and Design, Welding J. (N. Y.), 36:120s-130s (March 1957).

147. C. E. Taylor, N. C. Lind, and J. W. Schweiker, A Three-Dimensional Photoelastic Study of Stresses Around Reinforced Outlets in Pressure Vessels, Welding Research Council Bulletin No. 51 (1959).

148. M. Hetenyi, Handbook of Experimental Stress Analysis, John Wiley & Sons, Inc., New York, 1950.

149. M. M. Frocht, Photoelasticity, Vols. 1 and 2, John Wiley & Sons, Inc., New York, 1941 and 1948.

150. C. C. Perry and H. R. Lissner, The Strain Gauge Primer, McGraw-Hill Book Company, Inc., New York, 1955.

151. G. Ellis, Practical Strain Analysis by Use of Brittle Coatings, Proc. Soc. Exptl. Stress Anal., 1(1):46 (1943).

152. E. G. Coker and L. N. G. Filon, Treatise on Photoelasticity, Cambridge University Press, New York, 1959.

153. H. T. Jessop and F. C. Harris, Photoelasticity: Principles and Methods, Dover Publications, Inc., New York, 1950.

154. M. M. Leven, Quantitative Three-Dimensional Photoelasticity, Proc. Soc. Exptl. Stress Anal., 12(2):157 (1955).

155. M. M. Leven and A. M. Wahl, Three-Dimensional Photoelasticity and its Application in Machine Design, Trans. Am. Soc. Mech. Engrs., 80(8):1683 (1958).

156. C. E. Taylor and J. W. Schweiker, A Three-Dimensional Photoelastic Investigation of the Stresses Near a Reinforced Opening in a Reactor Pressure Vessel, Proc. Soc. Exptl. Stress Anal., 17(1):25 (1959).

157. J. D'Agostino, D. C. Drucker, C. K. Kiu, and C. Mylonas, An Analysis of Plastic Behavior of Metals with Bonded Birefringent Plastic, Proc. Soc. Exptl. Stress Anal., 12(2):115 (1955).

158. F. Zandman and M. R. Wood, Photo Stress, A New Technique for Photoelastic Stress Analysis for Observing and Measuring Surface Strains on Actual Structures and Parts, Prod. Eng., 27(9):167 (September 1956).

159. F. Zandman, Stress Analysis of a Guided Missile Tail Section with the Photoelastic Coating Technique, Proc. Soc. Exptl. Stress Anal., 17(2):135 (1960).

160. W. M. Murray and B. K. Stein, Strain Gauge Techniques, Technology Press, Massachusetts Institute of Technology, 1959.

161. P. K. Stein, Strain Gauge Readings, bimonthly publication, edited and published by P. K. Stein, 5602 E. Monte Rosa, Phoenix, Ariz.

162. C. Schabtach and R. J. Fehr, Measurement of the Damping of Engineering Materials During Flexural Vibrations at Elevated Temperatures, J. Appl. Mech., 11(2):A-86 (June 1944).

163. R. H. Kemp, W. C. Morgan, and S. S. Manson, Advance in High Temperature Strain Gauges and their Application to the Measurement of Vibratory Stresses in Hollow Turbine Blade During Engine Operation, Proc. Soc. Exptl. Stress Anal., 8(2):209-228 (1951).

164. R. H. Kemp, W. C. Morgan, and S. S. Manson, High-Temperature Strain Gauges and Their Application to Measurement of Vibratory Stresses in Turbosupercharger Buckets, Proc. Soc. Exptl. Stress Anal., 5(1):90-100 (1947).

165. R. E. Gorton, Development and Use of High Temperature Strain Gauges, Proc. Soc. Exptl. Stress Anal., 9(1):163 (1950).

166. J. E. Carpenter and L. D. Morris, A Wire Resistance Strain Gauge for the Measurement of Static Strains at Temperatures up to 1600°F, Proc. Soc. Exptl. Stress Anal., 9(1):191-200 (1950).

167. Symposium on Elevated Temperature Strain Gauges, Am. Soc. Testing Materl. Spec. Tech. Publ. 230 (1957).

168. R. L. Bloss et al., Reports NBS-4676, NBS-4747, NBS-4843, NBS-5286, NBS-6117, NBS-6245, NBS-6395, NBS-6526, NBS-6900, NBS-7004, and NBS-7161, National Bureau of Standards (progress reports on evaluation of resistance strain gauges at elevated temperatures), 1956-1961.

169. G. F. Brosius and D. Hartley, Evaluation of High Temperature Strain Gauges, Proc. Soc. Exptl. Stress Anal., 17(1):67 (1959).

170. F. R. Beyer and J. O. Smith, Evaluation of High Temperature Strain Gauges for the Enrico Fermi Reactor Vessel, paper presented at Society of Experimental Stress Analysis Meeting, Berkeley, Calif., Oct. 19-21, 1960.

171. J. J. Shrager, Evaluation at Temperatures up to 600°F of Seven Types of Strain Gauges Made of Karma and Armour Research Foundation Alloys A and B, Report NAMC-ASL-1011, Part II, Naval Air Material Center, 1957.

172. L. Herczeg and P. Beckman, High-Temperature Strain Gauges, Instruments and Automation, 31(3):460 (1958).

173. R. C. Smith and N. J. Rendler, Transducers for Strain Measurements in Intense Radiation Fields, Proc. Soc. Exptl. Stress Anal., 16(2):73-80 (1959).

174. A. V. DeForest, G. Ellis, and F. B. Stern, Jr., Brittle Coatings for Quantitative Strain Measurements, Trans. Am. Soc. Mech. Engrs., 64:A184 (1942).

175. G. Ellis and F. B. Stern, Dynamic Stress Analysis with Brittle Coatings, Proc. Soc. Exptl. Stress Anal., 3(1):102 (1945).

176. A. J. Durelli and J. W. Dally, Some Properties of Stresscoat Under Dynamic Loading, Proc. Soc. Exptl. Stress Anal., 15(1):43-56 (1957).

177. J. W. Dally, A. J. Durelli, and V. J. Parks, Further Studies, Proc. Soc. Exptl. Stress Anal., 15(2):57 (1957).

178. G. L. Lee, An Introduction to Experimental Stress Analysis, John Wiley & Sons Inc., New York, 1950.

179. F. M. Singdale, Improved Brittle Coatings for Use Under Widely Varying Temperature Conditions, Proc. Soc. Exptl. Stress Anal., 11(2):173 (1952).

180. M. Hetenyi, Beams on Elastic Foundation, University of Michigan Press, 1955.

181. M. G. Salvadori and M. L. Baron, Numerical Methods in Engineering, Prentice-Hall, Inc., Princeton, N. J., June 1956.

182. Chi-Teh Wang, Applied Elasticity, McGraw-Hill Book Company, Inc., New York, 1953.

183. B. E. Gatewood, Thermal Stresses, McGraw-Hill Book Company, Inc., New York, 1957.

184. D. N. De G. Allen, Relaxation Methods, McGraw-Hill Book Company, Inc., New York, 1954.

185. R. V. Southwell, Stress-Calculation in Framework by the Method of Systematic Relaxation of Constraints, I, II, and III, Proc. Royal Soc. (London), Pts. I and II [A]151(872):56-95 (Aug. 1, 1935); Pt. III [A]153(878):41-76 (Dec. 2, 1935).

186. R. V. Southwell, Relaxation Methods in Engineering Science, Oxford University Press, Fair Lawn, N. J., 1940.

187. M. L. Gossard, P. Seide, and W. M. Roberts, Thermal Buckling of Plates, Report NACA-TN-2771, Langley Aeronautical Laboratory, August 1952.

188. L. Ting and S. W. Yuan, On Radial Deflection of a Cylinder of Finite Length With Various End Conditions, J. Aerospace Sci., 25(4):230-234 (April 1958).

189. S. Timoshenko, Strength of Materials, Part I, 3rd ed., D. van Nostrand Company, Inc., Princeton, N. J., 1955.

CHAPTER 4

Heat-transport Systems

WAYNE L. CHASE
Atomic Power Development Associates, Inc.
Detroit, Michigan

Contents

4.1 General

4.1.1 INTRODUCTION

Nuclear energy is primarily a heat source. As with conventional heat sources, one of the most practical means of converting this heat to electrical energy is by use of the Rankine heat cycle. The poor efficiency and high cost of thermionic [1], thermoelectric [2], and magnetohydrodynamic [3] devices preclude their use in the near future in central-station and standard propulsion applications involving sizable amounts of energy.

The system used in fast reactors for transferring heat from the reactor requires a high heat-removal capability. Although there are potentially several heat-removal cycles and variations thereof, only one has been generally utilized for central-station fast reactor application. A primary radioactive sodium or NaK system removes heat from the reactor and transfers it to a secondary nonradioactive sodium or NaK system. From the secondary system this heat is transferred to produce superheated steam, which drives a turbine generator. This chapter is devoted to the primary and secondary liquid-metal systems and their auxiliaries; the steam cycle is discussed in Chap. 5.

4.1.2 FAST REACTOR HEAT-REMOVAL CYCLES

4.1.2.1 Direct Cycle

A simple method for transferring heat from the reactor to the turbine generator is to vaporize the coolant, which removes heat from the reactor, and use the vapor to drive the turbine (Fig. 4.1).

Argonne National Laboratory has examined several schemes for coupling [4-6] two cores into one reactor, one with a fast-neutron spectrum and the other with a near-thermal-neutron spectrum. Water boils in the thermal region, and the resulting steam is superheated in the fast region. A steam-cooled fast reactor Loeffler cycle [7] in which steam is produced at 1414 psia and 945°F has been studied. About one-third of the steam from the reactor is directed to the turbine; the remainder is used to vaporize the feedwater in an open type Loeffler boiler. Saturated steam from the Loeffler boiler is returned to the reactor by low-leakage steam circulators (Fig. 4.2). The large recirculation ratio and the problems involved in steam pump development are drawbacks to this scheme.

The direct mercury cycle [8] utilizes mercury at 600°F and superheats it to 900°F and 90 psia. The elimination of an intermediate cooling system is a prime factor in producing potential cost reductions over sodium-cooled systems. The poor nuclear properties of mercury preclude general acceptance of this system.

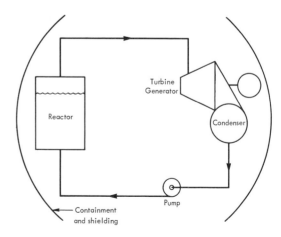

FIG. 4.1—Direct-cycle heat-transport system.

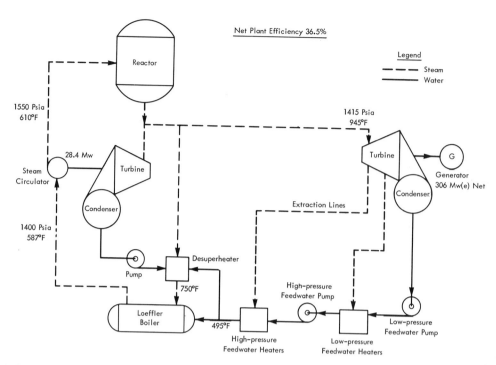

FIG. 4.2—Conceptual design of a steam-cooled fast breeder reactor. [From G.A. Sofer and R.D. Hankel, Trans. Am. Nucl. Soc., 4(1):35 (1961).]

4.1.2.2 Indirect Cycle

4.1.2.2.1 SIMPLE.   In an indirect simple cycle the primary coolant from the reactor flows directly to a steam generator, as shown in Fig. 4.3. A leak in the steam generator could result in at least three problems: (1) an introduction of water into the reactor, (2) the release of radioactivity into the steam system, and (3) a primary coolant-water reaction. The containment building or buildings would have to be designed to withstand any primary coolant-water reaction.

Reference 8 includes an evaluation of an indirect-cycle mercury-steam system. Mercury is vaporized and superheated in the reactor to a maximum temperature of 920 to 1000°F and is condensed in a condenser-boiler to produce 900°F 1800-psig superheated steam. Double-wall tubes in the steam generator minimize leakage. A third fluid in the steam generator has been used in sodium reactor systems and considered for other liquid-metal-cooled systems (Sec. 4.3.6.3). The third fluid can take the form of a monitoring gas, such as helium, or a heat-transfer medium, such as mercury. With helium the two tube walls must have essentially complete metal-to-metal contact with only small gaps for the gas to minimize the effect on overall heat transfer in the unit. Double-wall tubes with or without a stagnant heat-transfer medium may significantly affect heat transfer. An indirect simple cycle using a double-wall tube steam generator construction may be justified where space and weight requirements dictate. For central-station applications using sodium in the reactor, the concern about leaks between the radioactive

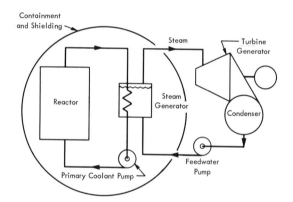

FIG. 4.3—Indirect-cycle liquid-metal heat-transport system without intermediate loop.

sodium and the water has, to date, precluded the elimination of an intermediate system.

4.1.2.2.2 BINARY.   The sodium-cooled reactor with a binary thermodynamic system will become attractive when higher sodium temperatures are achieved in the future. In this system sodium serves as a primary reactor coolant transferring its heat to mercury in a boiler. The mercury vapor operates a turbine and is then condensed in a steam boiler producing steam to operate a steam turbine [9, 10]. The binary cycle is shown in Fig. 4.4.

4.1.2.2.3 INTERMEDIATE LOOP.   Figure 4.5 shows a system in which the primary radioactive

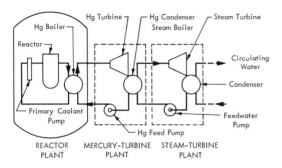

FIG. 4.4—Sodium-cooled reactor binary thermodynamic system [9].

sodium transfers its heat in an intermediate heat exchanger (IHX) to a secondary intermediate non-radioactive sodium system. The secondary sodium is circulated to the steam generator, where it produces superheated steam.

The advantages of the intermediate loop system are (1) hydrogenous materials are kept out of the containment structure housing the reactor, minimizing the possibility of increasing the reactivity, (2) the reactor containment structure can be designed for a lower pressure since it does not have to protect against the energy release of a sodium-water reaction, (3) leakage of radioactive sodium into the steam system is minimized, and (4) each secondary loop is completely separate. The sodium can be drained out of any one secondary loop without jeopardizing heat removal in the reactor.

The disadvantages are (1) increased pumping power, (2) added capital costs, (3) added space requirements, (4) added service systems, (5) added maintenance, and (6) lower thermodynamic efficiency.

4.1.3 DESIGN CRITERIA

4.1.3.1 Radioactivity and Radiation

Some of the nuclear properties of sodium are discussed in Chap. 2, and a detailed discussion of

shielding is given in Chap. 8. The core of a fast sodium-cooled reactor generates a fast flux greater than 10^{15} neutrons/cm^2/sec. An important consideration in the maintenance of pumps and intermediate heat exchangers is to minimize their neutron activation by locating them in fluxes of 10^4 neutrons/cm^2/sec or less. Since sodium has a high ratio of scattering to absorption, neutrons can scatter or stream along sodium pipes. Space required around pipes for clearance, expansion allowance, secondary containment, and for insulation provides gaps down which neutrons may stream. Bends in the pipes can be used to eliminate direct streaming between the reactor and the primary-system components.

Primary sodium coolant exposed during long-term fast reactor operation typically is activated to about 50 μc/g/Mw(t) (Chap. 8). It has two major isotopes: (1) Na^{24}, which is produced by the (n,γ) reaction, decays with a half-life of 15 hr, and emits two energetic gamma rays, and (2) Na^{22}, which is produced by the $(n,2n)$ reaction with neutrons above 11 Mev, decays with a half-life of 2.6 years, and emits one energetic gamma ray.

The radioactivity of the sodium effectively masks the radioactivity of fission products from failing fuel elements. This increases the problem of detecting failed elements. On the other hand, the necessity for providing adequate shielding for the radioactive sodium automatically provides the shielding required for a fuel-element failure.

4.1.3.2 Corrosion and Chemical Reactivity

Only a few common materials have good corrosion resistance in sodium at high temperature. One of these is 316 stainless steel, which shows good resistance at temperatures of 1200 to 1300°F. An analysis of materials at 1400°F for future reactors [11] indicates that type 316 stainless steel is relatively the most economical material.

The reaction between sodium and water below about 600°F normally produces sodium hydroxide

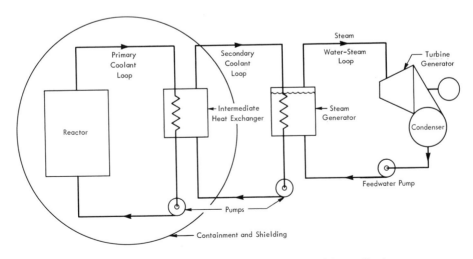

FIG. 4.5—Indirect-cycle liquid-metal heat-transport system with intermediate loop.

plus hydrogen. The injection of water or steam into an excess of sodium at a temperature exceeding the melting point of sodium hydroxide (600°F) produces sodium oxide, as discussed in Chap. 2. The design of the steam generator including the safety devices should (1) minimize the possibility of a sodium—water reaction (Sec. 4.3.6.1.1), (2) minimize the effects of a sodium—water reaction, (3) provide relief for reaction products, and (4) provide for the disposition of reaction products. All the secondary system should be designed to contain the reaction.

A pool of sodium reacts with air at a rate of less than 5 lb/sq ft/hr and burns with a short flame. The reaction of sodium in the air is a consideration in the design of the reactor containment building, as discussed in Chap. 6. The major problems resulting from the sodium—air reaction are the plugging of lines and equipment by the reaction products and the corrosive action of these products.

4.1.3.3 Temperature Considerations

A list of sodium temperature conditions for present-day sodium-cooled reactor systems is given in Table 4.1. These systems have been designed for rather moderate temperatures since the main objective of experimental demonstration plants is to provide experience

Table 4.1—Inlet and Outlet Temperatures of Sodium- and NaK-cooled Reactors

Reactor	Inlet, °F	Outlet, °F	Coolant
EBR-I	442	601	NaK
BR-5	806	932	Na
SRE	500	960	Na
Dounreay	392	752	NaK
Lampre I	842	1045	Na
Hallam	610	945	Na
EBR-II	700	890	Na
Fermi (300 Mw)	550	800	Na
Fermi (430 Mw)	600	900	Na
Rapsodie	482	644	Na

A larger reactor temperature rise is desirable to minimize the size of the components and the pumping power. The temperature rise is limited by thermal stress resulting from temperature transients. Chapter 3 discusses design conditions, stress limits, and methods of computing thermal stresses under both transient and steady-state conditions.

Flexibility is a primary consideration in the arrangement and support of a sodium system and its components (Secs. 4.2.1.1.2 and 4.3.4.1). Design allowance should be made for thermal expansion induced by any steady-state or transient temperature differences.

4.1.3.4 Fluid-flow Considerations

Sodium temperatures in fast reactors are sufficiently below the 1618°F boiling point of sodium to permit the use of a low-pressure cover gas in the primary sodium systems. Low pressure minimizes sealing problems, particularly for rotating com-

ponents, and permits gravity flow from the high point in the system to the heat exchanger, as in the case of Fermi. Design studies [12, 13] indicate that there is a limiting velocity and a maximum pipe diameter feasible for gravity-flow systems and that cavitation at the pump may also be a limitation.

One alternate to the gravity-flow system is to pressurize gas spaces, such as in the reactor, intermediate heat exchanger, and the pump. The pressurized system allows for a larger pressure drop in the section between the reactor and the pump suction. Other advantages of a pressurized system include less complex cover-gas systems (pressure control is not critical), small diameter reactor outlet pipes, minimizing of pump cavitation, and higher shell velocities in the IHX. Without pressurization and gravity flow, the size of the outlet pipes and the pump suction pressure are set by the pressure drop. Pressurization may range to 50 psia, depending on system conditions.

The total pressure drop in the primary system is of interest because it determines pump characteristics. A pressure drop across the core of about 100 psi has been generally used for a number of reasons, two of which are (1) core velocities greater than about 30 ft/sec create difficulties in the mechanical design of fuel support structures and (2) excessive pressure drops may produce cavitation at such locations as the inlet to subassemblies and control elements. Chapter 2 discusses cavitation problems further.

4.1.3.5 Emergency Cooling

Provision should be made to remove any heat the reactor core generates after loss of all pumps. This heat generation can be characterized by three successive time periods: (1) the time required after failure of the pumps to initiate movement of the control and safety rods to reduce reactor power, (2) the additional time required to reduce the neutron population in the core to essentially zero, and (3) the remaining time until pump recovery.

The decay heat can be calculated as shown in Chap. 7. The equivalent amount of power generated during the first two time periods is a function of the control-system response time, previous operating history, and core characteristics. The decay heat should be accurately calculated for each reactor and verified during low power tests. The integrated heat generation during the first two periods is insignificant compared to the heat-storage capacity of the primary coolant and to the heat generated during the gamma decay period. It is the third period for which emergency-cooling provisions should be made.

Several emergency-cooling methods are possible (Sec. 4.2.3), e.g., a separate coolant loop, auxiliary (pony) motors, and natural circulation. Prescribed sodium levels must be maintained for all cooling conditions. Secondary containment (Sec. 4.2.1.1.4) may be necessary to ensure maintenance of these levels after a primary containment rupture.

4.2 Heat-transport and Auxiliary Systems

The design of primary and secondary sodium heat-transport systems and the necessary auxiliary systems is discussed in this section. The schematic for a four-loop sodium-sodium-steam power conversion cycle is shown in Fig. 4.6.

4.2.1 PRIMARY SODIUM SYSTEM

4.2.1.1 Design Decisions and Methods

The discussion in Sec. 4.1.2 has established some of the criteria to be considered in the design of a primary sodium system. The design of the system consists of the following interdependent items: (1) operating conditions, (2) system arrangement, (3) piping design and layout, (4) emergency-coolant calculations (Sec. 4.2.3.2), and (5) secondary containment. The design and detail concepts of the various components should be integrated into the overall system (Sec. 4.3).

4.2.1.1.1 OPERATING CONDITIONS. Once the desired electrical output of the plant has been set, some limiting reference temperature in the primary system should be established. For illustration, a reactor outlet temperature of 1050°F and a steam pressure of 1500 psi have been selected.

A temperature driving force of 100°F is assumed between the primary and secondary loops and of 50°F between the secondary loop and the steam outlet of the superheater. The secondary sodium therefore leaves the intermediate heat exchanger at 950°F, and the superheated-steam temperature is 900°F.

On the temperature—enthalpy diagram (Fig. 4.7), a vertical line is drawn from the steam conditions of 900°F and 1500 psia (point 1) to the 950°F sodium temperature line (point 2). With a 100°F differential between the intermediate heat-exchanger primary sodium outlet and the secondary sodium inlet and a 300°F reactor rise, the steam-generator sodium outlet temperature is 650°F. The feedwater temperature should be optimized. For illustration a feedwater temperature of 430°F will be used. A vertical line drawn from the 430°F saturation point (point 3 on Fig. 4.7) to 650°F establishes the lower end (point 4) of the steam-generator sodium line. This procedure can be repeated for other sodium and steam conditions and can be integrated with steam-cycle analyses described in Chap. 5. The procedure can be refined as the design proceeds; for example, the actual temperature line for the sodium should be computed when the steam-generator design is known. The temperature differential (point 5-6, Fig. 4.7), called the "pinch point," denotes the transition to boiling and is a critical point.

For the conditions of this example, a gross plant thermal efficiency of about 40% is attainable. With a gross output of 180 Mw(e), the reactor thermal heat output Mw(t) is

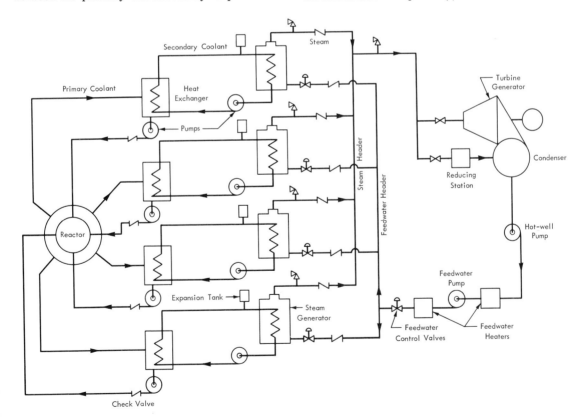

FIG. 4.6—Schematic diagram of four-loop liquid-metal heat-transport system.

$$Q = \frac{\text{Plant output}}{\text{Plant efficiency}} = \frac{180 \times 1000 \times 3415}{0.40}$$

$$\cong 1.54 \times 10^9 \text{ Btu/hr}$$

$$\cong 4.52 \times 10^2 \text{ Mw(t)}$$

This amount of heat energy is produced in the reactor and transmitted to the primary coolant. Two methods can be used for determining the amount of flow (W) necessary to remove this heat. Using the average specific heat c_p, we find $Q = W c_p \Delta T$, where ΔT is the reactor temperature rise.

With a reactor ΔT of 300°F, a specific heat (sodium at 900°F average temperature) of 0.303 Btu/lb/°F, and 1.54×10^9 Btu/hr heat output, the required flow is approximately 17×10^6 lb/hr of sodium equal to 2.83×10^5 lb/min, or 0.71×10^5 lb/min for each of four loops.

Using the sodium enthalpy ΔH, we find $Q = W(\Delta H)$. For sodium at 1050°F, H is approximately 364 Btu/lb; at 750°F, H is approximately 274 Btu/lb. This gives a ΔH of 90 Btu/lb, and the resultant W will be the same as in the first method.

The flow in gallons per minute = $7.48 \, W/\rho$ = 40,000 for ρ = 52.3 lb/cu ft at 900°F average reactor temperature. With the temperatures, temperature differentials, and flows established, the number of primary loops can be determined and a system-arrangement concept can be established.

4.2.1.1.2 SYSTEM ARRANGEMENT. Three possible concepts for the arrangement of the primary sodium system are (1) EBR-II design where all primary system components are located in a

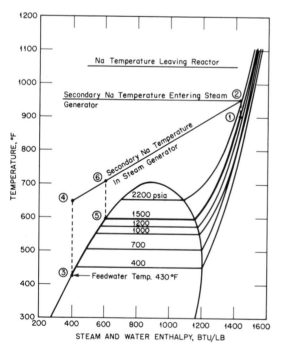

FIG. 4.7—Temperature-enthalpy diagram for fast reactor steam cycle.

large sodium-filled tank (Fig. 4.8), (2) Fermi type design where components are clustered around the reactor vessel and within the reactor containment building (Fig. 4.9), and (3) extended plant layout design where each primary loop is in a separate building outside the reactor containment building (Fig. 4.9).

The EBR-II design offers the following advantages: (1) secondary-system containment can be provided in a single large cylindrical vessel rather than in several tanks with connecting pipes, (2) there is only one free surface for which an inert cover gas must be provided, (3) the large sodium pool at reactor inlet temperature has a large heat capacity that serves to minimize temperature transients and is an excellent heat sink during emergency cooling (either the steam system or a completely separate cooling system can be utilized to cool the tank sodium) (Fig. 4.10), and (4) thermal expansion in the piping can be accommodated by leaky joints, such as slip-fit unions. The concept has two disadvantages: (1) shielding within the primary tank filled with sodium becomes increasingly difficult with larger size plants, and (2) the construction of the tank supports and the top closure becomes increasingly difficult as the tank size increases.

Although the extended plant layout design represents additional capital costs, it offers some advantages over the single-building arrangement: (1) removal of primary components for maintenance can be simplified by using inert gas in the building for this operation and removing the component without the use of transfer casks, (2) the building head room and volume are reduced, (3) the size of containment structure is minimized, (4) the sodium-air reaction, which is one of design criteria in determining the containment-building requirements, is reduced as a result of a smaller amount of air, and (5) segregation of components into several buildings minimizes interference during initial construction and during maintenance operations.

Regardless of the general arrangement concept, certain design features should be present in the individual loops of the primary system: (1) the reactor vessel generally should provide a common plenum for all loops [the coolant generally enters the reactor vessel at the bottom and leaves near the top below the shielding plug (Sec. 4.3.2)]; (2) each loop should contain a pump and one or more intermediate heat exchangers, and the primary coolant flow should usually be through the shell side of the heat exchanger (Sec. 4.3.5); (3) the pump should generally be located downstream from the intermediate heat exchanger, where it operates at the lowest system temperature; (4) loops used for emergency cooling should have sufficiently long hot and cold legs and sufficiently low pressure drops to promote natural circulation, or else a guaranteed power supply should be provided to either auxiliary pump motors or emergency-cooling loop pump motors; (5) stop or throttle valves are a source of increased maintenance and, where possible, should be eliminated (Sec. 4.3.4.2); and (6) heat-transport systems should be arranged for adequate draining and venting.

Before detailed layouts of individual loops are made, the number of loops should be determined.

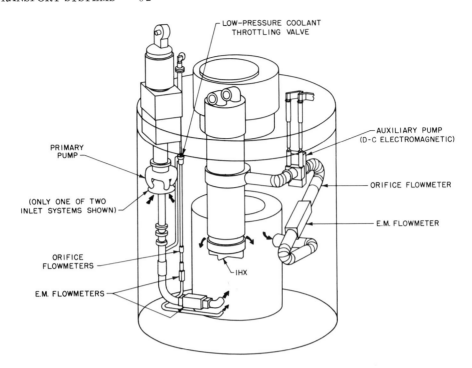

FIG. 4.8—EBR-II reactor inlet and outlet piping system [14].

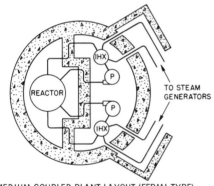

MEDIUM COUPLED PLANT LAYOUT (FERMI TYPE)

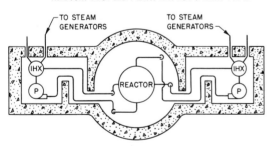

EXTENDED PLANT LAYOUT (PWR TYPE)

FIG. 4.9—Heat-transport system arrangements.

The determination of the number of normally operating primary loops is usually based on total flow (Sec. 4.2.1.1.1), allowable pressure drop, degree of plant reliability, size of available components, and allowable sodium velocities.

A one-loop system (Fig. 4.11) would probably be used only in a small interconnected plant or in a small peaking unit with an emergency-cooling loop to remove decay heat in the event of a pump failure. For a fixed plant size, as the number of loops increases, the flow per loop decreases; the pressure drop for the same size pipe decreases or the diameter of the pipe is decreased for a fixed pressure drop; the fraction of load dropped after failure of one loop decreases; component sizes decrease; and the sodium velocities are decreased for the same size pipe. Figure 4.11 shows designs for one- to four-loop systems within one containment building. The building diameter vs. number of loops can be determined only by an actual layout after sizing components and piping.

4.2.1.1.3 PIPING. After the reactor flow and the number of loops have been established, the loop line sizes can be determined. For a reactor flow of 17.2×10^6 lb/hr and inlet and outlet temperatures of 750 and 1050°F, respectively, a four-loop system would have a flow of 10,000 gal/min in the cold portion of the loop. The flow in the hot portion of the loop is determined by multiplying this flow by the inverse ratio of the densities, which in this case is 1.05.

4.2.1.1.4 SECONDARY CONTAINMENT. The primary system should be enclosed in secondary containment to prevent the sodium levels from dropping below the piping connections on the primary-system components in the event of a leak at any point below these connections. The secondary containment system can be divided into compartments. The volume of each compartment should be such that in the event of a leak the level

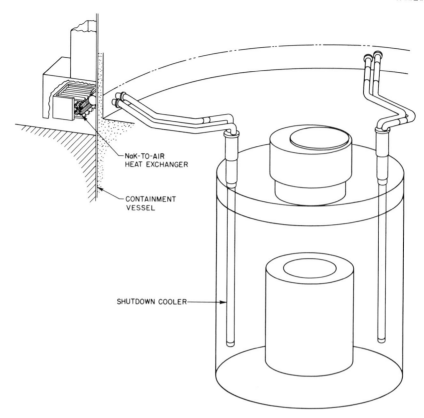

NaK-TO-AIR
HEAT EXCHANGER

CONTAINMENT
VESSEL

SHUTDOWN COOLER

FIG. 4.10—EBR-II shutdown cooling system [14].

in the primary system does not drop below that needed for emergency cooling. Consideration should be given to the difference in the volume between the operating temperature and the estimated temperature of the coolant during emergency cooling.

The containment system consists of a leaktight jacket enveloping the primary piping and the primary-system tanks. It would come into use only when there is a leak in the primary system. The secondary containment should have support provisions to pick up the increased load. The pressure for which containment should be designed is dependent upon the conditions under which the sodium is to be contained. If there are no relief valves, the design pressure should be equal to the maximum attainable pressure during the containment period. The steady-state design temperature of the containment should be the same as that of the pipe or tank that it contains if the system insulation is placed outside the containment. The time lag between the system and containment should be considered during transients.

The materials of construction should be suitable for containment of the sodium at the design pressure and temperature for the period of containment. In systems that are not highly stressed, chromium—molybdenum steels or even carbon steels can be considered, provided temperatures are kept within code limits. In rigidly anchored systems at the higher temperatures, the use of stainless steels should be considered because they allow higher stresses. Austenitic stainless steels should not

be used if the containment material is to be used as a medium for induction heating of the primary system.

A containment system can be completely enclosed or it can be open at the top to the underfloor atmosphere. If the system is closed, it should be designed either for the maximum expected pressure or provided with relief valves or relief diaphragms. The system can be open only if the expected pressure during containment does not exceed the static head of sodium.

A closed system can be an all-welded system, such as the primary tanks in EBR-II and Fermi. The Fermi primary tank has a relief valve. The relief valve can serve a dual purpose, i.e., to normally relieve excess gas pressure and to relieve excess pressures created by entry of sodium into the containment. The EBR-II primary tank provides complete containment for the primary system; no other containment is required around the piping. The containment around a piping system could be all welded, but, in general, it is preferable to use bellows to provide for axial and lateral movements. An inert gas should be maintained in the closed containment system to prevent a sodium-air reaction in the event of a leak. In a closed containment system, it may be possible to operate the primary system in the event of a leak. At EBR-II, if the leak is in the cold leg, the additional flow, up to some value, is readily supplied by the two primary pumps. If the leak is in the hot leg, the additional flow, up to some value, is readily supplied by the pumps;

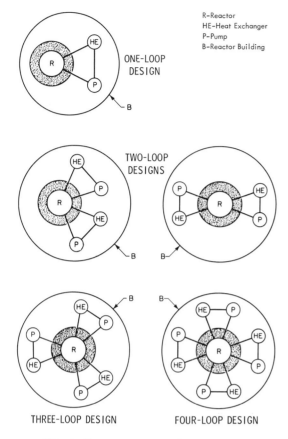

R—Reactor
HE—Heat Exchanger
P—Pump
B—Reactor Building

ONE-LOOP DESIGN

TWO-LOOP DESIGNS

THREE-LOOP DESIGN

FOUR-LOOP DESIGN

FIG. 4.11—Heat-transport system loop arrangements.

but, in addition, there is a temperature effect that must be accounted for. At Fermi, if there is a leak into the primary tank from the cold or hot leg, operation could probably continue up to a fixed limit. But, if a leak occurs outside the primary tank, the plant would be shut down because of the possibility of contamination since the containment system is open to the oxygen-depleted under-floor atmosphere. One solution would be a completely inert under-floor gas. This would create above-floor to below-floor sealing problems of a large magnitude.

Open containment systems simplify sealing problems. However, the leaktightness requirements of the system below the containment levels should not be compromised. The level above which the system can be open is the maximum coolant level of the primary system. The containment annuli are generally open to the below-floor ambient atmosphere around such components as the intermediate heat exchanger and the pump tanks.

The radial distance between containment and the primary-system component is a compromise among a minimum to reduce heat losses, a sufficient amount to permit free movement, and a maximum distance governed by the maximum allowable compartment volume. Hangers are required for the primary piping and the containment jacket. Separate hangers (Fig. 4.12) provide for differential movements between the primary piping

and outer containment. Such a system allows full use of the annular space for differential movement; however, hanger settings do not have sufficient range to include both the empty and filled loads. When a leak occurs, the containment hanger load changes from empty dry pipe to filled pipe, and the primary piping hanger load changes from filled pipe load to empty pipe load. When a tank leaks, the piping hanger is relieved to an amount equal to the buoyant force of the displaced piping volume. If constant-support pipe hangers are used, this load is transferred to the nozzles of the equipment. A joint hanger system allows the problem of shifting loads at the time of a leak. Spacers (Fig. 4.12) transmit support loads from pipe to containment but may involve expansion problems. A joint hanger system (Fig. 4.12) without spacers requires a design that uses a common support attachment and expansion joints in the containment system. Such a system satisfies the requirements of differential movement and of support.

There are many methods for heating the primary system: the annulus between the primary and the containment systems can be used as a container for a heating fluid, resistance electric heaters can be applied directly to the primary-system wall (in a manner to prevent burnout), the secondary containment can be used as the ferritic medium for induction heating, the piping itself can be a resistive load, and immersion heaters can be used. Insulation around the containment acts as an oven enveloping the primary system for the case where the containment is heated. The temperature of the primary system and the containment are approximately the same. If it is desirable to reduce the temperature of the containment and if adequate space is available for differential movement, insulation can be applied between the pipe and containment. The containment in this case cannot be used for heating but must be applied directly to the component. Heating details are given in Sec. 4.2.4.4.

Spark-plug type leak detectors (Fig. 4.13) should be installed at low points in the containment system to locate leaks. A drop in sodium levels is a check on this type of leak detection. A typical design of secondary containment piping, showing heating, insulation, and leak detection, is given in Fig. 4.13.

Containment design should include provisions for electromagnetic (EM) flowmeters. The annulus thickness should be a minimum. Electric leads from thermocouples and resistance thermometers should have room in the annulus for expansion loops between the rigid connections at the piping wall and those at the containment wall. In an open containment system, the leads may be brought out of the openings at the top of the system. Electrical penetrations in closed containment systems should be designed to the same integrity standards as the containment. Although welded connections are preferred on all penetration details, well designed and compatible brazed joints may be acceptable (see Chap. 2).

Where piping and containment systems are being erected concurrently, containment cylinders can be slipped over the open ends of piping assemblies. Where the piping has already been erected, the containment can be erected in half cylinders with two longitudinal seam welds. With the latter method

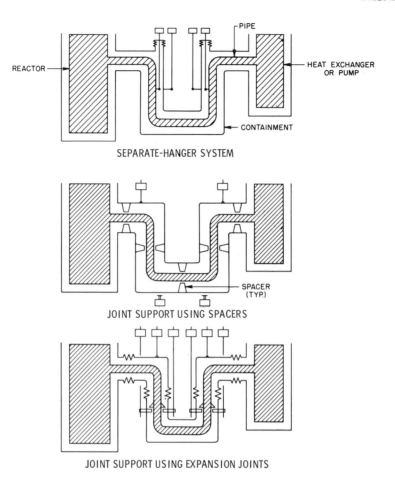

FIG. 4.12—Primary coolant system support schemes for secondary containment.

precautions should be taken to prevent weld splatter contacting the surface of the primary system. Elbows and tees can be installed by the same split construction method. The containment volume is hydraulically connected to the primary system at the time of a leak, and foreign particles in the containment system may contaminate the primary system. For this reason containment cleanliness is important.

The containment system should be given such nondestructive tests as are necessary to assure the integrity and leaktightness of the finished system. Rigid visual inspection should also be used in all cases. Welds should be checked by liquid-penetrant testing and radiography if possible. Ultrasonics is finding increasing applicability. Where possible, a system-integrity test using air should be applied to the system after erection. Water may be considered if the system can be completely drained after the test and all moisture eliminated from the system.

4.2.1.2 Specific System Designs

Several primary-system designs are described in the following sections. Chapter 11 gives an overall description of each installation except for the plutonium-fueled fast breeder reactor (PFFBR) system.

4.2.1.2.1 EXPERIMENTAL BREEDER REACTOR I (EBR-I). EBR-I operated at a maximum power of 1400 kw. The flow of NaK through the reactor is normally 290 gal/min (~128,000 lb/hr). The heat-transport system (Fig. 4.14) consists of a primary NaK coolant loop that removes heat from the reactor, a secondary NaK loop that removes heat from the primary NaK, a steam system that removes heat from the secondary NaK loop, and a turbine generator. The primary NaK flow is from an elevated constant-head tank into the reactor, through the inner blanket, and then through the core. From the reactor the NaK flows through the intermediate heat exchanger and then into a receiving tank. It is pumped continuously from the receiving tank up to the constant-head tank, which contains an overflow line to the receiving tank.

4.2.1.2.2 DOUNREAY FAST REACTOR [17]. The heat transport system (Fig. 4.15) has two notable features: downflow in the core and 24 primary loops. The multiplicity of loops ensures

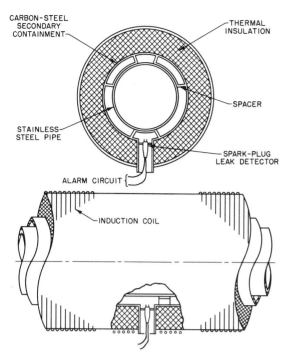

FIG. 4.13—Primary coolant system typical liquid-metal pipe section [15].

continuous cooling. If the flow is normally downward and pumps fail, there is a progressive changeover from downward to upward natural-circulation flow. A small liquid-metal heat exchanger in each primary circuit is connected to a system that rejects its heat to air by a natural draft through a stack. This system is always in operation.

The layout and design of the primary circuit has been dominated by the necessity to guard against coolant loss. Experience gained in the

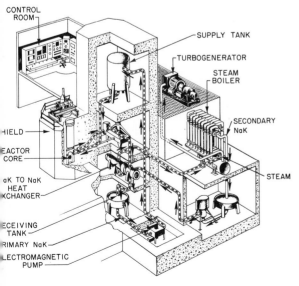

FIG. 4.14—EBR-I heat-transport system [16].

construction of the Windscale chemical-separation plants using stainless steel showed that it should be possible, given proper control of materials and fabrication techniques, to build a leaktight and completely drainable primary system, provided it was welded throughout and the circuit was designed for butt welding so that every weld could be radiographed and tested.

The primary–secondary intermediate heat exchangers (IHX) consist of one tube inside another. No valves were used because of their potential weakness. Components subjected to heavy working or welding stresses were stress-relieved, and, in addition to being X-rayed, all welds were pressure tested and leak tested with nitrous oxide or a halogen gas. Stainless steel was chosen for the material of construction because in the middle 1950's there was little available information on the behavior of carbon steels in a liquid-metal circuit. The United Kingdom Atomic Energy Authority (UKAEA) had also had considerable experience in the controlled fabrication of large plants made of stainless steel. Stainless steel would also make it easier to keep the circuit clean during erection, and hence no special cleaning of the system prior to being filled with liquid metal was thought necessary.

It was recognized that the use of NaK would be an advantage in the early stages of commissioning and operation when liquid metal could be circulated under varying temperature conditions without freezing. It was decided to operate the reactor with the NaK alloy as the coolant.

4.2.1.2.3 ENRICO FERMI ATOMIC POWER PLANT. The primary system (Fig. 4.16) is composed of three coolant loops having a common point in the reactor vessel. Each loop contains a sodium pump, a check valve, a blanket throttle valve, and the shell side of an intermediate heat exchanger. Primary sodium flows by gravity from the upper reactor vessel through three 30-in. pipes. Each of the lines supplies the shell side of an intermediate heat exchanger (IHX). The discharge of each IHX is connected to the pump suction by a 30-in. line. The discharge of each pump supplies a 16-in. line, which, in turn, supplies a 6-in. and a 14-in. line. The three 14-in. lines deliver approximately 87% of the flow to the plenum serving the reactor core. The three 6-in. lines deliver approximately 13% flow to the plenum serving the radial blanket. Flowmeters are located in both the 6-in. and the 14-in. lines. The flow of coolant to the blanket plenum can be adjusted by a throttle valve in each of the 6-in. lines.

The 30-, 16-, and 14-in. pipes are fabricated of 304 stainless steel plate. The wall thickness for all three of these pipe sizes is 3/8 in. The 6-in. piping is Schedule 40 seamless type 304 stainless steel pipe. The 30-in. piping is cold sprung 100% for 900°F operation, and the pump discharge piping is cold sprung 100% for 600°F operation.

All components of the primary coolant system are enclosed by secondary containment. Auxiliary 5-hp motors on each of the primary and secondary sodium pumps furnish the power to circulate

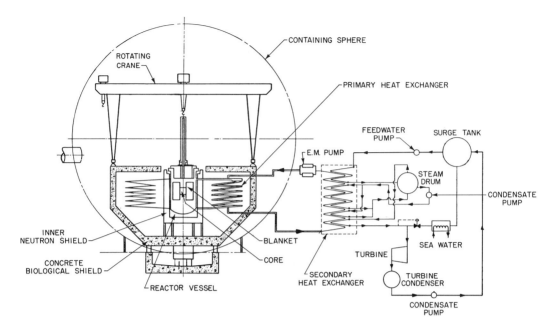

FIG. 4.15—Dounreay heat-transport system [17].

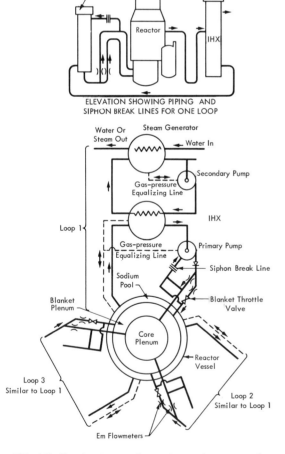

ELEVATION SHOWING PIPING AND
SIPHON BREAK LINES FOR ONE LOOP

FIG. 4.16—Fermi primary and secondary coolant system flow
diagram [31].

primary coolant to remove decay heat from the
reactor after shutdown.

4.2.1.2.4 EXPERIMENTAL BREEDER REAC-
TOR II (EBR-II). The pumps, heat exchanger, and
connecting piping of the primary system are disposed radically around the reactor vessel; the
equipment is at an elevation above the vessel
(Fig. 4.8). These items are immersed in sodium
contained in the primary sodium tank. The coolant
flow path is as follows: The mechanical coolant
pumps take in bulk sodium about 19 ft above the
bottom of the primary tank; coolant flow from the
pumps is downward to the connecting piping. The
flow from each separates into two pipes; one
enters the reactor high-pressure plenum, and
the second, the reactor low-pressure plenum,
with the smaller line supplying the low-pressure
plenum through an orifice and a valve. In all
regions of the reactor vessel, coolant flows upward
through the fuel and blanket subassemblies and into
an upper plenum chamber, which has a single 14-in.
outlet located on the opposite side of the reactor
vessel from the intermediate heat exchanger. The
connecting pipe between these two components is
designed to accomodate thermal expansion and
contains an auxiliary pump. The coolant flows
downward through the shell side of the heat
exchanger and discharges into the bulk sodium
in the primary tank. The heat-exchanger outlet
is approximately 7.5 ft above the center line of
the reactor to provide natural convection shutdown
cooling.

Ball-seat pipe couplings are used in the lines
between the main sodium pumps and the lower
plenums of the reactor vessel. This allows for
pump removal. The sodium line between the upper
plenum of the reactor vessel and the heat exchanger
shell is permanently attached to the cover of the
primary tank. The intermediate heat exchanger

tube bundle, the secondary sodium inlet and outlet nozzles, and the shield plug can be lifted out as a unit (Fig. 4.17).

When the reactor is in operation, coolant is supplied by the two primary sodium mechanical pumps. Flow to the low pressure plenum can be controlled by a valve in each circuit. During shut down conditions, when the reactor power is 1% or less of the design value, sufficient coolant flow is established by thermal convection to remove fission-product decay energy without exceeding the established fuel-alloy temperature limitations. For more drastic emergency shutdown conditions, including the case of complete failure of all pumps accompanied by reactor scram, analysis indicates that the fuel will overheat, but not dangerously. The relative elevations of the heat exchanger and the reactor were established to ensure natural circulation of the primary sodium.

The primary purpose of the auxiliary pump (Fig. 4.8) is to augment thermal convection under certain conditions of reactor shutdown. These conditions can result from any system malfunctions which destroy the normal temperature distributions which promote thermal convection. An example would be the case of a rapid reactor shutdown followed, after several seconds, by failure of the pumps. During the interim, the pumps would overcool the reactor and eliminate most of the temperature differential (and the thermal-convection head) which would normally exist across the reactor. The auxiliary pump ensures continuity of flow under these conditions. Auxiliary pump power is supplied from metallic rectifier units backed up by storage batteries. During normal operation these batteries float on the line and remain fully charged. In the event of a sustained power failure, the pump operates until the battery is discharged; the discharge results in a gradual decay of the flow rate and an ideal transition to thermal convection. Interlocks between the auxiliary pump and reactor controls prevent reactor start-up unless the pump is connected and operating with the batteries fully charged.

4.2.1.2.5 RAPSODIE. The heat released in the core and blankets of Rapsodie are removed by two parallel primary loops (Fig. 4.18 and Table 4.2). Each of the loops has a capacity of 10 Mw(t). For initial operation the sodium enters the reactor at 482°F and leaves at 644°F. However, the thermal equipment and the fixed part of the reactor are designed to allow temperatures of 360°F higher. The primary loops are symmetrically placed around the reactor. Each of these loops is located in a separate room. One of the two rooms has a tank for expansion of the sodium in the reactor vessel. From this tank, the sodium passes through the purification loop and then to an upper level in the reactor vessel.

Table 4.2—Rapsodie Primary Loop Data [18] (Per Loop)

Power, Mw(t)	10
Fluid	Sodium
Flow at average temperature, gal/min	1543
Temperature entering reactor, °F	482
Temperature leaving reactor, °F	644
Volume of sodium, gal	5400
Piping:	
Material	316 or 321 ss
Diameter (reactor to the pump), in.	11.8 ID/12.15 OD
Diameter (pump to the reactor), in.	7.88 ID/8.19 OD
Sodium velocity:	
In the reactor, max., ft/sec	10.35
In the 11.8-in. pipe, ft/sec	4.5
Pressure drop:	
In the reactor, psi	49
In the circuit, psi	3.8

The two loops have a common return line to the reactor and a common storage tank. The joint to the return line is made just before it enters the

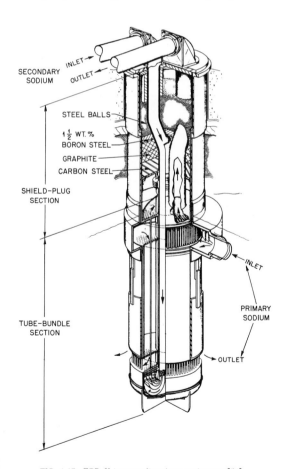

FIG. 4.17—EBR-II intermediate heat exchanger [54].

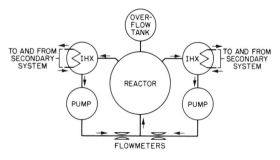

FIG. 4.18—Rapsodie primary sodium system [18].

primary shielding tank. The common tank is located in a room below the rooms containing the primary loops. The tank is surrounded by sufficient shielding to allow access to either of the primary loops after the reactor is shut down and that particular loop is drained. However, all primary equipment that may require cleaning or repairing periodically is accessible from the floor deck. Each has a removable shielding plug to facilitate removal of the equipment for maintenance. This type of maintenance can be carried out when the reactor is shut down and the loop is drained. The reactor vessel can remain full of sodium.

The reactor, the intermediate heat exchanger, and the pump each have a free surface that permits maintenance. With a free surface the shield plug of each piece of equipment is in a neutral atmosphere, and all the leakproof closures are at the level of the deck where they are easily accessible. Closures are made with a torus seal except for the reactor vessel, which uses a tin-bismuth dip seal.

The fluid in the secondary system is sodium. During the first phase of reactor operation, the heat production is dumped to the atmosphere through sodium-to-air heat exchangers. In the second phase these exchangers can be replaced by steam generators which could transmit the energy to a turbine generator.

4.2.1.2.6 PLUTONIUM-FUELED FAST BREEDER REACTOR (PFFBR) STUDY [12].

The primary system is composed of three coolant loops having a common point in the reactor vessel. Each loop contains a sodium pump, check valve, and the shell side of an intermediate heat exchanger (Table 4.3, Fig. 4.19, and Fig. 4.20).

Table 4.3—Performance Data for PFFBR Coolant Systems [12]

Sodium flow per loop, lb/hr	8.3×10^6
Sodium flow per loop, gal/min at 650°F	20,200
Pipe diameters:	
Reactor to IHX, in.	20
IHX to pump, in.	24
Pump to reactor, in.	20
Velocities in system:	
Reactor to IHX, ft/sec	22.4
IHX to pump, ft/sec	15.3
Pump to reactor, ft/sec	22.4
Design temperature, primary system, °F	1050
Operating temperatures:	
Reactor outlet to IHX, normal operation, °F	1000
IHX to pump to reactor, normal operation, °F	650
Shutdown and refueling, °F	600
Design pressure, primary system, psig	125
Material in primary system	304 ss
Pressure drop in system, ft of Na	223
IHX loss	17.0
Piping, reactor outlet to IHX	16.0
Piping, IHX to pump	8.0
Piping pump discharge to reactor	17.5
Reactor entrance and exit loss	11.5
Fuel element	141.0
Pump entrance loss	1.0
Check valve	11.0
Total sodium volume, cu ft	4500
Total sodium weight, lb	232,000
Cycle time, sec	33.4

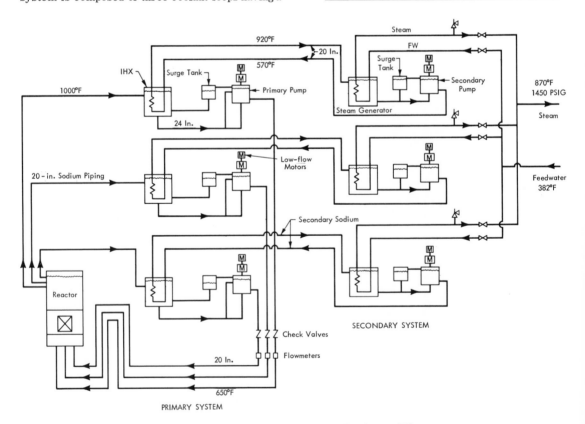

FIG. 4.19—PFFBR heat-transport system flow diagram [12].

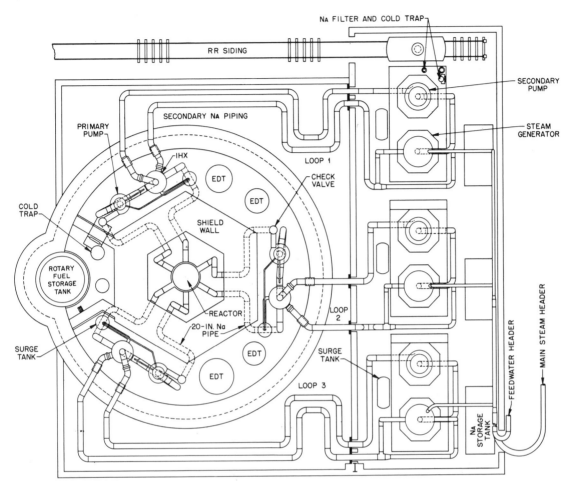

FIG. 4.20—PFFBR heat–transport system, plan view [12]. EDT represents equipment decay tank.

A ventilated space of 8 ft is provided adjacent to the reactor where the piping turns to go underneath the shield wall. There are no penetrations of the 11.5-ft-thick shield wall surrounding the reactor. The wall is laid out in a hexagonal pattern with the pump and IHX tank centered on a line parallel with one of the exterior sides. Coolant piping is located in tunnels 6 ft below the bottom of the shield wall. A minimum of four bends is taken in each piping run, and a distance equal to three trench widths is maintained between turns to prevent neutron streaming. Space is provided outside the shield wall to allow access of the crane hook to the IHX and pump tanks. Equipment storage tanks are located between the primary loops in the equipment compartment.

The primary piping is constructed of ASTM A-358 type 304 stainless steel. A wall thickness of 3/8 in. was selected for structural stability. Insulation is installed on the secondary containment, and induction heating is provided. Aerogel insulation is used in trenches and other close clearance places; conventional insulation is used at all other locations.

4.2.1.2.7 HALLAM NUCLEAR POWER FACILITY (HNPF) [19]. The primary system consists

of three independent loops, each of which is directly connected to the reactor vessel. Three independent loops were chosen for flexibility of operation. Thus, if one loop is out of service, the reactor can be operated with the remaining two loops. In event of failure of two loops, the reactor is shut down, and the third loop has the capacity to remove decay heat.

Each primary loop (Fig. 4.21) includes a variable-speed centrifugal pump, an intermediate heat exchanger, power-actuated valves in the reactor inlet and outlet lines, and a check valve in the inlet lines. The inlet line throttling valve is used mainly during reactor shutdown to control convective sodium flow for removal of decay heat from the reactor core. The check valve prevents reverse flow. The reactor vessel serves as an expansion tank for the primary loops. The reactor vessel, which is pressurized to prevent inleakage of air, is maintained at a positive pressure of 1 to 6 in. water by a helium atmosphere above the surface of the sodium pool.

The reactor outlet temperature during normal full-power operation is maintained constant at 945°F by the plant control system. At this temperature the sodium pool extends approximately 11 ft above the top of the moderator cans. During normal

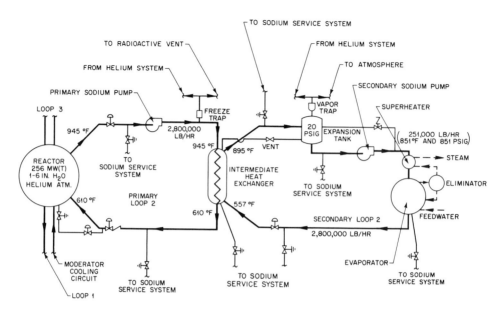

FIG. 4.21—Hallam (SGR) heat-transport system [77].

operation the sodium flow rate in each loop depends on the pump speed, which is adjusted by the plant control system to maintain the desired steaming rate of the turbine, with a minor trim on the primary loop to maintain a scheduled reactor inlet temperature (610°F for 100% load). Since all three circuits are controlled from a single control system, flow in the three circuits is balanced unless the operator desires to run any circuit at constant load or at a given ratio to the other two circuits.

All piping and components of the primary loops are located in shielded cells below the reactor room floor level. A nitrogen atmosphere is maintained in these cells, and the pressure is kept slightly above atmospheric. The reactor cavity and the pipe tunnels are separated by a diaphragm-seal assembly. Immediately outside the diaphragm seal are the inlet-line throttling valves and outlet-line blocking valves. The piping then passes through the shielded pipe tunnels to three individually shielded cells, each of which contains the lower portion of the pump and the intermediate heat exchanger of one of the primary loops. If the sodium piping and the intermediate heat exchanger of a shutdown loop are intact, the loop can be drained and its cell can be entered on a controlled basis while the reactor and the two remaining loops are in operation.

4.2.2 SECONDARY SODIUM SYSTEM

4.2.2.1 Design Discussion and Methods

The discussion in Sec. 4.1.3 has established the function and important criteria to be considered in the design of a secondary sodium system. The design of the system itself consists in establishing operating conditions, system arrangement, piping design and layout, and emergency cooling calculations (Sec. 4.2.3.2).

4.2.2.1.1 ESTABLISHING OPERATING CONDITIONS. The operating characteristics of the secondary system are determined by the characteristics of the primary system and of the steam cycle. As in the primary system, it is advantageous to establish a minimum flow rate in the IHX and steam generator. The minimum flow rate results in minimum shell diameter for a specified pressure drop in any design and minimum pump power.

4.2.2.1.2 SYSTEM ARRANGEMENT. The secondary-system intermediate heat exchangers can be located in one or more buildings designed to contain radioactivity; the rest of the secondary system components are in a separate building. Following are some secondary loop design features:

The loops in the secondary system can have a header or have no common point. The chief advantage of the header system is operating flexibility; all IHX's can supply all steam generators through a header system. The number of units and the number of loops do not have to be isolated while the remaining units continue to operate. A header system generally requires a multiplicity of valves. During a steam-generator leak, the water may enter any one of the other units and contaminate the entire system until the leaking unit can be isolated. A separate loop system can be operated with no valves, and in the event of a leak the water from the leaky steam generator does not contaminate the other loops. Maintenance requires complete loop outage with associated IHX, pump, and steam generator. The two systems are schematically illustrated in Fig. 4.22.

Unless a header arrangement is used, each loop contains an IHX, a pump, and a steam generator, and the number of loops is the same as in the primary system. The secondary sodium flow is usually through the tube side of the heat exchanger

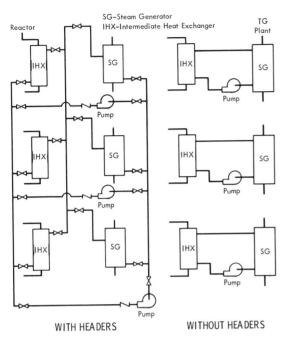

FIG. 4.22—Types of secondary heat-transport systems (intermediate loops).

(Sec. 4.3.5) and the shell side of the steam generator (Sec. 4.3.6).

The pump should normally be located at the outlet of the steam generator where it operates at the lowest system temperature.

If any secondary loops are used for emergency cooling (Sec. 4.2.3.1), they should have hot and cold legs of sufficient height to permit natural circulation, and the steam generator should be located above the IHX. Emergency-cooling calculations should be integrated with those for the primary system (Sec. 4.2.3.2).

The system should have adequate drain and vent connections. Systems should be filled from the bottom to prevent gas entrapment unless vacuum filling is used.

4.2.2.1.3 PIPING. The design of the secondary system piping is similar to the design of the primary system piping (Sec. 4.3.4.1). The maximum design pressure is governed by the pressure surge expected should a sodium—water reaction occur in the steam generator (Sec. 4.3.6.1.1.1). In the Fermi plant, for example, the system operating pressure is 20 psig, the maximum sodium—water reaction pressure is estimated at 175 psig, and the system design pressure is 300 psig.

The problems of secondary system layout and flexibility are simplified because of the reduced shielding requirements. Two additional anchors may be introduced into the system at the points where the piping penetrates the containment structure. If such anchoring is not desirable, a bellows can be designed around the piping to maintain containment while allowing the pipe to move. The integrity of the bellows should be assured by periodic testing.

4.2.2.2 Specific System Designs

Typical flow diagrams for secondary systems are shown for Fermi in Fig. 4.16, Hallam in Fig. 4.21, Dounreay in Fig. 4.15, and PFFBR in Figs. 4.19 and 4.20.

4.2.3 EMERGENCY-COOLING SYSTEM

4.2.3.1 General Considerations

Emergency cooling can be provided in several ways. One way is to provide a separate loop. This arrangement requires an auxiliary heat exchanger and either a gravity-flow or a pumped cooling loop separate from the normal cooling loops for the plant. An intermediate NaK loop, together with a heat sink external to the building, could be used to remove heat from the heat exchanger. Any pumps used in this scheme should be powered by a special emergency power supply with high reliability. Another method involves auxiliary pony motors attached to the main pump shafts. These motors, connected to an emergency power supply, turn the pumps at a low speed sufficient to supply the flow needed to remove decay heat. Finally, natural circulation can be provided, and, unless the power supply is guaranteed for the period of emergency cooling, the heat-transport system should be operable by natural circulation. The proper selection of relative elevations of the reactor, the intermediate heat exchanger, and the steam generator ensures emergency cooling by natural circulation. Careful determination should be made of the relative elevations and the system pressure drops to be sure that the sodium will circulate under the available thermal driving head. Check-valve pressure drop is an important consideration.

There are two advantages to using a separate loop to handle decay heat: (1) the loop is independent of normal operating requirements, allowing the normal operating loops to be designed for their chief function, i.e., power operation, and (2) the check valve for the loop can be designed for low pressure-drop requirements.

There are some disadvantages to a separate loop, e.g., increased heat losses, increased number of reactor vessel nozzles, and increased costs and space requirements.

In actual practice loss of flow after power failure is not instantaneous; pump coast-down after power failure gradually reduces flow. Methods for calculating natural circulation are referenced in Sec. 4.2.3.2.

4.2.3.2 Emergency-cooling Calculations

The heat-transport transient conditions following pump failure should be calculated to include pump flow decay, natural circulation, and behavior of the steam cycle.

4.2.3.2.1 PUMP FLOW DECAY. Immediately after power failure the sodium flow obeys the pump decay law. This law can be derived from the torque-balance equation, $T_m + T_P + T_I = 0$. References 20 and 21 contain information on pump flow decay.

4.2.3.2.2 NATURAL CIRCULATION. Natural circulation in a complete loop is due to the difference in weight of the two columns of liquid connected together to make a heat-transport loop, usually referred to as the hot leg and the cold leg. References 22 through 25 contain information on natural circulation.

4.2.3.2.3 STEAM SYSTEM. In the event of a total power failure, the feedwater flow stops very rapidly because in the steam loop the pressure stays relatively constant instead of decreasing as the square of the flow. Since the heat-transfer coefficient is practically proportional to the mean velocity (or mean flow), the heat transfer stops when the flow stops.

Flow can be reestablished in the steam generator by one of the following means: (1) increase, by a large amount, the inertia of the feedwater pump, (2) put a gas-cushioned hot-water capacity on the discharge of the feedwater pump and after the check valve, and (3) dump the steam very rapidly into the atmosphere. Steam is released

due to the pressure differential, and the hot water flashes to steam according to the pressure decay. The third means is the least costly one.

4.2.4 AUXILIARY SYSTEMS

4.2.4.1 Sodium Service Systems

The primary sodium service system stores and purifies the sodium received by tank car or other means and monitors and purifies the primary coolant as required during reactor operation. The major components of this system are storage tanks (Sec. 4.3.9), cold traps and other sodium purification equipment (Sec. 4.3.7), and plugging indicators and other contaminant-measuring devices (Sec. 4.3.8).

Sodium of high purity has a lower corrosion effect on the materials used in the primary coolant system. The sodium-purification system should maintain the sodium oxide content at or below a prescribed value. This value for stainless-steel systems is usually around 30 ppm. For reactors with niobium-, zirconium-, and tantalum-clad

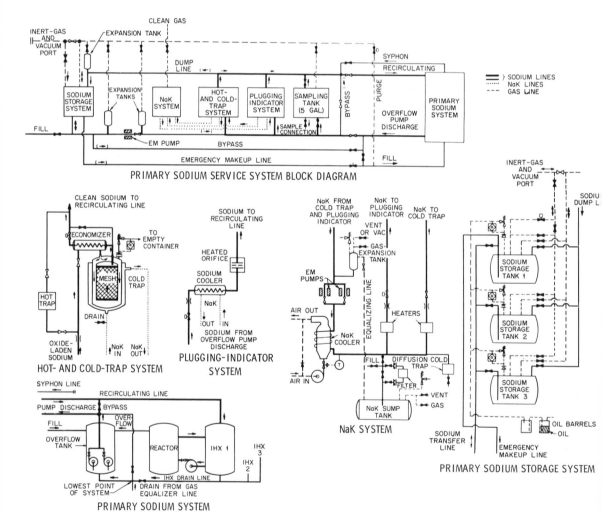

FIG. 4.23—Fermi primary sodium service system [31].

fuel, the requirement may be less than 10 ppm of oxygen. Storage space should be provided if it is necessary to remove the sodium from the primary system. Since Na^{24}, the principal radioactive isotope, has a 15-hr half-life, sufficient decay time should be allowed prior to draining the sodium into any unshielded facility.

The flow diagram for the Fermi primary sodium service system is shown in Fig. 4.23. Sodium received in railroad tank cars is melted by hot oil circulating through coils in the tank car. The sodium is transferred by putting a vacuum on the storage tank and pressurizing the tank cars with an inert gas. There are three storage tanks. Before the primary coolant system is filled, the sodium charge is purified by circulating the sodium through the cold-trap system. For system cleanup during reactor operation, a side stream of the primary coolant is pumped from the overflow tank to the cold trap and returned. Cold trapping is done on an intermittent basis, but frequently enough to maintain the sodium purity at prescribed levels.

The primary sodium service area, including flow-through sodium sampling facilities, should be shielded; limited access after a prescribed decay period can be allowed. An inert atmosphere should be maintained in the area to eliminate sodium–air reactions. Provisions should be made for the collection of sodium leaks.

The secondary sodium service system receives, stores, monitors, and purifies the secondary sodium

in much the same manner as the primary system but without shielding or containment. The Fermi secondary sodium system is shown in Fig. 4.24. The storage tanks are filled during the initial sodium loading of the secondary coolant system. The tanks can be used for dumping during shutdown since any one of the three secondary coolant loops can be drained to facilitate removal or repair of components. The tanks can also be used as a dump in the event of a sodium leak. The sodium is purified by a cold trap operating at a maximum pressure of 40 psi. The pressure head is supplied by any one of the three secondary sodium pumps or by the 100 gal/min electromagnetic pump installed in the cold-trap system. Connecting piping to the cold trap can be valved off automatically to ensure separation of the individual secondary loops. Four plugging indicators (one in each of the three independent loops and one in the cold-trap circuit) are used to monitor the oxide content of the secondary sodium.

Some simplifications in the secondary sodium over the primary system are possible: (1) air cooling is used for the cold trap and the plugging indicator, (2) tanks can be made of carbon steel and piping of chromium-molybdenum or carbon steel, and (3) secondary containment is eliminated.

4.2.4.2 Inert-gas Systems

The inert-gas systems provide and maintain an inert atmosphere over all liquid-sodium and NaK

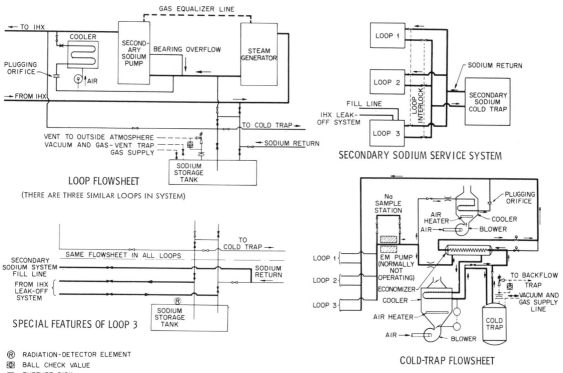

FIG. 4.24—Fermi secondary sodium service system [31].

surfaces to prevent oxidation of the liquid metals. The systems are also used to prevent inleakage of contaminants. The systems are characterized by negligible temperature transient activity and low demand. Auxiliary functions of the inert-gas supply system include (1) supply of purge gas for fuel-handling operations where radioactive gas and liquid metal are present, (2) transfer of liquid metal, and (3) inert gas for remote maintenance operations. In all of these applications the gas is relieved to the waste-gas disposal system as required (Sec. 4.2.4.3). Batch fluid transfer can be effected by pressurizing or by a combination of pressure and vacuum transfer. Centrifugal pumps (for batch or continuous transfer) may also require a static inert-gas pressure over the inlet to produce an adequate suction head.

Pipeline backflows from contaminated areas to clean areas are generally prevented by block valves, check valves, liquid seals, and other mechanical devices, and, if the contaminants are radioactive, the mechanical devices should be backed up by pressurized inert gas on the clean side of the mechanical device.

Closed radioactive systems also employ inert-gas spargers, which are gas lines penetrating to the bottom of a liquid-metal tank and are used to maintain suspension of solids. Inert-gas transfer jet pumps are also used for liquid transfer. For high lifts jet transfer is sometimes facilitated by the introduction of inert gas at the base of the jet dip tube, which reduces the effective density in the lift leg. Inert gases may also be used to provide an inert atmosphere wherever necessary to prevent a sodium–air fire in the event of a leak.

4.2.4.2.1 GENERAL CONSIDERATION. 4.2.4.2.1.1 Gas-selection Criteria. Cover gases should be chemically inert to sodium and other materials present and should not contribute to the deterioration of these materials under operating conditions. The nuclear properties of the cover gas should not create unreasonable shielding problems. Cost, availability, and application to the detection of fuel-element failure and system leaks are other considerations. Inert gases used for fast breeder reactors are limited at present to helium, nitrogen, and argon. Other rare gases are expensive and limited in availability. Gases such as CO_2 and CO are not used because of reactions with sodium. A comparison of the physical and nuclear properties of the three gases used is given in Table 4.4 and in Figs. 4.25, 4.26, and 4.27.

Helium is a fixed gas (chemically inert). Its nuclear properties are the most desirable of the three gases. Until about 1960 high cost and uncertain supply were the principal objections to its use; however, unrestricted commercial quantities are now available, and expanding production facilities are resulting in lower costs. Advantages are ready leak detection (by mass spectrometer), low pressure drop in lines, high heat-transfer coefficient, and applicability to regenerative absorber purifiers. (Cryostatic purification becomes practical only for very large systems.) Flowing helium apparently has a scouring action on the interior surfaces of containment; it sweeps out fission products and other objectionable adherents. Helium is difficult

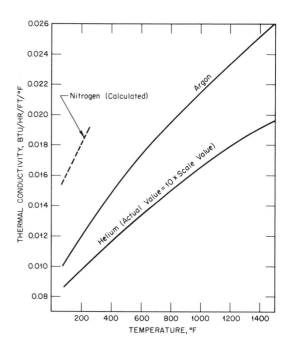

FIG. 4.25—Thermal conductivity of argon, helium, and nitrogen (at 1 atm). (Data from Report WADD–TR–61–96, 1964, and NBS Circular 564, 1955.)

to contain. Because of its low density and high diffusion rate, it is the least efficient gas for volume-displacement purging, and in recirculating systems it is the most difficult to pump.

The Hallam reactor (HNPF) employs a 1/4-psig helium blanket over the primary sodium and a 20-psig helium blanket over the secondary sodium. (The higher pressures employed over secondary sodium systems are designed to maintain a net positive suction head for the circulating pumps.) The SRE employs helium as a primary coolant blanket and nitrogen in the secondary liquid metal system.

The advantages of nitrogen are low cost and convenience of supply (e.g., a plant-site generator). The physical and nuclear properties of nitrogen are intermediate between helium and argon. Nitrogen

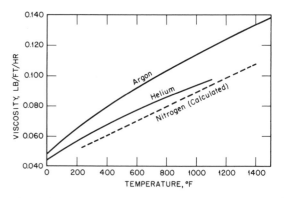

FIG. 4.26—Viscosity of argon, helium, and nitrogen (at 1 atm.). Note: To convert to centipose values, multiply by 1488/3600 = 0.412. (Data from Report WADD–TR–61–96, 1961, and NBS Circular 564, 1955.)

Table 4.4—Properties of Gases[*]
(At STP Unless Otherwise Noted)

	Helium	Nitrogen	Argon
Atomic number	2	7	18
Molecular weight	4.003	28.016	39.994
Density:			
G/liter	0.1785	1.2505	1.7838
Lb/cu ft at 70°F	0.01034	0.07247	0.1034
Specific gravity (air = 1)	0.1380	0.9672	1.380
Boiling point, °C/°F	−268.0/−452.1	−195.8/−320.4	−185.9/−302.6
Vapor density at boiling point, g/cm^3	0.016	0.00461	0.0059
Liquid density at boiling point, g/cm^3	0.125	0.804	1.3985
Heat of vapor at boiling point, cal/g	5.7	47.6	38.9
Melting point, °C/°F	−272.2/−457.7	−209.9/−345.8	−189.3/−308.7
	(at 26 atm)		
Vapor pressure at melting point, mm Hg		5.6	96.4
Heat of fusion at melting point, cal/g	<1	6.1	6.7
Specific heat:			
c_p, cal/g/°C at 15°C	1.25	0.248	0.125
c_p/c_v at 15°C	1.66	1.40	1.67
Thermal conductivity (k):			
Cal/sec/cm/°C	34.3×10^{-5}	58×10^{-6}	38.2×10^6
Btu/hr/ft/°F	0.995	0.1683	0.1109
Viscosity (μ)			
Centipoise at 70°F	0.0196	0.01744	0.02210
Centipoise at 700°F	0.033	0.031	
Centipoise at 1330°F	0.044	0.041	
Critical temperature, °C/°F	−267.9/−450.2	−147.1/−232.8	−122.3/−188.1
Critical pressure, atm	2.26	33.5	48.3
Critical density, g/cm^3	0.0693	0.311	0.536
Solubility in water, cm^3/g	0.0088		5.6

Gas	Mass number	Abundance	Half-life	Mode of decay	β energy (max.), Mev	γ energy (total), Mev	Activity[†] for (n, γ) reaction at 10^{10} neutrons/cm^2/sec, $\mu c/cm^3$	
							Zero decay	24-hr decay
Helium	3	0.00013	Stable					
	4	100	Stable					
Nitrogen	13		10 min	β^+	1.2	0.1	∼0	∼0
	14	99.6	Stable					
	15	0.38	Stable				1.29×10^{-6}	∼0
Argon	36	0.337	Stable			0.026		
	37		35 days	E.C.[‡]				
	38	0.063	Stable					
	39		265 years	β^-	0.565			
	40	99.6	Stable					
	41		110 min	β^-	2.2	1.4		
	42		3.5 years	β^-			3.76	9.78×10^{-6}

[*] Compiled from Refs. 26 and 27.

[†] Neglecting activity from sodium vapor and fission products present. Nitrogen activity assumes 1% argon impurity present. Helium activity assumes 1% air impurity present (containing 1% argon).

[‡] Electron capture.

is not entirely chemically inert and cannot be used over liquid-lithium systems. The Dounreay reactor formerly employed a nitrogen blanket over the primary liquid-metal coolant. Although the Dounreay operations were satisfactory, reactors designed for higher operating temperatures must take into consideration the possibility of nitriding embrittlement. Nitriding progresses most actively in the 850 to 1100°F range and generally occurs at the liquid-metal interface. Thin-section high-alloy parts (valve bellows, Bourdon tubes) are subject to fatigue failure in this environment. For these reasons nitrogen is used more as an auxiliary atmosphere in conjunction with secondary containment to prevent sodium fires.

Although argon is chemically inert, radioactivity wise it is the least desirable of the three gases. For example, the equilibrium activity of argon cover gas directly over the core of Fermi is computed to be 6×10^{-3} $\mu c/cm^3/$Mw(t) at STP owing to the formation of A^{41}. This figure does not include activity due to sodium vapor, fission products, and other impurities. Shielding for the Fermi argon pipe line is designed for one-third the AEC permissible dose rate, or 0.75 mr/hr, and utilizes 8 1/2 in. of steel. If helium were substituted for argon, the presence of radioactive Na^{24} vapor (gamma = 2.78 Mev) would require 3.2 in. of steel. These shielding requirements are based on the approximation of a line-source problem, disregarding pipe-wall shielding and self-shielding and assuming no decay in passage. This over-simplified estimate ignores concentrations, temperatures, pressures, sister isotopes, and additive effects.

Lubrication for pumps and compressors in contact with A^{41} should have good gamma-radiation stability.

Use of high-density argon gas as a displacement purge is efficient and permits the least contamination during refueling or maintenance. The argon leak rate is low by virtue of its mass. However, argon does not lend itself to mass spectrometer

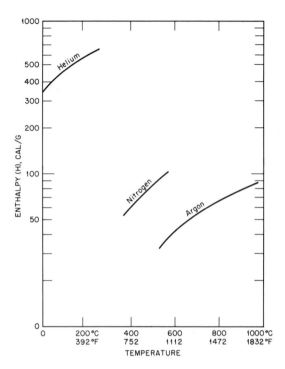

FIG. 4.27—Thermodynamic properties—enthalpy of argon, helium, and nitrogen (at 1 atm). Calories per gram × 1.8 = Btu per pound. (Data from Report WADD-TR-61-96, 1961, and NBS Circular 564, 1955.)

pickup, and leaks are difficult to locate except by radiation meters. It is difficult to determine such contaminants as nitrogen and oxygen in an argon atmosphere by chromatographic methods.

The Dounreay reactor was recently converted to argon cover gas. Argon is also used over the primary sodium in the EBR-II and over both primary and secondary systems in Fermi and is intended for use in Rapsodie.

Early indication of fuel-cladding rupture is important. The detection of fission products in the reactor cover gases is a promising technique. This consideration may influence the choice of cover gas. The principal gaseous fission products of fast breeder fuel are krypton and xenon isotopes plus some A^{41}. Of these, A^{41} is most readily detectable but would require that helium or nitrogen be used as a cover gas in lieu of argon. An alternate scheme for CO_2-cooled thermal reactors has fuel elements charged with helium to take advantage of the fast response of helium detectors in the event of a fuel-element leak. This technique applied to fast breeder reactors would limit the choice of reactor cover gas to argon or nitrogen.

4.2.4.2.1.2 Impurities. The terms employed to express the quality of commercial bottled gas are not standardized. For example, helium produced under the authority of the U. S. Bureau of Mines is stripped of natural gas and other heavy contaminants by adsorption in activated charcoal. Total contaminants (principally hydrogen and water vapor) are held to 10 ppm, but without guarantee, and the bottled gas may be sold as hospital grade,

welding grade, grade A, or grade xx. Welding-grade or lamp-grade nitrogen "compressed over water" is generally sold with a maximum dew-point guarantee and is of higher purity than gas "compressed over oil." Argon gas of welding quality is 99.995% pure. Nitrogen is 99.99% pure, and helium is 99.997% pure. (Fixed gases are not reported in these analyses.) The purity requirements for the Fermi argon cover gas are given in Table 4.5.

Table 4.5—Fermi Argon-gas Specifications

Content[*]	As purchased	Purified
A	99.996%	99.998%
O_2	10 ppm	Trace
N_2	10 ppm	10 ppm
H_2	5 ppm	5 ppm
CO_2	5 ppm	Trace
H_2O	5 ppm	Trace

[*] Neglecting other noble gases.

Process units for the further purification of commercial gas should be selected for the specific application. For example, no useful purpose would be served by stripping out traces of other noble gases from a helium system. Purification methods and equipment are discussed in Sec. 4.3.10.1.

Impurities may be introduced into cover-gas systems from residual air and water vapor, from inleakage during fueling and maintenance operations, or from degassing of reactor materials. Sodium—water reactions may develop pinhole leaks, which lead to hydride-hydroxide-monoxide contamination. Sodium vapor is always present in proportion to the partial pressure of sodium (Chap. 2).

Hydrogen in the cover gas can be obtained as free hydrogen from steel surfaces during degassing operations; from sodium—water reactions; and from alcohol, kerosene, ammonia, and other hydrogen-bearing compounds reacting with sodium. Hydrogen in a fast breeder core has a moderating effect that is objectionable. Hydrogen embrittlement from dissolved sodium hydride may result in fatigue of thin-section zirconium, niobium, and stainless-steel hardware. Even low concentrations of sodium hydride in sodium can be dissociated at reactor operating temperatures, and the nascent hydrogen liberated may materially accelerate the embrittlement process. The explosive range of hydrogen-air—argon mixtures is shown in Fig. 4.28. Critical ranges are not greatly affected by pressure changes (up to 4 atm) but are appreciably extended by elevated temperatures. For example, hydrogen-in-air mixtures are flammable in the 8 to 72% range at ambient temperature, and this range is increased to 6 to 82% at 750°F.

In practice, such compounds as sodium oxides, hydrides, hydroxides, and carbonate deposit out as hard tough complexes which build up at the liquid-metal surface. All these compounds may be present in bulk sodium within the solubility limits indicated in Chap. 2. They reduce heat transfer, restrict small passages, and plug up close-tolerance parts. If the concentration of these compounds is objectionably high, they can be removed by techniques and equipment discussed in Sec. 4.3.7.

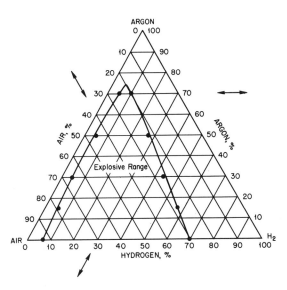

FIG. 4.28—Explosion limits in the system hydrogen—air—argon. Percent argon: 0.0, 15.0, 30.0, 50.0, and 70.0. Lower limits: H_2, 6.8, 6.0, 4.8, 4.4, and 4.4; air, 93.2, 79.0, 65.2, 45.6, and 25.6. Upper limits: H_2, 69.3, 57.0, 43.3, 27.0, and 10.3; air, 30.7, 28.0, 26.7, 23.0, and 19.7. [From J. Heiningen, Rec. Trav. Chem., 55:65 (1936).]

Sodium hydroxide (NaOH) is soluble in sodium to 100 ppm at 300°F and must be dissociated by pyrolysis (above 600°F) for a reduction below this level. In theory, NaH may also be decomposed by pyrolysis (above 750°F). Practical operations report successful cold trapping of NaH at 240°F (down to 10 ppm) and failure to decompose NaH in operations above 900°F owing to the suppression of dissociation by solution in excess sodium and by argon cover gas.

Nitrogen may also be considered an impurity in argon or helium systems owing to its possible nitriding at high temperatures.

Equipment and techniques for removing impurities in cover gas, either in use or prior to disposal, are discussed in Sec. 4.3.10.1.

4.2.4.2.2 DESIGN FEATURES. 4.2.4.2.2.1 Gas-supply Systems. Liquified gas storage may be economical even for a use as low as 20,000 cu ft per month if the use is constant. Liquid supply has the additional advantage of higher purity since less contamination is involved in transfer.

Gas supplies can be contracted by truck-trailer complete with a control cabinet and standby storage unit. The truck-trailer packages are usually 30,000 to 40,000 standard cu ft units at 2500 to 3000 psig.

Nitrogen can be generated at the plant site. Catalytic ammonia generators produce a clean supply of nitrogen in the 10,000 cu ft/hr range but require hydrogen traps. Gas- and oil-fired generators are available at 50,000 cu ft/hr and up but produce an impure product unsuitable for direct liquid-metal contact. Both oil- and gas-fired systems and smaller combustion-engine units require auxiliary purification systems, which makes them uneconomical for most nuclear-plant applications.

The initial Fermi nitrogen and argon storage facilities were tank farms consisting of standard gas cylinders mounted in banks and serviced by a truck-trailer. The permanent argon system was arranged in twin headers (one standby) at 2640 psig delivering metered gas at 200 psig to a NaK purification train downstream. Alarm and switchover to the standby header is provided. The Fermi argon-gas purification train is designed for 105°F service and operates at a lower ambient temperature. Process vessels include a backflow trap to protect supply piping from liquid-metal blowback, a purification tank, and a downstream entrainment trap. The control station, which distributes purified argon gas to the various plant facilities at 40 psig, includes metering units for accountability and for locating system leaks, a continuous oxygen analyzer, a spring-loaded valve relieving atmosphere at 45 psig, and a quick-closing valve. This valve is actuated by a high pressure and/or activity signal and isolates the reactor building from the inert-gas supply system as required by containment criteria.

4.2.4.2.2.2 Cover-gas Systems. Figure 4.29 illustrates the evolution of cover-gas systems for use with radioactive-sodium loops. System A is suitable only where the cover gas is the same as the ambient atmosphere and compatible with sodium. System B requires a flexible diaphragm, which may not be sufficiently reliable for use with sodium systems. With an inexpensive inert gas, system C would work if no radioactivity or sodium vapor were present in the effluent gas at point P_2. Since there is radioactivity in the inert-gas system, only schemes D and E can be used. System D should be capable of withstanding whatever pressures are generated by temperature changes within the sodium system. This requirement is difficult to meet with pump seals and other seals in the system. It is, however, the most reliable of all the systems available for sodium service and is very desirable from a maintenance standpoint. System E, a recirculating system like that used at Fermi, when operating properly, can provide the most uniform pressure over a liquid-metal system even when the temperature changes considerably. It prevents the radioactive gas from leaving the liquid-metal system and permits reuse of the gas. Gas that has been in contact with liquid metal may in some respects be purer than gas that is admitted; i.e., there may be fewer contaminants in the gas leaving the sodium. The contaminants in the entering gas may react with the sodium. This system requires a compressor. Compressor requirements are described in Sec. 4.3.10.3.

In the design of the cover-gas systems, certain precautions should be taken: (1) Provisions should be made to maintain prescribed pressure differentials on various components with large volume changes induced by liquid-metal temperature fluctuations. For example, pressurized mechanical seals and inflatable seals are maintained at pressures slightly greater than the pressures of the systems they service. (2) All pipe lines (including instrument signal lines) communicating with reactor containment should be fabricated in compliance with reactor-containment criteria. These lines should be provided with high-integrity fail-safe motor-operated block valves at the limits of the contain-

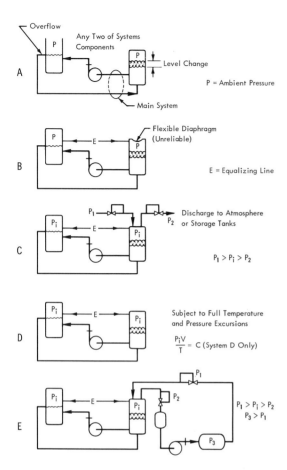

FIG. 4.29—Types of heat-transport inert cover-gas systems. The system shown in A is for liquids compatible with surrounding atmosphere; that in B is for liquids incompatible with air.

ment to effect reactor isolation in the event of an incident. (3) Condensing sodium vapor is a problem in communicating gas lines. All lines that might come in contact with sodium or sodium vapor should be heated (up to and including the appropriate block valves) and pitched to drain. Where there is a possibility of "burping," the exposed gas lines should be maintained at higher temperatures to prevent excessive stresses resulting from high-temperature sodium. Relief valves exposed to sodium may be backed up with rupture disks to shield the relief valve seats from solidified condensate. Special provisions are required in these relief valve–rupture disk assemblies to prevent pressure buildup in the space between the rupture disk and the valve seat caused by pin-hole leaks in the disk and/or temperature changes. Traps can be provided in relief lines to prevent a backsurge of air from failure of the relief valve to seat properly after a blowoff.

In Fermi the recirculating inert-gas system, shown in Fig. 4.30, maintains an argon blanket over the primary sodium units, e.g., the reactor proper, the primary sodium pumps, the overflow tank, and the intermediate heat exchangers. The recirculating gas system furnishes cooling gas to the fuel exit port and is an alternate supply of shaft purging gas to the primary sodium pumps and to the overflow pumps. The gas furnished can be recovered by the recirculating loop. The cover gas within the primary sodium units is equalized by interconnecting piping and is maintained at a positive pressure relative to the building to prevent inleakage of air. While the reactor is operating at constant temperature, there is no recirculation of gas. The effects of temperature transients in the primary sodium system are compensated for by discharge of cover gas, or makeup of cover gas from, the recirculating system. This transfer (in or out) is made through duplex (idle spare) pressure-regulating valves. Discharge is to a vacuum tank maintained at 10 psia, and makeup gas comes from a holdup and surge tank operated in the 20- to 35-psig range. The pressure differential is provided by three parallel gas compressors between the vacuum tank and the holdup and surge tank. The recirculating system also contains a vapor trap and cyclone separator installed downstream from the vacuum tank to protect the compressors from liquid-metal entrainment. Normal system operation requires only intermittent use of one compressor. The compressors cut in automatically in cascade to maintain 10 psia in the vacuum tank, and the lead compressor (the first compressor to come on the line) can be alternated to reduce the possibility of diaphragm-fatigue failure. The recirculating gas flow path (Fig. 4.30) is from the reactor through a breather line and twin regulating exhaust valves to a vacuum tank maintained at 10 to 12 psia. Gas passes from the vacuum tank through a sodium-vapor trap to three parallel compressors operating in cascade to maintain vacuum and discharge to a 35-psig surge tank. The surge tank supplies the reactor through twin regulating valves feeding to the reactor breather pipe. Two compressors can be operated simultaneously during refueling to supply cooling gas to the fuel exit port. The recirculating-gas loop is considered to be an extension of reactor-building containment. It relieves the waste-gas-disposal collection header through a manual valve. Clean argon is supplied manually from the inert-gas supply system by jumper hose makeup connections for miscellaneous periodic service and by permanent piping leads for purging, sealing, and servicing remote-maintenance operations. Flowmeters are installed on seal supply lines to signal leakage in excess of prescribed limits.

The secondary inert-gas system maintains an inert cover gas over the sodium in the steam generators, over the secondary sodium pumps, and in auxiliary units, such as surge tanks. The pressure-regulated supply lines to each of the steam-generator loops are equipped with individual flowmeters to indicate leaks. Secondary inert-gas systems relieve directly to atmosphere.

4.2.4.2.2.3 Auxiliary Atmospheres. Nitrogen can be used as an auxiliary atmosphere in portions of the reactor plant where a single failure would otherwise produce a sodium–air reaction. These and other typical applications of auxiliary atmospheres as used in the Fermi plant are described in subsequent paragraphs. Chapters 2 and 6 contain details on sodium–air reactions.

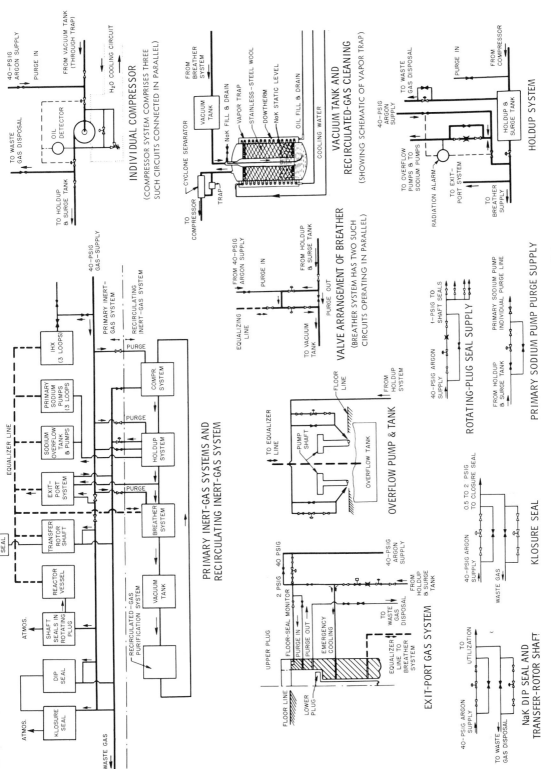

FIG. 4.30—Fermi primary inert-gas and recirculating-gas systems [31].

A typical sodium-air fire is characterized by low flames and dense Na_2O smoke. In theory, combustion temperatures can build up to the boiling point of sodium [29]. The ignition temperature for flowing sodium is about 250°F and ranges from 400° to 800°F over a still pool. When nitrogen is used to prevent open fires, sodium will not ignite, even at 1000°F, in an atmosphere containing less than 4% oxygen. However, slow oxidation with the evolution of smoke will continue down to 0.1% oxygen.

The Fermi containment building is separated by a steel and concrete floor into an above-floor section and a below-floor section. The floor is shielded to provide for above-floor access. The lower chamber is inaccessible and is serviced by an externally cooled depleted-air atmosphere. A secondary shell, or machinery dome, covers the reactor in the upper chamber to isolate any leaks in the reactor cover-gas system or the reactor seals. Below the floor the reactor vessel is encased in a secondary vessel, the primary shield tank, containing a nitrogen atmosphere under independent control. The pressure relations are covered in Chap. 6.

The below-floor atmosphere in Fermi is held to 130°F (max.) by two external cooling loops to prevent overheating and dehydration of the concrete biological-shield wall. These cooling loops are designed as extensions of the reactor-building containment. The 95% nitrogen below-floor atmosphere will prevent sodium fires in the event of a sodium leak. The primary shield tank requires an atmosphere of nitrogen to protect graphite shielding from oxidation; nitrogen will also prevent a sodium−air reaction in the event of a reactor-vessel leak.

The primary sodium service building, which contains cold-trap facilities, is sealed by an internal metal liner plate and is charged with nitrogen to prevent radioactive-sodium fires resulting from line rupture. This atmosphere is also continuously filtered and cooled by means of a closed external loop. Regulated makeup and exhaust lines maintain a slight positive pressure throughout the system.

The Fermi steam generators relieve on the sodium side through rupture diaphragms. To prevent sodium−air reactions or hydrogen−air reactions in the blowoff lines after disk rupture, the outlets are capped with light plastic diaphragms and the lines are charged with nitrogen.

4.2.4.2.3 DESIGN CALCULATIONS. 4.2.4.2.3.1 Purging or Makeup. Although some degree of mass displacement occurs during a straight-through purge of system atmosphere, the mechanism of exchange is more likely to approach perfect mixing owing to turbulence at the interface between the purged and purging gases. The initial displacement of air from a closed system by nitrogen gas can be considered a perfect mixing process down to 2% oxygen concentration. With a constant low purge rate, the instantaneous concentration of oxygen in the exhaust-gas stream is equal to the instantaneous concentration of oxygen averaged over the system volume.

For the continuous purging or makeup with clean gas (perfect mixing), the concentration of contaminants is reduced according to the relation:

$$C_{t_2} = C_{t_1} \exp(-Xt/V) \qquad (4.1)$$

where C_{t_1} = concentration of contaminant gas at time $t = 0$
C_{t_2} = concentration of contaminant gas at time t, min
V = system volume, cu ft
X = makeup or leak rate, cu ft/min
t = time, min

Given a 1000 cu ft system with an initial oxygen concentration of 0.21 (21%) oxygen in the purge gas and a purging rate of 20 cu ft/min, to reduce the oxygen concentration to 0.02 (2%) would require 113 min or 2260 cu ft of purge gas. Below 2% oxygen concentration, purging becomes less efficient, and further reduction can be accomplished more economically with a hot trap or vacuum where possible. Displacement of air by argon or helium is not economical. Where possible, large-volume systems should be evacuated. Pulling the pressure down to 100 μ absolute and refilling the system with clean argon or helium to atmospheric pressure reduces the original atmosphere to 132 ppm on the first cycle and to 0.017 ppm on the second cycle, assuming no inleakage of air during the vacuum cycle. For further economy, the gas backfill in the first cycle need not be full atmospheric pressure.

The purging of radioactive gas is complicated by the decay rate of the unstable isotopes present. The effect of radioactive decay combined with a perfect-mixing purge results in

$$C_{t_2} = C_{t_1} \exp\left[-\left(\lambda + \frac{X}{V}\right)t\right] \qquad (4.2)$$

where λ is the radioactive decay constant.

Diffusion rates control in instrument tubing and other small static systems. In these lines it may be necessary to oppose backdiffusion from contaminated areas by a sweep stream of clean gas. The mutual diffusion rate in a two-gas system is proportional to a diffusion constant D. Expressed in kinetic terms, Maxwell's diffusivity equation, with a constant 0.0166 derived by Gilliland [30], for gases A and B is

$$D = \frac{0.0166\, T^{3/2}(1/M_A + 1/M_B)^{1/2}}{P\left(V_A^{1/3} + V_B^{1/3}\right)} \quad \text{sq ft/hr} \qquad (4.3)$$

where M = molecular weight
T = temperature, °K
P = pressure, atm (abs)
V = volume of gas at boiling point, $cm^3/g/mole$

In this equation the gases A and B may diffuse at different rates. The coefficient D expressed the effect of temperature, pressure, and molecular weight on the diffusion rate in a two-gas system. Such a diffusion rate would also be determined by the length or the diffusion path and the instantaneous concentration differential between the two gas zones.

4.2.4.2.3.2 Allowable Leak Rate. Contamination of work-space atmosphere is permissible up to a level established for personnel safety.

If the contamination is introduced at some steady rate, as from a leak from reactor cover gas, the ventilation system should dilute the leak down to or below the maximum permissible level.

The total contamination introduced into any given work space in 1 hr is the product of the contamination level of the leak, A, and the volume leak rate V_L. The volume or air available for dilution is the product of work-space volume, V_1, and the number of air changes per hour, N, provided by ventilation.

The resulting contamination in the work space is

$$A_M = AV_L/(V_1N + V_L) \qquad (4.4)$$

If we assume that A_M is the maximum permissible value, then V_L is the maximum permissible leak allowed in 1 hr. Since the volume of the leak is negligible compared with the dilution volume, the equation can be written

$$A_M = AV_L/(V_1N) \qquad (4.5)$$

and the maximum permissible leak rate (per hour) is

$$V_L = \left(\frac{A_M}{A}\right)(V_1N) \qquad (4.6)$$

where A_M is specified by the AEC for the various isotopes of concern.

Activities of all other contaminants and fission products should also be included in fixing an allowable leak rate. The high leak rate of helium systems is explained by its low molecular weight and low viscosity since, according to Knudsen's law for molecular flow, flow rate is inversely proportional to molecular weight and, according to Poiseuille's law for viscous flow, inversely proportional to viscosity.

4.2.4.3 Waste-gas-disposal Systems

Waste-gas-disposal systems may be necessary to remove primary-system and fuel-handling-cycle system gases that may also be contaminated with radioactive fission-product gases and/or sodium vapor. Waste gas from other areas, such as containment building, ventilation systems, and decay-pool ventilation systems, is not normally radioactive and does not require a radioactive waste-gas-disposal system to handle it.

A waste-gas-disposal plant should conform to the following design criteria: (1) activity released to the atmosphere should be equal to, or below, specified maximum permissible concentrations in air, (2) provisions should be made to store any gas that cannot be disposed within these concentrations, (3) a suitable method of properly dispersing the gases in the atmosphere should be used to attain required dilution factors, and (4) sufficient capacity should be provided to handle the maximum possible release of waste gas from the gas systems.

There are two primary methods of waste-gas disposal: the waste gas can be stored for decay or vented up a stack with proper dilution factors. Perhaps the best waste-gas system is one in which these two methods are combined. Two holdup systems are in general use. In one of these the fission gases are adsorbed in preference to the inert gas. The fission gases do not remain adsorbed on the charcoal or adsorber but have a continuous atom exchange from the surface of the adsorbent and the gas. In effect they move from one adsorbent particle to the next and eventually out the end of the adsorber. They may remain in the adsorber long enough during this process to decay to acceptable levels for stack disposal.

In another holdup system (Fig. 4.31), the incoming gas enters the waste-gas collection header and then is fed to one of two absolute filters and compressed into one of the two decay tanks until the radioactivity levels allow stack disposal. When one decay tank is filled, the valves are switched to open the second tank. The system provides for intermittent discharge to the waste-gas system and allows sufficient dilution for the gas in one decay tank to be normally discharged to the stack after a few days. Decaying beyond 30 days is of little value since at that time the 10-year krypton is the controlling fission product.

No halide or metallic fission products will be evolved from the sodium surface since these either react with the sodium or are dissolved in the sodium. Studies indicate that the major gases evolved from the sodium are krypton and xenon [32].

4.2.4.4 Heating Systems

All sodium lines and sodium components should be provided, as necessary, with heating facilities to keep them above the melting point (208°F) of sodium. The need for thermal insulation is determined by the sodium operating temperature. Heating facilities are designed to heat from ambient to the desired temperature in a designated time. The Fermi sodium-heating elements are sized to heat the sodium to 400°F in 100 hr. To prevent sodium concentrate from solidifying and blocking lines, all associated cover-gas systems and lines exposed to sodium should be heated to, and including, the first line valve or rupture disk. Heating systems should be designed for sequence heating to avoid high pressures produced by thermal expansion of sodium in between two still-frozen sections.

Space heating of compartments is expensive and requires all hardware in the space to be designed for at least 400°F service. Circulation of heated gas in secondary containment systems is feasible and has been used in Rapsodie. The use of the piping system as a resistance unit (or of secondary containment housing) is highly efficient. Limitations of system geometry present problems in the control of current paths for even heat distribution and the elimination of electrical shorts at support points and end effects at equipment connections.

Trace heating by Dowtherm, Aeroclor, fused salts, and other liquids have had no known application to date; however, NaK has been used as a heat-transfer liquid in sodium systems, most commonly for cold traps and plugging meters. NaK is probably the only commercial heat-exchange medium with the required range for sodium systems (ambient to 1200°F). It requires many of the same precautions as the main sodium system design.

Two widely used heaters for sodium systems are low-frequency induction heaters using cables

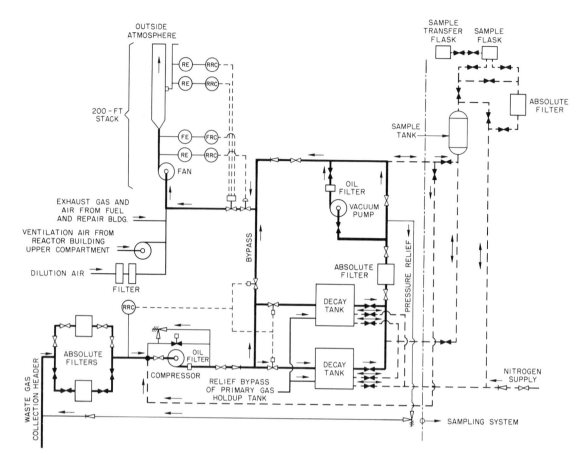

FIG. 4.31—Fermi waste-gas-disposal flow diagram [31]. RE, radiation element; RRC, radiation recorder-controller; FE, flow element; FRC, flow recorder-controller.

and tubular resistance heaters. The advantages and disadvantages of the two systems are listed in Table 4.6. Both systems can be monitored with thermocouple elements to signal failure, and induction circuits should include a grounding alarm. Signal circuits should be arranged to fail safe.

Induction-heating cable should be installed so that it does not interfere with adjoining flux fields, and individual coils should clear the carbon-steel sleeve by some 3 in. for best transformer geometry. Stainless-steel pipe should be encased in a carbon-steel sleeve to provide magnetic pickup. These requirements, together with 1000°F service insulation, may result in a 2-in. line becoming as large as 12 in. in outside diameter. Since induction-heating elements are on the outside face of the insulation, the induction load should be balanced for even heat distribution, with allowance for line hardware, turns, and end effects. Fermi installations use 12 turns of No. 10 wire per foot around sodium service lines; about 80% thermal efficiency is realized.

Tubular heaters are usually operated below rated voltage to extend service life. Arc protection may be necessary to prevent damage to the component in the event of a short. This protection can be accomplished automatically by ungrounded systems which fail safe when grounded, by balanced

systems which fail safe on unbalance, or by cladding installed between the heater tube and the piping. Alarms can also be used to indicate grounds or shorts. It is impractical to control large-scale electric heating circuits by variable voltage. Heating circuits are generally operated by off-on manual or thermostatic control. Heaters installed on piping to prevent thermal shock or a sodium freeze during accidental introduction of sodium should be in operation at all times.

4.2.4.5 Vacuum Systems

Vacuum may be necessary for (1) transfer of sodium, (2) purging operations, including degassing of systems, and (3) cleaning of hardware by vacuum distillation. The low sodium-vapor pressures at transfer temperatures allow transfer of sodium into tanks or vessels by vacuum. Vessels or tanks (and connecting devices) which use this process should be specified for vacuum service. Mechanical vacuum pumps should be provided with cold traps on the inlets to protect the pumps from liquid-metal condensate. In-line instruments subject to vacuum damage should be removed, valved off, or isolated by a freeze seal, and transfer lines should be closed against siphon action.

Table 4.6—Induction Heating Vs. Tubular Resistance Heating

Advantages	Disadvantages
Induction Heating	
1. Long life and low maintenance if radiation-resistant insulation is used	1. Impractical to induction heat flat surfaces
2. Induction coils can be wound around the insulation and thus are accessible during maintenance	2. Extraneous power losses in adjacent magnetic material
3. Quality control does not require X-ray of wire as may be the case for tubular resistance heaters	3. Possible uneven heating owing to flux discontinuities
4. Hot spots and burnouts are reduced	4. Stainless-steel pipe requires a carbon-steel jacket as a magnetic medium for induction heating; this also increases overall diameter of the component
5. The induction wire can itself be the lead wire thereby allowing accessible above-floor connections	
Resistance Heating	
1. Can be used on all types of surfaces; does not have to be wound around an object to obtain heating	1. May have a short life and require undue maintenance if not carefully fabricated and installed
2. Provides a large concentration of heat	2. May require a sheath between heater and component to prevent burn through of component during a short
3. Does not require magnetic material to induce heating	3. Expensive per unit length; may require X-ray to assure accurate centering of heater element
	4. Has to be placed inside insulation, making replacement difficult or impractical
	5. Subject to hot spots and possible burnout
	6. Connections to lead wires because of cost may have to be made below floor in inaccessible locations.

Economy is effected if purging operations are preceded by a vacuum pulldown (in the $500-\mu$ range). Vacuum distillation of sodium from hardware that has been submerged in liquid metal is less hazardous during operation than a mixed alcohol wash or a steam-spray process, particularly for radioactive parts and for apparatus in which large sodium deposits may be trapped. Typical operation is at 850°F and 500 μ.

4.3 Components

Components for sodium heat-transport systems generally are not standard items. They should be designed, fabricated, tested, handled, and installed for maintenance-free operation when operated within limits and should perform the functions for which they are intended within these limits.

Once a concept has been developed, the owner, the fabricator, a separate design firm, architect-engineer, or prime contractor should detail a set of specifications for the component.

4.3.1 GENERAL SPECIFICATIONS

The following sections cover those aspects of design, fabrication, handling, inspection, test, and installation which are common to all components for liquid-metal systems.

4.3.1.1 Applicable Codes

The codes that govern the design and fabrication of components used in fast reactor systems are the same as those used for other reactor systems [33]. Additional discussions about codes is given in Chaps. 3 and 6.

In general, the codes to be followed are those of the American Society of Mechanical Engineers (ASME), the American Standards Association (ASA), and the American Society for Testing Materials (ASTM). The designer should also be familiar with the laws of the state and/or municipality in which the reactor is to be located since all states do not accept the recommendations of the national groups.

The ASME publishes the Boiler and Pressure Vessel Code in several sections. Those sections which apply to pressure vessels for nuclear service are: Section I, Power Boilers; Section II, Material Specifications; Section III, Nuclear Vessels; Section VIII, Unfired Pressure Vessels; and Section IX, Welding Qualifications. The code is kept current by periodic revisions. In addition, the ASME considers questions pertinent to the code and requests for interpretations. When the replies to these questions and requests are approved by the ASME Board on Codes and Standards, they are published in Mechanical Engineering as Code Cases.

The design of nuclear pressure vessels is covered in appropriate sections of the Boiler and Pressure Vessel Code, applicable Code Cases, and the Addenda to the Code and to the Code Cases. The Code establishes minimum safety requirements for new construction but does not cover deterioration that may occur in service.

Nuclear power piping should conform to the latest edition of Section I, Power Piping, of the ASA B-31 Code for Pressure Piping and applicable nuclear cases as issued by the Committee on Nuclear Piping.

ASTM publishes the Book of ASTM Standards in ten volumes. Those volumes which apply to components for nuclear service are: Part I, Ferrous Metals (Specifications); Part II, Nonferrous Metals (Specifications) Electronic Materials; Part III, Methods of Testing Metals (except chemical analysis); and Part V, Masonry Products, Ceramics, Thermal Insulation, Acoustical Materials, Sandwich and Building Constructions, Fire Tests.

The Book of ASTM Standards is published every third year. Annual supplements containing the new and revised standards are published in the intervening years. These standards are used in the specifications of materials for service other than that covered by the ASME Boiler and Pressure Vessel Code. In some cases the ASTM and ASME materials standards are interchangeable. In such cases this fact is noted on the first page of the ASTM material specifications.

4.3.1.2 Materials

Materials for components and piping in sodium heat-transport systems include carbon steel, chromium-molybdenum steels, and stainless austenitic steels. Selection is based primarily on adequate mechanical properties at the proposed temperature of operation. EBR-I used type 347 stainless at 600°F. Fermi is using type 304 stainless steel at 900°F and 2 1/4 wt. % Cr-1 wt. % Mo steel at 820°F. The USSR BR-5 uses type 321 stainless steel at 900°F. Rapsodie plans to use type 316 or 321 stainless steel to 1000°F. Selection of materials should be based not only on operating temperatures and pressures but also on accident conditions within specified limits.

Sodium heat-transport systems have thus far been generally designed with stainless steels as the primary-system material. There is a lack of previous experience with the low-alloy chromium-molybdenum steels. To ensure satisfactory properties in addition to applicable ASTM specifications, the chemical composition is usually more stringently defined than the nominal composition of materials. As an example, the composition limits shown in Table 4.7 were required for type 304 stainless steel used in the Fermi plant. Of particular interest is the carbon content, 0.08 wt.% max. and 0.04 wt. % min. This range at Fermi was further restricted in certain special applications, such as the reactor pressure vessel. In these cases a 900°F tensile test showing a minimum strength was required if the material contained less than 0.052 wt. % carbon.

In the Fermi plant the following ASTM material specifications were required: (1) ASTM Specification A240-54 Grade S for plates, sheets, and strips (unfired pressure vessels); (2) ASTM A376-55T Grade TP304 for seamless austenitic pipe for high-temperature service (up to and including 12-in. diameter); (3) ASTM A358-55T Grade S for electric-fusion-welded austenitic chromium-nickel alloy steel pipe for high-temperature service (8-in. diameter and larger made from plate); (4) ASTM A213-55T Grade TP304 for seamless austenitic steam boiler, superheater, and heat-exchanger tubes; (5) ASTM A249-55T Grade TP304 for welded austenitic stainless-steel boiler, superheater, heat-exchanger, and condenser tubes; (6) ASTM A351-52T Grade CF8 and ASTM A296-55, as applicable, for stainless-steel castings; and (7) ASTM A182-55T Grade F304 and A336-55T Class F8, as applicable, for stainless-steel forgings.

Since sodium is a highly effective reducing agent, specific attention is placed on eliminating inclusions, especially in thin sections. Mass transport is of concern in systems containing both austenitic and ferritic materials. The latter is decarburized by sodium. Stainless steel can be carburized in sodium with excess carbon. A more detailed discussion of stainless-steel carburization is given in Sec. 4.3.7.3.2.

Table 4.7—Type 304 Stainless Steel

Allowable Chemical Composition Limits for Fermi [34]

Element		Composition,[*] wt. %				
		Castings	Forgings	Plate, sheet, strip	Rolled-bar stock	Pipe and tubing
Carbon	Max.	0.080	0.080	0.080	0.080	0.080
	Min.	0.040	0.040	0.040	0.040	0.040
Manganese	Max.	1.50	2.00	2.50	2.00	2.00
	Min.	None	1.00	1.00	1.00	1.00
Silicon	Max.	2.00	1.00	0.85	1.00	0.75
	Min.	None	0.50	0.40	0.50	0.40
Phosphorus	Max.	0.040	0.040	0.035	0.045	0.030
	Min.	None	None	None	None	None
Sulfur	Max.	0.050	0.035	0.030	0.040	0.030
	Min.	None	None	None	None	None
Chromium	Max.	21.00	20.00	20.00	20.00	20.00
	Min.	18.00	18.00	18.00	18.00	18.00
Nickel	Max.	11.00	11.00	11.00	11.00	11.00
	Min.	8.00	8.00	8.00	8.00	8.00
Cobalt		Cobalt analysis required for all material				

[*] Percentages subject to AISI tolerances.

4.3.1.3 Fabrication

All components in a heat-transport system should be carefully cleaned before the system is placed in service. In complex equipment where components are not readily accessible to cleaning fluids, each component should be cleaned before assembly and kept clean thereafter. In less complex equipment it may be cheaper and more desirable to clean the whole system after installation of components. The designer should carefully evaluate the system and all its parts to determine which parts can be cleaned after installation in the reactor plant and which parts should be cleaned during manufacture.

Cleanliness eliminates contaminants (1) which may block small passages in fuel elements, (2) whose nuclear properties could alter the reactivity of the reactor core, (3) which may react with the coolant, leading to the formation of oxides and hydroxides that have to be removed from the system before operation, and (4) which interfere with mass-spectrometer leak-test operations. Detergents are generally used to remove hydrocarbons, and thorough water rinsing is used to remove all traces of the detergent. After the components have been cleaned, provisions should be made to maintain this cleanliness. During shipment open ends of the components should be sealed weathertight, and silica gel or other drying agents should be placed inside the assembly to reduce condensation on the walls.

Surface finishes for materials in contact with, or exposed to, sodium may run from a fine finish of 10 μin. (rms) up to 250 μin. (rms), depending on the service intended. In some cases even a mill finish may be satisfactory. The surface finish should be sufficiently smooth (1) to provide for good ultrasonic testing and dye-penetrant testing; (2) to prevent undue stress concentrations particularly in thin members, such as bellows, or in highly stressed members, such as springs; (3) to seal mating surfaces or to provide a bearing surface for plastic sealing materials; (4) to reduce friction between sliding or rotating bearings; (5) to prevent galling of mating surfaces; and (6) to reduce mass transport and localized corrosion attack. Seal surfaces should have the finest finish. They may be lapped better than 10 μin. (rms). Bearing surfaces may vary to 64 μin. (rms.) General-purpose surfaces are around 250 μin. (rms).

Longitudinal and circumferential joints in tanks or vessels which contact sodium on one side only should be double butt welded or equivalent. Welds should have full penetration and be ground smooth to the inside of the tank or vessel. The electrodes or weld material to be used should produce a weld meeting the following standards: (1) the weld metal should have mechanical properties comparable to those of the parent metal, (2) the weld should be free from defects, porosity, and slag inclusions, (3) the weld should produce a clear radiograph, and (4) slag should be easily removed.

It is important to ensure that no potential leaks are blocked or covered during manufacture or assembly by slag, paint, oil, or other contaminants which could be attacked by the liquid metal. Coated electrode arc welding, because of possible small slag inclusions which may not show up under test, may result in a potential trouble spot after a reduction with sodium. One fabrication technique utilizes seal welds with bolts or other fasteners to take the structural load. Another technique utilizes an inert-arc sealing weld run on the inside of the vessel followed by a metallic arc structural weld [35].

Heat treatment of austenitic stainless-steel components to relieve stresses after welding is generally performed where possible to avoid stress corrosion from sodium hydroxide. This is important if inspection and/or repair is to be performed after the piece is removed from sodium and cleaned with any hydroxide-forming matter or exposed to a hydroxide-forming atmosphere.

4.3.1.4 Installation

Cleanliness should be stressed during installation. If work is done inside any of the components, a clean room should be installed over the component and the rigid cleanliness rules maintained. Grinding, cutting, or welding particles should be kept out of the components. Field erection of piping requires careful attention to maintain the cleanliness of the internal surface. The use of fusible inserts on field welds eliminates the need for internal access to piping. Where access is necessary, either to complete or repair a field weld, workmen should be provided with protective clothing to preclude the need for recleaning. On smaller size piping where access is not possible, the root pass in butt welds should be made with care since a repair would probably contaminate the inside surface. An inert-gas backup atmosphere should be used on all field welds to prevent oxidation of the metal in the vicinity of the weld. In the installation of valves in the piping, care should be taken not to damage the valves. For example, excessive heating at the weld ends may distort the valve seat.

4.3.1.5 Inspection and Testing

Inspection and testing of components and piping for heat-transport systems begins with the base material and is not completed until the entire system is accepted by the customer. Tests fall into the following sequence: (1) destructive tests on the base material to determine chemical and mechanical properties, (2) nondestructive tests on basic shapes, such as piping, sheets, castings, and forgings, (3) inspection of welds, (4) leak testing and performance tests of entire components or piping assemblies, and (5) leak testing and acceptance tests on completed systems.

Destructive tests are performed on the base metal to determine its metallurgical properties. Typical requirements for type 304 stainless steel, for example, are given in Sec. 4.3.1.2. Material should generally not be accepted without a minimum of two analyses of chemical and mechanical properties. If there is conflict between the two reports, a third analysis could be performed by an impartial laboratory. In addition to the above, a reference sample from each heat should be retained by the owner for further evaluation.

Principles and procedures of the various methods of nondestructive inspection are discussed in detail in Refs. 36–38. Besides visual inspection and mechanical measuring, the following techniques are used in the examination of basic fabricated shapes: ultrasonics, eddy current, radiography, fluid penetrants, and magnetic particle. For the Fermi plant ultrasonics and/or radiography were required for castings only. Radiography was performed in accordance with ASTM designations E71-52 and E94-52T with some minor additions, including the prohibition of permanent marking on any surface that would be exposed to sodium.

In ultrasonic inspection a beam of ultrasonic energy is directed at the component, and the energy transmitted through the component or reflected from it is indicated on an oscilloscope or a recorder. If there is no flaw within the part, the ultrasonic beam will travel through it with little loss of energy. Most commercial testing is done within the range of 1 to 25 Mc/sec. Ultrasonic tests are used to detect flaws, to measure thickness, and to study metallurgical structure. The method has high sensitivity, permitting detection of minute defects, and great penetrating power, allowing examination of extremely thick sections. It has good accuracy and fast response and thus permits rapid and automated inspection.

In eddy-current testing an eddy current is electromagnetically induced in the test specimen by means of external magnetizing coils or poles that do not touch the specimen. Eddy-current devices can measure thickness of metallic sheets and walls from one side only, measure thickness of nonmagnetic coatings on magnetic base materials and vice versa, identify or separate materials by composition and structure, and detect discontinuities in metallic materials. Low-frequency electromagnetic fields from 60-cycle power sources, variable-frequency motor-generators, or electronic oscillators are used for eddy-current testing of ferromagnetic materials and parts. Audiofrequency electromagnetic fields are used in tests on nonmagnetic metallic materials and electrical conductors to determine dimensions or detect discontinuities.

Radiography is used to detect internal flaws and defects in materials. With X rays or gamma rays, it is possible to detect shrink cavities, gas holes, cracks, and inclusions as small as 1% of the thickness of the section being examined. For sodium components maximum sensitivity is desired. A minimum of two exposures for each position is required. One of these can be retained by the owner for record.

Penetrants such as Zyglo and dye penetrant are useful in detecting surface fissures and cracks produced during grinding or heat treating. These defects may be obscured by seams, but their presence can cause fatigue failures. It is important that all the penetrant be removed before completing the welds. Magnetic-particle inspection reveals the same type of defect shown by fluid-penetrant methods, but with proper application it can show up flaws as much as 3/8 in. below the surface. Its use is limited to ferromagnetic materials. Inspection of welds can be made by liquid penetrant of the finished weld and sometimes of the root pass as well. The complete weld after the liquid penetrant test is also radiographed. In the Fermi plant all radiographed acceptance tests were in accordance

with the standards of the ASME Boiler and Pressure Vessel Code, Section VIII (P UW-51, Part M). The intent should be to eliminate defects that may propagate by themselves. Nonpropagating defects should not exceed the ASME Code standards.

In the leak testing of individual components, piping subassemblies, or completed assemblies, two objectives should be met: establish the leak rates and find the leaks. Hydrostatic or pneumatic gross leak tests should be made. Where recleaning is a problem, such as inside complex structures of the reactor vessel or inside complicated piping assemblies, a pneumatic test can be made. Both tests readily determine porous areas in materials. Leaks are discovered by a drop in the gas pressure over a predetermined period of time and/or by bubbles that form in a soap solution applied on the external surface of the component.

Mass-spectrometer leak testing may be performed by creating a vacuum within the component. When a prescribed vacuum has been achieved, the exterior is blanketed with an inert atmosphere (helium gas). The mass spectrometer, connected to the interior, detects the presence of helium if there is a leak.

Small leaks have been found in vessels after they have been heated that could not have been found before they were heated; therefore it is recommended that in some cases the pipe or vessel be heated to about 400°F before testing. Because of the expense involved in performing this test and the small likelihood of leaks developing in thick materials or multipass welds, the factors involved should be carefully considered before specifying this test.

An alternate method is to apply a slight excess pressure in the system and use an external detector. For large equipment two detectors of high sensitivity are available: the infrared gas analyzer, which uses nitrous oxide as a tracer, and the ionization type halogen detector, which uses chloroform, freon, or other volatile halogen compounds. Of the two, the infrared gas analyzer is perhaps the more sensitive. A mass spectrometer can also be used as an external detector; the inside of the component is, in this case, pressurized with helium.

References 39 and 40 cover aspects of radiographic testing; Refs. 41 to 44, ultrasonic testing; 45, eddy-current testing; and Refs. 46 and 47, liquid-penetrant testing.

The usual performance tests, such as pressure-drop determinations on valves, and flow, head, and power determinations on pumps, are performed on components for heat-transport systems. Water may be used with extrapolation or conversion of data for application to sodium. After it has been tested, the component should be completely disassembled and cleaned. Acceptance testing normally checks for proper connections, assembly, rotation, alignment, mechanical adjustments, and performance.

4.3.2 REACTOR VESSELS

4.3.2.1 Definition and Purpose

The ASME in the Boiler and Pressure Vessel Code, to clarify the use of the code for the design and fabrication of the several types of vessels used in reactor systems and to differentiate between these vessels, has defined a reactor vessel to be ". . . any vessel, any tube, or any assemblage of tubes, regardless of size, in which nuclear fuel is present and in which the nuclear chain reaction takes place." By this definition, for example, the tubes of a pressure-tube reactor are, collectively, a reactor vessel; also, a tank containing fuel sub-assemblies arranged in a critical array surrounded by a heat-transfer medium (reactor coolant) is a reactor vessel. The ASME Code Case 1270-N specifically does not make use of either the word "primary" or "containment" in its definition of a reactor vessel but reserves these terms for defining those vessels which are secondary or subordinate to the reactor vessel. By such definitions the ASME Code has established a consistent nomenclature for the several types and uses of vessels employed in reactor plants that are built under the requirements established by the code. For a more detailed discussion of the ASME Code, see Chaps. 3 and 6.

In addition to the basic purpose defined above, the reactor vessel provides: (1) a means of distributing coolant flow for the removal of heat generated in both the core and the blanket, (2) support for core and blanket subassemblies, (3) support, where necessary, for biological shield plugs, which, in turn, support fuel-handling and reactor-control mechanisms, (4) possible fuel-decay storage, and (5) space for thermal and radiation shielding. The reactor vessel is considered within the context of this chapter as a component in the heat-transport system. Fuel-handling mechanisms and fuel-decay storage are described in Chap. 7, shielding in Chap. 8, and control-rod drive mechanisms in Chap. 9.

The general arrangement of the Fermi reactor vessel is shown in Fig. 4.32. In the EBR-II design the primary tank supports the fuel-handling and reactor-control mechanisms. Sealing against the air atmosphere above floor is done at the top of the primary tank rather than at the reactor vessel.

4.3.2.2 Design Criteria

4.3.2.2.1 RADIATION AND RADIOACTIVITY. Safety and reliability of reactor vessels is the primary consideration of design since these vessels contain radioactive materials, are subject to high-level neutron and gamma irradiation, and are inaccessible for periodic examination and maintenance. Design, fabrication, and inspection are primary considerations; cost considerations are secondary.

High-level neutron irradiation affects the mechanical properties of the stainless steel used for the reactor-vessel shell. Although stainless steel does not suffer from a shift in the nil ductility temperature associated with ferritic steels, its properties do change and require evaluation and monitoring. Maximum radiation exposure is continually being extended. At present no significant deterioration of mechanical properties is reported for exposures up to 2.6×10^{22} neutrons/cm^2 of fast neutrons (greater than 1 Mev) [48]. For a life of 10 years, the fast flux is thus limited to 10^{13} neutrons/cm^2/sec. Surveillance specimens are being installed more extensively in reactors to monitor vessel materials.

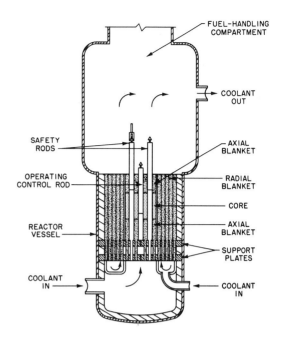

FIG. 4.32—Fermi reactor-vessel arrangement [31].

4.3.2.2.2 PRESSURE AND TEMPERATURE. Because of the high specific power in fast reactors, the cores are considerably smaller than those of thermal reactors; this should result in a somewhat smaller vessel even with a blanket surrounding the core. The low operating pressure of sodium-cooled fast reactors affects wall thickness, method of end closure, design of nozzles and other penetrations, internal shields and baffles, and external supports.

The temperature considerations relating to vessel design are primarily those resulting from temperature variations. The vessel itself should have provisions for gross thermal expansion and for equalization of this expansion where it is important to maintain a relative position between various components on or within the vessel. Flow passages should be carefully sized so that the coolant mass flow can match the heat generation well enough to minimize the temperature differences across internal structural members. Rapidly occurring temperature differentials can result from coolant-temperature transients and can impose severe thermal stresses within the vessel wall and other structural members. It is generally simpler to provide these members with thermal-shock protection, i.e., baffles or thermal shields, than to design the member for the thermal transient. Stresses resulting from transient as well as from steady-state conditions are covered in detail in Chap. 3. Details on thermal shielding are given in Sec. 4.3.2.4.2 of this chapter.

4.3.2.2.3. FLOW PATTERN. The coolant flow pattern required within the reactor vessel determines major features of the vessel design, such as internal baffling, location and number of nozzles, and pressure requirements for individual portions of the vessel. Determination of the flow pattern consists in establishing the number of passes, both in series and in parallel, past the fuel, blanket, and shielding, and the direction of flow. It may be desirable to distribute the flow to individual subassemblies so that there is a minimum of difference in the coolant exit temperatures between subassemblies. Individual orificing can be done within the fuel support structure, and additional orificing can be done in the subassembly. The pressure drop that can be attained through such orifices may be limited. For outer blanket elements requiring the least cooling, an additional pressure drop can be taken before the orifices by external valving through a separate line or by internal orificing from a high-pressure to a low-pressure plenum. In the first case the pump outlet flow in the primary loop can be split into two pipes, one to feed the core subassemblies and a smaller one to feed the radial blanket subassemblies. The vessel in this case has twice as many inlet nozzles as there are primary loops.

Sodium-cooled fast breeder reactors can have upflow or downflow of coolant through the core and blanket. The advantages of upflow are that the coolant is flowing in the direction of natural thermal circulation and the pressure is lowest at the top of the reactor, i.e., where it is necessary to make seals on equipment and rotating plugs. Upflow requires mechanical or hydraulic hold-downs. The advantages of downflow are that the temperature at the top of the reactor vessel is lowest, and thus control-rod drives, plug, and fixed fuel mechanisms are in the coldest part of the system; and the hydraulic forces on an individual fuel element are downward, and thus mechanical hold-down is not required.

With upflow, the simplest arrangement of nozzles and internal baffling results if the coolant is brought in at the bottom of the vessel and discharged near the top. In water reactors there are several overriding considerations that make it desirable to bring the coolant in near the top: (1) penetrations are avoided in the reactor vessel below the top of the core, (2) inlet nozzles can be more readily cut if the vessel needs to be replaced, and (3) the inlet coolant is along the vessel wall and cools it and the thermal shield. In contrast, in liquid-metal reactors: (1) containment protects against the failure in a lower penetration; (2) because of low pressure, lack of corrosion, and high metal ductility, the need for vessel replacement should be considerably lessened, and (3) cooling requirements in the vessel wall and the shield wall are small and can be handled by a small bypass of sodium.

4.3.2.2.4 FUEL SUPPORT AND HANDLING. Accurate alignment between the vessel, the plug, plug equipment, and the vessel internals are requirements that result from several design concepts normally embodied in sodium-cooled fast reactors, e.g., the reactor fuel elements are tightly held in a rigid core configuration to avoid reactivity effects due to inward fuel movement, the fuel-handling scheme requires that the fuel-handling mechanism be capable of accurately locating fuel elements under sodium in a completely closed and sealed vessel, and the control and safety rods, extension shafts, and drives require accurate alignment to ensure reliability of rod movement.

The Fermi and EBR-II reactors are designed to provide frequent replacement of fuel. For this reason both plants are designed so that refueling can be accomplished in a minimum of time. In both cases fuel handling is done internally within the primary sodium, and fuel is inserted in, and removed from, rotating storage racks. The rack in EBR-II is separate from the reactor vessel, i.e., it is in the primary tank, whereas in Fermi it is located in a part of the reactor vessel called the transfer-rotor section. The fuel-handling equipment is permanently located and operates through a single rotating plug in Fermi and through a double rotating plug in EBR-II. The plug provides biological shielding against full-power reactor operation.

In advanced reactors fuel replacement should be a more infrequent operation. For example, it should be possible to utilize a fixed plug with either refueling from the face of the plug or with removable fuel-handling machines installed to operate under sodium only during refueling (Fig. 4.33).

4.3.2.3 Support and Alignment

External supports of a reactor vessel should transmit the load of the vessel and its internal structures with a minimum increase in the vessel membrane stresses. The supports should be designed to allow for any differential expansion which may occur during start-up. The vessel radial movements should be taken up by flexure, rollers, pinned columns, or by other comparable arrangements. Vertical movement should be accounted for. Differential vertical movements may be accounted for by Belleville springs located in the columns or by self-compensating columns. The support design should minimize the movements produced by other attachments to the vessel, such as piping nozzles.

There are several advantages to be gained by supporting the vessel at the top flange: (1) the upper vessel flange is at the lowest vessel temperature, and radial motion is minimized, (2) the full load of the vessel plug can be taken directly into the support member instead of being carried through the thin vessel wall, and (3) the plug is kept at floor level, which minimizes vertical movement of equipment and reduces the need for expansion joints between the vessel and other containment.

In EBR-II the reactor vessel rests on the bottom structure of the primary tank. The primary tank is supported from a structure built upon the top of columns.

4.3.2.4 Vessel Components

4.3.2.4.1 PLENUMS. The reactor-vessel inlet plenum functions as a flow-distribution header for the incoming reactor coolant. If the coolant is distributed separately to the core and blanket, there are two plenums, one of high pressure for core flow and the other of low pressure for blanket flow. The inlet plenums should be designed to provide proper flow distribution to the core and blanket and also to remove the heat produced within the structure by neutron and gamma irradiation. In EBR-II the fuel support structure is integral with the inlet plenum. In Fermi the fuel support plates are removable and rest on a fixed structure. Differential movement between piping to the inlet plenums and the reactor is accommodated by suitable pipe

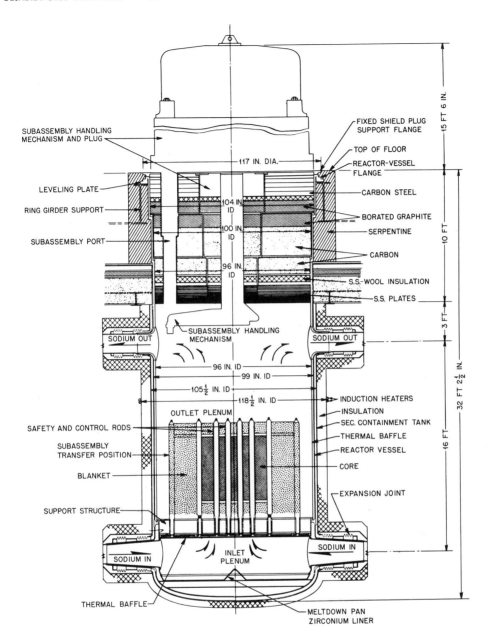

FIG. 4.33—PFFBR reactor vessel [13].

hangers and by piping flexibility. Reinforcement of piping penetrations is covered by the ASME Code.

For some reactor designs (Fermi, Dounreay, Rapsodie), a meltdown section was built into the lower plenum as part of the flow-distribution baffles. Its design is such as to spread molten fuel, in the event of core meltdown, into a flat noncritical configuration. It can be made of, or covered with, a material such as zirconium which does not form a low-melting eutectic with uranium or plutonium. Since the reactor vessel is usually made of materials that form such eutectics, the lower reactor-vessel head is lined either inside or out with a nonreacting material to form a secondary crucible for containing molten fuel in a noncritical array.

When a reactor outlet plenum is located above the core, its volume and/or height requirements may be determined by one or more of the following considerations: (1) sufficient height to allow proper coolant mixing, (2) sufficient height to fulfill the space requirements for fuel-handling and holddown mechanism, and (3) sufficient volume to provide a reservoir of constant-temperature coolant which will serve to reduce bulk coolant temperature transients during scram or other power changes. In the Fermi design the fuel-handling requirement dictated plenum size. In EBR-II the vessel cover is removed before refueling.

4.3.2.4.2 THERMAL SHIELDING.

The purpose of the thermal shield is to offer the following protection to the reactor vessel wall: (1) to minimize temperature transients, (2) to attenuate high-energy neutrons so as to avoid significant radiation damage, and (3) to reduce steady-state thermal stresses. The shield is normally made up of one or more cylindrical sections structurally separated from the vessel wall and from each other to maintain annuli for coolant flow. The plate thickness is determined by the maximum allowable temperature gradient within the plate. This gradient is produced by gamma and neutron heating; the higher the heating, the thinner the plate. If there is more than one plate, the inner plates are normally thinner than those close to the vessel wall. Provision should be made to prevent or reduce backflow into the thermal shield or blocking of flow from the thermal shield due to flow from the core or blanket subassemblies and internal circulation within the annuli.

4.3.2.4.3 PLUGS AND SEALS.

As discussed in Sec. 4.3.2.2.4, the complexity of the reactor-vessel plug is predicated primarily upon the fuel-handling concept. If rotating plugs are used, the major problem becomes the sealing of the plug against the vessel. The plug may be thick (up to 10 or 12 ft) and correspondingly heavy. The plug or plugs should be aligned for rotation during fuel handling. Differential expansion between vessel and plug should be accommodated. At Dounreay this is done by means of roller assemblies; at Rapsodie, by a combination of springs and flexible joints; and at Fermi, by a three-race bearing.

Two types of seals between the vessel and the plugs have been utilized, i.e., a rotating mechanical seal (Fermi) and a liquid-metal dip seal (EBR-II and Dounreay). While not in operation, the liquid metal may be partly frozen as in EBR-II. If a fixed plug is used, it can be sealed against the vessel flange by means of O-rings or other fixed seals.

4.3.2.4.4 OTHER VESSEL COMPONENTS.

A reactor vessel may also contain core, blanket, and shield support structures; fuel and blanket material

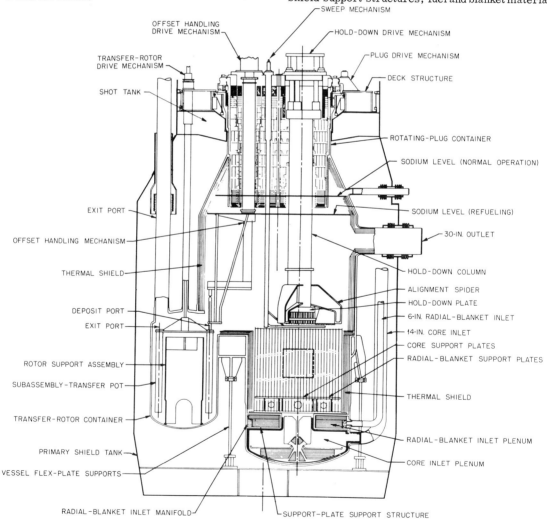

FIG. 4.34—Fermi reactor vessel [31].

in the form of subassemblies, subassembly hold-down devices, control rods, rod drives, reflectors, neutron sources, oscillators, fixed or rotating plugs, and fuel-handling mechanisms. Some of these items are discussed elsewhere in this chapter or in other chapters.

4.3.2.5 Specific Vessel Designs

4.3.2.5.1 FERMI REACTOR VESSEL. The reactor vessel shell (Fig. 4.34) is composed of four parts: the lower vessel, upper vessel, transfer rotor container, and the rotating plug. The vessel is designed and built in accordance with Section VIII of the ASME Boiler and Pressure Vessel Code as modified for all applicable nuclear vessel code cases. In addition, further integrity is incorporated by the use of conservative design criteria. The design is based on conditions and limits listed in Chap. 3. The design conditions that result from consideration of the operating conditions are given in Table 4.8.

The lower reactor vessel is cylindrical with a 111-in. inside diameter and with a dished elliptical 2 to 1 bottom head. The wall is 1 1/2 in. thick in the plenum region and 2 in. thick above. The lower portion of the vessel has three 14-in.-OD inlet nozzles supplying the core inlet plenum for core coolant flow and three 6-in.-OD inlet nozzles for supplying the radial-blanket inlet plenum. The blanket-flow plenum also serves as the support structure for the core and the radial-blanket support plates. The support plates rest on an outer ledger ring and an inner seal rail, which are welded to the top of the support structure. A meltdown section is located in the core-flow section inlet plenum (Fig. 4.35). It consists of a flat 1/8-in.-thick zirconium liner bolted to the top of a 1/2-in.-thick

Table 4.8—Fermi Reactor-vessel Steady-state Design Conditions [31]

	Pressure, psig	Temperature, °F
Inlet piping and nozzles	110	750
Core inlet plenum	93.5	1000
Remainder of reactor vessel	50	1000

baffle plate, which is a part of the shielding and baffling for the lower head of the vessel. The dimensions and geometry are such that material resulting from a meltdown can be collected in the shape of a flat circular subcritical slab, 7 ft in diameter. Three vertical baffles and a conical flow guide serve to direct coolant flow. The conical flow guide also serves, in case of a meltdown, to disperse the molten fuel as it enters the plenum and thus prevents a buildup of fuel in the center of the meltdown section. A secondary meltdown section is located immediately below the bottom head of the lower reactor vessel and follows the contour of the head. It consists of 6-in. cubes of 5% borated graphite bonded together with boron-containing cement to form a crucible capable of containing molten uranium.

The transition deck section connecting the lower reactor vessel and the transfer-rotor container to the upper reactor vessel consists of a flat dished head with vertical ribs and a deck plate as shown in Fig. 4.34. Brackets for the reactor-vessel support are welded under the transition section in line with the ribs. Eight flex-plate support columns, 2 in. thick and 7 ft long, made of carbon-steel plates support the vessel and allow for free thermal expansion while holding the center line of the upper reactor vessel in a fixed position. Some of the flex-plates are mounted on Belleville springs to prevent over-

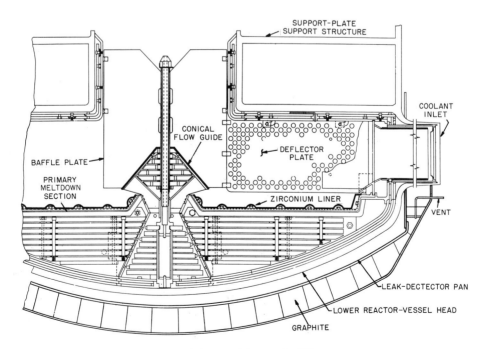

FIG. 4.35—Fermi meltdown section [31].

stressing of the support columns and the transition deck due to unequal growth during operation.

The upper reactor vessel is cylindrical and has an inside diameter of 170.5 in. It is 2 in. thick to a point 60 in. above the connection of the flat head to the lower reactor vessel and 1 1/2 thick above this section. Three 30-in.-OD sodium outlet nozzles are located in the upper section of the reactor vessel. These nozzles were pierced from 2-in.-thick plate and welded to extension nozzles that were machined to reduce the thickness gradually to the 3/8-in. thickness of the pipe. The plug container is an extension of the upper reactor vessel, which houses the rotating plug. It has a minimum inside diameter of 106 in. The wall thickness of the plug container varies from 1 1/2 to 1 3/32 in. It is stepped to maintain the biological shielding effectiveness of the rotating plug by preventing neutron and gamma streaming through the operating annulus between the rotating plug and the plug container. The 6-in. overflow nozzle and pipe which maintain reactor sodium level constant during operation, the 2-in. inert-gas equalizing lines and nozzles, and the dip-seal connections are located in the plug-container portion of the vessel.

A stainless-steel shield surrounds the blanket inside the lower and upper reactor-vessel walls. The section of shielding adjacent to the radial-blanket subassemblies is made up of two rows of solid stainless-steel subassemblies. The shield subassemblies are geometrically similar in outline to a radial-blanket subassembly. The remainder of the thermal shield in the lower vessel is made up of eight cylindrically formed stainless-steel plates. The cylindrical plates are 1/2 to 1 in. thick and are separated by 1/4- to 1/2-in. flow annuli. The total sodium flow through the thermal shield, including that through the steel subassemblies, is about 475 gal/min. The cylindrical plates are structurally separated from each other and the vessel wall. The total shield thickness in the lower vessel, including the vessel wall, is 12 in. The shield in the core and blanket inlet plena is made up of shield plates, the vessel wall, and other structural steel and has a total thickness of 12 in. The transition deck is covered with approximately 6 in. of shield plates.

The thermal shield in the upper reactor vessel is made up of vertical cylindrically shaped plates resting on the transition deck and has a total thickness, including the vessel wall, of 6 in. The cylindrical plates are structurally separated from each other and the vessel wall. The coolant flow from the lower reactor vessel thermal shield is directed into the upper reactor-vessel thermal shield through the transition deck.

The thermal-shield design limits the irradiation of the vessel wall to a neutron flux 1×10^{22} neutrons/cm^2 of 0.1 Mev neutrons which covers 20 years of reactor operation at a power of 430 Mw(t). The portion of the reactor vessel wall in the vicinity of the core horizontal center plane was designed for heat generation of 0.2 watts/cm^3, and the remainder for lower values.

The rotating shield plug, shown in Fig. 4.34, serves as an integral part of the biological shield and as a part of the fuel-handling equipment. Its 1 1/32-in.-thick stainless-steel shell contains layers of shielding materials and insulation. The shielding materials consist of 18 in. of stainless steel; approximately 6 ft of graphite, of which about 20% is borated to 1.5 at.%; and 3 ft 2 in. of carbon steel, which includes seven 2-in. support plates for the graphite, a stack of six 2-in. plates, and a 12-in.-thick cover plate. A layer of stainless-steel wool insulation reduces the temperature to design limits. The cover plate carries the hold-down assembly and the offset handling equipment. The deflection of the cover plate is limited to 15 mils to ensure that the offset handling mechanism is vertical. The 120-ton dead-weight load of the plug is transmitted to the reactor-vessel plug-container flange through the load-carrying ring and the ball-bearing assembly shown in Fig. 4.36. The plug gear is integral with the load-carrying ring. The intermediate race of the double-row ball bearing provides for differential thermal expansion between the load-carrying carbon-steel ring and the reactor-vessel flange of stainless steel. The ball bearings and races are designed to use a specially formulated molybdenum disulphide as a lubricant. The mechanical seal between the rotating plug and the plug container is achieved with a silicone rubber seal. The center of the seal is supplied with clean argon gas at approximately 1/2 psi above system pressure. The pressure seats the lips of the seal on the rotating-seal ring and assures that any leakage is into the vessel rather than out. Provision is made for a NaK dip seal to act in conjunction with the rubber seal in the event that sodium vapor in this area develops into a problem. All bolted covers and flanges are sealed with rubber O-rings and gaskets.

The entire reactor vessel is encased in a steel liner which, though not leaktight, is designed to direct any leakage to leak detectors located at the bottom of the liner. Electrical resistance heaters are located between this liner and a layer of thermal insulation to provide means of heating the vessel when desired. In addition to the leak-detector system, the entire reactor vessel is enclosed in the primary shield tank, which is a leaktight carbon-steel vessel designed to prevent excessive loss of sodium from the reactor vessel in the event of failure of any of the primary-system components within the primary shield tank.

4.3.2.5.2 EBR-II REACTOR VESSEL. In EBR-II the reactor (Fig. 4.37) is completely submerged within the large volume of bulk sodium contained in the primary tank. The reactor vessel is mounted on the bottom structure of the tank and a removable cover is provided. The vessel contains: (1) a lower grid-plenum assembly with inlet nozzles, (2) an inner radial neutron shield, (3) a subassembly hold-down and flow-baffle structure with outlet plenum and outlet nozzles, (4) a vessel cover, and (5) thermal baffles.

The grid-plenum assembly (Fig. 4.38) supports and locates the subassemblies and provides a plenum chamber which directs the inlet coolant flow. The grid consists of two stainless-steel plates interconnected by tubes welded to each plate in the outer blanket zone. Two coolant inlet plenum chambers are provided. The high-pressure chamber which supplies the core and inner blanket subassemblies is comprised of the space between the two grid plates. The coolant enters this plenum at the periphery, flows radially inward to the core and

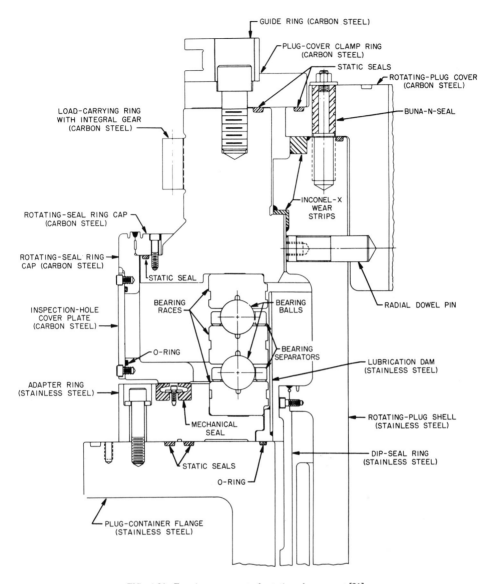

FIG. 4.36—Fermi arrangement of rotating-plug support [31].

inner-blanket zones, and then enters the subassemblies through the holes in the walls of the bottom adapters near the lower grid plate. The upper surface of the lower grid plate is stepped to vary the number of subassembly-adapter flow-entrance holes and thus provide orificing to match the heat-generation rate. The low-pressure coolant plenum which supplies the outer blanket is an annular chamber immediately below the lower grid plate. The coolant enters the plenum and flows into the bottom adapters of the outer-blanket subassemblies through the openings in their bottom ends.

The reactor-vessel cover provides the closure of the upper end of the reactor vessel and forms the upper surfaces of the outlet coolant plenum chamber. It also contains the upper portion of the neutron shield. During reactor operation when a sodium pressure differential of approximately 12 psi exists across the cover, a small amount of leakage

occurs through various openings for control-rod drives and fuel-handling mechanisms. This leakage flow is employed as a part of the neutron-shield cooling system in this region.

The vessel cover is raised and lowered by two shafts penetrating the small rotating plug mounted in the primary tank cover-plate structure. It is fastened to the reactor vessel by three remotely operated clamping mechanisms, and the raising and lowering mechanism is designed to permit free expansion of the lifting shafts. This arrangement avoids the large load that is present when internal pressure is transferred to the cover-lifting mechanism and also avoids problems associated with differential thermal expansion in the system.

In EBR–II the complete primary system is contained in the primary tank (Fig. 4.39). All the primary-system components, including the reactor sodium pumps, primary piping, heat exchanger, and

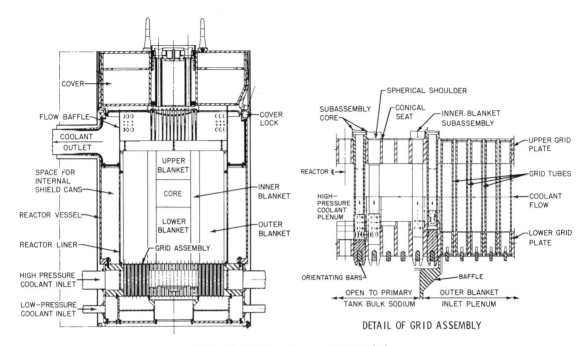

FIG. 4.37—EBR-II reactor-vessel assembly [14].

fuel-transfer and -storage system, are submerged in the 80,000 gal of sodium within the primary tank, under a blanket of argon gas. The pumps and heat exchanger are arranged radially around the reactor vessel and elevated somewhat above it.

The primary tank, primary structure, and biological shield comprise an integrated system that is designed to meet static-load requirements, maintain accuracy of alignment, and contain an internal energy release. The tank is surrounded by the primary structure and the biological shield.

The primary tank and the primary structure are completely independent of each other on all sides except the top. The primary tank is supported at the top, and all units entering the primary tank do so through the top. The combined primary structure and shield are designed to contain the energy release associated with a hypothetical nuclear accident. For design purposes an energy release equivalent to 300 lb of TNT at the center of the reactor was assumed. Although the primary tank would be destroyed, the structure surrounding the tank has

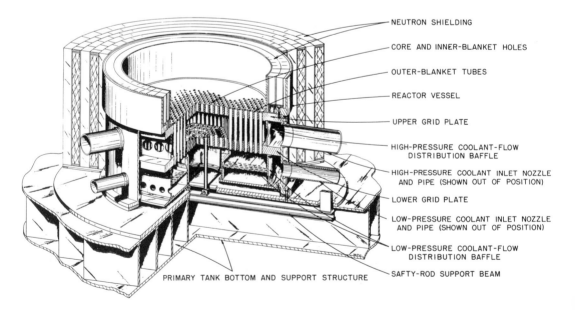

FIG. 4.38—EBR-II reactor-vessel grid assembly [14].

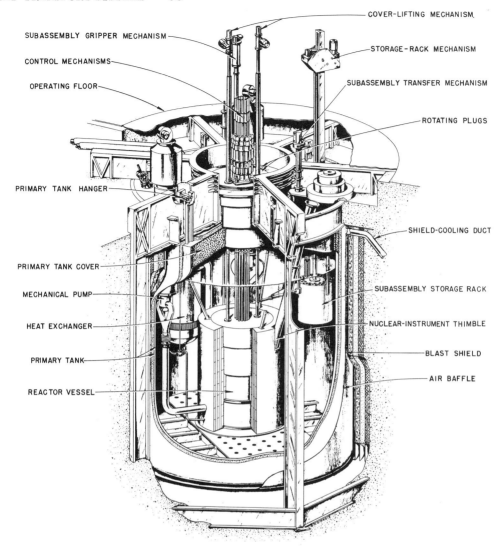

FIG. 4.39—EBR–II major reactor components and reactor primary tank [14].

been designed to contain this energy release without failure.

The primary tank is of double–wall construction (a tank within a tank) to provide maximum reliability for sodium containment. The tank is constructed of type 304 stainless steel. The inner tank is 26 ft in inside diameter, and the outer tank wall is 26 ft 11 in. in inside diameter. The space between the two tanks is filled with inert gas, which is monitored to detect leakage through either tank wall (sodium or air). The outside of the tank is insulated to minimize heat loss from the primary system.

The bottom of each of the tanks is stiffened with parallel beams. A radial stiffening structure is used for the primary tank cover, which is 32 3/4 in. deep. This depth is used for shielding and thermal insulation. The inner-tank bottom-plate structure is designed to support the reactor tank, the subassemblies, the neutron shield, and the load of sodium. This load is transferred by the tank wall to the top cover where the tank is supported. The outer-tank structure is designed to carry only the sodium load in the event a leak develops in the inner tank.

The primary tank and its contents and those components which are connected to the primary tank top cover are supported by six hangers. Each hanger is of a simple roller type. This design eliminates the possibility of secondary stresses in the primary tank cover due to horizontal loads developed in the hanger links and increases the reliability of symmetrical, unrestricted radial thermal expansion of the tank.

The primary tank design and the method of support are arranged to provide radial expansion about the vertical center line of the system. The most critical units, the reactor and the rotating plugs that locate the control drives and fuel-unloading mechanisms, are located on the physical center line of the system. Differential vertical expansion is avoided by using identical material for all equipment in the system and maintaining it at the same temperature.

The primary structure (Fig. 4.40) consists of a system of columns and beams which transmit the loads to the main internal building foundation. In combination with the biological shield, it forms a pressure vessel surrounding the primary tank. The bottom structure consists of six beams embedded in the heavily reinforced concrete with six columns connected to the beams. These columns are connected at the top to six radial beams which frame into circular rings located on the center line of the system. This tip structure, with additional stiffening members, provides the supporting structure for the primary tank and for the major primary-system components supported external to the primary tank. The material of this structure is USS Carilloy T-1 plate steel.

A ring of ordinary concrete (6 ft. thick) provides the radial biological shield, the inside diameter of which is at essentially the same diameter as the inside of the six vertical columns. The shield alone provides sufficient strength to carry the static loads imposed on the top structure. The steel columns are required to provide the strength required to withstand the assumed internal energy release.

4.3.2.5.3 DOUNREAY REACTOR VESSEL. The Dounreay reactor vessel (Figs. 4.41 and 4.42), approximately 20 ft high by 10 ft 6 in. in outside diameter, consists of a shell of 18/8/1 stainless steel, closed at one end and open at the other, with an outer casing of lighter gauge stainless steel forming a leak jacket. The main shell was designed for a working pressure of 50 psig and inlet and outlet coolant temperatures of 392 and 752°F, respectively.

The vessel support system consists of two sets of columns, 24 per set, one set on a 12-ft diameter

and the other on a 21.5-ft diameter. The columns are approximately 32 ft high and are interconnected at the 11-ft level and at the top. The vessel is supported from the top flange on 24 roller assemblies that bear on the top of the inner columns of the support structure. The rollers allow free differential expansion of the vessel in relation to the support structure.

The supporting structure within the reactor vessel supports the weight of the core and blanket (approximately 100 tons), ensures the correct geometry of the core and blanket, and divides the coolant flow to the core, inner blanket, and outer blanket. These internal supports are built up from a flange mounted on the inner skirt of the reactor vessel. The blanket support is mounted on a matched ring attached to the bottom of the vessel skirt. A true and level datum was ensured by making this ring after the vessel had been installed on its rollers. The structure supports the inner blanket assembly. The bottom support plate for the outer blanket is also carried on the support structure, and the top support plate is supported on the inner blanket assembly and the upper end of the vessel skirt. The core skirt is suspended from the inner blanket assembly and is located inside the core skirt. All of this supporting structure is designed for removal at some future date should this be required.

Additional features of Dounreay are as follows: (1) The blanket support structure is the main structural member supporting the total weight of the core and blanket and the load due to pressure drop across the core. It also acts as a plenum for the blanket outlet coolant. (2) The inner-blanket assembly is a vertically mounted skirt of hexagonal cross section, enclosing the five inner rows of breeder elements, and acts as a structural member from which the core skirt hangs. (3) The outer-blanket support consists of two plates, a bottom plate mounted on the blanket support box and an upper one mounted on the inner blanket assembly at the inside and on the reactor vessel at the outside. (4) The core skirt consists of a fabricated tube of hexagonal cross section hanging vertically from a flange located on the top inner-blanket plate and passing through the blanket support structure at its lower end.

Two rotating plugs form the closure for the top of the reactor vessel and provide a facility for orienting the refueling machine over any fuel or blanket element. The plugs are jacked onto bearings and are rotated only when the reactor is shut down. Sealing of the rotating members is by a mechanical bolted seal under normal operating conditions and by liquid-metal dip-seals during refueling (Fig. 4.43). The plugs are designed with the outer casing as the boundary of the coolant circuit, the inside of the plugs being completely sealed from the coolant and vented to atmosphere. So that the radiation level at the top of the plugs is reduced to an acceptable figure, both during operation and shutdown, the eccentric plug is filled with neutron and gamma shielding. The fabrication, inspection, and pressure testing were completed before the shield materials, graphite, and mild steel were loaded. The two rotating plugs are sealed against leakage of cover gas during normal reactor operation by a double O-joint ring. During refueling it is

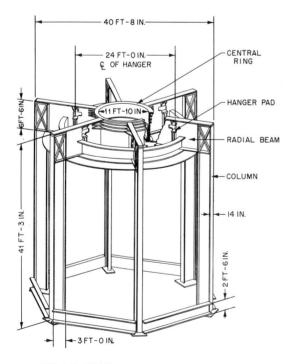

FIG. 4.40—EBR-II primary-tank support structure [54].

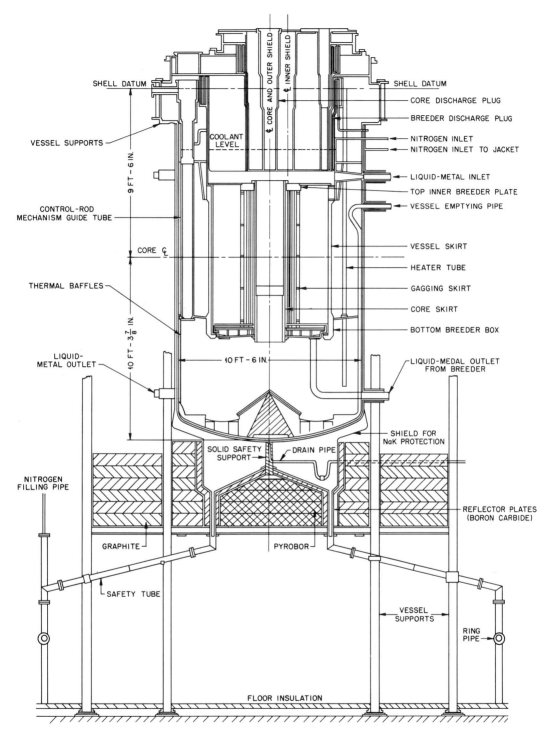

FIG. 4.41—Dounreay reactor, vertical section [50].

necessary to maintain a leaktight seal around plugs to prevent inleakage of air to the reactor and out-leakage of radioactive cover gas, which is maintained at less than 0.5 psig. A double seal is effected by two concentric rings dipping into a trough of liquid metal. As originally designed the inner seal contained sodium-mercury amalgam and the outer seal, mercury. When the reactor is pressurized, the liquid metal in these seals is discharged to a dump tank located on the plugs.

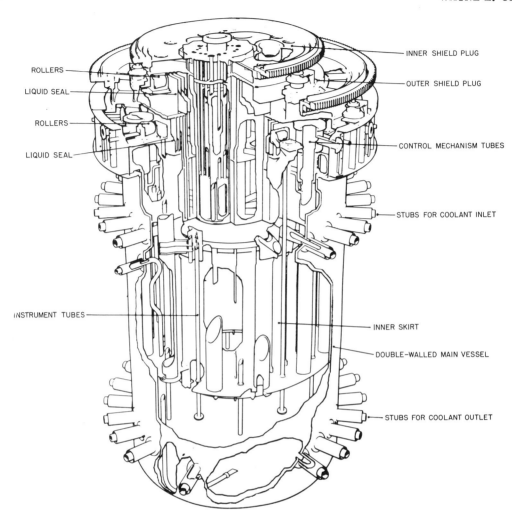

ROLLERS

LIQUID SEAL

ROLLERS

LIQUID SEAL

INSTRUMENT TUBES

INNER SHIELD PLUG

OUTER SHIELD PLUG

CONTROL MECHANISM TUBES

STUBS FOR COOLANT INLET

INNER SKIRT

DOUBLE-WALLED MAIN VESSEL

STUBS FOR COOLANT OUTLET

FIG. 4.42—Dounreay, cutaway view of reactor vessel and rotating shields [51].

4.3.2.5.4 RAPSODIE REACTOR VESSEL. The vessel, made of type 316 stainless steel, consists of four principal parts (Fig. 4.44). The lower part of the reactor vessel, in the form of a 12 mm (0.47 in.) thick elliptical cylinder, is joined on one end to an entrance nozzle and at the other end to a massive support flange. The support flange transmits the weight of internal parts of the vessel and of the vessel itself to five columns. The main vessel is made of 15 mm (0.59 in.) plate. A ring at the upper end of the reactor vessel allows the vessel to be operated under a vacuum. The uppermost part of the reactor vessel, located between the fixed plug and the large rotating plug, is terminated by an expansion joint tied to the fixed plug. The expansion joint allows axial expansion of the reactor vessel from the support flange.

A preheating jacket around the reactor vessel and the sodium pipes allows for circulation of nitrogen or helium to provide preheating, at 150°C (302°F), prior to the introduction of sodium at this temperature. The preheating minimizes thermal shock and prevents sodium from freezing. Gas enters concentric to one of the sodium outlet pipes and is distributed between the jacket and the reactor vessel in two flows. One flow preheats the lower part of the vessel and leaves concentric to the sodium inlet. The other flow heats the upper part of the vessel and exits concentric to the second sodium outlet pipe.

The space between the reactor vessel and the containment tank is occupied by stainless-steel containers filled with thermal insulation. The containers fill the space sufficiently to prevent, in the event of a rupture of the reactor vessel and its gas heating jacket, a sodium level lower than the exit pipes in the reactor vessel. The gas in the space between the reactor vessel and the containment tank is nitrogen. The cylindrical containment tank is made of plain carbon steel. Three reinforcing rings assure its ability to withstand a vacuum. At its upper end an expansion joint is connected to the fixed plug allowing expansion of the containment tank in an axial direction. Its mean temperature during operation of the reactor is approximately 250°C (482°F).

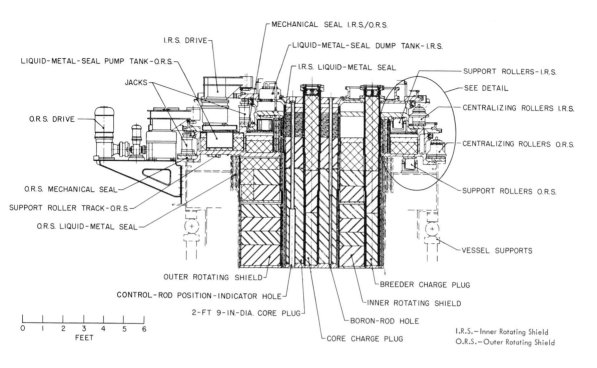

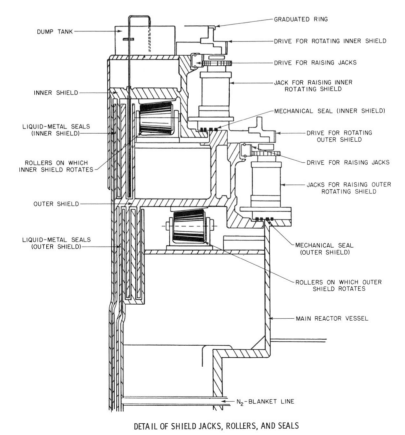

DETAIL OF SHIELD JACKS, ROLLERS, AND SEALS

FIG. 4.43—Dounreay, section through rotating shields. (From J. Tatlock et al., Proceedings of the Symposium on the Dounreay Fast Reactor, London, Dec. 7, 1960, Institution of Mechanical Engineers, London, 1961.)

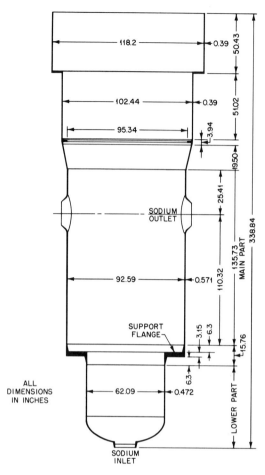

FIG. 4.44—Rapsodie reactor vessel [18].

ALL DIMENSIONS IN INCHES

upper half of the upper graphite. About 90% of the heat or 100 kw(t) is removed in the lower layer of borated graphite.

The large concentric rotating plug, carried by a set of ball bearings, contains two liquid-level indicators. There is a tin-bismuth liquid-metal dip seal between this plug and the fixed plug. A dynamic seal is located inside the ball bearing as a backup. The eccentric rotating plug, similarly sealed, is carried on the concentric plug through ball bearings. It carries the fuel-handling port and two experimental ports. A removable non-rotating plug contains seven ports, a central port for operating the core cover plate and six ports for the control-rod drive shafts. Each of the rotating plugs is driven by two motors, one at slow speed and one at fast speed. The position of each plug is determined by a circular magnetic pickup.

A rigid pentagonal structure between the flange plate of the fixed plug and the five support columns prevents the columns from bending. The fixed plug rests on the structure but is separated from the structure by springs. These springs have flexible joints at each end. The plug is thus able to expand radially without producing any adverse effects on the structure. Four keys, pinned to the

The flow baffle and diffuser assembly (Fig. 4.45) located in the entrance to the reactor vessel is carried by the reactor-vessel support structure. The purpose of the diffuser assembly is to assure a good distribution of coolant and to collect the fuel in the event of a meltdown. The flow baffle separates the coolant into a high-pressure zone of approximately 57 psig and a low-pressure zone of approximately 4 psig. The high-pressure zone cools the core subassemblies and the inner radial blanket subassemblies. The difference in the pressure is attained by the use of annular diaphragms which are part of the flow baffle. The flow baffle is designed to permit free differential expansion between the reactor vessel and the flow baffle during temperature transients.

The fixed plug and rotating plugs (Fig. 4.46) contain, traversing upward, a borated-graphite layer, a stainless-steel layer, a second layer of borated graphite divided into two parts by a carbon-steel plate, and finally another carbon-steel plate. To produce the required temperature reduction of about 470°C (846°F) from the bottom to the top of the plugs without too steep a gradient, two cooling systems are provided. The first system cools the lowest graphite, and the second system cools the

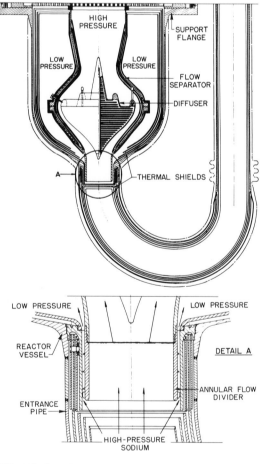

FIG. 4.45—Rapsodie reactor vessel lower-section flow baffle and diffuser assembly [18].

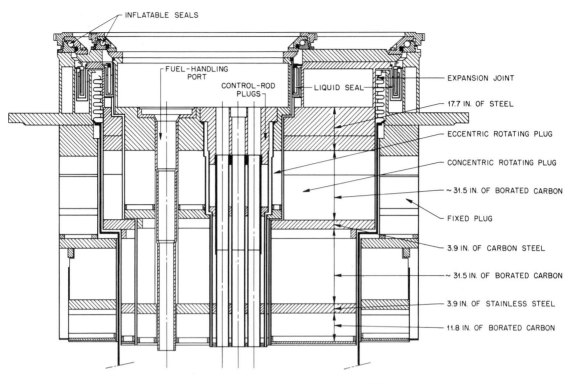

INFLATABLE SEALS

FUEL-HANDLING PORT

CONTROL-ROD PLUGS

LIQUID SEAL

EXPANSION JOINT

17.7 IN. OF STEEL

ECCENTRIC ROTATING PLUG

CONCENTRIC ROTATING PLUG

~31.5 IN. OF BORATED CARBON

FIXED PLUG

3.9 IN. OF CARBON STEEL

~31.5 IN. OF BORATED CARBON

3.9 IN. OF STAINLESS STEEL

11.8 IN. OF BORATED CARBON

FIG. 4.46—Rapsodie rotating-plug structure [18].

fixed plug, center the plugs. They slide radially in four grooves pinned to the pentagonal structure. Initial centering is made with removable jacks. Bolts prevent the expulsion of the plugs without restricting the radial movements.

So that its length can be maintained constant, each reactor-vessel support column is formed of three concentric metal tubes whose coefficients of expansion are such that the expansion of the inner and outer cylinder is compensated for by the expansion of the middle cylinder whose coefficient of expansion is twice as great as the other cylinders. The bottoms of the inner and middle cylinders are rigidly connected. The tops of the middle and outer cylinders are rigidly connected. The vessel is connected to the top of the inner cylinder. The foundation is connected to the bottom of the outer cylinder.

4.3.3 PUMPS

4.3.3.1 Introduction

Pumps used in primary and secondary sodium systems are either mechanical or electromagnetic. Several varieties of each type have been developed. The relatively high electrical conductivity of sodium and NaK make them most amenable to being pumped by electromagnetic means. However, recently demonstrated reliable operation of mechanical seals has resulted in the selection of centrifugal sump type pumps for many of the sodium heat-transfer systems.

Electromagnetic pumps have the advantages of (1) being hermetically sealed, (2) having no moving parts and hence being free from wear and maintenance and requiring no bearing lubrication of the kind needed for external drive motors, (4) having no free surface with controlled sodium levels and hence can be located more conveniently in the piping system, and (5) having characteristics that allow for flow control over a wide range by varying the magnitude of the input voltage or the frequency; for example, a prototype pump for the EBR-II secondary system provides for incremental changes of 1 gal/min up to 100 gal/min, increasing above this point at increments of 5 gal/min to a 5000 gal/min flow rate, as compared to a mechanical pump of comparable capacity with a minimum flow limit of 8% of design flow.

Electromagnetic pumps have the following disadvantages: (1) the pump duct is a thin-walled member (about 0.020 to 0.065 in. thick), requiring extreme care in design and fabrication and possibly a hermetically sealed secondary enclosure, (2) pump performance is affected adversely by entrained gas in the liquid and can result in a pump-duct burnout, the avoidance of which requires venting of gas from the pumping system and the prevention of gas entrainment, such as caused by turbulence in surge tanks, (3) electrical insulation is exposed to gamma and possibly neutron radiation, (4) fabrication techniques are not as conventional as for centrifugal pumps, requiring expensive inspection and testing techniques, and (5) efficiencies below 45% for most electromagnetic pumps, particularly a-c pumps.

4.3.3.2 Mechanical Pumps

Mechanical pumps for primary and secondary sodium systems are generally single-stage centrifugal units. The centrifugal design has been used because of its mechanical simplicity and the suitability of its hydraulic characteristics. The usual techniques for designing centrifugal pumps to obtain maximum efficiency are used except that ring-wear clearances are increased 50 to 100% over those used for normal low-temperature designs. This approach reduces the efficiency slightly but ensures long-time operation at high temperature by preventing contact of the wear-ring surfaces. It is especially necessary when the pumps are made from an alloy which has a high coefficient of thermal expansion, such as the 18-8 stainless steels.

New design approaches have been required to meet the rigid and difficult requirement of sealing the liquid metal to prevent any contamination by inleakage of air or fluids or outleakage of the liquid metal at joints and shaft penetrations. All types of rubbing face seals when in contact with liquid metals deteriorate rapidly owing to the high temperatures and the contaminants in the liquid metal. Nickel and copper braids applied as compression packing have a limited life because of wear at the rotating shaft. Four types of seals (Table 4.9) have been developed: membrane seals, frozen seals, gas seals, and mechanical-shaft seals.

4.3.3.2.1 MEMBRANE SEAL.

The membrane seal relies on separating the liquid metals from the air by a permanently sealed, thin, nonmagnetic metallic membrane. The interior rotating parts of the pump are submerged in the pumped fluid and derive the torque for rotation from an external rotating magnetic-field coupling through the membrane. The portions of the pump submerged in the liquid metal are supported by hardened-metal sleeve bearings or by hydrostatic bearings for high temperature use. The hydrostatic bearing employs the discharge pressure of the pump to equalize the pressure in hydraulic pressure pads located around the journal. The action of this bearing is to center the journal in a film of the pumped fluid.

Membrane-sealed pumps of two general varieties are commercially available in the smaller sizes. One, the canned-rotor pump (Fig. 4.47) has the pump impeller directly connected to the rotor of a polyphase motor, which is submerged in the pumped fluid. A tubular membrane, about 0.020 in.

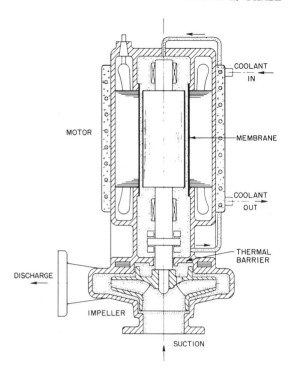

FIG. 4.47—Canned-rotor membrane-sealed pump [25].

thick, surrounds the rotor, completely enclosing the bearings and rotating parts. The stator windings which are wound with class H insulation, are placed outside the membrane, and the rotor is driven as in an ordinary polyphase motor. For high-temperature applications, the liquid metal circulating to the bearings and around the rotor is cooled by the fluid used to cool the stator windings. A thermal barrier is placed between the pump and motor sections to reduce the cooling load and prevent mixing of the hot fluids in the cooled region. The case around the stator may be designed to retain full pressure of the pumped liquid and thus provide protection against membrane ruptures.

The magnetic-drive pump has a thin circular diaphragm separating two disks, each containing permanent magnets. The outside disk is connected

Table 4.9—Mechanical Liquid-metal Pump and Seal Characteristics

Pump	Service	Max. eff.	Features	Difficulties
1. Canned-rotor membrane seal centrifugal	Low capacity; special designs for high capacity and temperature	65%	Positive stationary seal	Temperature limited to 575°F for ordinary bearings; no speed control; maintenance
2. Magnetic-drive membrane seal centrifugal	Low capacity; less than 450°F	60%	Positive stationary seal	Temperatures limited to 450°F; poor speed regulation; maintenance
3. Frozen seal centrifugal	High and low capacity; high temperature	75%	Easy maintenance; no rubbing parts in liquid metal	Leaks when auxiliary coolant lost
4. Totally enclosed centrifugal sump gas seal	High and low capacity; moderate temperature	75%	Positive stationary seal; no rubbing parts in liquid metal	Sump-level control; purified inert-gas supply required
5. Mechanical-shaft seal centrifugal sump	High and low capacity; high temperature	75%	Easier maintenance than (4).	Sump-level control; purified inert-gas supply required

to a conventional-drive motor, and the inner disk, which is submerged in the pumped fluid, is connected to the pump impeller. The submerged bearings are the type used in the canned-rotor pump except that cooling is not generally provided. Bearings can be designed to operate submerged. The other features are much the same.

The membrane seal offers the advantage of providing a positive seal that may be welded shut and is ideal for radioactive applications. It also tends to alleviate lubrication problems since the pumped fluid supports the parts rotating inside the seal case and no organic lubricant applied to bearings outside the case can find its way to the liquid metal. However, maintenance on the sealed bearings and pump parts is difficult. Pump cost is high because of rigid fabrication requirements and reduced pump efficiency owing to magnetic losses in the membrane and high friction losses at the rotor. Speed control and close regulation are difficult. Special cooling provisions are required for motor windings, permanent magnets, and bearings for operating temperatures above 400°F.

4.3.3.2.2 FROZEN SEAL. This type of vertically mounted pump is equipped with frozen seals at the case and at the shaft. The shaft seal is a special liquid-cooled gland inserted into the annulus normally occupied by the stuffing material. The liquid metal is frozen on the inner and outer annulus around the cooled gland. An inert atmosphere backs up the seals to prevent oxygen contamination. The inert atmosphere is regulated to maintain a pressure differential across the seals. The design of a frozen seal is not critical; the main requirement is to cool the liquid metal in the annuli below its freezing point. A secondary liquid coolant can be used for this purpose.

For sodium and other materials that melt between 200 and 400°F, the radial clearance of the annulus is about 0.030 in. This annulus is large enough to prevent the formation of a strong bond between the frozen material and the rotating shaft and small enough to prevent the extrusion of a solid plug by pressure differentials of 15 psi across the seal. In operation the frozen metal shears at the face of the rotating shaft, and, as the shaft rotates, the heat created by friction causes a thin liquid film to form about the shaft. With a well designed seal in sodium, the torque used for starting and running a frozen seal is no greater than that experienced with ordinary packing in a usual pump application. During running, the torque is perhaps somewhat less. Experiments with a 50-hp pump delivering 1285 gal/min against a 130-ft sodium head at a speed of 1460 rpm showed a power loss of less than 1 kw. About 2 kw of heat were removed at both the shaft seal and the case seal to maintain the sodium at the seal in a frozen state with the flowing sodium at 1200°F. Loss of the liquid coolant for prolonged periods is mitigated by the use of inert gas, which can temporarily be used as a backup until repairs can be made.

The primary pumps in the Sodium Reactor Experiment (SRE) are of the frozen seal type. An overall cross section of an SRE prototype is shown in Fig. 4.48; the actual primary pump and the seal arrangement is shown in Fig. 4.49. The case extension places the bolting for the head and case joint

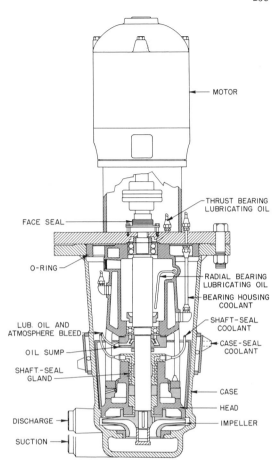

FIG. 4.48—SRE single-stage centrifugal pump [111].

in a cool region and provides the container for the inert atmosphere to protect the seals from oxygen contamination. The atmosphere is sealed at the floor plate by an O-ring seal on the case extension and a lubricated face seal on the shaft. Oil is fed to the bearings of the SRE prototype pump by an oiler whose lines pass through the floor plate. The excess oil is caught in the sump below the lower bearing and is removed continuously by being entrained in the inert-atmosphere bleed. Coolant lines

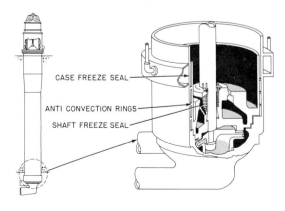

FIG. 4.49—SRE primary sodium pump details [111].

for the bearing housing and shaft freeze seal also enter through the floor plate. Removal of all the rotating parts from the shell is accomplished by unbolting the case joint, melting the freeze seal, and lifting out the parts in one unit without disturbing the piping. The primary SRE pumps are fabricated from type 304 stainless steel, except for the shaft and impeller, which are type 316 stainless steel.

The shaft is 3 in. in diameter, and the impeller is 13 1/2 in. in diameter. The lower radial bearings are packed with a special grease of good stability under irradiation. A 2-in.-thick steel shield protects the bearing. The frozen seal, when adapted to commercial pump designs, results in a low-cost, high-efficiency pump that should not be difficult to maintain since there are no rubbing parts submerged

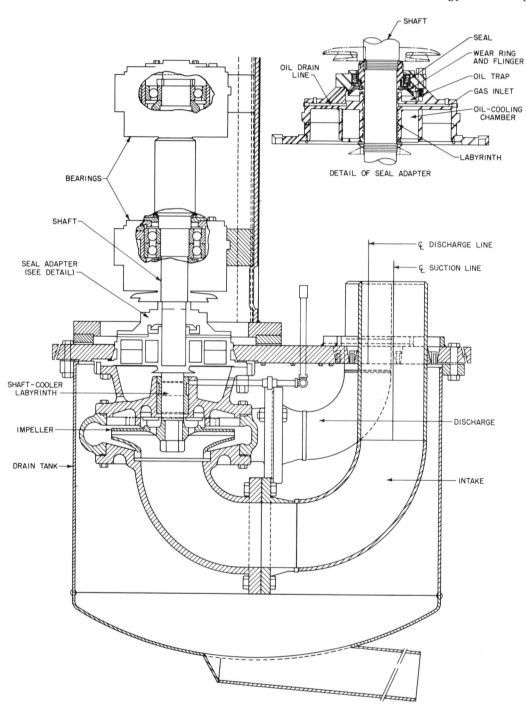

FIG. 4.50—Section through a 400-gal/min 126-ft-head gas-sealed mechanical pump.

in the liquid metal and the rotating parts can be easily removed.

4.3.3.2.3 GAS SEAL. Gas-sealed pumps do not have to be directly sealed against the liquid sodium. A relatively simple gas seal is easily maintained. The labyrinth gas seals operate on the principal of sealing an inert atmosphere above a free surface of the liquid metal. It is necessary to control the liquid level in the sump, especially if another free surface is present in the system. Such a pump is shown in Fig. 4.50. Included is an enlarged detail of the seal area. A labyrinth separates the driver and the sump preventing metal vapor from coming into contact with the motor windings and bearings. So that welding of the pump-case joint can be avoided, a sump-pump design is employed, and leakage is to the sump, where it is returned to the system.

Reliability is a prime requirement for the gas-sealed EBR-II pump. Some of the other major requirements [54] are (1) the pump motor and top shield plug flange assembly must be completely gastight to prevent leakage of the primary-system blanket inert gas, (2) a 6.5-ft (overall length) radiation shield plug must exist between the pump and the drive motor to conform to the top biological shield of the primary system, (3) the pump shaft must extend through the shielding and inert-gas blanket areas and into the sodium for proper impeller submergence, (4) the sodium "hydraulic" bearing must not require any external sodium source or auxiliary external equipment, and (5) the pump speed should be controllable from about 20 to 100% of speed with specified rates of acceleration and deceleration. A prototype EBR-II pump designed to circulate 5000 gal/min at a head of 107 ft (40 psi) and temperatures up to 700°F was successfully tested [55] for 16,000 hr with 251 starts (Fig. 4.51).

The 5000 gal/min test pump employs a standard rigid coupling. This pump requires a longer shaft

for coupling. The EBR-II pumps require a relatively long shaft to traverse the radiation shielding between the pump and the pump motor. The hydrostatic bearing in the test pump is also very similar, except that the EBR-II pump has additional hydraulic pads within the hydrostatic pressure pockets. The test pump has a two-speed 480-volt a-c motor and an auxiliary drive to provide operation at 10% of rated speed. Inspection of the pump after operation revealed that it was in excellent condition. No significant amount of sodium or sodium oxide had passed the upper labyrinth seal toward the motor enclosure. There was no evidence of corrosion or cavitation on the pump parts. All surfaces exposed to flowing sodium were in excellent condition. Of perhaps greatest interest was the condition of the hydraulic bearing that operates with sodium under pressure from the pump outlet. No hydrostatic-centering forces exist until some pump discharge pressure is established. During this brief interval after pump start-up, the bearing functions as a sodium "lubricated" journal bearing. The wear on the bearing was measured to be 0.001 to 0.002 in. Also noted were small grooves, perhaps 0.002 to 0.003 in. deep; these have not propagated or increased in subsequent operation. Neither the wear nor the light scoring effected operation since the nominal diametral clearance of about 0.017 in. was sufficient to prevent interference. (The EBR-II pumps are provided with additional pads in the hydraulic bearing, and these should result in even less wear.)

The mechanical centrifugal pumps (Fig. 4.52) are used as the main coolant pumps in the EBR-II primary cooling system [54]. Each has a maximum capacity of 5500 gal/min at 75 psi of 700°F sodium. The approximate EBR-II full power equipment of each pump is 4,730 gal/min at 56 psi head. Each 480-volt a-c motor for the EBR-II pump is capable of variable speed over a range of 10 to 100% of rated speed with adjustable acceleration and deceleration rates. Each pump is powered by a motor-generator set with an eddy-current coupling that provides variable frequency and voltage. The direct-coupled pump drives are special totally enclosed gastight motors. Labyrinth type seals are employed to minimize diffusion of sodium vapor into the motor enclosure. Each pump was given a comprehensive test with water at the vendor's plant. The tests were performed using the individual variable-speed power supply and control system provided for each pump. Tests were run over a wide range of pump speeds; the results corrected to sodium are shown in Fig. 4.53. The flow acceleration and deceleration rate was adjusted to meet the specified 0.3 to 0.5% per second of the actual flow rate throughout the full-speed range of the pumps. The water tests on each pump totaled about 30 hr of operation, including several starts. Disassembly and inspection following the tests revealed all parts in excellent condition. Each of the pump-motor assemblies was tested with a helium mass spectrometer to assure the required leaktightness. (All electrical connections are solid conductors equipped with hermatic seals where they penetrate the pump-motor frame.)

The radiation shielding installed in the shield-plug structure consists of carbon-steel balls to a depth of 33 in., 8 in. of insulation, and 34 in. of

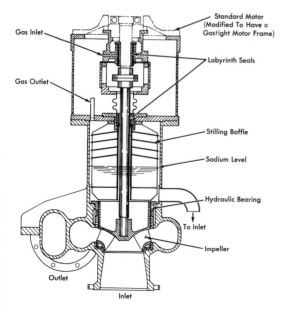

FIG. 4.51—EBR-II prototype, internal arrangement of mechanical pump [61].

Gas Inlet

Gas Outlet

Outlet

Inlet

Standard Motor (Modified To Have a Gastight Motor Frame)

Labyrinth Seals

Stilling Baffle

Sodium Level

Hydraulic Bearing

To Inlet

Impeller

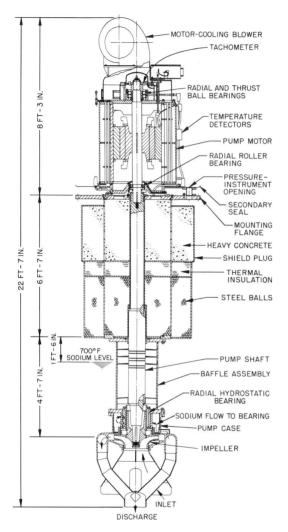

FIG. 4.52—EBR-II primary-system mechanical sodium pump [54].

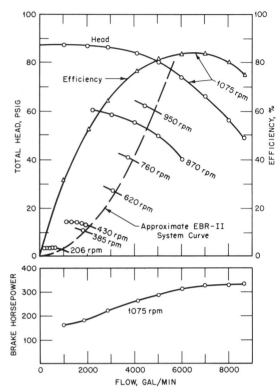

FIG. 4.53—EBR-II primary pump operating characteristics with sodium at 700°F [54].

high-density concrete. The center portion of this shield plug and the pump shaft are stepped to reduce radiation streaming along the vertical shaft.

The shaft in the 350-hp pump motor has a maximum diameter of 5.5 in. and is hollow to accommodate the draw bolt for the coupling immediately below the motor. The center distance between the upper ball thrust and radial bearing and the lower radial roller bearing is 4 ft 2.5 in. The pump shaft connects at the top of the shield plug to the motor shaft, projects downward through the shield plug, then through the spacing baffle assembly, and into the pump case, where it is located radially by a hydrostatic bearing. The pump impeller is overhung on the shaft immediately below this bearing. The center distance between bearings on the pump shaft portion is 10 ft 8.75 in., and the maximum shaft diameter is 9.5 in. This large diameter was selected to ensure that no vibrational instabilities will occur. The pump shafts are precisely balanced. Sodium is fed to the bearing from the impeller discharge. The hydrostatic pressures in the bearing shell act to center the bearing journal within the

bearing clearance. Pads within the hydrostatic bearing pockets provide an additional hydraulic centering action; this is desirable at start-up when the available pressures are insufficient for good hydrostatic bearing action. The bearing surfaces are hard faced with Colmonoy to minimize wear and galling.

The centrifugal type pump was selected in preference to the d-c electromagnetic pump because of the very favorable performance of the 5,000 gal/min centrifugal pump during the long-term loop tests. The success of the centrifugal pump can be attributed largely to the development of the hydraulic bearing, which resolved the most difficult problem in the design of the rotating sodium pumps.

4.3.3.2.4 MECHANICAL SHAFT SEAL. Although they may differ in various physical respects, all mechanical shaft seals are fundamentally the same in principle [56]. The sealing surfaces are located in a plane perpendicular to the shaft and usually consist of two adjacent highly polished surfaces, one surface being connected to the shaft and the other to the stationary portion of the pump. The polished or lapped surfaces, which, in general, are of dissimilar materials, are held in continual contact by a spring and form a fluidtight seal between the rotating and stationary members with very small frictional losses. A flow of lubricant past the seal faces is required to provide a pressure breakdown between the internal pressure and the atmospheric pressure outside the pump.

The wide variation in seal designs stems from the many methods used to provide flexible mounting of the seals. A mechanical seal is similar to a bearing in that it involves a close running clearance with a liquid film between the faces. The lubrication and cooling provided by this film cuts down the wear, as does a proper choice of seal-face materials.

Experience has shown that the surface finish of the seal is critical. In one application [57] it was necessary to modify and to relap all commercial seals to achieve lubricant leakage rates on the order of 5 to 15 cm^3 per day. Each seal face was hand lapped to a flatness of from one to two light bands, as measured with monochromatic helium light. It was necessary to reduce the runout of the rotor seal face (perpendicular to the axis of the rotation) to a maximum value of 0.0001 in. total indicator reading to obtain acceptable values of seal leakage. It was also necessary to locate the raised dam on the stator seal face concentric with the axis of shaft rotation.

As a result of satisfactory experience with mechanical-shaft-seal centrifugal sump pumps using hydrodynamic bearings, they were selected as the primary sodium pumps for Hallam and Fermi. In Hallam it was decided to use the open motor stationary-field coupling and mechanical-seal design for both the primary and secondary pump because this design proved satisfactory during prototype testing and it represented the lowest cost of acceptable designs. Zero leakage of the mechanical seal during prototype tests and a cost savings of $18,000 per unit over hermetically sealed motor and coupling design influenced the ultimate selection of identical seals for the primary and secondary loops [58]. The Hallam primary pumps are designed for a flow of 7200 gal/min against a head of 160 ft at a speed of 835 rpm, circulating 1000°F sodium. The secondary pumps have the same pumping requirements as the primary pumps, except that the design temperature is 900°F. The primary and secondary pumps are identical except for length. The primary pumps have a shield plug built into them. The pumps (Fig. 4.54) have three major independent parts: the pump case, the pumping element, and the variable-speed drive. Suction and discharge piping is welded to nozzles at the lower end of the pump case. The pump case is fabricated from type 304 stainless steel.

The pumping element consists of diffuser, impeller, bearing, shaft, and mechanical seal mounted on the inner barrel. This assembly includes all rotating parts and all close-clearance stationary parts. It is completely assembled before being installed in the pump case. An accurately sized ring below the impeller fits into a bore at the suction nozzle to separate suction and discharge pressure regions of the pump. Another ring fitting into a bore at the junction of the sphere and the cylinder separates discharge pressure from the free-surface region. The pressure above the free surface is the inert-gas pressure maintained by the reactor gas system at 2 psig. This package design makes possible removal and replacement of all parts that are subject to wear without removal of the sodium from the pump case.

The shaft has an oil-lubricated ball-type thrust and radial bearing at the top of the inner barrel and a hydrostatic radial bearing in the sodium close to the impeller. The shaft is hollow up to the solid portion through the shield plug. The hydrostatic bearing is used because it can operate on low-viscosity fluids with no metallic contact between the journal and the bearing. Pump efficiency is lowered because the bearing takes part of the flow from the discharge of the pump. A double oil-lubricated mechanical shaft seal is used in this pump. The thrust ball bearing is located between the seal assemblies. Oil is circulated through the seal bearing assembly by a gear pump. Heat generated by the seals and gear pump is removed by an oil-to-air radiator. The seals and bearing are mounted on a sleeve which is assembled into the seal housing. The seal bearing assembly can be checked for leakage before it is mounted on the pump shaft. Oil pressure at the seal is controlled by orifices to 25 psig. This pressure was selected to protect against accidental surges in gas pressure. Oil leakage is at the rate of about 3 gal per year per seal. The leakage from the lower seal is isolated from sodium by two sumps that will hold all the oil in the system, thus no oil contaminates the liquid sodium.

The design point for the Fermi primary pump is 11,800 gal/min of 600°F sodium at 310 ft total dynamic head. The efficiencies and shape of the performance curves given in Fig. 4.55 are typical for centrifugal pumps. The pump (Fig. 4.56) is mounted in a tank. The tank is connected to the pipe leading to the IHX. The suction is from the pump tank and the five volute discharge pipes are headered to a single 16-in. pipe that leaves the tank at the bottom. The slip fit at the discharge pipe makes it possible to remove the pump assembly from the pump tank. There are two sodium-lubricated hydrodynamic bearings. All parts of the pump that are in contact with sodium or sodium vapor are made of type 304 stainless steel, except the bearings, which have a Colmonoy inlay. Provision is made at the upper motor thrust bearings to isolate the lubricant from the motor shaft (Fig.4.57). Included in these provisions are oil slingers. The lubrication features and seals for the lower motor bearings are similar in design to the upper motor bearings. Grease-lubricated bearings are used for both upper and lower motor bearings. Grease will not flow as readily as oil, and a given quantity of grease accomplishes the same lubrication function as a larger quantity of oil. The pump shaft is provided with a high-integrity seal just above the pump plug at the floor level. The rotating mechanical seal (Fig. 4.58) prevents primary inert gas from escaping to the reactor building. This is the lowest point on the pump shaft at which a quantity of lubricant is located. The lubricant is Hooker Electrochemical MO-10 Fluorolube, a nonhydrogenous liquid. A seal prevents this oil from leaking into the primary system and directs any leakage to a sump. Leakage out of the upper rotating seal faces is also run off to a container.

The main motor drives for the primary pumps are 3-phase 60-cycle wound rotor motors rated at 1000 hp, 900 rpm, and 4800 volts. The sodium flow rate in each loop can be adjusted by varying the speed of the pump drive motors. This speed change is accomplished by varying the external electrical resistance of the rotor circuit. Liquid rheostats are used to provide continuous resistance changes.

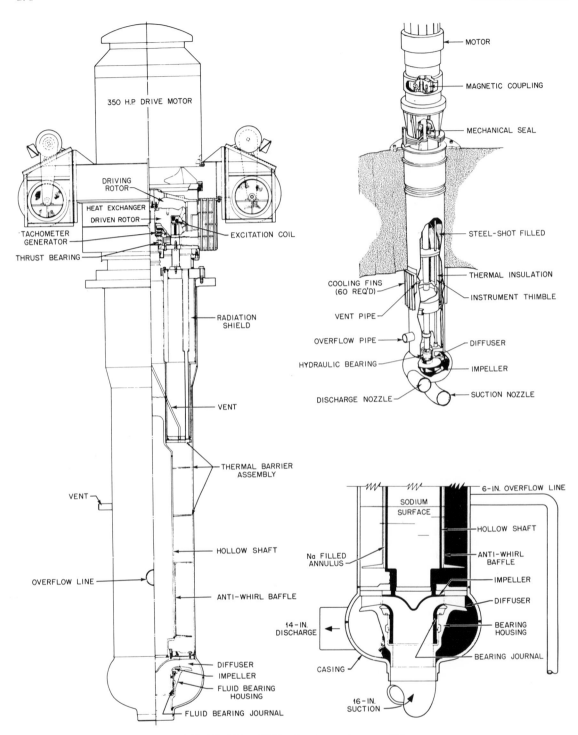

FIG. 4.54—Hallam (SGR) sodium free-surface pump [19].

Electric motors adjust the electrode position of the liquid rheostats. An auxiliary (pony) motor drive, consisting of a 5-hp gear head electric motor and a housing containing driving gears and an overriding cam clutch, is located on the top of each main pump motor. These motors are used for emergency cooling.

The Fermi secondary pumps are each designed to deliver 13,000 gal/min of sodium at a total dynamic head of 100 ft at 1000°F. The design is simpler than that of the primary pumps because it is not necessary to pull the volute for maintenance. In the secondary pump (Fig. 4.59), the single suction and single discharge connections are welded

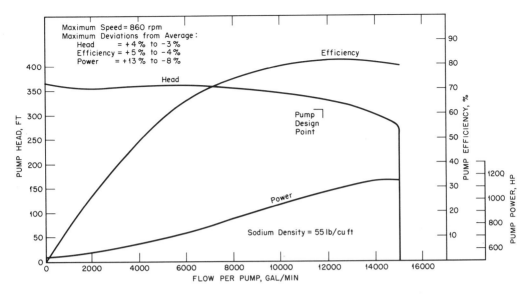

FIG. 4.55—Fermi primary sodium pumps average full-speed characteristics [31].

directly to the piping. The lower bearing is above the impeller and is sodium lubricated; the upper pump bearing is a combination radial and thrust bearing. An oil system lubricates and cools the mechanical shaft seals and the upper bearing. All pump parts in contact with sodium are of 2 1/4 wt. % Cr-1 wt. % Mo alloy. The pumps are driven by 350-hp 900-rpm induction motors. The speed governor control of the secondary sodium pumps is accomplished by means of an electronic circuit that controls the field excitation of an eddy-current coupling. Thyratron rectifiers are used to supply d-c excitation to the field. Dual circuitry is provided, and the standby tube is energized automatically when needed. A remote manual set of the desired speed into the tachometer speed governor control loop is obtained by means of a pneumatically positioned rheostat.

Sodium at 750°F has a viscosity comparable to water at 212°F. The high-temperature low-viscosity and consequently the low-load-carrying properties of liquid sodium result in bearing performance that requires development testing of each bearing combination for each particular service application. Bearing compatibility tests have been performed on a large number of material combinations. Although it is difficult to make generalizations concerning this subject, the following basic considerations are listed: (1) In general, soft bearing materials are unsatisfactory for use in liquid sodium because of corrosion. (2) Steel-to-steel contact surfaces having the same hardness may be subject to galling; with harder materials there is a definite improvement in bearing compatibility. (3) The limiting bearing load in all cases is the load that causes plastic deformation of the base material under the hard surface or the load at which welding of the surface occurs. Detailed results are given in Ref. 60.

4.3.3.3 Electromagnetic Pumps

All electromagnetic pumps utilize the motor principle, i.e., a conductor carrying a current in a magnetic field experiences a force. Since there are various means of creating the current and field, many different types of electromagnetic pumps have been conceived and studied. The design features and advantages of the various types are discussed in this section. The general advantages and disadvantages of electromagnetic pumps in relation to mechanical pumps are discussed in Sec. 4.3.3.1.

4.3.3.3.1 DIRECT-CURRENT FARADAY PUMP [25]. In the d-c conduction pump (Fig. 4.60), a thin-walled duct with copper conductors attached to opposite sides is located between the poles of an electromagnet. With a circuit equivalent to that of Fig. 4.61 and the following nomenclature, a set of equations has been derived. The equations are summarized below:

Nomenclature:

B = magnetic flux density in the liquid between the magnetic poles, gauss

E_c = counter electromotive force developed in the liquid as it moves through the magnetic field [$Bw/(10^8 s)$], volts

F = longitudinal force on the sodium ($BI_e r/10$), dynes

I = total current, amp

I_e = current traversing the liquid in the magnetic field ($10 \, ps/B$), amp

P = pressure developed, psi

Q = electrical power input to the duct (VI), watts

$R_B = R_w R_b/(R_w + R_b)$

R_b = effective resistance of the bypass paths through the liquid, ohms

R_e = effective resistance of liquid in strong-magnetic-field region, ohms

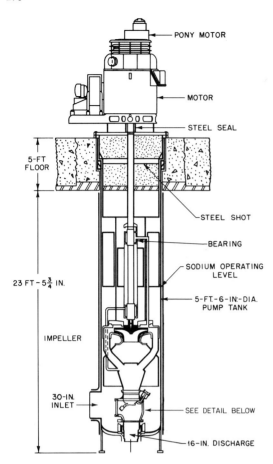

PONY MOTOR

MOTOR

STEEL SEAL

5-FT FLOOR

STEEL SHOT

BEARING

SODIUM OPERATING LEVEL

23 FT – 5¾ IN.

5-FT-6-IN.-DIA. PUMP TANK

IMPELLER

30-IN. INLET

SEE DETAIL BELOW

16-IN. DISCHARGE

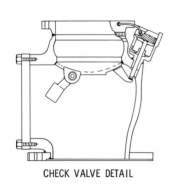

CHECK VALVE DETAIL

FIG. 4.56—Fermi primary sodium pump [31].

R_w = resistance of duct wall, ohms
S = duct height, in.
V = potential difference across the duct (E_c + $I_e R_e$), volts
W = flow, gal/min
p = pressure developed [$BI_e/(10s)$], dynes/cm^2
r = width of the pump duct parallel to the direction of current flow, cm
s = height of the duct in the magnetic-field direction, cm
w = liquid flow in the duct, cm^3/sec

In cgs units, solving network equations and substituting for I_e,

$$q = \frac{10^8 s}{B} \left[\frac{I R_w R_b}{R_w + R_b} - \frac{10 p s R_w R_b}{B (R_w R_b)} + R_e \right] \text{ cm}^3/\text{sec} \quad (4.7)$$

Converting to English units and rearranging yields the pressure developed

$$P = 5.7 \times 10^{-7} \frac{BI R_B}{S(R_B + R_e)} - \frac{B^2 W}{7 \times 10^{12} S^2 (R_B + R_e)} \text{ psi} \quad (4.8)$$

from which the static pressure can be obtained by setting $W = 0$.

The efficiency is obtained by knowing the electrical input to the duct in watts and the mechanical power, which is equal to 0.435 PW watts. Substituting for W the efficiency is

$$\text{Eff} = 1.74 \times 10^6 PS \frac{R_B - 1.75 \times 10^6 PS (BI)^{-1} (R_B + R_e)}{R_B (BI - 1.75 \times 10^6 PS)} \quad (4.9)$$

The efficiency does not include magnetic-field requirements or $I^2 R$ losses to the pump. The actual pressure is less than P by an amount that is a function of duct impedance.

Magnetic-field compensation for high-capacity pumps can be provided by reversing the return current, as shown in Fig. 4.62, and tapering the poles, as shown in Fig. 4.63. The matching of the field intensity with the drop in the current density can be accomplished by tapering the pole ends as shown in Fig. 4.63.

Separately excited many–turn high–voltage windings are subject to high-temperature insulation problems. Few-turn large-cross-section copper series windings, with drops of less than 1 volt, have few insulation problems and may not require auxiliary cooling.

The pump-duct material should have the following characteristics: (1) good corrosion resistance in sodium, (2) high electrical resistivity, (3) good weldability, (4) nonmagnetic, and (5) high-temperature strength.

The most commonly used materials are series 300 stainless steels, Nichrome (80 wt.% nickel-20 wt.% chromium), and Inconel X. The last two may not be desirable in high-temperature sodium near a neutron-activation zone. Low electrical resistivity and the joining of the conductor to the pump duct limits material choice, in general, to copper, aluminum, silver, nickel, and sodium or NaK. Figure 4.64 illustrates a pump design with the sodium-to-copper-to-sodium electrical conductor. With this conductor welds of copper to stainless steel can be avoided. Mass transfer and neutron activation should be evaluated in all cases.

Small pumps using rectangular sections formed from round tubes, though inexpensive, sacrifice integrity owing to the welding of the conductor to the thin tube wall, which is 0.025 to 0.0625 in. thick. The rectangular duct can be formed from four separate stainless-steel sheets welded together; two of these (parallel to the direction of current) can be thin, but the sheets composing the electrical junction can be heavier, adding strength and rigidity to the pump duct. The copper conductor, normally

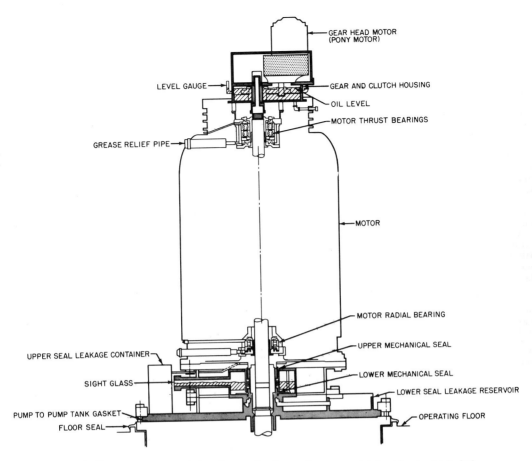

FIG. 4.57—Fermi primary pump-shaft-seal, motor-bearings, and pony-motor lubricant-barrier details [31].

made of many smaller bars stacked together in parallel, can be brazed directly to the stainless-steel sheets. Distortion of the heavy stainless-steel sheet is a problem.

The current requirements of d-c pumps range from the order of 1000 amps for small pumps (5 to 10 gal/min) to many thousands of amperes for high-capacity pumps supplied by rectifiers or generators with efficiencies of 20 to 40%. The voltage drop across the pumps is in the range of 1 to 2 volts. For higher efficiencies a homopolar generator, employing NaK as a liquid brush, can be used to produce large currents at low voltage and at efficiencies over 80%.

Pumps with capacities up to 10,000 gal/min have been built and tested. The 500 gal/min 25-psi primary circulating NaK coolant pump in EBR-II has a tapered Nichrome duct with a wall thickness of 0.025 in. The field winding consists of two turns of 6 in. by 6 in. cross section copper connected in series with the current path across the duct. Mica insulation is used, and no provision is made for external cooling. The current leads are brought out of an enclosure through stainless-steel bellows, which provide an insulating seal inasmuch as the leakage of current through the bellows is negligible. The enclosure is filled with helium. Leakage of liquid metal into the enclosure can be detected by the short circuiting of an insulated probe connected to an alarm circuit. The efficiency of the pump is 42% when pumping 300 gal/min at 40 psi.

The EBR-II primary coolant system includes one 14-in. d-c electromatic auxiliary pump [54] (Fig. 4.65). The pump has a capacity of about 500 gal/min at about 0.25 psig at 700°F. When the pump is powered by batteries alone, e.g., during an unexpected complete power failure with subsequent scram, the flow will continue at a minimum of 300 gal/min for about 20 min. The approximate EBR-II head requirement for a 500 gal/min flow is 0.22 psi. A 14-in. prototype primary auxiliary pump was constructed and assembled into a test loop designed to match approximately the desired hydraulic performance of the pump. Pump flow was read with an electromagnetic flowmeter. The differential head across the pump was read directly with an oil-filled manometer, using a balanced-level twin-seal pot arrangement. Power to the pump was supplied by a rectifier. The test data produced a head-capacity curve that is a straight line with the head decreasing slowly from 0.30 psi, at zero flow, to 0.24 psi at 600 gal/min. Tests on the actual EBR-II nickel-cadmium battery discharging through a resistance simulating the 14-in. auxiliary pump application provided data to estimate the discharge characteristics of the EBR-II installation, as shown in Fig. 4.66. Based on this available power and pump test data, the EBR-II primary system auxiliary pump flow rate variation with time has been plotted on the same figure. When only battery power is available, the primary-system coolant flow will continue for a period sufficient to prevent overheating and to ensure a smooth transition to natural circulation of the primary sodium coolant. The pump is located in the sodium line from the reactor to the IHX. It operates in series with the two main sodium pumps. The pumping section is incorporated in the 14 in. schedule 20 reactor outlet pipe, with no change in pipe cross section. The heavy electrical leads make no physical contact with the pipe. Electrical contact is made through a sodium-filled container. The double-walled electrically insulated container is welded directly to the pipe wall.

A 10,000 gal/min electromagnetic pump was developed and tested for possible use in the EBR-II (Fig. 4.64). It is equipped with a homopolar generator supplying 250,000 amp at 2.5 volts. The pump-power supply combination is a single compact unit aligned vertically to reduce electrical-conductor length between generator and pump. A functional description of the various components is given in Table 4.10, and a schematic diagram of the homopolar unit is shown in Fig. 4.67.

In contrast with the successful development of the centrifugal pump, considerable difficulty has been encountered with large d-c electromagnetic pumps. Extrapolation to large sizes, from experience with 500 to 1,000 gal/min units, introduces new and difficult problems. The power source is more complicated because of the extremely high currents

and low voltages. At the present time, large-sized centrifugal pumps are more reliable, more efficient, and more economical than d-c electromagnetic pumps.

4.3.3.3.2 ALTERNATING–CURRENT ELEC-TROMAGNETIC PUMPS. Alternating–current electromagnetic pumps for sodium and NaK in larger sizes are comparable to d-c electromagnetic pumps in size and weight. They have the advantage of utilizing conventional power sources. They have the disadvantage of requiring special provisions for cooling (either free or forced-air convection or forced-fluid convection). Development of a-c electromagnetic pumps has largely been centered around two types: the a-c Faraday and the induction or traveling field pumps.

The a-c Faraday pump [25] differs from the d-c type in the following respects: (1) a high current can be obtained from a transformer in proper time phase with the magnetic field in the gap, (2) the alternating nature of the magnetic flux requires the magnetic circuit to be laminated to avoid excessive magnetic losses, and (3) the secondary currents induced by transformer action in the sodium by the alternating field do not contribute to the pumping and cause an additional loss. Pumps of this type, with 10 to 15% efficiency, are commercially available at flows up to 50 gal/min, pressures up to 150 psi, and temperatures up to approximately 1600°F; above this temperature construction materials are limiting.

A large current can be developed directly in

ITEM NO.	DESCRIPTION	ITEM NO.	DESCRIPTION
1.	Oil Return Line	10.	Argon Supply
2.	Cooling Fins	11.	Pump Shaft
3.	Oil Supply Line	12.	Oil Inlet Pipe
4.	Oil Reservoir	13.	Spring Holder
5.	Stationary Face (Upper)	14.	Coupling and Seal Sleeve
6.	Rotating Face (Upper)	15.	Upper Leakage Drain
7.	Motor Shaft	16.	Key
8.	Cooling-air Duct	17.	Orifice
9.	Lower Leakage Drain	18.	Conical Seal

HALF SECTION OF SHAFT SEAL

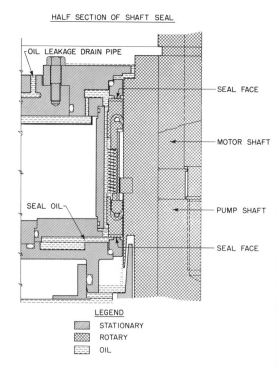

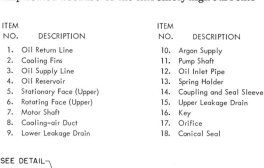

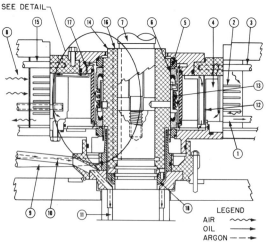

FIG. 4.58—Fermi primary sodium-pump mechanical seal [59].

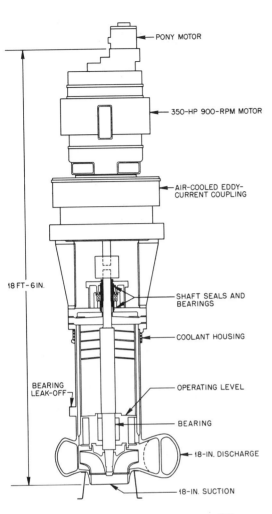

FIG. 4.59—Fermi secondary sodium pump [31].

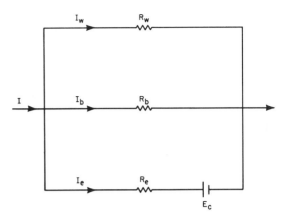

FIG. 4.61—Direct-current Faraday pump equivalent circuit [25].

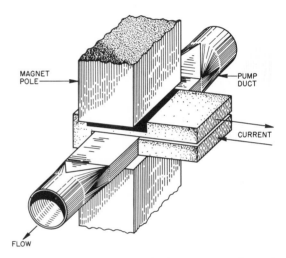

FIG. 4.62—Direct-current pump showing arrangement of current flow for field compensation [25].

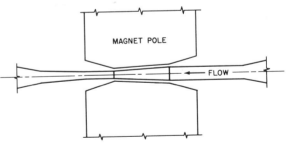

FIG. 4.63—Pump with tapered magnet poles and duct to provide field compensation [25].

moving sodium by electromagnetic induction. There are three major versions: the flat linear induction pump (FLIP), the annular linear pump (ALIP), and

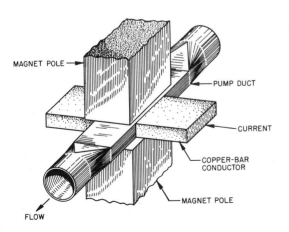

FIG. 4.60—Direct-current Faraday type pump [25].

the helical, or spiral channel, induction pump (SIP); all utilize the same principle of inducing current in the moving liquid by means of polyphase a-c multipole windings mounted in slotted fixed stators ajacent to the pump duct. Table 4.11 gives information about some typical induction pumps.

The linear induction type (FLIP) (Fig. 4.68) utilizes a moving magnetic field to induce currents in the liquid metal. The polyphase multipole

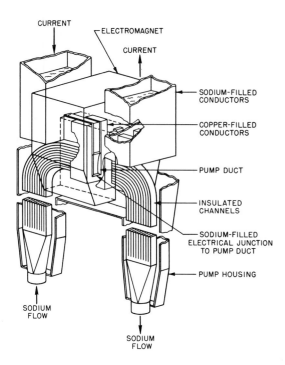

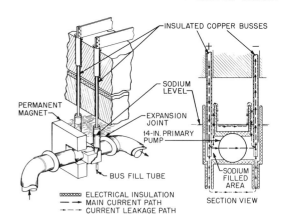

FIG. 4.65—EBR-II primary-system auxiliary pump [76].

FIG. 4.64—Cutaway perspective of 10,000 gal/min d-c electromagnetic sodium pump [61].

windings are contained in a magnetic core and produce a linear traveling wave of flux. Two stators, one on each side of the rectangular duct, induce currents in the sodium in a manner similar to that of an induction motor. An aspect ratio of approximately 24:1 for the duct cross section results in a satisfactory compromise between efficiency and power factor for a 60 cycle/sec design. The linear electromagnetic pump includes the duct; an outer casing, which mounts the stator punchings and can be made hermetically tight; transition pieces, which connect the rectangular duct to the

inlet and outlet nozzles; and an expansion joint to accomodate changes in the duct length with varying liquid-metal temperatures.

The EBR-II secondary coolant system features an a-c linear induction electromagnetic pump [54]. This pump has a capacity of 6,500 gal/min at 53 psig. The approximate EBR-II full-power flow requirement of the pump is 5,900 gal/min at 45 psig of 585°F sodium. Performance and life tests were conducted on an identically constructed, slightly smaller capacity (5000 gal/min), a-c linear electromagnetic pump. The reported test results [55] were based on 5,600 hr of operation at 5,000 gal/min with sodium at 850°F, plus an additional 1,000 hr at lower flow rates and temperatures. The total operating time with sodium was 8700 hr at full capacity and 850°F, plus an additional 1100 hr at reduced flow rates and temperatures. One of the major attributes of this type pump is the very fine flow control that can be achieved. Refinements were made in the control system for the motor-generator power supply, and stable flow rates down to approximately 7 gal/min were achieved. This type pump is also capable of reverse flow, a characteristic that will be useful in the EBR-II secondary system

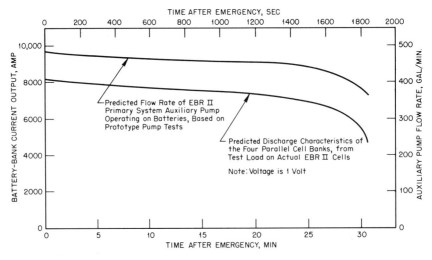

FIG. 4.66—EBR-II auxiliary-pump flow on battery power [54]. Note: voltage is 1 volt.

Table 4.10—Characteristics of a 10,000 Gal/Min Electromagnetic Pump Unit [61]

Item	Functional description	Capacity
Structural characteristics:		
Arrangement	Vertical alignment of components	
Over-all height	30 ft	
Over-all weight	35 tons	
Drive motor:		
Type	Induction, squirrel cage	1250 hp
Input voltage	3-phase, 60-cycle	2300 volts
Set connection	Direct	
Homopolar generator:		
Type	Liquid brush	250,000 amp, 2.5 volts
Brush conducting material	NaK eutectic, water-cooled, argon blanketed	
Machine winding	Excitation coil, Cu strap, water-cooled	13 turns
Field excitation	Separate d-c source, dry rectifier	2500 amp
Rotor	12-in. Fe rotor, Ag-soldered, Cu plugs	
Stator–NaK insulation	Stainless-steel double-walled cylinder	
Terminal ring	2 in. wide, Cu	
Temperature	Maximum operating	150°C
Losses, full load	Excitation, bearings	60 kw
Test loading	Maximum generator load current	425,000 amp, 1.8 volts
Test loading	Maximum generator field current	2450 amp
Efficiency	Overall full load	92%
Electromagnet:		
Excitation	Homopolar generator output, one-turn coil, series excited	250,000 amp
Flux density	Na-filled duct	7000 gauss
Core composition and weight	20 carbon-steel plates, 2 in. thick, $\frac{1}{8}$-in. spacing	16 tons
Gap dimensions	Between plates rectangular cross section	21 in. high, 6 in. wide, 42 in. long
Pump duct:		
Material	18 Cr-8 Ni stainless steel sheet	
Geometry, pumping region	Single duct at center of gap	21 in. high, 6 in. wide, 30 in. long
Geometry, flow regions	Multiple-channel duct on either side	12, $1\frac{5}{8}$ in. × 6 in. cross section
Insulation	Flat sheet, mica or ceramic	
Temperature limit	Curie point of iron	763°C

as a coolant "brake" to control natural-circulation rates. The Class H insulated windings operate at a lower temperature because of a thin thermal barrier and water cooling. The barrier can consist of alternate layers of stainless-steel screen and narrow strips of thin stainless steel. Heat derived from the iron and copper losses of the stators is removed by water cooling. Each stator assembly generally consists of a laminated punched stack, form-wound coils, coolant pipes, a structural stator plate, and metallic thermal insulation. The two stator assemblies can be electrically and mechanically independent. The laminated punching stack provides a low-reluctance path for the magnetic flux as in a conventional motor stator. The stator coils are very similar to the formed coils used in large induction motors, except the two coil sides lie in parallel planes since the slots in the punchings are parallel. The coils are insulated with glass-backed silicone-bonded mica tape. No seals are used in the primary sodium enclosure, the pump

duct. The electrical windings and magnetic structure are located in a secondary enclosure filled with inert gas during operation and sealed with a conventional O-ring.

The Dounreay primary pumps (Fig. 4.69) are of the a-c linear induction type. Each pump operates within a steel tank into which the stators can be lowered down guide rails on two sides of the access column and then clamped on to the built-in pump tube.

The helical induction type (SIP) (Fig. 4.70) utilizes a cylindrical multipole, polyphase a-c winding to produce a rotating magnetic field, which induces high currents in the sodium in space quadrature with the field. The sodium is contained in a thin-walled hollow cylindrical duct, which takes the place of an air gap in an induction motor. Currents flowing axially in the sodium interact with the field causing the fluid to rotate. Rotation of the fluid is transformed into axial movement by a thin metal helix in the sodium

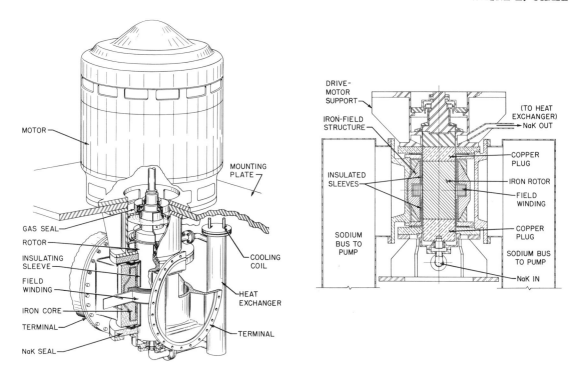

FIG. 4.67—Schematic diagram of 250,000–amp homopolar generator [61].

Table 4.11—Typical Induction Pumps [61]

Type	Application	Flow rate, gal/min	Pumping head, psi	Overall efficiency, %
FLIP	EBR-II secondary sodium system	6500	53	43
ALIP	Laboratory test system (Na) at Argonne National Laboratory	400	15	40
SIP	Laboratory test systems (Na) at Argonne National Laboratory	300	40	20
FLIP	Dounreay Fast Reactor, primary and secondary coolant systems			
	Sodium	400	30	30
	NaK (with some stator current)	400	15	23

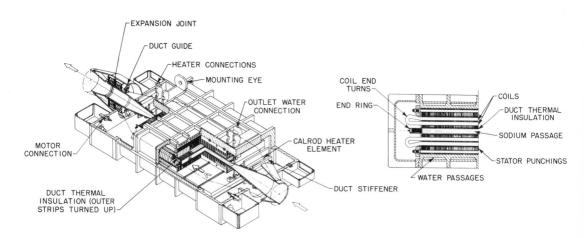

FIG. 4.68—Linear induction pump (water cooled) [25].

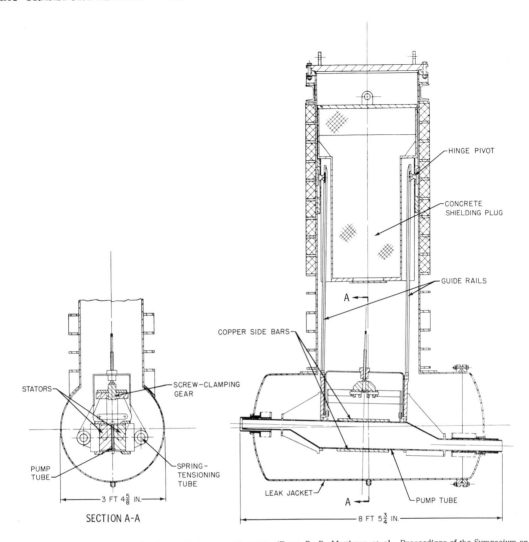

FIG. 4.69—Dounreay, arrangement of primary-electromagnetic pump. (From R. R. Matthews et al., Proceedings of the Symposium on the Dounreay Fast Reactor, London, Dec. 7, 1960, Institution of Mechanical Engineers, London, 1961.)

SECTION A-A

STATORS
PUMP TUBE
SCREW-CLAMPING GEAR
SPRING-TENSIONING TUBE
3 FT 4⅝ IN.

HINGE PIVOT
CONCRETE SHIELDING PLUG
GUIDE RAILS
COPPER SIDE BARS
LEAK JACKET
PUMP TUBE
A
8 FT 5¾ IN.

duct which is open at both ends to headers or collecting pipes; these pipes, in turn, are open to inlet and outlet nozzles. Up until the 1960's pumps of this type were built for flows as high as 400 gal/min and for high pressures (≥150 psi) at low flow rates (<5 gal/min) where compactness was required. Type 347 stainless steel, 0.030 in. thick, can be used for liners (forming the walls of the liquid-metal duct). The thermal insulation separating the duct walls and the stator iron can consist of 1/16 in. of phospho-asbestos. Forced-air cooling can be used to maintain a satisfactory winding temperature.

There has been some development of a combination helical induction and mechanical pump with an efficiency as high as that of a mechanical pump [63]. This pump (Fig. 4.71) has no moving parts in sodium and no seals or stuffing boxes. It uses an enclosed annulus that contains the sodium, with a rotating electromagnet in the center. This electromagnet is rotated by a motor that can be located internal to the shielding.

However, to change the flow, the field strength must be changed. The rotor is a helical electromagnet. The direct current is brought through slip rings on the shaft. The electromagnet central coil is cooled by windage only. The efficiency is

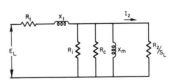

Electromagnetic pump equivalent circuit.

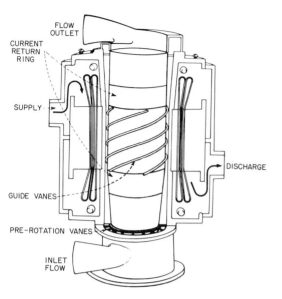

E_L	the input voltage per phase, volts
I_2	the equivalent secondary current per phase, amp
K_d and K_p	distribution and pitch factors, respectively
N_1	the number of primary conductors in series per phase
P	theoretical pressure developed, psi
Q	pump electrical output, watts
r	width of the pump duct, parallel to the direction of current flow, cm
R_1	the primary-winding resistance, ohms
R_2	the resistance of the liquid metal in the duct referred to the primary or stator winding, ohms
R_c	the resistance equivalent of losses in the duct walls referred to the primary or stator winding, ohms
R_i	the resistance equivalent of the iron losses, ohms
S	the resistance of the fluid (measured in the direction of the flux), in.
S_L	the slip = $W_s - (W/W_s) = 0.5194\ rs_Tf$
W	actual flow, gal/min
W_f	the width of the fluid (measured in the direction of current flow), in.
W_s	synchronous flow, gal/min

FIG. 4.70—Helical induction-pump cutaway. [From Product Engineering, 27(4):193 (1956).]

26% at 2000 gal/min, 37 psi, and 600°F. The efficiency should improve with an increase in size. The estimated cost is about half of comparable electromagnetic pumps.

The electrical performance of an electromagnetic pump can be represented by the circuit

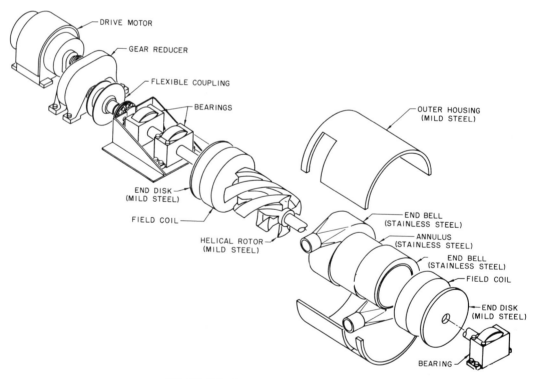

FIG. 4.71—Helical pump with unipolar rotor [63].

X_1	impedance of the primary-winding leakage reactance, ohms
X_m	the magnetizing reactance, ohms
f	frequency, cycles/sec
l	the length of the fluid under the stator (measured in direction of fluid flow), in.
n_p	the number of poles
ρ_f	the resistivity of the fluid at the operating temperature, ohm-in.
r	pole pitch, in.
s	duct height, cm

The values of R_1, X_1, and R_i are calculated as for induction motors. In practice, X_m can be neglected. The duct can be treated as a separate rotor with zero-resistance end rings. The value of X_m is calculated conventionally if the air gap is less than 1/4 pole pitch. R_2 can be calculated as a rotor with values of slip less than 30%

$$R_2 \cong 3\rho_f r (N_1 K_d K_p)^2 / (s\, l) \qquad (4.10)$$

The value of S_L can be determined for any value of W. The circuit can then be solved for E_2, and the pump output Q can be calculated. For a three-phase pump, the output in watts is

$$Q = 3 I_2^2 R_2 (1 - S_L)/S_L \qquad (4.11)$$

and the pressure per square inch is

$$P = 2.30\, Q/W \qquad (4.12)$$

The developed pressure is about $[(n_p - 1.5)/n_p]P$, taking into account field discontinuities. The output

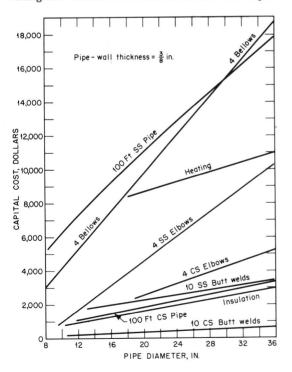

FIG. 4.72—Approximate costs for primary piping and containment.

pressure is the developed pressure minus pump hydraulic losses.

4.3.4 PIPING AND VALVES

4.3.4.1 Piping

The design of piping for a fast reactor follows the conventional piping code procedures for the determination of size and wall thickness. The piping configuration for flexibility is also planned by normal piping design procedures. Both flexibility and method of support are critical design areas because of the high operating temperatures.

4.3.4.1.1 PIPING SIZE. Line sizes for forced circulation are based on economics. The capital costs invested in the installed equipment for various line sizes amortized over the expected life are plotted against pumping power cost. Where the total cost reaches its lowest point determines the optimum line size.

As an example of this optimization, Fig. 4.72 was used for approximate capital costs of 100 ft of stainless-steel piping, with four elbows, enclosed in carbon-steel pipe with bellows. With 24-in. pipe as an example, the following tabulation can be made:

	Dollars
100 ft 24-in. pipe	$ 12,500
4 SS elbows	6,000
10 butt-welds	2,500
100 ft 30-in. CS pipe	2,750
4 CS elbows	4,200
4 bellows	15,300
10 CS butt-welds	400
30 in. insulation	3,000
30 in. heating	10,000
24 in. SS erection	42,000
30 in. CS erection	50,500
Total	$ 149,150

Using annual charges of 14% based on 30-year life (see Chap. 10 for details), the yearly cost for 24-in. piping is about $21,000. Other pipe-size costs can be calculated in the same manner, and the information can be plotted as is done in Fig. 4.73.

For the same system the annual power costs for pumping can be determined. The following is an example of the annual power costs.

With 0.71×10^5 lb/min as the flow per loop or 1200 lb/sec (Sec. 4.2.1.1.1), the power is 1200 H ft lb/sec, where H is the pressure drop in feet. With a conversion factor of 0.00136 for changing ft lb/sec to kilowatts, a pump efficiency of 0.75, a yearly plant factor of 0.80, and a combined energy and power charge of $ 0.006 per kw/hr, the annual pumping costs are approximately $91 H. The pressure drop in straight lines is

$$(fL/D)(v^2/2g) \qquad (4.13)$$

where f = friction factor based on Reynold's number $(Re = Dv\rho/\mu)$
L = length of pipe, ft
D = inside diameter of pipe, ft
v = velocity, ft/sec

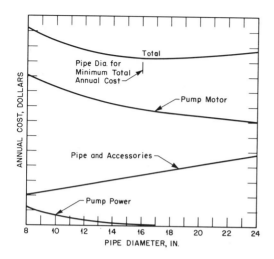

FIG. 4.73—Pipe-size optimization (pipe diameter vs. annual costs).

$g = 32.2$ ft/sec^2
ρ = density, lb/cu ft
μ = viscosity, lb/ft/hr

The values of f, Re, and the head loss in pipe can be found from charts in Chap. 2.

The pressure drop in elbows and fittings Δp for turbulent flow is

$$\Delta p = K\rho v^2/2g \qquad (4.14)$$

where K is a constant shown in tabular form in Chap. 2.

As the pipe size increases, the pressure drop and therefore the pump head requirements decrease, with a consequent decrease in pump costs. This should be evaluated by costing each pump size.

Each of the three curves, pipe cost, power cost, and pump costs, can be plotted as shown in Fig. 4.73. The sum of the curves gives the total cost, and the minimum cost gives the most economical pipe size. This is an overall simplified optimization since the following cost factors remain to be accounted for: (1) tank and vessel nozzles, (2) space occupied by the piping and equipment, (3) pipe-heating power costs, (4) heat losses, (5) maintenance costs, and (6) reflection of changes of pump capacity in the gross electrical load and in the capital cost of the plant.

A similar calculation for head (H) requirements can be made for gravity flow. For example, Fig. 4.74 shows the head requirements for moving 10,000 gal/min of sodium through various pipe sizes. More details on pressure drops are given in Chap. 2.

4.3.4.1.2 WALL THICKNESS. Normally the minimum wall thickness is determined by the ASME Code [64]:

$$S = \frac{PD}{2S_A + 2KP} + C \qquad (4.15)$$

where S = minimum wall, in.
P = maximum internal pressure, psig
D = outer diameter of pipe, in.
S_A = allowable stress due to internal pressure at operating temperature, psi

C = corrosion allowance, in.
K = coefficient dependent on temperature and material

When this formula is used, an addition should be made to the thickness to compensate for material removed in making mechanical joints and to provide additional mechanical strength where it may be necessitated by other factors, such as thermal gradients. For the term, P, the maximum pump discharge pressure should be used even on those portions of the system which operate at low pressure. The maximum allowable stress S_A for the material is taken from the code stress tables at the design temperature of the system. The design temperature for a primary coolant system should be equal to the maximum possible steady-state temperature. Other sustained stresses, such as gravity loads, may be important and should be considered.

As an example, with a pump discharge pressure, P, of 100 psig, a pipe diameter, D, of 30 in., a design temperature of 1050°F (which gives an allowable stress, S_A, of 6800 psi for 304 stainless steel), and a coefficient K of 0.4, S becomes 0.22 in. excluding corrosion allowance. The corrosion allowance is dependent on the system conditions and the experience gained from tests under these conditions.

4.3.4.1.3 LAYOUT. The primary considerations in piping arrangement are neutron attenuation (Sec. 4.1.3.1) and thermal expansion (Sec. 4.1.3.3). As Fig. 4.75 indicates, there are three methods of handling thermal expansion: (1) stiff piping and

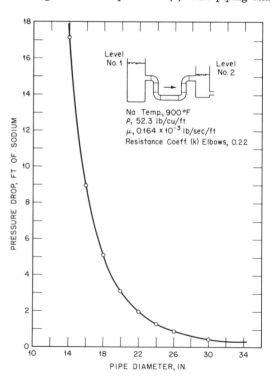

FIG. 4.74—Sodium pressure drop through piping system (100 ft of pipe and four elbows; 10,000 gal/min).

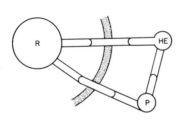

Problem
This Schematic Diagram Presents the Problem of the Design of a Coolant Loop Consisting of the Reactor, a Pump, Heat Exchanger, and Piping.

— Coolant Loop
— Shielding
— Reactor Bldg.

R, Reactor

HE, Heat Exchanger

P, Pump

SCHEME 1.

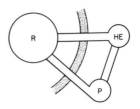

Pump and Heat Exchanger on Rollers.

No Need for Flexibility in Piping.

Poor Shielding Design.

Poor Pump Support.

SCHEME 2.

Pump and Heat Exchanger Anchored.

Piping Flexibility by Expansion Joints.

Poor Shielding Design.

Poor Integrity.

SCHEME 3.

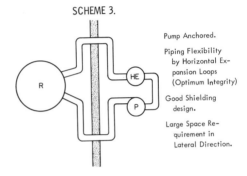

Pump Anchored.

Piping Flexibility by Horizontal Expansion Loops (Optimum Integrity)

Good Shielding design.

Large Space Requirement in Lateral Direction.

SCHEME 4.

Vertical Expansion Loops.

Good Integrity.

Good Flexibility and Shielding.

Good Shielding Design.

Minimum Lateral but Maximum Radial Space Requirement.

SCHEME 5.

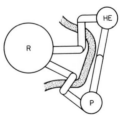

Vertical Offset Expansion Loop.

Good Integrity.

Good Flexibility and Shielding.

Optimum Use of Available Space.

FIG. 4.75—Primary piping layout schemes.

equipment not anchored (scheme 1), (2) fixed equipment with flexible piping using expansion joints (scheme 2), and (3) fixed equipment with flexible piping using expansion loops (schemes 3, 4, and 5).

It may be advantageous to anchor pumps with rotating shafts. The reactor usually acts as an anchor at the other end of the system. It may also be advantageous to allow the heat exchanger to move with the piping. Even if the heat exchanger is not anchored, the piping between it and the reactor should probably be flexible. If this piping is arranged to be stiff, the equipment should accomodate pipe expansion. The major disadvantage to such a system is the difficulty in designing acceptable equipment supports under varying circumstances. For normal operating conditions the heat exchanger can be supported so that no differential vertical expansion between exchanger and reactor shell occurs, permitting a rigid support. However, because transients might produce temperature differentials between the reactor and the heat exchanger, a solid support is not feasible. Moreover, any type of moving support requires damping to prevent response under vibrational loads. Because the best type of damping is hydraulic, such a support would have to be outside the radioactive area to permit inspection and maintenance. If the pump is anchored, it should be located as close as possible to the other anchor, the reactor, because the distance between anchors dictates the length of the expansion loop and the diameter of the containment building is established primarily on the basis of the space occupied by the primary loops. Piping expansion loops require more space and more material than expansion joints, but primary-system integrity is higher. The choice between vertical and horizontal expansion loops depends mainly upon the number of primary loops in the reactor plant. If there are only two loops, obviously 180° of the plant layout is available for each loop, and a horizontal expansion loop would probably make optimum use of the space. With several loops, more use should be made of the vertical space. In optimizing space requirements, remember that the flexibility in a thin-wall large-diameter piping system comes from elbows rather than from pipe sections because of the flattening effect on the elbows. Therefore, adding an elbow is better than adding length to the piping in an expansion loop.

4.3.4.1.4 FLEXIBILITY.

Stress calculations are a necessary part of layout studies. Flexibility should be designed into the system to accommodate the allowable moments on the vessels and the allowable stress for the piping. The usual procedure is to design a configuration for the loop and submit the design to a stress analyst for computation of the forces and moments in the system and the maximum stress in the system. References 64 through 68 contain some of the methods for determining pipe flexibility. In close-coupled sodium system layouts, the vessel-nozzle moments rather than piping stress will dictate the flexibility requirements. After the forces and moments in a piping system have been determined, the stresses, particularly at nozzles, should be evaluated. The following sample calculation uses the ASME Piping Code [64] method to determine piping stresses. The system is shown in Fig. 4.76.

(1) Nozzle Moments at Point 1

$$M_b \text{(bending moment)} = \left(M_z^2 + M_y^2\right)^{1/2} = 32,300 \text{ ft-lb}$$
$$M_t \text{(torsional moment)} = M_x = 6000 \text{ ft-lb}$$

(2) Nozzle Moments at Point 12

$$M_b = \left(M_x^2 + M_y^2\right)^{1/2} = 18,700 \text{ ft-lb}$$
$$M_t = M_z = 42,000 \text{ ft-lb}$$

(3) Reaction with 100% Cold Spring

If the tabulated moments and forces were based on the cold modulus E_c, then the nozzle reactions in terms of the calculated reaction F are:

Forces (Pounds) and Moments (Foot-pounds) Acting on Nozzles

Point	F_x	F_y	F_z	M_x	M_y	M_z
1	−4000	−1300	+1100	−6000	−12,000	−30,000
7				−8000	+18,500	+48,000
12	+4000	+1300	−1100	+5000	−18,000	+42,000

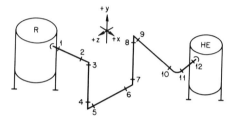

FIG. 4.76—Isometric diagram of piping system for stress analysis (lengths omitted).

$$F_h \text{(hot reaction)} = (1 - \tfrac{2}{3}C)\frac{E_h}{E_c} F$$

$$= \left[1 - \tfrac{2}{3}(1)\right]\frac{22.8 \times 10^6}{27.4 \times 10^6} F = 0.278 \, F$$

$$F_c \text{(cold reaction)} = CF = 1.0(F) = F$$

where C is a cold-spring factor equal to zero for no cold spring and 1.00 for 100% cold spring and E_h is the hot modulus.

The layout is satisfactory if the reactions (nozzle moments and forces) in the hot and cold conditions are within the allowable reaction used for design.

(4) Piping Stress (Maximum at Point 7)

$$S_E = \left(S_b^2 + 4S_t^2\right)$$
$$S_b = \left(iM_{bp}^2 + iM_{bt}^2\right)/Z$$
$$S_t = M_t/2Z$$
$$h = Sr_1/r_2^2 = 0.079 \, [30 \text{ in. dia.}, \tfrac{3}{8} \text{ in. wall}]$$
$$i \text{ (elbow)} = (0.9)/(h^{2/3})$$
$$S_b = 11,200 \text{ psi}$$
$$S_t = 43.7 \text{ psi}$$
$$S_E = 11,240 \text{ psi}$$

where: S_E = expansion stress, psi
S_b = resultant bending stress, psi
S_t = torsional stress, psi
i = stress intensification factor

M_{bp} = bending moment in plane of member = M_x, in.-lb
M_{bt} = bending moment in transverse plane = M_z, in.-lb
M_t = torsional moment = M_y, in.-lb
S = wall thickness, in.
r_1 = elbow radius, in.
r_2 = inside radius of elbow, in.
Z = section modulus, cu in.

S_E should not exceed allowable stress S_A given by the following formula:

$$S_A = k_f (1.25 S_c + 0.25 S_h)$$

S_c = 18750 psi from Code table

S_h = 8500 psi from Code table

k_f = 1.0 for < 7000 cycles (i.e. 1 cycle/day for approximately 20 years)

S_A = 25,500 psi for type 304 stainless steel and $S_E < S_A$

where: S_c = allowable stress at min. temp.
      S_h = allowable stress at max. temp.
      k_f = reduction factor for cyclic conditions for total number of full temperature cycles during life of plant

There are several methods whereby adequate pipe flexibility can be attained: (1) the anchor external to the reactor (pump or heat exchanger) may be moved closer to the reactor, thereby reducing the distance between anchors, (2) the length of the expansion loop may be increased in a direction perpendicular to the line between anchors or additional elbows may be added, (3) the diameter of the pipe may be reduced to the next standard size if the increased pressure drop can be tolerated, (4) the wall thickness of the piping may be reduced, if stress allows, to the next standard thickness, (5) the piping material may be changed (e.g., a change from stainless steel to chromium–molybdenum steel results in a smaller thermal growth and therefore smaller stresses and a change from type 304 stainless steel to type 316 stainless steel gives higher allowable stresses), and (6) if 100% cold spring gives excessive moments in the cold conditions, a 66% or 50% cold spring design may be adopted.

4.3.4.1.5 SUPPORTS. When the piping configuration has been decided upon, the system should be analyzed to determine the type of supports to be used and the location of the support attachments. Vibration studies should be made of the configuration to substantiate the location of the support attachments. The support design should be coordinated with secondary containment design (Sec. 4.2.1.1.4). Generally, piping supports are sized to support 100% of the weight of the piping and its contents so that there will be no moments imposed on the vessel for support of the piping. If the pipe supports are to carry all the piping load, allowances should be made for thermal growth that might cause vertical movement of vessel nozzles. For example, if a rigid rod were used as a pipe support and if this support were attached in the cold condition, the upward movement of the vessel nozzle would shift the piping load from its support rod to the vessel nozzle since the support is usually attached in a manner that allows freedom of motion of the pipe in an upward direction. A partial solution to this problem is the use of spring hangers. The spring is compressed at the time of erection so that adequate support is given at the operating position. However, at all other positions the amount of support depends upon the spring constant. Complete solution to the problem rests in the use of a constant-support hanger. This type is designed to render the same amount of support on the piping within all normal ranges of vertical movement. The support attachment to the piping may use welded lugs rather than a continuous ring around the pipe. A ring represents a change of section and may act like a restrictive band around the pipe circumference, preventing the rapid expansion of the pipe diameter at the time of a thermal transient. Welded lugs may require stress relief. Consideration could be given to supports external to the insulation.

4.3.4.2 Valves

4.3.4.2.1 USES. Valves may be installed in a sodium heat-transport system for the following purposes:

(1) To isolate a loop or a component. If it is desired to isolate one primary loop while continuing to operate the other loops, positive shutoff valves are needed in both supply and return lines. The loop can then be drained, and maintenance operations can be performed. Valves for loop isolation demand zero body leakage since the valve is the only barrier between maintenance personnel and the primary coolant. When loops are isolated for maintenance, biological shield walls must be used between the loops. If the reactor is shut down, shield walls need not be used between loops. There is always the possibility with valves of inadvertent closure, which would result in temperature surges in the reactor core due to reduced coolant flow. Valves should be designed for zero stem leakage and for remote operation. If the critical parts of major primary-system components, such as the intermediate heat-exchanger tube bundle and the pump impeller, were constructed so that they could be removed from liquid sodium without having to drain the system, stop valves could be eliminated from major primary-system components since there would be no need for isolation. Secondary loops are normally independent of each other although valves could be used to isolate a specific component.

(2) To throttle or control the quantity of flow. A portion of the reactor flow may be diverted through a line containing a throttle valve into the blanket subassemblies of the reactor. These subassemblies require only a fraction of the total flow. A typical valve for this service is shown in Fig. 4.77. Another application might be for a pump or heat-exchanger bypass where a fixed flow can be obtained by adjusting a valve.

(3) To control the direction of flow. Check valves in the heat-transport systems serve two purposes: to prevent thermal shock and pump reversal in a nonoperating loop and to allow operation of a plant while one loop is out of commission.

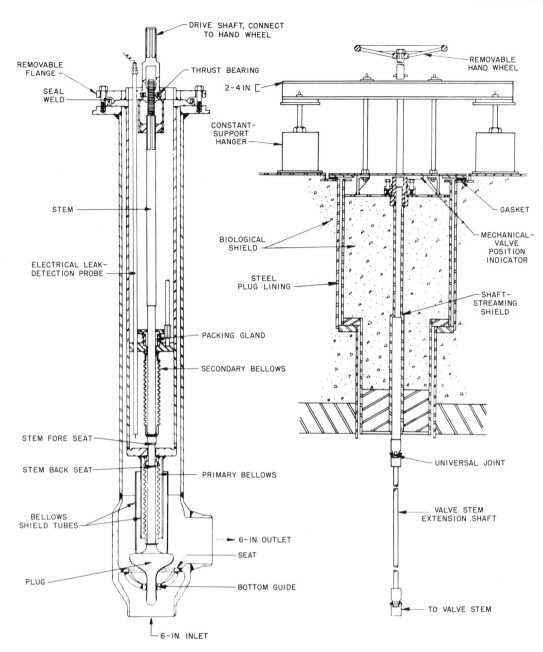

FIG. 4.77—Fermi throttle valve [31].

The valve generally closes on reverse flow. A common type is the tilting-disk check valve (Fig. 4.56).

(4) To drain a coolant system. A disadvantage of drain valves is the possible leakage of coolant, which could result in unscheduled draining of the coolant from the reactor core if the drain lines are not frozen. The location of drain valves at the low point in the system may make them inaccessible and require remote operation. Siphoning is an alternate method for draining sodium systems. Body design of drain valves should incorporate complete drainage.

The valves should be installed so that the system pressure is not on the stem side of the seat.

(5) To vent a coolant system. Vent valves are located at high points in coolant systems to eliminate gas pockets when the system is being filled and to admit gas during draining. During loop operation the valves may be left open for equalization of pressure between components. For this reason back-seating valves are often used as vent valves. This type valve has a seat from above the disk that seals off the valve body when in the full-open position. Complete valve body drainage is desirable.

4.3.4.2.2 VALVE DESIGN DETAILS. 4.3.4.2.2.1
Valve-seat Seal and Materials. Typical leakage
across a valve main seat and back seat when tested
with cold water at design pressure should not be
more than 1 cm^3/hr for valves 1 in. and smaller
and 2 cm^3/hr per inch of seat diameter for valves
over 1 in. The internal leakage requirements can
be met easily if all the following conditions are
fulfilled: (1) the seating faces have a sound and
homogeneous surface, (2) the mating faces of the seat
and disk have a good surface finish of 4 to 8 μin.,
(3) the seat and disks are carefully lapped and mated
to ensure continuous metal-to-metal contact on the
entire seating surface, and (4) satisfactory torque
can be applied at least in excess of 30 to 50% of the
pressure load.

Self-welding of the valve face to the valve seat
may occur if the pressure seating of the valve is
high and/or the valve is subjected to high temperatures in the presence of liquid sodium. Nitriding
of surfaces, stellite surfacing, or other hard sur-
facings are effective in preventing self-welding [69].

Screening studies have been performed on potential valve-seat materials for 1500°F service in
NaK. Molybdenum, tungsten, K-94 (88% tungsten
carbide, 12% cobalt), K-8 (96% tungsten carbide,
4% cobalt), and K-138A (65% titanium carbide,
15% niobium carbide, 20% cobalt) were found to be
the best materials. The combination of tungsten-
tungsten was found to be the best over-all combination tested. Lists of materials tested and details
of the tests are given in Ref. 60.

4.3.4.2.2.2 Stem Seal and Materials. No simple
stem packing has been devised that will provide a
satisfactory operating seal at high temperatures.
Some investigators have reported satisfactory static
seals for relatively high temperatures, such as
Inconel mesh packings or metal 0-rings. For
temperatures under 1000°F a wire-reinforced asbestos graphite has given good service. It may be
expected that after a period of operation the packing
will become permeated with sodium contaminants,
which might possibly bind the stem [25]. Double-
packing stem seals with a leak-off connection have
been used to minimize leakage.

Packless valves have proven most satisfactory
for liquid-metal systems. Of the several commercially available types, bellows-sealed valves with
all-welded construction have been used most extensively and with best results. For bellows-sealed
valves, total leakage for body, stubs, and bellows
should be undetectable on a mass spectrometer
within limits of sensitivity (less than 1×10^{-10}
standard ml of helium per hour).

In frozen stem-seal designs a cooling section is
placed around the valve stem to freeze a thin
annulus of sodium so that it becomes impossible
for molten metal to pass that point. Since the shear
strength of solid sodium is low, the frozen annulus
will shear when the valve is actuated.

4.3.4.2.3 CHECK-VALVES PROBLEMS. Immediately after the pump in one loop of a multi-
loop system is shut down, the flow in that loop
begins to decay. Within a very short period, the
pressure downstream of the pump exceeds the
pressure delivered by the decelerating pump, and
the flow tends to reverse. If the check valve were

an ideally designed valve, it would close at the instant the flow became zero in the dead loop. However, this condition cannot be attained because of
inertia of the disk, friction in the bearings, and in
some cases the normal, partially-open, hanging
position of the valve. Therefore, the flow reverses
to build up sufficient velocity to close the valve.
As the valve closes, fluid hammer occurs when
the disk reaches the seat and decelerates the
flowing liquid. The first layer of fluid next to the
disk sees the flow blocked in zero time. Even
though the disk takes a finite time to close, the
flowing liquid is moving at the same velocity as
the disk the instant before closure. At closure,
this fluid adjacent to the disk is compressed
somewhat, and the fluid behind it continues to
flow for another instant. The compression builds
up layer upon layer until the layer of fluid adjacent
to the common plenum, in this case in the reactor,
has been compressed somewhat [70]. The kinetic
energy of the flowing fluid is converted into the elastic energy of the stretched pipe and the compressed
fluid. This condition of zero fluid velocity and stag-
nation pressure spreads from the check valve to the
plenum chamber with acoustic velocity. After the
entire line is filled with compressed stagnant fluid
at a higher pressure than the fluid in the common
plenum, the high-pressure fluid begins to discharge
from the pipe back into the plenum chamber. Even
after the fluid in the pipe is at the initial pressure,
it continues to flow out of the pipe into the plenum
chamber because of the momentum of the fluid
column. Eventually, the momentum of the fluid
outflow is balanced by the adverse pressure
gradient, and the fluid comes to rest. The entire
fluid column is then stagnant at a pressure that is
lower than the plenum-chamber fluid pressure.
This pressure differential causes plenum-chamber
fluid to flow into the pipe at the plenum-chamber
pressure, with the initial velocity, magnitude,
and direction [71]. Chapter 2 has additional details on this problem.

Three methods of designing the check valves to
reduce fluid hammer [72] are: (1) the disk can be
moved to seat considerably faster by adding springs
to the valves or by using heavier counterweights,
(2) the disk can be decelerated as it approaches
the seat by piston devices which work against a
flow of fluid through an orifice or by spring actuators
on the valve itself, and (3) if space is available, a
gas-filled surge tank on the reactor side of the
check valve would absorb some of the energy of
the fluid hammer.

In method 2 the decelerating force acts through
the last portion of the valve stroke as a throttle,
providing snubbing action. This method may be
preferred where natural circulation is necessary
since a low pressure drop is one of the valve's
characteristics.

4.3.5 INTERMEDIATE HEAT EXCHANGERS

In the sodium−sodium−steam power conversion
cycle, the intermediate heat exchanger (IHX) transfers heat from the primary radioactive coolant to
the secondary nonradioactive coolant while maintaining a physical separation between the two.

Although the functions of the IHX and steam generator are different, many of the general design considerations are the same. These considerations are summarized here and discussed in more detail under steam generators in Sec. 4.3.6.1.

4.3.5.1 Design Considerations

4.3.5.1.1 GENERAL CRITERIA. A sodium-to-sodium IHX to meet the general requirements of a high-performance piece of heat-transfer equipment should have sufficient surface area, be designed to code, operate satisfactorily at part loads, and be reasonable in cost. Additional requirements are that it be designed to resist thermal shock and stresses, be accessible for maintenance, and have high integrity.

Steady-state thermal stresses as well as transient stresses due to thermal shocks are severe in the IHX because the high conductivity of both fluids places the bulk of the thermal resistance in the metal walls. Some design recommendations that could alleviate this problem are: locate the tube sheets outside the sodium, use thermal shielding, and ensure flexibility or freedom of movement to allow for thermal expansion. Because of the low design pressure in the IHX, flexibility can be designed into the shell of the unit as well as into the tubes.

The intermediate heat exchanger contains a radioactive fluid and should be located in a shielded compartment. The unit may be arranged in one of two ways to permit the removal of the tube bundle: (1) arranged to permit assembly and disassembly by remotely controlled tools with an opening through the shield to permit removal of the tube bundle, or (2) arranged with the shell of the unit extended through the shield and a shield plug inside the shell. The first design permits a more standard heat exchanger but requires complex maintenance tools. The second design permits the use of ordinary tools except for the equipment used in pulling or lifting the tube bundle, but it increases the complexity of the heat exchanger and demands a high-temperature material for the shield plug. Regardless of the method, it is desirable to accomplish removal of the tube bundle under the following conditions: (1) the tube bundle should either drain completely during removal or contain only nonradioactive coolant after removal, (2) it should not be necessary to cut either the primary or secondary piping (cutting requires draining of sodium and may require remote maintenance tools and accessibility to radioactive components), and (3) any dilution of coolant in the heat exchanger resulting from tube-bundle removal should be by secondary coolant leaking into the primary. Fulfillment of the last two conditions make it unnecessary to drain either the primary or secondary system prior to bundle removal. A possible alternative to bundle removal is the plugging of tubes in place through an appropriate arrangement of small shielding plugs as in the alternate IHX design for the Plutonium Fueled Fast Breeder Reactor (PFFBR) 150 Mw(e) plant (Fig. 4.78 and Sec. 4.3.5.2.3). All these repair methods are alternatives to the conventional scheme of valving off,

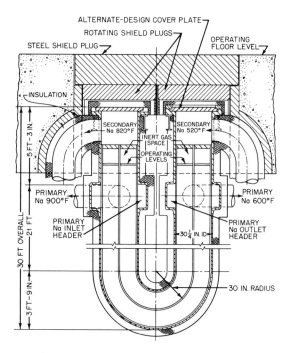

FIG. 4.78—PFFBR alternate intermediate heat exchanger [13].

cutting all lines, and removing the entire IHX, as practiced in the Hallam plant.

4.3.5.1.2 CONFIGURATIONS. In IHX configuration selection, many of the following basic decisions are influenced by accessibility considerations: (1) cylindrical shell-and-tube configuration vs. other arrangements, (2) primary coolant in the tubes vs. in the shell, (3) vertical vs. horizontal unit, (4) baffled vs. unbaffled unit, and (5) thermal expansion in the tubes vs. in the shell.

The basic shell-and-tube configuration has been used in all but a North American Aviation (NAA) small-scaled concentric cylinder unit used as an experimental model (Sec. 4.3.5.2.2). In EBR-II a complete continuous shell is not necessary because the primary coolant is discharged into the bulk sodium in the primary tank. The U-tube shell has received some consideration, as in the SRE IHX (Fig. 4.79 and Sec. 4.3.5.2.1) or the Los Alamos Scientific Laboratory (LASL) model (Sec. 4.3.5.2.2). In this shape, the tube must be repaired in place since the tube bundle is not removable.

Primary coolant in the shell allows more design freedom. If the nonradioactive coolant is in the tubes, it is not necessary to make the tube bundle drainable for removal. The major reason, however, is an economic one. The secondary system operates at a higher pressure than the primary system to prevent outleakage of radioactivity in case of a break in the IHX heat-transfer surface. In addition, the secondary system should be able to withstand the pressure surge of a sodium–water reaction in case of a steam-generator leak. It is more economical to put the higher pressure fluid in the tubes. Thermal baffling is of greater importance with primary

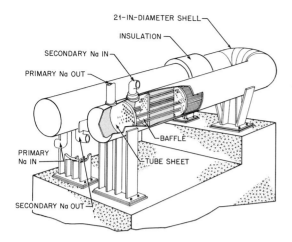

FIG. 4.79—SRE intermediate heat exchanger [25].

coolant in the shell because the primary may be subject to more severe thermal transients.

Accessibility for maintenance, including the handling of shield plugs and removal of tube bundles, is much simplified in a vertical unit compared to a horizontal one. If the tube bundle is to be removable, any baffles on the shell side should be part of the bundle, although attached to the bundle they are not as effective as if a portion of them were attached to the shell. Both baffles and vertical mounting are effective in reducing stratification of shell-side sodium at low flows or shutdown. Baffles also provide higher heat-transfer coefficients. They may be eliminated if the tubes and their supports are of such geometry as to effectively break up shell-side flow.

Thermal expansion can be built into the shell by the use of bellows, as in the Hallam unit (Fig. 4.80 and Sec. 4.3.5.2.1). Bellows can be designed to operate safely in this type of service; however, a failure in the bellows, which is a more sensitive item than a thick nonconvoluted shell, can be a major safety hazard.

In summary, the general configuration for an IHX may include: (1) a cylindrical shell and tube, (2) vertical mounting, (3) single-wall tubes carrying secondary sodium in the tubes, (4) removal tube bundle, (5) thermal expansion in tubes, (6) counter flow, and (7) a baffled shell carrying primary sodium.

Figure 4.81 shows some typical IHX designs. Schemes A through C show three methods of supporting and allowing for thermal expansion of the tube bundle in a simple one-pass arrangement: (A) support at the top tube sheet with thermal expansion by means of a sliding seal at the bottom tube sheet, (B) bottom tube sheet support with sliding top seal, and (C) support top and bottom tube sheets with expansion loops in the tubes. All three schemes require the shell side to be drained prior to bundle removal to prevent primary coolant from draining into the secondary system. In schemes D through F the secondary coolant connections are at the top of the unit, and withdrawal of the non-drainable bundle causes only some dilution of primary sodium by secondary. Because there is hot

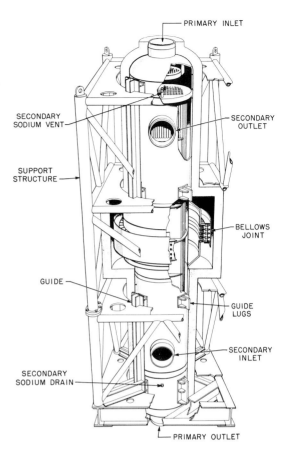

FIG. 4.80—Hallam (SGR) intermediate heat exchanger [78].

and cold fluid at the same end, a split tube sheet is desirable in these three cases. Schemes D and E are U-tube designs. Of these schemes, E appears less desirable because of the dead central section and the need for expansion loops in the tubes. Scheme F accomplishes the same as E with a smaller dead diameter. Other combinations can be made, such as the support arrangement in scheme C in conjunction with the downcomer feature of F.

4.3.5.1.3 SELECTION OF OPERATING CONDITIONS. A qualitative examination of the operating conditions, i.e., flow, coolant temperature rise, pressure drop, operating pressure, and log mean temperature difference, is useful. Minimum flow rate and hence maximum temperature rise have a definite advantage in the IHX (Sec. 4.2.2.1.1). The limitation on coolant temperature rise may be the thermal stress associated with a reactor scram. Because of the heat capacity of the primary system and the mixing from the reactor outlet, temperature transients resulting from a reactor scram are less severe in the IHX than in the reactor.

There is an economic advantage in minimizing the secondary sodium pressure drop in the IHX and allowing more drop in the steam generator in view of the higher cost of the steam generator per unit diameter. Establishment of operating pressures in

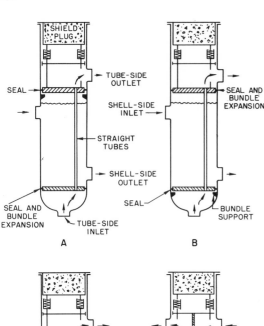

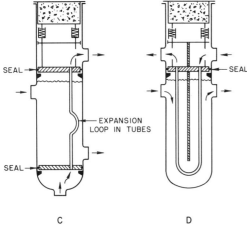

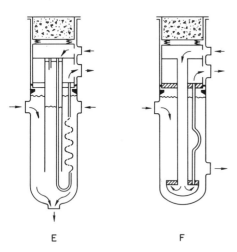

FIG. 4.81—Typical IHX configurations.

the IHX starts with the reference primary pressure, i.e., the pressure at the reactor shield plug seal. After proper correction for piping losses, the primary pressures are fixed, and a suitable dif-

ferential for protection against primary outleakage is added to fix the secondary coolant pressure.

Determination of terminal temperature differences is based on economics. For a given maximum reactor surface temperature, the cost of increasing the size of the IHX by reducing the terminal temperature difference should be balanced against the savings resulting from better steam conditions. The foregoing considerations of integrity and accessibility plus shielding requirements increase the costs of an IHX. Each system should be optimized to determine the best terminal temperature difference.

4.3.5.1.4 CALCULATION METHODS. Several different relations between the Nusselt and Peclet numbers have been proposed for calculation of heat-transfer coefficients. As shown in Chap. 2, considerable divergence in Nusselt number can be obtained for a given Peclet number depending upon the relation used. For example, at a Peclet number of 300, the Nusselt number ranges from 6 to 9. Although there are uncertainties associated with shell-side heat-transfer correlations, shell-side coefficients may be based on the following Nusselt numbers:

$$Nu = 0.212(D_e\,Pe)^{0.6} \text{ (cross flow)} \tag{4.16}$$

$$Nu = 0.106(D_e\,Pe)^{0.6} \text{ (axial flow)} \tag{4.17}$$

For the tube side, the Lubarsky-Kaufman equation [73] can be used:

$$Nu = 0.625(Pe^{0.4})$$

Pressure-drop calculations can be based on the best conventional fluid flow correlations available, accounting for momentum changes, frictional drop through the unit, and entrance, exit, and end losses. Friction factors inside tubes are based on:

$$f = 0.46/Re^{0.2} \tag{4.18}$$

as recommended by Ref. 74 for turbulent flow through smooth drawn tubes. Friction factors on the shell side may be based on

$$f = \frac{2}{3}\left[0.23 + \frac{0.11}{(P_1/D_0 - 1)^{1.08}}\right]\left(\frac{D_o\,G_{\max.}}{\mu}\right)^{-0.15} \tag{4.19}$$

as recommended by Ref. 74 for a staggered tube arrangement, where P_1 is tube pitch; μ is the viscosity; D_o is the outer diameter of the tube; and G is mass velocity. The 2/3 factor was incorporated to account for deviation of the relation from observed values for $(P_1/D_o) < 1.5$.

Discussion of the stress analysis is given in Sec. 4.3.6.1.4.2.

4.3.5.1.5 IHX SAMPLE CALCULATION. The following sample calculation represents a first approximation to sizing of an IHX unit for the design conditions used throughout this chapter.

Design conditions	Value
Type of IHX	One-pass, cylindrical, shell and tube
Total heat transferred (4 loops), Mw(t)	450
Heat transferred per IHX, Btu/hr	3.85×10^8
Primary sodium flow (shell side), lb/hr	4.25×10^6
Primary sodium inlet temp., °F	1050
Primary sodium outlet temp., °F	750
Secondary sodium flow (tube side), lb/hr	4.25×10^6
Secondary sodium inlet temp., °F	650
Secondary sodium outlet temp., °F	950
Tube material	304 SS
Fouling factor	None
Tube size:	
OD, in.	$5/8$
Wall thickness, in.	0.049
Number of tubes (n)	1500
Pitch (P_1) triangular, in.	$7/8$
Tube-side flow area, sq in.	328
Shell-side flow area, sq in.	533
Shell diameter, ft	2.96

To Find: (a) Over–all heat-transfer coefficient U (Btu/hr/sq ft/°F)

(b) Surface area A (sq ft)

(c) Effective tube length required $L_{(tube)}$ (ft)

(d) Pressure drop (tube side) $\Delta P_{(tube)}$ (lb/sq in.)

(e) Pressure drop (shell side) $\Delta P_{(shell)}$ (lb/sq in.)

(1) $v \text{ (ft/sec)} = \dfrac{W \text{ (lb/hr)}}{3600 \text{ (sec/hr)} \, \rho \text{ (lb/cu ft)} \, A \text{ (sq ft)}}$, average

$v_{(shell)} = \dfrac{4.25 \times 10^6}{(3600)(52.3)(533/144)} = 6.10 \text{ ft/sec}$

$v_{(tube)} = \dfrac{4.25 \times 10^6}{(3600)(53.2)(328/144)} = 9.74 \text{ ft/sec}$

(2) $Re = \dfrac{D_e \text{ (ft)} \, v \text{ (ft/sec)} \, \rho \text{ (lb/cu ft)}}{\mu \text{ (lb/sec-ft)}}$

$D_{e \, (shell)} = \dfrac{4 A_{flow} \text{ (sq ft)}}{(D_{shell} + n d_{tube})} = 0.058 \text{ ft}$

$Re_{(shell)} = [(0.058)(6.10)(52.3)]/(0.16 \times 10^{-3})$

$\cong 113,000$

$Re_{(tube)} = [(0.527/12)(9.74)(53.2)]/(0.178 \times 10^{-3})$

$\cong 141,000$

(3) $Pr = \dfrac{c_p \text{ (Btu/lb/°F)} \, \mu \text{ (lb/sec/ft)} \, 3600 \text{ (sec/hr)}}{k \text{ (Btu/hr/ft/°F)}}$

$Pr_{(shell)} = [(0.303)(0.16 \times 10^{-3})(3600)]/(38.5)$

$= 4.65 \times 10^{-3}$

$Pr_{(tube)} = [(0.305)(0.178 \times 10^{-3})(3600)]/(40)$

$= 4.9 \times 10^{-3}$

(4) $Pe = Re \, Pr$

$Pe_{(shell)} = 525$

$Pe_{(tube)} = 687$

(5) $Nu = 0.625 (Pe)^{0.4}$

$Nu_{(shell)} = 7.65$

$Nu_{(tube)} = 8.5$

(6) $Nu = \dfrac{h \text{ (Btu/hr/sq ft/°F)} \, D \text{ (ft)}}{k \text{ (Btu/hr/ft/°F)}}$

$h_{(shell)} = 5080$

$h_{(tube)} = 7750$

(7) Tube wall resistance $(R_w) = \dfrac{s_{(wall)} \text{ (ft)}}{k \text{ (Btu/hr/ft/°F)}}$

$\times \left[\dfrac{2 \text{(OD)}}{\text{(ID + OD)}} \right]$ (per unit of outside of tube area)

$R_w = 3.7 \times 10^{-4}, \text{ (hr)(sq ft)(°F)/Btu}$

(8) U (based on OD of tubes)

$1/U = \left[\dfrac{1}{h_i} \dfrac{\text{(OD)}}{\text{(ID)}} + R_w + \dfrac{1}{h_0} \right]$

where $h_i = h$ of tube side

$h_0 = h$ of shell side

$= [1.53 \times 10^{-4} + 3.7 \times 10^{-4} + 1.97 \times 10^{-4}]$

$U = 1390 \text{ Btu/hr/sq ft/°F}$

(9) $Q = UA \, \Delta T$ and substituting for Q, U, and ΔT

$3.85 \times 10^8 = (1390)(A)(100)$

$A = 2770 \text{ sq ft}$

(10) $L_{(tube)} = \dfrac{A}{n \pi \text{(OD)}} = 11.3 \text{ ft (effective)}$

(11) Tube side head drop $(\Delta h_{total}) = [(fL/D) + K_1 + K_2]$

$\times (v^2/2g)$

where K_1 and K_2 are contraction and expansion loss coefficients for entrance and exit losses.

From Chap. 2 for $Re = 141,000$ and $f = 0.0165$ for smooth pipe, assume $K_1 = 0.5$, $K_2 = 1.0$, and $L_{tube} = 15$ ft (actual length), then

$\Delta h_{(total)} = [5.65 + 0.5 \quad .0][(9.74)^2/64.4]$

$= 10.5 \text{ (ft of Na)}$

$= 3.9 \text{ psi total tube-side pressure drop}$

(12) Shell-side friction factor (f'') for cross flow [74]

$f'' = \left[0.23 + \dfrac{0.11}{(P_1/D_o - 1)^{1.08}} \right] (Re^{-0.15}/1.5) = 0.03$

where $P_1 = $ tube pitch, in.

$D_o = $ tube OD, in.

$1.5 = $ deviation factor [74]

(13) Cross-flow [74] pressure drop (Δh_{cr})

$\Delta h_{cr} = 4 f'' N (V^2/2g)_{(shell)}$, ft of Na

where N (number of tube rows) $= \dfrac{D_{(shell)}}{P_1} = 40$, for one flow configuration

$\Delta h_{cr} = 4.8 (V^2/2g)_{(shell)}$

(14) Total shell-side pressure drop (Δh_{shell})

$$\Delta h_{\text{shell}} = \Delta h_{cr} + \Delta h_{\text{axial}} + \Delta h_{\text{in}} + \Delta h_{\text{out}}$$

(last two terms are entrance and exit losses)

Assume $L_{\text{(tube)}} = 12.5$ ft

then fL/D axially $= 4.0$

$$= [4.8 + 4.0 + 0.5 + 1.0] \times \frac{(6.1)^2}{64.4}$$

$$= 6 \text{ ft of Na} = 2.2 \text{ psi}$$

(15) Summary of results:
$$\begin{aligned}
U &= 1390 \text{ Btu/hr/sq ft/}^\circ\text{F} \\
A &= 2770 \text{ sq ft} \\
L_{\text{(tube)}} &= 11.3 \text{ ft (equiv.)} \\
\Delta p_{\text{(tube)}} &= 3.9 \text{ psi} \\
\Delta p_{\text{(shell)}} &= 2.2 \text{ psi}
\end{aligned}$$

(16) Since the Δp's are low, calculation should be repeated with fewer and/or smaller tubes.

4.3.5.2 Specific Designs

Intermediate heat exchangers have been used in reactor plants and in experimental test loops. Design characteristics of existing and proposed designs are tabulated in Table 4.12.

4.3.5.2.1 HEAT EXCHANGERS IN EXISTING REACTOR PLANTS.

The EBR-I IHX is a conventional shell-and-tube design with all joints welded [25]. The secondary flow on the shell side is double pass, and the tubes are bent in a hairpin shape. The actual values of heat-transfer coefficient are lower than calculated, apparently because the primary side is not running full. There is a continuous amount of blanket gas drawn into the coolant stream from the reactor outlet free surface. Since the flow is downward in the primary side of the heat exchanger, an indeterminate amount of surface may be blanketed by gas.

The SRE IHX (Fig. 4.79) is a shell and U-tube unit [75]. During steady-state tests the log mean temperature difference was approximately 42% higher than the predicted value. The theoretical shell-side Nusselt number used in the design heat transfer was 209% above the experimental value. The off-design steady-state performance was due to excessive bypassing on the shell side and also to optimistic heat-transfer predictions. In the thermal transient tests, large temperature differences existed in the shell and tubes, and in some cases reverse flow occurred in the tubes [75].

In the Fermi IHX (Fig. 4.82) the tube bundle is removable after the shield plug has been removed. Neither primary nor secondary piping connections have to be cut. The tube-sheet seal between primary and secondary sodium is connected to a leak-off system where accumulated sodium can be pumped to a secondary-system storage tank. Each tube has a sine-wave bend to accommodate thermal expansion.

In the EBR-II IHX (Fig. 4.17) there is no continuous shell since the bundle is immersed in the primary tank [54, 76]. Flow from the reactor is directed by baffles to pass over the tubes and then return to the tank. Secondary sodium flows in piping that penetrates the shield plug.

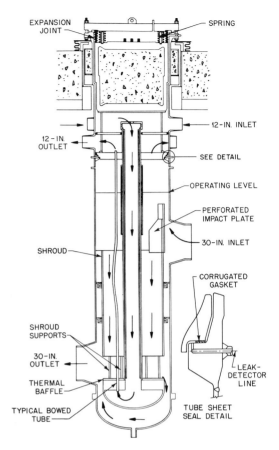

FIG. 4.82—Fermi intermediate heat exchanger [31].

The Hallam IHX (Fig. 4.80) is mounted vertically with a bellows in the center of the shell. This arrangement allows straight tubes and rigid attachment of the top and bottom tube sheets to the shell [19, 77, 78]. The support structure carries the weight of the unit at the bottom end and provides for vertical expansion at three other elevations along the length. Movement of the IHX is confined to the vertical direction, thereby removing torsional loads from the bellows. For repairs the entire unit, including the support structure, is removed. One IHX developed a leak late in 1962 [79].

Each Dounreay IHX (Fig. 4.83) consists of an inner stainless-steel pipe, 300 ft long and 4 in. in diameter, surrounded by a 6-in.-diameter outer stainless-steel pipe [17]. The unit is formed into seven loops. The inner and outer pipes are held concentric by means of spiders machined from solid stainless steel welded into the pipe. The secondary coolant flows through the annulus counter to the primary coolant flow. The center of each leg of the exchanger is clamped to a steel framework that is supported by a hanger through a pin joint from the vault roof. The exchanger can move in a radial direction.

The Rapsodie IHX (Fig. 4.84) consists of a fixed shell, a removable tube bundle, and a shield plug [18]. The vertical shell, made of stainless steel, is suspended from the top. Its lower section is sealed by a convex head. The sodium inlet nozzle is located

Table 4.12—Characteristics of Intermediate Heat Exchangers

Description	Primary coolant Type	Primary Inlet, °F	Primary Outlet, °F	Secondary coolant Type	Secondary Inlet, °F	Secondary Outlet, °F	Remarks	Design pressure, psig Tubes	Design pressure, psig Shell	Operating pressure, psig Tubes	Operating pressure, psig Shell	Design temperature, °F Tubes	Design temperature, °F Shell	Material Tubes	Material Shell	Shell ID, in.	Shell wall, in.
EBR-I	NaK	600	442	NaK	419	583	*							A-nickel		16	0.31
SRE	Na	960	500	Na	440	900	*	50	50	20		1200	1200	316 SS	304 SS	21	0.5
Fermi	Na	900	600	Na	520	820	†	300	50	40	2	1000	1000	304 SS	304 SS	68	
EBR-II	Na	883	692	Na	588	866	†	150	75		0.25	1000	1000	304 SS	304 SS	55	
Hallam	Na	945	610	Na	557	895	*	100	100			1000	1000	304 SS	304 SS		
Dounreay	NaK	662	392	NaK	338	626	‡							SS	SS	6	
Rapsodie (10 Mw)	Na	644	482	Na	428	590	†							316 SS	316 SS	34.8	0.63
MSA (1 Mw)	NaK	1500	1150	NaK	1100	1400	*			24	2.9			316 SS	316 SS	4	
Los Alamos (2 Mw)	Na	1100	850	Na	750	1000	†	300	300			1100	1100	316 SS	316 SS	8	0.237
NAA (concentric cylinder, spiral flow)					700	1020	§									24	
AEC study [70 Mw (t)]	Na	1050	730	Na	665	1140	†	125	100	125	100	1200	1200	304 SS	304 SS	49	0.5
AEC study [30 Mw (t)]	Na	1200	723	Na	777	1175	†	150	100			1200	1200	316 SS	316 SS	36	0.375
PFFBR [300 Mw (e)]	Na	1000	900	Na	570	920	†	150	125			1000	1050	316 SS	316 SS	84	
PFFBR [150 Mw (e)]	Na	900	650	Na	520	820	†	150	50			1000	1000	304 SS	304 SS	58	
PFFBR [150 Mw (e)] (alt.)	Na	900	600	Na	520	820	†	150	50			1000	1000	304 SS	304 SS	30	

Description	Flow, 10³lb/hr Primary	Flow, 10³lb/hr Secondary	Velocity, ft/sec Tubes	Velocity, ft/sec Shell	Pressure drop, psi Tubes	Pressure drop, psi Shell	LMTD, °F	Unit size, Mw(t)	Heat transferred, 10⁶ Btu/hr	Number tubes	Tube OD, in.	Tube wall, in.	Tube pitch, in.	Effective tube length, ft	Effective tube surface, sq ft	Overall heat-transfer coefficient, Btu/hr/sq ft/°F
EBR-I	114.6							1	3.95	102	0.75	0.065			495	400
SRE	485	485					60	20	68.4	316	0.75	0.058	1	18.7	1165	730
Fermi	5300	5300	4.4	3.3	4.7	3.4	80	143	489	1860	0.875	0.049	1.06		6200	985
EBR-II	3730	2500	2.9	2.5	4.6	5	48	62.5		3026	0.625	0.062	0.8125	9.16	4539	979
Hallam	2800	2800			7		50	80								
Dounreay	145.8	137.9						3								
Rapsodie (10 Mw)	675	875					54	10		888	0.551	0.079	0.78		378	
MSA (1 Mw)	45.5	40.3					72	1	3.68	35	0.375	0.022	0.59	300	904	
Los Alamos (2 Mw)	90.5	90.5	10	1.6	5.4	0.7	100	2	6.83	19	0.75	0.035		11.7	43	1560
NAA (concentric cylinder, spiral flow)	41.3	41.3				0.2		0.1	440	3		0.187			15.8	350
AEC study [70 Mw (t)]	1665	1665	9.3	2.3	8.5	14	59	70	239	1087	0.5	0.049	1		3740	1080
AEC study [30 Mw (t)]	1140	855	9.9	2.7	7.4	9.0	61.5	30	102.4	461	0.5	0.035		22.3	1340	1240
PFFBR [300 Mw (e)]	8300	8300			15	6	80	258	883	1200	1	0.042	1.25	30.5	8700	1270
PFFBR [150 Mw (e)]	8060	7980	16.1	11.4	15	6	80	217	740	567	1	0.042	1.375	41	6100	1600
PFFBR [150 Mw (e)] (alt.)	8060	7980	21.3	16.3	22	11.5	80	217	740	421	1	0.042		49.8	5500	1680

* Primary coolant on inside of tube.
† Primary coolant on shell side of tube.
‡ Primary in inner tube; secondary in outer annulus.
§ Both primary and secondary coolants are in helical ducts.

on the lower head. A jacket around the shell allows for preheating by hot nitrogen gas. Primary sodium flows in the shell and secondary NaK, in the tubes. The 888 stainless-steel tubes are welded to the tube sheets. The upper tube sheet is fixed, but the lower sheet is floating to allow for thermal expansion of the bundle. The tubes are located in 12 concentric layers. There is a bowed section in the upper part of each tube which allows for differential expansion between the tubes. The bundle is clamped at two points to prevent tube vibration induced by sodium flow. The inlet plenum to the tube bundle is formed by a convex head connected to the lower tube sheet. Two upper plates are connected by a sleeve forming an annular chamber between the sleeve and the NaK central inlet tube. Four pipes tied to the upper plate of the upper plenum carry the outlet NaK and lead into a single pipe. A vertical baffle is located around the entire tube bundle. The baffle distributes the flow of sodium through the tube bundle. A ring welded to the vertical sleeve and a flange welded to the shell of the heat exchanger also provide baffling for sodium flow. Three holes in the ring attached to the shell allow sufficient sodium flow to cool the annular space. Radial baffles are located between different openings in the vertical baffle surrounding the tube bundle. These baffles provide even flow distribution around the tubes in the tube bundle. The openings are sized to produce a good flow distribution. There are two liquid-level indicators in the space between the shell and the vertical sleeve surrounding the tube bundle.

4.3.5.2.2 HEAT EXCHANGERS IN TEST LOOPS.

The heat exchanger in the Los Alamos 2000-kw Sodium Test Facility is a vertically mounted conventional U-tube assembly with hairpin tubes. All equipment in the facility was designed on a 1/10 scale of actual equipment proposed for a molten-plutonium reactor plant having a capacity of about 20 Mw(t). In fabrication the shell was split and then welded together after the tube bundle and tube sheet had been laid in one half.

The NAA concentric-cylinder spiral-flow heat exchanger [89] utilizes neither tubes nor tube sheets. This 100-kw(t) model was constructed and tested to determine its heat-transfer characteristics and its ability to endure rapid thermal transients. It consists of a series of concentric cylinders with a continuous thin metal vane fixed in each of the annuli. The guide vanes conduct the fluid entering each annulus along a spiraling path to the flow exit. The guide vanes are welded in a spiral fashion around the outer peripheral face of each cylinder. A cylinder wall thickness of 3/16 in. is used to meet the most severe thermal stress conditions that might be expected.

Values of over-all heat-transfer coefficients were determined for Reynold's numbers between 10^4 and 10^5. For net heat transmission through two opposite walls, the following relation was found [89]:

$$Nu = 0.055 \, Pe^{0.8} \qquad (4.20)$$

For a similar geometry with heat flow through only one wall, the relation was[89]:

$$Nu = 0.15 + 0.12 \, Pe^{0.6} \qquad (4.21)$$

4.3.5.2.3 HEAT EXCHANGERS OF ADVANCED DESIGN.

As part of the AEC development program for high-temperature components in sodium reactor systems, design studies have been performed on 70-Mw(t)[90] and 30 Mw(t)[91] intermediate heat exchangers to operate with 1200°F primary inlet sodium. Other advanced designs have been made in conjunction with a second generation Fermi plant [13].

The 70 Mw(t) and 30 Mw(t) high-temperature IHX designs are essentially identical except for size (Fig. 4.85). To provide for freedom of differential expansion between tubes and shell and between different tubes, all tubes are provided with a prebent sine wave, i.e., a curved portion 48 in. long with 10 in. maximum offset, placed adjacent to the upper tube sheet. The tubes are placed in concentric circles, and the wave is given a double curvature to fit these circles. The area in the center, which is left without tubes, provides a turning area for the flow between the disk and doughnut baffles. The use of close overlapping disk and doughnut baffles (Ref. 74, p. 420) minimizes rapid stratification of sodium which usually occurs just prior to isothermal conditions. Tube-to-tube sheet welds are the most critical stress areas during transient conditions when the mass of the tube sheet does not cool as rapidly as the tubes and the tube contracts diametrically. To reduce this stress concentration, a trepanning operation is performed, making a riser at each tube penetration. The unit is designed to operate full of sodium, i.e., without a gas blanket. Because of the high operating temperatures, type 316 stainless steel was selected as the material of construction.

In the 300-Mw(e) PFFBR plant the IHX design is a U-tube unit with a primary sodium discharge standpipe in the center of the unit [12]. A flanged joint at the top of the shell allows removal of the bundle after secondary connections are severed. The shield plug in the operating floor is connected to the unit. The primary side of the IHX contains two gas blankets, one at the inlet end and one at the outlet end, with a 4-psi pressure differential between them at full-load conditions.

For the 150-Mw(e) PFFBR plant (Fig. 4.86) the IHX reference design has a flow plan similar to that for the large unit except that the directions of both the primary and secondary flows are reversed [13]. The standpipe serves as the primary inlet. Using the center tubes for upflow removes the possibility of gas entrainment with downflow. The shell temperature is low with this arrangement since the primary flow at the shell end is at the low outlet temperature. An involute tube-sheet pattern is used because it allows a shell-side flow area per tube in the outer annulus equal to that in the inner annulus.

For the 150-Mw(e) PFFBR plant, an alternate IHX design (Fig. 4.78) is based on in-place tube maintenance. This principle requires development since, to date, it has not been proven feasible. Both the shell and tubes are U-shaped and both tube sheets have inert gas on the primary side. The bolted seal-welded cover plate at the top of each plenum is removable for tube maintenance. The rotating shield plugs contain small individually removable plugs which, by indexing, can line up with each of the IHX tubes.

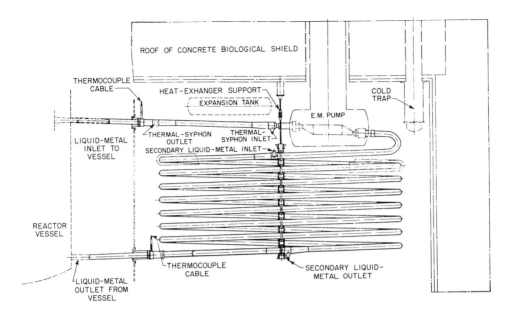

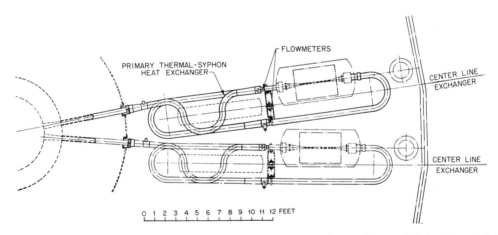

FIG. 4.83—Dounreay intermediate heat exchanger. (From R. R. Matthews et al., Proceedings of the Symposium on the Dounreay Fast Reactor, London, Dec. 7, 1960, Institution of Mechanical Engineers, London, 1961.)

4.3.6 STEAM GENERATOR

The steam generator in the sodium–sodium–steam power conversion cycle for fast breeder reactors transfers heat from the secondary sodium to the feedwater, which is preheated, evaporated, and superheated to produce high-temperature steam. In some designs this heating is done in a single unit. In other designs the three steps are carried out in two or three separate units.

The use of an intermediate loop in this cycle prevents interchange of water and radioactive sodium. However, in the steam generator sodium and water are separated only by a tube wall. The pressure difference between them is essentially equal to the steam pressure. Local temperature differences across the tubes vary as shown in Fig. 4.7. These temperature gradients occur in all

three zones, preheating, evaporating, and superheating. These temperature differences coupled with the high heat-transfer coefficients of the sodium and boiling water produce high heat-transfer rates within the steam generator, as much as 300,000 Btu/hr/sq ft in local areas. All these factors combine to make the steam generator a critical component in the heat-transport system of a fast breeder reactor.

4.3.6.1 Design Considerations

4.3.6.1.1 GENERAL CRITERIA. A sodium-heated steam generator should meet the general requirements of any high-pressure heat-transfer equipment: (1) sufficient surface area to meet or exceed design heat-transfer load under

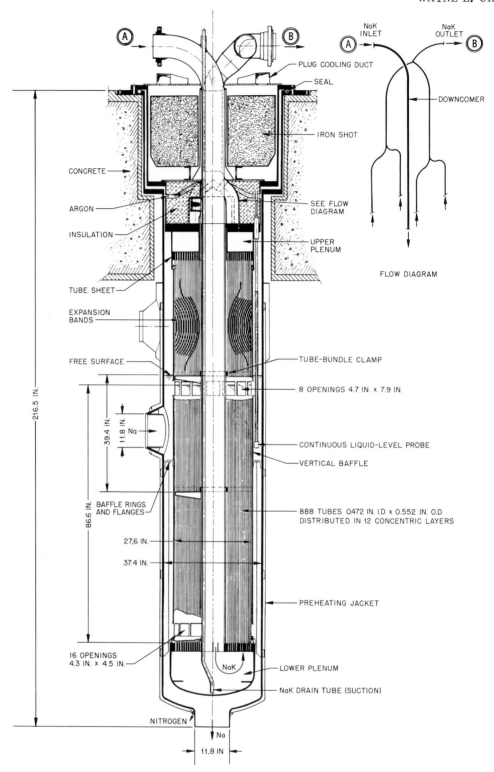

FIG. 4.84—Rapsodie intermediate heat exchanger [18].

expected service conditions, including anticipated fouling, (2) design according to applicable codes, (3) stable and predictable operation at part loads, and (4) minimum capital and operating cots commensurate with the required safety and reliability.

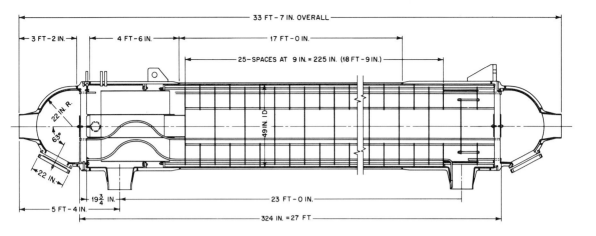

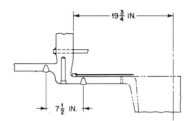

SHELL– AND–TUBE SHEET CONSTRUCTION (BOTH ENDS)

FIG. 4.85—AEC intermediate heat exchanger [90].

Because of the critical nature and severe service conditions of these units, additional requirements or extra emphasis on existing requirements are imposed. These requirements deal generally with three areas: minimizing the effects of a possible sodium–water reaction, reducing thermal shock and thermal stresses to tolerable values, and providing easy accessibility for inspection, maintenance, and repair.

4.3.6.1.1.1 Sodium–Water Reaction. Two approaches have been used to cope with a possible sodium–water reaction. One approach consists of providing double-walled tubes with double tube sheets. An intermediate monitoring fluid may or may not separate the water side tube from the sodium tube. The theory is to provide a system of such reliability that a leak of water will never contact sodium. Where a monitoring fluid is used, the fluid can be an inert gas, mercury, or other compatible fluid. Large reductions in over-all heat-transfer coefficients may result as compared with those for a single-walled tube if there is a poor bond. With an inert gas, gas-carrying grooves can be knurled into the outer surfaces of the inner tube, and the tubes can be roller expanded together to form a metallurgical bond. This scheme can provide a heat-transfer path with theoretically up to 95% the efficiency of a single-walled tube of comparable thickness. When the bond between the tubes is mechanical instead of metallurgical, there may be a decrease in the heat-transfer rate after temperature transients separate the bond. The

equivalent heat-transfer coefficient of the tube may be reduced from 5000 to less than 1000 Btu/hr/sq ft/°F. The use of double tube sheets complicates design, fabrication, inspection, and maintenance. The capital costs of such a unit may be as much as three times those of a comparable unit with single tube walls.

The other approach to possible sodium–water reactions is to provide the single-wall tube steam generator with facilities to handle the pressure effects from a major leak and to detect small leaks. In the case of small leaks, the sodium–water reaction of itself may not be vigorous enough to indicate the leak; instead it may indirectly be detected by the plugging effects of the insoluble reaction products dissipated in the sodium system. (Because of pressure difference the leakage normally will be water or steam into sodium. Care should be exercised to prevent a pressure reversal.) There are several methods of detecting a leak: (1) a plugging indicator in the sodium system (Sec. 4.3.8.1), (2) a hydrogen detector in the inert-gas space (Sec. 4.3.10.2), (3) a continuous hydrogen detector (currently under development) for the sodium system [92], and (5) possibly, a sodium resistance meter, such as a rhometer (Sec. 4.3.8.2).

Large-scale sodium–water reaction tests have been conducted by APDA. Water at about 900 psig and 350°F was passed through the seven tubes of a bayonet-tube heat exchanger containing 280 lb of 500°F sodium at 5 psig on the shell side. The shell was an 8 2/3-ft length of 12-in. pipe connected at the top to a 3 1/2-ft diameter 3-ft-high gas

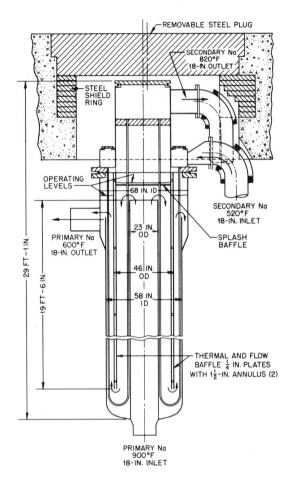

SECONDARY Na
820°F
18-IN. OUTLET

REMOVABLE STEEL PLUG

STEEL
SHIELD
RING

OPERATING
LEVELS

68 IN. ID

SECONDARY Na
520°F
18-IN. INLET

PRIMARY Na
600°F
18-IN. OUTLET

23 IN.
OD

SPLASH
BAFFLE

46 IN.
OD

58 IN.
ID

29 FT-1 IN.

19 FT-6 IN.

THERMAL AND FLOW
BAFFLE $\frac{1}{4}$ IN. PLATES
WITH 1$\frac{1}{2}$-IN. ANNULUS (2)

PRIMARY Na
900°F
18-IN. INLET

FIG. 4.86—PFFBR intermediate heat exchanger [13].

chamber fitted with a 30-in.-diameter rupture disk, designed to release at 37 psig and 750°F. To simulate a tube failure, a plug valve at the blind end of one tube was triggered open. The following temperature and pressure transients and resulting damage were observed:

The maximum reaction pressure at the point of simulated rupture was 175 psig and occurred 0.015 sec after the valve opened. The rupture disk ruptured 0.083 sec after the valve opened.

The maximum temperature occurred at both the reaction point and the rupture disk. Two temperature peaks were detected before the maximum temperature of 1950°F occurred at 2.37 sec, one at 0.23 sec at a temperature of 1160°F and another at 1.08 sec at a temperature of 1700°F. Fifty-eight inches above the reaction point the maximum temperature of 1770°F was observed at 1.13 sec, and 40 in. below the reaction point the maximum temperature was 1740°F at 4.71 sec. The 1950°F maximum temperature at the rupture disk occurred at 2.95 sec.

The reaction caused no significant damage to the tube bundle, steam chest, or shell interior; however, some distortion of the tube bundle did result. Outward bowing of all six steam tubes surrounding the simulated ruptured center tube was observed. Maximum bowing of an individual

tube after one test run was a 3/8-in. deflection at 1 1/2 ft above the reaction point. After three successive runs the maximum bowing of an individual tube was 1/2 in., also 1 1/2 ft above the reaction point.

Metallographic examination of representative specimens from all steam tubes and the steam chest revealed no evidence of cracks or severe deformation. Minute pitting on the outer diameter and very thin scale on the inner diameter of the tubes was found.

These tests suggest the following design provisions to cope with the effects of a large leak in a sodium-heated steam generator: (1) a shell design pressure sufficiently high to withstand the initial pressure pulse, (2) an adequate gas-filled surge volume to dampen the initial pressure pulse, (3) a large rupture disk to permit rapid release of pressure, and (4) separators in the discharge line from the rupture disk to separate particulate reaction products.

On the basis of the results of tests on sodium-water reactions reported above, an AEC-sponsored study for future development of high-temperature sodium-heated steam generators [95] indicated that single-wall tube designs may be adequate for steam-generator use.

Because of the relatively greater possibility of a leak developing at a weld, it is desirable that welds should be placed in such a fashion that the two fluids are not on opposite sides of the same weld. In the design of the EBR-II steam generator, this objective necessitated the use of double tube sheets (Sec. 4.3.6.3.1.5). Where circumferential welds are used in tubes, care should be taken to prove out the weld.

4.3.6.1.1.2 Thermal Stresses and Thermal Shock. In the steam generator the problems of steady-state thermal stresses, as well as transient stresses due to thermal shock, are aggravated by such features as the joining of thin to thick sections, as tubes to tube sheets, and nozzles to shells.

There are several basic design features that could be used to alleviate the thermal stress problem: (1) tube-to-tube sheet joints should be located in a gas space above the sodium with liquid-level control, (2) thermal shielding in the form of baffles should be provided in such areas as the sodium inlet and outlet nozzles and discontinuous shell sections to reduce temperature transients of coolant directly in contact with these areas, and (3) flexibility or freedom of movement should be provided for such items as tubes to allow for thermal expansion. This last objective has been achieved by designing tubes as bayonets, U-shapes, helical coils, sine waves, circular shapes, hockey sticks, and involutes.

4.3.6.1.1.3 Accessibility. The steam generator should be accessible for periodic inspection, periodic maintenance, and unscheduled maintenance. Since possible corrosion and erosion would most likely occur on the water side of the tube, inspection of the water side is the most critical. Straight-tube designs accessible to boroscope inspection, rather than coils or sine waves, may be preferred if water is inside the tubes.

The following design features, which are not necessarily compatible with each other, could serve to simplify accessibility to critical parts: (1) a removable tube bundle, (2) ability to drain the steam generator, and (3) tubes penetrating through the shell so that defective tubes can be plugged external to the shell without opening the shell, otherwise a head must be removed to get at a tube sheet.

4.3.6.1.2 CONFIGURATIONS.

Before the configuration of the steam generator can be selected, several basic decisions have to be made: (1) natural circulation or forced recirculation vs. once through, (2) shell and tube vs. other arrangements, (3) sodium in tube vs. sodium in shell, (4) baffled vs. unbaffled unit, (5) vertical vs. horizontal unit, and (6) shape of tube.

In natural-recirculation boilers the force available to produce flow comes from the difference in density of the fluids in the downcomer and riser portions of the steam drum-evaporator-superheater circuit. Ideally, the fluid in the downcomer is water at, or slightly below, saturation temperature and containing no steam bubbles. The feedwater is often injected at the top of the downcomer to quench steam bubbles. The heat absorbed in the riser produces saturation temperature and subsequently a water—steam mixture of lesser density than the water in the downcomer. The water and steam are separated in a steam drum above the riser, the water returning to the downcomer and the steam continuing to the superheater. Several evaporators may feed one steam drum or one superheater. In recirculating forced-circulation units, the same circuit is followed, but the flow is produced by a pump or pumps.

In a once-through forced-circulation steam generator, feedwater is pumped to the inlet of the unit. Preheating, evaporation, and finally superheating take place as the fluid proceeds through the unit. The pounds of steam produced are numerically equal to the water supplied. The unit has no steam drum.

The once-through unit provides a simple configuration with reduced heat-transfer area and has an inherent compactness that is reflected in a lower installed cost because of reduced material and space requirements and the ease of fabrication and erection. The unit would provide good integrity because of a minimum number of welds and points of possible leakage. The once-through steam generator requires a good and constant water purification system since most impurities introduced into the steam generator in feedwater remain in the evaporating section. A maximum concentration of about 0.1 ppm total solids is a general feedwater purity requirement for all once-through boilers, not just those heated by sodium. Control of once-through units is quite sensitive because of the small amount of water stored within the units. Fluctuations in feedwater flow are rapidly reflected back to the nuclear reactor since there is no thermal capacity of the magnitude provided by the steam drum of natural-circulation units.

The Fermi steam generators (Sec. 4.3.6.3.1.4) are once-through, and the EBR-II (Sec. 4.3.6.3.1.5) and the Hallam units (Sec. 4.3.6.3.1.6) are of the natural-circulation type.

The basic shell-and-tube configuration has thus far been used in most sodium-heated steam-generator designs because of the good strength properties inherent in the cylindrical configurations. There have been designs aimed at eliminating the massive tube sheets of the conventional tube-and-shell exchanger. Such a design is the natural-circulation unit for SRE (Sec. 4.3.6.3.1.2) in which the sodium-carrying tubes penetrate individually through the cylindrical portion of the shell and join into inlet and outlet headers. The intent was to avoid the stresses associated with joining thin tubes to heavy tube sheets. The penetration of the shell with tubes and the design of the outside header create other problems, such as differential expansion between the shell and the header.

Although there have been designs with sodium in the tubes and sodium in the shell, the latter appears economically preferable since the shell can be designed for the low sodium pressure. Steam in the shell would require a high-pressure shell design. Inspection of the water side is facilitated with water in the tubes.

Baffled units are preferred over unbaffled units because of their ability to reduce stratification at partial flows or shutdowns. The baffles also reduce the physical size of the units by providing higher heat-transfer coefficients. They act as barriers to slow down natural convection currents and improve the distribution of fluids over the heat-transfer surface. The disk-and-doughnut time baffles [74] are claimed to be the most beneficial in minimizing stratification effects and improving flow distribution. They can be placed closer together than the segmental type, thereby increasing fluid velocities with a smaller penalty on pressure drop.

Vertically mounted units are to be preferred over horizontal units because the latter are more prone to stratification into temperature layers of sodium in the shell side, i.e., the cold sodium layers at the bottom and the hot at the top. This, in turn, affects the water side. The water-side pressure drop is affected, and an instability may result. This effect can be avoided by increasing the pressure drop in any tube, i.e., orificing the tube. As a result of stratification, steam of different quality is produced by tubes at different elevations. Examples of such units are the horizontal once-through SRE unit (Sec. 4.3.6.3.1.3) and the horizontal APDA test unit (Sec. 4.3.6.3.2.1). Vertical mounting of a once-through steam generator produces greater stability of flow on the water side. Vertical stratification of the sodium affects all tubes alike.

A vertical unit baffled on the shell side can be drained by gravity flow. In a horizontal or inclined unit, drainage taps are necessary between every other baffle to avoid having the ring-shaped baffles pocket fluid between them on the lower half of the shell.

Some of the types of tubes used for sodium-cooled steam generators are bayonet, U-tube, straight-through with or without curvature, such as a sine wave for expansion, and coil or involute. In the bayonet arrangement each tube consists of two concentric tubes fastened to separate tube sheets at the top. The inner tube is open at the bottom, and the outer tube is sealed at the bottom. Coolant flows down the inner tube and returns up the annulus. It is preferable, from the standpoint of stability and proper circulation, for the water in the inner tube not to heat at all or only to preheat. Such an arrangement increases the size of the tube because of internal insulation and represents a somewhat inefficient use of heat-transfer area and of steam-generator volume.

In the U-tube design the two ends of the tube are joined to separate tube sheets. The fluid flows down one side of the U and up the other and is heated in transit. The major difficulties result when one leg, being hotter than the other, expands and causes differential stresses. It is also difficult to baffle the shell in the vicinity of the U bend. Heat losses reduce the heat-transfer efficiency.

Straight-through tubes must also contend with the difference in thermal expansion between the tube and the shell. Either a diaphragm expansion bellows connecting the shell with the tube bundle or a curvature in the tube can be used to allow for thermal expansion. Tubes with such a curvature do not lend themselves as readily to internal inspection as do bayonet or U-tube designs.

Considerable flexibility in the design of tube sheets and entrance and exit nozzles can be developed if a complex shape, such as a coil or involute, is accepted, e.g., the Fermi steam-generator design (Sec. 4.3.6.3.1.4).

4.3.6.1.3 SELECTION OF OPERATING CONDITIONS.

The selection of temperature conditions in heat-transport systems was discussed in Sec. 4.1.3.3. Present-day steam conditions are around 1050°F. Research and development is proceeding, under the sponsorship of the USAEC, of 1200°F sodium-cooled steam generators which will allow 1100°F to 1150°F steam conditions. The results may be used in the design of supercritical steam units, which may obviate some of the problems of the present-day once-through steam generator associated with its transition zones and water slugging. The 2.25 wt.% chromium-1 wt.% molybdenum used in some steam generators is limited because of its lower strength and decarburization above 800°F, to about 900°F, and to operating at reduced stress limits. Current development work on steam generators revolves around the use of type 316 stainless steel. This material is suitable for sodium service in excess of 1200°F but is limited in its use on the water side because of its susceptibility to short-term rapid stress corrosion in the presence of chlorides or hydroxides. The following conditions help to cause this susceptibility: high temperature, condensing steam, and residual stresses due to cold forming, tube rolling, or welding [94]. Laboratory tests have indicated that stress levels as low as 5000 psi with oxygen and chloride concentrations as low as 0.1 ppm are sufficient to initiate stress-corrosion cracking in austenitic stainless steels. A technique is being developed for coating or bonding the water side of the type 316 stainless steel with such materials as Inconel or nickel to protect the steel from stress corrosion and thus solve the problem of the water-side corrosion.

Once the steam temperature and the maximum secondary sodium temperature have been established, the effect of sodium temperature drop on the design of the steam generator should be determined. There are advantages to a minimum flow rate associated with a maximum temperature drop through

the steam generator, as discussed in Sec. 4.2.2.1.1. The thermal stress associated with reactor scrams and feedwater temperature changes limit sodium temperature changes through the steam generator. Because of the thermal inertia, i.e., heat capacity, of the primary and secondary sodium systems, temperature transients resulting from a reactor scram will be less severe in the steam generator than in the reactor, if sodium flow and the sodium temperature rise are the same in both the primary and the secondary sodium systems.

4.3.6.1.4 CALCULATION METHODS.

4.3.6.1.4.1 Heat Transfer and Fluid Flow. The following methods for designing a once-through steam generator were adapted from an AEC-sponsored study of high temperature sodium-heated steam generators [95]. The methods illustrate one design approach with steam flow in the tubes. The sample calculation at the end of this section was not part of the Ref. 95 analysis but gives an indication of the magnitude of heat-transfer coefficients obtained in these units. A similar treatment for natural-circulation steam generators is found in Ref. 91.

The heat-transfer surface of a once-through steam generator can be considered as three connecting zones, which correspond to the regions of superheating, boiling, and preheating of the water or steam. For each zone the heat transfer from the shell-side sodium to the tubes can be evaluated using empirical equations such as:

$$Nu = 0.212[(D_e)(Pe)]^{0.6} \quad \text{(cross flow)} \quad (4.22)$$

$$Nu = 0.106[(D_e)(Pe)]^{0.6} \quad \text{(parallel flow)} \quad (4.23)$$

where D_e is the equivalent diameter of the shell in inches. Throughout industry there is considerable difference of opinion as to which heat-transfer correlation should be used. The designer should consult the literature and choose the equation that most closely matches his specific exchanger geometry. If the sodium velocity varies across the tube bundle, the sodium heat-transfer coefficient has a different value for each of the concentric rows of tubes. The effect of velocity is averaged according to the exposed heat-transfer surface for each concentric row of tubes. This average velocity is used to arrive at a mean sodium heat-transfer coefficient. Pressure-drop correlations for the shell side are given in Sec. 4.3.5.1.4. The above correlations are two of several that can be used; see Chap. 2 for other relationships. The state of knowledge on shell-side coefficients is, at present, meager in scope.

For the superheating zone the heat transfer from the tube to the steam can be evaluated with a modified Colburn equation for forced convection:

$$Nu = 0.019(Re)^{0.8}(Pr)^{1/3} \quad (4.24)$$

For this equation all physical properties of the steam are evaluated at the bulk temperature.

For the boiling zone, the heat transfer from the tube to the operating water can be evaluated from an expression that includes both pool boiling and forced convection. Since it is generally accepted that the pool-boiling coefficient and the convection coefficient are directly additive, the expression for the total boiling heat-transfer coefficient is

$$h_2 = h_5 + h_6$$

where h_6 is the pool-boiling coefficient (Btu/hr/sq ft/°F) and h_5 is the convection coefficient (Btu/hr/sq ft/°F).

One of the correlations for evaluating the pool nucleate boiling coefficient (taken from pages 406 to 413 of Frank Kreith, Principles of Heat Transfer, International Textbook Co., Scranton, Pa., 1958)[96] is

$$\frac{c_p T_x}{h_{fg}} = 0.013 \left[\frac{(q/A)}{\mu h_{fg}} \left(\frac{g_0 \sigma}{g(\rho_L - \rho_v)} \right)^{1/2} \right]^{1/3} \left(\frac{c_p \mu}{k} \right)^{1.7} \quad (4.25)$$

where: c_p = specific heat of saturated liquid, Btu/lb/°F

T_x = temperature drop, hot surface to fluid, °F

h_{fg} = latent heat of saturated liquid, Btu/lb

q/A = heat flux, Btu/hr/°F

σ = surface tension of saturated liquid, lb/ft

ρ_L = density of saturated liquid, lb/cu ft

ρ_v = density of saturated vapor, lb/cu ft

k = thermal conductivity of saturated liquid, Btu/ft/hr/°F

μ = viscosity of saturated liquid, lb/hr/ft

Solving for (q/A), substituting $(h_6 T_x)$ for (q/A), and assuming g_0/g equals one,

$$h_6 = \frac{\mu h_{fg}}{[\sigma/(\rho_L - \rho_v)]^{1/2}} \left[\frac{c_p}{0.013 \, h_{fg}(c_p \mu/k)^{1.7}} \right]^3 T_x^2 \quad (4.26)$$

The first fraction and the denominator of the second, evaluated at constant pressure, are equal to a constant K; thus

$$h_6 = K T_x^2 \quad (4.27)$$

The convection coefficient for the liquid is evaluated from the following expression:

$$h_5 = 0.019 c_p G_T (G_T D_E/\mu)^{-0.2} (c_p \mu/k)^{-2/3} \quad (4.28)$$

where G_T is the fluid mass velocity (lb/hr/sq ft) and D_E is the equivalent diameter (ft).

Since the boiling coefficient depends on the value of T_x, the coefficient varies along the length of the tube. The effect of this variation on the required heating surface can be evaluated by the following method. A resistance circuit is made from the hot fluid to the boiling fluid as shown in Fig. 4.87. For simplification an approximation can be made that boiling occurs at $A_r = A_2$ assuming the fouling resistance has no thickness.

Balancing heat flows $h_1 \Delta T = h_2 T_x = (h_5 + h_6) T_x$, substituting for h_6 the pool-boiling coefficient $h_{bp} = K T_x^2$ from Eq. 4.27, and for ΔT the expression $\Delta T_T - T_x$ from the resistance circuit, the equation for ΔT_T becomes

$$\Delta T_T = \frac{h_5}{h_1} T_x + \frac{K}{h_1} T_x^3 + T_x \quad (4.29)$$

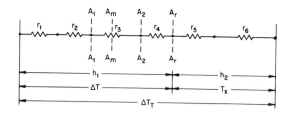

r_1 = Resistance of Sodium

r_2 = Resistance of Sodium Fouling

r_3 = Resistance of Tube Metal

r_4 = Resistance of Boiling-Water Fouling

r_5 = Resistance of Boiling Water (Convection)

r_6 = Resistance of Boiling Water (Pool Boiling)

A_1 = Outside Surface of Tube

A_2 = Inside Surface of Tube

A_m = Surface of Tube at Mean Diameter

A_r = Reference Surface at Which Boiling Occurs

ΔT_T = Total Temperature Drop—Sodium to Water

ΔT = Temperature Drop—Sodium to Boiling Surface

T_x = Temperature Drop—Boiling Surface to Water

$$1/h_1 = \sum_{i=1}^{4} r_i$$

$$1/h_2 = \sum_{i=5}^{6} r_i$$

FIG. 4.87—Thermal-resistance circuits for boiling section of steam generator.

Substituting for inlet and outlet conditions gives ΔT_{To} and ΔT_{Ti}, based on T_{xo} and T_{xi}.

The following steps can be taken: (1) differentiate Eq. 4.29; (2) substitute for $d(\Delta T_T)$ by making use of the fact that, given an element dl in length along the tube, the differential area is dA_r and the change in the ΔT_T along the tube is $d(\Delta T_T)$, $wc_p \, d(\Delta T_T) = -h_2 T_x \, dA_r = -K T_x^3 + h_5 T_x \, dA_r$; and (3) integrate dA_r from 0 to A_2 and T_{xi} to T_{xo}. The result is an expression for the area A_2, the required inside tube surface.

The following summarizes the basic equations:

$$\Delta T_{To} = (h_5/h_1) T_{xo} + (K/h_1) T_{xi}^3 + T_{xo} \quad (4.30)$$

$$\Delta T_{Ti} = (h_5/h_1) T_{xi} + (K/h_1) T_{xi}^3 + T_{xi} \quad (4.31)$$

$$A_2 = \frac{wc_p}{2h_1} \left(1 + \frac{h_1}{h_5} \right) ln \left(\frac{T_{xi}}{T_{xo}} \right)^2$$
$$+ \left(2 - \frac{h_1}{h_5} \right) ln \left(\frac{K T_{xi}^2 + h_5}{K T_{xo}^2 + h_5} \right) \quad (4.32)$$

The coefficients should be corrected to the proper reference surface.

For the preheating zone the heat transfer from the tube to the feedwater is first evaluated using the conventional convection coefficient to determine the tube metal temperature at the feedwater inlet. If this is determined to be above the saturation temperature, preheating is accomplished by boiling heat transfer. The procedure for thermal analysis is then the same as previously described for the boiling zone. If not, the same equation is used for the preheating zone as for the superheating zone.

The sodium fluid power consumption is evaluated from the shell-side sodium pressure loss. This loss is determined by dividing the overall nozzle-to-nozzle pressure drop into a series of smaller drops and evaluating each separately according to the formulas in Chap. 2.

The tube-side (water to steam) pressure losses are evaluated by using the friction-factor data found in the Reactor Handbook [97]. The two-phase multipliers based upon the Martinelli–Nelson correlation are also give in the Handbook.

The part-load variation in the thermal performance is determined by calculating the average equivalent heat-transfer rate for each part load. When the conventional number of transfer units (NTU effectiveness) type of heat transfer analysis [98] is applied, the corresponding terminal sodium temperatures can be predicted. For purposes of preliminary sizing, such as shown in the following sample calculations of heat-transfer coefficients, the following approximations for boiling film coefficients may be used: From 0 to 70% steam quality, 6000 Btu/sq ft/hr/°F; from 70 to 100% steam quality, 2000 Btu/sq ft/hr/°F.

Steam Generator Sample Calculation

Design conditions	Value
Type of steam generator	Once-through conventional, shell and tube
Heat transferred, Btu/hr	3.85×10^8
Sodium flow (shell side), lb/hr	3.17×10^6
Sodium inlet temperature, °F	950
Sodium outlet temperature, °F	650
Feedwater inlet temperature, °F	430
Steam outlet temperature, °F	900
Tube material	2.25 Cr–1 Mo
Fouling factor (h_f), Btu/hr/sq ft/°F	2000
Tube size:	
OD, in.	½
Wall thickness (t_w), in.	0.049
Number of tubes	1500
Tube-side flow area, sq ft	1.17
Shell-side flow area, sq ft	7.3
Steam pressure, psia	1500
Steam flow rate, lb/hr	3.77×10^5

To Find: (a) Overall heat-transfer coefficient U (Btu/hr/sq ft/°F) in each zone

(b) Total surface area required (sq ft)

(1) Shell-side coefficient at $T_{av.}$= 800°F, ρ = 53.2 lb/cu ft, μ = 0.178 × 10⁻³ lb/sec/ft, c_p = 0.305 Btu/lb/°F, k = 40 Btu/hr/ft/°F, D_e = 0.0157 ft,

$$v = \frac{W \, (\text{lb/hr})}{3600 \, (\text{sec/hr}) \, \rho \, (\text{lb/cu ft}) \, A \, (\text{sq ft})} = 2.27 \text{ ft/sec}$$

$$Re = \frac{D_e \, (\text{ft}) \, v \, (\text{ft/sec}) \, \rho \, (\text{lb/cu ft})}{\mu \, (\text{lb/sec/ft})} = 106,500$$

$$Pr = \frac{c_p \, (\text{Btu/lb/°F}) \, \mu \, (\text{lb/sec/ft}) \, 3600 \, (\text{sec/hr})}{k \, (\text{Btu/hr/ft/°F})} = 4.9 \times 10^{-3}$$

$$Pe = Re \, Pr = 522$$

$$Nu = 0.625 \, (Pe)^{0.4} = 7.6$$

$$h_o = (Nu)(k)/D_e \cong 2000 \text{ Btu/hr/sq ft/°F},$$
the shell-side tube coefficient

(2) Tube-side coefficient: Preheating section at T_{water} =513°F, ρ =48 lb/cu ft, μ = 7 × 10⁻⁵ lb/sec/ft, c_p = 1.19 Btu/lb/°F, k = 0.348 Btu/lb/°F, Pr = 0.863, v = $(W/\rho A)$ = 1.86 ft/sec, Re = 43000, Nu = 0.019 $(Re)^{0.8} \, Pr^{1/3}$ = 92.3, h_i = $(Nu \, k/D)$ = 960 Btu/hr/sq ft/°F, the inside tube coefficient.

$$1/U = \left\{ \frac{1}{h_i} \left(\frac{\text{OD}}{\text{ID}} \right) + \frac{t_w}{k_w} \left[\frac{2(\text{OD})}{\text{ID} + \text{OD}} \right] + \frac{1}{h_f} + \frac{1}{h_o} \right\}$$

$$= \left(\frac{10^4}{12.9 + 2.79 + 5.0 + 5.0} \right)^{-1}$$

U = 390 Btu/hr/sq ft/°F

(3) Tube-side coefficient: Boiling section

(a) U for 0 to 70% quality (assume h_i = 6000), only $\frac{1}{h_i}$ changes

$$U = \frac{10^4}{2.05 + 2.79 + 5.0 + 5.0} = 675 \text{ Btu/hr/sq ft/°F}$$

(b) U for 70 to 100% quality (assume h_i = 2000), only $\frac{1}{h_i}$ changes

$$U = \frac{10^4}{6.15 + 2.79 + 5.0 + 5.0} = 529 \text{ Btu/hr/sq ft/°F}$$

(4) Tube-side coefficient: Superheating section at T_{steam}= 750°F, ρ = 2.47 lb/cu ft, k = 0.032 Btu/lb/°F, μ = 2.3 × 10⁻⁵ lb/sec/ft, Pr = 1.15, v = 35.8 ft/sec, Re =129,000, Nu = 0.019 $(Re)^{0.8} \, Pr^{1/3}$ = 245, h_i= 234 Btu/hr/sq ft/°F

$$U = \frac{10^4}{52.5 + 2.79 + 5.0 + 5.0} = 153 \text{ Btu/hr/sq ft/°F}$$

Summary:

Water side			Sodium		LMTD, °F	$Q \times 10^{-6}$, Btu/hr	U, Btu/hr/sq ft/°F	$A = Q/U \times$ LMTD, sq ft
T, °F	H, Btu/lb	ΔH, Btu/lb	ΔT, °F	T, °F				
430	408	204	80	550	68	77	390	2900
596	612	388	151	630	89	145	675	2410
596	1000	168	66	781	213	64	529	570
596	1168	262	103	847	125	99	153	5200
900	1430			950				Total 11,080

*Since v_{steam} in the superheated section is only 35.8 ft/sec, the generator may be recalculated with fewer tubes.

4.3.6.1.4.2 Stress Analysis. Structural analysis is covered in Chap. 3. The AEC study [95] mentioned in Sec. 4.3.6.1.4.1 used the following criteria: (1) The U. S. Navy Code "Tentative Structural Design Basis for Reactor Vessels and Directly Associated Components," dated 1 April 1958, SSN/S51(551 B) Ser. 551B-596, was selected as a method for handling stress analysis of combined mechanical, hydrostatic, and thermal stresses, including conditions for the application of creep and stress rupture properties. (2) Allowable values for membrane stresses and stresses due to gross discontinuities were based upon figures given in the latest revisions of the Unfired Pressure Vessel Code as modified by Code Case 1234 and the values of yield strength and ultimate strength based upon the best available data. (3) The allowable values for pipe reaction stresses plus membrane and gross discontinuity stresses were taken as 90% of the yield strength. (4) Acceptable values for thermal stress and stress concentrations were taken from the Navy Code up to 700°F, which is the limiting temperature for these data. Beyond this, the values were assumed to vary with the ultimate strength. This assumption is in accord with available experimental results. Thermal stresses were treated as governed by Paragraph 5.1.4 of the Navy Code: "No stress limitation need be considered with regard to steady-state thermal stresses. All thermal stresses shall be considered as transient conditions."

Differential expansion between tubes and shell depends upon the flexibility developed by the particular tube shape and should be evaluated for each such shape. Tube sheet pressures can be calculated by the Horvay method (Chap. 3), which takes into account stress concentration in ligaments; whenever the tube sheet does not have tubes in a central core, it can be treated as a composite disk comprised of a central core without tube holes surrounded by an annular area with tube holes, which are, in turn, attached to a solid ring to which the shell and barrel are welded. For nozzle reaction stresses, Bijlaard's analysis [99] can be used in calculating required shell thickness at the sodium nozzles. Transient temperature differences resulting in thermal stresses can be calculated by the finite difference method of Schmidt [100], modified as explained in detail in Ref. 90. For additional discussion of transient thermal stresses, see Chap. 3.

4.3.6.2 Fabrication Development

As part of a high-temperature sodium-heated steam-generator development program, certain fabrication development work was carried out [101]. The following developments associated with this program are of general interest for future work and will be briefly discussed: tube-to-tube sheet welded connections, metallurgical examination of bimetallic tubes, and transition weld test.

The tube-to-tube sheet welded connections were a concern because of the rapid thermal transients possible in the unit. As an alternate to flush welds, welded connections with trepanned risers were considered. These risers would reduce the magnitude of the maximum stresses and would shift them away from the notch concentration points at the root of the weld.

In tests with carbon steel, 2.25 wt.% chromium—1 wt.% molybdenum steel, and type 316 stainless steel weld joints, the metals showed a suprisingly high resistance to damage from thermal strains. This resistance persisted even in defective carbon-steel welds that contained initial porosity. As a result of the tests, trepanning was to be omitted in several of the tube sheet welds. Even for the most critical welds, i.e., the upper tube sheet of the superheater, the trepanning could be reduced in height to 0.25 in. or simply to a semicircular groove surrounding the tube hole.

It was concluded that the most serious danger connected with a tube-to-tube sheet weld appears to be corrosion or stress corrosion in the crevice between the tube and the tube sheet. The tube and the tube sheet hole should be thoroughly cleaned before assembly and should be kept clean and dry to minimize this danger. The unit should not be tested under water pressure because the water will be driven into the crevice, and water or corrosion products may remain.

Because of the problem of stress corrosion, bimetallic tubing of 316 stainless steel clad with Inconel was selected during the design study. The Inconel protects the stainless steel from the high-temperature water and steam. Its strength properties are not as important. The minimum allowable thickness of Inconel is determined by the ability to produce tubing to commercial tolerances. For 1/2-in. tubes, this Inconel thickness is claimed by manufacturers to be 10 mils. As a result of mechanical tests, it was concluded that mechanically bonded bimetallic tubing is satisfactory for steam-generator service. In the transition weld test, a 4 1/2-in.-thick cylindrical joint between the chromium-molybdenum and stainless steels was successfully made and satisfactorily thermal cycled 165 times over a stress ranging up to 160,000 psi.

EBR-II problems consisted in providing reliable welding of the bonded duplex tubes of chromium-molybdenum to the sodium tube sheets of the superheater without the introduction of real or potential defects. The superheater originally designed is geometrically similar to the EBR-II evaporator, except that baffle tubes are not used and dimensions are generally smaller. The superheater utilizes a 0.596-in.-OD duplex tube with a total wall of 0.096 in. and a 1.109-in. pitch, whereas the evaporator utilizes a 1.438-in.-OD duplex tube with a total wall of 0.187 in and a 1.938-in. pitch. The smaller tube diameter and thinner wall of the superheater tube requires welding techniques superior to those used in welding the evaporator tubes. The welding development included a complete reexamination of all the welding parameters including welding current, wire speed, voltage, welding speed, bead size, and preheat temperature. Two welding procedures were investigated, spray transfer and dip transfer; both are modes of metal disposition. The principal difference between these methods is that the spray-transfer technique produces sound and reliable welds most of the time, with only an occasional imperfect one. The imperfections usually consist of overpenetration and violation of the nickel-phosphorus bond line. The dip-transfer method invariably incorporates a nonwetted area at the start of the weld cycle. Subsequent overlap of this area during the termination phase of the welding

Table 4.13—Performance Summary of Plant-size Steam Generators [102]

	EBR-I	SRE (natural circ.)	SRE (once through)	FERMI	EBR-II	HALLAM
Full-load heat transferred per unit, Mw(t)	3.92	20	20	143	62.5	85 (reentrant)
Type of unit	Falling film	Recirculating pancake tube	Once-through double-wall tube	Once-through single-wall involute tube	Recirculating duplex tube	Recirculating double-wall tube
Number of units per plant	1	1	1	3	1	3
Steam temperature, °F	529	654	825	780	840	833
Steam pressure, psig	393	600	605	900	1250	825
Feed-water temperature, °F	214	425	311	380	550	304
Feed-water flow per unit, lb/hr	3630	51,500	88,800	476,000	268,000*	251,000
Liquid-metal temperature In, °F	583	850	900	820	866	895
Out, °F	419	580	440	520	588	557
Liquid-metal flow, lb/hr	124,700	546,000	718,000	5,300,000	2,500,000	2,820,000

* 20,000 lb/hr blowdown.

cycle does not wet the area. Defects of this type create a vertical leak path through the weld which allows the sodium to leak to the atmosphere. Other improved welding techniques include the use of two weld passes; about 75% of the first pass is machined off prior to the start of the second pass. A second technique used a substantial weld overlay applied to the outer tube end, which was then partially machined off; the tube was redrawn to the original outside diameter before the first joint weld pass was made. Because of welding difficulties, the four superheaters were not manufactured. Two modified evaporator units were substituted with provisions for two additional units to be added at a later date.

4.3.6.3 Design, Fabrication, and Operating Experience [102]

4.3.6.3.1 PLANT-SIZE STEAM GENERATORS.
A performance summary of plant-size steam generators is given in Table 4.13.

4.3.6.3.1.1 EBR-I. The EBR-I steam generator has a separate economizer, boiler, and superheater (Table 4.14). Heat-transfer tubes in each component are similar and consist of a composite assembly of inner nickel, intermediate copper, and outer nickel tubes (Fig. 4.88). These tubes were assembled by mechanically drawing them together and thermally diffusion bonding them for good heat transfer. Total wall thickness of the tube is 5/16 in., of which 3/16 in. is nickel. An outer stainless-steel pipe makes up the shell of the heat exchanger, and a bellows provides differential thermal expansion. Thus, each heat exchanger has a single tube, with NaK flow in the shell side countercurrent to water or steam in the tube.

The vertical forced-circulation falling-film type steam generator limits the quantity of water in the system and increases the heat-transfer rate. The water film is established by a baffle at the top inner surface of the internal tube. The film runs to the bottom where excess water and generated steam are piped into a drum. Steam is separated in the drum and fed to the horizontal superheater.

Values were calculated for the heat-transfer coefficient in the economizer by dividing the nine-tubes-in-series unit into two parts, the first five tubes in nucleate boiling and the second four tubes in film boiling. The values were 508 Btu/hr/sq ft/°F and 204 Btu/hr/sq ft/°F, respectively. Temperature differentials in the second section are very low for boiling heat transfer; the gas blanket (characteristic of film boiling) may be responsible for the poor values obtained.

4.3.6.3.1.2 SRE Natural-circulation Unit. The SRE steam-generating unit comprises two natural-circulation evaporators, a steam drum, and a superheater (Table 4.15). The heat-transfer tube has a double wall; it contains sodium in an inner stainless-steel tube surrounded by a concentric carbon-steel tube. The annulus between tubes is filled with mercury. Each heat-transfer tube is formed into a horizontal coil connected to inlet and outlet headers mounted outside the evaporator shell. Each tube passes through an individual thermal sleeve in the shell (Fig. 4.89). The steam-water mixture is carried from the evaporator to the steam drum through two 10-in. risers. From there steam at 0.25% moisture (maximum) is carried by a 6-in. pipe to the superheater, which also contains double-tube horizontal coils; but the steam is inside the tubes to improve heat transfer through increased steam velocity.

The proprietary methods used for performing the coiling probably limit fabrication to a very few manufacturers. Under some transient conditions a large stress point may exist at the point where tubing is attached to the shell of the evaporators and superheater. This is particularly true of the connection between the inner and outer tubes on

Table 4.14—EBR-I Steam-generator Design and Operating Characteristics [102]

Physical design and geometry	Economizer	Evaporator	Superheater
Unit type	Forced circulation, falling-film boiler		
No. components per unit:			
Economizer	9 (in series)		
Evaporator	18 (in parallel)		
Superheater	4 (in series)		
Steam drums	1		
Shell-side geometry:			
Fluid contained	NaK	NaK	NaK
Materials	SS	SS	SS
Tube-side geometry:			
Fluid contained	Water	Steam	Steam
Type of tube	Three-layer composite	Drawn and diffusion bonded	
Material	Nickel OD; Copper–Nickel ID		
No. per component	1	1	1
Outside diameter, in.	$2\frac{5}{8}$	$2\frac{5}{8}$	$2\frac{5}{8}$
Individual wall thickness,* in.	$\frac{1}{16} - \frac{1}{8} - \frac{1}{8}$	$\frac{1}{16} - \frac{1}{8} - \frac{1}{8}$	$\frac{1}{16} - \frac{1}{8} - \frac{1}{8}$
Pattern	Single tube	Single tube	Single tube
Pitch, in.	Centered in shell	Centered in shell	Centered in shell
Thermal and fluid data per component			
Heat transferred, Btu/hr	1,432,000	4,560,000	368,000
Effective surface area, sq ft	5	5	5
Effective tube length, ft	9.56	9.56	9.56
Liquid-metal data:			
Temperatures, °F			
In			583
Out	419		
Flow rate, lb/hr	124,700	6,930	124,700
Fluid velocity, ft/sec	6.15	2.51	6.15
Water and steam data:			
Temperatures, °F			
In	214		
Out			529
Steam pressure, psig			423
Flow rate, lb/hr	3630	202	3630
Fluid velocity, ft/sec	3.43		58.8

*Dimensions for each layer of composite wall.

each coil, which is made just external to the shells. With steam on the outside of the heated tubes in the evaporator, the pressure capability of such a unit is limited to about 1000 psig.

This steam generator has been operated successfully at approximately two-thirds power. Considerable difficulty was experienced at initial start-up in maintaining water purity in the evapora-tors owing to accumulation of rust and preservatives during the several years between construction and initial operation. At low sodium flow the thermal gradient between inlet and outlet headers reversed the sodium flow in the bottom tubes, creating internal circulation of sodium within the evaporator and superheater sections. Otherwise the steam genera-tor is easy to control.

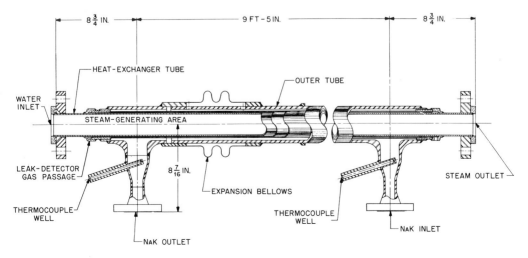

FIG. 4.88—EBR-I steam-generator tube [102].

Table 4.15—SRE Steam-generator Natural-circulation Design
and Operating Characteristics [102]

Physical design and geometry	Evaporator	Superheater
Unit type	Natural recirculation boiler	
No. components per unit:		
Economizer	0	
Evaporator	2	
Superheater	1	
Steam drums	1	
Shell-side geometry:		
Fluid contained	Water	Na
Outside diameter, in.	$63\frac{1}{2}$	58 I.D.
Wall thickness, in.	$1\frac{5}{16}$	
Overall length, ft	8.20	6.85
Flow baffles	None	None
Design temperature, °F	600	850
Design pressure, psig	600	300
Tube-side geometry:		
Fluid contained	Na	Steam
Type of tube	Double tube with Hg annulus	
Material	347 SS inside	347 SS—347 SS
	carbon steel outside	
No. per component	48	20
Outside diameter, in.	$1\frac{1}{4}$ inside	$1\frac{1}{4}$ inside
	$1\frac{1}{2}$ outside	$1\frac{1}{2}$ outside
Individual wall thickness, in.	0.065—0.090	0.065—0.085
Pattern	Horizontal coils, pancake stacked	
Design temperature, °F	600	850
Design pressure, psig	600	600
Thermal and fluid data per component unless noted (100% load)		
Heat transferred, Btu/hr (total unit)	60.5×10^6	
Effective surface area, sq ft	690	224
Overall heat-transfer coefficient, Btu/hr/sq ft/°F	580 clean, 470 service	263 clean, 243 service
Log mean temperature difference, °F	255	260
Liquid-metal data:		
Temperatures, °F		
In	818	860
Out	494	818
Flow rate, lb/hr	273,000	546,000
Fluid velocity, ft/sec	4.4	
Pressure drop, psi	42 total	
Water and steam data:		
Temperatures, °F		
In	300	490
Out	490	654
Steam pressure, psig		615
Flow rate, lb/hr	25,750	51,500
Recirculation	10 to 1 at full power	
General data:		
Water and steam-side safety valves	2 (one for 5% over pressure; the other for 10% over pressure)	
Size	3 in.	
Water quality	Navy standard boiler water	
Accessibility of interior surfaces of tubes and shells for inspection	Interior tube surfaces inaccessible; shell: evaporator, 3 ports; superheater, 3 ports	
Inspection techniques	Mass spectrometer, 0.003 μ cu ft/hr	
Drainable:		
Sodium side	Yes	
Water-steam side	Yes	
Piping	Yes	

4.3.6.3.1.3 SRE Once-through Unit. This horizontally mounted, 304 stainless steel, shell-and-
tube heat exchanger is in a U configuration; the
tube length in the double tube is 80 ft (Table 4.16).
The inner tube contains water, and sodium is on the
outside of the outer tube. Mercury in the annulus
serves as a leak detector for either of the two
concentric tubes since it is maintained at a pressure intermediate between the steam and the sodium.
The water and steam flow inside the tubes is coun-
ter-current to the sodium on the shell side. Tube
bundles are supported by "egg crates" on the shell

side (Fig. 4.90). Heat transfer is somewhat reduced in the U-bend of the tubes where supports
have been omitted to accommodate thermal expansion. Absence of baffles allows temperature stratification of sodium in the horizontal shell, which
produces uneven steam-temperature distribution at
the tube bundle exit. Superheated steam is produced in the top tubes, and saturated steam (and
perhaps some water) issues from the bottom tubes.
Mixing in the steam end bell and pipe produces
a mixed mean steam temperature corresponding to
that desired, but a thermal gradient and stress

Table 4.16—SRE Once-through Steam-generator Design and
Operating Characteristics [102]

Physical design and geometry	
Unit type	Once through, shell and tube, U-bend
Number of components per unit	
Economizer, evaporator and superheater	One integral component
Shell-side geometry:	
Fluid contained	Na
Outside diameter, in.	19
Wall thickness, in.	$3/8$
Overall length, ft	End of legs to end of U-bend, 41.33
Flow baffles	None
Design temperature, °F	1200
Design pressure, psig	50
Material	304 SS
Tube-side geometry:	
Fluid contained	Water and steam inside tube, Hg in annulus
Type of tube	Double tube with Hg annulus, U-bend
Material	All 304 SS
No. per component	199
Outside diameter, in.	$1/2$ inside, $11/16$ outer, $7/8$ at bend
Individual wall thickness, in.	0.050 inside, 0.054 outside, 0.069 bend
Pattern	Triangular
Pitch (center line to center line), in.	1.125
Design temperature, °F	1200
Design pressure, psig	750
Thermal and fluid data per component	
Heat transferred, Btu/hr	102.39×10^6
Effective surface area, sq ft	2790 Na side, 1580 water side
Effective tube length, ft	76
Log mean temperature difference, °F	100
Liquid-metal data:	
Temperatures, °F	
In	900
Out	440
Flow rate, lb/hr	718,000
Pressure drop, psi	7
Water and steam data:	
Temperatures, °F	
In	311
Out	825
Steam pressure, psig	625
Flow rate, lb/hr	88,800
Recirculation	None

exist vertically across the steam outlet tube
sheet.

Operation has been satisfactory from an integrity, performance, and control standpoint. The
steam generator has operated for approximately
16,000 hr, 8,000 hr of which were at significant
power levels approaching 20 Mw(t). All operating
time has been at full pressure, and maximum
sodium temperatures have varied from 750°F to
1060°F. Inspection of the internals on the steam
side after 16,000 hr indicated no observable deposits, corrosion, or other untoward phenomena.
The excellent condition of the steam generator is
primarily attributed to water treatment. Total dissolved solids have never been permitted to exceed
0.5 ppm, and pH has been controlled at 9.6 using
hydrazine and morpholine.

4.3.6.3.1.4 Fermi. The Fermi steam generators are vertical-shell, single tube wall, counterflow, once-through units (Table 4.17 and Fig. 4.91).
The tubes are serpentine involutes, trombone nested
in banks of eight to obtain maximum heat transfer.
They are attached to the stationary head by welding
and light rolling.

Once-through counterflow steam generation is
accomplished as follows. The feedwater enters at
the upper manifold and passes through the straight
downcomer portion of the tubes inside a sodium
flow shield. Preheating, boiling, and superheating is
accomplished in the involute sections on the outside
of the thermal shield. The steam leaves from an
outer manifold. The connection at the tube sheet is
a bolted and welded flange. Sodium enters the shell
through nozzles at the side of the unit and flows
out the nozzle located at the bottom of the shell.

During a cold hydrotest of the unit at 850 psi, an
unaccounted for leakage of 300 cm³ over 1 1/2 hr
was observed. A hot hydrotest was performed, and
steam was observed at a shell–side vent when the
vent was opened. The bundle was then removed
and examined. Metallographic examination of the
cracked tubes disclosed that the tubes failed as a
result of stress corrosion cracking. The tubes
were stressed during cold forming and were not
stress relieved after bending.

Some of the alkaline cleaning agent probably
was left in the tubes since they were not flushed
but were allowed to drip dry. The water analysis
indicated the presence of an alkaline solution; the
pH was considerably higher than would be expected
as a result of hydrazine, the only known addition.

The only cracks that were found occurred on the
sides of the bend, not on the inside or outside
radius of the bend. A considerable number of
cracks that started on the inside surface but did

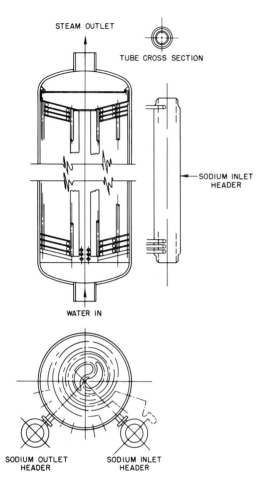

FIG. 4.89—SRE natural-circulation evaporator [81, 82].

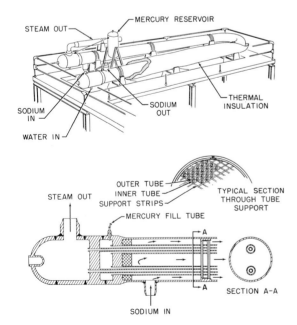

FIG. 4.90—SRE once-through steam generator [102].

not progress to the outside surface of the tube was observed. Thus it appears that all cracks originated on the inside surface of the tubes. All cracks were intergranular. They showed distinct amounts of corrosion product in the network of the crack. All indications pointed to stress corrosion cracking. Cracks were found in both the long- and short-radius bends, but no cracks were found in the single straight section that was examined.

4.3.6.3.1.5 EBR-II. The EBR-II steam-generator system consists of a natural-circulation evaporating section, a conventional steam drum, and a once-through superheating section (Table 4.18). The evaporating section is comprised of eight identical shell-and-tube heat exchangers connected in parallel on the tube side to a horizontal steam drum with internal moisture separation. Dry saturated steam leaves the top of the steam drum and flows downward to what, in the original design, were four identical shell-and-tube superheater units in parallel. Modifications were made as noted later.

The external design of the evaporators and superheaters is shown in Fig. 4.92. The internal details are shown in Fig. 4.93. Both evaporator and superheater shells are constructed of 2.25 wt.% chromium-1 wt.% molybdenum steel. Four evaporators have mechanically bonded duplex tubes, and four evaporators and four superheaters have metallurgically bonded duplex tubes. Each duplex tube consists of two single-length seamless tubes. The

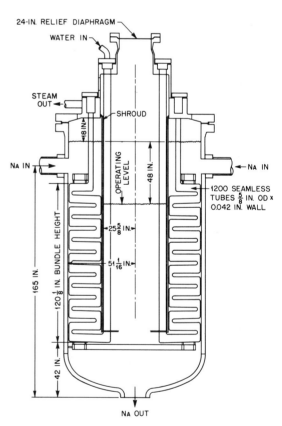

FIG. 4.91—Fermi steam generator [83].

Table 4.17—Fermi Once-through Steam-generator Design and Operating Characteristics [102]

Physical design and geometry
  Unit type   Once through, cross and counterflow, involute pattern
  Number of components per unit   Economizer, evaporator, and superheater in one
                                   integral component
                                   Steam drums, none

Shell-side geometry:	
Fluid contained	Na
Outside diameter, in.	$105\frac{3}{8}$
Wall thickness, in.	$1\frac{5}{8}$ to $2\frac{3}{4}$
Overall length, ft.	26.5
Design temperature, °F	1000
Design pressure, psig	Vacuum to 175
Material	2.25 wt.% Cr–1 wt.% Mo
Tube-side geometry:	
Fluid contained	Water–steam
Type of tube	Single seamless drawn tube
Material	2.25 wt.% Cr–1 wt.% Mo
Number per component	1200
Outside diameter, in.	$\frac{5}{8}$
Individual wall thickness, in.	0.042
Installed length, ft.	78.75
Pattern	Involute
Pitch, in.	0.872
Design temperature, °F	900
Design pressure, psig	Vacuum to 1000

	Preheat	Evaporative*		Superheat
		0-70%	70-100%	
Thermal and fluid data per section (100% load)				
Heat transferred, Btu/hr	82×10^6	223×10^6	95×10^6	89×10^6
Effective surface area, sq ft	2620	3390	830	3850
Overall heat transfer coefficient				
Btu/hr/sq ft/°F	402	734	565	210
Log mean temperature difference, °F	77.9	89.5	202	110
Liquid-metal data:				
Temperature, °F				
In		820		
Out		520		
Flow rate, lb/hr		5.29×10^6		
Fluid velocity, ft/sec		3		
Pressure drop, psi		1.39		
Water and steam data:				
Temperature, °F				
In		380		
Out		780		
Steam pressure, psig		900		
Flow rate, lb/hr		476,000		
Recirculation		None		
Pressure drop, psi		Approx. 10		
Fluid velocity, ft/sec		59		

General data

Water- and steam-side safety valves:	
No.	3
Size	4 in. (2), 3 in. (1)
Sodium-side relief device:	
No.	1
Size	24-in. rupture disk
Thermal shock protector for tube sheets	Argon inert-gas space above sodium level
Accessibility of interiors of tubes and shells for inspection	Shell can be entered through 24-in. rupture disk after draining; tubes can be reached by removing steam and water header cover plates
Stress analysis	Detailed (design basis, code, steady-state and transient thermal pressure, and combinations of these)
Inspection techniques	Ultrasonic, radiographic, dye penetrant, mass spectrometer leak, hydrostatic
Dry weight of complete assembly (not including support structure), lb	114,000
Drainable:	
Sodium side	Yes
Water–steam side	No
Piping	Yes
Water purity	Maximum solids 1 ppm, pH from 8.5 to 9.5

* Evaporative section broken down into two sections, 0-70% quality steam and 70-100% quality steam.

Table 4.18—EBR-II — Natural Circulation Steam Generator Design
and Operating Characteristics [102]

	Evaporator	Superheater
Physical design and geometry		
Unit type	Natural circulation evaporator and once through superheater	
Number of components per unit		
Economizer	0	
Evaporator	8 in parallel	
Superheater	4 in parallel	
Steam drums	1	
Shell-side geometry		
Fluid contained	Na	Na
Outside diameter, in.	20	14
Wall thickness, in.	0.375	0.312
Overall length, ft	30.17	31.5
Flow baffles	Staggered	Tube support only
Design temperature, °F	1000	1000
Design pressure, psig	150	150
Material	2.25 wt.% Cr—1 wt.% Mo	2.25 wt.% Cr—1 wt.% Mo
Tube-side geometry		
Fluid contained	Water	Steam
Type of tube	Duplex tube	Duplex tube
Material	2.25 wt.% Cr—1 wt.% Mo (both tubes)	2.25 wt.% Cr—1 wt.% Mo (both tubes)
Number per component	73	109
Outside diameter, in.	1.438	0.596
Total wall thickness, in.	0.187	0.096
Installed length, ft	27.67	29.67
Pattern	Straight, tube, triangular spacing	
Pitch, in. center to center	1.938	1.109
Design temperature, °F	800	900
Design pressure, psig	1500	1500
Thermal and fluid data per component unless noted (100% load)		
Heat transferred, Btu/hr/(total unit)	213×10^6	
Effective surface area, sq ft	620	440
Effective tube length, ft	22.5	25.75
Overall heat transfer coefficient Btu/hr/sq ft/°F	500 (predicted)	330 (predicted)
Log mean temperature difference, °F	63	89
Liquid metal data		
Temperature, °F		
In	794	866
Out	588	794
Flow rate, lb/hr	312,500	625,000
Fluid velocity, ft/sec	1.4	4.3
Pressure drop, psi (total unit)	14	
Water and steam data		
Temperature, °F		
In	550	580
Out	580	840
Steam pressure, psig		1250
Flow rate, lb/hr	31,000	62,000
Recirculation	4 : 1 (minimum)	
Pressure drop, psi (total unit)	22	
Fluid velocity, ft/sec		79
General data		
Water- and steam-side safety valves		
Number	2	
Sodium-side relief device		
Number	2	1
Size, in.	10	4 × 6
Type	Rupture diaphragms	Safety valve
Drainable		
Sodium side	Essentially	
Water—steam side	Yes	
Piping	Yes	
Tube sheet thermal protection:		
Outer	None	None
Inner	4 baffles-2 in. total thickness	4 baffles-2 in. total thickness
Water quality - Demineralized - 0.01 micromho conductivity		
Fe - 0.01 ppm		
Cl - 0.01 ppm		
Si - 0.01 ppm From demineralizer		
Tds*- 0.50 ppm		
All tube joints are welded		

*Tds - total dissolved solids.

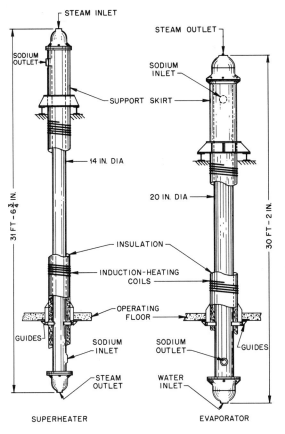

FIG. 4.92—EBR-II steam-generator components [54].

units have double wall tube sheets at each end; the outer tube is welded to the sodium tube sheet, and the inner tube is welded to the steam tube sheet. The space between the tube sheets is open to the atmosphere.

Maximum integrity was obtained by controlling tube fabrication from preparation of the furnace heat to the installation of the finished tube. Some difficulty was experienced in obtaining the desired cleanliness of the furnace heat; however, the tubing as supplied was free of inclusion concentrations greater than 4-0, 4-S as determined by SAE procedures. The tubing was also free of laps, seams, or cracks greater than 0.004 in. in depth, 0.015 in. in circumferential length, or 0.030 in. in longitudinal length. Each tube was subjected to hydrostatic, dye-penetrant, eddy-current, and ultrasonic tests prior to duplexing. After assembly into duplex tubes, the mechanically bonded tubes were helium mass-spectrometer leak tested, and the metallurgically bonded tubes were ultrasonically tested. A few mils had to be removed by surface grinding to ensure a good metallurgical bond.

The welding procedure, used successfully to attach the evaporator tubes to the sodium tube sheet, did not produce consistently reliable welds to these criteria on the smaller and thinner superheater tubes. The superheater tubes have an outer diameter of 0.596 in. and a 0.052-in.-thick outer wall. The object was to weld the outer wall only to the sodium tube sheet. Details of weld development are discussed in Sec. 4.3.6.2. The fabrication of the four superheaters was not completed, and two evaporators were modified and substituted for them. A core tube was centered within each tube in the modified unit, and it provided a 1/8-in. annulus for steam flow (Fig. 4.93). These two modified

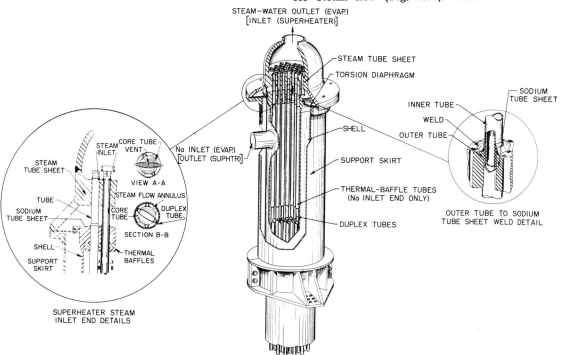

FIG. 4.93—EBR-II superheater and evaporator details [54].

Table 4.19—Hallam Natural-circulation Steam-generator Design
and Operating Characteristics [102]

Physical design and geometry

Unit type   Natural circulation, bayonet tube
Number of components per unit:
   Economizer   0
   Evaporator   1
   Superheater   1
   Steam drums   1

	Evaporator	Superheater
Shell-side geometry:		
Fluid contained	Water	Steam
Outside diameter, in.	$89\frac{1}{4}$	$60\frac{1}{2}$
Wall thickness, in.	$2\frac{5}{8}$	$2\frac{7}{8}$
Overall length, ft	32	21
Flow baffles	None	Orifice, every $4\frac{1}{16}$ in.
Design temperature, °F	550	950
Design pressure, psig	1000	1000
Material	2.25 wt.% Cr—1 wt.% Mo	2.25 wt.% Cr—1 wt.% Mo
Tube-side geometry:		
Fluid contained	Na	Na
Type of tube	Bayonet, outer tube duplex, with He gap	
Material	2.25 wt.% Cr—1 wt.% Mo	2.25 wt.% Cr—1 wt.% Mo
Number per component	679	559
Outside diameter, in.	1.330 inner	1.330 inner
	1.523 outer	1.523 outer
Individual wall thickness, in.	0.085 inner	0.085 inner
	0.072 outer	0.072 outer
Pattern	Rectangular	Triangular
Pitch, in.	2×2	2 equilateral
Design temperature, °F	950	950
Design pressure, psig	100	100
Thermal and fluid data per component (100% load)		
Heat transferred, Btu/hr	232.7×10^6	55.3×10^6
Effective surface area, sq ft	3680	2150
Effective tube length, ft	13.85	10
Overall heat transfer coefficient,	Clean, 800	Clean, 212
Btu/hr/sq ft/°F	Service, 570	Service, 175
Log mean temperature difference, °F	111	147
Liquid metal data:		
Temperatures, °F		
In	830	875
Out	559	830
Flow rate, lb/hr	2.82×10^6	2.82×10^6
Pressure drop, psi	8.15	6.28
Water and steam data:		
Temperatures, °F		
In	304	530
Out	530	833
Steam pressure, psig		825
Flow rate, lb/hr	2.51×10^5	2.51×10^5
Pressure drop, psi		26
General data		
Water- and steam-side safety valves:		
No.	4 (1 on superheater, 3 on eliminator)	
Size	$2\frac{1}{2}$	
Sodium-side relief device:	None	
Accessibility of interior surfaces of tubes and shells for inspection	Interior of tubes not accessible; shell side: evaporator has manhole, superheater has an escape opening	
Weights (dry) (not including supporting structure)	Evaporator 116,000 lb	
	Superheater 69,000 lb	
	Eliminator 11,600 lb	
Inspection techniques	Ultrasonic, radiographic, dye penetrant, magnetic particle, visual, mass-spectrometer leak test	
Drainable		
Sodium side	Completely	
Water-steam side	Completely	
Piping	Completely	
Water quality	Boiler feedwater total dissolved solids = 0 to 5 ppm	
Type of tube joint(s)	100% X-rayable butt weld	

evaporator units produce a steam temperature of about 820°F at 45 Mw(t).

During the final tube to sodium tube sheet welding procedure, the tubes were cold sprung to reduce stresses caused by differential expansion during severe over-temperature operation. During this process the shell was elongated about 1/8 in. relative to the tubes. The differential elongation was maintained during the tube to tube sheet welding and stress-relieving operation.

4.3.6.3.1.6 Hallam (Table 4.19). The Hallam steam generators are natural-circulation horizontally mounted units composed of an evaporator, a steam drum, and a superheater (Fig. 4.94). Sodium in the evaporators and superheaters is contained in reentrant thimbles. Hot sodium enters down a thermally insulated central tube, reverses flow at the end of the tube by impinging on an end cap on the outer tube, and flows back toward the inlet in an annulus between inner and outer tubes. It gives up heat by evaporating and superheating steam in contact with the outside of the outer tubes. The outer double-wall tube contains helium passages between the inner and outer portions. Inner and outer sections are swaged together for maximum heat transfer. Leaks in inner or outer sections produce a change in helium pressure. The use of double-walled bayonet tubes reduces thermal stresses.

The saturated steam—water mixture leaves the evaporator in four risers after some separation is effected in the top of the evaporator shell. Two drain lines return saturated water to the evaporator from the steam separator. Steam at 0.25% moisture enters the horizontal superheater and is passed over bayonet tube bundles similar to the evaporator bundles but heavily baffled to ensure maximum heat to steam from the bayonet tubes.

Two unusual fabrication techniques are automatic butt welding of tubes to tube sheets and tube caps and two-way ultrasonic testing of tubes. It is estimated that double-wall construction and the leak-monitoring system triple the cost.

Volatile chemicals are used to aid in maintaining low boiler solids. The use of high solids concentration in boiler water comparable to conventional boiler practice would result in plugging of the orifice type baffles in the superheater.

4.3.6.3.2 MODEL BOILERS. 4.3.6.3.2.1 APDA U-tube (Table 4.20). The prototype once-through steam generator is of shell-and-tube construction with an effective length of approximately 48 ft (Fig. 4.95 and Table 4.20). The U-shape eliminates differential expansion problems between the shell and tubes. The shell is made of schedule 160 stainless-steel pipe. A thermal sleeve barrier between the shell and the shroud band consists of two thin-walled (50 mils) type 304 stainless-stell sleeves with a layer of Quinterra insulation (approximately 2 mils) sandwiched between the two sleeves. A shroud band made of 2-in. schedule 10 type 304 stainless-steel pipe surrounds the tube bundle to provide a desirable flow pattern parallel to the tubes. Seven full-length water-stream tubes are centered in the shroud band flow path and are held in place by tube supports of the spider web type. The tube sheets are enlarged to include an additional row of 12 dummy tubes, drilled part way into each tube sheet. A thermal barrier, consisting of a 5-in.-thick piece of type 304 stainless steel, is located on the NaK outlet side of the water-end tube sheet and a 1 3/4-in.-thick piece of type 304 stainless steel is located on the NaK inlet side of the steam-end tube sheet to eliminate thermal shocks on the main tube sheets. A dummy tube sheet with twelve 1/4-in.-OD type 304 stainless-steel tubes feeds the water into the dummy tubes in the main tube sheet. From there the water flows into the main water box and into the seven active tubes. At the steam outlet end, steam from the active tubes is fed into the 12 dummy tubes, out through twelve 1/4-in.-OD type 304 stainless-steel tubes, and into the steam outlet chamber.

The entire unit, including the single-walled tube design, successfully withstood one year of operation with cycling conditions equivalent to a number of

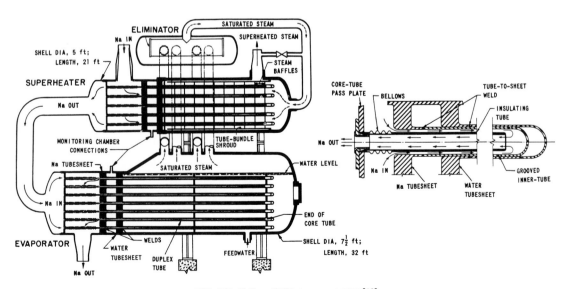

FIG. 4.94—Hallam (SGR) steam generator [19].

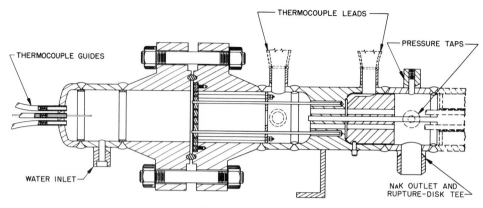

HEAD END OF BOILER

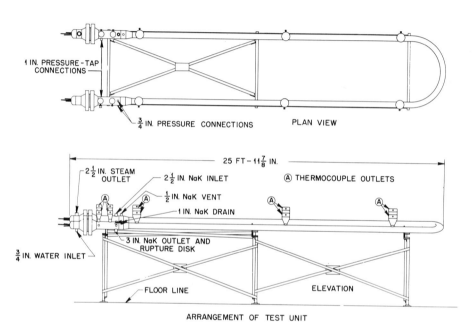

PLAN VIEW

ARRANGEMENT OF TEST UNIT

FIG. 4.95—APDA U-tube steam-generator model [84, 85].

years of normal operation. Of the 25 unscheduled shutdowns that occurred during the year, none resulted from failure in liquid-metal components or in the once-through steam generator. There was no evidence of either water-side or liquid-metal-side deposits extensive enough to cause measurable losses in heat transfer or increases in pressure drop.

During normal operation the steam-hot NaK sheet has a much smaller differential temperature than the water-cold NaK tube sheet. During 85% load transient tests, the steam flange developed a small leak to the atmosphere at a steam temperature of approximately 690°F, or 100°F above the saturation pressure. A larger thermal block on the steam-hot NaK end would have been a desirable change for this unit.

4.3.6.3.2.2 APDA Bayonet Unit. The unit (Fig. 4.96) is of the vertical shell and bayonet tube once-through type (Table 4.21). Feedwater enters the insulated inner tube of the bayonet tube and flows from top to bottom without being heated. It then flows vertically upward in the space between inner and outer tubes and is heated, evaporated, and superheated by a counterflow of NaK on the shell side. A free NaK level is maintained below the steam tube sheet so that the tube sheet is not exposed to NaK and is less subject to thermal shock. The space between the NaK level and the tube sheet is filled with argon gas.

The steam generator has an effective length of 20 ft. There is a 4-in.-OD, 0.125-in.-thick shroud inside the 6-in.-ID shell. With the shell it forms an annulus to contain the NaK bypass flow which dampens thermal transients and prevents shell stresses. A set of four baffles between the shell and shroud keeps this annulus NaK flow to a minimum. A set of 11 baffles between the shroud and steam tubes serves to create sufficient turbulence

Table 4.20—APDA U-tube Steam-generator Model Design
and Operating Characteristics [102]

Physical design and geometry
  Unit type   Once-through, counter flow U-tube
  Number of components per unit
    Economizer, evaporator, and superheater   One integral unit
    Steam drums   0
  Shell-side geometry:
    Fluid contained   NaK
    Outside diameter, in. $4\frac{1}{2}$
    Wall thickness, in.   0.531
    Overall length, ft   50
    Flow baffles   Shroud
    Design temperature, °F   1000
    Design pressure, psig   1200
    Material   304 SS
  Tube-side geometry:
    Fluid contained   Water–steam
    Type of tube   Single seamless
    Material   304 SS
    Number per component   7
    Outside diameter, in.   0.50
    Individual wall thickness, in.   0.050
    Installed length, ft   48.1
    Pattern   Equilateral triangle
    Pitch (center to center), in. $\frac{3}{4}$
    Design temperature, °F   1000
    Design pressure, psig   1300

		Evaporative*		
	Preheat	0-70%	70-100%	Superheat
Thermal data per section (100% load)				
Heat transferred, Btu/hr	1,182,000	1,190,000	509,000	542,000
Effective surface area, sq ft	18.85	11.30	3.00	10.45
Overall heat transfer coefficient, Btu/hr/sq ft/°F	556	1190	799	330
Log mean temperature difference, °F	118.5	94.6	226	168
Liquid-metal data (per unit):				
Temperature, °F				
In		900		
Out		450		
Flow rate, lb/hr		30,200		
Pressure drop, psi		7.4		
Water and steam data (per unit):				
Temperatures, °F				
In		175		
Out		800		
Steam pressure, psig		1200		
Flow rate, lb/hr		2770		
Recirculation		None		
Pressure drop, psi		13.5		
Fluid velocity, ft/sec		2 water, 70 steam		

General data
  Water and steam side safety valves
    No.   1
    Size $1\frac{1}{2}$ in.
  Sodium-side relief device   Rupture disk in the NaK dump line connected
                                       to the unit shell
  Accessibility of interior surfaces of   Tubes are accessible through flanged ends,
    tubes and shells for inspection   shells are inaccessible
  Scope of stress analysis furnished   Complete steady-state analysis
  Inspection techniques   Hydrostatic tests, pneumatic test
  Tube sheet thermal protection   Stainless-steel blocks on NaK side of each
                                       tube sheet
  Drainable
    Sodium side   Yes
    Water–steam side   Yes
    Piping   Yes
  Water treatment   Water having a purity of less than 0.1 μmho
                                      conductivity and a silica content of approxi-
                                      mately 0.02 ppm was used; ammonium hydroxide
                                      addition maintained a pH of about 9.7

*Evaporative section broken down into two sections, 0–70% quality steam and 70–100% quality steam

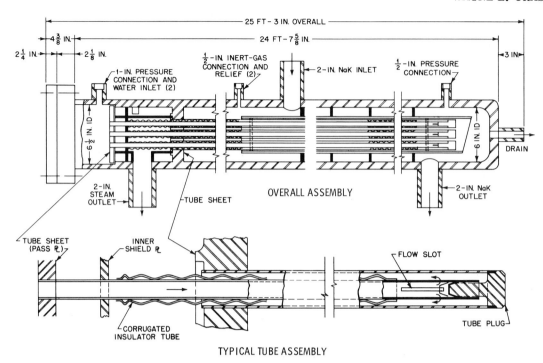

FIG. 4.96—APDA bayonet-tube steam generator [86, 87].

to keep the steam tubes in constant contact with hot NaK. The bayonet water tube is thermally insulated from the steam tube by a 3/4-in.-OD, 0.0125-in.-thick corrugated tube welded to the water tube top and bottom. The space between the corrugated tube and the water tube is filled with argon gas at about 15 psi. The outer tube slides over a tube plug welded to the bottom of the steam tube to allow for differential expansion and to keep the water tube centered.

A shield plate installed in the steam chest reduces the amount of feedwater preheating through the water pass plate (tube sheet). Installed in the steam chest is a 4-in.-diameter shroud to reduce heat leakage to the containing metal. The only operating problem encountered involved the pass plate. A broken compressed asbestos gasket between the water pass plate and its mating shoulder in the steam generator shell permitted considerable feedwater to bypass the water and steam tubes and pass directly to the steam chest area, tempering the steam in the chest.

After replacement of the gasket, the steam temperature began to fluctuate, but control of the unit was not affected. When steam-temperature fluctuations increased 30°F in 5 min, it was decided to seal weld the pass plate to the inside diameter of the steam-generator shell. After this repair no further trouble was experienced during the remaining 360 hr of operation. This method of repair would be impractical if the water tube bundle were to be lifted out at moderate to frequent intervals.

Actual heat-transfer performance was inferior to the predicted design performance. This was more pronounced at the lower loads. There was steam-to-feedwater heat leakage through the corrugated insulating tubes surrounding the feedwater tubes. Suspected hot leakage prompted installation of a thermocouple in the bottom of the center water tube to check for feedwater preheating. Feedwater temperatures at the bottom of the tube exceeded water inlet temperature by 29°F at 106% load and by 113°F at 11% load.

4.3.6.3.2.3 Hallam Model. A 3-Mw(t) model of the Hallam steam generator was tested for 8000 hr. The model is composed of one 19-tube bayonet bundle in the evaporator and a similar 19-tube bundle in the superheater, identical with the large unit in design and in the dimensions of individual tubes. A series of thermal cycle and thermal shock tests corresponding to at least a 20-year operating life of the full scale unit were imposed. A leak developed after about 2000 hr of operation. It was traced to a weld defect in the end cap of one of the bayonet tubes. This defect was repaired with no significant difficulty. Disassembly of the steam generator following the entire test indicated no damage to any of the parts. The steam generator exhibited heat-transfer characteristics slightly higher than calculated, was easily controlled, and, in general, performed satisfactorily.

Average corrosion rates were acceptable for a 20-year lifetime. One area of each of two tubes exhibited a corrosion rate approximately twice that of the average. These areas were shallow grooves on the top side of the tubes, extending roughly parallel with the axis of the tube for about 4 in. These areas were attributed to the position of the downcomer, which contained a higher concentration of oxygen-bearing feedwater than the average of all water in the evaporator section. The position of the downcomer has been corrected in the full-scale unit.

Table 4.21—APDA Bayonet Steam-generator Model Design
and Operating Characteristics [102]

Physical design and geometry
  Unit type   Test unit: bayonet tubes, counterflow,
                                                           once-through

  Number of components per unit
    Economizer, evaporator, and superheater   One integral unit
    Steam drums   0
  Shell-side geometry:
    Fluid contained   NaK-56
    Outside diameter, in. $7\frac{1}{2}$
    Wall thickness, in.   0.680
    Overall length, ft   25.25
    Flow baffles   11 modified disk and doughnut
    Design temperature, °F   1000
    Design pressure, psig   1500
    Material   304 SS
  Tube-side geometry:
    Fluid contained   Water, steam
    Type of tube   Bayonet, outside steam tube single
                                                           wall
    Material   2.25 wt % Cr—1 wt % Mo
    Number per component   7
    Outside diameter, in.   Outer, 1; inner, $\frac{1}{2}$
    Individual wall thickness, in.   Outer, 0.065; inner, 0.035
    Installed length, ft   23.25
    Pattern   Triangular
    Pitch, in. $1\frac{1}{4}$
    Design temperature, °F   850
    Design pressure, psig   1000

	Preheat	Evaporative	Superheat
Thermal data per section (100% load)			
Heat transferred, Btu/hr	217,000	1,225,000	343,000
Effective surface area, sq ft	8.82	7.56	9.59
Overall heat transfer coefficient, Btu/hr/sq ft/°F	486	1748	328
Log mean temperature difference, °F	51	92.5	109

Liquid-metal data:
  Temperatures, °F
    In   820
    Out   520
  Flow rate, lb/hr   26,000
  Pressure drop, psi   Approx. 8
Water and steam data:
  Temperatures, °F
    In   430
    Out   780
  Steam pressure, psig   900
  Flow rate, lb/hr   1880
  Pressure drop, psi   1.96
General data
  Water and steam side safety valves
    No.   1
    Size $1\frac{1}{2}$ in.
  Sodium-side relief device   Rupture disk in the NaK dump line connected
                                                           to the unit shell
  Accessibility of interior surfaces of   Tubes are accessible through flanged end;
    tubes and shells for inspection   shell is inaccessible
  Scope of stress analysis furnished   Complete steady-state analysis
  Inspection techniques   X-ray, hydro, pneumatic, Zyglo, ultrasonic
  Drainable
    Sodium side   Yes
    Water—steam side   No
  Water treatment   Water having a purity of less than 0.1 μmho
                                                           conductivity and a silica content of approxi-
                                                           mately 0.02 ppm was used; ammonium hydroxide
                                                           addition maintained a pH of about 9.7

4.3.6.3.2.4 LASL Model. The steam-generating unit in the 2000-kw Sodium Test Facility
consists of an evaporator, a superheater, and an
economizer (Table 4.22). The economizer between
the superheater and the evaporator cools the sodium
to decrease the temperature difference between
sodium and boiling water and thus the thermal
stresses in the evaporator.

The evaporator and superheater are of the once-
through design without steam drums. The three
heat exchangers are of the shell-and-tube type,
and the three shells are welded together in a
series to form a continuous horizontal U-bend
unit (Fig. 4.97). Doughnut baffles are used to prevent
channeling of sodium along the outside of the tube
bundle and to provide support for the tubes. There

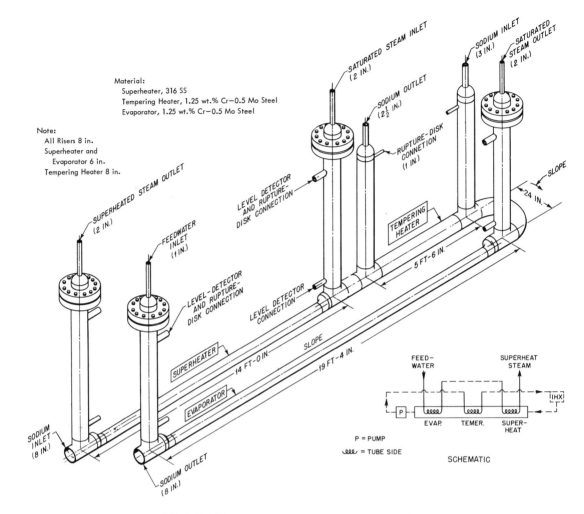

FIG. 4.97—LASL isometric layout of steam-generating unit [88].

is a single tube wall between sodium and steam or water. A helium-gas space serves as a thermal shield in each vertical lag between shell-side sodium and the tube sheet. Remotely operated valves were installed to vary the amount of sodium flowing through the tube side of the economizer. In this manner sodium temperature to the evaporator and steam temperature from the evaporator could be controlled.

The unit exhibited a fluctuating steam flow, pressure, and temperature at less than 50% of design load. A marked difference existed between steam temperature out of the top and bottom rows of tubes in the evaporator steam outlet header. As a result it was necessary to operate with slightly superheated steam coming out of the evaporator to prevent moisture from entering the superheater. Orifices were installed in the evaporator inlet tubes to increase pressure drop across the unit and to attempt to equalize the flow of water and steam through the tubes. Stability improved, the difference in temperature between the top and bottom rows of tubes became less, and evaporator outlet steam temperatures and total steam flow reached a steady

condition more rapidly following a steam flow transient. Stable operation at 40% load is possible.

The operating experience of the unit has been satisfactory, and design heat-transfer coefficients were conservative. The experiment was terminated as planned after 9500 hr of operation. Reference 104 contains results of a post-operation examination.

4.3.6.3.3 AEC STEAM-GENERATOR DESIGN STUDY. As part of the AEC sodium components development program, one 30-Mw(t) steam generator has been built for test at the AEC Sodium Components Test Installation (SCTI) at AI (Table 4.23). A second unit, 35 Mw(t), is now being designed and being built for test at the same installation.

The 30-Mw(t) steam generator (Fig. 4.98) is a once-through type and can be classed as shell-and-tube construction incorporating a fixed tube bundle, sine-wave tubes, and disk and doughnut baffles. The unbaffled portion of the steam generator is used for a sodium gas blanket and a rupture disk. The channel ends are hemispherical and each includes a manway to provide access to the tube sheet for inspection and maintenance.

Table 4.22—LASL Steam-generator Model Design and Operating Characteristics [102, 103]

Physical design and geometry
  Unit type — Once through, horizontal U, shell and tube
  Number of components per unit
    Economizer, evaporator, and superheater — Separate tube bundles in one continuous shell
    Steam drums — None

	Tempering exchanger	Evaporator	Superheater
Shell-side geometry:			
Fluid contained	Na	Na	Na
Outside diameter, in.	$8\frac{5}{8}$	$6\frac{5}{8}$	$6\frac{5}{8}$
Wall thickness, in.	0.322	0.280	0.280
Overall length, ft	6.67	20.5	16.17
Flow baffles	Doughnut	Doughnut	Doughnut
Design temperature, °F	1000	800	1000
Design pressure, psig	300	300	300
Material	1.25 wt.% Cr—0.5 wt.% Mo	1.25 wt.% Cr—0.5 wt.% Mo	316 SS
Tube-side geometry:			
Fluid contained	Na	Water and steam	Steam
Type of tube	Single tube	Single tube	Single tube
Material	1.25 wt.% Cr—0.5 wt.% Mo	1.25 wt.% Cr—0.5 wt.% Mo	316 SS
Number per component	19	19	14
Outside diameter, in.	$\frac{3}{4}$	$\frac{5}{8}$	$\frac{5}{8}$
Total wall thickness, in.	0.035	0.050	0.050
Installed length, ft	17.5	29.5	27.0
Pattern	Triangular	Triangular	Triangular
Pitch, in.	$1\frac{1}{2}$	$1\frac{1}{8}$	$1\frac{1}{4}$
Design temperature, °F	1000	800	1000
Design pressure, psig	300	1100	1000

	Tempering exchanger	Preheat sec.	Boiling sec.	Superheater
Thermal and fluid data per component (100% load)				
Heat transferred, Btu/hr	5.65×10^6	9.69×10^5	4.156×10^6	1.694×10^6
Effective surface area, sq ft	28.0	24.8	41.4	36.6
Effective tube length, ft	7.5		21.3	16.0
Overall heat transfer coefficient, Btu/hr/sq ft/°F	1085	431	940	238
Log mean temperature difference, °F	186	90.5	107	195
Liquid-metal data:				
Temperatures, °F				
In	938	584	733	1000
Out	733	550	584	938
Flow rate, lb/hr	90500	90500	90500	90500
Fluid velocity,* ft/sec	1.63S, 10.0T	2.86	2.89	2.76
Pressure drop,* psi	0.18S, 3.77T		0.76	0.54
Water and steam data:				
Temperatures, °F				
In	550 †	400	535	535
Out	750 †	535	535	925
Steam pressure, psig				900
Flow rate, lb/hr		6250	6250	6250
Pressure drop, psi			10.0	10.0
Fluid velocity, ft/sec				58.7

	Superheater	Tempering exchanger	Evaporator
General data			
Water- and steam-side safety valves			
No.	1		1
Size, in.	$1\frac{1}{2}$		$1\frac{1}{2}$
Sodium-side relief device			
No.	2	None	2
Size, in.	3		3
Type	Rupture disk		Rupture disk
Inert-gas vol., cu ft	1.9	1.6	1.4
Drainable:			
Shell side	Yes	Yes	Yes
Tube side	No	No	No
Weights (complete assembly), lb			
Dry	2000	600	1700
Operating	2270	800	2000
Type of tube joint	Internally welded, crevice free	Internally welded, crevice free	Rolled and welded

Table 4.22—LASL Steam-generator Model Design and Operating Characteristics (continued)

Water treatment	Pretreatment of make-up water in a two-bed anion-cation demineralizer; continuous polishing treatment in a mixed-bed demineralizer designed to pass about 10% of the total system circulation rate; continuous oxygen removal through a conventional deaerating feedwater heater; continuous oxygen scavenging by introduction of an aqueous hydrazine solution at the boiler feed-pump suction; pH control through addition of ammonia to the system
Typical feedwater analysis	
Total solids, ppm	1.0
Fe, ppm	0.1
Si, ppm	0.1
Zn, ppm	0.4
Cl, ppm	0.1
Oxygen, ‡	5.0
pH	8.8
Tube-protection	Protected from thermal shocks by an inert gas space
Accessibility of interior surfaces of tubes and shells for inspection	Flanged connections provided on steam and water sides of superheater and evaporator to permit inspection of tube sheets and interior of vertical legs of tubes; shell sides cannot be inspected; tube side of tempering heat exchanger cannot be inspected
Scope of stress analysis	Pressure stresses in tubes, shells, and tube sheets; thermal stresses across tube walls; and thermal stresses due to differential expansion between tubes and shell
Inspection techniques	Tubes were inspected by ultrasonic, radiographic, and dye-penetrant methods before installation; all welds subjected to radiographic, dye penetrant, and helium mass-spectrometer inspections, except evaporator tube-to-tube sheet welds which were not inspected radiographically; both the completed evaporator and superheater tube side were subjected to hydrostatic test and mass-spectrometer inspection; shell sides of all units and tube side of tempering heat exchanger were subjected to mass-spectrometer inspection
Unusual fabrication techniques	Internally welded, crevice-free, fully radiographable tube-to-tube sheet joints on superheater and tempering heat exchanger

* S, shell side; T, tube side.
‡ Oxygen analysis by Beckman continuous automatic analyzer.
† The tempering medium is sodium, not water (see Fig. 4.97).

Feedwater enters the steam generator through the lower channel. The feedwater is preheated to a saturated liquid, evaporated to a saturated vapor, and superheated in a once-through vertical pass through the tubes, countercurrent to the shell-side sodium flow. High-quality superheated vapor is supplied to the turbine inlet control valve from the upper channel. Sodium flows on the shell side downward through the unit. The sodium side of the steam generator is constructed of type 316 stainless steel. The tubes feature a bimetallic construction with a 0.032-in.-thick Inconel inner tube on the water side bonded to a nominal 1/2-in.-OD stainless steel tube with a 0.072-in. wall thickness. The bundle is slightly oversize and actually is compressed into the shell to prevent sodium from flowing directly to the outlet connection along the periphery of the shell without giving up its heat. A thermal shield prevents entering sodium from reaching the tubes adjacent to the inlet sodium. This shroud is made from two concentric cylinders with a gas space in between to give adequate insulation. There are relief-vent ports at both the top and bottom. The shroud is attached to the stationary head and is provided with tube-support baffles on the inside to space the straight portions of the tubes.

4.3.7 SODIUM-PURIFICATION EQUIPMENT

Oxygen is usually present in liquid sodium as sodium oxide. Other impurities are carbon, hydrogen, nitrogen, and calcium. Detailed information about these impurities and their solubility in sodium is given in Chap. 2.

Since calcium preferentially reacts with oxygen, it is gradually removed with precipitation or cold trapping. With the possible exception of carbon, the other impurities normally are removed to some degree by taking advantage of their temperature-dependent solubilities in sodium. However, other methods of purification of sodium exist. Some of the existing methods of sodium purification are filtering, cold trapping, hot trapping, and distillation. These are discussed below.

4.3.7.1 Filters

For gross purification of bulk sodium, filters can be used in the line between the tank car or other shipping containers and the sodium system. Filters have also been used in a crude cold trapping system where it is not necessary to have high-purity sodium. With filters sodium is cooled below the oxide saturation temperature and then passed through the filter, which removes precipitated solids within filter limits. The filters used are usually stainless-steel micro-metallic filters. The major difficulty with filters is their tendency to plug. They should be removable for periodic cleaning.

4.3.7.2 Cold Traps

Cold traps are crystallizers or precipitating chambers for removing materials that have a temperature-dependent solubility. The cold trap is designed to reduce the temperature of the in-

Table 4.23—AEC 30-Mw(t) Once-through Steam-generator Model Design
and Operating Characteristics [102]

Physical design and geometry	
Unit type	Once-through, vertical shell and tube
Number of components per unit	
Economizer, evaporator and superheater	One integral unit
Steam drums	0
Shell-side geometry:	
Fluid contained	Na
Outside diameter, in.	$32\frac{7}{8}$
Wall thickness, in.	$\frac{7}{16}$ and $1\frac{1}{8}$
Overall length, ft	45.25
Flow baffles	Disk and doughnut
Design temperature, °F	1200
Design pressure, psig	150
Material	316 SS
Tube-side geometry:	
Fluid contained	Water and steam
Type of tube	Bimetallic, metallurgically bonded
Material	Inner, Inconel; outer, 316 SS
Number per component	300
Outside diameter, in.	$\frac{1}{2}$
Individual wall thickness, in.	Inconel, 0.024; SS, 0.072
Total wall thickness, in.	0.096
Installed length, ft	40.33
Pattern	Radial
Pitch, in.	Radial, 1; circumferential, 1
Design temperature, °F	1200
Design pressure, psig	2500

	Preheat	Evaporator	Superheat
Thermal data per section (unless noted) (100% load)			
Heat transferred (total unit), Btu/hr		102×10^6	
Effective surface area, sq ft	140	400	720
Overall heat transfer coefficient			
Btu/hr/sq ft/°F	395	495	278
Log mean temperature difference, °F	150		
Liquid-metal data (total unit):			
Temperatures, °F			
In	1175		
Out	777		
Flow rate, lb/hr	855,000		
Fluid velocity, ft/sec	2.70 to 4.22		
Pressure drop, psi	12.3		
Water and steam data (total unit):			
Temperatures, °F			
In	600		
Out	1050		
Steam pressure, psig	2200		
Flow rate, lb/hr	116,000		
Pressure drop, psi	35.3		
Fluid velocity, ft/sec	4.95 water; 79.0 steam		

General data	
Steam-side safety valves	One safety valve set for 2750 psig, with a capacity of 35 lb/sec of superheated steam at 1050°F
Shell-side relief devices	One 12-in.-diameter rupture disk on steam generator rated for 165 psig at 1200°F; one relief valve recommended as follows: (a) inlet, $1\frac{1}{2}$-in. pipe size, capacity, 2 cu ft/sec (minimum) of cover gas at 140 psig and 1100°F, set pressure, 140 psig
Inert gas volume	28 cu ft provided in upper portion of steam generator

coming sodium below the saturation temperature of the oxide or other impurity, provide sufficient residence time for precipitation, provide sufficient surface area for grain growth of the material being removed, and provide sufficient capacity for the volume of impurities expected during the life of the cold trap.

There are two basic types of cold traps, natural circulation and forced circulation. Natural-circulation cold traps depend on density differences caused by temperature changes to circulate sodium through the trap. This type of trap can be quite elaborate or simply a short piece of pipe acting as a cold stub on part of the sodium system. Although primarily used for sodium monoxide, this type of trap does remove other materials having a temperature-dependent solubility in sodium. These traps have been known to remove up to 20% of their volume of oxide. A straight piece of pipe tends to remove oxide at a faster rate than

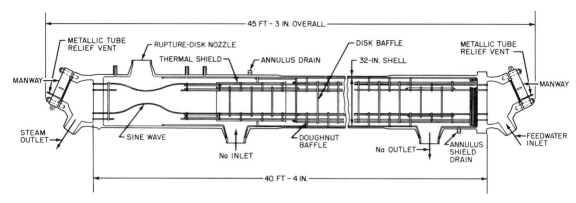

FIG. 4.98—AEC 30-Mw(t) steam-generator design [105].

a small pot connected by smaller piping to the system. Natural-circulation cold traps are simple and require no attention after they are installed. They will continue to remove oxide at a slow rate until they attain full capacity (about 20% of trap volume) of oxide. They reduce oxide to the saturation level at the trap temperature. One type of trap is shown in Fig. 4.99.

The cold trap is effective in removing sodium oxide from the sodium regardless of the type of packing used. However, forced-circulation cold traps packed with knitted wire gave the best results in tests. This type of trap is capable of containing up to 20 vol.% sodium oxide before significant flow restriction is evident. Packings of metal Raschig

rings or 1/4-in.-mesh screens are not as effective as the knitted mesh [106]. Operating experience and analysis of difficulties with cold-trap designs is included in Ref. 107.

In a small-scale experiment [108] sodium hydride was removed from a static sodium system by a natural-circulation cold trap. The NaH content dropped from 0.0200 to 0.011 wt.% NaH in 168 hr with the cold trap adjusted to 270°F at the coldest point; the pot remained at 800°F (3 wt.% NaH had been added to the pot). When the trap was heated to 800°F, much of the hydride was returned to the pot.

Most cold traps in high-temperature systems operate with an economizer. The economizer is a heat exchanger in which the sodium to the trap is cooled by reheating sodium from the trap prior to its return to the main sodium stream. The economizer, together with the cooling jacket on the cold trap, provides sufficient cooling to precipitate any oxide to a saturation temperature slightly above the

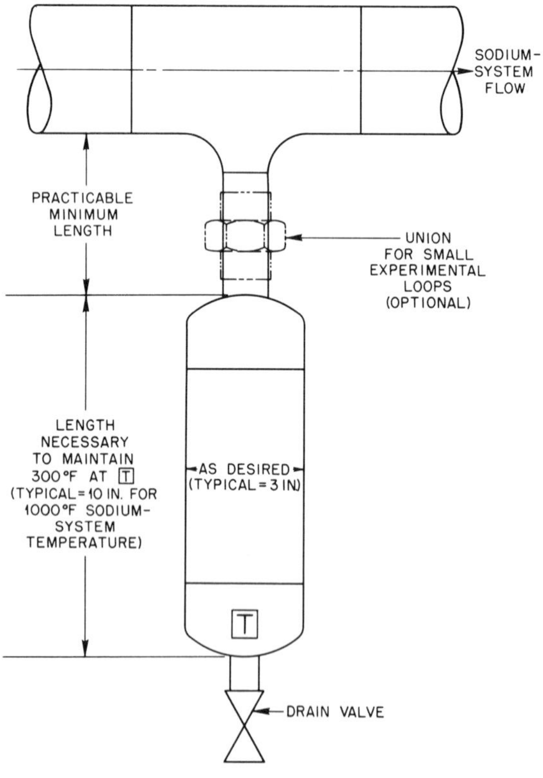

FIG. 4.99—Natural-circulation cold trap [25].

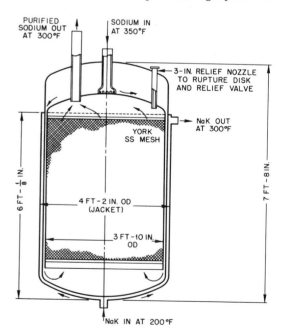

FIG. 4.100—Fermi cold trap [31].

freezing point of sodium. Cold traps are normally operated in conjunction with plugging meters. During the cleanup operation the cold trap should be operated at a temperature that will not risk plugging of the cold trap. This temperature should be somewhat above the plugging temperature of the sodium. The temperature of the cold trap should also be controlled to prevent the oxide in the trap from going into the solution and back into the system being serviced.

The oxide capacity of the cold trap consists in the total volume minus the actual volume of packing excluding the free volume in the packing. The net volume should be sufficient for all the oxide precipitated during the useful life of the trap. Experimental determinations [107] have shown that the apparent density of sodium oxide in the knitted mesh often used in cold traps is 0.02 lb/cu in. This density multiplied by the mesh volume gives an indication of the amount of sodium oxide properly designed cold traps will hold. A suitable residence time [25] in the packed section of the cold trap is 5 min. The volume of a large cold trap should be about 1 to 2% of system inventory. The trap should be able to trap down to or below 10 ppm O_2. The system oxygen concentration as a function of time is given by

$$(x - x_c)/(x_0 - x_c) = \exp[(-W/V)t] \qquad (4.33)$$

where x = concentration of O_2 in the system at any time t in minutes, ppm
x_0 = initial system concentration ($t = 0$), ppm
x_c = saturation concentration at cold-trap outlet temperature, ppm
W = trap flow, gal/min
V = system inventory, gal

Three inventory turnovers should bring the system oxygen concentration down to x_c if the oxygen concentration is below the saturation level. This applies only to dissolved oxygen. It may be necessary to cold trap for longer periods to dissolve the oxides precipitated in the system.

The Fermi cold trap shown in Fig. 4.100 is a 500-gal tank capable of handling 100 gal/min of sodium. The incoming sodium is cooled below the oxide-saturation temperature by the NaK-cooled jacket on the trap. NaK flows in at the bottom of the trap and out near the top of the jacket. The York mesh packing, together with the flow reversal at the bottom of the shroud, successfully removes precipitated oxides or other precipitated impurities.

Two cold traps were designed and tested for Hallam SGR [19]. The conditions were 40 gal of sodium per minute at 350°F and 10 gal/min at 607°F. The final pressure drop with 200 lb of Na_2O in the trap was less than 7 psi for each trap. Both cold traps were designed for a 20-psig drop with 200 lb of oxide.

Design A, Fig. 4.101, is a 20-in.-diameter trap 9 ft long with a cooling jacket over the lower 8 ft. The lower 6 ft is packed with 24 lb/cu ft stainless wire mesh. The internal economizer is a 6-in.-diameter tube 6 1/2 ft long with an 18-ft coil of 2 3/8-in. tubing at the upper end. Sodium enters the unpacked dome and flows past the coil and through the packing. Disk and doughnut baffles in the mesh lengthen the sodium path and prevent bypassing. The flow is reversed at the bottom of the packing and enters the 6-in. economizer pipe out through the 2 3/8-in. coil. Spiral-flow dividers in the coolant jacket prevent bypassing of coolant.

Design B, Fig. 4.101, is a cold trap with a 22-in.-diameter shell 8 ft long. An inner 20-in. shell open at one end serves as an economizer. The inner shell contains the coolant coil, an 18-in.-diameter helix of 2 3/8-in.-OD tubing 94 ft long. Sodium enters the inner shell and passes through stainless mesh and around the coolant coil. At the bottom

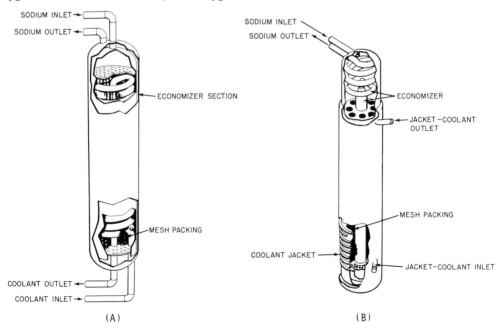

FIG. 4.101—Hallam (SGR) cold traps [19].

the direction is reversed, and sodium flows up the outside annulus formed between the inner and outer shell. Economizing takes place in this section.

Design A is better from the thermal standpoint; design B is better from the cost standpoint.

Modified cold-trap baskets were made for operation in the Dounreay main primary system bypass circuits. These baskets do not incorporate a regenerator and have wide coolant passages to minimize the possibility of blockages. Separate cooling is supplied to each unit by individual fans. Figure 4.102 (part A) shows the internal arrangement of one of these baskets. These cold traps are capable of cooling 1 gal/min each through a temperature range of 60°C (108°F). For a reactor inlet temperature of 200°C (392°F), the minimum saturation temperature achievable would therefore be 140°C (284°F), which gives no margin beyond the desired level. Slightly larger cooling fans were installed, which should extend this cooling range by about 20°C (36°F). The trapping temperature could, of course, be lowered by reduction of coolant flow rate, but this is undesirable both because it would reduce cold-trap capacity and also because it could only be attained by reducing the main current flow, which would require a power reduction. The cold-trap loop, being independent of main circuit flow, can, of course, be operated to suit any conditions. The baskets now installed in this loop are as shown in Fig. 4.102 (part B). The coolant annulus is 2.7 in. wide compared with 0.25 in. in the original design. A steel mesh is used as a filter, and the internal regenerator is omitted since the loop is fitted with a separate regenerative heat exchanger. There

is no internal bypass in the basket; flow is controlled entirely by the pump in the circuit.

The EBR-II cold trap consists of a 500-gal tank filled with type 304 stainless-steel wire mesh to provide supplementary surface area to enhance sodium crystallization and deposition. A regenerative heat exchanger is incorporated in the main sodium stream to reduce overall heat losses in the cold-trap system. A cold-trap operational temperature of 350°F is maintained by a secondary sodium cold-trap coolant loop. Two types of analytical devices are used to determine the sodium quality. A plugging indicator is mounted on the cold-trap inlet line to monitor the concentration of impurities in the primary tank sodium. Two vacuum-cup samplers are used to remove sodium samples for chemical or radiological analysis. Samples may be taken from either the cold-trap inlet or discharge line. Parts of the cold-trap circuit lie below the level of sodium in the primary tank. Since radioactive primary sodium is circulated in the cold-trap system, it is essential to eliminate the possibility of an accident or equipment failure that would result in the syphoning of primary tank sodium. Therefore a surge tank is included in the cold-trap inlet line at its highest point of elevation. An argon-gas blanket pressure is maintained such that, under static conditions, the sodium level is just below the surge-tank discharge opening. With the pump operating the level rises sufficiently to establish flow. The power supply to the pump is interlocked to a sodium vapor monitor at the cold-trap floor level to cut out when a sodium leak is detected and thereby "break" the inlet sodium

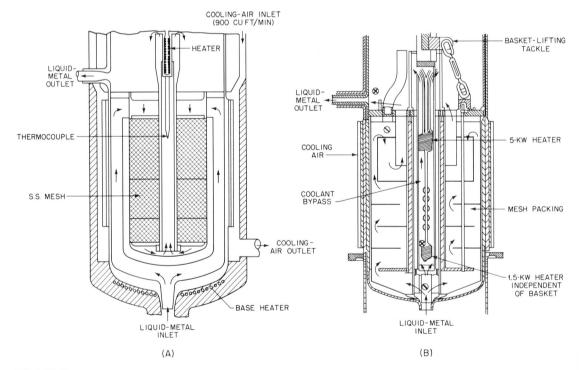

FIG. 4.102—Dounreay cold trap. (A) Cold trap for permanent cold-trap loop. (B) Modified basket of main circuit cold trap. [From J. L. Phillips, Nucl. Eng., 9(92):10–16 (January 1964)].

line at the surge tank. In addition, an argon–gas line is provided for positive gas addition to ensure breaking the sodium column in an emergency.

4.3.7.3 Hot Traps

The purpose of a hot trap is to getter system contaminants that the cold trap is not capable of removing. Although the following discussion is limited to zirconium and stainless steel as getters, it should be noted that titanium, tantalum, niobium, vanadium, uranium, and plutonium are potential hot-trap materials. It should also be noted that these materials, if used in the reactor core or other locations, act as getters and thus change the character of the material. One material, however, may be used to protect another. For example, a zirconium hot trap at LAMPRE protects tantalum in the core.

4.3.7.3.1 OXYGEN HOT TRAPS. Zirconium hot traps can be used after cold trapping to reduce the oxygen content of sodium below that obtainable from cold traps alone. This reduction is accomplished by selective absorption on a high-temperature zirconium surface with a large exposed area. The cold trap is isolated at the time the hot trap is in operation.

The process by which zirconium getters oxygen is strongly temperature dependent. The zirconium oxide form is very stable. The equilibrium partial pressure of oxygen over zirconium oxide at $1200°F$ has been established to be 10^{-30} atm compared to a pressure of 10^{-20} atm over sodium oxide [112].

In SRE each of the two hot traps is a stainless-steel tank containing 0.004-in.-thick zirconium sheet, as shown in Fig. 4.103. Sodium enters the

trap at the bottom and flows upward through the zirconium sheet element, which is corrugated to allow for sodium flow. Each trap contains 240 lb of zirconium, which gives a trapping surface area of about 350 sq ft based on 0.004-in. sheet. A flange at the top of the hot-trap tank permits removal and replacement of the zirconium element. As further insurance against leakage of sodium, a cooling jacket is provided just below the flange to freeze any sodium that would rise beyond the removable plug which supports the zirconium element.

Heaters on the outside of the hot-trap tank raise the temperature of the sodium in the hot trap to higher than the hottest core zirconium. Typical operating conditions are: sodium flow, 10,000 lb/hr; inlet temperature to regenerative heat exchangers, 950°F; and hot-trap average temperature, 1200°F.

In Dounreay each hot trap is designed so that 2.1 lb/sec of NaK coolant from the associated primary loop is bypassed through the hot trap, where it is heated to 1110°F and passed over zirconium foil. The trap contains a main vessel containing a heat exchanger, foil carriers, heat

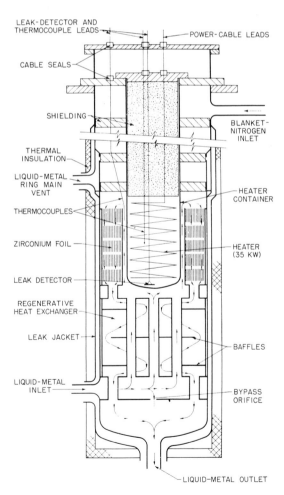

FIG. 4.104—Dounreay hot trap. (From R. R. Matthews et al., Proceedings of the Symposium on the Dounreay Fast Reactor, London, Dec. 7, 1960, Institution of Mechanical Engineers, London, 1961.)

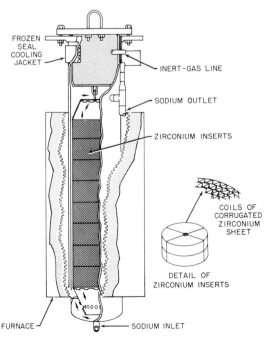

FIG. 4.103—SRE hot trap [111].

container tube, and heater, arranged as shown in Fig. 4.104. The main vessel has a secondary containment jacket.

4.3.7.3.2 CARBON HOT TRAPS 4.3.7.3.2.1 General Considerations. Many of the desired properties of austenitic stainless steel depend on its low carbon content. During operation of sodium-cooled reactors, the carbon in sodium and the carbon in the surface of the stainless steel attain an equilibrium based upon their temperatures and concentrations.

Excess carbon in sodium will carburize stainless steel at temperatures above 800°F and possibly at lower temperatures. There is a consequent change in the physical properties, such as embrittlement. Filtering, hydrocloning, cold trapping, and hot trapping have been used with some success to remove carbon from sodium, as evidenced by unofficial APDA reports. Evidence indicates that carbon can be in sodium in at least three forms, particulate carbon, dissolved carbon, and dissolved and/or particulate sodium carbonate, as evidenced by unofficial GE-APED reports. Some data on the solubility of carbon in sodium are given in Chap. 2. The mechanism of carburization is still in the process of being determined.

Reference 113 indicates that the surface carbon in stainless steel saturates at increasing values of effective carbon as shown in Fig. 4.105. The correct interpretation of the results of carburization studies is made difficult by uncertainties as to the types of carbon which cause carburization of stainless steel and the lack of precision in present analytical methods for small amounts of carbon in sodium. The carbon concentration in the sodium used in these experiments was measured by the Van Slyke oxidation method. This method does not usually account for all the carbon-containing compounds present in sodium. There is no assurance that the kind of carbon it measures actually carburizes stainless steel, and the method is neither very accurate nor reproducible by different laboratories. For these reasons it is recommended that considerable caution be exercised before this information is used for design purposes.

Table 4.24 lists several material specimens that were exposed to carbon in sodium [114] and indicates the carbon gain in the specimen after 200 hr in 1300°F sodium. Reference 114 indicates that the table gives some measure of carbon gettering ability of the different materials. Reference 114 also indicates that the curves for equilibrium content of carbon at various temperatures may actually cross for two different materials (Fig. 4.106). Figure 4.107 from Ref. 114 shows the diffusion coefficient vs. reciprocal of the temperature for the two materials.

The relative rates of carburization of type 304 stainless steel and type 410 stainless steel at 1300°F were calculated [113] for various carbon levels in sodium (Fig. 4.108).

4.3.7.3.2.2 Design Method and Description. The mean carbon gain of a sheet of stainless steel carburized in liquid sodium can be calculated [113] by assuming the sheet as an infinite slab. Reference 113 indicates that $(C_m - C_0)/(C_s - C_0)$ is proportional to $(Dt)^{1/2}/s$ for certain carbon gains,

where C_m = mean carbon content of the steel after exposure, %
C_0 = initial carbon content of the steel, %
C_s = surface carbon content of the steel in equilibrium with liquid sodium, %
D = diffusion coefficient, cm^2/sec
t = exposure time, sec
s = sheet thickness, cm

The resulting equation, once the proportionality constant is determined, can be put into useful form, which can be represented by nomography, as shown in Figs. 4.109 and 4.110 adapted from Ref. 113. The nomographs merely serve as illustrations.

The carbon hot traps at both SRE and Fermi are very similar in appearance to an oxide hot trap. The primary difference is in the packing material, i.e., stainless steel is used for the carbon hot trap and zirconium is used for the oxide hot trap. A cutaway design of a carbon hot trap is shown in Fig. 4.111. In operation the sodium enters the hot-trap economizer at about 600°F and the hot trap at about 1200°F. In the hot trap it is heated to 1250 to 1300°F. Stainless-steel carburization removes carbon from the sodium. The sodium reenters the system through the economizer.

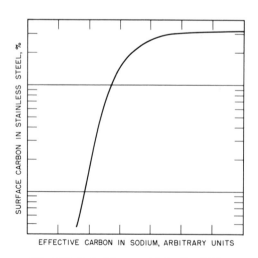

FIG. 4.105—Carburizing potential of sodium [113].

Table 4.24—Carbon Gain of Specimens Exposed to Carbon-saturated Sodium at 1300°F for 200 Hr

Material*	Initial carbon, %	Average carbon after exposure, %
9 Cr–1 Mo	0.10	1.84–1.84
5 Cr–0.5 Mo–Ti	0.08	1.60–1.66
Type 430 SS	0.08	1.58–1.62
7 Cr–0.5 Mo	0.10	1.50–1.64
Type 410 SS	0.10	1.50–1.55
5 Cr–0.5 Mo	0.10	1.39–1.45
2.25 Cr–1 Mo	0.12	1.27–1.35
5 Cr–0.5 Mo–Si	0.10	1.01–1.14
1.25 Cr–0.5 Mo	0.12	0.90–0.91
Type 304 SS	0.06	0.72–0.78
0.5 Cr–0.5 Mo	0.12	0.55–0.64
Zr	Nil	0.05–0.06
Cr	Nil	0.04–0.05

*Figures in front of metal indicate weight percent of alloy constituents.

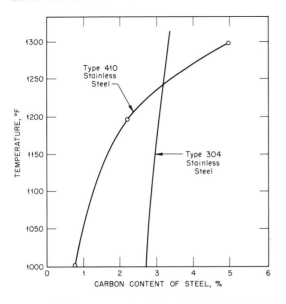

Fig. 4.106—Carbon content of type 304 and type 410 stainless steels in equilibrium with carbon-saturated sodium [114].

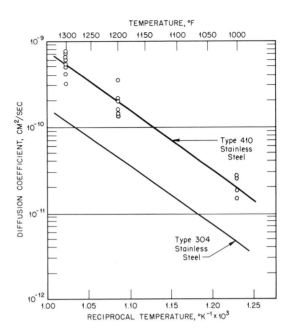

FIG. 4.107—Diffusion coefficients for carbon in type 304 and type 410 stainless steels [114].

4.3.7.4 Distillation

Successful purification of sodium by vacuum distillation has been carried out on a small scale [115]. The Russian BR-5 reactor reportedly uses a plant-scale distillation system for purification.

4.3.8 OXIDE MEASURING AND INDICATING DEVICES

4.3.8.1 Plugging Indicators

In the chemical analysis of sodium for oxygen, sodium samples must be withdrawn from the sodium system. It is difficult to avoid contamination of these samples. Chemical analysis necessitates the use of a full complement of chemical analytical equipment. A plugging indicator eliminates these disadvantages since it is an inline device capable of determining saturation temperature. It contains no moving parts. The plugging indicator consists of a flowmeter, a heat exchanger, a flow restriction or orifice, and thermocouples, as shown in a typical design in Fig. 4.112. Flow under constant head is maintained by a small pump or by system pressure drop at constant flow.

A determination is made by slowly lowering the temperature of the flowing sodium with a cooler located just ahead of the flow restriction. When the saturation temperature is reached, sodium oxide precipitates, plugs the flow restriction, and causes a sharp break in the plugging indicator flow rate. By means of a solubility curve (Chap. 2), this temperature can be directly related to the oxygen content. After a determination cooling is stopped, and the bypass temperature is returned to normal. The oxide plug quickly redissolves, and the plugging indicator is ready for another determination. This device has been thoroughly tested for oxygen contents ranging from 10 to 200 ppm. For single de-

terminations in this range, the standard deviation was found to be 10 ppm. Its agreement with chemical methods was found to be within the precision of both devices, i.e., the standard deviation for the difference between determinations by both methods [25] was 10 ppm. In the 10 to 80 ppm range, the holes in the flow restriction should be about 0.030 in.; for determinations above 80 ppm, they should be about 0.050 in.

The plugging indicator may be subject to interference from other impurities that precipitate in the measured temperature range. The plugging indicator could conceivably be adapted for determination of other temperature-soluble impurities in sodium or in other liquids.

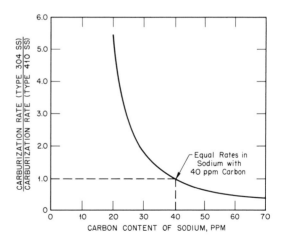

FIG. 4.108—Relative carbon gettering rates of type 304 and type 410 stainless steels at 1300°F [114].

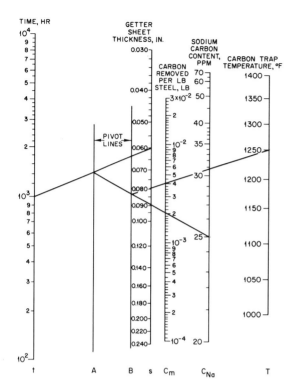

FIG. 4.109—Nomograph for carbon–trap design with type 304 stainless steel [114].

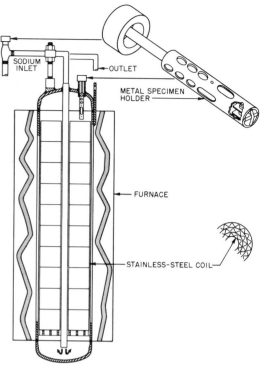

FIG. 4.111—Carbon hot trap [113].

4.3.8.2 Resistivity Meter

The Rhometer (Fig. 4.113) is a current transformer potentiometric device for the measurement of resistivity of flowing liquid metal [116]. The detector component consists of a double–loop transformer coil with a primary excitation winding of N turns producing constant flux and two secondary windings producing readout. A single–turn toroid pipe designed to carry the flowing liquid metal forms one of the secondary coils, and a probe coil of n turns forms the other. The single–turned toroid coil imposes a load that varies with the conductivity of the flowing liquid metal, and the probe coil senses this loading effect on the primary circuit. The high sensitivity of this meter is achieved by bucking out the signal representing absolute resistivity at meter set point and measuring only the change in primary excitation due to a change in contamination of the liquid–metal stream.

In the theory of conductivity on which the design of the Rhometer is based,

$$\rho \sim (2m/e^2)(v/\rho_e L)$$

where ρ, the absolute resistivity, is a function of the electron mass, m, the electron charge, e, the effective velocity of the electron v, and electron distribution density, ρ_e. These factors are assumed to hold fairly constant within the operating range of the meter. The symbol L represents the mean free path of the electron through the atomic lattice structure of the conductor metal, such that the ratio L/v expresses the time lapse between collisions of an

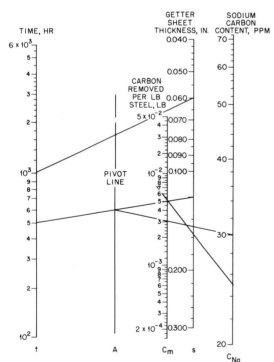

FIG. 4.110—Nomograph for carbon–trap design with type 410 stainless steel (1300°F only) [114].

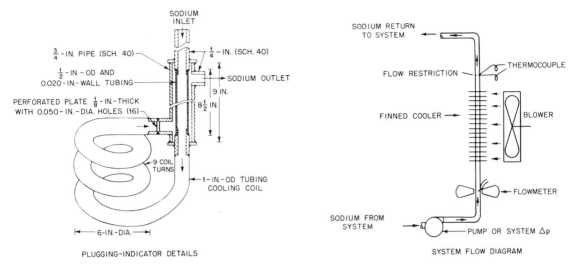

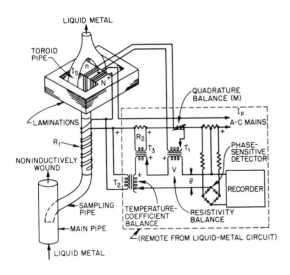

PLUGGING-INDICATOR DETAILS

SYSTEM FLOW DIAGRAM

FIG. 4.112—Oxide plugging indicator [25, 117].

electron with the lattice. In a steady-state liquid-metal system, the value of L is finite because of certain characteristic imperfections in the atom lattice structure and because of additional irregularity of lattice structure brought on by thermal oscillation of the lattice, which is a function of absolute temperature. The structural component of L is independent of temperature and is not perceptibly affected by phase change, but it may

be influenced by the presence of a very low concentration of soluble impurities. The values of the ratio,

Change in absolute resistivity (ppm)
Change in contamination (ppm)

range from 100 to 1000. The sensitivity of the resistivity meter in detecting contamination is brought about by this anomaly: a change in concentration of impurities on the order of only $1/10^6$ may produce a change in absolute resistivity on the order of $1/10^4$. For example, 1 ppm of oxygen in sodium increases the resistivity by approximately 0.5×10^{-9} ohm-in. Any other soluble impurity can be detected.

Typical results of resistivity vs. oxide plugging-indicator temperature are shown in Fig. 4.114. These results, together with an oxide solubility curve, relate resistivity to oxide contamination in sodium.

The advantages of this toroidal device over conventional potentiometric metering of liquid sodium are threefold: (1) no probes are required in the sodium stream, (2) no adjustment is required for bypass current through the main channel of sodium flow around the meter, and (3) the multiple-turn probe coil multiplies signal voltage for greater response.

With reference to Fig. 4.113 the resistance R_1 is the sodium-temperature compensator, a noninductive coil in close thermal contact with the toroid inlet. Resistance R_2 is a resistor with zero thermal coefficient, sensing primary excitation current and reflecting variations in the input voltage. Transformer T_1, T_2, and T_3 are multiple-tap transformers functioning as individual amplitude controls and designed to produce null balance for the three principal system variables: quadrature, T_1; excitation voltage, T_2; and temperature-compensation signal, T_3.

The toroid proper is some three inches in mean diameter, constructed of 1/2-in. stainless-steel tubing. The core is made of 0.004-in. lamina-

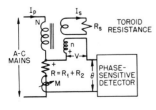

FIG. 4.113—Rhometer [118].

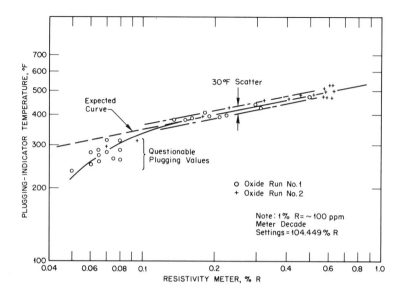

FIG. 4.114—Plugging-indicator temperature vs. percent resistivity [118].

tions of supermumetal, and both core and windings are thermally insulated from the toroid by asbestos tape.

Design for null balance is based on the following theory. If the magnetization current is negligible, the transformer ratio will hold true for primary and secondary windings,

$$I_p N_p = I_s N_s \qquad (4.34)$$

In this case N_s is unity and N_p is N; then

$$I_p = I_s/N \qquad (4.35)$$

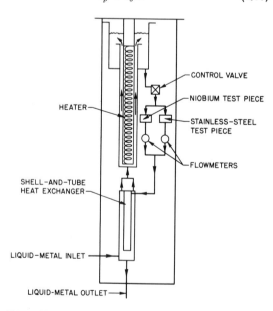

FIG. 4.115—Schematic of Dounreay corrosion meter. (From R. R. Matthews et al., Proceedings of the Symposium on the Dounreay Fast Reactor, London, Dec. 7, 1960, Institution of Mechanical Engineers, London, 1961.)

The voltage V_s required to drive the current I_s in the toroid is measured by the voltage V set up in the probe coil. Resistance R_s in the toroid (metal tubing and flowing liquid metal in parallel) may be expressed as

$$R_s = V_s/I_s = V/(nNI_p) \qquad (4.36)$$

where $V = nV_s$.

To balance out the primary current I_p, a net resistance $R = R_1 + R_2$ is placed in series with the primary coil N such that

$$V = RI_p \quad \text{and} \quad R_s = R/(nN) \qquad (4.37)$$

In this relation balance can be affected by adjustment of R or n. Since n is fixed, the adjustment is to R and is simulated by selection of the appropriate transformer taps. As R_s increases, the output of the probe coil must also increase. This increased output can be compensated back to zero by resetting the bias voltage in the readout circuit (not shown) to produce zero output from a phase rectifier. Bias checks are required periodically.

4.3.8.3 Corrosion Meter

A corrosion meter can be installed in a side stream of the reactor coolant system to indicate oxygen content by the corrosion effect on a perforated plate in series with a flowmeter. The flowmeter is extremely sensitive to small changes in flow. As the oxide-bearing sodium passes through the plate, it corrodes the material of the plate in the vicinity of the holes, enlarging them somewhat. This corrosion is indicated by an increase in flow. These devices are difficult to calibrate and lack the precision and ease of operation of the plugging indicator.

An experimental oxide corrosion meter was installed in Dounreay for checking the performance of the hot traps in removing oxide from the NaK

(Fig. 4.115). The unit included a regenerative heat exchanger, an electric heater, and a control-valve control block, all mounted in one of the vessels originally provided for a hot trap. The complete unit can be removed by means of a shielded cask for renewal of the cylinders or other maintenance. The corrosion meter has not been proven in use.

4.3.8.4 Sampling Devices

Sampling liquid sodium for laboratory analysis of the oxygen content without contaminating the sample requires careful techniques. The contamination can be an appreciable fraction of the total oxygen in the sample.

Handling and analysis of sodium from a radioactive reactor system requires that the complete procedure be conducted behind considerable shielding. For detailed techniques the interested reader is referred to Refs. 120 through 122.

It should be noted that online sampling and online reduction preparatory to analysis are being accomplished at EBR-II and were accomplished by KAPL-SIR-Mark A. At EBR-II the reduction is by vacuum distillation. At Mark A it was by the Pepkowitz mercury-amalgam method.

At Dounreay approximately 100 cm^3 of NaK can be taken in a nickel beaker from one of the vessels originally provided for a hot trap. The NaK is distilled off and the oxide is left in the beaker. The residue in the beaker is then treated chemically to determine the quantity of oxide present in the sample. The entire process is done remotely inside shielded equipment. Dip samples are obtained at

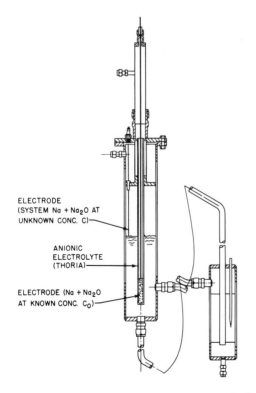

ELECTRODE
(SYSTEM Na + Na$_2$O AT
UNKNOWN CONC. C)

ANIONIC
ELECTROLYTE
(THORIA)

ELECTRODE (Na + Na$_2$O
AT KNOWN CONC. C$_0$)

FIG. 4.116—Electrochemical cell for oxygen determination [119].

SRE through the reactor shield plug. Fermi uses an online sampling device, i.e., a stainless-steel coil which is frozen and then disconnected and removed.

4.3.8.5 Electrochemical Cells

Electrochemical cells have been under development for some time. One such cell is being developed by Argonne National Laboratory for installation in the Fast Reactor Equipment Test (FARET). This cell, with one electrode of sodium saturated with sodium oxide at a known concentration and the other with sodium oxide at the unknown concentration of the sodium system, has a solid oxide electrolyte and is used to measure the oxygen content of sodium continuously. The voltage of the cell changes with the oxygen content of the sodium.

A schematic diagram of the ANL electrochemical cell is shown in Fig. 4.116. This cell has operated at temperatures up to 650°F utilizing an electrolyte of zirconia. Fused thoria is expected to overcome this temperature limitation. A unique advantage of this cell is that the accuracy of its measurements should increase with decreased oxygen concentrations in the sodium [119].

4.3.9 STORAGE TANKS

Sodium-cooled heat-transport systems normally include a dump tank or storage tank. The principal functions are (1) to provide convenience in handling coolants at the initial filling of a system, (2) to be available for emergency use when it is necessary to drain the system for major repairs or adjustments, (3) to aid in the removal of impurities that have accumulated in the coolant, and (4) to be available for storage of an emergency supply of coolant. These tanks should be sized to handle the inventory of the coolant system. Several tanks may be required. The limitations on tank size may be imposed by such considerations as space or configuration at the site or by shipping regulations.

The approach to the design of storage tanks for liquid metals is generally conventional except in the selection of materials, fabrication, and inspection. Special requirements in these categories applicable to all components are discussed in Sec. 4.3.1. Only considerations specific to storage tanks are reviewed here. Most storage tanks fall into the category of unfired pressure vessel since they have external heating and/or a cover gas. The foregoing considerations require that these tanks be designed in accordance with the ASME Code for Unfired Pressure Vessels, Sec. VIII, plus applicable nuclear codes. Chapter 2 contains information on the compatibility of the various coolants with container materials, including temperature limitations of specific materials and their corrosion rates. Such contaminants as oxygen, nitrogen, or carbon dissolved in the liquid or present as a compound in suspension contribute in a large degree to corrosion in storage tanks. Thus a corrosion allowance should be included when the plate-thickness requirements are determined since the complete exclusion of these contaminants is not always possible. A good grade of low alloy steel such as SA-387 firebox Grade A (0.5 wt. % chromium-0.5 wt. %

molybdenum) could be used at temperatures of 600 to 700°F.

Specific attention should be paid to supports, openings, heating and insulating, and relief devices. Tank supports are located so as to prevent sagging or vibration as well as to properly distribute the loads due to the weight of the vessel completely filled with coolant. Supports are usually anchored to a floor or foundation, and allowance must be made for free expansion of the tank. Longitudinal expansion is generally limited to one direction by making one support a complete anchor. Construction material is generally steel. The design of nozzles and requirements for attachment are adequately covered by the ASME Code. In general, all openings in liquid-metal coolant tanks should be located on top of the tank. Bottom connections are not recommended because of safety considerations. A manhole opening should be included for inspection access during fabrication as well as for future inspection.

Insulation and heating are required because most liquid-metal coolants require heat to maintain them in a liquid state. In addition, the coolant temperature in a heat-transport system should be balanced prior to making a transfer, to reduce thermal shock to the system. Resistance type heaters attached to the outside of the tank have been successful in maintaining the desired temperatures. Induction or other heating can also be used.

A typical design of a pressure-relief system in a sodium storage tank is shown in Fig. 4.117. The relief system consists of a rupture disk designed to fail at the maximum allowable working pressure of the vessel backed up by a pressure-relief valve. An oil seal can be added to the relief system to prevent the possibility of back flow of air into the sodium tank. A small-diameter line with an excess-flow valve allows venting of the space between the rupture disk and pressure-relief valve. Under sudden pressure surges, this excess-flow valve closes and thus does not circumvent the function of the relief valve.

4.3.10 GAS-SYSTEM COMPONENTS

4.3.10.1 Purification Equipment [123, 124]

As discussed in Sec. 4.2.4.2, a sodium heat-transport system may require purification of the gas entering the cover-gas system and removal of

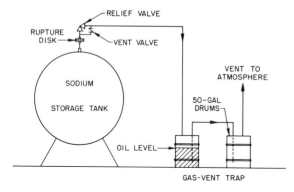

FIG. 4.117—Sodium storage-tank relief system.

fission-product gases from the cover gas over the primary coolant system.

The most common gaseous impurity in the gas supply is oxygen. It is perhaps most easily removed by bubbling the entering gas through NaK and reacting the oxygen with the NaK. This step also tends to remove any water vapor that may be present, but it does not remove carbon-bearing gases or nitrogen. Usually these gases are in sufficiently low concentrations in the entering inert gas to be of no consequence. Other metallic getters are also effective for removing gaseous contaminants. For instance, calcium fixes nitrogen in the form of calcium nitride, and such common materials as iron fillings and copper have been used at 1000 to 1200°F to remove oxygen [125]. Brass, copper, cerium, and uranium also getter oxygen [127]. Another method of purifying the entering inert gas is to pass it through an absorbent, such as charcoal, molecular sieves, or silica gel [126-130].

It is general practice to locate the purification or monitoring system in the primary gas supply line to forestall accidents or sabotage. The Dounreay facility and EBR-II employ a NaK bubbler to remove contaminants such as oxygen and water vapor. The Fermi argon-purification train consists of a NaK bubbler at ambient temperature (with increased residence time) and a continuous oxygen detector sensitive to 1 ppm. The interior of the purification tank is fitted with a Raschig-ring section to extend surface contact and a woven wire-mesh section to prevent liquid carry over. The downstream entrainment trap is also fitted with a woven wire-mesh section and with a high-level alarm to signal carry-over.

Heavier impurities are not completely removed by the activated-charcoal adsorbers used in the final polishing of commercial helium. These fractions can be more completely adsorbed by Linde Co. molecular-sieve material and can be further stripped in titanium or uranium hot traps. Hydrogen in helium can be converted with a copper oxide hot trap, and the resulting water vapor can be removed in a molecular-sieve column.

There are several possible methods of removing fission-product gases, such as krypton and xenon, from the effluent cover gas. The most common is adsorption on molecular-sieve material, silica gel, or activated carbon [131-139]. Sufficient residence time must be allowed in the adsorber bed to permit radioactive decay. Distillation techniques have been used extensively to separate air into its gaseous components. However, initial equipment costs are high. Separation of the three major components of the gas stream (argon or helium, xenon, and krypton) is feasible but would require considerable development work.

Absorbents for krypton and xenon are limited since these gases have no reactions with the normal chemical reagents. However, some data are available for absorption of these gases in nitromethane [140]. The Ostwald coefficient (the volume of the gas absorbed by one volume of solvent) determined in nitromethane at 770°F is 0.145 for argon, 0.380 for krypton, and 1.14 for xenon. From this it can be determined that the amount of liquid required to effect the desired absorption would be considerable; also there cannot be complete separation of the fission gases from the inert gas.

If the gas leaving the sodium system is to be recompressed, it is desirable to remove sodium vapor from this gas. The most common method is to cool the gas below the freezing point of sodium, thus freezing out the sodium vapor or causing it to condense on a cold surface. One of the most efficient ways of removing the sodium vapor is by a vapor trap in which the sodium vapor is bubbled through NaK at a temperature of less than 150°F. This form of vapor trap has been shown experimentally to remove better than 98% of the incident sodium vapor.

4.3.10.2 Monitoring Equipment

Methods of analysis for impurities should be appropriate to the cover gas. Both helium and argon pose special problems. Water vapor in either helium or argon can be measured directly in the 1 to 20 ppm range provided the sample line is heated to prevent condensation. The phosphorus pentoxide-phosphoric acid equilibrium cell is one of the most sensitive detectors; it registers a change of 1 megohm for each additional ppm of water vapor in a gas sample stream. Traces of hydrogen in an inert atmosphere can be converted by a copper oxide hot trap and metered as water vapor.

In the analysis of impurities in helium by chromotography, Linde molecular-sieve material is preferred in the adsorber solumn since activated charcoal does not adsorb or desorb nitrogen and oxygen quantitatively. Ionization meters are not definitive in the presence of fixed gases. Other special problems are the separation of argon and oxygen in the elutriation process (sometimes accomplished by lowering column temperature) and the control of sequence in the separation of nitrogen and krypton, which is a function of the procedures employed in adsorbent regeneration.

In the analysis of argon cover gas, oxygen can be metered directly in the 1 to 20 ppm range. Here again the gaseous ionization detectors are not so satisfactory as paramagnetic cells or liquid-electrolyte ionization cells. Hydrogen content can be determined directly as the first fraction through in a chromotography train. If helium is also present, twin columns are generally employed, one with helium elutriation and the other with argon elutriation. This is done to achieve selectivity without column chilling. Sodium vapors are reported detectable in 1×10^{-7} mole concentration by bubbling a gas stream through thymolsulfonphtalein (thymol blue). Low concentrations of petroleum vapors may be detected by an infrared comparison cell with a chopper circuit arrangement.

Fission-product monitoring is covered in Chap. 9.

The evolution of hydrogen from secondary sodium furnishes an early warning of a water leak. Continuous hydrogen monitors have been devised to give a prompt indication of hydrogen buildup [141,142]. Automated chromatography trains are available as well as a conductivity meter [143] and a submerged detector element which operates on the diffusion of hydrogen through a nickel membrane with pickup by a Pirani gauge [141].

4.3.10.3 Compressors

There are basically two types of compressors that can be used for compressing the inert gas in a cover-gas system for liquid metals, the rotary compressor and the direct-displacement compressor. The compressor should (1) be completely gastight since the gas is radioactive and cannot be allowed to leak out of the system, (2) be so designed that failures do not break the containment of the compressor, (3) not admit extraneous material into the gas system, and (4) provide the full pressure required over the entire operating temperature range of the gas.

There are available high-speed rotary gas-lubricated compressors that can handle the flows and pressures required in most liquid-metal gas systems. The primary advantage of this type of compressor is the complete containment of the gas. It needs no external stuffing box since the motor and compressor section is enclosed in an integral containment and the gas acts as a lubricant for the bearings. With this type of compressor intermittent operation should not be considered.

Oil-driven diaphragm type compressors contain the gas completely separate from the compressing medium, permit very little contamination, and provide high integrity. Should the diaphragm rupture, oil can enter the gas stream. However, a catch tank and oil detectors minimize this problem.

A piston compressor is more suitable where the gas is to be discharged to the waste-gas system. These compressors commonly use multiple seals with a pressurized clean-gas chamber between the seals. Where it can be used, the piston compressor is less costly than the other types.

For Fermi, oil-driven diaphragm compressors were selected in preference to canned rotary compressors for the recirculating cover gas because of the limited service life of rotary compressor bearings in intermittent service. Oil monitors are mounted in each compressor discharge as an additional safeguard against the introduction of oil (hydrogen) into the reactor core. The compressors unload at 38 psig to prevent backup of radioactive gas into the 40-psig supply system. The waste-gas system compressor is a single-effect piston unit.

Glossary

A	area, sq ft; contamination, $\mu c/cm^3$
B	magnetic flux density, gauss
C	corrosion allowance, in.; carbon content, %
C_t	concentration of contaminant gas at time t
D	diffusion constant; diameter, ft
D_e	equivalent diameter, ft
E	electromotive force or voltage, volts; modulus of elasticity
F	force, dynes or lb
G	mass velocity, lb/hr/sq ft
H	enthalpy, Btu/lb or cal/g
ΔH	change in enthalpy, Btu/lb
I	current, amp
K	constant
L	length, ft; mean free path
M	molecular weight, moment, ft-lb

N	air changes per hour; number of transformer turns
N_1	number of primary conductors per phase
Nu	Nusselt number
P	pressure, psi or atm
P_1	tube pitch, in.
Pe	Peclet number
Pr	Prandtl number
Q	heat transferred, Btu/hr
R	electrical resistance, ohms
R_w	thermal resistance of tube wall, (hr)(sq ft) (°F)/Btu
Re	Reynolds number
S	stress, psi; height, in.
S_L	slip
T	temperature, °F or °K; torque
T_x	temperature drop, °F
ΔT	temperature difference, °F
U	overall heat transfer coefficient, Btu/hr/ sq ft/°F
V	volume, cu ft, cm³, or cm³/g/mole; potential difference, volts
V_2	volume leak rate, cm³/hr
W	flow, lb/hr, gal/min
W_f	width, in.
X	makeup or leak rate, cu ft/min; reactance, ohms
c_p	specific heat, Btu/lb/°F
f	friction factor; constant; frequency, cycles/ sec
g	32.2 ft/sec²
h	heat-transfer coefficient, Btu/hr/sq ft/°F
Δh	pressure-head drop, psi or ft
i	stress intensification factor
k	thermal conductivity, Btu/hr/ft/°F or cal/ sec/cm/°C
k_f	stress-reduction factor
h_{fg}	latent heat of saturated liquid, Btu/lb
l	length, in.
m	electron mass
n	frequency, cycles/sec; number of transformer turns
n_p	number of poles
p	pressure, dynes/cm²
Δp	pressure drop, psi
q	heat flux, Btu/hr/sq ft
r	width, cm
r_1, r_2	radius, in.
s	height or thickness, cm or in.
t	time, min or sec
v	velocity, cm/sec or ft/sec
w	flow, cm³/sec
x	concentration, ppm
λ	radioactivity decay constant
μ	viscosity, lb/ft/hr, lb/ft/sec
ρ	density, lb/cu ft
ρ_e	electron distribution density
σ	surface tension of saturated liquid, lb/ft

References

1. H. M. Ogle, G. I. Samstad, and C. A. Von Damm, Nuclear Thermionic Fuel Element Experiments, J. Advanced Energy Conversion, 2:353 (1962).
2. R. W. Fritts, The Development of Thermoelectric Power Generators, Proc. IEEE, Special Issue on New Energy Sources, 51(5):713 (1963).
3. D. J. Rosa, Nonequilibrium Ionization in MHD Generators, Proc. IEEE, Special Issue on New Energy Sources, 51(5):774 (1963).
4. B. J. Toppel and R. Avery, Coupled Steam Superheater Concept, Trans. Am. Nucl. Soc., 2(2):149 (1959).
5. R. Avery et al., Coupled Fast-Thermal Power Breeder, J. Nucl. Sci. and Eng., 3:129 (1958).
6. R. R. Rohde, R. Avery, W. V. Dewey, and B. J. Toppel, Conceptual Design of a Coupled Fast-Thermal Steam Superheating Reactor, Trans. Am. Nucl. Soc., 4(1):34 (1961).
7. G. A. Sofer and R. D. Hankel, Conceptual Design of a Steam-cooled Fast Breeder Reactor, Trans. Am. Nucl. Soc., 4(1):35-36 (1961).
8. J. O. Bradfute et al., An Evaluation of Mercury-cooled Breeder Reactors, USAEC Report ATL-A-102, Advanced Technology Laboratories, October 1959.
9. A. Forcella, CNEN Program for a Mercury Binary Cycle Nuclear Power Plant, paper presented at the 1962 Nuclear Congress, unpublished, New York, Engineers Joint Council, New York, June 1962.
10. C. C. Randall, S. S. Bloxam, W. E. Gunson, E. W. Ruppen, D. B. Scott, and E. E. Smith, Study of Mercury Binary Cycles for Nuclear Power Plants, Report WCAP-1832, Westinghouse Electric Atomic Power, July 31, 1961.
11. A. Amorosi, Advanced Fast Reactors, paper presented at the 1962 Nuclear Congress, unpublished, Atomic Power Development Associates, Inc., June 1962.
12. A Plutonium-Fueled Fast Breeder Atomic Power Plant, Report APDA-129, Atomic Power Development Associates, Inc., April 1959.
13. 150-Mw Plutonium-Fueled Fast Breeder Atomic Power Plant, Report APDA-136, Atomic Power Development Associates, Inc., March 1960.
14. EBR-II selected illustrations distributed by Argonne National Laboratory at the Advisory Committee of Reactor Safety Meeting, Arco, Idaho, March 17-18, 1961.
15. Enrico Fermi Fast Breeder Reactor Plant, USAEC Report APDA-115, Atomic Power Development Associates, Inc., Nov. 1, 1956.
16. Experimental Power and Test Reactors, USAEC Report TID-4562, p. 16, November 1956.
17. H. Cartwright, J. Tatlock, and R. R. Matthews, Dounreay Fast Reactor Basic Problems in Design, in Proceedings of the Second United Nations International Conference on the Peaceful Uses of Atomic Energy, Geneva, 1958, Vol. 9, p. 316, United Nations, New York, 1958.
18. C. P. Zaleski and L. Vautrey, Le Reacteur Rapide Surregenerateur, Vols. 1 and 2, Commissariat à l'Energie Atomique, France, Oct. 23, 1961.
19. Final Summary Safeguards Report for the Hallam Nuclear Power Facility, USAEC Report NAA-SR-5700, Atomics International, Apr. 15, 1961.
20. D. Burgreen, Flow Coastdown in a Loop After Pumping Power Cutoff, Trans. Am. Nucl. Soc., 2(2):65-68 (November 1959).
21. G. M. Boyd, Jr. et al., Transient Flow Performance in a Multi-loop Nuclear Reactor System, Trans. Am. Nucl. Soc., 2(2):68, 69 (November 1959).
22. R. C. Martinelli and L. M. K. Boelter, The Analytical Prediction of Superposed Free and Forced Viscous Convection in Vertical Pipe, University of California Press, Berkeley, Calif., 1942.
23. D. C. Hamilton, F. E. Lynch, and L. D. Palmer, The Nature of the Flow of Ordinary Fluids in a Thermal Convection Harp, USAEC Report ORNL-1624, Oak Ridge National Laboratory, 1954.
24. S. K. Hellman, G. Habetler, and H. Babrov, Use of Numerical Analysis in Transient Solution of Two-Dimensional Heat Transfer Problem with Natural and Forced Convection, Mech. Eng., 76:683 (1954).
25. Liquid-Metals Handbook, Sodium NaK Supplement, Atomic Energy Commission and Department of the Navy, July 1955.
26. Matheson Gas Data Book, The Matheson Company, Inc., East Rutherford, N.J., 1961.
27. High Purity Gases, (Brochure), Linde Co., Div. Union Carbide Corp., 270 Park Ave., New York.
28. J. Heiningen, Influence of Argon, Nitrogen, Helium, and Carbon Dioxide on the Explosion Limits of Hydrogen, Carbon Monoxide Methane, and Butane in Air, Rec. Trav. Chim, 55:65-75 (1936).
29. J. D. Gracie, A Study of Sodium Fires, USAEC Report NAA-SR-4383, Atomics International, Oct. 15, 1960.
30. E. R. Gilliland, Diffusion Coefficients in Gaseous Systems, Ind. Eng. Chem., 26:681 (1934).
31. Enrico Fermi Atomic Power Plant Technical Information and Hazards Summary Report, Power Reactor Development Company, Vols. 1, 2, and 3, October 1962.
32. J. Bagley, Liquid Sodium Absorbs Gaseous Iodine, Nucleonics, 20(10):100 (October 1962).
33. Design and Construction Practice, Sec. IX, Power Reactor Technol., 4(2):44 (March 1961).
34. D. A. Quinn and R. C. Williams, Material Specification and Testing Procedures for Liquid Metal Systems Components, APDA Specification 10-12, Atomic Power Development Associates, Inc., Feb. 26, 1956.
35. R. Hurst and S. McLain (Eds.), Progress in Nuclear Energy,

Series IV, Technology and Engineering, McGraw-Hill Book Company, Inc., New York, 1956.

36. R. C. McMaster (Ed.), Nondestructive Testing Handbook, The Ronald Press Company, New York, 1959.

37. Symposium on Nondestructive Tests in the Field of Nuclear Energy, Am. Soc. Testing Mater. Spec. Tech. Publ. No. 223, 1958.

38. W. J. McGonnagle, Nondestructive Testing, McGraw-Hill Book Company, Inc., New York, 1961.

39. American Society of Mechanical Engineers, ASME Boiler and Pressure Vessels Code, Section VIII, Unfired Pressure Vessels.

40. Radiographic Testing, Am. Soc. Testing Mater. Standards, Part 3, E94-62T, p. 155, 1962; Radiographic Control of Quality, Part 3, E-142-59T, p. 963, 1959.

41. Ultrasonic Contact Inspection of Weldments, Am. Soc. Testing Mater. ASTM Std., Part 3, E-164-62T, p. 993, 1962.

42. Resonance Methods of Ultrasonic Inspection, Am. Soc. Testing Mater. ASTM Std., Part 3, E-113-55T, p. 1008, 1955.

43. Reflection Method Using Pulsed Longitudinal Waves Induced by Direct Contact, Am. Soc. Testing Mater. ASTM Std., Part 3, E-114-55T, p. 1013, 1955.

44. Ultrasonic Inspection of Heavy Steel Forgings, Am. Soc. Testing Mater. ASTM Std., Part 3, A-388-59, p. 1003, 1959.

45. Test for Electrical Conductivity by Use of Eddy Currents, Am. Soc. Testing Mater. ASTM Std., Part 3, B-342-61T, p. 543, 1961.

46. Liquid Penetrant Testing of Materials, APDA Specification 40-4, Atomic Power Development Associates, Inc., Dec. 15, 1955.

47. Liquid Penetrant Inspection, Am. Soc. Testing Mater. ASTM Std., Part 3, E-165-60T, p. 855, 1960.

48. R. E. Bailey and M. A. Silliman, Effects of Irradiation of the Type 347 Stainless Steel Flow Separation in the EBR-I Core, Am. Soc. Testing Mater. Spec. Tech. Publ. No. 233, 1958.

49. J. Tatlock et al., Design, Manufacture, and Construction of Fuel Element Core, Reactor Vessel, Fuel Element Handling, and Shielding, in Proceedings of the Symposium on the Dounreay Fast Reactor, London, Dec. 7, 1960, arranged by the Institution of Mechanical Engineers under the aegis of the British Nuclear Energy Conference, Institution of Mechanical Engineers, London, 1961.

50. Fast Reactor Descriptive Manual, British IG-Report-170(D), Vol. 1, Section A. 2.

51. Dounreay Fast Reactor photographs, document released under terms of the UKAEA/PRDC agreement of Aug. 8, 1958, revised Jan. 19, 1959.

52. J. Am. Soc. of Naval Eng., 66(1):247-249 (1954).

53. R. W. Ratz, Performance of HNPF Prototype Free-Surface Sodium Pump, USAEC Report NAA-SR-4336, Atomics International, June 30, 1960.

54. L. J. Koch, W. B. Lowenstein, and H. O. Monson, Addendum to Hazard Summary Report Experimental Breeder Reactor-II (EBR-II), USAEC Report ANL-5719, Argonne National Laboratory, June 1962.

55. O. S. Seim and R. A. Jaross, Characteristics and Performance of 5000 gpm ac Linear Induction and Mechanical Centrifugal Sodium Pumps, Proceedings of the Second United Nations International Conference on the Peaceful Uses of Atomic Energy, Geneva, 1958, Vol. 7, p. 88, United Nations, New York, 1958.

56. I. Karassik and R. Carter, Centrifugal Pumps, F. W. Dodge Corp., New York, 1960.

57. A. G. Grindell, W. F. Boudreau, and H. W. Savage, Development of Centrifugal Pumps for Operation with Liquid Metals and Molten Salts at 1100-1500°F, Nucl. Sci. Eng., 7(1):83-91 (January 1960).

58. R. W. Atz, R. E. Ball, and D. E. Cullman, Design and Testing of Sodium Pumps for the Hallam Nuclear Power Facility, Mech. Eng., 83:85 (October 1961).

59. Personnel Training Program Plant Manual, Power Reactor Development Company, EFAPP, prepared by Commonwealth Associates, Inc., Reactor Auxiliary Systems Unit V — Liquid Metal Pump, 1960.

60. C. R. Tipton, Jr. (Ed.), Reactor Handbook, 2nd ed., Vol. 1, Interscience Publishers, Inc., New York, 1960.

61. J. R. Dietrich and W. H. Zinn, Solid Fuel Reactor, Addison-Wesley Publishing Co., Inc., Reading, Mass., September 1958.

62. R. R. Matthews et al., Design and Construction of Heat Transfer Circuits, Steam Generating Plant, and Reactor Control System, in Proceedings of the Symposium on the Dounreay Fast Reactor, London, Dec. 7, 1960, arranged by the Institution of Mechanical Engineers under the aegis of the British Nuclear Energy Conference, Institution of Mechanical Engineers, London, 1961.

63. R. S. Baker, Theory, Design, and Performance of Helical-Rotor Electromagnetic Pump, USAEC Report NAA-SR-7455, Atomics International, May 31, 1963.

64. Code for Pressure Piping, ASA B 31.1, American Society of Mechanical Engineers, New York, 1955.

65. S. W. Spielvogel, Piping Stress Calculations Simplified, McGraw-Hill Book Company, Inc., New York, 1943.

66. M. W. Kellogg Co., Design of Piping Systems, John Wiley & Sons, Inc., New York, 1956.

67. A. R. C. Markl, Piping Flexibility Analysis, Trans. Am. Soc. Mech. Engrs., 77(2):127-149 (February 1955).

68. S. Crocker, Piping Handbook, McGraw-Hill Book Company, Inc., New York, 1945.

69. D. O. Leeser and R. C. Williams, Evaluation of Material Wear and Self-Welding in Na-Cooled Reactor Systems, Report APDA-126, Atomic Power Development Associates, Inc., August 1958.

70. R. M. Rosser, Check-Valve Designed to Reduce Water-Hammer, Power Eng., 66:72-73 (May 1962).

71. P. Lieberman and E. A. Brown, Pressure Oscillations in Water-Cooled Nuclear Reactor Induced by Water-Hammer Valves, J. Basic Engineering, 82:901-911 (December 1960).

72. J. Parmakian, Waterhammer Analysis, Dover Publications, Inc., New York, 1963.

73. B. Lubarsky and S. J. Kaufman, Review of Experimental Investigations of Liquid-Metal Heat Transfer, Report NACA-1270, National Advisory Committee for Aeronautics, 1956.

74. W. H. McAdams, Heat Transmission, 3rd ed., McGraw-Hill Book Company, Inc., New York, 1954.

75. K. W. Foster, Thermal Performance of the SRE Main Intermediate Heat Exchanger, USAEC Report NAA-SR-3775, Atomics International, June 16, 1961.

76. L. J. Koch et al., Construction Design of EBR-II; an Integrated and Unmoderated Nuclear Power Plant, Proceedings of the Second United Nations International Conference on the Peaceful Uses of Atomic Energy, Geneva, 1958, Vol. 9, p. 323, United Nations, New York, 1958.

77. Design Practice: Hallam, Sec. VII, Power Reactor Technol., 5(3):39 (June 1962).

78. R. Chipman, R. Galantine, and J. Susnie, Stress Analysis of Bellows for the HNPF Intermediate Heat Exchanger, USAEC Report NAA-SR-4534, Atomics International, Apr. 15, 1962.

79. O. J. Foust et al., Hallam Nuclear Power Facility—Reactor Operations Analysis Program, Semiannual Progress Report 1, Sept. 1, 1962, to Feb. 28, 1963, USAEC Report NAA-SR-5401, Atomics International, July 1, 1963.

80. S. Lawroski et al., Reactor Development Program Progress Report, USAEC Report ANL-6328, Argonne National Laboratory, February 1961.

81. Natural Circulation Double Tube Steam Generator, Report NAVSHIPS-351-0506, Bureau of Ships, November 1956.

82. R. D. Welsh, Preliminary Test of Natural-circulation Double-tube Steam Generator, USAEC Report NAA-SR-3969, Atomics International, Dec. 1, 1959.

83. Enrico Fermi Atomic Power Plant, Report APDA-124, Atomic Power Development Associates, Inc., January 1959.

84. R. H. Jones, T. E. Lempges, H. J. Williams, and J. Wooton, Operating Experience and Results of Testing the First APDA Prototype Liquid-metal Once-through Steam Generator, USAEC Report AECU-3700, Atomic Power Development Associates, Inc., December 1957.

85. J. J. Morabito and R. H. Shannon, Test of a Once-through Steam Generator with a Liquid Metal as a Heat Source, ASME Paper 55-A-189, American Society of Mechanical Engineers, November 1955.

86. R. H. Jones, R. H. Costello, T. E. Lempges, and H. J. Williams, Report on Test of a Bayonet Tube Once-through Type Steam Generator, unpublished data, Atomic Power Development Associates, Inc., October 1959.

87. Liquid Metal Heated Steam Generator, Alco Products, Inc., letter to Atomic Power Development Associates, Inc., Jan. 11, 1958.

88. L. A. Whinery, 2000 Kilowatt Sodium Test Facility, USAEC Report LAMS-2541, Los Alamos Scientific Laboratory, 1961.

89. J. S. McDonald, Experimental Evaluation of a Concentric-Cylinder Spiral-Flow Heat Exchanger, USAEC Report NAA-SR-3747, Atomics International, Oct. 15, 1959.

90. Intermediate Heat Exchanger, Preliminary Design, USAEC Report APAE-41, Vol. 1, Alco Products Inc., Feb. 28, 1959.

91. IHX and Steam Generator Final Design, USAEC Report APAE-78, Vol. 1, Alco Products, Inc., Sept. 30, 1960.

92. H. Strahl, A Device for Continuous Detection of Hydrogen in Sodium, USAEC Report NAA-SR-6986, Atomics International, May 1962.

93. R. H. Jones, H. J. Williams, and J. A. Murphy, NaK-Water Reaction Test, USAEC Report AECU-3193, Atomic Power Development Associates, Inc., December 1956.

94. Report on Stress-Corrosion Cracking of Austenitic Chromium-Nickel Stainless Steels, Am. Soc. Testing Mater. Spec. Tech. Publ. No. 264, 1960.

95. 30 Mw Heat Exchanger and Steam Generator for Sodium Cooled Reactor Systems, Report APAE-112, Vol. 1, Alco Products, Inc., Jan. 31, 1962.

96. Heat Transfer Notes, Massachusetts Institute of Technology summer session, 1958.

97. J. F. Hogerton and R. C. Grass (Eds.), Reactor Handbook, Engineering, 1st ed., Vol. 2, Chap. 1.5, p. 722, USAEC Report AECD-3646, 1955.
98. L. A. London and W. M. Kays, Compact Heat Exchangers, The National Press, Palo Alto, Calif., 1955.
99. Tentative Structural Design Basis for Reactor Pressure Vessels and Directly Associated Components (Pressurized Water Cooled Systems), Bureau of Ships, PB151987, Dec. 1, 1958.
100. W. H. Giedt, Principles of Engineering Heat Transfer, D. Van Nostrand Company, Inc., New York, 1957.
101. Research and Development Reports for Sodium to Sodium Intermediate Heat Exchanger and Sodium to Water Steam Generator, USAEC Report APAE-81, Alco Products, Inc., October 1960.
102. J. J. Morabito and H. O. Muenchow, Sodium Heated Steam Generator Summary, USAEC Report TID-18072, Atomic Power Development Associates, Inc., Sept. 19, 1962.
103. Quarterly Status Report on Lampre Program for Period Ending May 20, 1960, USAEC Report LAMS-2438, Los Alamos Scientific Laboratory, 1960.
104. H. I. Bowers and W. E. Ferguson, Structural Materials in LASL Liquid Sodium Systems, Trans. Am. Nucl. Soc., 6(2):364 (November 1963).
105. 30 Megawatt Heat Exchanger and Steam Generator for Sodium Cooled Reactor System, USAEC Report APAE-112, Vols. 1-4, Alco Products, Inc., Jan. 31, 1962.
106. G. Billuris, Experimental Investigations of the Removal of Sodium Oxide from Liquid Sodium, GEAP-3328, General Electric Atomic Power, Jan. 18, 1960.
107. R. B. Hinze, Control of Oxygen in a Large Sodium System, USAEC Report NAA-SR-3638, Atomics International, December 1959.
108. S. J. Rodgers and J. W. Mausteller, Removal of NaH from Na by Cold Trapping, USAEC Report NP-6030, Mine Safety Appliance Company, January 1955.
109. D. E. Williams, A Study of the Sodium-Hydrogen-Oxygen System, Report NRL-33, Naval Research Laboratory, June 1952.
110. M. Sittig, Sodium—Its Manufacture, Properties and Uses, ACS Monograph No. 133, Reinhold Publishing Corp., New York, 1956.
111. C. Starr and R. W. Dickinson, Sodium Graphite Reactors, Addison-Wesley Publishing Company, Inc., Reading, Mass., September 1958.
112. F. E. Bowman and D. D. Cubicciotti, Use of Zirconium in Liquid Sodium Systems, A.I.Ch.E., 2(2):173-176 (June 1956).
113. D. I. Sinizer and E. N. Pearson, Relationship of Carburizing Potential to Operating Temperature Limits in SRE, USAEC Report NAA-SR-Memo-7804, Atomics International, 1962.
114. W. J. Anderson, Removal of Carbon from Liquid Sodium Systems, USAEC Report NAA-SR-6386, Atomics International, Dec. 1, 1961.
115. G. W. Horsley, The Purification of Sodium by Vacuum Distillation, British Report AERE-M/R-1152, 1953. (Classified)
116. A. R. Eames, The Rhometer as an Impurity Indicator for Liquid Metal Circuits, British Report TR-6-377(D), 1962.
117. I. L. Gray et al., Control of O_2 in Sodium Heat Transfer Systems, Liquid Metal Technology, Part I, Vol. 53, No. 20, p. 13, American Institute of Chemical Engineers, New York, 1957.
118. Evaluation of the Blake Sodium Resistivity Meter, USAEC Report APDA-149, Atomic Power Development Associates, Inc., Oct. 15, 1962.
119. R. M. Adams and A. Glassner, Reactor Development Program Progress Report, pp. 27-28, USAEC Report ANL-6780, Argonne National Laboratory, Sept. 15, 1963.
120. The Analysis of Sodium Metal and Sodium-Potassium Alloy (collected Capenhurst Methods), British Report IGO-AM/CA-100, March 1958.
121. H. Steinmetz and B. Minushkin, Experimental Determination of Contaminants in Sodium, Report NDA-2154-6, Nuclear Development Associates, Aug. 30, 1961.
122. H. E. Perrine, Collected Methods for Analysis of Sodium Metal, USAEC Report GEAP-3273, General Electric Atomic Power, October 1959.
123. E. A. Cernam, Purification of Argon, Helium and Xenon, A Bibliography, USAEC Report CNLM-1802-2, Pratt and Whitney Aircraft Div., Middletown, Conn., September 1959.
124. A. L. Kohl and F. C. Riesenfeld, Gas Purification, p. 556, McGraw-Hill Book Company, Inc., New York, 1960.
125. D. S. Gibbs et al., Purification of the Rare Gases, 48(2):289-296 (February 1956).
126. M. S. Foster et al., Helium Purification Unit for High Purity Inert Atmosphere, USAEC Report ANL-6652, Argonne National Laboratory, December 1962.
127. Lampre-I Final Design Status Report, USAEC Report LA-2833, Los Alamos Scientific Laboratory, January 1962.
128. J. Malgiolio et al., The Purification and Gas Chromatographic Analysis of Helium, USAEC Report PWAC-352, Pratt and Whitney Aircraft, June 1961.
129. C. F. Hale and K. E. Rapp, Removing Major Contaminants From Nitrogen Generator Gas, USAEC Report K-1477, Oak Ridge Gaseous Diffusion Plant, November 1961.
130. H. Bernard et al., Gas Handling System for the Processing-Refabrication Experiment, USAEC Report NAA-SR-2309, Atomics International, August 1958.
131. L. A. Weller, The Adsorption of Krypton and Xenon on Activated Carbon, USAEC Report MLM-1092, Mound Laboratory, May 1959.
132. M. Steinberg, B. Manowitz, and J. Prajansky, The Recovery of Xenon and Krypton by an Absorption Process, USAEC Report BNL-542, Brookhaven National Laboratory, January 1959.
133. W. K. Kenney and A. M. Eshaya, Adsorption of Xenon on Activated Charcoal, USAEC Report BNL-689, Brookhaven National Laboratory, September 1960.
134. R. C. Koch and G. L. Grandy, Retention Efficiencies of Charcoal Traps for Fission Gases, USAEC Report NSEC-7, Nuclear Science and Engineering Corp., August 1957.
135. J. M. Holmes, Design of the Dissolver Off-Gas System for the Idaho Chemical Processing Plant, USAEC Report CF-52-11-39, Oak Ridge National Laboratory, Nov. 5, 1952.
136. G. H. Prigge, Application of Activated Carbon in Reactor Containment, USAEC Report DP-778, E. I. DuPont de Nemours & Co., September 1962.
137. M. H. Lloyd and R. A. McNees, Adsorption of Krypton and Xenon by Various Materials, USAEC Report ORNL-3228, Oak Ridge National Laboratory, December 1961.
138. K. C. Koch and G. L. Grandy, Retention Efficiencies of Selected Absorbents for Krypton, USAEC Report NSEC-12, Nuclear Science and Engineering Corp., April 1958.
139. A. H. Peters, Application of Moisture Separators and Particulate Filters in Reactor Containment, USAEC Report DP-812, E. I. DuPont de Nemours & Co., December 1962.
140. H. L. Friedman, The Solubilities of Sulphur Hexafluoride in Water and of the Rare Gases, Sulphur, Hexafluoride and Osmium Tetroxide in Nitromethane, J. Am. Chem. Soc., 76:3294-3297 (June 20, 1954).
141. H. Strahl, A Device for Continuous Detection of Hydrogen in Sodium, USAEC Report NAA-SR-6986, Atomics International, December 1960.
142. K. A. Davis, Detection Device for Hydrogen in Sodium, USAEC Report NAA-SR-5732, Atomics International, January 1962.
143. R. L. Hooker, Hydrogen Detector for Monitoring Uranium Cladding Failures, USAEC Report DP-568, E. I. DuPont de Nemours & Co., March 1961.

CHAPTER 5

Steam-Electric Plant

CHARLES M. HEIDEL and PHILLIP E. HEIDMAN

Contents

The steam-electric portion of a fast breeder reactor power plant is not appreciably different from its counterpart in a conventional fossil-fueled installation. Some features, such as steam dumping, feedwater treatment, and emergency cooling, are, however, developed to a higher degree in the fast breeder plant.

This chapter is intended to aid in the economic selection of steam conditions, cycle arrangements, and auxiliaries.

5.1 Optimization of Plant Conditions

Reducing the cost per kilowatt-hour at the bus bar has been the chief incentive for decreasing heat rates in fossil-fueled plants. Reductions in heat rates have been achieved by increasing steam pressures and temperatures, reheating, increasing feedwater temperatures, lowering turbine exhaust pressures, improving boiler efficiency, improving the internal efficiency of turbines, and reducing mechanical and electrical losses. For economies to be realized at the bus bar, assuming a fixed fuel cost per equivalent ton of coal, the net increase in the combined capital charges and operation and maintenance expense (expressed in mills per kilowatt-hour) should be less than the improved heat-rate savings (expressed in mills per kilowatt-hour). Sometimes, through a better understanding of heat transfer, fluid flow, and thermodynamics, improved heat rates can be obtained at no additional cost.

Similar economic incentives to utilize higher temperatures and pressures, as well as other improvements that result in economic reductions in heat rates, should apply also to nuclear power plants, particularly fast breeder reactors cooled with liquid metals. To date, sodium-cooled reactors have been built to demonstrate their feasibility and their reliable operation. Their true potential has not been fully explored.

To determine the temperature, pressure, and other operating conditions that will result in the lowest cost per kilowatt-hour at the bus bar, the plant and fuel-cycle conditions must be optimized by establishing several sets of conditions and determining the cost per kilowatt-hour for each set. To be complete, an optimization study should encompass core design; blanket design; refueling procedures; shielding design; primary- and secondary-system conditions; piping, pump, heat-exchanger, and steam-generator design; steam-system conditions; and steam-system components. Table 5.1 lists some of the parameters (and their values) that could be considered in determining what sets of conditions will be used in the plant optimization study.

If reactor temperature differences are extended to values higher than those used in the past, greater advantage can be taken of advanced technology and experience, which indicate that thermal stresses produced by the operation of reactors with 500°F temperature differences are not excessive with proper design. Extension of thermal outputs to 3000 Mw(t) is in line with the tendency in this country toward large interconnecting power pools with large generating units. The extension of steam pressures up to 5000 psig agrees with modern station steam practice of utilizing supercritical pressure cycles and taking advantage of once-through steam generators. Supercritical operation decreases the effect of temperature differences between the water side and the liquid-metal side of heat exchangers. Extending steam temperatures to 1200°F and limiting the reactor outlet temperature for this steam to 1400°F may be feasible in the future with available metals. As Chap. 4 indicates, the present feasible reactor outlet sodium temperature is 1200°F.

Table 5.2 lists some combinations of reactor plant and steam plant conditions that should be

Table 5.1—Nuclear Power Plant Design Parameters

Parameter	Unit	Range of parameter
Reactor temperature difference	°F	300, 400, 500
Reactor power thermal output	Mw	400, 800, 1200, 1600, 2000, 2400
	10^6 Btu	1365, 2730, 4095, 5460, 6825, 8190
Intermediate heat-exchanger log mean temperature difference	°F	50, 100, 150, 200
Steam generator log mean temperature difference	°F	50, 100, 150, 200
Steam pressures	Psig	850, 1450, 1800, 2400 3500, 5000
Steam temperatures	°F	800, 900, 1000, 1100, 1200
Condenser back pressure	In. Hg	1, 2, 3
Feedwater temperature	°F	200, 300, 400, 500
Sodium reheat		Reheat to be considered for pressures of 1450 psig and above

studied for optimization. The reactor plant conditions will be discussed briefly before proceeding on to the steam plant conditions.

5.1.1 REACTOR CONDITIONS

The four important parameters in the reactor are (1) fuel temperature, (2) fuel-cladding temperature, (3) temperature rise across the reactor, and (4) reactor inlet coolant temperature.

In fast reactors the chosen fuel will, in general, be the one with the highest burnup capability consistent with safety (Chap. 1). The fuel should be driven close to its maximum temperature to allow for the largest temperature drop from fuel to coolant. This will permit the largest ligament between fuel elements and thereby the smallest number of fuel elements. With a heat-transfer coefficient of 18,000 Btu/hr/sq ft/°F and a maximum heat flux of approximately 720,000 Btu/hr/sq ft, the temperature rise from coolant to the fuel cladding is 40°F. The thermal conductivity for stainless steel, Inconel X, and Nimonic is about 12; for Zircaloy, about 8; and for zirconium, about 9.5. With a thermal conductivity of 10 and 0.015 in. of cladding, the temperature rise through the cladding is about 90°F; therefore the cladding temperature is about 90 + 40 = 130°F higher than the coolant temperature at the point of maximum heat flux. This will probably drop off to one-half this value (65°F) at the core outlet. With a maximum to

average outlet coolant temperature ratio of 1.13, without hot channel factors, the maximum cladding temperature will run about 75 to 100°F higher than the reactor outlet coolant temperature. This means (Table 5.2) that the cladding temperature may run from 1100 to 1300°F, depending on the condition chosen. The temperature may determine the choice of materials. Some of the reactor core structure may also run from 1130 to 1356°F. The temperature again may determine the choice of materials.

The temperature rise across the reactor affects, for a fixed reactor inlet temperature, the temperature of the fuel, fuel cladding, and reactor structure; the amount of coolant flow; and thereby the pumping power.

Other considerations include the core pressure drop as it may be affected by the reactor temperature rise and by the heat-transfer requirement.

5.1.2 SODIUM HEAT-TRANSPORT SYSTEM

The items of prime concern in the sodium heat-transport system are (1) size of the pipes, (2) number of loops, (3) capacity of the pumps, (4) required pump head, (5) size of intermediate heat exchangers and steam generators, and (6) materials of construction. The reactor temperature rise as it affects the sodium flow, the reactor outlet temperature, the pressure drop through the reactor, and the terminal temperature difference are the factors to be considered in the listed items. The

Table 5.2—Combinations of Plant Conditions for Optimization Studies
[2140 Mw(t) plant, 7.3 × 10^9 Btu/hr]

Reactor ΔT, °F	Terminal T (steam to reactor outlet), °F	Reactor outlet, °F	Steam temperature, °F	Reactor inlet, °F	Steam generator Na outlet, °F	Primary- and secondary-system total flow of sodium, 10^7 lb/hr
500	100	1000/1100/1200	900/1000/1100	500/600/700	400/500/600	4.82
400	100	1000/1100/1200	900/1000/1100	600/700/800	500/600/700	6.02
300	100	1000/1100/1200	900/1000/1100	700/800/900	600/700/800	8.02
500	150	1050/1150/1200	900/1000/1050	550/650/700	400/500/550	4.86
400	150	1050/1150/1200	900/1000/1050	650/750/800	500/600/650	6.02
300	150	1050/1150/1200	900/1000/1050	750/850/900	600/700/750	8.02
500	200	1100/1200	900/1000	600/700	400/500	4.82
400	200	1100/1200	900/1000	700/800	500/600	6.02
300	200	1100/1200	900/1000	800/900	600/700	8.02

Note: 1. Assume same ΔT through IHX and SG sodium as through reactor.
2. Assume specific heat of sodium equal to 0.303.
3. The first figures in each of the third through sixth columns correspond as do the second and third figures.
4. Steam pressures can be chosen from Table 5.1.

cost of the heat-transport system should be evaluated for each set of parameters. The kilowatt-hours used for pumping power should also be evaluated for each flow and pressure condition.

5.1.3 TURBINE-GENERATOR, CONDENSER, AND FEEDWATER SYSTEM

Plant steam and feedwater conditions are major considerations in the design of a nuclear electric power plant. Variables, such as initial steam pressure and temperature, final feedwater temperature, and condenser pressure, may have a marked effect on the initial plant investment and a lasting effect on the operational costs of the plant. Bartlett [1] lists 13 factors that influence steam power-plant thermal efficiency. Table 5.3 lists some of the conditions chosen for several existing fast reactor plant steam cycles.

The size of the turbine generator has generally been a function of the size of the system it is intended to serve. Units equal to approximately 10% of the system size have been added historically. Other factors, such as anticipated system growth rate, pooling potential, and reserve margin requirements, have become increasingly dominant influences, particularly pooling by interconnections, resulting in units far in excess of 10% of system capacity.

Manufacturers of power-plant equipment can supply a broad range of turbines and accessories to meet many combinations of steam pressures and temperatures within material limitations. The selection of the optimum steam cycle is a matter of economics rather than a compromise to meet available equipment specifications.

Figure 5.1 illustrates the effect that the steam temperature and pressure at the turbine inlet have on the purchase price of an 1800-rpm tandem-compound double-flow (TCDF) and a 3600/1800-rpm cross-compound double-flow (CCDF) turbine generator. Curve A of Fig. 5.1 indicates the increased cost associated with manufacturing turbines capable of operating at temperatures near saturation or in the so-called "wet region" where turbine blades, particularly those in the lower stages, are susceptible to impact erosion resulting from high-moisture-content steam impinging on the turbine blading.

Curve B of Fig. 5.1 shows a cost reduction brought about by increasing the steam temperature to 150°F superheat and thereby eliminating some of the problems arising from operating in the wet region. Curve C, for throttle conditions of 1000°F-1000°F reheat, shows an increased cost that is

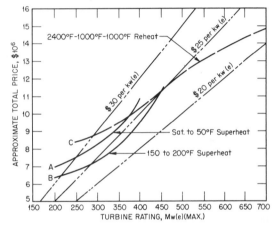

FIG. 5.1—Turbine-generator rating vs. total cost. Curves A and B, 1800-rpm TCDF turbine 850 to 1450 psig. Curve C, 3600/1800-rpm CCDF turbine 1800 to 2400 psig.

Table 5.3—Comparison of Fast Breeder Reactor Steam Cycles

	EBR-I	EBR-II	Dounreay	Fermi
Nameplate rating, kw(e)	300	20,000	15,000	150,000
Generator voltage, volts	480	13,800	11,000	18,000
Power factor	0.80	0.85	0.85	0.85
Frequency, cycles/sec	60	60	50	60
Phases	3	3	3	3
Turbine speed, rpm	4015	3600	3000	1800
Turbine type	Single flow	Single flow	Multistage impulse	Tandem compound single flow
Throttle flow, lb/hr	3530	248,000	96,000	963,235
Throttle temperature, °F	550	837	527	780
Throttle pressure, psig	400	1250	185	850
Final feedwater temperature, °F	214	550	104	340
Condenser back pressure, in. Hg abs	1.5	1.5	2.0	1.0
Condenser surface, sq ft	600	16,000	12,500	110,000
Circulating water:				
Inlet temperature, °F	65	70	60	56
Outlet temperature, °F	75	82	104	70
Flow, gal/min	600	23,600	25,800	133,800
Number of condensate pumps	2	1	2	3
Number of heater feed pumps	1	1	12	0
Number of closed feedwater heaters	0	3	0	3
Number of deaerators	1	1	2	1
Boiler feed pumps				
Type*	MD	TD	MD	MD
No.	1	1	12	3
Number of steam generators	1	2	12	3
Net plant thermal efficiency, %	17	28	N.A.†	30

*MD, motor driven; TD, turbine driven.

†N.A., not available.

primarily the result of the extensive use of high-chromium-content alloys required in the manufacture of turbines operating in this temperature range. The use of reheaters to increase thermal efficiency and to avoid excessive moisture in the lower turbine stages is discussed in Sec. 5.3.3.

5.1.3.1 Steam Temperature and Pressure

The steam temperature is equal to the reactor outlet temperature minus the sum of the temperature difference across the intermediate heat exchanger and the temperature difference across the steam generator. The terminal temperature differences can be optimized by determining the effect a change in the terminal difference has on the cost of the heat-transport system. In general, a decrease in the terminal temperature differences of either unit will result in an increase in size and cost of the heat-transport equipment. An increase in the difference will result in a lower steam temperature, a higher turbine heat rate, and increased turbine equipment costs. For parallel or counterflow steam generators, heat-transfer surface can be estimated by applying the following equation to the water preheating, saturation boiling, and superheating sections of the steam generator (see Fig. 5.2).

$$Q = UA(\Delta T_m)$$

where Q = total heat transferred, Btu/hr
U = heat-transfer coefficient, Btu/hr/sq ft/°F
A = heat-transfer surface of the heat-exchanger section under consideration, sq ft
ΔT_m = log mean temperature difference = $(\Delta T_1 - \Delta T_2)/\ln(\Delta T_1/\Delta T_2)$

The following assumptions are made to complete an example in which the superheating section heat-transfer area is approximated for two different superheat conditions (see Fig. 5.2).

1. The overall heat-transfer coefficient (U) is constant and is assumed to be 250 Btu/hr/sq ft/°F.
2. Total heat transferred (Q) is taken as 3.3×10^8 Btu/hr.
3. $\Delta T_1 = 50°F$ in Case I and 25°F in Case II.
4. $\Delta T_2 = 250°F$ in both Case I and Case II.

Solving for the heat-transfer area for the superheating section in the counterflow steam generator for this case:

Case I:

$$A_1 = \frac{Q}{U(\Delta T_m)} = \frac{3.3 \times 10^8}{250(50 - 250)/\ln(50/250)}$$

$$A_1 = \frac{3.3 \times 10^8}{250 \times 124} = 1.06 \times 10^4 \text{ sq ft}$$

Case II:

$$A_2 = \frac{3.3 \times 10^8}{250(25 - 250)/\ln(25/250)} = \frac{3.3 \times 10^8}{250 \times 97.8}$$

$$A_2 = 1.35 \times 10^4 \text{ sq ft}$$

Figure 5.3 illustrates the effect that various initial temperatures and pressures have on the turbine heat rates of a 300 Mw(e) TCDF 1800-rpm turbine generator operating in a four feedwater heater cycle and of a 3600/1800-rpm cross-compound reheat unit operating in a five and seven heater cycle. For example, a plant with an initial pressure of 1000 psig and an initial temperature of 820°F has a turbine cycle heat rate of 9175 Btu/kw-hr. Raising the throttle steam temperature to 920°F decreases the rate to 8940 Btu/kw-hr.

This change in heat rate has three possible economic effects: (1) a higher electrical output if the reactor size is fixed, which results in a capability credit; (2) a reduction in reactor size for a given electrical capacity; and (3) a reduction in fuel cost for a given electrical output.

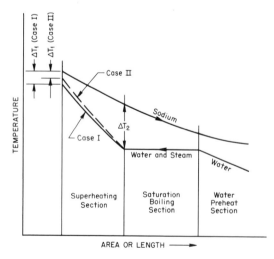

FIG. 5.2—Steam-generator terminal temperature differences.

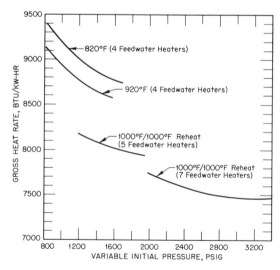

FIG. 5.3—Steam pressure vs. turbine gross heat rate for various steam temperatures and numbers of feedwater heaters. Curves are based on constant initial temperature and optimum final feedwater temperature.

Increasing the throttle temperature 100°F increases the cost of the feedwater heaters, piping, and other equipment owing to higher heat duty requirements and metallurgical considerations. On the other hand, feedwater and steam flows will be reduced, and this will result in some savings in boiler feed pumps, condenser, and other equipment.

Davis and Creel [2] compared five different steam conditions and turbine types ranging from 2400 psig and 1000/1000°F to 3500 psig and 1000/1025/1050°F for a 300-Mw conventional coal-fired plant. Much of this work is directly applicable to a steam-condition study for a nuclear station. Table 5.4 illustrates the reduction in net station heat rate made possible by the use of high pressures and temperatures.

Table 5.4—Reduction in Heat Rate for Several Steam Conditions*

Steam conditions	Turbine type†	Btu/kw-hr
2400 psig, 1000/1000°F	TC4F-26	Base
2400 psig, 1050/1000°F	TC4F-26	58
3500 psig, 1000/1000°F	TC4F-26	152
3500 psig, 1000/1000/1000°F	TC4F-26	315
3500 psig, 1000/1025/1050°F	TC4F-26	384
3500 psig, 1000/1000°F	TC4F-26	Base
3500 psig, 1000/1000°F	TC4F-29 and CC4F-29	75
3500 psig, 1000/1000°F	CC2F-38	119
3500 psig, 1000/1000°F	CC2F-43	186

*From R. W. Davis and G. C. Creel, Economics of the Selection of 3500-psig Double Reheat for a 200-Mw Unit, in *Twenty-fifth American Power Conference*, Illinois Institute of Technology, Chicago, 1963.
†TC4F, tandem compound four flow; CC4F, cross compound four flow; CC2F, cross compound double flow.

Petersen [3] compared three different steam conditions for fossil-fueled units of 300-, 400-, 500-, and 600-Mw capacity. He concluded that the economic choice between 2400 psig vs. 3500 psig for large capacity units is not clear cut and cites the factors that influence the final selection of steam conditions.

5.1.3.2 Value of 1 Btu/kw-hr

Before a comparison of alternate plans can be made, the value of 1 Btu/kw-hr must be determined. The value of 1 Btu/kw-hr of plant heat rate over one year may be expressed as (1 Btu/kw-hr) × (plant output in kw-hr/year) × (fuel cost in dollars/ Btu). The fuel cost (in dollars/Btu) may also be expressed as (fuel cost in dollars/kw-hr)/(plant heat rate in Btu/kw-hr). As an example, for a plant with a 1000-Mw(e) net generating capacity, a plant factor of 80%, a plant heat rate of 8000 Btu/net kw-hr, and a fuel cost of two mills/net kw-hr, the value of 1 Btu/net kw-hr in the plant heat rate over one year is as follows:

$$\text{Fuel cost} = \frac{\$0.002/\text{net kw-hr}}{8000 \text{ Btu/net kw-hr}} = \$0.25/10^6 \text{ Btu}$$

(1 Btu/net kw-hr) × (10^6 net kw) × (0.80) × (8760 hr/year) × ($0.25/10^6$Btu) = $1752/year.

The value of 1 Btu/kw-hr capitalized at 14.5% equals $1752/0.145 = $12,000. A 100 Btu/kw-hr reduction in heat rate would justify a capital expenditure of $1,200,000 or, for each mill/kw-hr,

a 100 Btu/kw-hr reduction justifies an expenditure of $600,000.

5.1.3.3 Regenerative Cycle

Regenerative cycles are used in most nuclear electric plants today and have been widely accepted in the steam electric power industry for years as the most direct method of increasing thermal-cycle efficiency. The regenerative process involves heating the feedwater on its return trip to the steam generator by bleeding or extracting steam at various stages of the turbine and transferring the energy to the feedwater via a heat exchanger.

Figure 5.4 is a feedwater and steam-cycle diagram for a 300-Mw cross-compound turbine generator operating at 2400 psig and 1000/1000°F heat with seven stages of feedwater heating [4].

Figure 5.5, adapted from [5], is a feedwater and steam-cycle diagram for a 1000-Mw(e) plant operating at 3500 psig and 950°F with sodium reheaters. This diagram is for illustrative purposes only.

In nuclear applications the regenerative cycle assumes new importance as a method of reducing thermal shocks and accompanying stresses on the heat-transport system by supplying feedwater at an elevated and essentially constant temperature. Some plants utilize an open, or direct-contact, type heat exchanger placed in the low-pressure region of the feedwater circuit. Steam for feedwater heating is extracted from the turbine during normal operation and is supplied by an auxiliary source, such as a small heating boiler, for start-up operation and other special situations. The other feedwater heaters in the cycle are generally closed, or shell-and-tube, heat exchangers of conventional design.

The optimum number of feedwater heaters required is determined by balancing the heat-rate improvement against capital investment for a given cycle.

The following tabulation by Bartlett [1] indicates current practices in the nonnuclear power industry; it should prove practical for nuclear application even though the fuel cost to investment ratio may be slightly higher for fossil-fuel plants:

20,000 to 50,000 kw(e)	4 or 5 heaters
50,000 to 100,000 kw(e)	5 or 6 heaters
100,000 to 200,000 kw(e)	5, 6, or 7 heaters
Over 200,000 kw(e)	6, 7, or 8 heaters

The actual number of feedwater heaters can be determined only after a careful evaluation of thermodynamic effects as well as installation and maintenance costs. Figure 5.6 is a graph of heat-rate reduction as a function of the number of feedwater heaters for various throttle pressures at a constant throttle temperature. It illustrates the significant heat-rate improvement that is realized by the addition of the first four or five feedwater heaters and the diminishing effect as more heaters are added. Higher throttle pressures will further increase the number of feedwater heaters that can be economically justified. Figure 5.7 shows the optimum final feedwater temperature vs. the

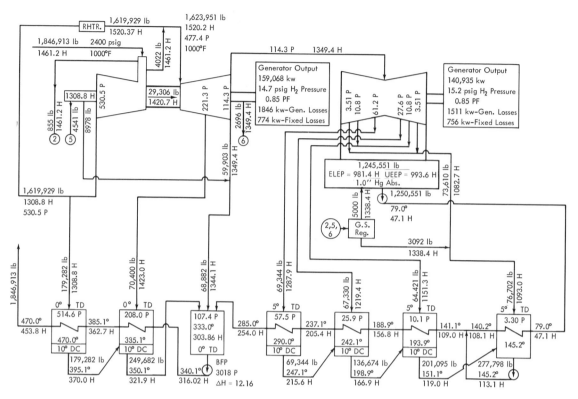

FIG. 5.4—A 300-Mw(e) plant heat-balance diagram. Legend: H = enthalpy, Btu/lb. Temperature = °F. Lb = flow, lb/hr. P = pressure, psia. PF = power factor. LSB = last-stage blade. BFP = boiler feed pump. RHTR = reheater. CCDF = cross-compound double-flow. Kw = kw electrical. G.S. Reg. = gland-seal regulator. DC = drain condenser. TD = terminal difference. ELEP = expansion-line end point. UEEP = used-energy end point. Gross heat rate = [1,846,913(1461.2−453.8) + 1,619,929(1520.37−1308.8)]/300,003 = 7344 Btu/kw-hr; net heat rate = [1,846,913 (1461.2−453.8) + 1,619,929 (1520.37−1308.8)]/300,003−7312 = 7528 Btu/kw-hr. 300,000 kw at 3.5 in. Hg. 3% makeup. 2400 psig 1000/1000°F. CCDF-43 in. LSB 3600/1800 rpm. Gen. No. 1:204,000 kva at 30 psig H₂ pressure and 0.85 PF. Gen. No. 2:180,000 kva at 30 psig H₂ pressure and 0.85 PF. (From R. C. Spencer, K. C. Cotton, and C. N. Cannon, ASME Paper 62-WA-209, American Society of Mechanical Engineers.)

number of feedwater heaters for various steam pressures.

For illustration, a nonextraction heat rate will be determined for a turbine operating at 2400 psig and 1000°F steam conditions exhausting at 1 in. Hg absolute in the condenser.

$$\text{Nonextraction heat rate} = \frac{TSR \, (h_s - h_c)}{\eta}$$

where TSR = theoretical steam rate, lb/kw-hr

h_s = enthalpy of steam at the throttle, from Ref. 6, Btu/lb

h_c = enthalpy of liquid at the condenser, from Ref. 6, Btu/lb

η = overall turbine efficiency (assumed at 80%)

From the Theoretical Steam Rate Tables [7], we find that at the above conditions TSR = 5.352 lb of steam per kilowatt-hour.

$$\text{Nonextraction heat rate} = \frac{5.352 \, (1462 - 47)}{0.80}$$

$$= 9,466 \text{ Btu/kw-hr}$$

From Ref. 8 we find that for the specified throttle conditions the percentage of heat-rate reduction for six, seven, and eight heaters would be 14.4%, 14.8%, and 15.2%, respectively.

The heat rate for six heaters is 9,466 (100 − 14.4) = 8,103 Btu/kw-hr; for seven heaters, 9,466 (100 − 14.8) = 8,065 Btu/kw-hr; and for eight heaters, 9,466 (100 − 15.2) = 8,027 Btu/kw-hr.

The heat-rate improvement realized by the addition of the first six heaters is approximately 1,363 Btu/kw-hr. The addition of a seventh heater would lower the heat rate by 38 Btu/kw-hr, and an eighth heater would lower the heat rate by an additional 38 Btu/kw-hr. In Section 5.1.3.2 it was determined that 1 Btu/kw-hr is worth approximately $12,000 of investment; hence the first six heaters would easily justify the required capital expenditure. As the number of heaters increases, the percentage of heat-rate improvement diminishes, and consequently justifiable capital expenditure decreases. The seventh and eighth heaters could together justify the expenditure of about $900,000. The cost of heaters and related piping, valves, and other equipment increases proportionally with pressure and temperature.

Fuel technology advances in breeder reactors may result in the addition of a plant with a fuel-cost component that is much lower than the fuel-cost components of the other power plants in the power system under consideration. The question

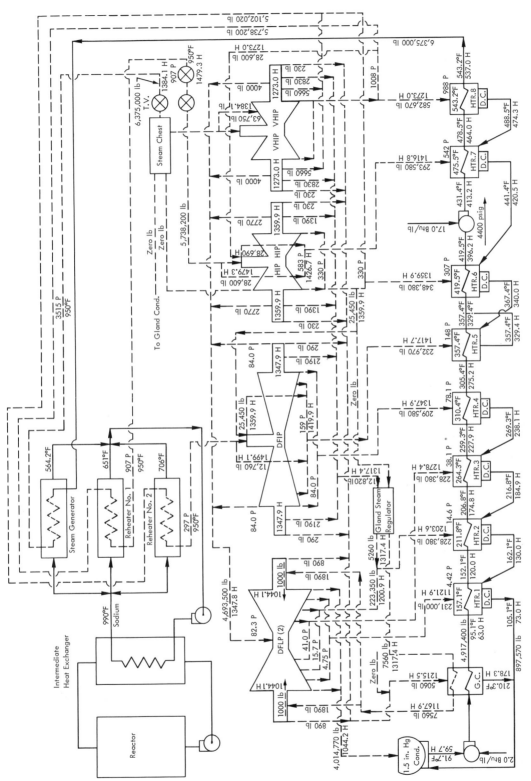

FIG. 5.—A 1000-Mw(e) plant heat-balance diagram. Legend: VHIP = very high pressure. HIP = high pressure. DFIP = double-flow intermediate pressure. HTR. = heater. P = pressure, psia. DC = drains cooler. G.C. = gland condenser. H = enthalpy. T.V. = throttle valve. Calculations are based on no radiation losses to heaters or extraction piping located in condenser neck. Liquid-sodium-cooled reactor steam turbine cycle. Reactor power of 2140 Mw(t), turbine power of 993 Mw(e), and cycle efficiency of 46.4%. Heat rate = [637500 (1384.1−537.0) + 5738200(1499.1−1359.7)]/613761 + 370070 = 7348 Btu/kw-hr.

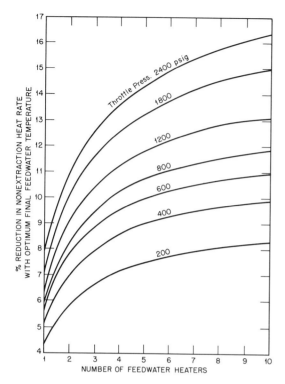

FIG. 5.6—Number of feedwater heaters vs. reduction in nonextraction heat rates for a range of steam pressures. Steam conditions: throttle pressure, 200 to 2400 psig; throttle temperature, 900°F; exhaust pressure, 1 in. Hg.

then would be: What criteria can be used to evaluate heat-rate improvement? For a fixed reactor thermal output, the improved heat rate results in the production of more kilowatt-hours. These kilowatt-hours can be used to reduce more costly kilowatt-hours produced at the other plants if

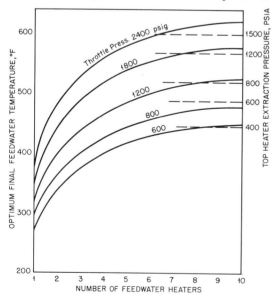

FIG. 5.7—Number of feedwater heaters vs. optimum final feedwater temperature for various throttle pressures at 1 in. Hg.

analysis indicates the capitalized incremental saving is more than the additional required capital investment. Assuming the unit to be added is to operate in a system with fossil-fueled plants, the overall system fuel cost can be used as the parameter for preliminary purposes, i.e., the cost of heat-rate improvement for the nuclear station is balanced against the average system fuel cost. For example, if a 1000-Mw(e) nuclear plant with an average system fuel cost of $0.30 per million Btu has a plant heat rate of 8000 Btu/kw-hr and if the addition of a seventh feedwater heater will improve the plant heat rate by 37 Btu, the capacity credit resulting from increased generation may be evaluated by

$$\Delta kw = \frac{HR_1 - HR_2}{HR_2} \, kw$$

where HR_1 = original heat rate (8000 Btu/kw-hr)
HR_2 = improved heat rate (7963 Btu/kw-hr)
kw = kilowatts associated with the HR_1 heat rate
Δkw = increase in generation
$$= \frac{8000 - 7963}{7963} \times 1,000,000 = 4650 \text{ kw}$$

Assuming the average system heat rate is 10,000 Btu/kw-hr and the nuclear plant factor (PF) is 0.80, then

$$4650 \text{ kw} \times 8760 \, \frac{hr}{year} \times 0.80 \, PF \times \frac{\$0.30}{10^6 \text{ Btu}} \times 10,000 \, \frac{Btu}{kw\text{-}hr}$$
$$= \$97,700/\text{year}$$

Capitalized at 14.5% = $674,000

In this oversimplified example an expenditure less than $674,000 would be justified to facilitate the generation of the additional 4650 kw. On the basis of the following assumed costs for the heater, generator, and transformer, a seventh heater could be added to the cycle:

High-pressure feedwater heater	$150,000
Piping	15,000
Generator, incremental $10/kw(e)	46,000
Transformer, incremental $1.00/kw(e)	5,000
	$216,000
Overhead and contingency including design and engineering, 40%	86,000
Total expenditure	$302,000

Theoretically, the additional generating capability would also change the next block of generation by some small increment of time, the result of which would be a so-called "capacity credit." This effect has been neglected in the example.

5.1.3.4 Exhaust Conditions[9]

In determining the effects that various components have on the cycle heat rate and efficiency, the designer should give careful consideration to the heat sink or condenser. In a regenerative cycle the condenser receives 65 to 80% of the total throttle steam flow and condenses it to the liquid state by transferring the latent heat to the circulating or cooling water. The analysis required to determine the optimum size of a main unit condenser in nuclear applications is made more complex by the special requirement for dump steam disposal and, for once-through steam generators, the need to avoid condensate contamination. These special features are discussed in Secs. 5.2.3 and 5.4.

In general, the selection of the condenser is dependent on the operating savings resulting from gains in overall cycle efficiency balanced against capital cost.

Table 5.5 shows the relation between cooling-water temperatures and recommended exhaust pressures. For a given cooling-water temperature, a decrease in exhaust pressure will result in an increase in condenser size until at some point further decreases become uneconomic.

Table 5.5—Recommended Turbine Exhaust Pressures for Various Cooling-water Temperatures

Cooling-water temperatures, °F	Recommended minimum absolute pressure, in. Hg
60	1.0
70	1.5
80	2.0
85	2.5
90	3.0
95	3.5

Table 5.6 shows the effect of three different exhaust pressures on the design of a single-pass condenser serving a 1000-Mw(e) unit.

This comparison shows that an improvement in exhaust pressure from 2 in. Hg abs to 1 in. Hg would require doubling the condenser surface and cooling flow. The attendant higher cost, both in investment and operation, must be balanced against gains in cycle efficiency and resulting fuel savings by lowering the expansion line end point.

5.1.3.5 Turbine Heat Balance

With the approximate steam conditions, turbine type, and number of feedwater heaters established,

a turbine heat balance is prepared to determine steam—water qualities and flows in the various steam-cycle components. The turbine manufacturer usually supplies a complete heat balance for his equipment at design conditions, i.e., 100% of capability. It may be desirable for the purchaser to work out his own heat balances. For example, at partial load operation, the corresponding lower steam and water flows affect the performance of pumps, heaters, controls, piping, and other equipment. The plant designer may wish to investigate the effect of changing the heat duty on a particular feedwater heater. In either case a revised heat balance is required. To facilitate the procedure, turbine manufacturers supply a "thermal kit" containing pertinent information for the particular turbine. The following items are generally included in the kit:

1. Summary of design and operating conditions including throttle flow, generator output, heat rates, and pressures and temperatures at admission, exhaust, and all extraction points.
2. Curve showing pressure vs. flow for all extraction points.
3. Curve showing gland leakages vs. throttle flow at various loads.
4. Curve showing gland leak-off enthalpy vs. throttle flow.
5. Curve showing turbine exhaust loss vs. volumetric condenser flow.
6. Turbine expansion lines at various loads plotted on a Mollier diagram.
7. Generator efficiency data on fixed and variable losses.

Equipped with the above information, the engineer can proceed with the necessary calculations using methods outlined by Bartlett [1] and Salisbury [8].

Spencer, Cotton, and Cannon [4] have developed a simplified method that enables the engineer to predict performance of turbine-generators in the 100- to 1000-Mw range through the application of prepared tables and curves.

The cycle heat balance provides the designer with the necessary tool for determining (1) gross turbine heat rate, (2) net turbine heat rate, and (3) plant heat rate as follows:

Table 5.6—Condenser Comparison for Exhaust Pressures of 1, 1.5, and 2 in. of Mercury

	1 in. Hg	1.5 in. Hg	2 in. Hg
Steam flow, lb/hr	4,000,000	4,000,000	4,000,000
Heat removed, Btu/lb steam	997	985	975
Exhaust pressure, in. Hg abs	1.0	1.5	2.0
Steam temperature, °F	79.0	91.7	101.1
Heat transfer coefficient, Btu/hr/sq ft/°F	545	545	545
Log mean temperature differential, °F	11.8	19.6	25.4
Cooling-water temperature rise, °F	12.3	20.6	26.7
Cooling water required, gal/min	647,000	382,000	292,000
Surface required, sq ft	620,000	369,000	282,000
Assumptions:			
Cooling-water temperature, °F	60	60	60
Terminal temperature difference, °F	6.7	11.1	14.4
Tube size (OD), in.	7/8	7/8	7/8
Tube gauge (BWG)	18	18	18
Tube material	Admiralty	Admiralty	Admiralty
Cooling-water velocity, ft/sec	7.0	7.0	7.0

$$\text{Turbine gross heat rate} = \frac{Q_S}{\text{kw(e) gross}}$$

$$\text{Turbine net heat rate} = \frac{Q_S}{\text{kw(e) gross} - \text{kw(e)} \, BFP}$$

Plant heat rate

$$= \frac{Q_S}{\eta_B [\text{kw(e) gross} - \text{kw(e)} \, BFP - \text{kw(e) aux.}]}$$

where Q_S = heat supplied = (throttle flow) (throttle
    enthalpy-final feedwater enthalpy)
BFP = boiler feed pump
η_B = boiler efficiency
kw(e) aux. = auxiliary power requirements

Auxiliary power requirements include all pump,
crane, and compressor drives; air conditioning;
lighting; controls; heating; and any other plant
power requirements.

5.2 Feedwater–Steam Systems and Control

5.2.1 CONTROL

The feedwater system is the portion of the
cycle from the condenser hot well to the steam
generator, including feedwater heaters, pumps,
necessary controls, and piping.

The steam system encompasses the equipment
necessary to handle the steam flow from the steam
generator to the turbine throttle valve and the extraction steam from the turbine to the feedwater
heaters, plus any special requirements for handling
dump steam to the condenser.

The water–steam system must function not only
at maximum load but through the entire range of
operation from zero thermal input through start-up
to normal operation and back to zero. The system
should also be able to handle abnormal operating
conditions.

There are two basic methods of feedwater–
steam cycle control. One concept is for the turbine
to utilize all the steam produced by the reactor.
Normal control maintains the temperature of the
steam-generator outlet sodium and the temperature
of the feedwater by controlling the feedwater flow
to the steam generator. Reactor output controls
generator output. In Fig. 5.8 the feedwater regulating valve (A) is positioned to maintain constant
sodium outlet temperature (B). The boiler feed
pump speed control (C) is positioned by differential
pressure (D) across the feedwater regulating valve
(A). Turbine throttle-valve position (E) is controlled by maintaining constant steam-generator
outlet pressure (F).

As the fast reactor becomes increasingly a part
of the power economy, the control concept will
probably change to fossil-fuel type control where
the reactor output is controlled by electrical system demand. In this concept a demand signal for
load pickup is transmitted to the turbine governor
and throttle valve. The increased valve opening
results in a greater flow through the turbine, which

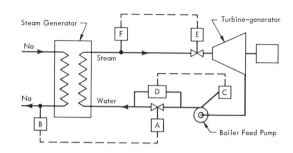

FIG. 5.8—Schematic diagram of feedwater and steam control.

causes a corresponding decrease in steam pressure
and temperature. The drop in steam temperature
and subsequently in the sodium temperature is
anticipated and transmitted to the reactor control
rods, which are repositioned for a higher thermal
output. Simultaneously a pressure-control device in
the main steam line signals the boiler feed pumps
for an increase in water flow to the steam generator, returning the system to equilibrium. A decrease in electrical load requirements has the
opposite effect.

An even more direct method of control, one
particularly applicable to once-through boilers,
consists of regulating the reactor control rods
directly to give the desired electrical generator
output. Steam pressure is maintained by adjusting
the turbine governor.

In general, control should include the following
modes of normal and abnormal operation: (1) normal start-up, (2) normal control in operating range,
(3) normal shutdown, (4) normal control during
refueling, (5) abnormal control after reactor-
initiated scram with feedwater and sodium flows
normal, (6) abnormal control after water–sodium
reaction, (7) abnormal control, loss of feedwater,
shutdown including emergency cooling, and (8) abnormal control, loss of sodium flow. Chapter 9
contains additional information regarding methods
of control.

5.2.2 FEEDWATER PURITY [10]

Boiler feedwater-quality requirements are high
in a fast breeder installation utilizing once-through
steam generators because in the once-through
boiler solids blowdown through a drum connection
is not possible. Solids entering the steam generator
will foul heat-transfer surfaces or precipitate on
turbine blading.

The need for installing filters ahead of the bypass deionizer in once-through systems is questionable. When they are most needed, at start-up, they
tend to plug up quickly with corrosion products.
Normally there is not enough suspended material
to warrant use of filters. The system should be
very clean on initial start-up, makeup water should
be of high quality, and control of dissolved-metal
contamination should be maintained. On an installation of the 1000-psi steam pressure class, where
the boiler feedwater is not in the radioactive exposure region and the material is relatively free from
chloride corrosion, the following requirements are
in order:

Total solids = < 50 ppb (parts per billion)
Reactive silica = < 20 ppb
Conductivity = < 0.5 μmho (after removal of amine by cation exchange)
Iron = 5 to 10 ppb
Copper = 5 to 10 ppb
Oxygen (dissolved) = < 5 to 7 ppb
pH = 8.8 to 9.2 (after amine addition)

Equipment necessary to achieve desired feedwater quality usually includes a condensate makeup demineralizer, floc filters on condenser hot-well effluent, and a mixed-bed polishing demineralizer. Unlike a conventional steam generator in which there is a recirculation of boiler water, a once-through unit cannot remove accumulated solids by blowdown. Therefore the only way to maintain the required feedwater quality is by deionizing some of the condensate to remove solids that enter the system in the makeup, in leaking condenser cooling water, and through corrosion of the system piping. In once-through boilers fired by fossil fuels, it is customary to install bypass deionizers capable of handling 30% of the total condensate. A deionizer of similar capacity for sodium-heated steam generators could be used. It should be designed on the basis of 30 gal/min per square foot of resin bed. A deaerator in the feedwater cycle is necessary to maintain dissolved-oxygen requirements. Introduction of some amine may be necessary to achieve pH control features.

Any use of stainless steels in high-temperature steam generators requires strict control of chlorides, fluorides, and oxygen in the final feedwater. Concentrations of chlorides and fluorides should be limited to approximately 10 ppb, and oxygen should be essentially zero.

The use of a natural- or forced-circulation boiler would not change the above purity requirements appreciably. However, where boiler drums are used in the steam cycle, it might be possible to eliminate the mixed-bed condensate polishing demineralizer and depend on boiler blowdown during start-up to eliminate dissolved solids.

The purity of makeup should be such as to keep the system impurities below set limits using the feedwater quality-control equipment. A separate demineralizer section may be needed for makeup.

The feedwater in present sodium-cooled fast breeder reactors is not directly exposed to radioactivity owing to the interposition of the secondary sodium system. Consequently the problem of radiolytic decomposition of the water does not arise.

5.2.3 HEAT-DUMP SYSTEMS

When the normal steam flow path is disrupted because of sudden loss of the turbine generator, either the reactor is immediately shut down or an alternate steam flow path is provided. So that repetitive shutdowns with resultant rapid temperature transients can be avoided, fast power reactors have been provided with an alternate steam flow path to the heat sink.

Each of the three fast breeder reactor plants built has heat-dump design unique to the particular project. The Fermi plant and the EBR-II plant each use the main steam condenser as the heat sink but provide a steam dump to the condenser by bypassing the turbine. The United Kingdom Atomic Energy Authority (UKAEA) Dounreay plant uses a separate steam-dump condenser as the device for bypassing the turbine.

The Fermi heat dump is shown in Fig. 5.9. When the turbine stop valves and control valves are closed suddenly because of a mechanical or electrical machine fault, the two large steam-dump valves located at the deaerating heater immediately open and admit steam to the steam space in the deaerator. The steam-dump valves reduce the steam pressure from the operating pressure of 600 psig to the 130-psig heater pressure. The admission of large quantities of heat to the deaerator increases the internal pressure above the set pressure of the condenser dump valve, opening the valve and dumping the heat to the main condenser. There are two reasons for this two-step dump process. One reason is to maintain a constant final feedwater temperature under all conditions of operation with a once-through steam generator to mitigate thermal transients. When the turbine is lost from service, all extraction steam is lost to the closed feedwater heaters. Feedwater heating is accomplished in the No. 4 open deaerating heater by dumping all steam to this heater prior to admitting it to the steam condenser. The other reason is to avoid severe damage to the steam condenser and turbine exhaust end which would occur on failure of the desuperheating on feedwater.

The EBR-II heat dump is shown in Fig. 5.10. This dump is a one-step dump. When the turbine control valves close, steam is admitted directly to the steam condenser through a pressure-reducing valve and a desuperheating station. The dump piping in the EBR-II condenser is in the lower section of the condenser whereas the dump piping in the Fermi is at the top of the condenser. The

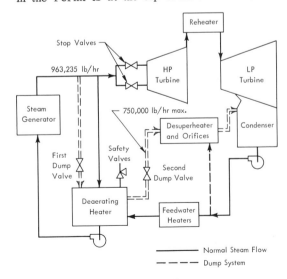

FIG. 5.9—Fermi steam-dump system.

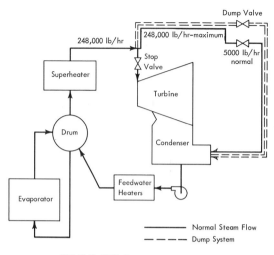

FIG. 5.10—EBR-II steam-dump system.

damage in the EBR-II condenser would be limited to the lower condenser structure if the source of desuperheating water failed. The EBR-II steam-generator design also has an evaporation drum. Limited concern is exercised over cold water entering the drum. Dilution of the feedwater with hot water in the drum avoids the need to provide live-steam feedwater heating between the condenser and steam drum.

The Dounreay heat-dump design (Fig. 5.11) is different from the two previously described. This design provides the ultimate in reliability but incurs a greater first cost. A separate steam condenser is used for start-up and emergency purposes. The condensing water flow is continuous; thus the condenser is ready for service when an emergency trip-out of the turbine occurs.

The heat-dump system has been discussed in terms of its function under emergency circumstances. These systems can also be used to dump

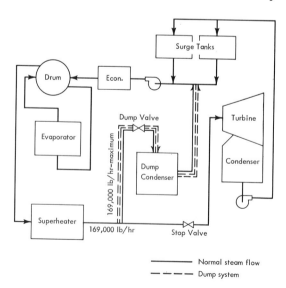

FIG. 5.11—Dounreay steam-dump system.

low levels of heat during start-up, shutdown, and decay-heat periods. Steam and/or water is circulated through the steam generators and heat-dump systems until the desired pressure–temperature operating conditions are met. This is generally in the range of 20 to 30% of reactor power. When the flow pressure and temperature reach the required condition, the steam is transferred from the dump to the turbine. Generally the broad range of water and/or steam flows to be handled by the heat dump is such that separate valves and piping systems are required.

5.3 Turbine Generator

The turbine generator for a nuclear electric power plant presents no new problems to the turbine designer. The electric generator requires no change, assuming a turbine of proper speed capability. The turbine is easily adapted to the fast breeder steam cycle and control conditions. One adaptation may require the use of constant reactor thermal-output load control as contrasted with a fossil-fueled plant where the electrical output is controlled by the turbine governor mechanism to hold a constant speed (i.e., constant frequency in a-c electrical output).

5.3.1 TURBINE CONTROL

Since the nuclear plant makes no special demands on the turbine except a minor change in the basis of control, it is necessary to consider only two turbine-output control mechanisms in ordinary use: (1) the simple throttle valve, which controls turbine output by adjusting steam pressure entering the first turbine stage nozzles, and (2) the multiple valve control, which controls turbine output by partial peripheral admission to the first turbine stage. Each of these multiple valves is a simple throttle valve, and each admits steam to its own sector on the periphery of the first turbine stage. The valves operate in sequence, each in its turn, from fully closed to fully open. Turbine output is controlled by adjusting the steam pressure on only one section of first turbine stage nozzles at any one time.

The advantage in multiple valve control is improved economy at reduced loads, obtained with a higher investment for the control mechanism. This difference is illustrated in the turbine heat-rate curves of Fig. 5.12.

The potential low fuel cost for the fast breeder reactor plant and the restriction to an essentially constant load indicate a system loading of the plant at high capacity. At high capacities heat rates with simple or multiple valve control differ little. A base-load plant leads to the choice of the turbine with simple throttling control for the nuclear plant.

A constant thermal-energy output from the reactor is obtained by the reactor control rods. All available fluctuations in operating conditions within the plant are compensated for by variations in turbine output. This may be accomplished by using the turbine throttle valve to control the pressure of the steam leaving the steam generator. No basic

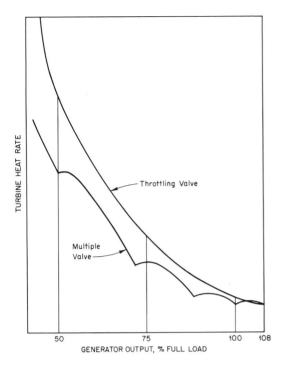

FIG. 5.12—Turbine heat-rate curves showing throttling vs. multiple-valve control of turbine.

the turbine, still within the limit imposed by Carnot's principle. Moreover, the end point of a steam-turbine expansion process is limited by a combination of theoretical and practical considerations to a relatively small region of the steam chart (see Fig. 5.13).

Examination of the chart shows an initial pressure vs. initial temperature relation, including the capability of the unit. As the initial temperature is increased, there is an increase in the initial pressure required to convert the resulting increase in heat availability into mechanical work in a simple turbine. An expansion from an initial point outside the region outlined in Fig. 5.13 gives a turbine exhaust condition with a moisture content that is too high. The increase in pressure required to keep the exhaust within the bounds imposed results in higher construction costs, which can be justified only for units of large capability. Units of large capability require the higher pressures, otherwise the volumetric flow at the turbine exhaust becomes prohibitively large.

The pressure and temperature limitations have resulted in the ASME Preferred Standards [11], which delineate the optimum pressure—temperature capability relations accepted in common practice for the conventional steam power plant. Economics in power production has to date resulted in the use of the largest practical units. The growth of the power industry in recent years has increased

change in the turbine control mechanism is involved, merely the substitution of a control impulse from steam pressure instead of the control impulse from turbine speed (a-c output frequency as in the conventional plant). This assumes the existence of sufficient nonnuclear plants in the system to absorb any variations and maintain a constant total system load to fit the system demand.

A control impulse from turbine speed is maintained to protect the turbine in case of emergencies, such as a generator trip-out. The trip-out is inoperative except when turbine speed attains some predetermined value, around 2% above normal operating speed. In ordinary operation the speed regulation is much closer than 2%, and the turbine throttle valve operates simply as a steam-pressure regulator.

In normal operation with good reactor output control, fluctuations of turbine output should be comparable to, or less than, those of a frequency-regulating turbine.

5.3.2 TURBINE CONDITIONS

By Carnot's principle the ability to produce mechanical work from a working medium in any cyclic process is limited by the highest temperature and the temperature range of the cycle. The efficiency of such a cycle is $(T_2 - T_1)/T_2$ where T_2 is the top temperature of the working fluid and T_1 is the temperature of the rejected working fluid. Central-station heat engines operate on the modified Rankine cycle. In the simple steam turbine, work availability is more readily related to pressure ratio in the adiabatic expansion process within

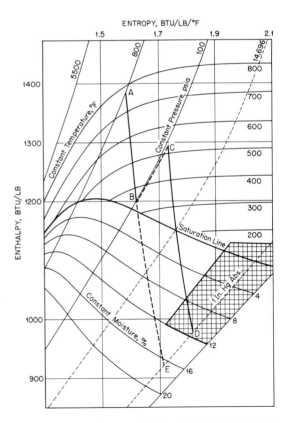

FIG. 5.13. Steam-turbine expansion line. (Courtesy Allis Chalmers Electrical Review, 2nd Quarter, 1961.)

optimum unit sizes beyond those included in the preferred standards.

Reheat has become a means of increasing the total energy transport for a given turbine exhaust flow. Reheat, as used in the conventional steam plant, not only reduces the turbine designer's problems but pays for itself through lower heat rates. A fast breeder reactor, with potentially low fuel costs, requires a reexamination of the use of reheat.

5.3.3 MOISTURE ELIMINATION

The moisture content of steam flowing through turbine blading should be kept below 10 or 12%. Greater amounts produce excessive erosion and an unduly high maintenance charge. A turbine expansion from 900°F and 900 psi would produce a moisture content of about 16% in the last turbine wheel. Blade life would be somewhat less than twenty years, and the stage efficiency penalty (1.15% for each 1% of moisture present in new blading) would be increased by loss of blade form through erosion.

Moisture elimination can be accomplished in several ways. Among these are the following: (1) reheat, (2) moisture separation, and (3) by-passing throttle steam to a lower turbine stage.

Moisture separation is most effective in increasing the ratio of turbine work to volumetric flow at exhaust. It has, compared to reheat, less efficiency gain. Moisture separation can be accomplished with moisture-extracting blading or with an external moisture separator. It introduces no complications in the cycle arrangement.

Reheat offers attractive gains in efficiency but introduces complications in the cycle arrangement unless accomplished locally with steam from a point located on the boiler side of the turbine throttle. In the initial stages of sodium-cooled fast reactor technology, simplicity requirements lean to compensating for the low initial temperature restriction of the nuclear plant with some form of moisture extraction or with local reheat using throttle steam as the heat source. Steam-reheat circuits and liquid-metal circuits to a local reheater are being explored as means of reducing moisture problems for future units.

Moisture control in the turbine exhaust can be accomplished by the use of moisture-extraction blading in each third or fourth turbine stage after this moisture region is reached. Moisture content can be reduced to 2 or 3% at a small efficiency cost in the moisture-extraction stage. This is more than compensated for by the resultant gains in the moisture-extraction stage and in the remaining stages.

Modern turbine blading ordinarily uses a blunt nose on the blade at the entrance similar to the leading edge of an airplane wing. Stage efficiency dictates this form if the turbine is to operate any considerable portion of the time at off-rating loads. A high-efficiency blade with sharp-angle incidence profile can be designed for a particular loading, but the stage efficiency falls off more rapidly with changes in loading than it does with the round-nose blade. A round-nose moving blade is readily con-

verted to a moisture-extraction blade by thickening the entrance and introducing a moisture-trapping groove on the side of the blade where all large moisture droplets strike. These droplets are thrown out into the steam extraction space by centrifugal force and are extracted to the feed-heating system.

Moisture extraction can also be accomplished in an external moisture separator. Because of the large volumetric flow in the lower turbine, this becomes a bulky and expensive piece of apparatus. In reality it is a large number of separators operating in parallel. The pressure loss through the separator is compensated for by resultant gains in the remaining turbine stages. Moisture content can be reduced in this manner to about 1%.

Moisture is eliminated primarily to increase blading life, but its elimination is necessary when the moisture content exceeds about 12%, regardless of the thermal gain. The manner in which it is accomplished is determined by comparing the economies of the various methods. Moisture control in the turbine exhaust, by passing throttle steam to a lower turbine stage, is the least desirable of the three methods named. The ratio of turbine work to volumetric exhaust flow decreases, and there is a large decrease in efficiency. It does have the advantage of being simple; it provides adequate protection in the lower turbine stages, and it has a low initial investment.

5.4 Condenser

5.4.1 USE OF CONDENSER AS STEAM DUMP

The main turbine condenser in a nuclear plant, in addition to performing the normal function of condensing steam leaving the turbine exhaust, may serve as a steam-dump disposal unit during reactor tests, start-ups, or in the event of a turbine-generator trip [12]. In the latter case the condenser should be capable of handling large volumes of steam at relatively high pressures and temperatures. This usage will generally impose more rigid requirements on the condenser manufacturer to prevent steam-side erosion of shell or tubes by the steam. The condenser should also be designed to meet the rigid condensate- and feedwater-purity requirements imposed by the use of once-through steam generators. Steam-dump disposal systems are generally designed to handle all, or a portion of, the total primary steam flow. For example, at the Fermi plant (Fig. 5.9) the dump system is designed for 750,000 lb/hr or approximately 50% of the full-load throttle flow. The remainder is vented to the atmosphere through safety valves. The steam is at 2.5 psia and 175°F when it enters the condenser as compared to 1 in. Hg absolute and 80°F exit conditions during normal operation. Eight 36-in.-diameter pipes in the condenser neck handle the steam volume. Even with this relatively large area, near-sonic steam velocities are attained.

5.4.2 COMPARTMENTED HOT WELLS

The need for high-purity feedwater has led to the development of compartmented hot wells as a method for determining when and where cooling-water contamination occurs. The hot-well storage section is divided into a number of small compartments monitored by a conductivity recorder. A tube leak is detected by a resulting rise in conductivity, and an alarm signals the plant operator. The compartmented section involved is removed from service until corrective measures have been taken. A vertically divided water box is one method used for isolating leaking tubes or tube holes. In the event of a leak, the side involved is valved off, and operation continues at reduced load with the remaining side.

Welding the condenser tubes to the tube sheet [13] is another technique developed for improving the integrity of the condensate–steam side of the condenser. Condenser manufacturers differ as to the best method of tube welding, but essentially it consists of running a seal weld around the tube ends after the tube has been rolled into the tube sheet.

Use of double tube sheets improves steam-space integrity. Four tube sheets are used instead of the customary two. The twin sheets at either end of the condenser are spaced a few inches apart. This space is filled with condensate, which, in turn, is circulated through a conductivity instrument. Circulating water entering this space through a leaking tube hole is sensed by the instrument, and the proper alarm system is energized.

5.4.3 COOLING TOWERS

Where the natural supply of cooling water is insufficient, cooling towers can be used to cool the circulating water before it is passed through the condenser. Water is brought into intimate contact with air by spraying or by conducting heat to the cooler air and by evaporation. (Note that warming the air by conduction also allows more evaporation.) The amount of heat conduction depends on the temperature of the air whereas the amount of evaporation (and evaporative cooling) depends on the pressure, temperature, and relative humidity of the air. A cooling tower is most efficient when located in a region of low temperature or low humidity, or both. The circulating water is cooled to a low temperature, which results in low back pressures and high thermal efficiencies. Three types of cooling towers, atmospheric, natural draft, and forced draft, are commonly used. The forced-draft type is most commonly utilized because it provides a large flow of cooling air independent of prevailing winds, as contrasted with the atmospheric type, and independent of high temperature differences, as contrasted to the natural-draft type. The forced-draft type minimizes recirculation of moisture-laden air and thus prevents a loss in efficiency due to the use of relatively high humidity air.

A fourth type of condenser cooling, a so-called "dry-cooling-tower cycle," was recently introduced into this country. This cycle utilizes a closed heat exchanger located inside a natural- or mechanical-draft cooling tower and a direct-contact condenser. Figure 5.14 is a simplified flow diagram of two conventional cooling cycles and the dry-

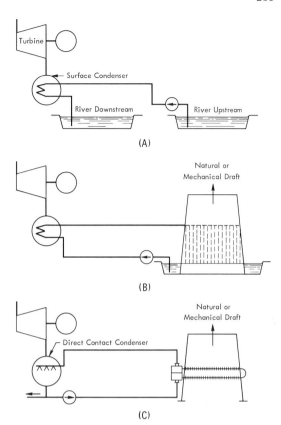

FIG. 5.14—Simplified flow diagrams for the basic condensing systems. (A) Once-through cooling cycle. (B) Conventional cooling-tower cycle. (C) Dry cooling-tower cycle. (From G. R. Reti, Dry Cooling Towers, in Twenty-fifth American Power Conference, Illinois Institute of Technology, Chicago, 1963.)

cooling-tower cycle. Reti [14] points out that the most important advantage offered by the new system is a substantially decreased water requirement for the power plant.

The following are approximate water requirements for a thermal power plant including boiler makeup and miscellaneous domestic needs.

Conventional once-through condenser cooling	600 (gal/min)/Mw(e)
Wet-cooling-tower operation	30 (gal/min)/Mw(e)
Dry-cooling-tower cycle	2 (gal/min)/Mw(e)

5.5 Boiler Feed and Condensate Pumps [15]

5.5.1 CHOICE OF BOILER FEED PUMPS

Boiler feed pumps are generally classified as either horizontally or vertically split. This terminology refers to the pump-casing bolting flange, which, in the horizontally split casing, runs in a plane parallel to the axis of rotation. This type construction was introduced originally to provide easy access to the pump internals and is still in wide use where pressure limits permit. Increasing boiler pressures and correspondingly higher inner casing pressures have made it necessary for pump manufacturers to utilize the vertically split casing, which eliminates the distortion and the resultant inner-stage leakage inherent in the horizontal design.

The demarcation line between horizontally and vertically split casings is not clearly defined. A working pressure of 1250 psi has been generally accepted as the upper limit for the horizontally split casing.

The economic choice between a variable-speed device, e.g., hydraulic couplings, and throttling valves for controlling feedwater hinges on the load demand to the plant. If the plant is to be operated at or near full load, throttling valves should be economical because they have a lower first cost and partial-load penalties will be small. Hydraulic couplings at partial loads generally prove more economical because of the lower power requirements. The higher first cost is offset by operating-cost savings.

The power requirements for each pumping system are determined from the hydraulic head, flow, and unit-efficiency curves (see Fig. 5.15). The relative values of power vs. load on the unit for the two systems can be determined from Fig. 5.16. To facilitate the comparison, the pump head-capacity curve at pump speed N_1 has been assumed to be the same for flow W_1 for both the variable-speed pump and the constant-speed pump.

Variable-speed pump power requirement:

$$W_1 = \text{rated flow} \qquad W_2 = \text{partial flow}$$

$$P'_1 = \frac{W_1 H_1}{K} \times \frac{1}{\eta_1} \qquad P'_2 = \frac{W_2 H_2}{K} \times \frac{1}{\eta_2}$$

Throttling-valve power requirement:

$$W_1 = \text{rated flow} \qquad W_2 = \text{partial flow}$$

$$P_1 = \frac{W_1 H_1}{K} \qquad P_2 = \frac{W_2 H'_2}{K}$$

where P' = power requirement with a variable-speed device

P = power requirement with throttling valves

K = conversion constant

W = pump flow

H = hydraulic head

η = efficiency of variable-speed device

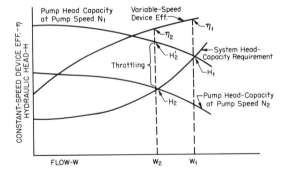

FIG. 5.15—Boiler feed pump head and variable-speed device efficiency.

The savings in operating costs can be determined by a number of methods. One of these methods uses the yearly load-duration curve to predict the amount of generation at various power levels. Normally there will be a series of load-duration curves for a machine which define the load for various periods over its life. Each period should be treated separately. The savings are converted into present-day dollars for a comparison of the difference in first costs.

Figures 5.16 and 5.17 illustrate how savings can be evaluated. In Fig. 5.16 kilowatt input is plotted vs. percentage of full load for both methods of operation. Figure 5.17 is a load-duration curve, actual and approximated.

From Fig. 5.16 and the curve approximation of Fig. 5.17, for a variable-speed device:

$$\text{Kw-hr savings/year} = [(\Delta kw_2 \times 0.20) + (\Delta kw_1 \times 0.30)$$
$$- (\Delta kw_0 \times 0.40)] \times 8760$$
$$\text{Power savings (\$/year)} = (\text{kw-hr savings/year})$$
$$\times \text{plant power cost (\$/kw-hr)}$$
$$\text{Sum of power savings} = (\text{power savings/year})$$
$$\times \text{sum of present worth factors}$$

The sum of the power savings evaluated for the years of equipment life is compared with the difference in first costs between the two methods, and the economic choice is based on an evaluation of these savings.

5.5.2 CHOICE OF BOILER FEED PUMP DRIVES

The economic evaluation of turbine drives vs. electric-motor drives for the main boiler feedwater pumps consists of an evaluation of the efficiency of the drive and its cost. The flow of power for each method is shown schematically in Fig. 5.18.

In Fig. 5.18:

Z = energy at the throttle necessary for net electrical output

b = required pump energy

X = energy at the main turbine throttle necessary for motor-drive

Y = energy at the main turbine throttle necessary for turbine-drive

η_m = efficiency of the motor-drive

η_{td} = efficiency of the turbine-drive

η_{mt} = efficiency of the main turbine

η_g = efficiency of the electrical generator

η_t = efficiency of the electrical transmission

η_{hc} = efficiency of the hydraulic coupling

The major influence on the ratio of X to Y is the size of the unit. The efficiency of the motor-drive systems initially increases rapidly with increasing unit size and then tends to flatten out as the unit increases further in size. The turbine-drive system efficiency increases with size at a slower rate but will approach the efficiency of the main turbine.

The energy flow diagrams in Fig. 5.18 are meant to be used only as guides in understanding the flow of energy. The performance of each system

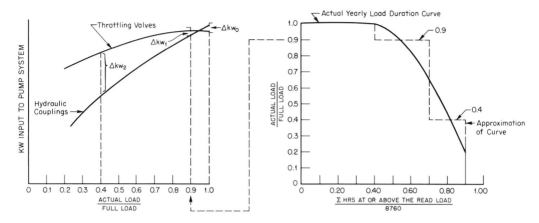

FIG. 5.16—Boiler feed pump power input vs. percent of load.

FIG. 5.17—Boiler feed pump yearly load duration curve.

is determined by computing a heat balance for the cycle. A heat balance is necessary because the distribution of steam flow in the main turbine and feedwater heaters can be changed by the steam-turbine drive. There is an optimum location of the turbine inlet and exhaust points in the cycle; it is determined by the overall efficiency and the ability of the cycle to handle the exhaust from the turbine drive. In general, it can be said that for economic reasons the inlet for the turbine should be at some extraction point in the main turbine. Also, the exhaust from the turbine drive should be used to supply one or more of the feedwater heaters in the cycle. After the optimum location of the turbine drive has been determined, the difference in the heat rates between the two drive systems can be evaluated as outlined previously.

The first cost difference between the two drive systems includes the following items:

1. Pump: When a turbine drive is used, a high-speed pump can be utilized, thereby lowering the pump investment.

2. Drive System: The initial turbine-drive cost is higher than a comparable motor-drive.

3. Modification to Main Turbine-generator Unit: The main turbine requires modification to accomodate the change in steam distribution if a turbine-drive is used.

4. Piping and Valves: There is an increase in the piping and valve investment for a turbine-drive system.

5. Steam Generator: Based on a fixed net electrical output, the steam-generator size changes, depending upon the heat-rate difference of the two systems.

6. Main Turbine-generator Unit: Based on a fixed net electrical output, the size of the main turbine-generator unit is reduced when a turbine-drive system is used.

7. Main Transformer and Switchgear: The main transformer and switchgear required for the turbine-drive systems is less expensive.

8. Start-up Motor and Pump: When steam-turbine-drives are used, a small motor-pump unit must be used to start the plant.

Extensive studies should be made in each particular case to determine the best solution. As the size of the main turbine units increase, the boiler

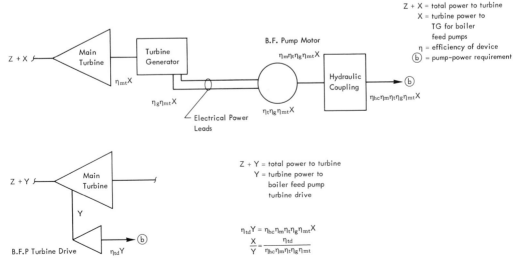

FIG. 5.18—Boiler feed pump power requirements.

feed pump sizes increase, and, in general, pressures increase. The use of turbine-drives for boiler feed pumps has been extended to many modern large-size units. References 16 and 17 cover some of the aspects of turbine-drives.

In general, turbine-drives extract steam from the reheat point of the main turbine for a single reheat. At the Philadelphia Electric Company Eddystone supercritical plant, with 1050/1050 reheat, the turbine receives steam from the first cold reheat and exhausts to the second cold reheat. As in the case of the Eddystone plant, where high pressures of over 5500 psi are developed, several pumps in series may be needed, and a mixture of motor-drives and turbine-drives may be used.

Another development has been the use of boiler feed pumps driven by the main turbine-generator shaft. With cross-compound machines a half-size boiler feed pump can be connected to each of the two shafts. The use of direct-connected pumps should be evaluated in a manner similar to the motor-driven vs. turbine-driven pumps. End-space requirements and boiler feed piping become the main problems with direct-drive units.

5.6 Electrical Systems

The electrical requirements (Fig. 5.19) to ensure continuity of service for a nuclear power plant are not appreciably different than those for a fossil-fuel plant. The following items are generally considered good practice by the power industry for plants serving extensive power systems (see also Chap. 9).

5.6.1 CONTINUITY OF VOLTAGE SUPPLY

5.6.1.1 Transmission

Two high-voltage transmission lines should be used to serve as a source for plant auxiliaries and to distribute plant generator output to the system. The two lines should leave the plant on separate structures so that both lines would not be taken out of service for any one electrical failure. These two sources, with adequate interconnections, provide a reliable means of serving auxiliary power to the power plant. The two lines should terminate at the plant through individual circuit breakers.

5.6.1.2 Auxiliary Electrical System

The main plant high-voltage auxiliary electrical system can be operated ungrounded to provide, in the event of a single-phase ground fault, an alarm allowing operators time for an orderly shutdown without interruption of service. The high-voltage auxiliary should be supplied by two separate transformers, each energized from one of the high-voltage lines. The secondaries of the transformers should be operated in parallel for continuity.

A third source of high-voltage auxiliary power can be provided by a transformer energized from the high side of the main generator transformer. This transformer normally serves as a standby source of power for all large motors in the plant. An extreme, adverse condition causing the outage of both transmission lines (L_1, L_2) and the generator breaker would remove all sources of power except the No. 3 auxiliary transformer (Fig. 5.19).

5.6.1.3 Low-voltage Supply

Low voltage for small motors may be supplied through transformers of the sealed dry type which are practically immune to trouble. These transformers can be operated radially and should be provided with an automatic throw-over for continuity.

5.6.2 SYSTEM-SERVICE TRANSFORMER PROTECTION

The two system transformers providing the auxiliary power in the switchyard should be physically isolated to prevent double jeopardy in case of fires. The transformers should also be protected by relaying via differential relays, overload relays, and reverse-power relays.

5.6.3 MAINTAINING AUXILIARY POWER WITH GENERATOR

Normally the auxiliary power is served by the two high-voltage transmission lines and the generator operating in parallel. In case of severe system trouble, which would eliminate the two lines, the generator should be able to carry the auxiliary load for sufficient time to allow for an orderly reactor shutdown.

5.6.4 BATTERIES AND GENERATOR FOR EMERGENCY SERVICE

Two separate d-c batteries should be provided for the functions listed below.

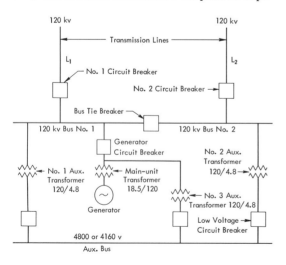

FIG. 5.19—Nuclear power plant main electrical supply system.

1. Control Battery:
   High transmission voltage breaker control
   High auxiliary voltage breaker control
   Low auxiliary voltage breaker control
   Annunciator
   Transmission voltage line carrier relaying
2. Power Battery:
   Turbine generator emergency bearing-oil
   pump
   Generator hydrogen-seal oil pump
   Emergency lighting in strategic locations
   including the control room
3. Emergency Generator:
   To supply the power battery requirements
   and recharge the battery

References

1. R. L. Bartlett, Steam Turbine Performance and Economics, McGraw-Hill Book Company, Inc., New York, 1958.
2. R. W. Davis and G. C. Creel, Economics of the Selection of 3500-psig Double Reheat for a 200 Mw Unit, in Twenty-fifth American Power Conference, Illinois Institute of Technology, Chicago, 1963.
3. H. J. Petersen, The Economics of 2400 psig vs. 3500 psig for Large Capacity Units, in Twenty-fifth American Power Conference, Illinois Institute of Technology, Chicago, 1963.
4. R. C. Spencer, K. C. Cotton, and C. N. Cannon, Method for Predicting the Performance of Steam Turbine Generators (16,500 kw and larger), ASME Paper 62-WA-209, American Society of Mechanical Engineers, New York.
5. Study of Mecury Binary Cycles for Nuclear Power Plants, USAEC Report WCAP-1832, Atomic Power Department, Westinghouse Electric Corporation, July 31, 1961.
6. J. H. Keenan and Frederick G. Keyes, Thermodynamic Properties of Steam, John Wiley & Sons, Inc., New York, 1936.
7. J. H. Keenan and Frederick G. Keyes, Theoretical Steam Rate Tables, American Society of Mechanical Engineers, New York, 1938.
8. J. K. Salisbury, Steam Turbines and Their Cycles, John Wiley & Sons, Inc., New York, 1950.
9. Condenser Handbook, Worthington Corporation, 1960.
10. S. B. Applebaum, Modern Water Treatment Developments for Boiler and Nuclear Plants, ASME Paper 4145, American Society of Mechanical Engineers, New York, March 1959.
11. AIEE Group of Joint AIEE-ASME Committee on Steam Turbine Generators, Preferred Standards for Large 3600-rpm Three-phase 60-cycle Condensing Steam Turbine Generators (larger than 10,000 kw rated capacity), ASME Standard No. 100, January 1953, AIEE Nos. 60 and 602, January 1953.
12. R. A. Wilson, Condenser Arrangements for Dumping Large Quantities of Steam, in Twenty-first American Power Conference, Illinois Institute of Technology, Chicago, 1959.
13. R. A. Wilson, Welding Non-ferrous Tubes to Tube Sheets, Field Experience in Welding Tubes, Allis-Chalmers Manufacturing Co., 1957.
14. G. R. Reti, Dry Cooling Towers, in Twenty-fifth American Power Conference, Illinois Institute of Technology, Chicago, 1963.
15. Karassik and Carter, Centrifugal Pumps—Selections, Operation and Maintenance, F. W. Dodge Corp., New York, 1960.
16. A. G. Mellor, E. L. Pace, and J. F. Ransome, Economics of Turbine Drives for Boiler Feed Pumps, in Eighteenth American Power Conference, Illinois Institute of Technology, Chicago, 1956.
17. J. A. Tillinghast, Turbine Driven Feed Pump Best, Electrical World, 144(22):66-69 (1955).

CHAPTER 6

Plant Structures, Containment Design, and Site Criteria

NORMAN T. PETERS AND JOHN G. YEVICK*
Atomic Power Development Associates, Inc.
Detroit, Michigan

Contents

This chapter is written specifically for the designers of fast breeder power plants. The chapter draws upon experience gained in the design, construction, and operation of fast reactor plants; however, it should also be useful to those engaged in the design, construction, and operation of other reactor plants. It has been written to encompass site and structures from the time of site selection, through the erection and operation phases, with emphasis on the reactor building and its containment vessel.

6.1 Plant Site and Building Arrangement

6.1.1 SITE-SELECTION CRITERIA

The selection of a suitable reactor site for a nuclear reactor plant requires not only the evaluation of factors normally considered in the selection of an industrial site but also an evaluation of the effect of the possible release of radioactivity from the reactor. The following are some of the more important factors to be considered in choosing a reactor site: (1) population density in the area surrounding the site; (2) uses of the area, i.e., industrial, farming, or residential; (3) physical characteristics of the site, i.e., seismology, meteorology, geology, and hydrology; (4) characteristics of the reactor, i.e., type of reactor, maximum power load, engineering features, unique features, and refueling schedule; (5) economic consideration of location with respect to load center; (6) location near a large body of water which could provide condensing cooling water, unless cooling towers are to be used; (7) adequacy of site size,

i.e., is it large enough to accommodate future additions to the reactor plant; (8) transportation facilities; and (9) attitude of the local communities toward the construction of the power plant at the site being evaluated.

The process of reactor site selection is not a precise science. Exact values cannot be assigned to many of the variables involved in site evaluation. The major steps in the process are (1) acquisition of basic data that present the essential features of the reactor plant, (2) determination of the preferred region based on the siting factors, (3) studies of the preferred region to find the best sites and to eliminate sites lacking basic requirements, (4) field inspection, (5) selection and land options, and (6) evaluation for final selection.

The basic plant data include (1) water requirements, such as quantity, continuity, and quality; (2) waste and waste-disposal requirements, (3) labor (construction and operation) requirements, (4) isolation requirements, (5) plant acreage requirements, and (6) electrical-transmission and equipment-transportation requirements.

The preferred region for a reactor plant may be determined by such factors as location of the plant near load centers, water availability, availability of many good sites to choose from, and community acceptance. The basic data and other requirements should be matched with the physical features of each site, starting with a systematic analysis of available maps and area surveys. Field inspection of the chosen sites should be employed to more adequately gauge the terrain, changes in the area from map data, and items not covered by maps, such as pollution sources and unmapped sinkholes. Air surveys may be of assistance. Field inspection will determine the apparent direction of population growth in the area, which may affect future isolation and thereby limit expansion. Selection of site and option procedure should be based on available data, requirements, and costs. In general, the best plant site is one located near an adequate source of water, with good hydrology for waste disposal, near a railroad or truck road, with adequate isolation, and with good meteorology. An existing power supply close at hand and a nearby

---

*Now with the U. S. Atomic Energy Commission.

populated area where labor and supplies are readily available may be prime economic considerations. After options and rights of way have been obtained, a thorough survey and study should be made to determine whether or not the choice was the correct one or, in the event of two or more options, to determine the final selection.

Sites for fast reactor plants have essentially the same requirements as those for other types of reactors. For example, most fast reactors contain plutonium fuel, an alpha emitter, but the hazard associated with this emitter is present in all power reactors that contain U^{238} and produce plutonium. Fission-product yields from fast fission differ slightly from yields from thermal fission. The total fission-product inventory is a function of power level and duration of operation and is independent of the type of reactor. In fast reactors there is usually a higher concentration of fission products than in thermal reactors because of relative compactness and increased power density. This is usually offset by the use of smaller subassemblies. The net result is that the total radioactivity handled per subassembly is about the same for either a thermal reactor or a fast reactor operating at the same power level. Site isolation requirements are set by safety guides that are based principally on reactor power level.

The use of sodium as a coolant should present no siting problems outside the limits set by national safety guides. The ability to handle large quantities of sodium in reactors has been successfully proven. Chapter 2 discusses the properties and methods of handling sodium. Sodium has an advantage over other coolants in that it would absorb such fission products as iodine and bromine in the event of an incident [54]. A dominant difference between the design of a sodium-cooled fast reactor and high-pressure reactors is the use of thin-walled components in the former. The large temperature differences generally encountered in fast reactors and the use of sodium as heat-transfer agent do present a problem in thermal transients. The increased structural flexibility might require special consideration in designing against external loading imposed by earthquakes, for example.

The low operating pressures, coupled with an ability to handle higher energy densities in heat storage and transfer, result in compactness which leads to reduced size of reactor building, components, piping, and associated structures. This, in turn, results in decreased transportation requirements and may in some instances give a wider choice of site selection.

6.1.2 SITE STUDIES

6.1.2.1 Meteorology

Meteorology is the science dealing with the atmosphere and its phenomena. Nuclear-power-plant sites require a meteorological analysis to determine the probable course of events in the disposal of airborne radioactive wastes. Such wastes may be from either normal or abnormal operation of the reactor plant. A knowledge of local meteorology should be used to determine favorable conditions for the release of normal radioactive and waste gas. The design for abnormal radio-active gas released during an incident should be in accordance with limits set by national safety guides.

Some of the meteorological parameters that require study are (1) wind direction and speed, (2) atmospheric stability as measured by the vertical temperature distribution, including rates, and (3) precipitation records. The scope of a meteorological program depends on the magnitude of the possible pollution and the number of people it may affect. On the basis of meteorological data and diffusion studies, reactor sites can be evaluated to determine which is best suited for disposing of waste gases and which provides the greatest protection to the population. The capacity of waste-disposal equipment is based on the capacity of the atmosphere at a particular location and the diffusion rates. Site buildings can be located to minimize radioactive contamination. Meteorological studies can be used to determine waste-gas disposal-stack heights. A lapse is generally defined as a decrease in temperature with altitude; and an inversion, as an increase in temperature with altitude. If inversions lie below a reasonable height (100 to 200 ft), stacks may be constructed to vent gases above the inversion.

The atmospheric dispersion of fission products released from a reactor plant at the time of an accident is determined mathematically, with Sutton's equation [1] serving as the basic equation. More extensive work has been done on this equation, which was limited to distances on the order of 1 km and near-adiabatic conditions of atmospheric stability [2]. New observations were made using x, y, and z coordinate distances from the source. Reference 2 shows Cramer's equation, which is based on Gaussian concentration distributions and introduces dispersion coefficients σ_y and σ_z instead of the diffusion coefficients C_y and C_z. An improved method of calculating dispersion is proposed; it is called the method of moving averages. In Ref. 3 the following Gaussian interpolation formula is discussed:

$$X = \frac{q}{\pi \sigma_y \sigma_z u} \exp\left[-\frac{1}{2}\left(\frac{y^2}{\sigma_y^2} + \frac{h^2}{\sigma_z^2}\right)\right] \qquad (6.1)$$

where X = ground-level air concentration, curies/m^3
q = source strength, curies/sec
u = average wind speed, m/sec
h = height of the source above the ground, m
y = lateral (cross-wind) distance from the plume axis, m
σ_y^2, σ_z^2 = dispersion coefficients, m^2

Conversion factors: meters × 3.2808 = feet; meters^2 × 10.7636 = square feet; meters^3 × 35.3134 = cubic feet.

The dispersion coefficients σ_y^2 and σ_z^2 are dependent upon x, the distance from the source, and upon the meteorological conditions. A table describing these conditions and charts from which the dispersion coefficients may be read directly are shown in Ref. 4. Since the concentration is at ground level, z is equal to zero.

Modifications of this formula are offered [4], such as introducing the effect of the reactor building on plume dilution and fumigation conditions during temperature inversions. Other modifications account for cross-wind integrated concentration, long-period average concentration and maximum concentration, and distance of required concentration from the source. Formulas are also used with this equation to evaluate cloud width and height, deposition and washout of the cloud, and radioactive-cloud dosage calculations. For total internal dosage and external beta dosage, relations given in terms of Sutton's equations can be converted[3] by the following substitutions: $\sigma_y^2 = 1/2 C_y^2 x^{2-n}$ and $\sigma_z^2 = 1/2 C_z^2 x^{2-n}$. Reference 4 discusses plume height and width and dispersion coefficients based on various meteorological categories. Reference 5 discusses a total population dosage with appropriate high- and low-dosage cutoffs taken into account. If the area inside ground-level isodose contours can be calculated, computation of the total population dosage is simplified. A plot of this area vs. concentration values is shown for the various meteorological categories in Ref. 5. Table 6.1 gives examples of diffusion parameters determined at the Fermi plant site by a technique that was based on the release of fluorescent-particle tracer material in conjunction with air sampling and theodolite tracking.

Table 6.1–Diffusion Parameters at
Fermi Plant[*]

Lapse rate	n	C_z	C_y
Inversion	0.55	0.08	0.40
Weak lapse	0.25	0.35	0.40
Strong lapse	0.20	0.40	0.40

[*] From Sec. V, p. 504.9, Ref. 6.

6.1.2.2 Geology

A detailed investigation should be made of the geological conditions at the site, with emphasis on the soil conditions at the proposed reactor-building location. The study should include (1) character of overburden and of rock formation, such as cost of excavation, design of foundation, and location of underground water-storage structures, (2) capacity of the soil to receive and to absorb radioisotopes in water, including the determination of porosity of the substrata to establish the rate of flow of groundwater, (3) corrosiveness of the soil and conditions which might promote electrolysis to determine the effect on underground structures, and (4) the ability of the soil to support the power-plant structures.

6.1.2.3 Seismology

One of the physical characteristics of the site is the earthquake history of the area. Data should be obtained showing the frequency and the intensity of such occurrences. The usual procedure is (1) to determine the earthquake activity of the area from local records and records of the U. S. Coast and Geodetic Survey, (2) to determine the geological features of the site, such as structures, composi-

tion, and faulting, (3) to predict the earthquake frequency and intensity based on precedent, and (4) to evaluate the hazard from distant earthquakes.

Earthquake intensities are expressed as ground acceleration in fractions of the acceleration due to gravity. It is this acceleration which gives rise to earthquake forces. These intensities are measured in one of two scales, the Rossi-Forel scale (maximum X) or the Modified Mercalli (MM) scale (maximum of 12). The response of the structures to earthquake waves depends on the natural frequency of the structure and the spectrum intensities of the forcing function. The relation between maximum accelerations recorded and the periods associated with them are analyzed in Ref. 7. Lateral-force design coefficients as a function of the rigidity of structures are discussed in Ref. 8. In Ref. 8 attempts are made to establish minimum acceptable standards for different zones of equal earthquake probability. Since reactor structures are highly rigid structures which, in general, closely follow the ground motion, the relative displacement between reactor components and external connections would be low. Resultant stresses would also be low. Internal reactor components will see the same dynamic loads as the force function; that is, very little damping would occur. In such cases alignments would be critical.

The equal-seismic-probability map originally issued by the U. S. Coast and Geodetic Survey [9] and withdrawn in 1954 indicates large areas in the United States which require no earthquake provisions. It is up to the designer to determine whether any provisions should be made in the analysis of a reactor plant. Reference 10 recommends earthquake intensities be applied with at least Mercalli 5 as an absolute minimum. References 11 through 14 contain additional information concerning seismological criteria. For a new concept in seismic design, reference may be made to the latest edition (1961) of the Uniform Building Code [9]. Section 6.2.2.4.3 covers additional features of seismic design.

6.1.2.4 Hydrology

Thorough studies should be made of the ground-water and surface water hydrology of the reactor site and the surrounding area. The following information should be obtained: (1) depth of water table; (2) elevation, direction, and rate of flow of groundwater as an indication of the behavior of waste disposal in the ground; (3) effect of changing water-table elevation temperatures; (4) characteristics of surface water, e.g., flow time, currents, impoundments, suspended and bed-load characteristics, and biological aspects; (5) restrictions in the use of surface water including the effects of upstream use; (6) the effect of radioactive and other wastes from the plant on downstream uses; and (7) the effect of ice conditions on the local hydrology.

The effort to be placed on such studies depends on the importance of the possible effects of reactor operation on the stream, the surrounding area, and the population. Pumping tests should be made to determine the permeability of the soil and bed rock at the reactor site and the pattern of natural drainage. Underground streams to a residential area would be objectionable. If settling basin is available at the site, all drainage can be conducted into it. Waste materials could be allowed to decay in the basin before being discharged into a flowing steam. High-water conditions may require shore protection to prevent site flooding. On a lake the maximum critical high-water point will occur at the time of a maximum on-shore wind during a period when the lake surface is at a maximum elevation. For the amount of shore protection needed, it may be necessary to construct models of several wall slopes to determine run-up and over-topping. At the Fermi plant on Lake Erie, it was found that an off-shore bank slope of stone riprap at a one to six slope and with a maximum run-up of 5 ft would take care of any predictable high-water condition. All buildings should be waterproofed up to the finished grade level.

6.1.2.5 Population Studies

Human safety is the foremost consideration in nuclear-power-plant design. Although uniform standards can be set for radiation and pressure limits, determination of the actual radiation exposure under hypothesized conditions is dependent on a complex set of variables. For example, meteorological conditions at the time of an incident may be such that inhabitants located two miles from the plant site are exposed to more radiation than others located only one mile from the site.

The Atomic Energy Commission has published in Ref. 15 reactor-site criteria that set forth a number of the factors considered by the AEC in the evaluation of reactor sites. One of the factors is the population density and use characteristics of the site environs, including, among other things, the exclusion area, low-population zone, and population-center distance.

The site-criteria guide defines these population areas as follows (see Fig. 6.1):

1. Exclusion area is that area surrounding the reactor in which the reactor licensee has the authority to determine all activities, including exclusion or removal of personnel and property from the area.

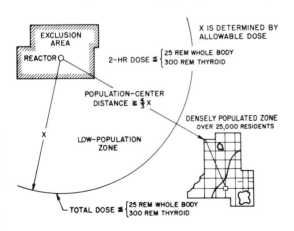

FIG. 6.1—Diagram of AEC reactor-site characteristics. The allowable dose determines X.

This area may be traversed by a highway, railroad, or waterway, provided these are not so close to the facility that they interfere with normal operations of the facility and provided appropriate and effective arrangements are made to control traffic on the highway, railroad, or waterway in case of emergency to protect the public health and safety. Residence within the exclusion area shall normally be prohibited. If there are residents, they shall be subject to immediate evacuation. Activities unrelated to operation of the reactor may be permitted in an exclusion area under appropriate limitations, provided that no significant hazards to the public health and safety will result.

2. Low-population zone is the area immediately surrounding the exclusion area which contains residents, the total number and density of which are such that there is a reasonable probability that appropriate protective measures could be taken in their behalf in the event of a serious accident. The AEC guides do not specify a permissible population density or total population within this zone because the situation may vary from case to case. Whether a specific number of people can, for example, be evacuated from a specific area or instructed to take shelter on a timely basis, will depend on many factors, such as location, number and size of highways, scope and extent of planning, and actual distribution of residents within the area.

3. Population-center distance is the distance from the reactor to the nearest boundary of a densely populated center containing more than about 25,000 residents.

The radiation-dose criteria determining the size of the population areas are as follows:

1. An exclusion area of such size that an individual located at any point on its outer boundary for 2 hr immediately following onset of a postulated fission-product release would not receive a total radiation dose to the whole body in excess of 25 rem or a total radiation dose in excess of 300 rem to the thyroid from iodine exposure.

The whole-body dose of 25 rem referred to above corresponds numerically to the once in a lifetime accidental or emergency dose for radiation workers which, according to the National Committee on Radiation Protection (NCRP) recommendations, may be disregarded in the determination of their radiation-exposure status [16]. However, neither its use nor that of the 300-rem value for thyroid exposure as set forth in these site criteria guides are intended to imply that these numbers constitute acceptable limits for emergency doses to the public under accident conditions. Rather, this 25-rem whole-body value and the 300-rem thyroid value have been set forth in these guides as reference values that can be used in the evaluation of reactor sites with respect to potential reactor accidents of exceedingly low probability of occurrence and low risk of public exposure to radiation.

2. A low-population zone of such size that an individual located at any point on its outer boundary who is exposed to the radioactive cloud resulting from a postulated fission-product release (during the entire period of its passage) would not receive a total radiation dose of the whole body in excess of 25 rem or a total radiation dose in

excess of 300 rem to the thyroid from iodine exposure.

3. A population-center distance of at least one and one third times the distance from the reactor to the outer boundary of the low-population zone. In applying this guide, due consideration should be given to the population distribution within the population center. Where very large cities are involved, a greater distance may be necessary because of total integrated population dose considerations.

Analytical methods have been used in determining the characteristics of existing reactor sites; the results are tabulated in Table 6.2. The calculated distances are based on the site-criteria guide.

The Experimental Breeder Reactor-I (EBR-I) and EBR-II plants are located in a large exclusion area near Arco, Idaho. The United Kingdom Atomic Energy Authority (UKAEA) Dounreay plant is isolated at the northern tip of Scotland, and the Commissariat, à l'Energie Atomique (CEA) Rapsodie plant is located in an isolated area near Cadarache, France. The Enrico Fermi plant is located 30 miles south of Detroit, Mich., on the shores of Lake Erie. All the sites essentially conform with the AEC siting distances discussed in this section.

6.1.2.6 Ecological Radioactivity Studies

Surveys should be conducted from the start of site purchase to determine the radiological environment of the locality. These data will pro-vide information establishing the basic levels of radioactivity and the variations of these levels. This information, in conjunction with continuing measurements of environmental activity after routine operations have begun, will provide a basis for evaluation of the impact of reactor operation upon the ecology of the area. The survey should include such items as surface water and groundwater. Milk from the area can be analyzed for gross-beta activity. In addition, radiochemical procedures should be employed to provide a measure of the levels of specific radionuclides present in plant and animal life. So that a pattern can be established, several test locations may be selected over a radial distance up to 40 miles from the site. Where environmental studies have already been made of the area, these can be used to reduce the expense of new surveys. In any case, surveys are necessary after the start of plant operation.

6.1.3 SITE ENGINEERING

When a site has been approved for the construction of a nuclear power plant, the following engineering steps are usually taken: (1) the soil is prepared to carry construction equipment; (2) roads are constructed from highways to the site and on the site; (3) marshy areas may require extensive drainage and muck removal; (4) fill dirt is added to bring the ground to desired levels for the construction area; (5) the plant acreage is determined on the basis of a building-arrangement study, with sufficient area provided for

Table 6.2—Calculated Radial Distances for Selected Reactors [17]

Reactor*	Type[†]	Power level, Mw(t)	Exclusion area		Area of low population	Population center	
			Calculated distance, miles	Actual distance, miles	Calculated distance, miles	Calculated distance, miles	Actual distance, miles
Dresden	BWR	630	0.50	0.50	7.4	9.9	14.0
Con. Ed.	PWR	585	0.48	0.30	7.0	9.4	17.0
Yankee	PWR	485	0.42	0.50	6.3	8.4	21.0
Enrico Fermi	FBR	300	0.31	0.75	4.5	6.1	7.5
Shippingport	PWR	270	0.31	0.40	4.1	5.6	7.5
Consumers	BWR	240	0.30	0.50	3.9	5.2	135.0
Hallam	SGR	240	0.30	0.25	3.9	5.2	17.0
Pathfinder	BWR	203	0.29	0.50	3.4	4.6	3.5
Bodega Bay	BWR	202	0.20	0.25	3.4	4.6	3.0
Peach Bottom	GCR	115	0.26	0.57	2.4	3.2	21.0
NASA	MTR	60	0.22	0.50	1.6	2.1	3.0
CVTR	PWR	60	0.22	0.50	1.6	2.1	25.0
Elk River	BWR	58	0.22	0.23	1.5	2.0	20.0
Vallecitos	BWR	50	0.21	0.40	1.4	1.9	15.0
Piqua	OMR	48	0.21	0.14	1.4	1.8	27.0

* The distances for all reactors were based on the same assumption with respect to fission-product release from the fuel and containment vessel and the subsequent dispersal events. There can be considerable differences between reactor types in the events that could result in a major accident and the releases that might be experienced. This must be examined on an individual basis for each reactor, and the distances must be determined accordingly.

[†] BWR, boiling-water reactor.
   PWR, pressurized-water reactor.
   FBR, fast breeder reactor.
   SGR, sodium—graphite reactor.
   GCR, gas-cooled reactor.
   MTR, materials-test reactor.
   OMR, organic-moderated reactor.

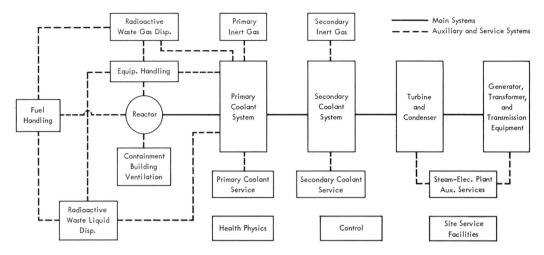

FIG. 6.2—Block diagram of a fast breeder reactor plant system.

construction equipment and for buildings and storage; (6) if heavy equipment is to be delivered to the site by rail, a rail spur line to the main right-of-way is constructed; (7) an adequate power supply is brought to the site to provide power for construction equipment (the rail right-of-way may be used for the power line); (8) meteorological and geological measuring stations are installed in locations that will not interfere with construction of the plant; and (9) a plot plan, showing a proposed building arrangement, is made preliminary to foundation work on the building.

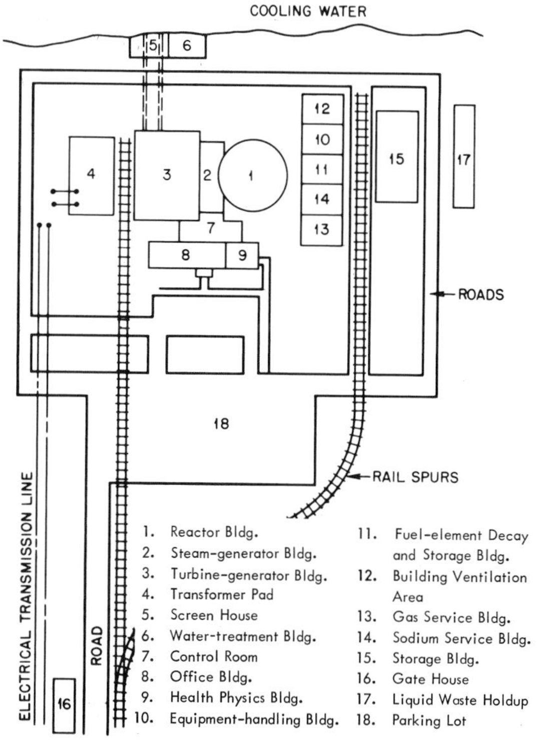

6.1.4 BUILDING ARRANGEMENT AND SITE LAYOUT

A building-arrangement study should be made prior to determining the plot plan. This arrangement should then be adapted to the site with the orientation, elevation, and location that best suit the site and the service facilities.

In the building-arrangement study, the location of each building is determined by the function of the system that is housed and by such considerations as radioactive contamination (see Sec. 6.1.2.1). Service systems to the primary system should be located adjacent to the reactor building; equipment-repair buildings and office buildings can be located at a reasonable distance. The size of the building required for each system should be based

1. Reactor Bldg.
2. Steam-generator Bldg.
3. Turbine-generator Bldg.
4. Transformer Pad
5. Screen House
6. Water-treatment Bldg.
7. Control Room
8. Office Bldg.
9. Health Physics Bldg.
10. Equipment-handling Bldg.
11. Fuel-element Decay and Storage Bldg.
12. Building Ventilation Area
13. Gas Service Bldg.
14. Sodium Service Bldg.
15. Storage Bldg.
16. Gate House
17. Liquid Waste Holdup
18. Parking Lot

FIG. 6.3—Plot plan incorporating systems shown in block diagram of Fig. 6.2.

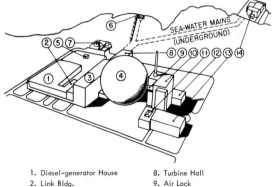

1. Diesel-generator House
2. Link Bldg.
3. Heat-exchanger House
4. Reactor Sphere
5. Transformer Bldg.
6. Outfall
7. Diesel-generator Oil Store
8. Turbine Hall
9. Air Lock
10. Element Storage Bldg.
11. Control Room
12. Active-element Storage Pond
13. Administration Bldg.
14. Sea-water Pump House

FIG. 6.4—Layout of buildings at Dounreay.

on equipment size and piping layouts. A typical systems diagram, as shown in Fig. 6.2, is useful in estimating the housing requirements for the sytems necessary in a nuclear power plant. A plot plan which may not be typical of all plants but which accommodates the systems of Fig. 6.2 is shown in Fig. 6.3. Figures 6.4, 11.36, 11.42, 11.53, 11.54, 11.63, and 11.64 show building arrangements for the Dounreay, EBR-II, Enrico Fermi, and Rapsodie plants.

6.2 Reactor Building

6.2.1 GENERAL CRITERIA

6.2.1.1 Purpose of the Reactor Building

The reactor building houses the radioactive portion of the heat-transport system. The building serves: (1) to contain fission products and other radioactive material that may be accidentally released from the reactor, (2) to contain the liquid-metal coolants that may be released from the reactor and the heat-transport system and products of the chemical combination of these coolants with air, (3) as the substructure and superstructure for the radioactive heat-transport system and associated equipment, and (4) as a barrier against fragments and components behaving as missiles following a large, sudden energy release.

6.2.1.2 Containment Vessel

6.2.1.2.1 SELECTION. The selection of a reactor containment vessel is based on the need to contain, in the event of an incident, released fission products and coolant within prescribed limits at the lowest cost. Some types of containment are (1) steel pressure containment shells enclosing the radioactive heat-transport system, (2) confinement structures, such as a mill type building, from which radioactivity can be released through special devices, such as filters, (3) prestressed steel-lined concrete pressure vessels, and (4) modified CP-5 type with external expansion volume.

Important differences between containment vessels and standard pressure vessels are (1) containment vessels are normally not under pressure, (2) personnel access to containment vessels should be through locks to avoid impairment of containment integrity, (3) ventilation-air supply and exhaust should be provided, (4) safety valves defeat the purpose of the vessel, (5) missile shielding and leaktightness require special attention, (6) many different penetrations of the vessel are necessary, and (7) provision should be made for inflow to balance any oxygen depletion.

Smith and Randolph [18] discuss a number of alternatives considered for a reactor-building design which can apply to containment buildings for fast reactors. The following criteria were used in the evaluation: (1) ease of design and construction of the containment shell, (2) ease of design and installation of air locks and penetrations, (3) accessibility for inspection and strength and tightness testing, (4) economy in materials costs, and

(5) ease of design and construction of the transition between the containment-vessel wall and the foundation.

6.2.1.2.2 REQUIREMENTS. The design of the concrete foundation, the piling structure, retaining walls, and the transmission of support of the equipment inside the building to the building foundation follow normal engineering design procedures. The use of a steel containment vessel in the reactor-building design is a departure from normal practice. A containment vessel, according to the ASME Code Case 1270N, is an outer vessel that encloses the reactor vessel or a portion of the primary coolant circuit or both. The vessel is designed to contain the products resulting from a nuclear or nonnuclear incident at the temperatures and pressures associated with the incident. Leakage should be within prescribed limits. The vessel should be protected from missiles or adequate in itself to contain missiles without penetration.

Although reactors are carefully designed with elaborate control systems and other safety features to eliminate or minimize the possibility of fission products' escaping from the reactor system, reactor plants should be designed for a credible sequence of events which would culminate at the containment-vessel wall. Figure 6.5 is a block diagram, adapted from Ref. 19, of the course of events of an accident. Reactivity insertions, loss of coolant, and stoppage of coolant flow may result in such a series of events as shown in Fig. 6.5.

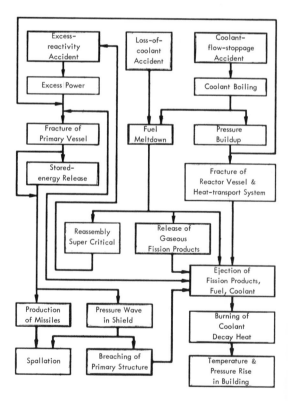

FIG. 6.5—Scheme of possible events that may determine reactor-building containment requirements [19].

For design purposes maximum hypothetical accidents in fast reactors are usually based on fuel meltdown and reassembly [20-22]. The resultant release of energy is translated into pressure and temperature vs. time histories. References 23 through 36 contain details of problems involved in violent nuclear-energy releases. The effect of missiles from such incidents, means of reducing pressures and temperatures, and methods of minimizing fission-product release should be considered in the design of the containment vessel.

A series of reactor or heat-transport system failures could occur simultaneously and result in a heat-generation rate greater than the heat-removal rate. A partial meltdown of the core materials may result in the release of gaseous fission products into the coolant and the inert-gas system. If a high pressure develops, these gases and vapors may escape through the equipment seals. The vessel and its penetrations should be capable of containing these products within prescribed limits. Vacuum-relief devices may be needed to prevent an excessive negative pressure on cool-down if significant oxidation has occurred. Valves and piping systems leaving the containment vessel to noncontainment systems should be closed on action of alarms that indicate an incident may occur or has occurred.

The reactor-building containment vessel should also be capable of providing containment for nonnuclear accidents. These include leakage of radioactive cover gas, leakage of coolant, any resultant reaction products, and the products of any incident occurring during the transport of fuel.

Although a building containment vessel may be capable of confining fission products at incident pressures and temperatures, provision should also be made to prevent breaching of the vessel wall by such projectiles as an ejected control rod or some other part of the reactor. Barriers of sufficient strength should be located between the core and the containment vessel for missile protection. Although projectiles from external sources, such as a falling aircraft, are possible, provisions normally are not made to protect the containment vessel against such incidents. There is a very low probability of occurrence and an even lesser probability of such projectiles' penetrating the reactor system and causing a radioactive-material release.

Individual studies may indicate that gaseous fission-product removal after an incident is possible through the use of sized filters, scrubbers, and a storage room.

Individual studies may also indicate that, after adequate removal of fission products, pressures can be reduced by the same equipment that removes the fission products or by other means, such as oxygen-limiting equipment.

6.2.1.3 Housing Requirements

The reactor building serves to house the reactor, the primary coolant system, and the intermediate heat exchanger. A layout can usually be made to fit in a cylindrical or spherical building (Figs. 6.6 and 6.7). An alternate design could have the reactor and the primary system in separate containment buildings. The design of the reactor containment building would be based on a nuclear incident. The design of the housing for the pumps and heat exchangers would be based on a sodium—air reaction with provisions for containing any fission products present in the coolant. A mill type building might be sufficient housing for the primary system. Cognizance would have to be taken of either the interaction between the nuclear incident and the primary system via the primary coolant piping or, in the event of an incident in the primary system, its interaction with the reactor. Quick-closing valves may have to be provided to separate the two systems. A separate emergency coolant loop would probably have to be completely contained in the reactor building to adequately cool the reactor after such isolation.

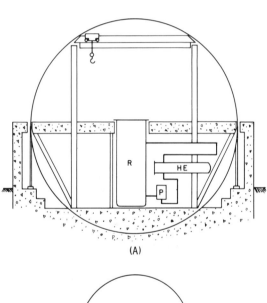

(A)

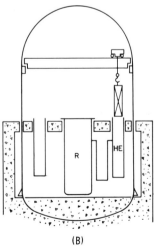

(B)

FIG. 6.6—Effect of reactor-building shape on systems layout. A, spherical containment building showing horizontal layout. B, cylindrical containment building showing vertical layout.

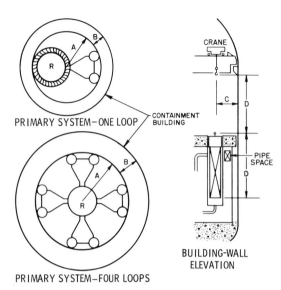

PRIMARY SYSTEM—ONE LOOP

PRIMARY SYSTEM—FOUR LOOPS

CONTAINMENT BUILDING

BUILDING-WALL ELEVATION

FIG. 6.7—Sizing of reactor-building radius and height. A, radius required to house primary-system components. B, extra length required for C distance, for pipe space, and for structural steel. C, minimum distance between crane-hook coverage and containment-vessel wall. D, height of equipment removable with building crane.

6.2.2 REACTOR-BUILDING DESIGN

6.2.2.1 Shape, Volume, Diameter, and Height

6.2.2.1.1 SHAPE. Fast reactors, such as EBR-II and Fermi, have been designed in accordance with Sec. VIII of the ASME Pressure Vessel Code, a requirement set by Code Case 1270N. This code case requires the use of pressure vessels as containment. Section III of the ASME Boiler and Pressure Vessel Code, Rules for Construction of Nuclear Vessels, has been issued and should be used as the guide for all future reactor plant pressure-vessel designs. Dounreay and Rapsodie are also contained in a pressure vessel. It is expected that the fast reactor designs for the next few years will include pressure-vessel containment unless new developments result in other types of containment. The use of gastight vessels may be even more imperative with the conversion to plutonium operation. The simplest shape is a sphere, e.g., Dounreay (Fig. 6.8). The wall thickness for spheres (Sec. 6.2.3.5.3) is approximately one-half that required for cylinders of equal diameter. The EBR-II, Fermi, and Rapsodie buildings are vertical cylinders with elliptical or hemispherical heads. Figure 6.6 illustrates how the configuration of the primary-system components may dictate the shape of the containment vessel. A horizontal layout in a sphere, as shown in (A) of Fig. 6.6, may require greater access than a vertical layout in a cylinder, as shown in (B). A horizontal cylinder configuration has been used at PWR and may be suitable for some purposes particularly where additional floor space is needed. If fuel-element storage and decay space is to be within the reactor building, such as EBR-I, a horizontal cylinder might be appropriate.

6.2.2.1.2 VOLUME. If the design pressure of the vessel is based on a liquid-metal—air reaction, the oxygen-limiting process results in lower pressures and temperatures if the building volume of air is minimized. Economically, volume should be minimized since the cost is a function of height, diameter, and the volume of internal concrete and steel.

6.2.2.1.3 DIAMETER. When the design includes more than two primary coolant loops, the reactor is generally located in the center of the containment building (Fig. 6.7). With a single or two-loop layout, it may be economically desirable to offset the reactor from the building center (Fig. 6.7). With the loops symmetrically spaced around the reactor, the resultant reactions of the piping at the reactor can be more easily balanced.

The layout for a cylindrical containment building can be made with a circle of radius A drawn to enclose the equipment (Fig. 6.7). The building radius is determined by adding a distance B that accommodates the minimum distance from the crane hook to the wall and additional space for pipes, ducts, and structural steel. Where direct access to components is necessary for maintenance or operating purposes, space should be provided around the equipment, and the diameter of the building should be correspondingly increased. Figures 4.14, 4.15, 11.36, 11.40, 11.50, 11.53, 11.61, 11.72, and 11.73 show layouts of EBR-I, Dounreay, Fermi, and Rapsodie reactor buildings.

6.2.2.1.4 HEIGHT. The height of a cylindrical building or the diameter of a sphere for housing purposes can be obtained from an elevation layout of the arrangement of the primary-system components. This can be done in the following order: (1) the external concrete foundation and the internal concrete support pad are designed to provide adequate structural support for the building internals and to provide an adequate building foundation,

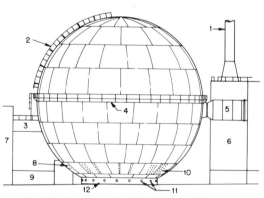

1. Thermal Syphon Chimney
2. Rotating Ladder
3. Pipe Bridge
4. Wind Girder
5. Air Lock
6. Active-element Storage Bldg.
7. Heat-exchanger Bldg.
8. Adaptors for Lower Secondary Heater Pipes
9. Pipe Way
10. Adaptors for Power Cables
11. Access Holes
12. Skirt

FIG. 6.8—Elevation of reactor-building sphere. [From N. T. Barrett, Struct. Eng., 36(3):86 (March 1958).]

(2) the primary-system components are supported on an internal pad, (3) shielding walls and floors are drawn in at correct thicknesses, (4) structural beams and columns are included for the support of the components and the floors, (5) ventilation ducts are provided, and, where these penetrate shield walls or floors, a circuitous route for shielding purposes is necessary, (6) the distance from the top of the operating floor to the high-lift position of the crane hook is determined by the length of the longest piece of equipment that is to be removed from below the floor, with a shielding coffin adding to the height requirement, (7) the space occupied by the building crane follows conventional practice, and the shape of the upper head usually provides natural headroom for the crane, and finally (8) the upper head of the vessel is designed so that it does not restrict horizontal movement of the crane carriage. In this procedure it has not been necessary to consider the location of grade with respect to building elevation.

6.2.2.2 Reactor-building Elevation

Figure 6.9 illustrates several reactor containment-building elevations in relation to grade or ground level. Scheme (A), which shows the containment vessel above grade, may be necessary if the topographical conditions indicate the presence of rock at or just below grade level. Support columns or brackets provide horizontal stability. The below-floor area may require shielding to compensate for the loss of earth shielding. Personnel and equipment access to the above-floor area is above grade. This scheme has the advantage of providing complete access to the external wall of the containment vessel for periodic inspection. The problems of corrosion are minimized. The disadvantages are extensive biological shielding and reduced lateral stability.

Schemes (B) and (C) show that added lateral stability and increased earth shielding are made available by lowering the reactor building into the ground. Corrosion protection may be necessary if part of the building is below the water-table elevation. The design and erection of the lower half of the vessel should include provisions for inspection in accordance with the ASME Code [72, 73]. Piping penetrations of the building should be above the water table. If the site is on a lake or river, the maximum high-water level may have a bearing on the building elevation.

6.2.2.3 Structural Design

Containment-building structural-design problems are discussed in the following paragraphs.

6.2.2.3.1 LATERAL STABILITY. A vessel supported at the bottom may require a horizontal restraint to provide lateral stability. The horizontal projected surface above ground may result in a considerable wind load on the building that requires the bottom head to be locked into the foundation concrete.

6.2.2.3.2 TRANSMISSION OF EQUIPMENT LOAD. The support of the building internals must be

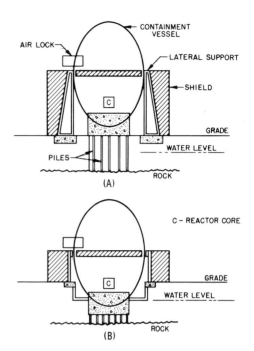

(A)

(B)

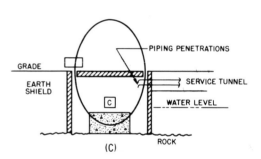

(C)

FIG. 6.9—Effect of building elevation on vessel support.

carried through the vessel wall to the foundation. Structural designers may use one of two methods to accomplish this transmission of load. (1) They may pour concrete to completely cover the internal and external surfaces, with the load well distributed and a minimum of local stress at any point in the head. This method requires provisions for any possible horizontal differential expansion between the metal and the concrete such as may occur at the time of an accident. (2) They may transmit the internal loads to the foundation through the containment-vessel wall using steel columns. This method is illustrated in Fig. 6.10, on pages 13-171 of Ref. 82, and in Fig. 11.73.

6.2.2.3.3 CLEARANCES. The building design should provide for sufficient clearances between the steel containment vessel and the internal and external concrete structures to allow for the thermal growth of the vessel at design temperature and pressure conditions as well as at conditions at the time of a postulated accident. The clearances should conform to shielding requirements. Figure 6.11 shows

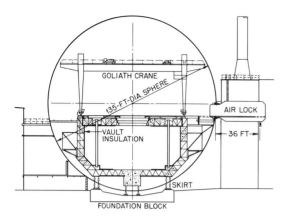

FIG. 6.10—Vertical section through vault and sphere. [From N. T. Barrett, Struct. Eng., 36(3):94 (March 1958).]

details of the fiber glass blankets that are used to form an expansion joint between the concrete and the vertical portion of the lower steel head at the Fermi plant. Figure 6.12 is a detail of the stepped radiation seal inside the vessel wall at the operating floor. The gap should be sufficient to prevent interference between the concrete structure and the vessel wall during the predicted high temperature of any accident. Figure 6.13 shows that the initial exterior gap should be larger than the interior gap since the vessel will expand radially.

6.2.2.3.4 BOTTOM-HEAD SHAPE ON CYLINDRICAL VESSEL. The Unfired Pressure Vessel Code [72] allows the use of ellipsoidal, torispherical, hemispherical, or flat heads. As shown in Sec. 6.2.3.5.3, code formulas give the following wall thicknesses for an 80-ft-diameter 20-psig A201-steel 100% radiographed vessel: (1) 0.29 in. for a hemispherical head, (2) 0.58 in. for an elliptical

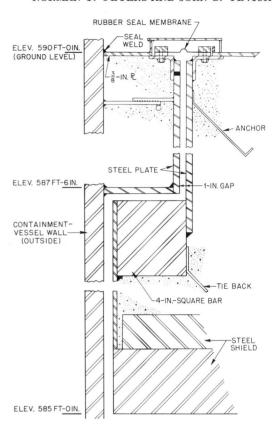

FIG. 6.12—Fermi gas and radiation seals in reactor building at the operating floor [6].

head, and (3) 1.03 in. for a torispherical head. As shown in the UA-4 appendices of Ref. 72, the crown radius (L) and the knuckle radius (r) can be varied with a constant diameter. As the L to r ratio is increased, the thickness correspondingly

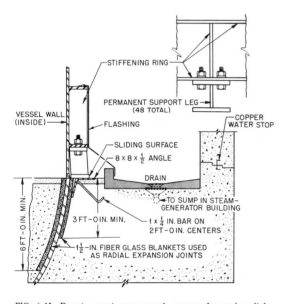

FIG. 6.11—Fermi containment-vessel support leg and radial-expansion joint [6].

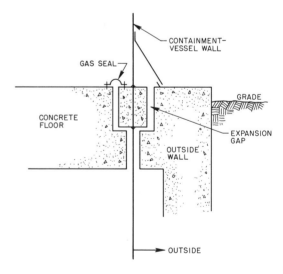

FIG. 6.13—Details at intersection of walls and floor of the reactor building.

increases. The thickness for a flat head is covered in paragraph UG–34 of Ref. 72.

6.2.2.4 Conventional Design Considerations

The reactor building must conform to the local building regulations for such conventional factors as wind load, snow load, earthquake design, and floor loads.

6.2.2.4.1 WIND LOAD. The containment building should generally withstand a horizontal wind pressure load of 10 lb per square foot (psf) of projected building area up to a height of 40 ft above the ground and 20 psf for surfaces above that point [37]. Specifications for water tanks, by comparison, recommend the use of 30 psf for flat surfaces, 18 psf for cylinders, and 15 psf for spheres. These numbers may be increased 50% in hurricane areas. The wind force on the building is:

$$F_w = PA_s \qquad (6.2)$$

where F_w = wind force
A_s = exposed surface
P = wind pressure

$$P = C_D \rho u^2 / 2g \qquad (6.3)$$

where C_D = shape factor
ρ = density of air
u^2 = wind velocity
g = acceleration due to gravity

Table 6.3, using an air density of 0.075 lb/cu ft, gives the last term of Eq. 6.3 for various wind velocities.

Table 6.3—Values of $\rho u^2/(2g)$ for Different Wind Velocities

Wind velocity, mph	$\rho u^2/(2g)$, psf
40	4.01
50	6.27
60	9.02
70	12.28
80	16.04
90	20.30
100	25.06

Selection of a value for the shape factor (C_D) can make little use of aeronautical data on drag coefficients because of the much higher Reynolds number involved. For a 100-mph wind large containment vessels have a Reynolds number in the vicinity of 7×10^7. Data on spheres and cylinders do not go beyond Re = 10^6 with coefficients of 0.2 for spheres and 0.35 for cylinders [37]. Coefficients of 1.25 and 1.5 have been used at Fermi for large spheres and cylinders, and the corresponding wind pressures are approximately 30 and 35 psf, respectively.

Figure 6.14 is an example of how to determine the wind load on the vessel walls. Local buckling due to wind pressure can occur in the vessel wall and cause local deflections. The wind pressure is a contributing factor in the design of the internal stiffeners in the vessel wall [38].

6.2.2.4.2 SNOW AND ROOF LOAD. For a snow load and/or the load of repair or maintenance men working on the roof of the building, 30 psf for the vertical projected area is used. With insulation there is an additional 10 psf [37].

6.2.2.4.3 SEISMIC DESIGN. An adequate seismic analysis should be a part of every nuclear-power-plant design effort, even though the reactor is to be constructed in an inactive earthquake area [39]. Design requirements for earthquake resistance may in some cases dominate other considerations. The analysis should examine the effect on all structures inside and outside the containment building. USAEC report TID-7024, Nuclear Reactors and Earthquakes, should be consulted for information on seismic design.

Earthquake design should be looked into carefully. A qualified seismologist may be retained as a consultant. It may be advisable to equip the reactor plant with a seismometer as part of the plant safety system [39].

Earthquakes are classified by magnitude and intensity. The maximum possible earthquake magnitude based on energy considerations is MM 8.7 (Sec. 6.1.2.3). The intensity depends on the type of soil or rock in the area. General design practice [37] has been to provide for a horizontal and a vertical earthquake load, each equal to 0.1 times the vertical load normally supported. In Japan, local code factors are multiplied by 1.5 to give a value of 0.2 g for horizontal acceleration for the reactor building and a value of 0.4 g for horizonal acceleration acting simultaneously with 0.2 g of vertical acceleration for vital equipment and their supports. Vital components of the Humboldt Bay plant in California are designed for 8 MM, which corresponds to a horizontal acceleration of 0.25 g with periods of from 0.1 to 0.3 sec. Nonnuclear parts are designed using factors of 0.2 times the live load. The Oak Ridge EGCR is designed for horizontal accelerations of 0.05 g acting simultaneously with 0.025 g of vertical acceleration. A sample earthquake design calculation is shown in Fig. 6.15 where 0.1 times the dead weight in both horizontal and vertical directions is used. References 7 through 14 contain additional detail design information.

6.2.2.4.4 LIGHTNING PROTECTION. Laboratory experiments [41] have been performed to simulate lightning strokes on metal containers. For this test a 3/8-in. steel plate was tested with 430 coulombs in the arc. The plate could not be punctured, but a crater 3/16 in. deep and with an area of 0.28 sq in. was formed. It was felt that to puncture such a plate would require several thousand coulombs; actual lightning measurements show maximum values of 240 coulombs. The use of lightning rods and ground wires for steel structures is a design detail subject to local building codes.

6.2.2.4.5 INTERNAL LOADS: STEADY STATE AND TRANSIENT. The reactor containment building is designed for loads imposed on the structure by the dead and live loads of the equipment, piping, shield walls, and floors. Examples of how these loads are transmitted through the containment

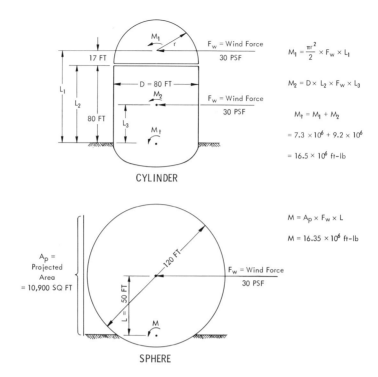

$$M_1 = \frac{\pi r^2}{2} \times F_w \times L_1$$

$$M_2 = D \times L_2 \times F_w \times L_3$$

$$M_t = M_1 + M_2$$

$$= 7.3 \times 10^6 + 9.2 \times 10^6$$

$$= 16.5 \times 10^6 \text{ ft-lb}$$

$$M = A_p \times F_w \times L$$

$$M = 16.35 \times 10^6 \text{ ft-lb}$$

FIG. 6.14—Wind loads on reactor building.

building to the concrete foundation below the building are shown in Figs. 6.10, 11.61, 11.73 and on pages 13-171 of Ref. 82. The load of overhead bridge cranes can be transmitted to the building foundations either through steel columns resting on a concrete slab inside the building or through the containment-building walls. Gantry type cranes are supported by their own column legs, and the

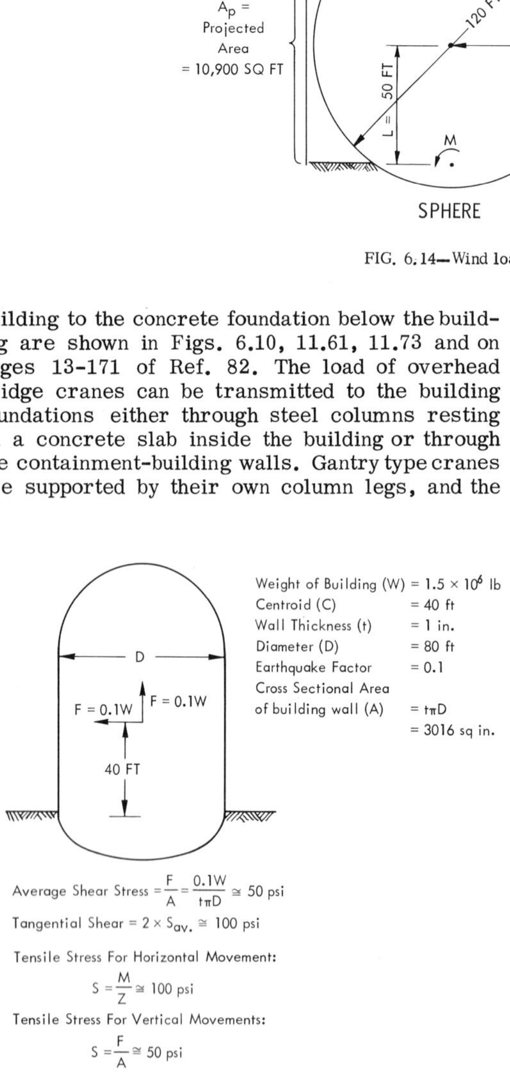

Weight of Building (W) = 1.5×10^6 lb
Centroid (C) = 40 ft
Wall Thickness (t) = 1 in.
Diameter (D) = 80 ft
Earthquake Factor = 0.1
Cross Sectional Area
of building wall (A) = $t \pi D$
= 3016 sq in.

Average Shear Stress $= \frac{F}{A} = \frac{0.1W}{t\pi D} \cong 50$ psi

Tangential Shear $= 2 \times S_{av.} \cong 100$ psi

Tensile Stress For Horizontal Movement:

$$S = \frac{M}{Z} \cong 100 \text{ psi}$$

Tensile Stress For Vertical Movements:

$$S = \frac{F}{A} \cong 50 \text{ psi}$$

FIG. 6.15—Earthquake loading computations.

load is transmitted through the building floor, where the crane rails are located, to the building foundations.

6.2.2.5 Design of Penetrations and Attachments

Building penetrations are required for the heat-transport-system, vacuum-break, ventilation, cooling, liquid-metal-service, and gas-service piping; electrical, instrumentation, and control wiring; personnel and equipment access; and fuel transfer. Penetrations should be designed for the same containment provisions as the building. Penetrations welded into the containment-vessel wall should be tested at the time of erection. Penetrations that have deteriorating joints, such as gaskets, bellows, and soldered, brazed, or packed stem joints, should be tested periodically. Depending on the size, number, and location of the penetrations, it may be necessary to reinforce the containment vessel at points of penetration. Figure 6.16 shows diagrams of typical building penetrations. Figure 6.17 is the Enrico Fermi penetration diagram.

6.2.2.5.1 ELECTRICAL PENETRATIONS. Cable penetrations use a packed-gland design both inside and outside the containment-vessel wall. During an accident the inside joint may fail, but the external joint, at a lower temperature will retain its integrity. This design has been successfully used for bulkhead penetrations by the U. S. Navy.

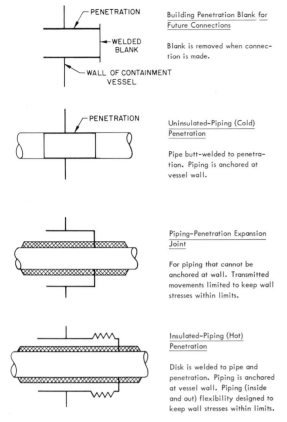

PENETRATION

WELDED BLANK

WALL OF CONTAINMENT VESSEL

Building Penetration Blank for Future Connections

Blank is removed when connection is made.

PENETRATION

Uninsulated-Piping (Cold) Penetration

Pipe butt-welded to penetration. Piping is anchored at vessel wall.

Piping-Penetration Expansion Joint

For piping that cannot be anchored at wall. Transmitted movements limited to keep wall stresses within limits.

Insulated-Piping (Hot) Penetration

Disk is welded to pipe and penetration. Piping is anchored at vessel wall. Piping (inside and out) flexibility designed to keep wall stresses within limits.

FIG. 6.16—Schematic diagrams of typical reactor-building piping penetrations.

Experiments have been performed to determine the necessary D distance from the vessel wall to the external joint, D being the distance required to maintain the temperature of the outer gland below prescribed values during maximum incident conditions. One test showed that with a 644°F temperature inside the vessel, the temperature of an attached tube in a 100°F external ambient atmosphere will drop, at the outer gland, to 212°F in 12 in., 180°F in 18 in., and 108°F in 48 in. Tubing penetrations using silver solder should also have a D distance that will maintain the temperature at the time of an incident.

6.2.2.5.2 GASKETED JOINTS. Gaskets should have resiliency for leaktightness under normal conditions and should withstand the high design temperatures. Natural-rubber gaskets give good resilience up to about 220°F. Above this temperature, less resilient silicone materials can be used. Figures 6.25 and 6.26 illustrate gasketed joints.

6.2.2.5.3 AIR LOCKS. At least two airlocks should be installed to provide access for personnel and materials in a manner that will not jeopardize the containment integrity. The locks should be large enough to accommodate the largest piece of equipment or the largest group of people expected to pass through and still permit operation of the doors. Each lock penetrates the vessel shell and is sealed at both ends by doors. These doors must be interlocked so that at least one door is always closed. The doors should preferably open into the building so that internal pressure will help to seat them. Equalizing valves should be provided to permit operation of the doors when the vessel is under internal pressure. If the doors open outwardly or if external pressure is possible, the dogging for the doors should be such as to keep the doors sealed. The air locks should be designed for the same containment pressures and temperatures as the reactor building proper.

Air-lock penetrations require the same special design attention as do other large openings. Consideration should be given to live loads passing through the locks [42]. A curtain wall of insulation should be provided to cover the inside of an air lock to prevent uneven heating and associated buckling during any high-temperature accident conditions. Safety precautions should be taken to ensure that personnel cannot be trapped inside the building with the outer door left in an open position, which would preclude the opening of the inner door. Means should also be provided for access to the building if personnel are incapacitated while in the building with the inner door open.

The air lock on the Fermi plant is shown in (B) of Fig. 6.26. The shell of this lock has a nominal diameter of 8 ft. The bulkhead openings are rectangular with rounded corners and have a nominal size of 6 ft by 3 ft 6 in. The operation of the lock is such that both doors must be closed before either door can be opened. The plant has two air locks. The second lock is an escape lock and is provided for use in the event that it is not possible to use the personnel lock, which is located on the opposite side of the building. The shell of the escape lock has a nominal diameter of 6 ft, and the bulkheads are round with a nominal diameter of 3 ft. The operation of this lock requires that both doors be closed before either can be opened. A method has been provided for closing the outer door of the escape lock from inside the reactor building. Both air locks are accessible from the operating floor. The two doors on each lock open toward the inside of the vessel. The design provides for pressure equalization on both sides of a door before the door can be opened. The equalization line of one door must be closed by means of a handwheel before the second door can be opened. A bolted and sealed emergency hatch and window are provided in the outer door of the personnel lock. The hatch provides a possible means of admitting ventilation, food, or tools required for repairs in the event that personnel should become trapped in the lock owing to a malfunction. Design pressure for the doors are the same as for the reactor building. Both locks have been pressure tested and stamped in accordance with the ASME Code at 40 psig and have been successfully leak-rate tested while installed in the vessel. The penetrations for the electrical and communications circuits that are

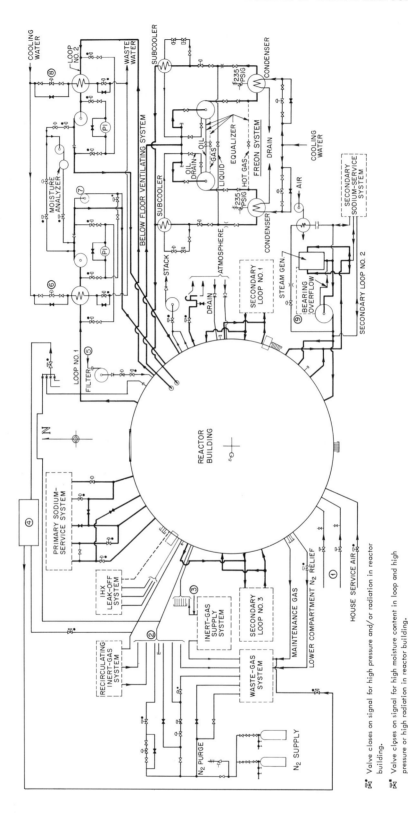

FIG. 6.17—Piping systems that penetrate the reactor building [6]. 1. Control air: valve closes for high pressure or high radiation in reactor building and loss of air pressure in line. 2. Inert-gas exit port, inert-gas pump purge, N_2 supply to lower reactor building, P.S.T. reactor-vessel exit port vent, 3. Primary inert clean gas header, 4. Fission-product detector and cover gas. 5. Air to above-floor region. 6. Closes for high moisture in loop No. 1. 7. Neutron-counter cooling loop. 8. Closes for high moisture in loop No. 2. 9. Gas-equalizer line.

⌦ Valve closes on signal for high pressure and/or radiation in reactor building.

⌦ Valve closes on signal for high moisture content in loop and high pressure or high radiation in reactor building.

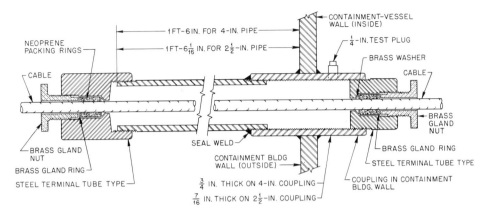

CABLE PENETRATION

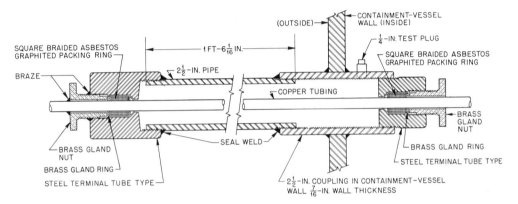

TUBING PENETRATION

FIG. 6.18—Reactor-building electrical-penetration details [6].

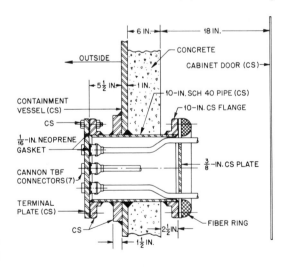

FIG. 6.19—EBR-II electrical-penetration detail [44]. Note: Cannon TBF connectors and neoprene gaskets can withstand 30 psi at 250°F without leaking.

installed inside the air locks are gastight; they are of a design similar to that used for the electrical penetrations in the containment-vessel wall. All

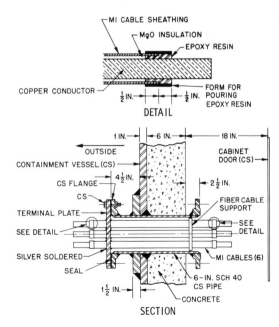

FIG. 6.20—EBR-II electrical-penetration detail [44].

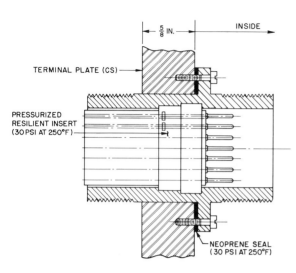

FIG. 6.21—EBR-II Cannon TBF connector [44].

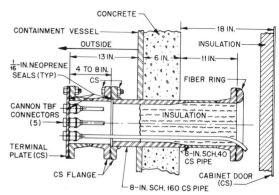

FIG. 6.23—EBR-II electrical-penetration detail.

such penetrations pass through the inner bulkhead of the air locks, and the cables are taken to the inside of the containment vessel. There are no penetrations in the side walls of the air lock, and the only penetrations in the outer bulkhead are those required for the operation of the lock mechanism.

The air lock at Dounreay [43, 76] has a much smaller volume than the spherical reactor containment vessel, but, with its stiffened constructions, the pin supports, bellows, machined components, and mechanical gear, the air lock presented problems of design and erection that, to some extent, were more difficult to solve than the sphere problems. During operation the air locks are the only means of access to the containment building. The doors are interlocked so that only one can be opened at a time; thus building containment is maintained. The air locks are designed to carry the same pressure and vacuum as the building. They carry a floor and rail tracks on which a rail car capable of transporting multiton loads can run. The shape of the air lock can be seen in Fig. 6.8.

The lock consists of a 15-ft 9-in.-diameter cylinder where it enters the sphere. A cutting plane through a sphere always produces a true circle, and this geometrical property was used to arrange a section in the sphere for the air lock to enter. The air lock axis is not truly radial to the sphere, but the introduction of a 12-ft 6-in.-diameter trimming sphere served to provide circular cutting planes and a means of compensating the opening. This rimming sphere is joined to the main sphere, using butt welds, by a jointless forged compensating ring that carries the sockets for the trunnion pins. If the air lock were pressurized to 18 psig and at the same time were carrying its full superload, a vertical force of 30 tons and a horizontal force of 50 tons would be applied to each pin. Stiffeners are provided to spread these loads into the sphere and to carry the bending moments arising when the bogie wheel loads are at the inner door jamb. The doors and jambs are welded fabrications with machined mating faces and a U section silicone-rubber seal. The doors are so hung that an internal pressure from the sphere forces them onto their seats. They are clamped to the jamb by cam type clamps mounted on the jamb, these clamps being chain operated from a single drive. The door opening and closing gear and the clamping

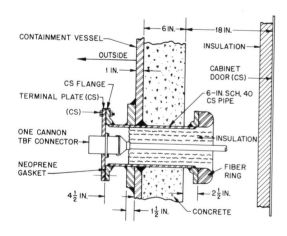

FIG. 6.22—EBR-II electrical-penetration detail.

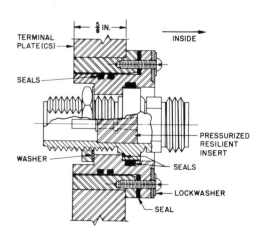

FIG. 6.24—EBR-II electrical-penetration detail.

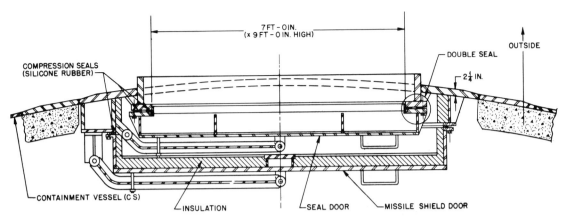

FIG. 6.25—EBR-II equipment door detail [44]. Note: Entire door assembly made of carbon steel. Silicon rubber seals good for 450 to 800°F. Both doors reinforced for 30 psig.

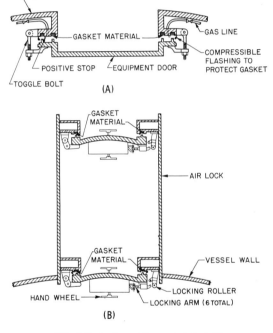

FIG. 6.26—Equipment door and air lock [6].

gear are power operated but are fitted with emergency manual operation for use in the event of an electrical failure. A section of the floor in the air lock and in the sphere has to be lowered to allow the doors to open, and this portion of the floor is also power operated, again with emergency manual operation.

Figure 6.27 shows the details of the 3-ft-wide by 6-ft-high personnel air lock used on the containment vessel of the EBR-II. The design uses a double seal, one inflatable seal and one compression seal. The seal area is insulated since the natural-rubber seals have an allowable temperature of only 220°F. Both doors are provided with motor operation and manual operation. Only one door opens at a time. The air-lock cylinder and the door frames are of the same grade steel as the building wall. The air lock is protected against internal missiles by a 14-in.-thick wall of reinforced concrete in front of the lock. A small emergency air lock (Fig. 6.28) has the same features as the large lock.

The EBR-II equipment air lock (Fig. 6.29) is located below the operating floor and has two 5-ft-diameter circular horizontal openings. Each door can be motor or manually operated. The doors are interlocked and open only one at a time. The shielded fuel coffin dictated the size of this lock.

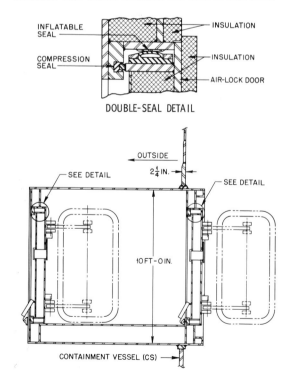

FIG. 6.27—EBR-II personnel air lock [44]. Air lock and doors made of carbon steel. The natural-rubber seals are good to 220°F.

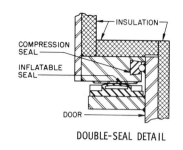

DOUBLE-SEAL DETAIL

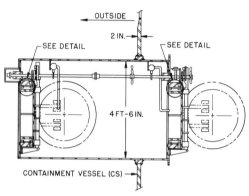

FIG. 6.28—EBR-II emergency air lock [44]. Air lock and doors made of carbon steel. The natural-rubber seals are good to 220°F.

Additional air-lock design information is given on pages 13–172 of Ref. 82 and on page 108 of Ref. 38.

6.2.2.5.4   EQUIPMENT DOORS. Equipment doors may be used in reactor buildings to provide access for large equipment. A flanged and gasketed joint is used on the door. The joint may be hinged

or may be moved to the open position on a monorail. The gasketed joint should be leakproof during normal operating conditions and also at the time of an accident.

Figure 6.25 shows the design of the equipment (freight) door for the EBR-II plant. The seal door is protected against uneven heating by an internal wall of insulation. Uneven heating of the door at high temperatures may lead to buckling of the structure and unsealing of the flanged joint. The door design also shows a heavy metal shield to protect the door against missiles.

Figure 6.26, (A), illustrates the double gasket seal design of the equipment door for the Enrico Fermi plant. It is held closed by twenty-four 1 1/4-in. steel bolts located around the periphery. Two grooves, 1 in. by 3/4 in. in cross section, have been machined in the edge of the door jamb. These grooves are filled to a depth of 15/32 in. with gasket material. Two tongues, 1/2 in. by 1 in. in cross section, located along the edge of the door, mate with the grooves in the jamb when the door is closed. Tightening the bolts causes the tongues to depress the gaskets and provide the desired seal. Positive stops are provided to prevent damage to the gaskets at high pressures. The gaskets are effectively in series, and the void between them is pressurized with air. An interlock requires the seal to be pressurized before the reactor can be made critical. Loss of seal pressure will not scram the reactor but will sound an alarm. The door is interlocked to prevent operation of the reactor fuel-handling mechanism and to prevent withdrawal of the safety rods while the door is unsealed.

A discussion of single-door operation is presented in Sec. 6.2.5.1.

6.2.2.5.5   VACUUM-RELIEF VALVES. Relief valves attached to the building should be free to

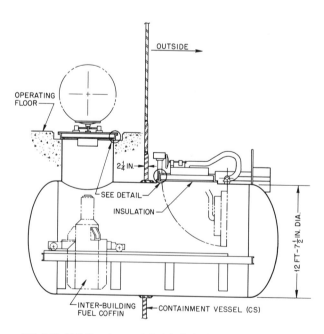

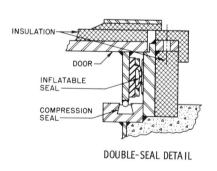

DOUBLE-SEAL DETAIL

FIG. 6.29—EBR-II equipment air lock [44]. Air lock and doors made of carbon steel. The natural-rubber seals are good to 220°F.

open in the range of - 2 to - 5 psi differential and yet be leaktight during incident conditions. During the latter condition the pressure inside the building will aid in seating the valve. The seat and disk should be periodically inspected and maintained to ensure leaktightness. Figure 6.30 shows a design for the vacuum-relief valve attachment used at the Fermi plant. Flanged connections are available at both ends for periodic pressure testing of the valve. The plastic bag over the inside connection prevents condensation and the introduction of foreign particles into the valve body and onto the valve seat. The inlet of the valve is turned down and covered with a wire mesh to protect it against "bird-nesting" and other foreign matter. Section 6.2.3.4 discusses the determinant conditions for relief-valve design.

6.2.2.5.6 PIPING SYSTEMS. Systems attached to and penetrating the building are shown schematically in Fig. 6.31. Sections of these systems, which are designed for conditions less severe than those for which the reactor containment vessel is designed, require a means of isolation. Such sections include threaded or flanged joints, rupture disks, relief valves that would relase at a pressure less than the incident pressure, or sections with manually operated valves that might be left open. Systems supplying air into the building would contribute to the sodium—air reaction and thus require isolation. Systems that supply inert gas into the building would reduce the sodium—air reaction and may not require isolation if designed for containment. All systems should be analyzed in detail to determine whether or not isolation is required. Piping penetrations are shown schematically in Fig. 6.16, in detail for the Enrico Fermi plant in Figs. 6.32 and 6.33, and for the EBR-II plant in Figs. 6.34 to 6.36.

6.2.2.5.7 INTERNAL ATTACHMENTS. Attachments to the containment vessel, other than the penetrations enumerated above, may include air-conditioning and ventilating equipment, light fixtures, crane-support ring, cable rig for electrical supply to the crane, access ladder for the crane, cable and instrumentation trays, and stepped seals at the operating floor. These attachments should be considered under all pressure and temperature conditions in the design of the containment vessel.

6.2.2.5.8 EXTERNAL ATTACHMENTS. Attachments to the containment vessel may include air locks or relief valves where the center of mass is located externally. Also included are cable trays, lightning masts and ground wires, insulation, access ladders, and stepped seals. Service tunnels are generally supported on an independent foundation and connected to the reactor building by bellows type penetrations.

6.2.2.5.9   FUEL-ACCESS   ATTACHMENTS. These attachments take many forms. Tanks, tubes, equipment doors, air locks, and other variations are used (Figs. 6.37 and 6.38). The chute shown in (A) of Fig. 6.37 is in the form of a tube penetrating angularly through the wall. Part (B) shows a horizontal tank filled with coolant. With this method, if coolant leakage to the atmosphere presents a public safety hazard, additional containment should be provided to enclose the tank. A rotor in a tank with a port in the building and a port outside the building is shown in (C). The tank and the outside port are designed for containment conditions. A bolted gasketed door is shown in (D). When tube or tank designs are used, a termination of building containment must be provided in the form of a valve or a closure. This closure must be leaktight at the

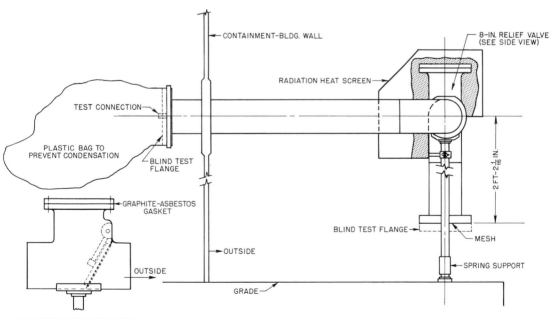

SIDE VIEW OF RELIEF VALVE

FIG. 6.30—Vacuum-relief valve [6].

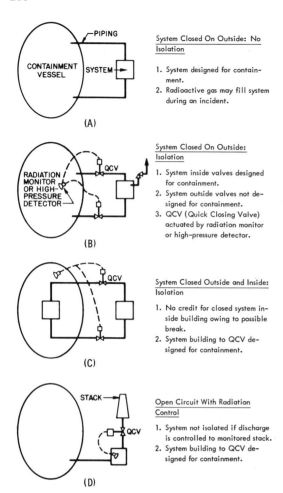

System Closed On Outside: No Isolation

1. System designed for containment.
2. Radioactive gas may fill system during an incident.

(A)

System Closed On Outside: Isolation

1. System inside valves designed for containment.
2. System outside valves not designed for containment.
3. QCV (Quick Closing Valve) actuated by radiation monitor or high-pressure detector.

(B)

System Closed Outside and Inside: Isolation

1. No credit for closed system inside building owing to possible break.
2. System building to QCV designed for containment.

(C)

Open Circuit With Radiation Control

1. System not isolated if discharge is controlled to monitored stack.
2. System building to QCV designed for containment.

(D)

FIG. 6.31—Design of systems penetrating the reactor building.

time of any accident within prescribed limits. Periodic leak-rate testing should be performed on this closure during the life of the plant. Part (A) of Fig. 6.38 illustrates an equipment air lock sufficiently large to allow for entrance and exit of fuel in whatever form it may be, i.e., shielded, unshielded, with coolant, or without coolant. The lock may require tracks to accommodate rail cars. The method illustrated in (B) uses a vertical transfer station in the reactor building to transfer through the building into a transfer tunnel, which can be equipped with a conveyor or a cask car. Chapter 7 on fuel handling presents more details on fuel access.

6.2.2.6 Service Tunnels

Service piping and other lines between the reactor building and other buildings may be contained in below-grade service tunnels and particularly so if the tunnels are to contain piping carrying radioactive fluids. Biological shielding is required for such piping. Locating service tunnels below grade allows for a practical arrangement of concrete slab and earth shielding. Tunnels should be independent structures with no direct connection to the reactor building. This prevents damage to either the reactor building or the piping when the reactor building expands and contracts due to temperature changes. Conventional pipe sleeves with or without bellows may be used for penetrations into the service tunnel. Penetrations for piping and other lines into the reactor building are described in Sec. 6.2.2.5. Figure 11.61 illustrates the type of service tunnels used for the Fermi plant. Service tunnels for the French Rapsodie reactor plant are also shown in Fig. 11.72.

A forced-air ventilation system supplying the service tunnel may be necessary to remove piping heat losses. Crawl space should be provided for

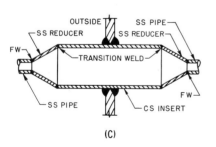

(A)

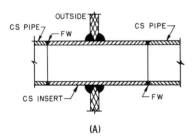

F.W FIELD WELD
C S CARBON STEEL
S S STAINLESS STEEL

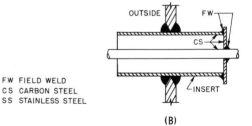

(B)

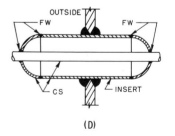

(C)

(D)

FIG. 6.32—Reactor-building piping-penetration details [6].

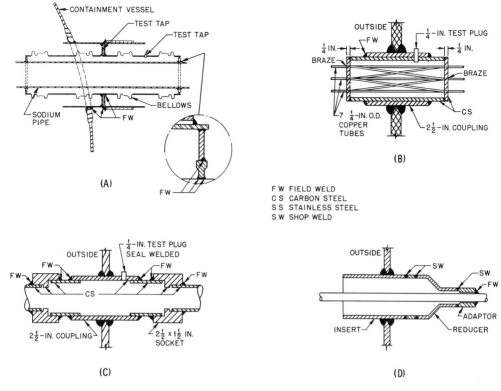

F W FIELD WELD
C S CARBON STEEL
S S STAINLESS STEEL
S W SHOP WELD

FIG. 6.33—Reactor-building piping- and tubing-penetration details [6].

pipeline maintenance. The atmosphere in the service tunnels should not be common with the atmosphere in the reactor building. In addition to piping, the tunnels may contain cable trays for supporting electric-power and instrumentation lines.

6.2.2.7 Ventilation, Heating, and Cooling

The ventilation, heating, and cooling systems for reactor buildings are designed primarily on the basis of the different atmospheres required for the

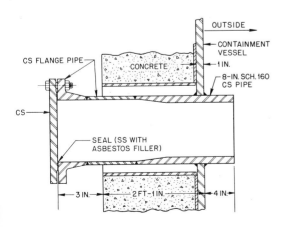

FIG. 6.34—EBR-II spare mechanical penetration.

various sections of the building. Areas normally accessible to personnel should have an air atmosphere. Areas housing equipment containing sodium should have an inert atmosphere or dry depleted air. Depleted air with less than 5 wt. % oxygen will not readily support combustion of sodium in a pool burning type incident [45].

The operating pressure of the atmosphere selected for a particular system (Fig. 6.39) is based upon the criteria described in Sec. 6.2.2.8. The heating and cooling loads can be calculated after the pressures and atmospheres have been selected. Cooling is generally required in equipment compartments to remove gamma and neutron heating loads and heat from thermal-insulation losses.

The inert-gas or the oxygen-depleted-air supply system can be operated on a continuous or intermittent basis to replace leakage losses. Control of the systems can be either manual or automatic, depending upon the degree of leakage and the degree of oxygen depletion required. If leakage is small and if the oxygen is within allowable limits, intermittent manual operation may be permitted. Refer to Chap. 4 for more details on inert-gas systems.

Heating, cooling, and moisture control of incoming air should be provided in areas accessible to personnel. Conventional air-conditioning units and systems can be used. Provision should be made for monitoring and purging personnel areas to detect and remove radioactive contamination. Systems connected directly to the reactor building should

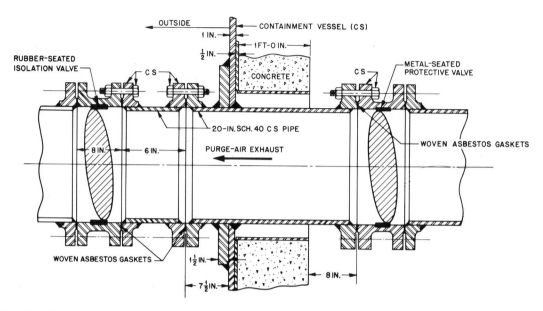

FIG. 6.35—EBR-II mechanical penetration [44]. This pipe is employed only to purge building atmosphere in the event of small sodium fires or other minor air-contamination accidents not involving significant radioactivity. Both valves are normally closed. If open temporarily for purging, both close automatically in the event of a major incident. The metal-seated valve is not gastight; its purpose is to prevent significant communication of building atmosphere with rubber-seated isolation valve, which is gastight.

conform to the same containment requirements as the reactor building itself. Quick-closing valves should be used where necessary to isolate one system from another in the event of a nuclear accident.

Figure 6.40 shows two relatively simple methods of removing heat from that portion of the reactor building which contains the reactor and the primary heat-transfer components. With the method using a cooling coil wrapped around the building, the

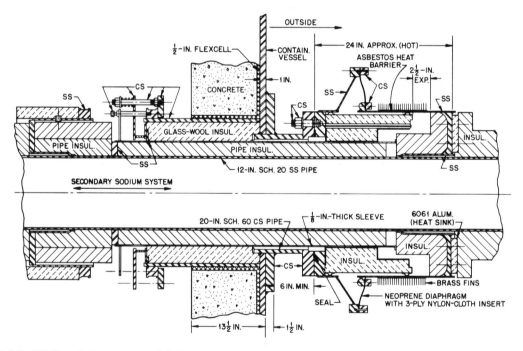

FIG. 6.36—EBR-II mechanical penetration [44]. This pipe carries secondary-system sodium between the main heat exchanger and the steam generator. The flexible-seal arrangement shown is necessary to accommodate pipe thermal expansion (it is impractical to provide an expansion loop inside the reactor building). Operating-temperature range of the sodium, 500 to 900°F. CS, carbon steel. SS, stainless steel.

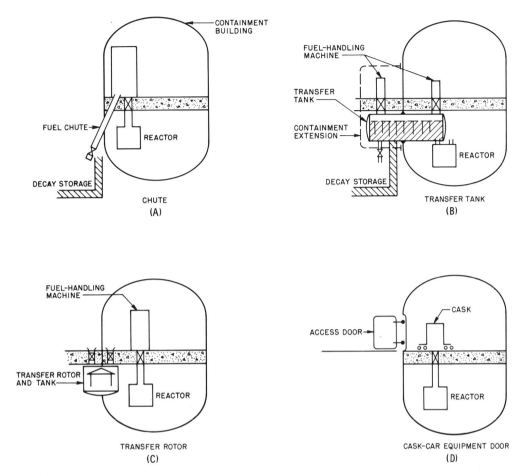

FIG. 6.37—Fuel-transfer schemes.

coils should have sufficient capacity to handle normal operating heat loads, but consideration could also be given to the heat loads produced under sodium—air reaction conditions. The second scheme, using refrigerant, such as Freon, requires protective shielding. Freon and methyl chloride refrigerants break down under irradiation to produce corrosive products, such as hydrofluoric or hydrochloric acid. Ammonia also dissociates under irradiation [46], but the products are not corrosive, and there is a radiochemical equilibrium point at which the decomposition products, N_2 and H_2, recombine to give ammonia. The operation and maintenance problems inherent to refrigeration systems located within radiation areas can be eliminated by locating the required compressors and cooling coils external to the reactor building (Fig. 6.41) or by providing special shielding.

6.2.2.7.1 COOLING LOADS. Typical loads for a heat-removal system used in normal operation include gamma and neutron heating of the biological shield, heat losses through the insulated surfaces of the heat-transport system, insulation penetrations, electrical and equipment losses, body heat, and solar radiation.

The nuclear-heat load in the primary shield depends upon the extent of neutron and gamma radiation that leaks into the shield from the reactor and upon the manner in which radiation is absorbed in the shield. The core, breeder blanket, and shield design determine the neutron leakage out of the reactor. The important factors are reactor power level; core power distribution, geometry, and spectrum; core-material composition; blanket thickness, density, and composition; and shield composition.

An estimate [47] of the total shield cooling load due to nuclear heating, H_N, can be made as follows:

$$H_N \text{ (in kw)} = 1.25 \, pfE_c/E_p \qquad (6.4)$$

where p = total reactor fission power (core and blanket), kw

f = fraction of neutrons produced in the reactor which leak into area outside the insulated reactor

E_c = average energy (Mev) produced in the shield external to the reactor per neutron captured in the shield

E_p = average energy (Mev) produced per fission divided by the average numbers of neutrons produced per fission

1.25 = factor to account for gamma-ray heating in the shield and heating from extraneous radiation sources in the shield, such as primary coolant lines carrying radioactive coolant

In fast breeder reactor designs, the neutron-leakage fraction, f, can be expected to vary from 0.005 to 0.05. The lower value would apply to a fast reactor having a large core with low power density and a soft spectrum and which contains considerable structural and coolant poison material and is surrounded by a thick high-density low-burnup blanket. The higher value would apply to a reactor having the opposite configuration. The energy release per fission neutron produced, E_p, depends upon what particular isotope of uranium or plutonium is being fissioned and upon what the fission energy is. For a U^{235} fast system, E_p would be about 80 Mev. The energy release per neutron capture in the shield, E_c, ranges from 3 to 8 Mev and depends upon the type of neutron-absorbing material used in the shield. The lower value applies to absorptions in boron; the upper value applies to absorptions in steel or concrete.

If the values above are used in Eq. 6.4, the shield cooling load for a fast reactor may range from approximately 0.02% to 0.65% of the reactor's power. A reduction in the external-shield cooling load (as much as 90% in some cases) can be achieved by arranging the shield materials and

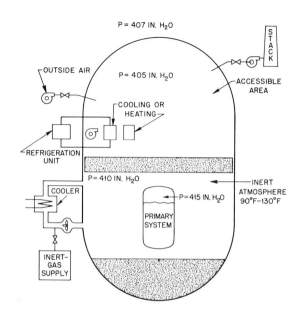

FIG. 6.39—Schematic diagram of reactor-building ventilation, heating, and cooling.

insulating barriers in such a way that most of the shield heat is transferred into the reactor coolant. Chapter 8 presents detailed information on gamma and neutron heating in shields.

The reactor, the heat exchangers and pumps, and the piping are insulated to prevent heat loss to the

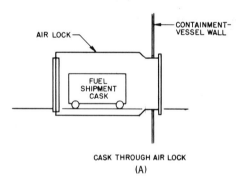

CASK THROUGH AIR LOCK
(A)

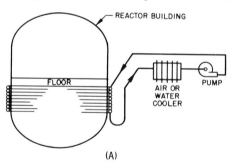

(A)

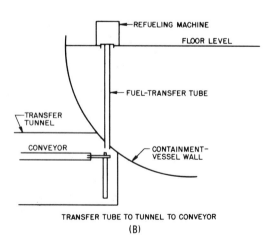

TRANSFER TUBE TO TUNNEL TO CONVEYOR
(B)

FIG. 6.38—Fuel-transfer schemes.

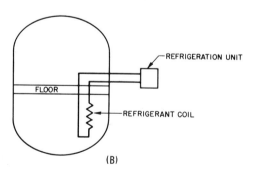

(B)

FIG. 6.40—Methods of removing heat from the reactor building.

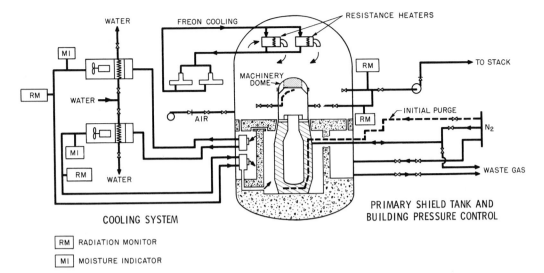

FIG. 6.41—Containment-vessel flow diagram [6].

atmosphere. The amount and type of insulation to be used should be based upon a reasonable, e.g., 130°F, limiting temperature for the surface of the insulation. This limits the insulation heat loss.

As an example of losses from insulated surfaces, Table III-8 of Ref. 48 shows that for an 8-in. pipe with an 850°F operating temperature the heat loss is 401 Btu/hr/linear ft for conventional insulation. This corresponds to 178 Btu/hr/sq ft. If there were 4000 sq ft of surface with this operating temperature, the loss would amount to approximately 0.7×10^6 Btu/hr as a part of the cooling load. Other surfaces at operating temperatures would make up the balance of the cooling load.

When equipment is operated by electric motors, the heat to be removed from the motors as a part of the cooling load is determined from:

$$Q \text{ (in Btu/hr)} = 2544 \, hp \times (1.00 - \text{eff.})$$

where hp represents motor horsepower and eff. represents motor efficiency. Motor efficiencies are approximately 0.80 at 1 hp, 0.88 at 10 hp, and up to 0.94 at horsepowers ranging from 1000 to 1500. The heat loss from motors during reactor operation may range from 0.03 to 0.04% of the reactor thermal power.

If the conditioned air space is to be maintained at a habitable temperature, the effect of solar radiant heat must be considered, particularly if the reactor building is uninsulated. Reference 49 illustrates a method of computing solar radiation in which the cosine of the incident angle is multiplied by the direct solar radiation, which is a function of the solar altitude. Values of solar radiant heat range from about 0.06% of the reactor power for plants of 100 Mw(e) size down to 0.015% of the reactor power for plants of 500 Mw(e) size.

Miscellaneous cooling loads include necessary heat removal from floors, walls, lights, and heat or missile shields. This category also includes the dehumidification of air during periods of high humidity. The range of cooling loads that may be expected in a reactor containment building are listed in Table 6.4.

Table 6.4—Range of Cooling Loads for Reactor Containment Buildings (Based on Fermi Experience)

	Cooling load in 1000 Btu/hr for two reactor output levels	
	100 Mw(t)	500 Mw(t)
Nuclear heating in shields	70 to 2,000	340 to 10,000
Losses from insulated surfaces	350 to 600	1,500 to 2,500
Machinery losses	100 to 120	500 to 600
Solar radiation	150 to 200	200 to 400
Miscellaneous	20 to 30	80 to 150
Total	690 to 2,950	2,620 to 13,650

6.2.2.7.2 HEATING LOADS. The heating load for a conditioned air space is the amount of heat required to treat incoming outside air to the desired conditions. This load must account for the heat lost through the reactor building walls and the heat contributed by electrical equipment, by personnel, and by heated surfaces, such as walls and floors. For a 500-Mw(t) plant a typical heating-load requirement may reach 1,000,000 Btu/hr when based upon a 50°F rise from an outside ambient of 20°F.

The heating system should be capable of carrying the entire plant heating load during winter-time reactor shutdown periods when there is no appreciable heat being furnished by the primary coolant systems. In a sodium-cooled fast reactor plant, electric heating should be used to avoid the use of steam or water heating systems within the containment building.

6.2.2.7.3 SEPARATION OF VENTILATION SYSTEMS. Biological shields usually divide the reactor building into two zones, one above and one below the operating floor. The separation of the two zones permits the use of an inert atmosphere in the reactor and the primary system compartments. Separation of the areas allows for design temperatures in the areas adjacent to the primary coolant which are higher than the design temperature of about 100°F in the area above the floor.

Below-floor cooling is necessary the entire year. The design should consider the possibility of utilizing the below-floor heat for above-floor winter heating to reduce the total electrical consumption though not the capability described in Sec. 6.2.2.7.2. A large temperature gradient between the reactor and the secondary concrete shielding will reduce the mass-flow requirements for the inert cooling gas. A large temperature gradient can be achieved by placing a large part of the shielding within the reactor vessel thermal insulation, thereby rejecting the heat to the primary-system coolant. A ventilated air space can be used to separate the concrete shield from the primary shield and the gas coolant can be conducted to the concrete shield before going to the high-temperature primary shield so that the concrete receives the benefit of the lower gas temperature. The temperature of the concrete should be kept below 200°F to maintain the shielding properties of the concrete. Section 8.11.6 of Chap. 8 presents a more detailed discussion of concrete as a shield.

6.2.2.7.4 BELOW-FLOOR SYSTEM. A below-floor system should be designed to (1) maintain the oxygen content below prescribed limits (generally 5 wt. % O_2 for sodium-cooled reactors), (2) maintain the moisture content of the atmosphere below prescribed limits, which should be sufficient to prevent corrosion of structural materials and to preclude a moist-air condition in the event of a sodium leak, (3) maintain design pressure and temperature conditions, (4) allow for equipment maintenance work to be performed after the required shutdown period, (5) maintain shield temperatures at or below design temperatures, and (6) maintain containment integrity for all normal and abnormal design conditions.

6.2.2.7.5 ABOVE-FLOOR SYSTEM. An above-floor system that includes heating, cooling, dehumidifying, and ventilation should be designed to (1) provide heating or cooling to keep the region within specified temperature ranges, (2) provide dehumidification to prevent any condensation of moisture within the building, (3) provide fresh-air ventilation for personnel areas, (4) maintain the building pressure at a specified level (Sec. 6.2.2.8), and (5) maintain building containment. Moisture condensed by cooling apparatus located within the reactor building should be removed from the building.

6.2.2.8 System Pressures

The normal pressure of each distinct atmosphere in the reactor containment building should direct flow from areas of low radioactivity to areas of higher radioactivity. As shown in Fig. 6.39, the above-floor pressure should theoretically be less than the outside atmospheric pressure so that any leakage will be into, rather than out of, the building. Since the above-floor area is accessible to personnel, the under-floor pressure should theoretically be less than the above-floor pressure

so that its atmosphere will not infiltrate into the personnel area. For a nonpressurized reactor the primary-system pressure should theoretically be the lowest since the inert gas above the sodium is the most radioactive or potentially radioactive atmosphere. Any leakage between the primary system and the above- or below-floor areas should be towards the primary system. Diffusion of radioactivity through seals should be a consideration in any design. If the primary sodium system is pressurized, leakage of the inert cover gas should be prevented by hermetically sealing the system with leakfree pressuretight seals. In actual practice, even for gravity-flow primary sodium systems, the theoretical desirability of inleakage to prevent escape of radioactivity cannot be entirely met since it may be more desirable to keep the inert cover gas pressure in the primary system at a slight positive pressure to prevent inleakage of air which could cause the formation of sodium oxide and other undesirable reaction products. The cost of inert gas to maintain this condition is relatively minor compared with the increased burden placed upon the sodium-purification equipment. In practice the under-floor pressure is kept at a higher pressure than the above-floor pressure to prevent additional O_2 contamination, which would increase the sodium—air reaction. The above-floor area is monitored for possible radioactive-gas leakage, and any gas detected is disposed of in the waste-gas system. This leakage problem is more readily controllable than an inleakage problem.

The inert cover gas system may have interconnected gas volumes supplied by a constant-pressure recirculating pump or may have each gas volume isolated and supplied independently. If the isolation scheme is used, repetitive filling to replace gas lost through leakage is avoided, and consequently less maintenance of the inert-gas compressors is required. In the interconnected system the pressure of the cover gas is allowed to follow the barometric changes, and either new gas or compressor operation is required to replace gas lost through leakage. To minimize leakage, the differential pressures should be at a minimum consistent with the ability of the system to maintain this minimum. Differential pressure controllers should be utilized to control the required differentials. Radiation monitors should be installed to indicate cover gas leakage at the system seals. Chapter 4 contains details of inert cover gas systems.

6.2.2.9 Alternate Types of Reactor Buildings

All power reactors have some form of containment structure which acts as a final barrier against the spread of hazardous radioactive contaminants to the surroundings in the event of an accidental release of radioactivity from the enclosed reactor system. In most cases this has taken the form of a steel pressure vessel that is capable of withstanding the maximum pressure anticipated during a maximum credible incident [50]. Some designs have been developed which do not use a complete containment pressure vessel but still accomplish containment of accidentally released radioactive contaminants. Reactor-plant designs, proposed in locations other than the United States, have used underground structures or structures in a hillside (Sec. 6.2.2.9.2). Advantage is taken of the earth to provide shielding and some incident protection, but special provisions have to be made to prevent the release of fission products to the atmosphere. Other designs are discussed in Secs. 6.2.2.9.1, 6.2.2.9.3, 6.2.2.9.4, and 6.2.2.9.5.

6.2.2.9.1 HEMISPHERE. The hemispherical reactor containment building, shown in Fig. 6.42, employs a design that may be suitable for sodium-cooled reactors. The building is composed of a steel hemispherical shell, 190 ft in diameter, anchored and sealed to a circular reinforced-concrete wall. A gastight flat floor slab on which all equipment is mounted completes the building. The circular concrete wall to which the hemispherical shell is anchored and pressure-sealed is faced with 1/4-in. steel plate and has a spread footing 3 ft thick and 8 ft wide. Both the wall and its spread footing are covered by an embankment of earth that slopes gently away from the building.

6.2.2.9.2 UNDERGROUND CONSTRUCTION [33, 52, 53]. Nuclear power plants are suitable for underground installations for a number of reasons. They require (1) relatively little earth removal as compared to a fossil-fueled plant because of their compactness, (2) no oxidant with the resultant complex air intakes, (3) relatively simple fuel-storage problem, and (4) modest air circulation.

The preferred location is in the side of a solid-rock hill for horizontal access. Vertical access is more costly but can be used. The following problems require resolution in an underground nuclear plant: (1) water supply for normal power require-

ments, (2) emergency water supply, (3) steam removal during emergency (this may require several independent exhaust lines possibly combined in part with emergency access tunnels for personnel, with the exits of the tunnels widely dispersed to make it unlikely that they would all be plugged by an accident), (4) control of groundwater seepage (this may require suitable linings in locations of low seepage and avoidance of locations where seepage is excessive), (5) contamination of underground water supplies by leakage of radioactive material (this may require a special lining if the rock is known to be porous), and (6) water seepage into tunnels (this may require emergency provisions for decontaminating the water).

The additional cost for underground construction of a reactor is chiefly due to excavation. Excavation for a typical reactor and turbogenerator equipment may require the removal of about 3,000,000 cu ft. Access tunnels would have a small volume compared with this: 500 ft of 12- by 17-ft tunnel, large enough for full railway clearance requires only 100,000 cu ft of excavation. At a nominal figure of 75 cents per cubic foot for the tunnel and 50 cents per cubic foot for the large chambers where quarrying techniques may be used, the excavation cost comes to $1,575,000. This estimate applies to a bare cavity. In some locations a lining will be required which is capable of excluding water seepage and preventing fission-product leakage after an accident while at the same time is snug enough to make use of the containment strength of the rock. In locations where seepage is slight, the lining may be simpler.

6.2.2.9.3 CONCRETE REACTOR BUILDING [40]. In France prestressed-concrete pressure vessels are being used for the gas-cooled reactor vessels of plants G1 and G2. The typical shell is a concrete vertical cylinder prestressed both ver-

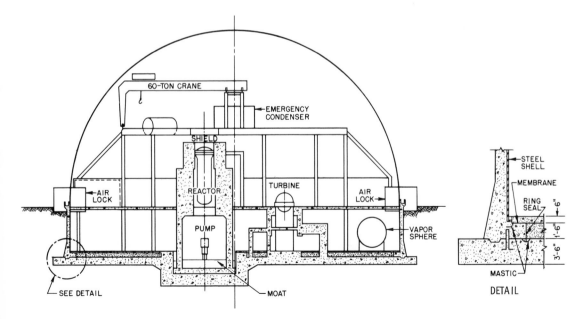

FIG. 6.42—Hemispherical reactor building, BONUS Reactor [51]..

tically and horizontally so that the concrete stress is zero when the shell is loaded at the maximum design pressure. The top of the cylinder is capped by a steel hemisphere, and the bottom is sealed to a concrete floor. The concrete is placed under a compressive stress of 2000 psig at the time of construction. The attachment of the steel head to the concrete cylinder is a difficult design problem. The pressure that such a building can withstand has not been established. Reference 54 shows leakages of the order of 1% per day for a 2,000,000 cu ft building. This rate was determined from leakage experiments of air through concrete panels and joints.

A composite concrete and steel containment vessel has been designed for the Heavy Water Components Test Reactor (HWCTR) at the Savannah River Plant [40]. Prestressed concrete is used below grade, and a 70-ft steel dome is anchored to the concrete above grade. The design pressure is 24 psig and the test pressure is 29 psig. The concrete thickness is 18 in. The test leakage rate is 0.58% of free volume per day.

6.2.2.9.4 BUILDING WITH CONVENTIONAL WALL AND ROOF PANELS [55].

The Research and Development Branch for Nuclear Safety, Division of Reactor Development, AEC, has sponsored structural components of conventional buildings that may serve as housings for nuclear reactors. Air-leakage measurements were made of building construction panels that were sealed inside test vessels with a differential pressure applied across the panels. The volumetric leak rates were computed by measuring the pressure differentials as a function of time. After the major leak paths had been determined, additional tests were made with improved methods of construction.

The tests indicated that the leakage rate of large metal-panel buildings can be reduced to 1% of the contained volume per day, provided the pressure differentials do not exceed a maximum of 0.5 psi and provided improved construction methods are used. Large concrete buildings can be constructed with an internal-pressure capability up to 5 psig which leak less than 1% of their contained volume per day at 5 psi differential. This contrasts with such pressure vessels as Fermi, EBR-II, and Dounreay, which leak less than 0.1% per day at internal pressures on the order of 25 psig.

6.2.2.9.5 REACTOR BUILDING WITH EXTERNAL EXPANSION VOLUME.

The gastight building of the type used to house the CP-5 research reactor at the Argonne National Laboratory utilizes a containment design that may, with proper design, be adapted for fast reactors.

The CP-5 building was designed on the principle that a second container for fission products outside the reactor itself would afford a considerable measure of protection against the dispersion of fission products following a reactor incident. The gastight portion of the main building (Fig. 6.43) is cylindrical in shape and is constructed of concrete. Access into or out of the gastight portions of the building is through either a personnel air lock with two sliding doors or a truck air lock with overhead doors. These doors are on each side of an air chamber and are interlocked in such a manner that the building always remains sealed. Ventilation is provided by centrifugal fans that maintain a slight negative building pressure (approximately 1/4 in. H_2O pressure) at all times. Air is introduced and exhausted through large concrete ducts, each of which contains dampers that are automatically closed in the event of excessive radioactivity in the building air. Liquid seals are also provided in each duct to ensure the gastight feature. Exhaust air passes through a holdup room with a capacity of about 1 min of air flow before passing to the exhaust stack. This air holdup allows the fan motors to be stopped and dampers and seals to be closed automatically before radioactive air reaches the exhaust stack. Following a possible release of radioactivity in this building, the negative pressure is maintained in the building by a separate "vapor dome" with a floating diaphragm attached to a flange at the bottom of a steel hemisphere. The diaphragm will fall slowly to maintain a negative pressure in the building. The space above the diaphragm is connected by pipe to the reactor building, and the space below is vented to the atmosphere. The volume is such that an inleakage of 1,000 cu ft/day could take place for 20 to 30 days after an incident. The tightness of a reactor building with a separate vapor dome can be tested by closing the building in the same fashion in which it would be closed following a radioactive-contamination incident and allowing the vapor dome to expand to its largest volume. This volume and the time required for its filling are measures of the leakage rate of the building when corrected for changes in the humidity, temperature, and atmospheric pressure. All internal surfaces of concrete for the CP-5 containment building are painted with three coats of a vinyl resin paint which seals the pores of the

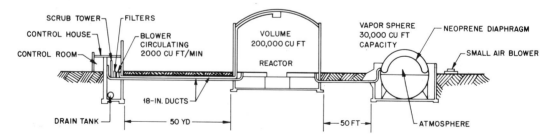

FIG. 6.43—Reactor building with separate expansion volume, CP-5. (From H. Etherington (Ed.), Nuclear Engineering Handbook, p. 13-163, McGraw-Hill Book Company, Inc., New York, 1958.)

concrete and provides a surface that can be easily decontaminated of radioactive products. The normal building leakage approximates 0.5% of its volume per day with a pressure differential of 1/8 in. H_2O.

An adaptation of such a system to a fast reactor could consist of a below-floor containment with depleted air to eliminate the sodium—air reaction. The inleakage of air would be counterbalanced by inert-gas makeup and a circulating system that would be shut off during an incident when the separate dome would come into play. It would probably be necessary to institute an emergency inert-gas makeup to the reactor building during an incident. A connection would be installed from the below-floor unit to a separate dome such as CP-5 to maintain the inleakage.

6.2.2.10 Protection of Reactor-building Internal Structural Members Against Sodium-leakage Effects

Where it is likely that a quantity of sodium might be spilled from a system, containers for the leaking sodium, such as spill pans, can be provided. Since the total quantity of smoke and heat liberated per unit time will vary directly with surface area, shallow spill pans should not be used as containers for large-volume leaks. Shallow spill pans can serve as collection devices; they should be sloped to conduct the metal to suitable closed vessels. Since cooling has a depressing effect on reaction rate, the closed vessels should be placed, if possible, so that they can be cooled by convective currents in the gaseous medium surrounding them. An alternate to having closed vessels is to line the sodium-component compartments with steel so that they can serve as containers. This is done at the Fermi plant.

Liquid sodium should not be allowed to contact concrete. Where sodium might contact column bases and other support members located within the spill-pan area, pipe sleeves and skirts welded to the pan should be installed. If there is a danger of sodium spilling into the sleeve from an overhead leak, a suitable sheet-metal cap should be provided over the open end and adequate space should be left between cap and sleeve to afford good convection cooling inside the sleeve. The protection of structural members against the detrimental effects of sodium that might leak or spill from a process system can be accomplished in a number of ways [56]. These include (1) prevention of contact of structural members with leaking sodium by the use of such items as spill pans and equipment enclosures, (2) removal of leaking sodium, (3) pressure-control measures to prevent buildup of excessive internal pressures, (4) water-control measures to exclude water from a potential spillover, and (5) smoke-control measures, if there is a possibility of smoke being generated, to remove quickly any caustic fumes that might be evolved. Where the possibility is high that sodium may jet or be blown beyond the limits of a spill pan, deflectors or collectors should be installed. The thermal insulation commonly used on high-temperature piping systems also serves to collect and conduct away small amounts of leaking sodium. If the thermal insulation is backed up by a long strip of 0.002-in.-thick stainless-steel foil of sufficient width to cover the bottom half of the insulation, this strip being held in place by a steel jacket, sodium leaking from any point along the pipe can be conducted to a collection point, and the leaking metal can be confined. Equipment enclosures of light-gauge sheet metal secured by sheet-metal screws to a steel frame can be added to a spill pan to minimize the smoke nuisance from a sodium spill. The secondary containment system at Fermi provides an excellent means of containing sodium leaks.

A satisfactory method of sodium-smoke abatement is desirable. Reference 57 discusses different systems for liquid-metal-smoke abatement; these systems include two types of scrubber systems, an electrostatic precipitator, and two types of filters. It is assumed in Ref. 57 that the method of smoke abatement should have a weight collection efficiency of at least 90% to be economical. After 90% of the particulate in liquid-metal smoke has been removed, the effluent becomes practically invisible, and the remainder can be dissipated in the atmosphere. As a result of the tests using sodium, NaK, and lithium, the following conclusions and recommendations were made: (1) either a scrubber system or a modified electrostatic precipitator with smoke-removal efficiencies on the order of 99% is recommended for use in the abatement of liquid-metal smoke, (2) capillary-cell filter units, as manufactured, will not adequately abate liquid-metal fumes, and filter casings packed with bulk Dynel fiber will not reduce liquid-metal smoke without developing prohibitive pressure losses, and (3) use of the dry, bonded Dynel fiber filter for liquid-metal fumes is not feasible since the filter tends to load up owing to the hygroscopic nature of the fumes at a rate that makes its use impractical for this purpose.

The discharge of any effluent should be based on design limits that account for meteorological conditions as well as the condition of the effluent, such as its radioactivity or its chemical effects.

6.2.3 CONTAINMENT-VESSEL DESIGN

6.2.3.1 Design Pressure and Temperature

The containment vessel should be designed to maintain containment integrity for all conditions of normal and abnormal operation. The design conditions should be based on a series of hypothesized but credible accidents which would produce the maximum building temperature and pressure. Containment vessels for fast reactors containing liquid-metal fuels may be designed on the basis of any one of several studies and experiments. Examples of some of the studies are: (1) a liquid-metal—air reaction, described in Sec. 6.2.3.1.1, and (2) a nuclear incident that generates a large energy release. One approach is to design on the basis of a sodium—air reaction and then analyze the resulting structure for inadequacies in the event of a nuclear incident. This section will present only the liquid-metal—air reaction using sodium as the coolant. Dounreay, EBR-II, and Fermi were designed on the basis of a sodium—air reaction.

The use of an inert gas or an oxygen-depleted air atmosphere surrounding the reactor and heat-transport-system components reduces the amount of oxygen available; thus a sodium leak would require access to the above-floor air for reaction to occur. Since full isolation between the above-floor air and the below-floor inert atmosphere may not be feasible, the design should include the possibiltiy of sodium leakage followed by a rupture of the operating floor. All piping and air ducts leading into the containment vessel should be closed rapidly if a sodium—air reaction occurs to prevent air from being fed into the vessel.

In an analysis of the potential hazards associated with a sodium—air reaction, it is necessary to consider the effects of various types of accidents involving the release of sodium into the reactor-building atmosphere. Although the presence of moisture in the above-floor air can be considered, as in Sec. 6.2.3.1.1, its contribution to the total energy is small, on the order of 5% for a relative humidity of 30% and 300,000 cu ft of air. Sodium exposure to the atmosphere can be studied in three broad categories: (1) stagnant pool, (2) pressurized spray, and (3) mass ejection. Of these, mass ejection is potentially the most severe. The resulting sodium—air reaction would occur primarily while the sodium is in flight. The heat of reaction would be transferred directly to the atmosphere, with little energy being lost initially to structures or the building wall. The heat of this reaction is almost completely utilized (initially) in raising the temperature and pressure of the building atmosphere.

The only effective difference between the mass ejection and the high-pressure spray discharge is one of reaction rate. Under given temperature conditions the rate of reaction is a function of the rate of sodium surface exposure, which depends upon the mass rate and particle size of the sodium discharge. In a spray discharge it is improbable that a very large discharge rate and a fine-particle dispersion could exist simultaneously. The ejection of a large mass of finely dispersed sodium results in optimum conditions for the most severe reactions.

6.2.3.1.1 SODIUM—AIR REACTIONS: MASS EJECTION OF SODIUM [44,58]. According to Ref. 58 the predominant reaction that occurs when high-temperature molten sodium in a finely divided state is mixed with air is oxidation of the sodium to form sodium peroxide

$$2Na + O_2 \rightarrow Na_2O_2 \qquad (\Delta H = -124\,kcal/mole\ O_2) \quad (6.5)$$

Reaction 6.5 appears to proceed until all oxygen is combined before additional sodium reduces the sodium peroxide to sodium monoxide

$$Na + \tfrac{1}{2}Na_2O_2 \rightarrow Na_2O \qquad (\Delta H = -20\,kcal/mole) \quad (6.6)$$

The presence of water vapor in the initial phase of the reaction results in the formation of sodium hydroxide

$$Na + HOH + \tfrac{1}{2}Na_2O_2 \rightarrow 2NaOH$$

$$(\Delta H = -85\,kcal/mole\ HOH) \quad (6.7)$$

On the basis of energy derived from these reactions, the theoretical atmospheric pressures and temperatures for a contained sodium—air reaction have been calculated and are shown in Fig. 6.44. These curves show the theoretical maximum temperature and maximum pressure obtained as a function of the quantity of sodium ejected into an experimental reaction vessel, assuming 100% reaction (of sodium or oxygen, whichever is limiting) and no heat loss to the vessel wall. The experimental vessel [58] used in performing the test was 3 ft in diameter, 10 ft high, and had a volume of 72 cu ft. Sodium was located in a reservoir below the vessel which was separated from the vessel interior by a thick rupture diaphragm. Beneath the sodium reservoir was a reservoir containing hydrogen and oxygen which was separated from the sodium reservoir by a thin rupture diaphragm. Sodium was ejected at a temperature of 400°C, in quantities varying from 0.45 to 3.5 lb and in times varying from 3 to 10 msec. The initial vessel conditions for pressure, temperature, and oxygen concentrations were atmospheric. The ejection was by ignition of the H_2 and O_2. The sodium to oxygen molar ratio varied from 0.51 to 4.07.

There are three reaction zones indicated in Fig. 6.44. Zone I represents the region where the peroxide reaction predominates and where the heat of reaction is distributed between nitrogen, sodium peroxide, and residual oxygen. Zone II represents the region of peroxide reduction by additional sodium, with the additional heat of reaction distributed between the nitrogen and the reaction products sodium peroxide and sodium monoxide. Zone III represents the region where all oxygen has been converted to sodium monoxide and where additional sodium remains unreacted. In zone III the heat capacity of the excess sodium is effective in reducing the overall system temperature. In this zone the partial pressure of sodium vapor is not included in the pressure curve. It is assumed that in a real system the container walls and

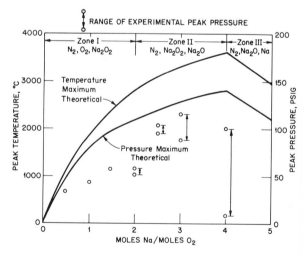

FIG. 6.44—Sodium—air reaction: mass sodium ejection, peak temperatures vs. various sodium to oxygen ratios [58].

component surfaces would act as condenser plates for sodium vapor; consequently its partial pressure would not contribute to the pressure stress imposed upon the containment vessel.

Postulation of the intermediate sodium peroxide step in the formation of sodium monoxide is principally reflected in the temperature values within zone I. Initially, in the oxygen-excess system, the oxidation of a given quantity of sodium results in higher temperatures than would be experienced by direct monoxide formation

$$2Na + \tfrac{1}{2}O_2 \rightarrow Na_2O \qquad (\Delta H = -104\,\text{kcal}) \quad (6.8)$$

It is emphasized that the curves presented in Fig. 6.44 are those for an ideal system of zero reaction time and, as such, represent a theoretical upper limit for conditions encountered in a real system. In a real system a discrete time interval is required for mixing and reaction. During this reaction period the atmospheric temperature becomes sufficiently high for appreciable heat loss to the cold reactor-building surfaces. Further heat loss, in the actual case, results from the incomplete reaction of sodium while in the air. The unreacted sodium not only absorbs heat, but, when it impinges on the reactor-building structures, it helps to transfer heat from the atmosphere to the wall. Thus an actual-system maximum temperature would be less than the theoretical value by an amount dependent upon the magnitude of these heat losses. The mixing and reaction processes in the actual case are too complex to permit complete analysis; the necessary information is lacking on the details of the ejection process and the sodium—air reaction rates. Realistic estimates of maximum temperatures and pressures attainable in practice can be obtained only through experimental testing. Results of the experimental test program are plotted in Fig. 6.44 for comparison with the theoretical curves.

In the opinion of some observers [83] the experimental results of Fig. 6.44 indicate that the primary reaction product consists entirely of the monoxide, Na_2O. At the temperatures involved in a sodium—air reaction, the peroxide is highly unstable, and the reaction would not take place. The peroxide decomposes at 646°C [Brewer, Chem. Rev., 52 (1953)]. An equilibrium calculation for the sodium—air reaction assuming Na_2O as the end product has been carried out in detail and is given in Ref. 59. The calculation is based on a constant-volume adiabatic equilibrium and represents the maximum sodium—air accident as applied to a containment-vessel incident. Reference 59 results are 129 psig and 1959°C, lower than Ref. 44 results. Another factor to be considered is the equilibrium that exists between Na_2O and its reactants, as covered in Ref. 59.

In any attempt to extrapolate these theoretical or experimental results to large containment systems, it must be remembered that the rate of pressure falloff in a large reactor building would be considerably lower than in the experimental vessel owing to the much smaller ratio of surface area available for cooling to gas volume and because the building-surface heat capacity is smaller. The steel in the experimental reaction vessel has

a total heat capacity of 130 kcal per degree centigrade of temperature rise. This large heat capacity contributes greatly to the rapid rate of system-pressure reduction observed immediately after the establishment of peak pressure (the pressure normally returning to atmospheric within 3 min from the time of sodium ejection). The relative heat capacity of the experimental reaction vessel, for example, is about twelve times that of the EBR-II reactor building, Fig. 11.50. Accordingly, a higher average wall temperature would be produced in the EBR-II reactor building (perhaps 180°C in the most pessimistic case), with correspondingly reduced heat-transfer rates and slower pressure falloff. Because of the much larger mean diameter of a reactor building, the effective heat-transfer rate to the wall during the pressure buildup period, effected principally by unreacted sodium and reaction-product transport, would be comparatively lower, and the peak pressure would be somewhat higher. Effective propagation of the secondary dispersion mechanism to include the entire building atmosphere would be much less likely to occur in the larger system.

Every effort was made in the experimental system to achieve optimum reaction conditions. It is unlikely that these conditions could be met accidentally in the larger system. In the EBR-II reactor building, the range of the quantity of sodium ejected and the range of the ejection energy employed in this investigation correspond to a mass ejection of from 2,900 to 23,000 lb of 300°C sodium with ejection energies of from 4.1×10^4 to 14×10^4 kcal (equivalent to 90 to 310 lb of TNT).

If a nuclear accident of sufficiently large magnitude to effect ejection of significant amounts of sodium were to occur, the reactor-building atmosphere could be expected to include fission products and plutonium as well as activated sodium. At the conclusion of fallout, the atmosphere would probably consist essentially of nitrogen and volatile or gaseous fission products, the major portion of the nonvolatile fission-product particles having been swept down by the falling reaction products. Thereafter, any atmosphere leakage from the containment vessel would involve only relatively small fractions of the radioactive material originally introduced.

6.2.3.1.2   SODIUM—AIR REACTION: POOL BURNING [59]. Mass ejection of sodium into air results in the most severe reaction. If the possibility of such an explosive ejection can be eliminated by design, other possibilities of a sodium—air reaction should be considered.

Where the radioactive sodium components are located in an inert atmosphere below the operating floor of a reactor building, leaking sodium would collect in a pool in the bottom of the building. The inert atmosphere, if maintained in this region, would prevent burning. Although the multiple-containment design of the reactor system reduces the probability of a major leak to a low value, for purposes of design it can be assumed that a major leak does occur and that at the same time the seals between the upper and lower compartments fail allowing air from the area above the reactor operating floor to enter the area underneath the operating floor which would cause the sodium to burn. The sodium burning area is taken as the area of the reactor operating floor. Basic data on the burning rate of liquid sodium are needed. Once combustion begins, the burning rate is governed principally by two factors, the oxygen concentration in the atmosphere, which continually decreases because of the burning, and the resulting temperature of the gas. Experiments have been carried out to determine this burning rate [59, 60], and, from the results of the experiments, it was possible to establish the mechanism of burning in a sodium pool. Experimental sodium-pool burning tests indicate that the burning rate is almost independent of the sodium temperature in the temperature range considered and that the sodium–air reaction is controlled by a diffusional mechanism rather than by the velocity of the chemical reaction.

If the reaction between sodium and oxygen takes place on the surface of the sodium, then the burning rate is independent of the number of sodium molecules, and the burning rate is given by

$$B = k n_O \sqrt{T_g} \qquad (6.9)$$

where B = burning rate
$\qquad k$ = a constant
$\qquad n_O$ = oxygen concentration
$\qquad T_g$ = gas temperature

Based on the sodium–air accident, the times vs. temperature profiles of the reactor-building atmosphere and containment-vessel shell can be calculated [59] using the initial sodium burning rate of 5 lb/hr/sq ft and the burning mechanism as expressed in Eq. 6.9. As the sodium burns, the atmosphere in the building is heated and, at the same time, the oxygen in the atmosphere is consumed. The hot gases, oxygen and nitrogen, give up their heat to the metal containment-vessel shell and to the extraneous metal in the building, i.e., crane girder, structural supports, and other material. The containment-vessel shell transfers heat to the outside atmosphere, but the extraneous metal does not.

Basing the burning rate on the simple collision mode, Eq. 6.9 gives

$$\frac{B(t)}{B(0)} = \frac{n_O}{n_O^0} \left[\frac{T_g}{T_g(0)} \right]^{\frac{1}{2}} \qquad (6.10)$$

where $B(t)$ is the burning rate corresponding to the oxygen concentration of n_O moles and temperature T_g and $B(0)$ is the initial burning rate corresponding to the initial oxygen concentration of n_O^0 moles and temperature $T_g(0)$.

The oxygen concentration is given by:

$$n_O = n_O^0 - b \int_0^t B(t')\,dt' \qquad (6.11)$$

where b is a conversion factor relating the total amount of sodium burned to the amount of oxygen consumed. Substituting Eq. 6.11 in Eq. 6.10 and differentiating the resulting expression to eliminate the integral gives

$$\frac{dx}{dt} = \frac{x}{2T_g} \frac{dT_g}{dt} - kx\sqrt{T_g} \qquad (6.12)$$

where

$$x = B(t)/B(0)$$

and

$$k = b\,B(0) \Big/ \left[n_O^0 \sqrt{T_g(0)} \right]$$

Equation 6.12 gives the necessary differential expression for burning rate as a function of the gas temperature. The heat input of the burning sodium is obtained by multiplying the burning rate by the heat of combustion of liquid sodium going to Na_2O and the area of burning sodium. The heat of combustion is about 3900 Btu/lb of sodium burned [61]. The assumption is made that the burning rate of sodium at constant temperature is proportional to the amount of oxygen present in the building and that the burning continues until the building atmosphere is depleted to 5 vol. % oxygen. The latter assumption is justified by the experimental work reported in Ref. 45. At oxygen concentrations of 5 vol. % and below, no sodium burning was observed.

The schematic drawing of the Fermi reactor building shown in Fig. 11.61 should be used as an aid in defining the temperatures and heat-transfer coefficients involved. The following nomenclature is used:

		Units
$B(0)$	= initial burning rate of sodium	Btu/hr/sq ft
$B(t)$	= burning rate of sodium at time t	Btu/hr/sq ft
n_g	= total moles of gas in the reactor building at time t	lb-moles
n_i	= moles of nitrogen	lb-moles
n_O	= concentration of oxygen at time t	lb-moles
n_O^0	= initial concentration of oxygen	lb-moles

Temperatures

T_g	= gas in reactor building	°R
T_m	= bulk metal of the containment-vessel shell	°R
T_m'	= bulk extraneous metal in the reactor building	°R
T_a	= outside ambient	°R
$T_g(0)$	= initial reactor-building atmosphere	°R

Heat-transfer coefficient

U_i	= overall based on the temperature differences $(T_g - T_m)$ and $(T_g - T_m')$	Btu/hr/sq ft/°R
U_o	= overall based on the temperature difference $(T_m - T_a)$	Btu/hr/sq ft/°R

Areas

A	= heat-transfer area of the containment-vessel shell	sq ft
A_i	= surface area of the extraneous metal within the reactor building	sq ft
A_s	= area of burning sodium	sq ft

Volumes

V_1	= above-floor volume	cu ft
V_2	= below-floor volume	cu ft

Specific heats

c_g	= at constant volume of the reactor-building atmosphere	Btu/lb-mole/°R
c_m	= of the metal	Btu/lb/°R

Weights

W_m	= containment-vessel metal shell	lb
W'_m	= extraneous reactor-building metal	lb

The differential equations are set up by making heat balances on the reactor-building atmosphere, containment-vessel metal shell, and the extraneous metal within the reactor building. For the reactor-building atmosphere

$$B(t) - U_i A(T_g - T_m) - U_i A_i(T_g - T'_m)$$
$$= \frac{d}{dt}\left\{ n_g c_g [T_g - T_g(0)] \right\} \tag{6.13}$$

The total number of gas moles is given by

$$n_g = n_i + n_O \tag{6.14}$$

where n_O is given by Eq. 6.11 and n_i is the moles of inert nitrogen. If c_g is treated as a constant, Eq. 6.13 becomes

$$B(t) - U_i A(T_g - T_m) - U_i A_i(T_g - T'_m)$$
$$= n_g c_g \frac{d}{dt}[T_g - T_g(0)] + c_g[T_g - T_g(0)]\frac{dn_O}{dt} \tag{6.15}$$

If Eqs. 6.11 and 6.14 are substituted in Eq. 6.15 and the equation is differentiated and divided through by $c_g n_i$, Eq. 6.16 results

$$\frac{B(t)}{c_g n_i} - \frac{U_i A}{c_g n_i}(T_g - T_m) - \frac{U_i A_i}{c_g n_i}(T_g - T'_m)$$
$$= \left(1 + \frac{n_O}{n_i}\right)\frac{dT_g}{dt} - \frac{bB(t)}{n_i}[T_g - T_g(0)] \tag{6.16}$$

Now if

$$B(t) = x B(0)$$
$$k_5 = U_i A/c_g n_i$$
$$k_6 = U_i A_i/c_g n_i$$

are substituted and if Eq. 6.10 from which

$$\frac{n_O}{n_i} = \frac{B(t)}{B(0)}\frac{n_O^0}{n_i}\left[\frac{T_g(0)}{T_g}\right]^{1/2} = x\frac{n_O^0}{n_i}\left[\frac{T_g(0)}{T_g}\right]^{1/2}$$

is utilized, Eq. 6.16 becomes

$$\frac{x B(0)}{c_g n_i} - k_5(T_g - T_m) - k_6(T_g - T'_m)$$
$$= \left\{1 + \frac{xn_O^0}{n_i}\left[\frac{T_g(0)}{T_g}\right]^{1/2}\right\}\frac{dT_g}{dt} - \frac{xb B(0)}{n_i}[T_g - T_g(0)] \tag{6.17}$$

Let

$$k_1 = [T_g(0)]^{1/2} n_O^0/n_i$$
$$k_2 = B(0)/c_g n_i$$
$$k_3 = bB(0)[T_g(0)]/n_i$$
$$k_4 = bB(0)/n_i$$

and transpose to arrive at

$$\left(1 + \frac{xk_1}{T_g^{1/2}}\right)\frac{dT_g}{dt} = x(k_4 T_g - k_3 + k_2) - k_5(T_g - T_m)$$
$$- k_6(T_g - T'_m) \tag{6.18}$$

Similarly a heat balance on the metal containment shell gives

$$U_i A(T_g - T_m) - U_o A(T_m - T_a) = W_m c_m(dT_m/dt) \tag{6.19}$$

Upon rearrangement Eq. 6.19 becomes

$$dT_m/dt = k_7 T_g - (k_7 + k_8)T_m + k_8 T_a \tag{6.20}$$

where

$$k_7 = U_i A/W_m c_m \qquad\qquad k_8 = U_o A/W_m c_m$$

Finally, a heat balance on the extraneous metal in the containment vessel gives

$$U_i A_i(T_g - T'_m) = W'_m c_m(dT'_m/dt) \tag{6.21}$$

or

$$dT'_m/dt = k_9(T_g - T'_m) \tag{6.22}$$

where

$$k_9 = U_i A_i/W'_m c_m$$

The sodium–accident model is now represented by Eqs. 6.12, 6.18, 6.20 and 6.22.

The film heat-transfer coefficient, h_i, on the inside of the building can be assumed to have a value of 2 Btu/hr/sq ft/°R. During the burning of the sodium, large convection currents are established which should tend to increase the normal value of the film heat-transfer coefficient considerably. Also, during the initial period in which the gas is being heated, large temperature differences exist between the gas and the metal. On the basis of considerations, the value of 2 for the film coefficient appears to be reasonable. For a value for the overall heat-transfer coefficient, U_i, based on the temperature difference between the gas temperature, T_g, and the bulk-metal temperature, T_m (or T'_m), the metal resistance must be included. Since this will give a negligible correction to U_i, a value of 2 Btu/hr/sq ft/°R can be used for the overall coefficient. Similarly the overall heat-transfer coefficient, , based on the temperature difference (T_m-T_a) can have a value of 2. Reference 65 should be consulted for a detailed discussion of heat-transfer coefficients. If only material above the reactor operating floor is taken into account as heat-absorbing material, assuming the sodium–air incident to take place underneath the reactor operating floor, the calculations will tend to be conservative. The use of extraneous heat-absorbing surfaces in containment-vessel design to minimize a pressure rise is not unique [62].

The initial burning rate of sodium of 5 lb/hr/sq ft applies to a normal atmosphere, i.e., 21 vol. % oxygen. In the assumed accident the normal atmosphere above the operating floor and the inert depleted atmosphere below the operating floor are assumed to mix. It is assumed that this mixing takes place before the accident begins. The resulting depleted atmosphere lowers the initial burning rate in accordance with Eq. 6.10. The total gas volume for the accident consists of V_1 cu ft of normal air above the operating floor at 70°F and V_2 cu ft of depleted air, with 5 vol. % oxygen, at about 140°F below the operating floor. The mixing of these two gas volumes results in an atmosphere containing

$$\frac{21 V_1 + 5 V_2}{V_1 + V_2} \quad (\text{Vol.} \% \, O_2) \qquad (6.23)$$

at a temperature of

$$\frac{530 V_1 + 600 V_2}{V_1 + V_2} \quad (^\circ R) \qquad (6.24)$$

When the oxygen-concentration correction is applied to the initial burning rate,

$$B_2(0) = \frac{n_{O2}}{n_{O1}} B_1(0)$$

where $B_2(0)$ = burning rate for depleted atmosphere
   $B_1(0)$ = burning rate for air
   n_{O2} = available oxygen for burning in depleted atmosphere
   n_{O1} = available oxygen for burning in air

or

$$B_2(0) = \left[\frac{(21 V_1 + 5 V_2)/(V_1 + V_2) - 5}{21 - 5} \right] B_1(0) \; (\text{lb/hr/sq ft}) \qquad (6.25)$$

for the initial burning rate in the depleted atmosphere accounting for no burning below the 5 vol. % O_2. The initial heat input is given by Eq. 6.25 multiplied by $(3900 \times A_s)$, where the 3900 refers to the heat of combustion per pound of liquid sodium and A_s is the area of the burning sodium. The constant b in Eq. 6.11 can be evaluated as follows for the reaction of sodium and oxygen going to Na_2O:

$$b = (3900 \times 23 \times 4)^{-1}$$

$$= 2.787 \times 10^{-6} \text{ moles of oxygen/Btu}$$

where 3900 is heat of combustion in Btu per pound of sodium, 23 is the molecular weight of sodium, and 4 is the assumed initial molar ratio of sodium to oxygen. Initally the gas temperature is taken equal to Eq. 6.24, and all metal temperatures are taken at 70°F. The ambient outside temperature, T_a, is assumed to be 70°F. It should be noted that in the differential equations all temperatures are absolute (°R). Constants used are summarized in Table 6.5. Because of the form of the sodium-accident equations, a computer solution should be used rather than an analytical solution. A typical solution of the system of equations using the constants of Table 6.5, which is one set of calculations made for the Fermi plant, is given in

Fig. 6.45. A summary of the calculations is given in Table 6.6.

The system of four equations (Eqs. 6.12, 6.18, 6.20, and 6.22) is solved by means of a fourth-order Runge-Kutta model. For this method the truncation error introduced at each stage of the integration is of the order $(\Delta t)^5$, where Δt is the change in the independent variable. The initial value of Δt can be chosen to be 0.001 hr. As a check on the combined truncation and round-off error, the computer program should be designed to perform the following test after each set of 10 successive integrations. First, the program checks the interval length by halving the value of Δt, recomputing the last point, and comparing the two results (i.e., the two sets of values of the dependent variables). The tolerance in this case is 0.001. If the test fails, the program continues with the new (halved) interval. However, if the results of the test are favorable, the original interval is doubled, and the last point is recomputed. If there is a favorable comparison, the calculation proceeds with the doubled interval; otherwise, it proceeds with the original interval. The pressure as a function of time can be calculated by the ideal gas law, $P = n_g R T_g / V$, where V is the volume of the containment building, 333,000 cu ft for the example used at Fermi. The total number of gas moles can be calculated from Eq. 6.14, where n_O is given by Eq. 6.10.

The peak gas temperature is insensitive to the value of the overall heat-transfer coefficient, U_o, and therefore would be insensitive to the outside ambient temperature, T_a. Calculations on a containment building insulated on the outside indicate that the effect of the insulation on the peak gas temperature is negligible. It does, however, have a considerable effect on the peak metal temperature, T_m. In one example the insulated calculation shows a maximum T_m value of 400°F as compared with the uninsulated value of 253°F, assuming no fission-product-decay heating. A change in U_i will greatly affect the peak gas temperature. A change of 25% in the value of U_i will produce a change of about 25% in the peak gas temperature. If it is assumed, contrary to experiment [45], that all the oxygen is to react, then calculations show that the gas pressure of 26 psig may be increased to about 30 psig. The blanketing of the burning sodium by the combustion products would decrease the magnitude of the incident. This may be a relatively small effect since the peak gas temperature and pressure are reached in a relatively short time.

Assume, as a final example, the improbable case in which the sodium burns only on top of the operating floor and only the gas space above it is involved. This condition results in a more severe accident, with a calculated gas pressure of about 40 psig and a gas temperature of 1660°F for the example. Such an accident is unrealistic because whatever gave access to the sodium may also provide for mixing of the above- and below-floor atmospheres. Furthermore, in the reactor floor there usually are a number of openings to the reactor area underneath the floor which are normally sealed off by gas seals. During the course of the sodium—air incident, these gas seals would probably be destroyed, and the free volume underneath the floor would be made available for

Table 6.5—Constants for Sodium-pool Burning-accident Calculations [59]
(Fermi)

k	$= b\,B(0)/\,n_O^0\sqrt{T_g(0)}$	$= 0.0662$		k_5	$= U_i\,A/c_g n_i$	$= 8.46$
k_1	$= \sqrt{T_g(0)}\ n_O^0/n_i$	$= 3.07$		k_6	$= U_i\,A_i/c_g n_i$	$= 8.53$
k_2	$= B(0)/c_g n_i$	$= 14600$		k_7	$= U_i\,A/W_m\,c_m$	$= 0.479$
k_3	$= b\,B(0)\,T_g(0)/n_i$	$= 112$		k_8	$= U_o\,A/W_m\,c_m$	$= 0.475$
k_4	$= b\,B(0)/n_i$	$= 0.204$		k_9	$= U_i\,A_i/W_m'\,c_m$	$= 0.586$

V_1 = 233,000 cu ft volume above operating floor
V_2 = 100,000 cu ft volume below operating floor

Mixing of above- and below-floor atmosphere:
  $(21V_1 + 5V_2)/(V_1 + V_2) = 16.6\%\ O_2$ (from Eq. 6.23)
Initial burning rate:
  $B_2(0) = \big[(16.6 - 5)/(21 - 5)\big] \times 5 = 3.63$ lb/hr/sq ft (from Eq. 6.25)
Initial heat input:
  $3.63 \times 3900 \times 3800 = 5.38 \times 10^7$ Btu/hr
where 3800 is the area of the burning sodium, sq ft

T_a	$= 530°$R	outside ambient
$T_m(0) = T_m'(0)$	$= 530°$R	initial temperature containment-vessel shell and extraneous metal
$T_g(0)$	$= 549°$R	initial temperature of mixed above- and below-floor atmosphere
U_i	$= 2$ Btu/hr/sq ft/°R	overall heat-transfer coefficient inside air to metal
U_o	$= 2$ Btu/hr/sq ft/°R	overall heat transfer coefficient outside air to metal
b	$= 2.787 \times 10^{-6}$	moles oxygen/Btu
n_O^0	$=$	initial moles of oxygen
c_g	$=$ Btu/lb-mole/°R	specific heat at constant volume of the reactor-building atmosphere
n_i	$=$	moles inert nitrogen
W_m	$= 503,600$ lb	weight of containment-shell metal
W_m'	$= 411,600$ lb	weight of extraneous metal
A	$= 15,640$ sq ft	heat-transfer area of shell
A_i	$= 15,750$ sq ft	surface area of extraneous metal

additional expansion. Assuming the two gas volumes do mix, the resulting pressure would be only 28 psig for the example quoted.

6.2.3.1.3 SODIUM—AIR REACTION: SODIUM SPRAY. Experiments have been performed [63] to determine the pressure effects when sodium is sprayed into a closed steel tank of oxygen-depleted air. The tank used was 30 in. in diameter and 49 in. long. One pound of sodium at 850°F was forced into the tank in 20 sec. In four experiments in which the oxygen content of the tank air was varied, the following results were obtained:

Experiment No.	Initial O_2 content, vol. %	Maximum pressure attained, psig	Time to reach max. pressure, sec
1	21.0	38	6
2	10.5	34	10
3	5.3	26	21
4	0.6	8	8

Figure 6.46 shows the pressure as a function of time for each experiment, and Fig. 6.47 shows the building pressure as a function of oxygen content.

The probable extent and effect of sodium sprays in air [64] is such that this reaction is generally not considered in the design of the containment vessel. The burning rate is influenced far more by total surface area than by drop size as such — the use of atomizers in combustion-chamber practice is governed solely by the need to produce a large surface area. For sodium spray to burn at the rate of 1 lb/sec and produce appreciable pressures, an area of spray approaching 1000 sq ft is required. Pressures of 30 to 100 psi in sodium circuits are not adequate to produce good atomization even in a spray atomizer with properly designed swirl chamber. Emerging through a hole at 30 psi, sodium—potassium alloy behaves like other liquids, such as paraffin, and forms a pencil jet of about the same size as the hole, which finally breaks up into drops that are large compared with the hole size. Fine drops of about 150 to 200μ are associated with the spray from a 0.020-in. hole, and the quantity of liquid metal is negligible. A tear in a pipe or a hair crack will produce slightly better atomization than this but not to any appreciable extent.

About 50 holes of 1-mm diameter are required to pass 1 lb/sec, and each jet would have to be something like 200 ft long for burning to be completed at this rate. The sodium would generally collect in pools, and the reaction would continue as a pool-burning reaction. Although study of the problem shows that sprays are not dangerous as a means of promoting very rapid pressure and

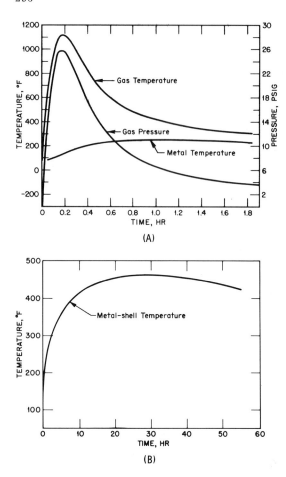

(A)

(B)

FIG. 6.45—Sodium—air reaction (pool burning), uninsulated reactor containment-building temperatures and pressures vs. time [59]. (A) Without fission-product heat. (B) With fission-product heat.

temperature rises, there are a number of simple precautions that will control fully the extent to which they can arise. If all the pipe-work and the vessel are covered, a spray cannot readily get out into the air. This precaution fits in very well with the suggestion of lagging all coolant pipes for heat-insulation purposes.

6.2.3.2 Fission-product Heating [66]

The containment-vessel temperature is affected by the decay heat of fission products that have been

Table 6.6—Summary of Calculations for
the Sodium-pool Burning
Accident [59]

(Uninsulated, Without Fission-product Heating)

Quantity	Maximum value[*]	Time, hr[†]
T_g, °F	1115	0.183
T_m, °F	253	1.0
T_m', °F	350	1.4
x	1.33	0.08
P, psig	25.8	0.175

[*] Values from (A) of Fig. 6.45.

[†] Time at which maximum value occurs.

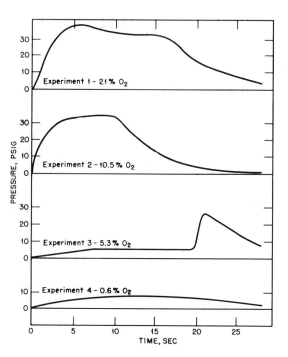

FIG. 6.46—Sodium—air reaction test (sodium spray). Reactor-building pressure vs. time curves for various oxygen contents. [From E. Hines, A. Gemant, and J. K. Kelly, Nucleonics, 14(10):39 (1956).]

released into the atmosphere following the sodium-burning phase. This decay heating will have a neg-ligible effect on the gas temperature since the gas temperature peaks shortly after the accident. (In Ref. 66 calculations for the Fermi plant show a peak in 7 min.) It may be assumed that decay heat-ing starts at the time the metal-containment temperature is at a maximum as a result of the sodium—air incident. Depletion of the oxygen in the building would decrease the temperature; however, fission-product heating continues to increase the vessel-wall temperature. Calculations for the

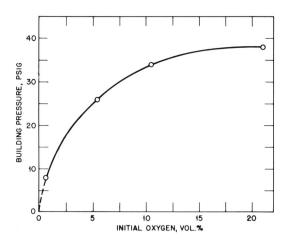

FIG. 6.47—Sodium—air reaction test (sodium spray). Reactor-building pressure vs. initial oxygen content. [From E. Hines, A. Gemant, and J. K. Kelley, Nucleonics, 14(10):41 (1956).]

Fermi plant showed that it takes over 24 hr for the vessel wall to reach its maximum temperature when fission-product heating is included, as contrasted to 1 hr to reach maximum temperature when only the sodium—air reaction is considered. The maximum temperature is reached when heat production from fission-product decay is in equilibrium with the containment-vessel-wall losses.

In installations where weather conditions are such that temperatures do not go below the nil ductility temperature, insulation on the outside of the containment vessel should be omitted so that the vessel can more effectively dissipate heat in the event of an incident. In the calculations for the Fermi containment vessel, it was found that 1 in. of insulation would cause the metal shell to reach 650°F, whereas without insulation the temperature would go to 460°F, assuming both sodium burning and decay heating.

Calculations for decay heat can be treated as a separate problem from sodium burning. Decay heat has a negligible effect on the gas temperature. The decay heating is a function of the operating power and integrated power prior to shutdown. The integrated power is a function of fuel burnup. The decay-heat calculations consist of a heat balance on the contents of the containment vessel with Way—Wigner decay heating as a heat source. For purposes of calculation the surface area of the containment vessel above the operating floor is assumed available for heat transfer to the outside ambient, and the resulting equation is

$$\Delta Q = H - UA(T_m - T_a) - W_m c_m (dT_m/dt)$$

$$+ \sum W_i c_i (dT_i/dt) \qquad (6.26)$$

where ΔQ = change in total heat content, Btu/hr
  H = Way—Wigner decay heating, Btu/hr
  U = overall heat-transfer coefficient from the bulk metal containment vessel to the outside atmosphere, Btu/hr/sq ft/°R
  A = wall area of the upper portion of the containment vessel, sq ft
  T_m = bulk temperature of the containment vessel wall, °F
  T_a = outside ambient temperature, °R
  $W_m c_m$ = heat content of containment vessel wall, Btu/°R
  $W_i c_i$ = heat content of various items of structure and components ($i = 1, 2, \ldots$ Btu/.°R)

In Eq. 6.26 the terms on the right side of the equation refer to the heat gained by the various pieces of equipment in the building. Heat gained by the nitrogen atmosphere left in the building can be neglected for the times considered since it is small in comparison with the other terms. The temperatures of the metal and concrete structures inside the building change less rapidly, because of longer time constants, than the wall temperature. This results in a ΔQ at least equal to $\sum W_i c_i \, dT_m/dt$, where $W_i c_i$ now includes the containment-vessel wall; therefore

$$\Delta Q = H - UA(T_m - T_\alpha) \sum W_i c_i \, dT_m/dt \quad (6.27)$$

gives a solution for T_m satisfactory for design purposes. The Way—Wigner heating, H, is given by

$$H = a\left[t^{-0.2} - (t + t_1)^{-0.2}\right] \qquad (6.28)$$

where t is the time in hours since shutdown, t_1 is the time at power, and a is given by

$$a = 0.038P \qquad (6.29)$$

where P is the prior operating power in watts. Substituting Eq. 6.28 in Eq. 6.27 gives

$$\frac{dT_m}{dt} + \frac{T_m}{t_0} = \alpha t^{-0.2} - \alpha (t + t_1)^{-0.2} + \frac{T_a}{t_0} \quad (6.30)$$

where

$$t_0 = \Sigma W_i c_i / (UA) \qquad \alpha = a / \Sigma W_i c_i$$

Equation 6.30 is a first-order linear differential equation whose solution gives rise to indefinite integrals of the form

$$\int e^x x^{-0.2} \, dx \qquad (6.31)$$

which can be solved by expanding $\exp(x)$ and integrating termwise. The solution to Eq. 6.30 is given by

$$T_m - T_a = \alpha \exp(-x_1)\Big\{[(T_0 - T_a)/\alpha] + t^{0.8} \, G(x_1)$$

$$+ \exp(-x_2) \times [t^{0.8} G(x_2) - (t + t_1)^{0.8} G(x_3)]\Big\}$$
$$(6.32)$$

where

$$T_m = T_0 \text{ at } t = 0;$$
$$x_1 = t/t_0;$$
$$x_2 = t_1/t_0;$$
$$x_3 = (t + t_1)/t_0$$

and

$$G(x_i) = \sum_{n=0}^{\infty} \frac{x_i^n}{n!(n + 0.8)} \qquad (6.33)$$

For small values of x, $G(x)$ can readily be evaluated by using the series definition; however, for large values of x, an asymptotic expansion is preferred. With integration by parts the asymptotic expansion for $G(x)$ is given by

$$G(x_i) = \frac{e^{x_i}}{x_i}\left[1 + \frac{0.2}{x_i} + \frac{(0.2)(1.2)}{x_i^2} + \cdots\right] \quad (6.34)$$

For the cases considered both $G(t_1/t_0)$ and $G[(t + t_1)/t_0]$ can be evaluated by the asymptotic expansion of Eq. 6.34 since these arguments are both very much greater than 1 (Table 6.7). Expanding these functions using the first two terms of Eq. 6.34 transforms Eq. 6.32 into

$$T_m - T_a = a \exp(-t/t_0)\Big\{[T_0 - T_a)/a] + [t^{0.8} G(t/t_0)]$$

$$+ t_0(t_1 + 0.2t_0)\left[t_1^{-1.2} - (t + 1)(t + t_1)^{-1.2}\right]$$

$$\times \exp(t/t_0)\Big\}$$

$$(6.35)$$

Table 6.7—Fission-product-heating Parameters [66] for Equation 6.35

Quantity	Unit	Normal Way–Wigner		Way–Wigner (× 2) [67-69]	
		Case I	Case II	Case III	Case IV
U	Btu/hr/sq ft/$^\circ$R	1	2	1	2
t_1	hr	3975	3975	3975	3975
a		1.63×10^7	1.63×10^7	3.26×10^7	3.26×10^7
α		41.8	41.8	83.6	83.6
t_0 *	hr	24.9	12.45	24.9	12.45
T_a	$^\circ$F	70	70	70	70
T_0 †	$^\circ$F	265	265	265	265

* For A_1 = heat-transfer area of 15,640 sq ft.

† Maximum value of T_m from sodium–air incident without fission-product heating.

The above equations were applied to calculations for the Fermi plant, which has 3×10^6 lb of steel for a heat sink. Two values of the overall heat-transfer coefficient, U, were used. An overall heat-transfer coefficient of about 2 Btu/hr/sq ft/$^\circ$R would seem reasonable, but a value of 1 was also chosen. The parameters used to calculate the decay heating are given in Table 6.7. Table 6.8 summarizes the results of decay heating on an uninsulated building. In (B) of Fig. 6.45 the results of the calculation for Fermi of a sodium—air reaction with an uninsulated building including fission-product heating are shown.

Case IV of Table 6.8 would probably be more representative of the real situation than other cases since a heat-transfer coefficient of about 2 Btu/hr/sq ft/$^\circ$R can be expected. With a value of $(T_m - T_a)$ exceeding 200°F, a heat-transfer coefficient much larger than 1 Btu/hr/sq ft/$^\circ$R can be expected. It should also be noted that case IV assumes a factor of 2 on Way—Wigner, which is conservative. The assumption that the sodium—air incident and the decay-heating incident calculations can be considered as separate problems is now apparent from the values of t given in Table 6.8, with the possible exception of case II. The design temperature for the Fermi containment vessel was 650°F at an internal pressure of 32 psig [70].

The maximum temperature of 490°F, reached in 14 hr at approximately atmospheric pressure, can be compared with a design metal temperature of 650°F at 32 psig. The predicted values are based on a conservative assumption of sodium—air reaction plus total decay heating. Since the predicted values are well within design values, the need for after-incident cooling systems is obviated. The reactor power rating to which a plant could be designed, using buildings approximately the size of Fermi or EBR-II, has not been accurately determined. Certainly the sodium—air reaction is not a determinant since it is area and rate limited, but the decay heat, set by the power of the reactor,

may be a limiting function. The EBR-II design temperature and pressure are 650°F and 24 psig [44]. The Dounreay design temperature and pressure are 140°F and 18 psig [43].

6.2.3.3 Other Coolant Reactions

If coolants other than sodium are to be considered for use in the primary system, the design-pressure and -temperature calculations would follow the same basic principles established for sodium. For comparison purposes Table 6.9 lists the heat given off during coolant reactions with oxygen at 298°K.

Table 6.9—Heats of Reaction for Various Coolants

Reaction	Kcal/mole
$2Na + \frac{1}{2}O_2 \rightarrow Na_2O$	−99.4
$2Na + O_2 \rightarrow Na_2O_2$	−155.2
$Na + O_2 \rightarrow NaO_2$	−62
$2Li + \frac{1}{2}O_2 \rightarrow Li_2O$	−142.57
$2Li + O_2 \rightarrow Li_2O_2$	−151.9
$3Li + \frac{1}{2}N_2 \rightarrow Li_3N$	−47.45
$2K + \frac{1}{2}O_2 \rightarrow K_2O$	−86.4
$2K + O_2 \rightarrow K_2O_2$	−118
$K + O_2 \rightarrow KO_2$	−67.6

The heats of formation at the higher temperatures may be computed with the aid of the formula and table in Ref. 71. Sodium—potassium alloy (NaK) forms Na_2O preferentially and should have the same heat of formation as the sodium reaction giving Na_2O. Sodium—water reactions are not covered. Designs should exclude water in the containment building. Humidity should also be a controlled item if it might become a problem requiring control.

Table 6.8—Summary of Results on Decay Heating (Uninsulated Building) [66]

Case*	U, Btu/hr/sq ft/$^\circ$F	Correlation	Maximum T_m, $^\circ$F	Time to reach maximum, hr
I	1	Way—Wigner	425	23
II	2	Way—Wigner	320	7.5
III	1	Way—Wigner (× 2)	715	31
IV	2	Way—Wigner (× 2)	490	14

* See Table 6.7 for case parameters.

6.2.3.4 Vacuum Relief of Containment Vessel

(See Sec. 6.2.2.5.5 for a description of the relief valve.) The containment vessel should be capable of withstanding an external pressure within the limits of the relief devices provided. Net external pressure may exist if the barometer rises, if the air in the vessel is suddenly chilled (unlikely condition but credible), and if, following an extensive coolant fire, cooling produces an oxygen deficit. The additive effect of these three conditions would produce a substantial pressure differential as a credible possibility. It can be shown by calculation that a sphere of Dounreay size and thickness [64] will probably buckle inward at a differential pressure of 4 psi but not at lower pressures. The stress in the steel at the buckling pressure is about 3000 psi. When buckling occurs under a pressure of 5.5 psi (estimated for the three stated conditions), its effect will be seen as a dimple about 25 ft in diameter, the center of which has moved about 20 in. toward the center of the sphere. At the same time there will be a local increase in stress due to the bending induced, and the stress around the buckled portion may rise to the yield point although the strain is quite acceptable.

The maximum allowable external pressure on a containment vessel can be determined from Ref. 72. For example, an 80-ft-diameter, D, cylindrical vessel with a length, L, of 25 ft of vessel between any two stiffener rings and with a 1-in. wall thickness, t, will, by virtue of internal pressure, have the following maximum allowable external pressure:

$$P_a = \frac{B}{D/t} = \frac{2000}{960} = 2.08 \text{ psi} \qquad (6.36)$$

The factor B is obtained from Fig. UCS-28.2 of Ref. 72 using an L/D ratio of 0.313, a D/t ratio of 960, and a design temperature of 650°F.

A relief valve should be provided if it is possible for the external pressure to be in excess of the design pressure. The vacuum breaker should be designed for the worst possible conditions with conservative assumptions. As the basis of this design, it is assumed that a sodium incident has occurred and that all the oxygen in the building has been consumed by the burning sodium and the remaining nitrogen is at some elevated temperature and pressure. After the incident the residual gas in the building will slowly cool down to a point where the temperature is such that any further cooling will reduce the pressure below atmospheric. The valve can be designed so that when the pressure in the vessel reaches a -2 psi the valve will open and allow a flow of air that will keep the pressure at -2 psi. It can further be assumed that the additional air brought into the building through the valve will not cause any additional sodium combustion.

The temperature at the time the containment vessel reaches -2 psi (12.7 psia assuming a normal pressure of 14.7 psia) is calculated as follows: Note that the quantity (nT/p) is a constant before and after the incident, n being the number of gaseous moles, T, the absolute temperature,

and p, the pressure. If it is assumed that the building originally contained 1 mole of air at 80°F and 1 atm pressure, after the incident it will contain 0.79 moles of nitrogen. Therefore, the temperature, T_2, at which the pressure becomes 12.7 psia is

$$T_2 = (n_1/n_2)(p_2/p_1)T_1 = (1/0.79)(12.7/14.7)(540)$$
$$= 591°\text{R} \qquad (6.37)$$

At temperatures below 131°F the pressure will exceed the -2 psi. The rate at which air must be introduced to maintain this differential will depend upon the heat transferred from the gas to the outside and upon the temperature of the incoming air. For a conservative estimate, assume no heat storage in the metal walls of the containment vessel. Consider an energy balance (the first law of thermodynamics) on the gas

$$\Delta E = -Q \qquad (6.38)$$

where ΔE is the increase in internal energy of the gas from the time the valve opens to some time t and $-Q$ is the heat transferred from the gas to the outside atmosphere. Assuming ideal gases

$$\Delta E = n_g c_v (T_g - T_a) - n_g(0) c_v (T_g(0) - T_a) \qquad (6.39)$$

where $n_g, n_g(0)$ = moles of gas in the containment vessel at time t and $t = 0$, respectively

$T_g, T_g(0)$ = temperature of the gas in the containment vessel at time t and $t = 0$, respectively, °R

T_a = temperature of the incoming air, °R

c_v = specific heat at constant volume, Btu/lb-mole/°R

The heat transferred, Q, is given by

$$Q = -\int_0^t UA[T_g(t') - T_a] dt' \qquad (6.40)$$

where U represents the overall heat-transfer coefficient and A, the area for heat transfer. Substituting Eqs. 6.39 and 6.40 into Eq. 6.38 and differentiating, the resultant equation with respect to the time is

$$\frac{d}{dt}(n_g c_v T_g) - w c_v T_a = UA(T_g - T_a) \qquad (6.41)$$

where dn_g/dt has been replaced by w. The term $d(n_g c_v T_g)/dt$ vanishes since $n_g T_g = pV$, where V is the volume of the containment building and p is the assumed pressure of 12.7 psia which, under the assumption of the model, is a constant. Therefore, Eq. 6.41 yields

$$w = UA(T_g - T_a)/c_v T_a \qquad (6.42)$$

which is the desired relation. Note that for the quantity $n_g T_g$ to be a constant, the temperatures must be expressed in degrees absolute. The maximum flow rate will result at time $t = 0$ when T_g is at its largest value. With typical values

A = 15,000 sq ft
U = 0.69 Btu/hr/sq ft/°R

c_v = 5 Btu/lb-mole/°R
T_g = 591°R at t = 0
T_a = 440°R (-20°F)

w, the required capacity for the vacuum relief valve, is equal to 710 lb-mole/hr or 3800 cu ft/min.

6.2.3.5 Code Design of the Containment Vessel

Section VIII of the ASME Boiler and Pressure Vessel Code [72] is the generally accepted standard in the United States for the construction of unfired pressure vessels designed for over 15 lb/sq in. In some states the use of the code is required by law. Code Case 1272N covers the requirements pertaining to containment vessels and intermediate containment vessels. Section III of the ASME Boiler and Pressure Vessel Code, Rules for Construction of Nuclear Vessels, has been issued and should be used as the guide for all future reactor plant pressure-vessel designs.

Modification of the code was required because a containment vessel, for example, differs from a conventional unfired pressure vessel in many features of design and construction. Some differences are (1) the design pressure and temperature of the vessel is based on a once-in-a-lifetime occurrence (2) personnel access must be available without losing containment (air locks), (3) safety valves for high internal pressure are not used, (4) provisions are made for air ventilation, (5) leaktight penetrations must be provided for many and various pipes, tubes, and cables, (6) field construction is necessary with a minimum of shop fabrication, (7) pneumatic leak tests are hampered by the temperature effects on the large internal volume typical of containment vessels, (8) wind, snow, and earthquake loads must be considered, (9) portions of the vessel wall may not be accessible for inspection after final erection.

6.2.3.5.1 CODE CASES. The ASME Boiler and Pressure Vessel Code ruled originally in Code Case 1224, and later in Case 1270N, that containment vessels must be built in accordance with the specifications given in Ref. 72 or 73, with exceptions as modified by nuclear cases and with code jurisdiction to end at the first pipe joint outside the reactor. Case 1224-1 defined a containment vessel as an outer vessel that encloses the reactor vessel or portions of the primary coolant circuit or both and has as its purpose the containment of the radioactive substances that would be released in the event of an accident or failure of the reactor vessel or the primary coolant circuit or both. Case 1270N superseded and included Case 1224-1. This case added the requirements that all welds were to be of the double-welded butt type and were to be fully radiographed. Case 1271N removed the requirement of the hazardous nature of the material that might be released. It further stated that if such devices were installed adequate provision must be made for safe disposal of the effluent.

Case 1272N referred specifically to containment and intermediate containment vessels and outlined the following: (1) stress relief of all welded joints was waived with provisions, (2) provision for corrosion protection shall be made in accordance with UG-25 of the code, and (3) inspection of welded joints in the lower parts of the containment vessel during pneumatic tests is waived with provisions. Case 1272N-1 added a new paragraph which stated that containment vessels could be designed in accordance with the formulas and rules of Ref. 72 with allowable stresses 1.1 times those given in Table UCS-23, Ref. 72, provided certain requirements were met. Case 1270N-2 allowed the equivalent of a double-welded butt type joint as defined in Par. UA-60 (o), Ref. 72, and Par. P-101(d), Ref. 73, except for transitions in diameter, which may be angle joints provided the angle formed does not exceed 30 deg. Case 1272N-3 revised the requirement for fluid penetrant inspection in lieu of radiography on the welds for doors and nozzles. The welds are to be detailed according to UA-6, UG-34, and/or UA-48 and Fig. UW-16.1 (Ref. 72). Also ultrasonic inspection was added. Secondary stresses shall be calculated on the assumption of elastic behavior which, when combined with primary stresses, shall be limited to three times the allowable stress values of Table UCS-23, Ref. 72. The total primary stress shall be limited to 1.1 times the allowable membrane stress and 1.5 of this amount for combined general membrane, general-bending, and local-bending stress values. Case 1272N-4 outlined the requirements for welded joints and the radiography of the four categories of joints previously cited in Par. UW-3 of Case 1272N-3 with a paragraph added on welded attachments. Attachments other than studs must be of impact-tested material unless they are subsequently stress relieved. Also, the attachment must extend 16 times the attachment-weld thickness. Provision for corrosion protection must be made in accordance with Par. UG-25, Ref. 72. Specifications on allowable stresses were as previously cited. Case 1270N-4 had no significant changes for containment vessels. Case 1270N-5 established that the special requirements of Par. UW-2, Ref. 72, do not cover all provisions against deterioration, which may occur in service as a result of such factors as corrosion, erosion, radiation effects, and instability of materials and of operating conditions such as transient thermal stress, mechanical shock, and vibratory loading. The purchaser's specifications should incorporate requirements with respect to these effects to ensure integrity throughout the intended life of the containment vessel.

6.2.3.5.2 MATERIALS FOR WELDED-STEEL CONTAINMENT VESSELS. Carbon and low-alloy steels are suitable for use in the construction of steel containment vessels. The material requirements for vessels built to code are covered in Subsection C, Part UCS, Ref. 72, and in code cases issued to cover specific modifications for nuclear applications. Since the vessel is normally exposed to the elements and is used near ambient temperature, the material selection should be based upon low-temperature mechanical properties and low-temperature allowable stresses. The material chosen should have the required tensile strength and adequate impact strenth and resistance to brittle-failure design temperatures.

Reference 74 should be used in the selection of the carbon or low-alloy steel for the containment building. This specification covers five classes of steel and requires that these steels have minimum acceptable impact-strength values at specified testing temperatures, and that the tests be made in accordance with the simple-beam Charpy type of test. Table 6.10 lists plate specifications and minimum test temperatures.

Table 6.10—Reactor-building Steel Plates
Recommended for Use at
Low Temperatures* [74]

Class	ASTM specification and grades	Minimum test temperature, °F
1	A201 and A212 flange or firebox quality	−50
2	A203, grades A and B, firebox quality	−75
3	A203, grades D and E, firebox quality	−150
4	A353 firebox quality	−320
5	A410 firebox quality	−150

* The notched-bar impact properties shall not be less than 15 ft-lb when tested at the specified temperature.

Brittle failures can occur under static conditions: an impact load is not the only requirement for failure [38]; notch effects and residual stresses are also necessary [43]. Neutron radiation has a significant effect on the notch ductility of ferritic steels [75]. Although the containment vessel is not subjected to neutron radiation, structural material close to the reactor should be checked for radiation effects. Code Case 1272N specified that stress-relief requirements are waived provided plates and forgings exposed to the elements (not inside a heated enclosure) conform to Specification SA-300 for plates and SA-350 for forgings. These materials should meet the impact-test requirements of Par. UG-84 at a temperature at least 30°F below the lowest recorded ambient temperature of the area in which the vessel is to be erected (the lowest test temperature can be assumed to be -50°F for any part of the United States). In regard to stress relief, Par. UGS-56, Ref. 72, requires stress relief for (1) all thicknesses of chromium—molybdenum steels having a chromium content greater than 0.70%, (2) steels A202, A203, A204, and others that have a molybdenum content greater than 0.05% and a chronium content not greater than 0.70 and thicknesses greater than 0.58 in., (3) steels A212 and A105 with 1-in. thickness, and (4) all other steels with thicknesses above 1 1/4 in. which may be used in welded construction. The Code Case 1272N waives stress relief for materials listed under Group P1 in Table UCS-23, Ref. 72, for thicknesses over 1 1/4 in. and up to 1 1/2 in., inclusive, provided a preheat of 200°F is used during welding. Corrosion protection shall, in compliance with Code Case 1272N, be in accordance with UG-25, Ref. 72. The requirements are not mandatory for containment vessels.

A tabulation of containment vessels [76] shows that plate complying with ASTM A201 and A300

was used for constructing the spheres at West Milton, N. Y.; Dresden, *Morris, Ill.; Indian Point,* N. Y.; Big Rock, *Mich.; and Yankee, Rowe, Mass.* In buildings using vertical containment vessels with formed heads, A201 and A300 were used for the Experimental Boiling Water Reactor at Argonne National Laboratory (EBWR); the Enrico Fermi Fast Breeder* at Lagoona Beach, Mich.; Air Force Nuclear Engineering Test Reactor (AFNETR) at Dayton, Ohio; the Boiling Water Reactor (BWR),* Elk River, Minn.; SM-1A at Fort Greely, Alaska; and the Plutonium Recycle Test Reactor (PRTR) at Richland, Wash. ASTM A212 material was used for the Vallecitos Boiling Water Reactor (VBWR) at Pleasanton, Calif. In buildings using vertical containment vessels with formed heads and flat (concrete) bottoms: (1) A201 and A300 were used for the Heavy Water Components Test Reactor (HWCTR) at Aiken, S. C.; (2) A283 was used for the Massachusetts Institute of Technology (MITR) at Cambridge, Mass., and the Horace Hardy Lester Reactor (HHLR) at Watertown, Mass.; and (3) A285 was used for the National Aeronautics and Space Administration Plum Brook Reactor (NASA-TR) at Sandusky, Ohio.

6.2.3.5.3 WALL THICKNESS. The containment-vessel wall thickness is computed after the design pressure has been determined and after the vessel shape, diameter, and material have been selected. The following formulas are found in Sec. UG-27, Ref. 72.

Cylindrical shells:
$$t = \frac{PR}{SEff - 0.6P} \tag{6.43}$$

Spherical shells:
$$t = \frac{PR}{2SEff - 0.2P} \tag{6.44}$$

Ellipsoidal head:
(Mfgr's standard head)
$$t = \frac{PD}{2SEff - 0.2P} \tag{6.45}$$

Hemispherical head:
$$t = \frac{PL}{2SEff - 0.2P} \tag{6.46}$$

Torispherical head:
$$t = \frac{0.885 PL}{SEff - 0.1P} \tag{6.47}$$

where t = minimum required thickness, exclusive of corrosion allowance, in.
P = design pressure, psig
R = inside radius, in.
S = maximum allowable stress value, psi
Eff = joint efficiency
D = inside diameter of the head skirt, in.
L = inside spherical or crown radius, in.

In all cases the wall thickness is proportional to the design pressure. If a joint efficiency of one is assumed and the pressure effect is neglected, the wall thickness is also inversely proportional as the allowable stress for cylindrical shells and torispherical heads but inversely proportional as twice the allowable stress for spheres, ellipsoidal heads, and hemispherical heads, which makes these

---

*Containment vessels built to ASME Boiler and Pressure Vessel Code.

shapes attractive in some respects. For welded joints the maximum allowable joint efficiency is specified in Par. UW-12, Ref. 72.

From the wall-thickness formulas, a cylindrical containment vessel with formed heads, a design pressure of 20 psig, a diameter of 80 ft, 100% radiography, and made of A201 material would require a wall thickness of 0.58 in. for the cylindrical walls, 0.29 in. for a hemispherical head, 0.58 in. for an elliptical head, and 1.03 in. for a torispherical head.

The effect of reducing radiographic inspection of welded joints from 100% inspection to spot inspection increases the required wall thickness from 0.58 to 0.687 in. A containment vessel in the shape of a sphere with design criteria comparable to a cylindrical vessel, assuming a diameter of 120 ft, would require a wall thickness of 0.44 in. The maximum allowable external pressure can be calculated after the wall thickness has been determined by the preceding method. The calculation is detailed in Sec. UG-28, Ref. 72. It should be noted that the L term used in external-pressure calculations is the maximum length of vessel section between any two stiffener rings.

6.2.3.5.4 DESIGN DETAILS. Stiffening rings may be required on the inside surface of a cylindrical containment vessel to prevent overstress or distortion under the maximum allowable external pressure. The number and location of the stiffeners are determined by the calculation for maximum allowable external pressure, Sec. 6.2.3.5.3. The size and shape of the stiffener ring(s) are determined in accordance with Par. UG-29, Ref. 72. The procedure is to select a member, determine its area and moment of inertia, then, using the chart in Appendix V and the formula in UG-29, Ref. 72, determine the required moment of inertia. The selected ring is satisfactory if the required moment of inertia is smaller than the actual value for the ring section. Details of the attachment of the ring to the vessel are covered in Par. UG-30, Ref. 72.

Openings in the containment vessel for piping penetrations should be circular, elliptical, or obrounds, according to Par. UG-36, Ref. 72. All such openings require reinforcement in the form of additional wall thickness in the material surrounding the opening. The amount of reinforcement required, in terms of cross-sectional area, is determined by the product of the diameter of the opening and the thickness of the vessel or head. The diameter is taken in the plane of the finished opening. The thickness is computed from the appropriate wall-thickness formula in Sec. 6.2.3.5.3. The dimensional boundaries of the reinforcement are given in Par. UG-40, Ref. 72; details are shown in UG-280, Ref. 72.

Vessel supports are treated in Appendix G, Ref. 72. Design calculations are not given because of the many variables in shape and size of vessels. Generally, the following precautions should be taken: (1) the supports should be designed so that localized stresses are not set up in the vessel wall when the vessel undergoes deformation due to thermal growth. This may be done by adding reinforcement material or by using a heavier vessel-wall thickness

at the vessel support attachments. (2) Continuous welds around the periphery of support brackets will ensure a rigid attachment. (3) Adequate flexural strength must be provided in support columns. An alternate design would use slotted holes and supports that can move in a radial direction.

6.2.3.5.5 CODE REQUIREMENTS FOR FABRICATION, WELDING, AND TESTING. The following parts of Ref. 72 have particular application to containment vessels: Part UG, General Requirements for All Methods of Construction and All Materials; Part UW, Requirements for Unfired Pressure Vessels Fabricated by Welding; and Part UCS, Requirements for Unfired Pressure Vessels Constructed of Carbon and Low-alloy Steels.

Part UG [72] specifies the requirements for materials, design, openings and reinforcements, brazed and stayed surfaces, ligaments, fabrication, inspection and tests, code stamps and reports, and pressure-relief devices for all unfired pressure vessels and vessel parts regardless of how constructed. Since welded construction is the most practical and is the accepted present-day standard for pressuretight containment vessels, only welding methods will be considered in this chapter.

Part UW covers the materials, design, fabrication, and testing of welded vessels. Qualification by specific tests is mandatory for the welding procedure to determine its suitability to ensure welds that will meet requirements. It is also mandatory that the welders be tested to determine their ability to apply the welding procedure properly. Arc- or gas-welding processes are restricted to shielded carbon arc, shielded metal arc, submerged arc, inert-gas metal arc, atomic-hydrogen metal arc, oxyhydrogen, and oxyacetylene. No mechanical pressure or blows shall be applied except as permitted for peening. Welding shall be performed under specified temperature conditions. The plates shall be fitted, aligned, and retained in position during the welding operation by bars, jacks, clamps, or tack welds. Longitudinal and circumferential joints shall have an alignment tolerance equal to an offset of one quarter of nominal plate thickness with a maximum of 1/8 in. for longitudinal joints and 3/16 in. for circumferential joints. Weld-reinforcement (or crown) thickness shall be restricted to a maximum of 3/32 in. for plates up to 1/2 in. thick, 1/8 in. for plates 1/2 to 1 in. thick, and 3/16 in. for plates over 1 in. thick. Each welder is required to stamp his identifying number, letter, or symbol adjacent to, and at intervals of not more than 3 ft along, the welds he makes, or, as an alternative, the fabricator must keep a record. A suitable stencil or other surface marking can be used.

The permissible types of welded joints for pressure vessels are listed in Table UW-12 and are further clarified, in four categories, for nuclear applications in Code Case 1272N-4. This case identifies joints of Category A and B as Type No. 1 of Table UW-12 with full radiography required. Flanged-head nozzle connections that do not have joints accessible to radiography must be inspected by either magnetic-particle fluid penetrant or by an ultrasonic method. The dimensions and shape of the end preparation shall be such as to permit complete fusion and complete joint penetrations. Where tapered transition sections occur, the tapered length should not be less than four times the offset.

Joint efficiencies to be used in the wall-thickness formulas are taken from Table UW-12 and depend on the type of joint and the degree of inspection. Openings may be located in, or adjacent to, welds provided there is no need for additional reinforcement. When nozzles or other connections are attached to the vessel, sufficient welding should be provided to develop the strength of the reinforcing part, considering shear or tension, whichever is applicable. Specific requirements are outlined in UW-16 for welding attachments to the vessel. These attachments include necks abutting the vessel wall, necks inserted with and without added reinforcing elements, nozzles with integral reinforcement, and fittings with internal threads. Plug welds may be used in lap joints, in reinforcement around openings, and in structural attachments not subjected to pressure. Fillet welds may be used as strength welds for pressure parts.

Section UG outlines specific requirements for inspection and the certification of inspection for all vessels that are to receive the Code U symbol. The code requires a hydrostatic or a pneumatic test if a hydrostatic test is impractical. The pneumatic test has been used on all the containment vessels, and the code requires the test pressure to be 1.25 times the maximum design pressure multiplied by the lowest ratio (for the materials of which the vessel is constructed) of the stress value for the test temperature to the stress value for the design temperature. The procedure is to increase the pressure gradually to one-half the test pressure and then increase in steps of one-tenth the test pressure until the test pressure is reached. The pressure is then reduced to 80% of the test pressure to permit inspection. Upon completion of fabrication, testing, and satisfactory inspection, the Code U stamp can be affixed to the vessel.

6.2.4 REACTOR-BUILDING CONSTRUCTION

Construction of the reactor building comprises foundation work, erection and fabrication of the containment vessel, testing of the vessel, completion of concrete work both inside and outside the vessel, and, finally, completion of the penetrations.

6.2.4.1 Foundation Preparation

Figure 6.48 shows an example of how concrete foundations are prepared for the erection of either a spherical or a cylindrical containment vessel. When the building elevation has been established, the foundation is designed in accordance with the soil conditions. If piling is not necessary in the case of a cylindrical vessel, a concrete pad is poured on the subsurface rock structure. This pad serves as a base upon which to construct the concentric cylinders that support the containment vessel. Figure 6.49 shows a sequence of the concrete pours and a view of the temporary supports for the Fermi plant.

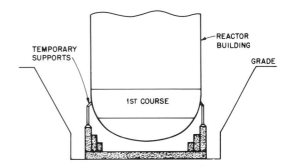

INITIAL ERECTION OF CONTAINMENT VESSEL

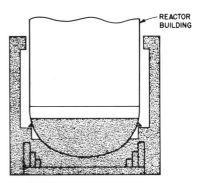

COMPLETED CONSTRUCTION

FIG. 6.48—Reactor building, concrete foundations.

6.2.4.2 Containment-vessel Fabrication and Erection

6.2.4.2.1 SHOP FABRICATION. Because of the large size of the containment vessel, essentially all construction and erection must be done at the plant site. Where possible, subassemblies are prefabricated in the shop because of the advantage that shop facilities have for welding, inspecting, stress relieving, and testing.

Material for the containment vessel is ordered according to ASTM standards (Sec. 6.2.3.5.2). Specified tests should be performed and certified copies of the test reports made available. Detail fabrication drawings are made, and identification numbers are assigned to each plate in the vessel. After being cut from flat plate, each piece is shaped or formed to fit the curvature of the vessel. After the ends are trimmed to meet final dimensions, they are prepared for welding. See Fig. 6.50 for typical full-penetration end-preparation details. Adjacent pieces may be joined in the shop to form a subassembly; however, the size is limited by shipping restrictions. The detail design drawings should show all penetrations and areas of reinforcement that are located and inserted into the plate before shipment to the field. Handling brackets should be welded to the assemblies in such a position that the site crane can support them while they are being positioned for welding. Building attachments that require stress relief should be

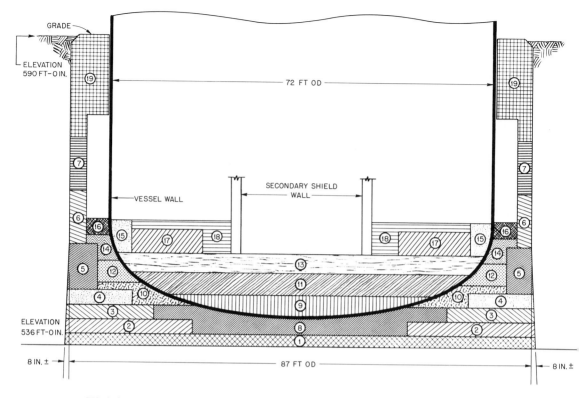

FIG. 6.49—Fermi reactor-building foundation details [6]. Numbers indicate the sequence of installation.

fabricated and stress relieved in the shop before shipment to the reactor plant site.

6.2.4.2.2 FIELD ERECTION.

An erection tower, a mast, and a boom adjacent to the foundation are usually required for handling all parts of the vessel during erection. The crane should be able to cover the entire height of the vessel as well as the movement area of the shipped subassemblies (i.e., area bounded by the unloading area and by the farthest point on the vessel wall). Temporary support columns are required to support the empty vessel through fabrication and testing.

The first assemblies to be welded into position are those forming the ring to which the supports are attached. The lower head and the walls are then completed. Access to both the inside and the outside of the walls must be maintained to allow the double-welding of the butt joints. Cleats and wedges can be used to position the plates for welding. A considerable amount of assembly welding can be performed on the ground before the assembly is raised into position by the crane. Automatic welding machines weld the longitudinal and circumferential seams. When each weld is completed, it is radiographed, and each film is properly identified.

Techniques have been developed to facilitate erection and welding of the plates. The crane lowers the plate into position where it is held in place by wedges. A welding machine then welds the straight seams. Just prior to the welding operation, the joint is preheated to the required temperature by a torch. Grinding and chipping are performed before additional passes are made. After completion of the weld, the surface is ground smooth for radiography. The weld may be ground flush, or it may have a crown (see Par. UW-51, Ref. 72 for allowable thicknesses). Weld defects discovered by visual or by radiographic means should be repaired by removing the defect down to sound metal and then rewelding. Repaired sections should be radiographed. Stress relief of subassemblies can be performed in the field if a gas-fired furnace of the proper size is constructed.

A manhole in the center of the bottom head can be used to provide access to the vessel interior during construction. The manhole serves another function; if there is a possibility of a rise in groundwater level, the manhole prevents damage resulting from the buoyant movement of the vessel

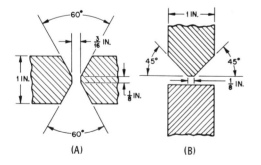

FIG. 6.50—Containment-vessel wall welding details. (A) Typical double-welded butt joint (both sides bevelled). (B) Typical double-welded butt joint (one side bevelled).

upon its supports. If some construction is to be performed inside the vessel before completion of the vessel, careful consideration should be given to the ability of each piece of equipment to withstand the pressure test. A building crane, if it is supported by the vessel walls, may have to be erected before the upper head of the vessel is completed. The completed vessel should be given an integrity pressure test at 1.25 times the design pressure and a soap-bubble test at the design pressure [72]. Any leak found by the soap-bubble test, no matter how small, should be ground out and rewelded; the reweld should be radiographed. There must be complete access to all external surfaces of the vessel for this test. The vessel should be retested after repairs are completed.

6.2.4.3 Containment-vessel Pressure Test (Refs. 33, 43, 72, 77-80)

Containment-vessel pressure tests have two purposes: (1) to establish the strength integrity of the containment vessel and (2) to establish the leakage rate. The leakage rate establishes the basis for determining the radiation dosages that would be encountered in the event of a nuclear incident. Pressure vessels generally are hydrostatically tested to 1.5 times the maximum allowable pressure multiplied by the ratio of the allowable stress value at test temperature to that at design temperature. Reference 72 allows a pneumatic test in lieu of the hydrostatic test for vessels which cannot be safely filled with water and for vessels in which traces of the testing liquid cannot be tolerated. The pneumatic test is made at 1.25 times the maximum design pressure stamped on the vessel multiplied by the ratio of the allowable stress value at the test temperature to that at the design temperature. For example, if a vessel of A201 Grade B plate has a design pressure of 20 psi and a design temperature of 700°F, the test pressure would be 26.2 psig at a test temperature of 70°F.

Table UCS-23, Ref. 72, shows no difference in the maximum allowable stress values from -20°F to 650°F. For vessels with a design temperature of 650°F or less, the test pressure would be 1.25 times the design pressure. In no case should the pneumatic test pressure exceed 1.25 times the maximum allowable pressure of the vessel as defined in Par. UA-60(e), Ref. 72.

Initially the internal pressure should be increased gradually to one-half the test pressure and then increased in increments of one-tenth of the test pressure until the full test pressure is reached. The code does not specify how long the pressure should be held; however, it should be held long enough to assure the integrity of the vessel at this pressure. The pressure should then be reduced to four-fifths of the test pressure and held for a time sufficient to permit inspection of the vessel.

After the building-strength test and local leak-detection tests have been completed, the vessel is ready for the leakage-rate test. Reference 80 defines leakage rate as the percentage by weight of the original content of air pressurized to the test pressure which would escape during a 24-hr

period. If possible the test should be performed during relatively static weather conditions. There are two test methods; the <u>absolute method</u> in which leakage is measured by means of direct pressure and temperature detectors properly located to provide an average air temperature and the <u>reference method</u> in which pressure differentials are measured between the vessel and reference vessels erected inside the vessel to assume the temperatures of the contained air within a reasonable time lag (see parts A and B, respectively, Fig. 6.51).

The reference method has been very successful [79]. The reference tanks should be checked for leaktightness before being put into use, and they should be located where they can best reflect the contained-air temperature. With reference tanks a differential pressure that develops between the two containers cannot be attributed to temperature effect, and hence this effect can be eliminated. A measured differential pressure can only indicate leakage from the outer containment vessel. Experience with steel vessels has shown that a leakage less than 0.1% of the total weight of air contained in the building at design pressure can be measured with reasonable accuracy.

6.2.4.3.1 ALLOWABLE LEAKAGE. Table 6.11 shows results of leakage-rate tests performed on containment vessels. These tests were conducted at approximately the design pressure of the vessel. The leakage in each case was well within the specified allowable.

The basis on which the leakage rate is calculated should be specified. For example, Table 6.12 indicates the variation in actual leakage for the same building volume when, in each case, the allowable leakage is identical in weight percent but is based on a different initial weight of air. The initial weight of air in each case is dependent on the test pressure. The code requires that the containment vessel be tested at 1.25 times the design pressure, in pounds per square inch gauge, condition 2 of Table 6.12. Condition 1 of Table 6.12, design pressure, is generally used to test for leakage.

It should be noted that, to determine the actual leakage out of the building during an accident, a complete history of the accident should be calculated up to the point where the pressure inside is at least equal to the outside pressure. The history

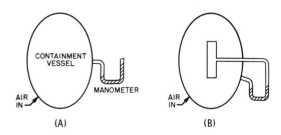

FIG. 6.51—Pressure test of reactor building. (A) 1. Pressurize vessel and hold. 2. Drop in pressure indicates a leak. 3. Temperature and barometric correction required. (B) 1. Use an inner chamber and pressurize both chamber and containment vessel to same pressure and hold. 2. Drop in vessel pressure on manometer. 3. Temperature correction minimized by this method.

Table 6.11—Results of Containment-building Leakage Tests* [79]

	Time for test	Ambient temperature, °F	Max. test pressure, psig	Min. test pressure, psig	Calculated[†‡] leakage (in 24 hr), %	Allowable*[‡] leakage (in 24 hr), %
West Milton, N.Y. 5,964,00 cu ft	32 hr	39 to 73	14.2	12.2	0.1	
Dresden, Ill. 3,591,300 cu ft	29 hr	29 to 47	28.5	26.0	0.0157	
Indian Point, N.Y. 2,144,700 cu ft	24 hr	47 to 68	25.4	24.1	0.014	0.1
Lagoona Beach, Mich. 366,000 cu ft[§]	56 hr	20 to 39	31.8	30.8	0.036	0.043
Dayton, Ohio 739,000 cu ft	9 days	7 to 49	12.8	10.3	0.0012	0.1
Elk River, Minn. 415,000 cu ft	5 days	49 to 78	22.9	19.7	0.05	0.1
Rowe, Mass. 840,000 cu ft[§]	53 hr	50 to 85	16.7	15.8	0.021	0.1

* These tests do not include penetration leakages.

[†] Based on test pressure.

[‡] Calculated and allowable leakages in % are either pressure loss in % of initial absolute pressure or, with equal initial and final temperatures, % of initial weight of air.

[§] Volumes for Lagoona Beach and Rowe appearing in this table are "free" or net volumes.

should include the pressures and the temperatures. Only an integrated history over any particular period can establish what the leakage will be for that period. The leakage will rise to a maximum and then fall, as shown in Fig. 6.45.

The allowable pressure decay per day of 0.035 psi for condition 1 indicates the need for reliable and accurate instrumentation.

6.2.4.3.2 TESTING PROCEDURE. Equipment located inside the building should be capable of withstanding the test pressure. The following test equipment is necessary: (1) an open-end mercury manometer connected between the building and the outside atmosphere, (2) a water manometer located outside the building between the building atmosphere and the reference tanks, (3) air pressurizing lines from the compressors with separate lines to the air locks, (4) pressure gauges and pressure recorders located externally and connected to the building atmosphere, (5) temperature indicators for recording temperature data at representative locations inside the building, and (6) instruments for recording barometric pressure, temperature, wind velocity, and relative humidity of the outdoor atmosphere.

If the air locks with both doors closed are not able to sustain an internal pressure equal to the building pressure, they may be tested at lower pressure prior to the building test. When this test has been completed, the inner door may be opened so that the air lock is open to the building pressure.

Pressurizing should be performed if possible with night air and at a time of low humidity. The test period shall be no less than 24 hr. The atmospheric temperatures and pressure should be close to the original conditions at the completion of the test period. If personnel access is necessary during the test, personnel decompression procedures should be followed. One method is outlined in Ref. 80. A log should be kept of hourly readings of internal pressure, temperature, humidity, manometer readings, barometric pressure, and outdoor temperature and humidity. Reference 80 uses the following formula for computing the leakage rate for the absolute method:

$$\% \text{ leakage in 24 hr } = \frac{24}{H}\left(1 - \frac{T_1 P_2}{T_2 P_1}\right)100 \quad (6.48)$$

For the reference method:

$$\% \text{ leakage in 24 hr } = \frac{24}{H}\left[\frac{T_1(P_2' - P_2)}{T_2 P_1} - \frac{(P_1' - P_1)}{P_1}\right]100$$

$$(6.49)$$

where H = duration of test, hr

T_1 = mean absolute temperature of the containment-vessel air at the start of the test

Table 6.12—Example of Allowable Leakages for Different Specified Conditions

Test condition	Pressure at beginning of period, psia	Temperature, °F	Air in building, lb	Leakage = 0.1%/day,* lb/day	Allowable pressure decay,* psi/day	Leakage,[†] scf/day
1. Design pressure	35	70	89,205	89.2	0.035	1190
2. Code test[‡]	40	70	102,000	102	0.040	1360

* Based on same temperature at beginning and end of test.

[†] Obtained by converting pounds of air at temperature to standard conditions of 70°F and 14.7 psia.

[‡] Code test = 1.25 × design pressure in psig.

T_2 = mean absolute temperature of the containment-vessel air at the start of the test

P_1 = absolute pressure of the containment-vessel air at the start of the test

P_2 = absolute pressure of the containment-vessel air at the completion of the test

P_1' = absolute pressure of the reference tanks at the start of the test

P_2' = absolute pressure of the reference tanks at the completion of the test

6.2.4.4 Reactor-building Superstructure Construction

The next step after erection and testing of the containment vessel is the completion of concrete and steel construction adjacent to and inside the reactor building. The following construction sequence would normally be followed: (1) The portion of the containment vessel adjacent to concrete should be covered with a corrosion-resistant paint or pitch. All welded joints should be painted with primer after the soap-bubble and leak-rate tests. (2) The concrete external to the lower head should be poured (Fig. 6.48). This is an excellent application for the grout-intrusion method of pouring concrete because it assures complete bearing between the vessel and the foundation. By this method the forms are filled with the dry aggregate consisting of crushed stone or gravel varying in size from 5/8 to 3 in. The stone is placed lightly against the bottom of the vessel. A cement grout is then pumped into the aggregate; the grout level rises and forms itself around the vessel head. A 5-psi pressure is generally used in placing the grout. To counteract the effect of this pressure against the head, concrete is simultaneously poured inside the vessel to form the internal concrete pad. Expansion-joint material should be placed adjacent to the inside and outside surfaces of the head near its vertical portion. (3) When sufficient concrete has been poured and has set so that it can render support to the vessel, the temporary steel support legs can be disconnected. If the concrete has enclosed the lower portions of the legs, the legs should be cut with torches and only the upper halves removed. The concrete can then be poured up to the level of the base of the permanent support legs, and the supports can be attached. (4) The vessel is anchored on its external concrete pad by pouring the inside concrete pad to cover the inner surface of the bottom head. The expansion-joint material should be in place at the near-vertical surfaces of the head before the concrete is poured. (5) The concrete wall adjacent to the ouside surface can then be poured by conventional methods. Figure 6.13 shows the details of a gas and radiation seal at the containment-vessel-wall—concrete juncture. It may be advisable to only partially complete the erection of the exterior concrete wall since access may be necessary into the building through a temporary opening, the bottom of which may be lower than the elevation of the completed wall. (6) A temporary opening can be cut out of the wall of the containment vessel to provide an entrance for all the building internals. The opening should be of sufficient size to allow the largest piece of equipment in the building to be brought in on a rail car or by truck. A temporary opening is not necessary if a permanent equipment door of sufficient size is provided. (7) Light and heat should be provided inside the building. A ventilation system may also be needed. (8) Rail or truck access, if necessary, should be provided up to and into the building. For this purpose temporary wood trestles can be constructed adjacent to the vessel. (9) Construction of walls and floors inside the building should be closely coordinated with the erection of equipment. (10) When construction and erection have been completed or when the remainder of the equipment can be introduced through the equipment door, the temporary opening can be closed. This is done by replacing and rewelding the same plate that was removed. A double-welded butt joint should be used. There should then be 100% radiographic inspection of the joint and magnetic-particle inspection of both inside and outside welds. The completed joint should be leak tested to correspond with the leak-rate test applied to the entire vessel. This can be accomplished by covering the joint area with a vacuum box. If a reduced pressure is maintained in the box, the joint can be checked for leaktightness.

6.2.4.5 Equipment Erection

Owing to the restrictions in the working area inside the reactor building, it is necessary to program the erection of equipment. Only a limited number of men can work in the building at one time, and work must progress from the center out and from the bottom up to prevent closure of an area where work is uncompleted. Ventilation, lighting, and power are necessary. The erection workmen should be constantly reminded of requirements for high standards of workmanship and cleanliness.

When the concrete pad has sufficiently cured, the reactor vessel, primary tank, and associated structures should be brought into the building. Usually they are brought in through the temporary opening on rails or on a truck bed. The next step is to lift, with the building crane or other type of crane, these pieces off the rail car or truck, upend them, and move them into position. Once the reactor is in place, work can progress radially. Piping to the heat exchangers and pumps should be erected after these components are in place since the piping must be pulled to close cold-spring gaps and the vessels must be firmly attached to their foundations. The pouring of any internal concrete shield walls between the reactor and the primary-system components should be done after the piping is installed to allow for grouting in the piping wall sleeves after the piping is erected. Otherwise, the piping may have to be altered to match the location of the wall sleeve, and the pipe sleeve would have to have enough clearance to accommodate cold-spring movements. Correspondingly, floor sleeves should be located in relation to tanks or piping after they are in place. Service piping can be installed after installation of the primary vessels and primary piping. The operating floor can be poured after instrumentation and electrical materials are installed, and construction can be completed on above-floor equipment. Adequate support should be provided for heavy thicknesses of wet concrete. If the concrete is handled in separate pours, the joints should be designed to minimize radiation streaming.

6.2.4.6 Penetrations

6.2.4.6.1 NONDETERIORATING TYPE PENETRATIONS. Penetrations that are installed as a part of the containment-vessel wall should be supplied in lengths a few inches longer than required so that the blank end portion of the cylinder can be removed (Fig. 6.16).

In Fig. 6.52 the four steps to the completion of the penetration are illustrated. In (A) it is shown that a circumferential cut is made in the cylinder. Piping that has been inserted into the penetration

cylinder is shown in (B). The pipe should be welded to the penetration with welds of integrity equal to those used on the containment-vessel seams. For this reason radiographable welds are desirable. The pipe section at the penetration could be made in the form of a T for attaching the penetration. After dye-penetrant and radiographic inspection of the welds, the welds should be given a pneumatic pressure test and a leak test, similar to the containment-vessel test. A plate (C) can be attached to the inside end of the cylinder to close off the penetration. Attaching the plate to the pipe or the cylinder without welding will facilitate removal. The test equipment used should be leaktight. The method of test-plate removal is shown in (D). Removal of the plate allows for the thermal movement of the pipe. In summary, each penetration should successfully pass the following tests: (1) weld radiography, (2) dye-penetrant, (3) pneumatic pressure, and (4) leakage.

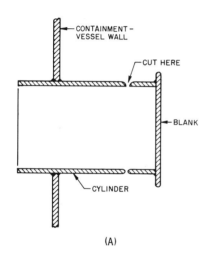

(A)

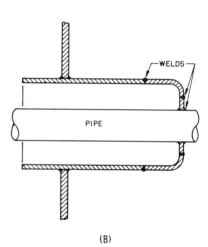

(B)

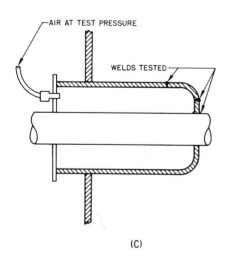

(C)

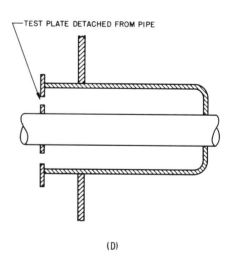

(D)

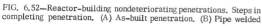

FIG. 6.52—Reactor-building nondeteriorating penetrations. Steps in completing penetration. (A) As-built penetration. (B) Pipe welded into penetration. (C) Pneumatic test on penetration. (D) Completed penetration.

6.2.4.6.2 DETERIORATING TYPE PENETRATIONS. This category includes penetrations that do not use welded joints but meet code requirements. Included are thin-wall flexible joints, such as bellows (Fig. 6.16), packed-gland seals, soldered joints, and gasketed joints. In addition to an acceptance test at the time they are fabricated, arrangements should be made for periodic tests of these penetrations during the life of the plant. This can be provided by attaching test connections. Penetrations in this category should be model tested in the laboratory prior to design acceptance under pressure and temperature conditions duplicating the design conditions of the containment vessel. Figure 6.53 shows an arrangement for a permanently installed test station for periodically leak testing penetrations.

6.2.5 REACTOR-BUILDING OPERATION

The operation of the reactor-building system is an important part of containment. While the reactor is operating, access should be allowed only through air locks (Sec. 6.2.2.5.3) which have two interlocked doors opening inward, each of which could serve as containment. All piping systems that are a part of the containment system (Sec. 6.2.2.5.6) should have their isolation valves kept to specified operability. Deteriorating type penetrations should be periodically tested and replaced if necessary. The reactor building should be given a periodic leak test as a proof of the integrity of the total system.

6.2.5.1 Single-door Access

A single door may be necessary for large-equipment removal and replacement or for a fuel-handling cask car (Sec. 6.2.2.5.4). The containment system is breached when the single door is opened. During this period it is necessary to eliminate any possibility of a reactor accident or the release of fission products to the atmosphere inside the reactor building. An interlock system should be designed with a sequence similar to the following: (1) the safety and control rods should be in a fixed position of maximum hold-down of reactivity and the operating mechanisms delatched from the rods; (2) fuel-handling equipment in the reactor should be locked out of operation to prevent the possibility of a single subassembly being moved with possible subsequent inadequate cooling, meltdown, and release of fission products; (3) the heat-transport system should be in operation to remove decay heat from the reactor core, and the emergency cooling system should be available for immediate use; (4) the radioactivity of the atmosphere inside the reactor building should be within prescribed limits for release to the outside atmosphere. Only when the above four conditions are met should the door be opened. Maintenance or fuel-replacement operations should not be performed until the door is closed and the containment restored.

Precautions should be taken to prevent an inadvertent opening of a single door. Covers could be placed over all or a portion of the bolted connections so that the door could not be completely unbolted. The cover should be removable only through a key interlock scheme. Removal of the key should be dependent upon an indication that not only is the door fully bolted but also that the bolts are tight and the gasket is leakproof.

A key interlock scheme is shown in Fig. 6.54. The interlock provides two safeguards: (1) it cannot be removed unless the pressure in the seal is 5 psig and (2) it assures the replacement of the sheet-metal bolt cover. The bolt cover may be attached to the door by light fasteners; it prevents tampering with any of the bolts. Insertion of the key would allow the lock to be unbolted and the cover to be removed. The interlock barrel is attached to the bolt cover, requiring detachable electrical leads. If the gasket deteriorates and the pressure is insufficient, the space would have to be pressurized by opening the valve from the air supply to permit insertion of the key.

6.2.5.2 Air-lock Access

If the plant is designed so that personnel have access to the reactor building while the reactor is operating, an air lock (Sec. 6.2.2.5.3) should be used. With an air lock, one door is always closed, and either door provides complete containment in itself. Rigid administrative control should be exercised over the entry of persons into the building during operation, maintenance, and refueling. Records should be kept not only of the names but also of the time spent in the building and the exposure. Before any personnel enter the building, they should obtain clearance from the health physicist. An accident can be postulated in which one or more personnel in the building leave the inside door open and are unable to reach the inside door to close it so that a rescue party can open the outside door.

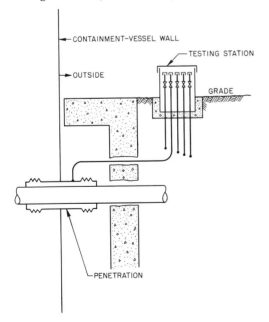

FIG. 6.53—Arrangement of permanent station for periodic test of penetrations.

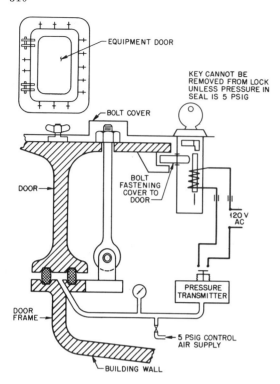

FIG. 6.54—Reactor-building equipment-door interlock.

As protection against such a possibility, an emergency air lock can be provided in the reactor building, preferably on the side opposite the normal full-size air lock. Maintenance personnel, prior to entering and after leaving the building through the air lock, should be processed through a change room. Before entering the change room, maintenance personnel should deposit their tools in a special receptacle. A health physics building incorporating a change room is shown in Fig. 6.72.

6.2.5.3 Maintenance of Inert Atmosphere

When inert atmospheres are specified in the containment design of the plant, it is necessary to provide administrative control to monitor and maintain the specified atmosphere. Nitrogen, argon, helium, or oxygen-depleted air can be used. It is generally necessary to monitor the oxygen and the moisture content. All monitor and sampling devices should be equipped with isolation valves. Oxygen content can be monitored by the conventional Orsat analysis method, or, for a more accurate determination, a spectrographic analysis can be used. Unless an area can be completely sealed, it is advantageous to specify oxygen-depleted air rather than pure nitrogen.

The supply of inert gas for the inert atmosphere can be handled with a manual-control gas station. If a constant supply is to be bled into the area with a corresponding relief, isolation valves will be needed on the lines. A means of reducing the oxygen content of an air atmosphere is available in "oxygen getters," which circulate air over powdered copper or some other reducing agent. Recharging is done by circulating hydrogen through the "getter," which reverts the oxidized agent back into a reducing agent.

6.2.5.4 Periodic Building Leak Tests

It is desirable that a periodic leak test be performed on the reactor building for the purpose of demonstrating the continuing integrity of the containment vessel. During an extended period of operation, a leak may have developed in the wall or its penetrations. A periodic test would detect the presence of such a leak. Periodic testing of penetrations is covered in Secs. 6.2.2.5 and 6.2.4.6. Repetitive leakage tests should also be performed after repairs or modifications which could affect building integrity.

It may not be possible to duplicate the preinstallation test conditions after the reactor and heat-transport systems and components are installed. The following are possible limitations: (1) vessels and piping may not be capable of withstanding the external test pressure, and it may not be feasible to increase the internal pressure simultaneously; (2) seals between volumes may not withstand the differential test pressures; (3) instrumentation that cannot be vented, isolated, or removed from the building may suffer damage; and (4) large pressure differentials between compartments may damage walls and floors.

The periodic leak tests should be designed within these and possibly other limitations. The test could be performed on a weekend reserved for this purpose. After the test equipment has been installed, the reactor is interlocked out of operation, the test pressure is imposed, and the leakage is measured over a period of time. Test data should include the average air temperature in the vessel and all other pertinent data that might affect the pressure. Where volumes (such as above and below a floor) are separated by seals, the volumes should be simultaneously pressurized to keep the differential pressure within limits. All isolation valves in piping systems should be closed during the test. It may be necessary to operate cooling coils for heat removal from such equipment as pump motors. The effect of temperature on a large gas volume is a major difficulty in these tests (Fig. 6.55). At the time of construction, the building constructor may have used reference tanks. However, this may not be possible after the equipment has been erected in the building. Periodic checks with a low test pressure may be adequate to determine the presence of holes (gross leaks). It can be shown that there is little advantage in using high pressures for leakage-rate tests. For example, consider the presence of a 1/4-in.-diameter hole and the use of various test pressures for the leakage-rate test. The instantaneous flow at the beginning of the test period is given by the orifice flow formula

$$w = 12KA\rho_1 Y \sqrt{(2g\,\Delta P/\rho_1)} \qquad (6.50)$$

where w = flow of air, lb/sec

K = orifice coefficient (about 0.6 for Re above 4000)

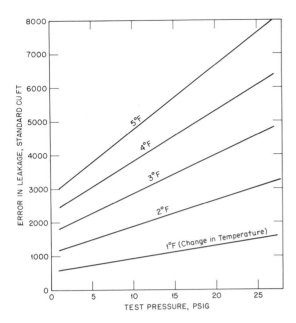

FIG. 6.55—Reactor-building ambient-temperature effect on leakage measurements.

A = area of hole, sq ft

ρ_1 = upstream weight density, lb/cu ft, at 2 psig $\rho_1 = 0.085$

Y = expansion coefficient, which is dependent upon the ratio $\Delta P/P_a$, where P_a is the absolute test pressure. For a 2-psig test pressure, Y is 0.97

ΔP = the test-gauge pressure for all pressures below the critical-velocity pressure (13.1 psig), psig

To give a comparative basis upon which to compare leakage under various test pressures, Fig. 6.56 shows the rate of leakage through a 1/4-in. hole at the start of the test. There is an advantage in using 2 psig rather than 1 psig. However, there is less advantage in going from 2 psig to 10 psig. Figure 6.57 shows the hole size vs. various

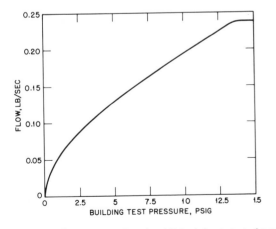

FIG. 6.56—Leakage rate through a 1/4-in. hole at start of test.

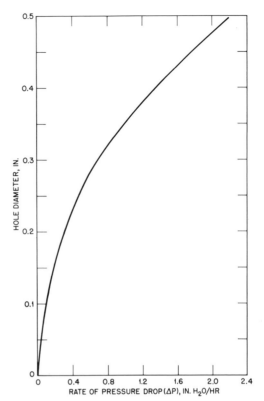

FIG. 6.57—Reactor-building leakage test rate of pressure drop in reactor building vs. single hole size during a 2-psig building test.

rates of pressure drop during a 2-psig building test. The pressure decay on which the change in flow is dependent should be considered for 24-hr test periods. All calculations and curves in this section are based on a constant pressure.

6.3 Materials of Construction

6.3.1 CONCRETE

Conventional design and pouring techniques can be used for structural concrete. When concrete is used for shielding, its density and water content should be considered. Shield thickness can be reduced when concrete density is increased. A high-density aggregate is used to increase the density of concrete. Where concrete may normally have a density of 140 lb/cu ft, shielding specifications may require a minimum density of 150 lb/cu ft. Higher densities can be obtained; however, the cost rises sharply with the special aggregates and special pouring procedures required. Table 6.13 gives the costs and thicknesses of several shielding materials.

Aggregates for conventional concrete consist of sand, gravel, crushed rock, blast-furnace slag, or other inert material. Table 6.14 shows a typical sample concrete report. The properties of other aggregates (limonite, magnetite, and barytes) used to increase concrete density are shown in Table 6.5 of Ref. 81.

Table 6.13—Costs and Relative Thicknesses of Shield
Materials [81]

Shield material	Specific gravity	Relative thickness required, ft	Installed cost, dollars/cu yd
Water	1.0	21.0	
Standard concrete	2.3	9.1	150
Barytes concrete	3.5	6.0	250
Iron-aggregate concrete	5.6	3.8	800

The grout-intrusion method can be used in placing concrete. By this method the dry aggregate is placed in position and the cement grout is pumped up through the aggregate. This method is particularly applicable where a good bearing-surface contact is needed below an erected tank, such as with the containment vessel. It is also claimed that this method results in less porosity. All air is pushed up ahead of the grout. It should be noted that a layer of water is usually used on top of the grout to saturate the aggregate and to act as a cushion, allowing complete penetration of the grout. Where it is not possible to obtain monolithic pours, concrete joints must be closed with a step design. A straight (unstepped) joint at right angles to a floor or wall represents a source of radiation leakage or a streaming path in the shield. Where temperatures in excess of 200°F must be tolerated, successful results have been obtained by using serpentine as aggregate. Serpentine allows the concrete to hold its water of hydration to 800°F; however, it also reduces the density of the concrete to approximately 130 lb/cu ft. The strength is also reduced. If concrete is to be used as a gamma shield, the retention of moisture in the concrete is not important. However, if the concrete is to be used for effective neutron shield-

Table 6.14—Sample Concrete Report

Item	Unit	Value
Materials per cubic yard of concrete		
Cement	lb	400 (4.25 sacks)
Fly ash	lb	100
Sand	lb	1200
Limestone 6A	lb	800
Limonite	lb	1600
Total water	lb	280
3 Я pozzolith	lb/sack cement	1.4
Laboratory results		
Slump	in.	2½
Air content	%	1.70
Density	lb/cu ft	161.4
Aging 7 days*		
Total load	lb	90,000
Stress	lb/sq in.	3,180
Aging 28 days*		
Total load	lb	136,000
Stress	lb/sq in.	4,800
After drying in an oven to a constant weight at 150°F		
Wet weight at start	lb/cu ft	161.4
Dry weight after drying	lb/cu ft	151.2
Total load after drying	lb	116,500
Strength	lb/sq in.	4,120
Lost due to drying	%	6.38

* After curing in moist room at 70°F, 95% relative humidity.

ing, a minimum of 6% water should be retained in the concrete. The hydrogen in the water acts as an effective moderating agent. It has been recommended that concrete for shields be moist cured for 28 days.

6.3.2 STRUCTURAL STEEL

Structural-steel design in a reactor plant follows conventional practice. Radiation damage is not a significant factor. Thermal-expansion movements must be accommodated in the structural steel design. Structural-steel beams and columns performing critical support functions, if exposed to possible sodium fires, should be fireproofed in accordance with building codes. The support of any such component as piping, tanks, heat-transport-system equipment, or operating floor could be considered critical.

6.4 Structures Other Than Reactor Building

The following descriptions of the buildings and structures common to a liquid-metal-cooled fast reactor plant bring out the purpose or function of the structure and some of its features. The descriptions cover most of the buildings that could be present in a fast breeder plant. This does not mean that the buildings described should necessarily be incorporated into a plant design. Those structures that contain sodium should be designed for sodium leakage and any possible sodium—air reaction. Buildings that may contain fission products or other radioactive substances should be properly shielded, and consideration should be given in the design of the buildings to the proper release of radioactive products.

6.4.1 STEAM-GENERATOR BUILDING

The steam-generator building is usually located adjacent to the reactor building and may contain part of the secondary coolant piping, the secondary pumps, the steam generators, part of the feedwater and steam systems, and the secondary coolant service system. If a radial pattern of plant layout as shown in Fig. 6.58 is used, the secondary coolant piping runs will be shorter and therefore will have fewer flexibility requirements. The straight-line pattern is advantageous for the layout of steam and feedwater piping but requires long secondary coolant piping runs. With the radial pattern a yard crane would have to be used for the vertical removal of components, whereas with the single building one permanent crane would suffice. Shielding requirements may pose difficult problems with the radial pattern because of the necessity of locating components opposite piping penetrations. Since the radioactivity level of the secondary-system coolant does not require biological shielding, all piping and equipment are accessible. At the Fermi plant (Figs. 6.59 and 6.60), a portion of the north wall facing the reactor building has been constructed of concrete for shielding purposes. This shield wall protects operators in the

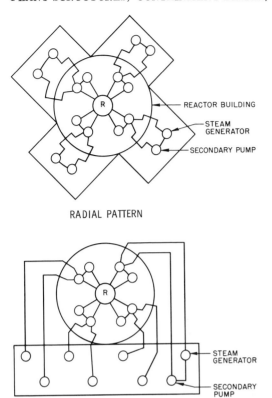

RADIAL PATTERN

IN-LINE PATTERN

FIG. 6.58—Steam-generator arrangements.

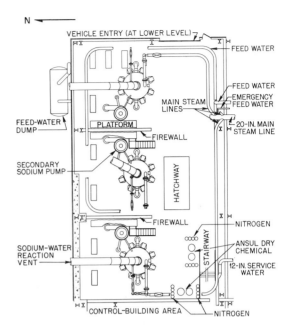

N ◄──

FIG. 6.60—Fermi operating-floor steam-generator building, plan view [6].

isolate a sodium fire resulting from a steam-generator or piping leak. The structural steel including columns should be enclosed in a manner such as that shown in Fig. 6.61. Masonry walls should be covered with sheet metal where there is a possibility of contact with sodium. The fireproofing may include plaster on metal lath supported 1 1/4 in. from the steel surfaces. The ground coat may include vermiculite—plaster aggregate in fibered

adjoining control building during certain radioactive maintenance operations. The steam-generator building should be designed to contain and

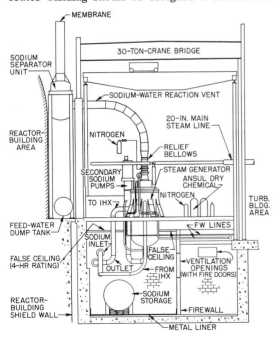

FIG. 6.59—Fermi steam-generator building elevation [6].

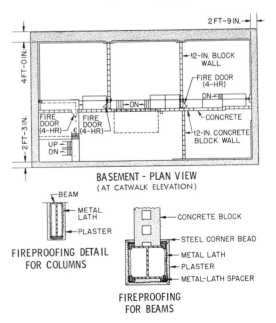

BASEMENT - PLAN VIEW
(AT CATWALK ELEVATION)

FIREPROOFING DETAIL
FOR COLUMNS

FIREPROOFING
FOR BEAMS

FIG. 6.61—Fermi steam-generator building fire-protection details [6].

gypsum. The floor and walls of the isolated compartments should be steel lined (but welded) so that they will form a large collection pan to contain any possible sodium leak. Fireproof doors should be used for access to the building and to rooms in the building. Steel walkways should service these doors. Walls or partial walls may be constructed between units so that a fire in one unit will not affect the steam generators or secondary loops. Typical fire-resistance rating is 4 hr. Structural columns should also be fireproofed. A typical leakproof roof consists of main steel trusses with steel purlins formed into the trusses; a deck of standard double-rib deck-plate 20-gauge cold-rolled steel and 1 1/2-in.-deep ribs; decking spot welded to the purlins; vapor seal and 1 1/2-in. rigid board insulation applied over the steel deck; conventional vapor-seal felts; and a four-ply tar and gravel composition roof. Ventilation of the steam-generator sodium—water reaction relief device should be directed to an accumulator and separator outside of the building. All ventilation of the building can be of conventional design. Some provision for heating the building during shutdown operations is necessary. Fire-fighting equipment should include smoke detectors that sound alarms to indicate an affected generator. A system similar to the Ansul Met-L-X system should be installed. Met-L-X is a silicone-coated sodium chloride. Each fire station should have ample capacity to extinguish any predictable fires.

6.4.2 PIPING TUNNELS

All piping penetrations of the reactor building which contain a liquid-metal coolant should be sheltered in a weathertight and watertight enclosure or tunnel. The heating elements and insulation attached to the piping are thereby protected, and a possible sodium—water reaction is avoided. Ventilation systems should be designed to remove heat from the enclosure. Where radioactive piping is carried through a tunnel, the proper amount of earth and concrete shielding should be provided on top of the tunnel.

6.4.3 TURBINE-GENERATOR BUILDING

This building houses the main steam and feedwater piping, the turbine-generator, the feedwater pumps, and water-treatment facilities. It is of conventional design with some variations. The turbine can be oriented with its shaft pointing toward the reactor building to prevent, in the event of a failure of the turbine spindle, flying missiles from being directed toward the reactor building. Where steam-dump systems are used with once-through steam generators, piping as large as 36 in. in diameter may be required in this building.

6.4.4 ELECTRICAL SUBSTATION

This facility follows conventional design.

6.4.5 CONTROL BUILDING

The control building should be designed to take into account (1) the need to divide the control building into several sections, e.g., normal reactor control, normal steam-electric plant control, emergency reactor plant control, emergency steam-electric plant control, remote refueling control, and remote handling of radioactive equipment; (2) the proximity of sodium and the need to preclude the entry of sodium—air or sodium—water reaction products; and (3) the proximity of radiation and the need to restrict radiation dosages to personnel in the control building to below-tolerable limits for any operations that may be carried on in the building.

The control building may be divided into two sections, one for reactor-plant control and the other for the steam-electric plant. The reactor plant control room, in addition to housing the control equipment for the reactor, the primary and secondary coolant systems, and the fuel-handling equipment, may also contain the control equipment for the remote handling of radioactive component parts. A shielding wall may be needed between the control building and the reactor building to protect personnel in the control building when equipment is being withdrawn from the below-floor shielded area. A room of equivalent size should be provided below the control room for control relay equipment. The multiplicity of control lines from the equipment to the control building may make it necessary to locate the control building at an elevation and location that keeps the length of cable runs at a minimum. Figures 6.62 to 6.64 show layouts of the control building at the Fermi plant. Control-building penetrations, such as cables, gas lines, and ventilation ducts, should be kept to a minimum to avoid radiation streaming. Penetrations should be installed in such a manner that persons in the area near the penetrations will be protected against radiation if such protection is necessary. It may be necessary to add shielded exits from the control room. Where cable trays have any possibility of being damaged by sodium—water reaction products, the trays should be covered with sheet steel. The cable trays may be of the metal ladder type. Heating and air conditioning should be provided for the control rooms. The possibility of sodium—water reaction products gaining entrance to the control building should be minimized. One method is to keep the building under a slight positive pressure. All ventilation air should be filtered. The walls of the control building should, in general, be solid-block construction with no windows and, preferably, with no doors on the sides toward the reactor building, the steam-generator building, or the sodium service building. It may be necessary to have fireproof doors. Smoke generated by wiring fires should be vented outside the control building. Fire extinguishers should be located in the control building, and sprinkler systems should be installed if necessary.

6.4.6 FUEL-HANDLING FACILITY

New fuel received on the Fermi site is stored in the fuel-handling facility; thus provisions

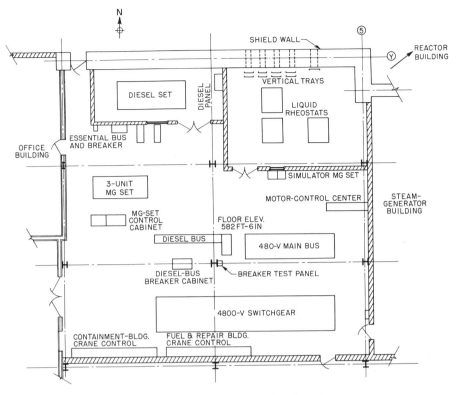

FIG. 6.62—Fermi control-building first floor [6].

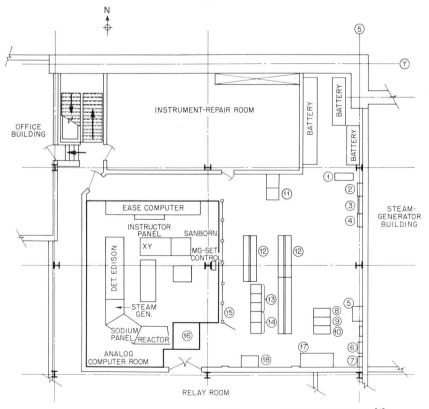

1. Battery Cutoff Switch
2. D-C Main Cable
3. Fuse Comp't. and Grd. Det.
4. D-C Dist. Battery Cable
5. 75-kva Transformer
6. Main Ltg. Dist. Panel
7. Main Dist. Panel
8. Offset Handling Mech.
9. Shield-plug Drive
10. Hold-down Plate
    and Transfer Rotor
11. Rad. Mont. and Tracer Lab.
12. Relay Rack
13. } Steam and
14. } Feedwater Control
15. Railing
16. Removable Inclined Ramp
17. Safety-system MG Set
18. Safety-system Bus and Control Cent.

FIG. 6.63—Fermi control-building second floor [6].

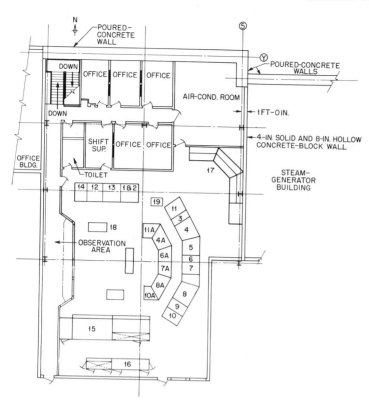

1. Inert Gas
2. Inert Gas
3. Key Interlock
4. Plant Monitoring
4A. Fuel-element Handling
5. Reactor Safety
6. Reactor Start-up
6A. Reactor Start-up
7. Reactor Operating
7A. Reactor Start-up
8. Primary Sodium System
9. Secondary Sodium System
10. Steam and F W System
10A. Steam and F W System
11. Aux. Station Power
11A. Aux. Station Power
12. Primary Sodium Service System
13. Secondary Sodium Service System
14. Waste Gas
15. Operating Panel
16. Secondary Panel
17. Remote-maintenance Panel
18. Data Logger
19. Transfer-function Analyzer

FIG. 6.64—Fermi control-building third floor [6].

should be made for storage, inspection, and transfer. Spent fuel is removed from the reactor, and, unless it is processed inside the reactor building, it is taken directly from the reactor to a fuel-handling building. Here, the radioactive fuel subassemblies are cleaned of residual sodium, placed in a pool of water for decay of radioactivity, inspected, and prepared for shipment off the site in shielded casks. Monitoring of radioactive leakage, including fission-product release, is necessary. If the subassembly is to be cut apart to separate core materials from structural materials or to allow examination of the materials for radiation damage, a remote machining facility should be provided. Wastes, both liquid and gaseous, from this building should be processed through disposal systems. The distance between the reactor building and this facility will be determined by the particular fuel-handling method to be used. A chute or conveyor that transfers the fuel from one building to the other will require the buildings to be adjacent to each other. If the fuel is handled in a shielded cask car, the buildings can be some distance apart. If possible, the railroad spur should be inside the building so that any accident in handling spent fuel will take place inside the building. Figures 6.65 and 6.66 show views of the Fermi facility. The fuel-handling building should be designed for all hazards associated with criticality, sodium–air, or sodium–water reactions. Chapter 7 contains the details of fuel handling.

6.4.7 SERVICE BUILDINGS

6.4.7.1 Sodium Service

The need for a separate sodium service building should be studied for each particular reactor. EBR-II incorporates sodium services in the reactor building. Fermi has a separate building. The sodium-service building houses sodium receipt and storage facilities and sodium-purification equipment. If storage tanks are provided for draining the primary system, the walls and ceiling of the tank room should be shielded. The shielding thickness will depend on the Na^{24} decay in the primary system and the remnant Na^{22} activity. The roof can be a combination of precast and poured concrete slabs. The purification room, since it circulates radioactive sodium, should be shielded against Na^{24} activity. The atmosphere of purification and storage rooms should be nitrogen or depleted air. The rooms can be sealed with steel liners; if the liners are used, the rooms would also serve in part as sodium-leak containers. Penetrations can be sealed with epoxies. The thick concrete walls may require cooling to prevent overheating and resultant cracking. An inert-gas circulating system should limit the concrete temperature to around 150°F. The ventilation equipment should be installed in a nonradioactive room. Provisions should be made for equipment removal, such as removable bolted plates on the outside wall, removable slabs, and the cutting of a welded inner plate. Penetrations between radioactive rooms and

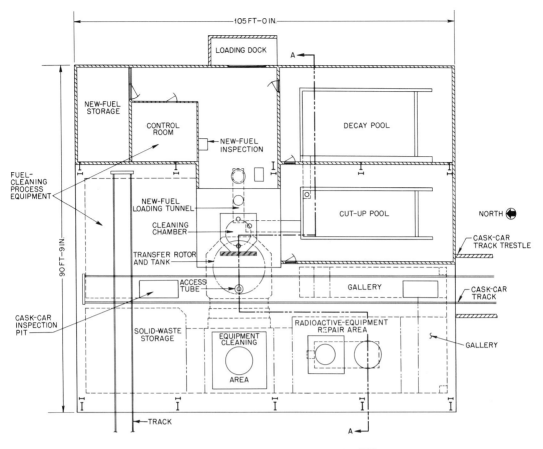

FIG. 6.65—Fermi fuel and repair building (plan) [6].

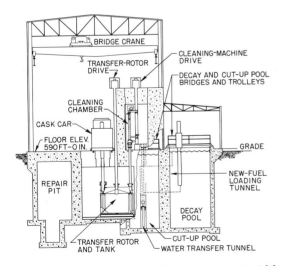

FIG. 6.66—Fermi fuel and repair building (sectional elevation) [6].

nonradioactive accessible rooms should be stepped to prevent streaming. Valves in the radioactive rooms should be operated remotely through the shielded walls, either electrically or manually. Figures 6.67 to 6.70 show the sodium-service building and equipment for the Fermi plant.

6.4.7.2 Inert-gas and Waste-gas-disposal Building

The need for a separate inert-gas building should be evaluated for each reactor. This description

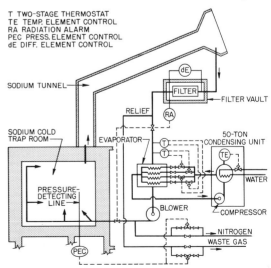

FIG. 6.67—Fermi sodium-service building cold-trap room [6].

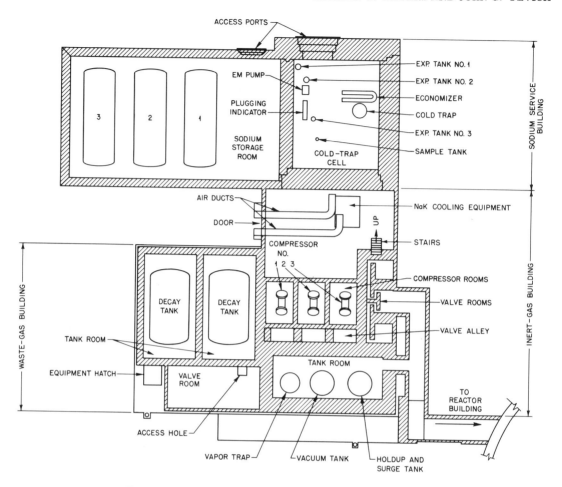

FIG. 6.68—Fermi sodium–service, inert–gas, and waste–gas buildings [6].

considers a separate building housing extensive inert-gas facilities. If an inert-gas building is deemed necessary, it could house (1) the primary-system inert-gas compressors, the vapor trap, holdup and vacuum tanks, valves, piping, and associated equipment and (2) the inert-gas-supply purification and distribution equipment for all gas systems, including pressure and flow regulators. Fission-product detectors can be housed in the inert-gas building if the system recirculates and purifies the gas from over the primary-system sodium. Shielding of the building is necessary if the inert gas or any of its impurities are radioactive while in the gas-service building. Access to holdup tanks can be by means of stepped concrete plugs. Floor drains should be equipped with threaded plugs that are removed only during maintenance. This avoids accidental drainage of radioactive products in the event of a leak of contaminated fluids. The drains should be provided with traps. The inert-gas building should be adequately ventilated and cooled to avoid concrete temperatures in excess of 150°F. Ducting to waste-gas disposal should also be provided to purge compressor rooms in the event of radioactive-gas leakage. The inert-gas building can be designed to serve as a waste-gas-disposal building, or a waste-

gas-disposal building can be erected adjacent to the inert-gas building. The waste-gas-disposal structure houses compressors, filters, vacuum pumps, valves, and decay storage tanks. As in the inert-gas building, shielding, drains with removable seal plugs, stepped concrete plugs for access, and ventilation may be needed. Figures 6.68 to 6.70 show plan views of the inert-gas and waste-gas buildings at Fermi.

6.4.7.3 Gas-disposal Stack

Some of the main sources of gaseous radioactive wastes from a sodium-cooled fast reactor are (1) venting of gases from over the sodium interface in primary-system components which have become activated or whose impurities have become activated, (2) release of gaseous fission products from either leaky fuel elements or vented fuel elements, (3) irradiation of cooling atmosphere in the below-floor area of the reactor building, (4) venting of chambers used to clean fuel and other components, (5) venting of laboratory hoods, (6) venting of plutonium and other radioactive fuel-handling equipment, (7) evaporation of radioactive liquid wastes,. and (8) incineration of radioactive

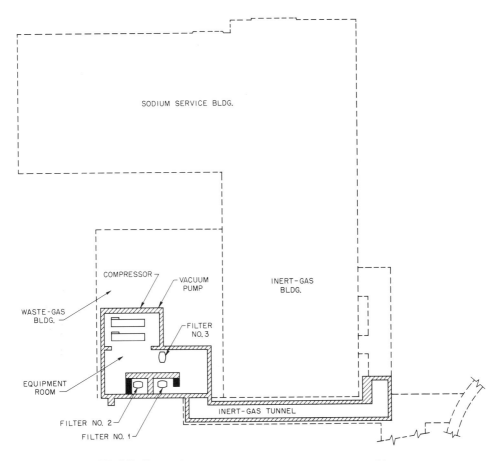

FIG. 6.69—Fermi sodium-service, inert-gas, and waste-gas buildings [6].

solids. The following factors should be studied in the design of a stack: location on the site, height, diameter, effluent, wind velocity, stack-effluent temperature, and stack emission. The various patterns of plume behavior which are considered to lead to maximum surface concentrations are fumigation, looping aerodynamic downwash, trapping, and deposition. The stack should be located on the downwind side of the site and, to prevent downwash, should not be located close to a high structure. The height of the stack should be at least 2 1/2 times that of any building within 20 stack lengths of the stack. Stack diameter will determine the exit velocity of the effluent, which, for the prevention of downwash, should be equal to, or in excess of, the maximum wind velocities anticipated. Laboratory-model studies can be made to determine the dilution factor. If the maximum flow and the radioactivity level of the effluent are known, studies can be made for all wind velocities and directions, for inversions, and for all plume behavior patterns. The waste gas can be slowly released into the stack, and air dilution can be provided by an axial-vane fan installed in the breeching. The stack at the Fermi power plant was designed for a maximum concentration of 1.0 rc/m^3 of effluent at the ground level. A dilution factor of 100:1 will always be satisfied if stack discharge is limited to the periods when the wind velocity exceeds 3 mph. The Fermi stack is made of 1/4-in. plate, is 200 ft high, and is 6 ft in diameter for the lower 15 ft and 3 ft in diameter for the remainder of the height. The stack is guyed in three directions and at three levels.

6.4.7.4 Emergency Power

Housing and structures should be provided with emergency power equipment which may be supplied by a diesel generator set or by large batteries. If batteries are used, an adequate ventilation system must be installed in the battery room to prevent hydrogen accumulation.

6.4.7.5 Equipment-maintenance Facility

Replaceable radioactive components of the primary or secondary coolant systems should be handled in shielded coffins. Nonradioactive components can be handled in bags to prevent exposure of the residual sodium to the air. These nonradioactive components include such items as heat-exchanger bundles and pump internals. After the

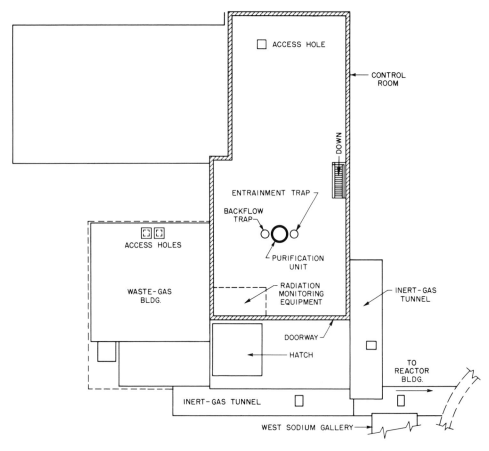

FIG. 6.70—Fermi sodium-service, inert-gas, and waste-gas buildings [6].

radioactive component has been withdrawn, it can be inserted into a decay tank or pit for a period of time necessary to permit personnel access for repair purposes. From the reactor building the part should be taken into a building equipped with shielded facilities for removing the residual sodium and preparing the part for repair. Cleaning pits and liquid-waste-disposal facilities should be provided. Crane facilities should be provided for handling the part after it is in the building. Remote machining facilities should not be necessary if the radioactivity has been allowed to decay. Figures 6.65 and 6.66 show the Fermi maintenance facility. Provisions should be made in the containment building for the removal of any piece of equipment designed for removal and replacement. Such a provision includes air locks and equipment doors (Secs. 6.2.2.5.3 and 6.2.2.5.4) interlocked as described in Secs. 6.2.5.1 and 6.2.5.2. Chapter 4 contains more details on maintenance operations.

6.4.7.6 Ventilation

A separate building may be provided to house the supply and exhaust blowers, heat exchangers, quick-closing valves, dehumidifiers, and refrigeration equipment required for the reactor building. Shielding requirements around such equipment may not be necessary if advantage is taken of the rapid decay rate of radioactive nitrogen by the use of sufficiently long duct runs. Equipment connected to the reactor building should be treated as an extension of reactor-building containment. The building should be provided with heating, floor drains, and such services as steam, condensate, control air, service air, and cooling water. A plan view of the Fermi ventilation building is shown in Fig. 6.71.

6.4.7.7 Health Physics

The design of the health physics building should incorporate all features required of such a building, particularly those which may be needed during an emergency. A health physics building should contain (1) a health physics laboratory, (2) offices and medical treatment rooms, (3) locker room and shower room for use by company employees and visitors entering radioactive areas, such as the reactor building, (4) equipment for monitoring and laundering contaminated clothing, (5) disposal facilities for radioactive tools and instruments and small parts, and (6) a waste-discharge system. The floor plan of the Fermi health physics building is shown in Fig. 6.72. All rooms in the building that may become contaminated with radioactive material should have either strippable material on the floors and walls,

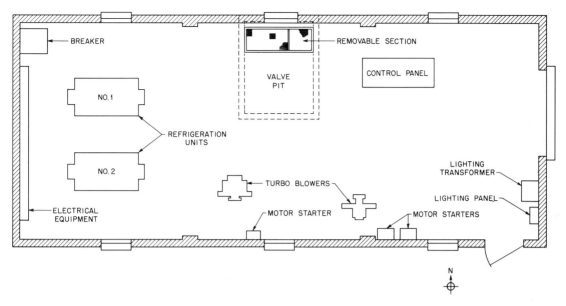

FIG. 6.71—Plan of Fermi ventilation-building equipment layout[6].

such as Liquid Tile, or easily decontaminated non-penetratable material, such as stainless steel. The waste-discharge system in the building should preferably be through two separate systems, a normal-waste system and a radioactive-waste system. Access to the reactor building is monitored and controlled through the health physics building. Maintenance workers, operators, and visitors should pass through this facility upon leaving or entering the reactor building through the personnel air lock. Personnel working in the reactor building should have a clothes-change room and washing facilities that are rigidly controlled by the health physics department. Clothing used in the building should be disposed of in such a manner as to minimize handling. All personnel leaving the building should go through hand and foot monitors. If maintenance or operating personnel work on contaminated equipment in the gas service or reactor coolant service building, the change room should also serve these buildings or a similar facility should be made a part of these buildings. There should be an emergency shower installation as close to the reactor building as possible.

6.4.7.8 Offices, Warehouses, Parking Facilities, Gate House

These buildings can be designed and constructed in accordance with normal power-plant design practice. For public-relations purposes it may be advisable to provide an atomic-power information center either in the office building or in a separate building. The center should be able to accommodate large groups of visitors. It serves the important function of educating the public in the development of atomic energy. The office building may, in addition to offices, contain conference rooms, a kitchen, and a cafeteria. During construction the warehouse can serve as a shop for the assembly

and construction of such items as reactor parts, instruments, and shield structures for installation in the reactor building.

6.4.7.9 Screen House and Water-treatment Building

These buildings are of conventional design. The water-treatment building houses equipment for water purification; it can also serve as a service building during construction. A heating boiler can be housed in this building. Where ice is present the concrete walls in both buildings may have to be reinforced to withstand the force of the ice. Figure 6.73 is a plan view of the screen house and the plant-services building for Fermi.

6.4.7.10 Test Facility

If it is felt necessary to perform tests on the various reactor components in liquid sodium at operating temperatures, a test-facility building should be constructed either on the plant site or on a nearby site. This facility would require liquid-metal handling equipment, piping loops with associated pumps, flowmeters, heat exchangers, and testing instrumentation. Tanks should be available for control-rod drop tests and for fuel-element pressure-drop tests. Offices for operating personnel and rooms for calculations and the writing of reports should be provided.

6.4.7.11 Water and Sewer Systems

Figures 6.74 to 6.76 are schematic diagrams of the Fermi potable-water, service-water, and sewer systems.

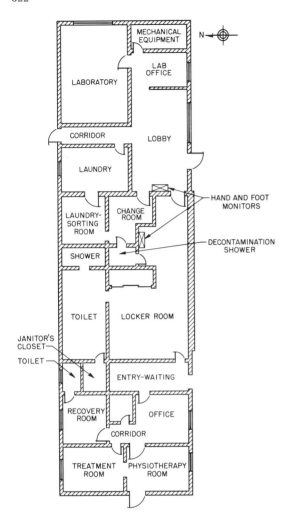

FIG. 6.72—Fermi health physics building [6].

Glossary

A area, sq ft

B burning rate, lb/hr/sq ft; a containment-vessel factor

b a conversion factor relating the total amount of sodium burned to the amount of oxygen consumed, moles oxygen/Btu

C_D shape factor for drag resistance

c_g specific heat of building atmosphere at constant volume, Btu/lb-mole/°F

c_m specific heat of metal, Btu/lb/°F

D diameter, in. or ft

Eff welding-joint efficiency as a fraction equal to, or less than, 1; or motor efficiency

E average energy, Mev; gas energy

F force, lb

f fraction of neutrons produced in the reactor which leak into area outside insulated reactor

g acceleration due to gravity (32.2 ft/sec²)

h height of the source above the ground, meters

hp horsepower

H Way—Wigner decay heating, Btu/hr; nuclear heat in shield, kw

K orifice-flow coefficient

k a constant used in sodium—air reaction analysis

L inside spherical or crown radius, in.; also length, ft

M moment, lb-ft or lb-in.

n concentration, lb-mole; moles of gas

P pressure, psia

p total reactor fission power (core and blanket), kw; pressure, psi

Q total heat content, Btu/hr; heat transferred

q source strength, curies/sec

R inside radius, in.

S stress, psi

T temperature, °F

t thickness, in.; time

U overall heat-transfer coefficient, Btu/hr/sq ft/°F

u velocity, meters/sec, ft/sec, mph

V volume, cu ft

W weight, lb

w flow, lb/sec

X concentration, curies/m³

Y expansion coefficient, as a fraction less than 1

x variable

y lateral (cross-wind) distance from the plume axis, meters

z vertical distance from ground, meters

Z section modulus, cu in.

σ dispersion coefficients, meters

ρ density, lb/cu ft

References

1. O. G. Sutton, The Problem of Diffusion in the Lower Atmosphere, Quart. J. Roy. Meteorol. Soc., 73:257 (1947); and A Theory of Eddy Diffusion in the Atmosphere, Pro. Roy. Soc. London, 13A:143 (1932).
2. F. A. Gifford, Jr., Atmospheric Dispersion, Nucl. Safety, 1(3):56 (March 1960).
3. F. A. Gifford, Jr., Atmospheric Dispersion Calculations Using the Generalized Gaussian Plume Model, Nucl. Safety, 2(2):56 (December 1960).
4. F. A. Gifford, Jr., Use of Routine Meterological Observations for Estimating Atmospheric Dispersion, Nucl. Safety, 2(4):47 (June 1961).
5. F. A. Gifford, Jr., The Area Within Ground-level Dosage Isopleths, Nucl. Safety, 4(2):91 (December 1962).
6. Enrico Fermi Atomic Power Plant, Technical Information and Hazards Summary Report, Power Reactor Development Company, 1962.
7. M. A. Biot, Analytical and Experimental Methods in Engineering Seismology, Proc. Am. Soc. Civil Engrs., 108:365 (1943).
8. E. Y. W. Tsui, Aseismic Design of Structures by Rigidity Criterion, Proc. Am. Soc. Civil Engrs., J. Struct. Div., 85:81–106 (February 1959).
9. Uniform Building Code, Vol. 1, Pacific Coast Building Officials Conference, Los Angeles, 1952 edition. (See inside of back cover which contains a map of the United States showing zones of aseismic probability.)
10. R. R. Alvey, Seismic Aspects of Nuclear Facilities, Symposium on Seismic Considerations for Nuclear Facilities, Cleveland, Ohio, May 4–8, 1959, Joint Meeting on Structural and Construction Division of the American Society of Civil Engineers.
11. R. W. Abbett (Ed.), Earthquake and Earthquake-resistant Design, American Civil Engineering Practice, Vol. III, pp. 34-02—34-23, John Wiley and Sons, Inc., New York, 1957.
12. F. Neuman, Earthquake Intensity and Related Ground Motion, University of Washington Press, Seattle, Wash., 1954.
13. K. J. Wooton, Designing an Earthquakeproof Nuclear Power Station, The New Scientist, 5(127):913–917 (1959).
14. Japan Plans to Build Nuclear Reactor, Modern Power and Engineering, 53(4):70–71 (1959).
15. Reactor Site Criteria, Federal Register, Title 10, Code of Federal Regulations, Part 100, Apr. 12, 1962.
16. National Committee on Radiation Protection, Maximum Permissible Body Burdens and Maximum Permissible Concentrations

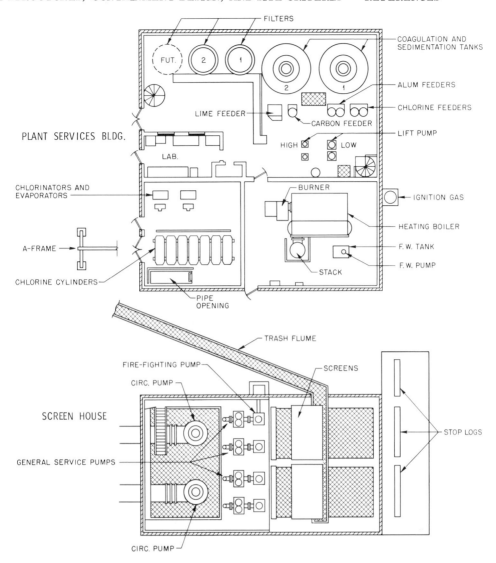

FIG. 6.73—Fermi plant services building and screen house [6].

of Radionuclides in Air and Water for Occupational Exposure, National Bureau of Standards Handbook 69, Superintendent of Documents, U. S. Government Printing Office, Washington, D. C., June 5, 1959.

17. J. J. DiNunno, F. D. Anderson, R. E. Baker, and R. L. Waterfield, Calculation of Distance Factors for Power and Test Reactor Sites, USAEC Report TID-14844, Mar. 23, 1962.

18. T. H. Smith and B. H. Randolph, Selections of a Reactor Containment Structure, Nucl. Sci. Eng., 4:762-784 (1958).

19. R. O. Brittan and J. C. Heap, Reactor Containment, Proceedings of the Second United Nations International Conference on the Peaceful Uses of Atomic Energy, Geneva, 1958, Vol. 11, p. 66, United Nations, New York, 1959.

20. H. A. Bethe, Bethe-Tait Accident, filed as Bethe Exhibit No. 2 in the Matter of the Power Reactor Development Company, AEC Docket F-16, 1957.

21. W. J. McCarthy, R. B. Nicholson, D. Okrent, and V. Z. Jankus, Studies of Nuclear Accidents in Fast Power Reactors, Proceedings of the Second United Nations International Conference on the Peaceful Uses of Atomic Energy, Geneva, 1958, Vol. 12, p. 207, United Nations, New York, 1959.

22. H. A. Bethe and J. H. Tait, An Estimate of the Order of Magnitude of the Explosion When the Core of a Fast Reactor Collapses, British Report RHM (56)/113, April 1956.

23. F. Porzel, Some Hydrodynamic Problems in Reactor Containment, Proceedings of the Second United Nations International

Conference on the Peaceful Uses of Atomic Energy, Geneva, 1958, Vol. 11, p. 85, United Nations, New York, 1959.

24. J. Bohannon and W. Baker, Simulating Nuclear Blast Effects, Nucleonics, 16(3):71-77 (March 1958).

25. W. E. Baker and J. D. Patterson, Blast Effects Test of a One-quarter Scale Model of the Air Force Nuclear Engineering Test Reactor, Report BRL-1011, Ballistic Research Laboratory, Aberdeen Proving Ground, March 1957.

26. W. R. Wise, NOL Reactor Vessel Containment Program, Report NAVORD-4542, Naval Ordnance Laboratory, June 1957.

27. N. Zabel, Containment of Fragments from Runaway Reactor, Technical Report No. 1, Standard Research Institute, Apr. 2, 1958.

28. W. E. Baker, Scale Model Tests for Evaluating Outer Containment Structures for Nuclear Reactors, Proceedings of the Second United Nations International Conference on the Peaceful Uses of Atomic Energy, Geneva, 1958, Vol. 11, p. 79, United Nations, New York, 1959.

29. E. M. Fisher and W. R. Wise, Jr., Containment Study of the Enrico Fermi Fast Breeder Reactor Plant, Report NAVORD-5747, Naval Ordnance Laboratory, Oct. 7, 1957.

30. W. R. Stratton et al., Analysis of Prompt Excursions in Simple Systems and Idealized Fast Reactors, Proceedings of the Second United Nations International Conference on the Peaceful Uses of Atomic Energy, Geneva, 1958, Vol. 12, p. 196, United Nations, New York, 1959.

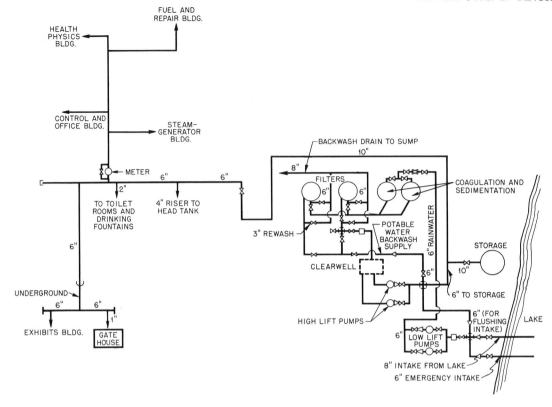

FIG. 6.74—Fermi potable-water system [6].

31. F. B. Porzel, Design Evaluation of BER (Boiling Experimental Reactor) in Regard to Internal Explosions, USAEC Report ANL-5651, Armour Research Foundation, January 1957.

32. H. O. Monson and M. M. Sluyter, Containment of EBR-II, Proceedings of the Second United Nations International Conference on the Peaceful Uses of Atomic Energy, Geneva, 1958, Vol. 11, p. 124, United Nations, New York, 1959.

33. R. O. Brittan, Reactor Containment, USAEC Report ANL-5948, Argonne National Laboratory, May 1959.

34. Theoretical Possibilities and Consequences of Major Accidents in Large Nuclear Power Plants, USAEC Report WASH-740, March 1957.

35. S. McLain and R. Brittan, Safety Features of Nuclear Power Reactors, ASME Paper 57-A-265, American Society of Mechanical Engineers.

36. W. McGuire and G. P. Fisher, Report on Containment Studies of the Enrico Fermi Atomic Power Plant, Power Reactor Development Company, Ithaca, New York, May 1959.

37. L. S. Marks, Mechanical Engineer's Handbook, 5th ed., pp. 1541 and 1537, McGraw-Hill Book Company, Inc., New York, 1951.

38. Nuclear Reactor Containment Buildings and Pressure Vessels, Proceedings of a Symposium Organized by the Department of Mechanical, Civil and Chemical Engineering of the Royal College of Science and Technology, Glasgow, Scotland, May 17–20, 1960, Butterworth and Co., Ltd., London, 1960.

39. Seismic Considerations in Nuclear Power Plants, Nucl. Safety, 3(4):58 (June 1962).

40. W. R. Gall, Reactor Containment Design, Nucl. Safety, 3(4):52 (June 1962).

41. Effect of Lightning on Thin Metal Surfaces, AIEE Trans., 61:559–564 (1942).

42. W. C. Siler and L. P. Zick, Design Considerations for an Atomic Power Reactor Containment Structure, paper presented at American Society of Civil Engineers Convention, Oct. 15, 1956.

43. N. T. Barrett, Housing the Dounreay Fast Reactor, Structural Engineer, 36(3):85–97 (March 1958).

44. L. J. Koch et al., Hazard Summary Report Experimental Breeder Reactor II (EBR-II), USAEC Report ANL-5719, Argonne National Laboratory, May 1957.

45. C. O. Nelson and D. B. Nelson, Sodium–Air Reaction Experiments, USAEC Report KAPL-639, Knolls Atomic Power Laboratory, Jan. 1, 1952.

46. R. E. Wyant, The Effect of Nuclear Radiation on Refrigerants, REIC-Memo-16, Battelle Memorial Institute, June 30, 1959.

47. R. E. Mueller, Memorandum P-62-150, Atomic Power Development Associates, Inc.

48. C. B. Jackson (Ed.), Liquid-Metals Handbook, Sodium–NaK Supplement, Superintendent of Documents, U. S. Government Printing Office, Washington, D. C., July 1, 1955.

49. Heating, Ventilating, Air Conditioning Guide, published annually by the American Society of Heating and Air-Conditioning Engineers, Inc., New York.

50. M. H. Fontana, Containment of Power Reactors, Nucl. Safety, 2(1):55 (September 1960).

51. Boiling Nuclear Superheat (BONUS) Power Station, Vol. IV, Preliminary Hazard Summary Report, USAEC Report TID-8524, June 1960.

52. D. Inglis and G. Ringo, Underground Construction of Power Reactors, USAEC Report ANL-5652, Argonne National Laboratory, January 1957.

53. C. Beck, Engineering Study on Underground Construction of Nuclear Power Reactors, USAEC Report AECU-3779, April 1958.

54. Annual Technical Progress Report, AEC Unclassified Programs, USAEC Report NAA-SR-6370, Atomics International, Aug. 15, 1961.

55. R. L. Koontz et al., Low Pressure Containment Buildings, Component Tests and Design Data, USAEC Report NAA-SR-7234, Atomics International, Mar. 15, 1963.

56. J. D. Gracie and J. J. Droher, A Study of Sodium Fires, USAEC Report NAA-SR-4383, Atomics International, Oct. 15, 1960.

57. H. K. LeMar, Liquid-Metal Smoke Abatement, Report PWAC-235, Pratt and Whitney Aircraft Division, Nov. 1, 1957.

58. J. R. Humphreys, Jr., Sodium–Air Reactions as They Pertain to Reactor Safety and Containment, Proceedings of the Second United Nations International Conference on the Peaceful Uses of Atomic Energy, Geneva, 1958, Vol. 11, p. 177, United Nations, New York, 1959.

59. E. Garelis, Sodium–Air Accident Study for a Sodium Cooled Reactor, USAEC Report AECU-4161, Atomic Power Development Associates, Inc., Apr. 6, 1959.

60. H. H. Gott and T. C. Waters, The Dounreay Reactor, Part I, Criteria of Design, and Part II, Structural Design and Construction, British Report RHM (56)/129, March 1956. (See also

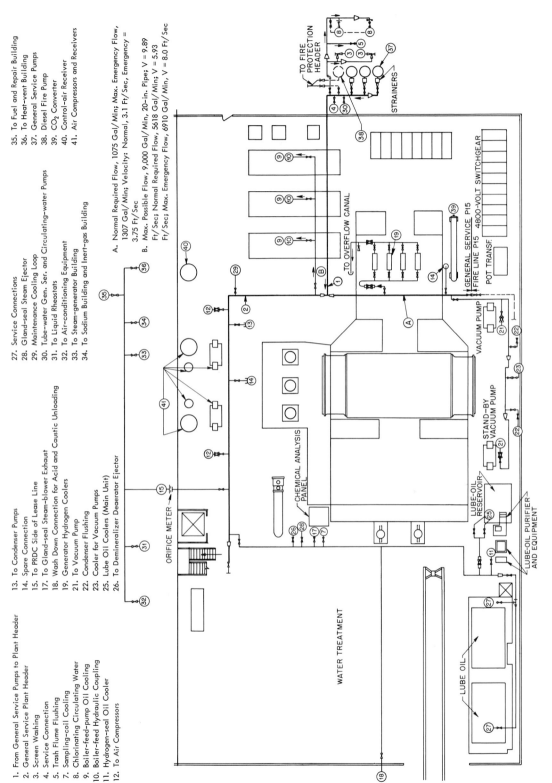

FIG. 6.75—Fermi general-service water system [6].

1. From General Service Pumps to Plant Header
2. General Service Plant Header
3. Screen Washing
4. Service Connection
5. Trash Flume Flushing
7. Sampling-coil Cooling
8. Chlorinating Circulating Water
9. Boiler-feed-pump Oil Cooling
10. Boiler-feed Hydraulic Coupling
11. Hydrogen-seal Oil Cooler
12. To Air Compressors

13. To Condenser Pumps
14. Spare Connection
15. To PRDC Side of Lease Line
17. To Gland-seal Steam-blower Exhaust
18. Wash Down Connection for Acid and Caustic Unloading
19. Generator Hydrogen Coolers
21. To Vacuum Pump
22. Condenser Flushing
23. Cooler for Vacuum Pumps
25. Lube Oil Coolers (Main Unit)
26. To Demineralizer Deaerator Ejector

27. Service Connections
28. Gland-seal Steam Ejector
29. Maintenance Cooling Loop
30. Tube-water Gen. Ser. and Circulating-water Pumps
31. To Liquid Rheostats
32. To Air-conditioning Equipment
33. To Steam-generator Building
34. To Sodium Building and Inert-gas Building

35. To Fuel and Repair Building
36. To Heat-vent Building
37. General Service Pumps
38. Diesel Fire Pump
39. CO_2 Converter
40. Control-air Receiver
41. Air Compressors and Receivers

A. Normal Required Flow, 1075 Gal/Min; Max. Emergency Flow, 1307 Gal/Min; Velocity: Normal, 3.1 Ft/Sec, Emergency = 3.75 Ft/Sec
B. Max. Possible Flow, 9,000 Gal/Min, 20-in. Pipe; V = 9.89 Ft/Sec; Normal Required Flow, 5618 Gal/Min; V = 5.93 Ft/Sec; Max. Emergency Flow, 6910 Gal/Min; V = 8.0 Ft/Sec

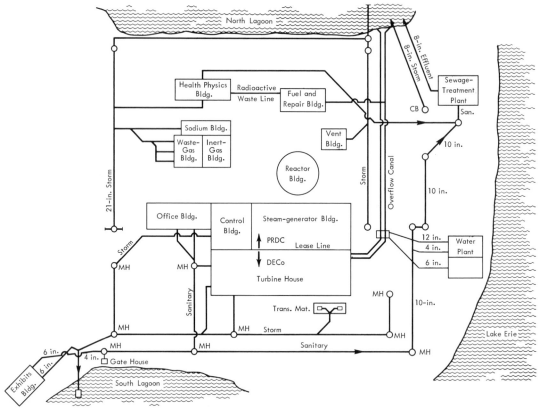

FIG. 6.76—Fermi storm- and sanitary-sewer system [6].

H. H. Gott and G. Flook, Design Conditions for Reactor Containing Sphere, British Report FRDC/P-70, 1954, and Engineering, The Dounreay Fast Reactor, 280-2, Aug. 26, 1955).

61. J. P. Coughlin, U. S. Bur. Mines Bull. 542, 1954.

62. A. Kolflat and W. A. Chittenden, Electrical World, 148:53-57 (1957).

63. E. Hines, A. Gemant, and J. K. Kelley, How Strong Must Reactor Housings be to Contain Na-Air Reactions, Nucleonics, 14(10):38-41 (October 1956).

64. H. H. Gott and G. Flook, Design Conditions for Reactor Containing Sphere, British Report FRDC/P-70, 1954.

65. W. H. McAdams, Heat Transmission, 3rd ed., p. 172, McGraw-Hill Book Company, Inc., New York, 1954.

66. E. Garelis, The Treatment of the Effect of Decay Heat on Reactor Containment Vessels, paper presented at the American Nuclear Society Winter Meeting, 1958.

67. I. G. Dillon and I. Burris, Jr., Nucl. Sci. Eng., 2:567-581 (1957).

68. J. F. Perkins and R. W. King, Energy Release from the Decay of Fission Products, Nucl. Sci. Eng., 3:726-746 (1958).

69. J. D. Blomeke and M. F. Todd, Uranium-235 Fission-Product Production as a Function of Thermal Neutron Flux, Irradiation Time, and Decay Time, USAEC Report ORNL-2127, Oak Ridge National Laboratory, 1957.

70. Enrico Fermi Atomic Power Plant, Technical Information and Hazards Summary Report, Power Reactor Development Company, June 1961.

71. A. Glassner, The Thermochemical Properties of the Oxides, Fluorides, and Chlorides to 2500°K, USAEC Report ANL-5750, Argonne National Laboratory, 1957.

72. Section VIII, ASME Boiler and Pressure Vessel Code, Unfired Pressure Vessels, 1959 Edition.

73. Section I, ASME Boiler and Pressure Vessel Code, Power Boilers.

74. ASTM Standards, Part I, Ferrous Metals, Specification A 300-58.

75. J. R. Hawthorne, L. E. Steele, W. S. Pellini, Effects of Nuclear Radiation on the Properties of Reactor Structural Materials, ASME Paper 61-WA-332, American Society of Mechanical Engineers, Nov. 26, 1961.

76. L. P. Zick, Design of Steel Containment Vessels in the U.S.A., Nuclear Reactor Containment Buildings and Pressure Vessels, Butterworth and Co., Ltd., London, 1960.

77. J. Zissi and E. Diehl, Leak Rate Test, Power Plant Building, West Milton Site, USAEC Report M-6065, Knolls Atomic Power Laboratory, September 1953.

78. S. Untermyer and D. Layton, Leakage Testing on the Boiling Water Reactor Enclosure, USAEC Report VAL-33, Vallecitos Atomic Laboratory, September 1957.

79. R. V. McGrath and L. P. Zick, Testing of Nuclear Containment Vessels, The Water Tower, pp. 13-17, Chicago Bridge and Iron Co., Oak Brook, Illinois, January 1961.

80. Proposed Standard for Leakage Rate Testing of Containment Structures for Nuclear Reactors, ANS 7.62, American Nuclear Society.

81. Theodore Rockwell III (Ed.), Reactor Shielding Design Manual, D. Van Nostrand Co. Inc., Princeton, N. J., 1956.

82. H. Etherington (Ed.), Nuclear Engineering Handbook, McGraw-Hill Book Company, Inc., New York, 1958.

83. Personal Communication, E. Garelis, General Electric Co., to M. Barrett, AEC, July 5, 1963.

84. Selected list of EBR-II illustrations, issued March 1961 by Argonne National Laboratory, at ACRS Meeting, Arco, Idaho.

CHAPTER 7

Fuel Handling

JACK STADER
Commonwealth Associates, Inc.
Jackson, Michigan
and
JOHN G. YEVICK*
Atomic Power Development Associates, Inc.
Detroit, Michigan

Contents

7.1 Introduction

The loading and unloading of solid-fueled sodium-cooled fast breeder reactors involves the removal and replacement of irradiated fuel complicated by the following:

1. Fuel radioactivity: Gamma and beta radiations are emitted by irradiated and recycled fuel.

2. Decay heat: The energy released in the radioactive decay processes of fission products in the fuel is great enough during the first few hours after shutdown of a power reactor to melt the fuel-element cladding or sheathing in a very few minutes if adequate cooling provisions are not made. The exact rate of temperature rise of a given fuel element depends on the design of the fuel element, the reactor power, and the time of irradiation.

3. Coolant radioactivity and chemical activity: The sodium coolant used in a fast reactor is radioactive and some of it remains on the fuel subassembly removed from the reactor. Its chemical activity prevents handling schemes which permit exposure of the fuel elements to water or air.

4. Damaged fuel elements: The fuel elements may be warped or damaged by corrosion or cladding failure and thus make handling difficult.

5. Criticality hazard: New and irradiated fuel subassemblies present a potential criticality hazard.

6. Maintenance: Fuel-handling equipment may become radioactive if kept in the reactor or may become contaminated by either radioactive sodium or fission products. Maintenance is difficult.

The following general criteria may lead to the solution of the problems presented by the six conditions listed. All unloading operations should be conducted remotely, and irradiation protection should be provided for personnel. Cooling should be adequate at all times to remove the decay heat.

Cleaning facilities may be needed to remove radioactive sodium. Wash solutions should be cleaned by ion exchange and diluted or stored before disposal. Spills or leaks of radioactive sodium should be prevented. Remote cleanup procedures may be necessary to clean up inadvertent spills or leaks that would contaminate any section accessible to personnel.

It may be necessary to provide some method of leak detection to detect leaking subassemblies and thus prevent contamination. Leaky elements should be contained in sealed cans to minimize the spread of contamination. Subassemblies should be handled carefully to avoid damage to irradiated fuel and possible fission-product release.

Spacing of subassemblies in new and decay storage areas should be such as to avoid criticality under any condition. Consideration should be given to the mediums in which the subassemblies are stored, to the possibility of inadvertent flooding, and to the presence of reflector material.

Irradiated subassemblies should be kept in storage for a specified period to reduce fission-product activity and decay heat to prescribed levels compatible with shipping and processing requirements.

The radiochemical activity of recycled plutonium and U^{233} should be contained by precautionary measures such as dry-box handling and/or shielding.

Remote maintenance of fuel-handling equipment may be necessary, and cleaning facilities may be

Table 7.1—Fast Reactor Fuel Subassembly Characteristics

Reactor	Cross section of subassemblies	No. of subassemblies	Diameter or dimension across flats, in.	Length, in.	Weight, lb
EBR-I	Round rods*	217 core rods 138 blanket rods	0.448 0.964	∼110†	‡
	Hexagonal§	7 core 12 blanket	$2\frac{7}{8}$ $2\frac{7}{8}$	112.75†	‡
BR-5	Hexagonal	80 core 40 blanket	1.02 ‡	32.7	‡
Dounreay	Round annular rods	367 core 1872 blanket	0.752 1.385	48.35 98.00	∼50 80
EBR-II	Hexagonal	61 core 576 blanket	2.290 2.290	91-53/64	∼76 ∼134
Fermi	Square	105 core 531 blanket	2.646 2.646	96-9/16	121 core 161 blanket
Rapsodie	Hexagonal	553 (core and blanket)	1.96	∼66	‡

* Round rods for Mark I and II cores were not placed in subassemblies.
† Includes extension through plug.
‡ Information not available.
§ Rods for Mark III and IV cores were placed in subassemblies.

needed to decontaminate the equipment.

This chapter is limited to the following basic refueling operations: (1) solid-fuel sodium-cooled reactors, (2) vertical subassemblies of various but relatively small cross sections, (3) refueling from top of the reactor, (4) unloading of one subassembly at a time, and (5) refueling only during reactor shutdown.

The characteristics of fuel subassemblies in existing reactors are described in Table 7.1. The use of relatively small subassemblies is motivated by several factors: (1) reactivity limitations, (2) heat-transfer limitations during refueling, (3) criticality problems during decay storage, and (4) refueling-machine design problems. Refueling from the top of the reactor prevents sodium leakage through seals. The same holds for control-rod operation from the top.

Fuel handling in a fast reactor is characterized by several important considerations generally not met in other reactors, e.g., the use of sodium as a coolant, high specific power, and restricted core movements. The problems encountered with sodium are covered in Chaps. 2, 4, 8, and 11. The comparative degree of heat concentration can be illustrated by the following facts: the Boiling Water Reactor (BWR) and Pressurized Water Reactor (PWR) operate at 815 to 1550 kw(t)/cu ft and the Sodium Graphite Reactor (SGR) operates at 124 kw(t)/cu ft as compared with over 20,000 kw(t)/cu ft for fast reactors [1]. This reflects directly on decay-heat generation during fuel handling, decay storage, and fuel shipment. Fast reactor cores have small clearances between subassemblies since relatively large reactivity perturbations take place whenever a physical change occurs in the size of the core. This results in the need for careful restriction of core movements at all powers and has considerable effect on fuel-handling-equipment design.

Fast reactor refueling has an advantage in that relatively small amounts of fuel are handled on a per year basis. For example, a 615-Mw(t) PWR core containing 39,000 kg of 2.7% enriched uranium, with

a potential burnup of 25,000 Mwd/tonne average and with an average life of approximately 5.55 years, refuels 9000 kg/year or approximately 15 kg/Mw(t) [2], whereas a 700-Mw(t) fast reactor with a ceramic core containing 3250 kg plutonium plus uranium, 25% enrichment, with a potential burnup of 100,000 Mwd/tonne average and an average life of approximately 1.3 years, refuels 2500 kg/year or approximately 3.5 kg/Mw(t) [3]. The smaller quantities of fuel and number of subassembly units handled allows for flexibility in fuel-handling design and procedures.

7.2 Methods of Fuel Handling

7.2.1 INTRODUCTION

The design selected for the fuel-handling scheme is greatly influenced by the frequency of unloading. Infrequent refueling may allow for the use of slow operating devices with long setup times and considerable manual operation, but it requires a high degree of equipment reliability during refueling and equipment accessibility for maintenance. Frequent refueling requires a design carefully integrated into the reactor plant, which will permit fast and accurate unloading using simple, foolproof, long-life equipment with provisions for maintenance. The maintenance of fuel-handling machines incorporated into the reactor is difficult. The reliability of such machines should be assured.

7.2.2 FUEL-HANDLING CYCLES

Some of the existing methods for handling fuel are diagrammed in Figs. 7.1 to 7.4. A method for advanced plants is shown in Fig. 7.5.

The fuel-handling cycle is generally not reversible, i.e., the process from new-fuel receipt to insertion of the fuel into the reactor cannot be

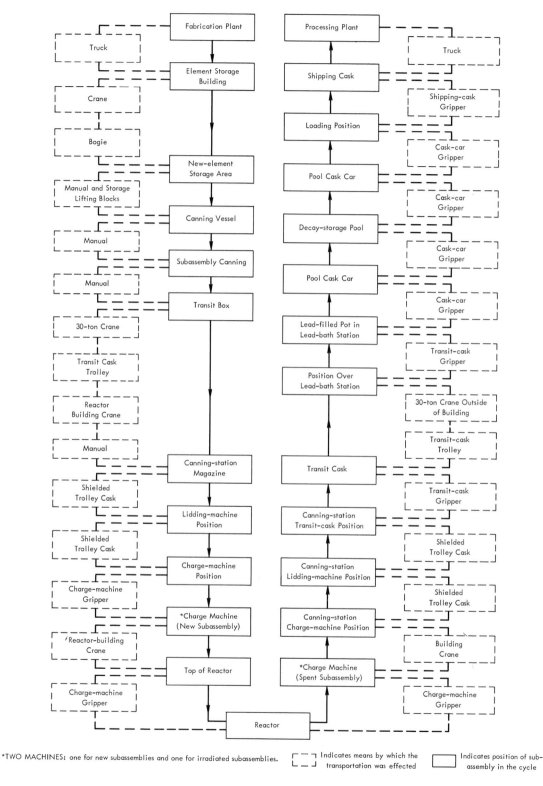

FIG. 7.1—Dounreay fuel-handling-system block diagram.

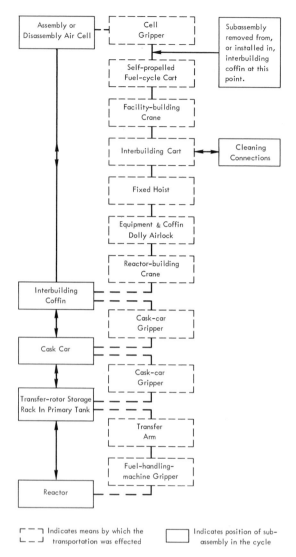

FIG. 7.2—EBR-II fuel-handling-system block diagram.

completely reversed. The flow charts of Figs. 7.1 to 7.5 have the following in common: fuel receipt and inspection → storage of new fuel → transfer to reactor using a cask → transfer from reactor to decay storage → inspection → shipment to reprocessing facility.

7.2.3 FUEL HANDLING INTERNAL TO THE REACTOR

7.2.3.1 Introduction

Movement of fuel subassemblies within the reactor complex may encompass one or more of the following: (1) transfer from one position in the core to another position in the core, (2) transfer from one position in the blanket to another position in the blanket, (3) transfer from either core or blanket to a decay storage position within the reactor, (4)

transfer from the core, blanket, or decay storage position to an exit-port transfer position or to a storage rack, (5) transfer from the exit-port transfer position or storage rack to an external cask, (6) transfer from an external cask to an exit-port transfer position or storage rack within the reactor, (7) transfer from the exit-port transfer position or storage rack to the core or blanket, (8) direct transfer from a core, blanket, or decay storage position to an external cask, and (9) direct transfer from an external cask to a core, blanket, or decay storage position.

This chapter will not cover the advisability of carrying out internal core and blanket transfers (operations 1 and 2) except to state that such transfers may be made for the following reasons: safety precautions during start-up or to program fuel and blanket burnup.

The advisability of decay storage within the reactor (operation 3) will be discussed in more detail. The use of an exit-port transfer position located in the reactor may be advantageous in reactors with fixed decay storage positions, as shown in the PFFBR cycle of Fig. 7.5. Rotating storage racks that receive fuel from the reactor and position the fuel for transfer out of the reactor are used in EBR-II and Fermi. In this case initial transfer from the reactor core is made to the rotating storage rack.

7.2.3.2 Existing Fuel-handling Systems Internal to Reactor

To accomplish any combination of tasks described in Sec. 7.2.3.1 requires that the fuel-handling system must be capable of performing the necessary tasks in a minimum of time and with the greatest degree of safety. The system must have maximum accessibility for maintenance. None of the existing schemes for fast reactors assures an optimum refueling down time. The refueling time for fast reactors should be shorter than that for thermal reactors, but considerable refueling experience needs to be gained at prototype and experimental plants such as Fermi, Dounreay, EBR-II, and Rapsodie. Refueling times for thermal reactors are shown in Table 7.2. The refueling time in Table 7.2 includes inspection and maintenance of reactor and fuel-handling equipment not normally accessible for inspection and repair.

Table 7.2—Refueling Times for Thermal Reactors [4-7]

		No. of days to refuel	
		Scheduled	Actual
Shippingport PWR	Seed 1	90	134
	Seed 2	52	44
	Seed 3	*	32.5
Yankee PWR	1st reloading	60	120
Dresden BWR	1st reloading	120	*

* Information not available.

The EBR-II and Fermi fuel-handling systems can accomplish operations 1 through 7 listed in Sec. 7.2.3.1. The Dounreay fuel-handling system can accomplish operations 1 through 3, 8, and 9. Rapsodie will essentially duplicate the Dounreay

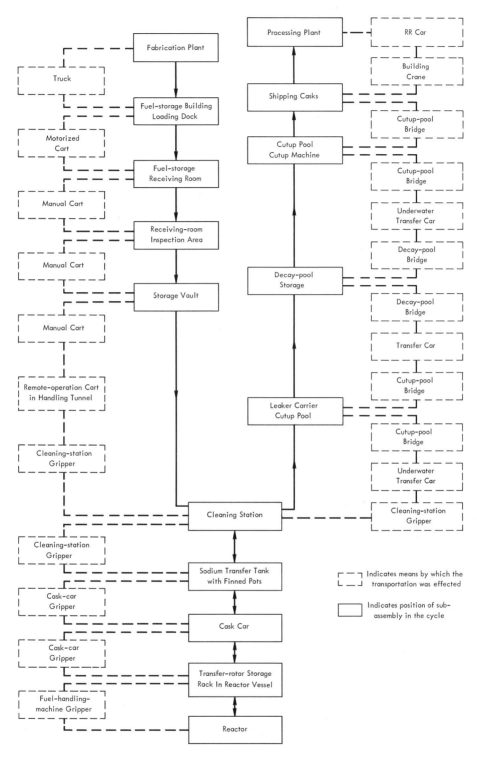

FIG. 7.3—Fermi fuel-handling-system block diagram.

type of operation. Both EBR-II and Fermi utilize a storage rack or transfer rotor as an intermediate stopover point for the fuel before its removal from the reactor primary sodium. In EBR-II this provides a means of decay storage for several weeks prior to removal of fuel to the pyrometallurgical processing plant. In Fermi the transfer rotor serves three purposes: (1) it provides for lateral

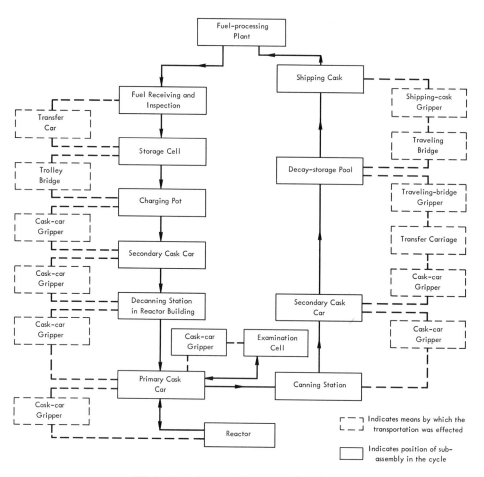

FIG. 7.4—Rapsodie fuel-handling-system block diagram.

displacement of the fuel so that it can be removed through an exit port independent of the rotating plug (this eliminates a cask car from above the reactor and keeps inviolate the gastight machinery dome above the reactor), (2) it provides for storage of fuel immediately after removal from the reactor, if this is deemed necessary, and (3) it allows for the removal of fuel independent of any operations internal to the reactor. The Dounreay and Rapsodie type of fuel handling is possible because the subassemblies are removed from the reactor at sufficiently low burnups to reduce the decay-heat problem and because the reactor top face is arranged in a manner that provides space for the refueling equipment. Table 7.3 summarizes the characteristics of existing refueling schemes at the reactor.

The double roating plug, consisting of a rotating eccentric plug within a rotating concentric plug, each plug being driven by an independent drive, allows for the positioning of one or more access holes in the eccentric plug over any desired position within the reactor. The fuel-handling machine can be fixed as a normal part of the reactor complex, such as in EBR-II, or it can be brought into position with a cask or a cask car, such as in Dounreay and Rapsodie. Further descriptions are covered in Sec. 7.9. The single rotating plug is used in

conjunction with a rotating offset handling arm submerged in sodium that positions the arm over any subassembly, as in Fermi. This arrangement is further described in Sec. 7.9.

Attaching shielded extensions to the top of each subassembly, with the extensions penetrating a fixed shield plug, makes it possible to refuel from the top face of the reactor. The EBR-I uses this system. For EBR-I a cask is brought into position by a crane. A top shield plug is removed prior to refueling. This plug normally reduces radiation streaming to below set limits.

The advantages and disadvantages of the various existing systems are listed in Table 7.4.

7.2.3.3 Proposed Fuel-handling Systems

Several proposed systems that have merit are (1) fixed plug with an under-sodium fuel-handling mechanism operating on a polar-coordinate principle, as proposed [8] for advanced plutonium-fueled fast breeder reactor (PFFBR); (2) a shielded compartment [9-11] above the reactor (Fig. 7.6) with an inert atmosphere, a removable reactor cover, handling lugs on fuel subassemblies exposed for viewing, equipment for viewing the refueling procedure, indexed crane carrying a grapple, and decay-

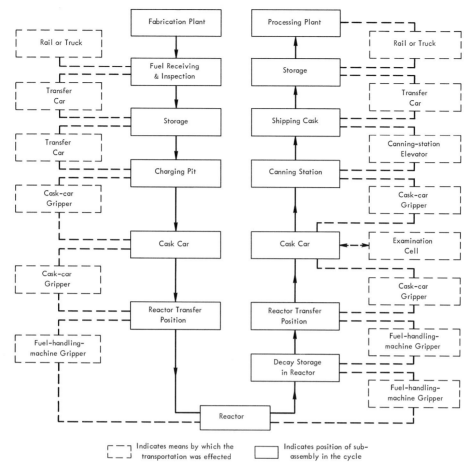

FIG. 7.5—PFFBR fuel-handling-system block diagram.

storage facilities; and (3) a modified EBR-I scheme consisting of shielded extensions on fuel subassemblies which project above the sodium level, a removable reactor cover (including control-rod drives), which can be replaced during refueling by a rotating shielded plug, and a shielded fuel-handling cask installed above the plug for refueling. Scheme 3 has been considered by Argonne National Laboratory for the fast core test reactor FARET

[12, 13]. The advantages and disadvantages of these three systems are listed in Table 7.5.

The systems described and compared in Secs. 7.2.3.2 and 7.2.3.3 cover the main types in use or proposed and are shown schematically in Fig. 7.7. Other refueling systems that may have merit include (1) a fuel-handling machine similar to proposed system 1, but with the entrance port located at an angle outside the vessel plug and the exit port

Table 7.3—Characteristics of Existing Fuel-handling Systems at the Reactor

Reactor	Reactor plug	Type of fuel-handling machine used to handle fuel in the reactor	Fuel-handling machine (internal or external to reactor)*
EBR-I	Fixed	Shielded cask	External
BR-5	Double rotating	†	External
Dounreay	Double rotating	Shielded cask	External
EBR-II	Double rotating	Permanent subassembly gripper mechanism	Internal
Rapsodie	Double rotating	Shielded cask car	External
Fermi	Single rotating	Permanent offset handling mechanism	Internal

* External: machine located outside of reactor. Gripper moves in and out of the reactor through refueling ports.
  Internal: gripper part of machine always submerged under sodium.
† Information not available.

Table 7.4—Advantages and Disadvantages of Existing Refueling Schemes

System	Advantages	Disadvantages
A. Double rotating plug; fixed machine with gripper continuously under sodium (EBR-II)	1. Continuous availability 2. Does not require indexing of the refueling machine body as in EBR-I 3. Fixed calibration 4. Simple operation 5. Allows for rotation of gripper	1. High inertia of a plug may cause severe damage in case of fuel subassembly hang-up 2. Radial bearings may be continuously in sodium or sodium vapor 3. Requires radioactive maintenance of reactor equipment 4. Contains a complex of external mechanisms that require maintenance 5. Possibility of long-term damage by sodium contaminants 6. Long-term outage for removal of normally inaccessible equipment 7. Hang-up of fuel possible 8. Space requirements for plug drives 9. Difficult, if not impractical, to instrument the core 10. No visual observation of fuel subassemblies 11. Requires release of control and safety rods from their drives
B. Double rotating plug; refueling cask brought into position; gripper in sodium only during removal and insertion of fuel (Dounreay, Rapsodie)	1. Refueling-machine bearings are kept in sodium or sodium vapor for only a limited period 2. Nonradioactive maintenance of gripper and carrier after a wash-down 3. Accessible for maintenance between refueling periods 4. Minimal reactor outage for maintenance of fuel-handling equipment 5. Allows for rotation of gripper 6. Does not require indexing of the refueling-machine body	1. High inertia of a plug may cause severe damage in case of hang-up 2. Available only after a large number of preparatory operations 3. Possibility of radioactive contamination 4. Requires a complex of external mechanisms 5. Hang-up of fuel possible 6. Space requirements for plug drives 7. Difficult, if not impractical, to instrument the core 8. No visual observation of fuel subassemblies 9. May require release of control and safety rods from their drives
C. Single rotating plug with offset fuel-handling mechanism; gripper continuously under sodium (Fermi)	1. Eliminates one rotating plug and drive mechanism with attendant maintenance 2. Reduces floor-space requirements 3. Continuous availability 4. Fixed calibration 5. Simple operation 6. Does not require indexing of the refueling-machine body 7. Reduces size of rotating-plug complex, the reactor vessels, and surrounding tanks	1. Disadvantages of scheme A 2. Additional moving parts in sodium 3. No rotation of gripper thus requires self-orientation of subassemblies
D. Refueling at top face of plug; fuel subassemblies attached to shield plugs acting as extension handle (EBR-I)	1. Complete accessibility to refueling machine for maintenance 2. No radioactive maintenance 3. Minimum danger of fuel hang-up 4. No gripper-mechanism hang-up 5. No bearings or moving parts in sodium or sodium vapor 6. High probability of instrumenting the core 7. Reduces complexity of fuel-handling mechanism 8. Eliminates need for orientation of fuel subassembly internal to the reactor 9. Visual refueling eliminates need for extensive calibration 10. Design may be such as to avoid the need for disconnecting the control and safety rods from their drives 11. Lowest in reactor outage for repair of fuel-handling machine	1. Requires wide separation of top of fuel subassembly extensions at the top surface of reactor shield plug (impractical with vertical subassemblies in high-density cores to do this); requires latticed core (difficult to accomplish) 2. High probability that the core and plug design will be complex to accomodate accessibility for refueling at the top face 3. Radioactive streaming problems may require complex shielding design or a removable top shielding plug such as at EBR-I 4. Fuel-handling mechanism must be long enough to accomodate the length of the fuel subassembly plus the extension which is at least equal in length to the shield plug plus any plenum between the plug and the subassembly 5. Each subassembly penetration requires extensive sealing to prevent release of sodium vapor and radioactivity into the above-floor atmosphere

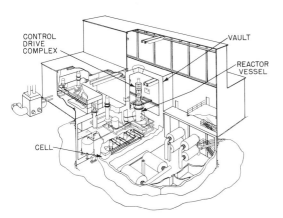

FIG. 7.6—Fuel-handling system using a shielded compartment above the reactor [11].

located at an angle at the side of the reactor and with an outlet directly into a decay-storage pool, and (2) pressure tubes for refueling under load. The development of the latter has been scarce, but the future will probably see development of this idea for liquid-metal-cooled reactors.

7.2.4 FUEL HANDLING EXTERNAL TO REACTOR

The scheme for movement of fuel outside the reactor complex, i.e., between reactor and reprocessing plant, will depend on many factors. The factors can be divided into six or more categories. Each of the six categories considered here is designated as follows:

A. Type of decay storage.
B. Location of fuel-reprocessing facilities.
C. Location of fuel-examination facilities.
D. Type of on-site fuel cleaning, if any.
E. Type of fuel canning, if any.
F. Location of on-site disassembly of fuel subassembly.

(Other categories and subcategories may include type of cask car, location of canning stations, location of disassembly, extent of disassembly, location of cleaning facilities, and type of fuel reprocessing.)

A. Type of decay storage:
A.1 The fuel has not been irradiated sufficiently long to require storage, or it has been decaying sufficiently long in the reactor complex to require no further decay storage outside the complex.
A.2 The fuel requires further decay storage in sodium outside the reactor complex.
A.3 The fuel requires further decay storage in water outside the reactor complex.
B. Location of fuel-reprocessing facilities:
B.1 On-site.
B.2 Off-site.
C. Location of fuel-examination facilities:
C.1 On-site examination of irradiated fuel.
C.2 Off-site examination of irradiated fuel or no examination.
C.3 Interim examination.
D. Type of on-site cleaning:
D.1 Steam cleaning of subassembly.
D.2 Ultrasonic cleaning of subassembly in oil bath.

D.3 Alcohol cleaning of subassembly.
D.4 Ammonia cleaning of subassembly.
D.5 No on-site cleaning.
E. Type of fuel canning:
E.1 Canning subassembly in an alloy for shipment to processing plant.
E.2 No canning of subassembly in alloy.
F. Location of fuel-subassembly disassembly:
F.1 On-site disassembly of fuel subassemblies prior to shipping to on-site or off-site processing.
F.2 No prior disassembly.

Table 7.6 lists several combinations of these items, which can be designated as schemes. The resulting schemes categorize reactors. Many other schemes devised from Table 7.6 or above could be considered for fuel-handling external to the reactor. For example, an A.1–B.1–C.3–D.2/D.3/D.4–E.2–F.2 scheme would be a variant of the EBR-II scheme that allows for examination of the subassembly prior to shipping to processing and allows for an advanced method of cleaning. This variant would allow, by proper design of a subassembly, fuel examination after irradiation to determine the remaining fuel life with a view to the possible return of the subassembly to the reactor for further irradiation. An alternate to steam cleaning would reduce the sodium–water reaction hazard. Table 7.6 columns are not arranged in operational sequence. The sequence may vary. The sequence of operations for various reactors is shown in Figs. 7.1 to 7.5.

The decision to can subassemblies should be based on an evaluation of cooling requirements and the removal of sodium by the canning metals. A system for removing sodium by such a metal as lead, tin–bismuth, lead–antimony, or by an aluminum–silicon eutectic, combined with an increase in the heat-transfer capabilities of the subassembly, should provide a means of simplifying fuel handling. With external storage in a sodium decay pool and no on-site dimensional examination or disassembly, a station for canning the subassembly in metal or alloy could follow decay storage. This can be applied to on-site or off-site reprocessing.

The decision to examine fuel subassemblies on-site should be based primarily on three factors: Can anything be learned that might be applied to future fuel loadings? Should a subassembly be examined to determine whether or not it should be returned to the reactor for further burnup? Is an examination needed to determine if the subassembly is a leaker? The location of on-site examination cells depends on several factors: If the fuel is to be returned to the reactor, then an examination cell close to the reactor should be considered. If a canning station is located in the reactor building, the examination should precede the canning. If the examination is for the purpose of determining if the subassembly is a leaker, the examination should be made prior to decay storage to avoid contaminating the storage facility.

The decision to disassemble on site prior to shipping to reprocessing should be based primarily on whether or not the reprocessing scheme requires such disassembly and whether or not individual fuel elements are to be examined prior to shipment. Disassembly should be done after decay storage and prior to shipment.

If a subassembly is canned in an alloy or a

Table 7.5—Proposed Fuel-handling Systems for Fact Reactors

System	Advantages	Disadvantages
A. Fixed plug, with a polar-coordinate fuel-handling mechanism inserted only during refueling; separate port and machine for inserting and removing subassemblies	1. Bearings and other moving parts are in sodium only during refueling 2. No radioactive maintenance after cleaning 3. Accessible for maintenance between refueling 4. Eliminates need for rotating plugs 5. Normal radiation streaming is reduced to a minimum 6. No reactor outage for maintenance of fuel-handling machine 7. Reduces number of reactor seals and thereby the leakage of sodium vapor or radioactivity into above-floor atmosphere	1. Bearings and other moving parts in sodium 2. Possibility of fuel hang-up 3. Complex mechanisms operating under sodium and a complex drive system operating above the reactor 4. Impractical to instrument core 5. May require removal of control- and safety-rod drives, rod extensions, and plug containing same to provide room for the fuel-handling mechanism 6. Requires complex storage facilities for the fuel-handling machine and the control-rod drive complex 7. Should consider a degree of probability of maloperation of the mechanism under sodium and consequent long-term reactor outage for repair
B. Shielded refueling compartment above reactor	1. Visual control of refueling reduces calibration to a minimum 2. No radioactive maintenance of fuel-handling equipment 3. Continuous accessibility of fuel-handling equipment 4. No rotating plugs with attendant drives and complex bearings, seals, and servicing 5. No reactor outage for maintenance of fuel-handling machine 6. Radiation streaming is no problem because of external shield walls 7. Minimum danger of fuel hang-up 8. Fuel-mechanism hang-up minimized 9. No bearings or moving parts in liquid sodium 10. Fuel-handling machine can be considerably simplified 11. Orientation of a fuel or blanket subassembly is a simple operation 12. Shielded compartment may be able to serve as part of the containment building	1. Plug, control-rod drives, and safety-rod drives used during normal operation are removed and stored for refueling, creating a complex moving and storing problem 2. Entire shielded compartment becomes part of the reactor vessel and, as such, during refueling, it is the first line of defense against a nuclear incident; required compartment design may become exceedingly difficult 3. Space within the shielded compartment is subjected to sodium vapor and to the release of fission-product gases from damaged fuel elements; this may require extensive waste-gas systems to maintain the space within the compartment at desirable vapor and radiation levels 4. The shielding requirements of the shielded compartment will probably be extensive, complex, and costly 5. Bearings and moving parts in sodium vapor are subject to contamination if the compartment leaks and the inert-gas system is not able to keep space clear of contaminants 6. Problem of sealing the reactor from the above-floor area is now transferred to the much larger surface area of the shielded compartment 7. Control and safety 8. Size of compartment may dictate containment-building size if the compartment cannot be used as the containment 9. Probably impractical to instrument core
C. Modified EBR-I system	1. Continuous accessibility to fuel-handling machine 2. Bearings and moving parts in sodium or sodium vapor only during refueling 3. Nonradioactive maintenance of most of the fuel-handling machine proper at all times, with nonradioactive maintenance of the gripper and its carrier after cleaning 4. Allows for rotation of gripper 5. Minimal reactor outage for repair of fuel-handling machine	1. No visual control 2. Shield plug, control-rod drives and shafts removed and stored for refueling, creating a complex moving and storage problem 3. Rotating-plug removal increases the moving and storage problem 4. Impractical to instrument core 5. Replacement of fixed plug with rotating plug requires an inert-gas atmosphere; the reactor at this period may require containment, such as a dome with an inert atmosphere and a crane capable of removing the fixed plug and installing the rotating plug, with reverse operation performed after refueling; machinery dome could be removed for actual refueling 6. Sealing between reactor and above-floor atmosphere is complex

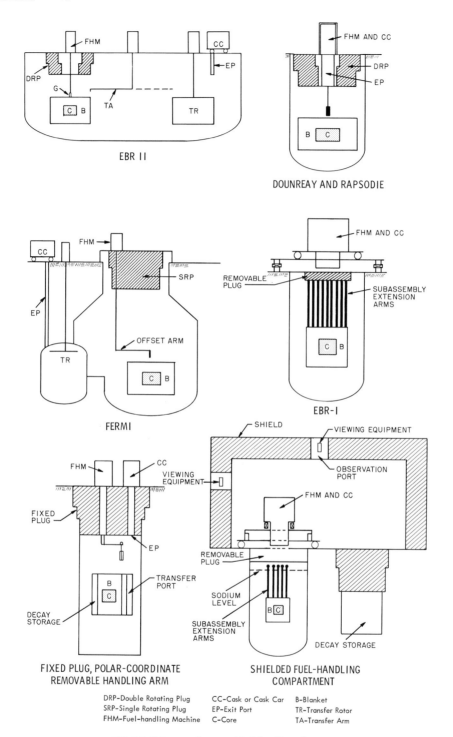

FIG. 7.7—Existing and proposed fuel-handling schemes.

metal, there is no need for further cleaning. Cleaning would also be questionable if a sub-assembly were to be returned for further burnup. Any cleaning may leave hydrogenous or other residues undesirable in the reactor. On the other hand, some form of nondestructive nonresidue cleaning may be necessary to allow for visual and dimensional inspection. Cleaning is generally mandatory if the subassembly is to be stored un-canned in a decay-storage water pool. Section 7.4 discusses cleaning in more detail.

All the systems described use solid shield

Table 7.6—Schemes for Fuel Handling External to the Reactor

Scheme No.	Scheme	No decay storage A. 1	Decay storage (water) A. 2	Decay storage (sodium) A. 3	On-site processing B. 1	Off-site processing B. 2	On-site examination C. 1	Off-site examination C. 2	Steam cleaning D. 1	Alcohol cleaning D. 2	Ultrasonic and oil cleaning D. 3	Ammonia cleaning D. 4	No on-site cleaning D. 5	Alloy canning E. 1	No alloy canning E. 2	Disassembly prior to shipment to processing F. 1	No disassembly prior to shipment to processing F. 2
1	Dounreay		×		×		×							×			×
2	EBR-II*	×			×		×		×						×		×
3	Fermi		×			×	×		×						×	×	
4	Rapsodie		×		†	†	×							×			×
5	Proposed			×		×								×			×
6	Proposed	×				×	×							×			×

* Disassembly is part of on-site pyrometallurgical reprocessing.
† Information not available.

material between the core and the top face of the reactor. Liquid shield materials are not used because of their hydrogenous nature. The use of liquid metal for gamma shielding has been considered and has some merit. Additions of poison to the liquid metal may be necessary to provide neutron attenuation. Chapter 8 covers shielding in detail.

7.3 Heat Transfer During Fuel Handling

7.3.1 HEAT-TRANSFER PROBLEMS

During refueling heat-transfer problems may exist for fuel and blanket subassemblies in the following positions: (1) core, (2) blanket, (3) decay positions within the reactor, (4) in transit from any one designated position in the reactor to any other designated position within the reactor, such as from the core to a decay position, (5) in transit from any position in the reactor to an external cask, (6) transit cask, (7) in transit from the cask to any other position, (8) external sodium-filled storage racks, canning stations, or examination pits and in transit from these positions to cleaning stations, secondary casks, coffins, or decay pools, (9) secondary casks, coffins, or cleaning, and (10) in transit from these casks, coffins, or cleaning stations to decay pools, cut-up pools, and disassembly stations and in these positions.

The list is indicative of where heat transfer is associated with operations shown in Figs. 7.1 through 7.5. The designer, the heat-transfer analyst, the structural analyst, and the nuclear engineer should work as a team to resolve any problems associated with the removal of decay heat from fuel and blanket subassemblies. Section 7.10 covers several selected heat-transfer problems which can be used as guides.

The basic approach to solution of a heat-transfer problem is as follows: (1) knowledge of the decay heat during refueling, decay storage, shipment, and disassembly (see Sec. 7.10); (2) a statement of the

heat-transfer problem with its boundary conditions; (3) a method for attacking the problem; (4) the solution; (5) the application of the solution to design; and (6) where necessary, a test to confirm the final design. Section 7.10 presents examples of limiting heat-transfer problems associated with subassemblies in finned pots filled with sodium (calculations of heat losses with natural convection), bare subassemblies (calculation of heat losses to an inert-gas environment with natural convection), time to reach the critical operating temperature upon loss of forced cooling, and forced-convection requirements in a cask car.

7.3.2 DECAY-HEAT REMOVAL

Decay heat is generated under various conditions and in various locations. A list of some of these and of means for removing the heat is given below.
1. Submerged in sodium (in reactor, transfer rotor, or decay pool)
    (a) Forced circulation of sodium
    (b) Natural circulation of sodium
2. In cover gas above reactor coolant
    (a) Forced circulation of inert gas (finned pot, bare subassembly)
    (b) Natural circulation of inert gas (finned pot, bare subassembly)
3. In cask car, interbuilding coffins, and other similar devices
    (a) Forced circulation of inert gas (finned pot, bare subassembly)
    (b) Natural circulation (finned pot, bare subassembly)
4. In cleaning station
    (a) Steam cleaning (inert gas, steam, water)
    (b) Oil cleaning (natural circulation, forced circulation)
    (c) Alcohol, ammonia, and other cleaning (the reaction of dissolving agent can be used as the heat-removal agent)
5. In decay pool, cut-up pool, or examination pool submerged under water
    (a) Forced circulation of water
    (b) Natural circulation of water

6. In shipping cask
   (a) Forced or natural circulation of water
   (b) Forced or natural circulation of inert gas
   (c) Forced or natural circulation of liquid metal
   (d) Forced or natural circulation of alcohol, kerosene, organic compounds, or other coolant fluid

Adequate cooling of a subassembly in a fixed location or in transit should be provided. Each case should be analyzed to determine whether natural circulation will keep the subassembly temperatures within prescribed limits or whether forced convection is necessary.

The subassembly, while submerged in sodium in the reactor, can be cooled by forced or natural circulation of the sodium. The adequacy of the cooling method should be determined when the subassembly is moved from the sodium or when it is in a position within the reactor other than the normal core or blanket position, for example, when the subassembly is in a decay position within the reactor. Analysis of heat transfer from a subassembly in transit through the reactor cover gas may indicate the need for forced cooling. Temperatures of the subassembly and the surrounding structures should be kept within design limits for all conditions, including a hang-up caused by mechanism or other malfunction.

Heat removal may be facilitated during transfers by placing the subassembly in a sodium-filled container. Fins may be added to the container to improve the heat transfer.

If the decay heat from a subassembly is sufficiently low, heat removal may be accomplished by radiation, conduction, and free convection.

The cask into which the subassembly is withdrawn is generally cooled by the forced convection of an inert gas, such as argon, helium, or nitrogen. Several heat-transfer schemes are possible; for example, an inert gas can be recirculated through an inert gas-to-air heat exchanger, and the air can be exhausted by duct connections to the outside air, or an inert gas can be recirculated through an inert gas-to-NaK-to-air heat exchanger (fluids other than NaK can be used, e.g., Dowtherm).

7.4 Fuel Cleaning

7.4.1 CLEANING REQUIREMENTS

7.4.1.1 Purpose of Cleaning

When fuel assemblies are removed from a reactor, they carry with them some of the primary coolant and some of the fission products contained in the coolant. When the primary coolant is a liquid metal that is not compatible with the coolants in the decay facility or in a shipping cask, the primary coolant must be removed from the fuel assembly. Even though coolant compatibility may not be a problem, fission products in the primary coolant may make cleaning necessary to avoid radioactive contamination problems in subsequent processing steps.

7.4.1.2 Factors Affecting Cleaning System

7.4.1.2.1 CLEANING EFFECTIVENESS. The amount of residual primary coolant that can be tolerated on a cleaned fuel assembly depends on the compatibility of the primary and decay coolants and on the fission-product content of the primary coolant. For instance, when sodium is to be used as a primary coolant and water as a decay coolant, an efficient fuel-cleaning process should be used to avoid sodium—water reactions. In this instance, it is also desirable to keep the sodium carry-over to a minimum to avoid corrosion problems due to sodium hydroxide in the water. When the primary coolant contains significant quantities of fission products, the level of fission products that can be tolerated in the decay, inspection, and shipping operations may be a factor deciding the cleaning effectiveness required.

7.4.1.2.2 FUEL COOLING. Adequate cooling must be provided for the fuel assembly during cleaning. The cooling required is dictated by the maximum permissible fuel temperatures and the purpose for which the fuel elements are desired, i.e., is the intent only to avoid melting the fuel elements or to maintain their irradiated condition for adequate examination. The cooling required may range from convection gas cooling to forced liquid cooling.

7.4.1.2.3 FUEL-ELEMENT DAMAGE. Fuel-element and subassembly damage can occur during cleaning as a result of excessive temperature, thermal shock, pressure excursions, or corrosion. Excessive temperatures can cause melting and the attendant contamination cleanup problems. At lower temperatures, where melting is not of concern, metallurgical changes may still result in spurious fuel-examination data. Thermal shock, pressure excursions, and corrosion not only can create mechanical damage that interferes with an evaluation of the examination data but can also increase the likelihood of fuel-cladding ruptures and fission-product leakage.

7.4.1.2.4 RADIATION SHIELDING. Biological shielding requirements are a major factor in the design of a fuel-cleaning system. Shielding requirements affect the building structure and frequently necessitate remote operation of equipment. Remote-operation equipment is complicated to design and presents problems in reliability and maintenance. Designing for reliability is complicated by the fact that some established materials which function well in normal service may not be acceptable because of poor resistance to radiation. If acceptable material substitutes are not available, the equipment may require local shielding or installation outside the biological shielding.

7.4.1.2.5 CONTAINMENT. Containment of radioactive materials is mandatory. The radiation hazard varies with the material and specific radioactivity, and each system should be evaluated individually. Very small leakages can quickly exceed permissible tolerances. As with all systems containing radioactive fluids, considerable attention should be given to design, fabrication, and testing to ensure a high-integrity system. Where a possibility exists for a cleaning-system malfunction that could lead to the melting of fuel elements, provisions should be made to contain the fission products released and to decontaminate the affected equipment.

7.4.1.2.6 WASTE DISPOSAL. The method to be used for disposal of radioactive wastes from fuel cleaning can have a major effect on the type of cleaning system selected. Plant location may determine whether waste will be disposed of in liquid form via settling basins, storage tanks, or metering into flowing water or whether it will be shipped in concentrated liquid or solid form to a disposal site. In any event, temporary storage facilities at the plant site should be provided to allow radioactivity to be reduced to levels acceptable for the disposal method employed.

7.4.2 CLEANING METHODS

The two basic methods of cleaning liquid metal from a fuel subassembly are reactive cleaning and nonreactive cleaning. Reactive cleaning employs a cleaning agent that reacts chemically with the liquid metal to form removable reaction products. Nonreactive cleaning employs a cleaning agent that dissolves or emulsifies the liquid metal so that it can be flushed from the subassembly surface.

7.4.2.1 Reactive Cleaning

7.4.2.1.1 CLEANING WITH WATER. Sodium–water and potassium–water reactions are (reaction energy ΔH at 298°K or 25°C) [14]

$$Na + H_2O \rightarrow NaOH + \tfrac{1}{2}H_2$$
$$\Delta H^\circ_{298} = -33.67 \text{ kcal/mole} \tag{7.1}$$

$$2Na + H_2O \rightarrow Na_2O + H_2$$
$$\Delta H^\circ_{298} = -31.08 \text{ kcal/mole} \tag{7.2}$$

$$K + H_2O \rightarrow KOH + \tfrac{1}{2}H_2$$
$$\Delta H^\circ_{298} = -33.46 \text{ kcal/mole} \tag{7.3}$$

Reaction 7.1 is expected at 225°C. If such a reaction took place, half the H_2 would remain in the hydroxide. Actual observation (Ref. 15) indicated only reaction 7.2 in the range 200°C to 350°C (392°F to 662°F) for concentrations of hydrogen less than 350 ppm at 1 atm of helium. Reference 16 indicates that the stability of NaOH in the presence of excess sodium is governed by the partial pressure of hydrogen in the temperature range 400°F to about 600°F and water-vapor pressures greater than 10 mm. Reference 14 indicates that reaction 7.1 proceeds below approximately 600°F, which is the melting point of NaOH based on calculations of free energies. The reactions are exothermic and can cause sharp temperature rises if the reaction rate exceeds the heat removal rate. Such tem-

perature rises can damage a fuel assembly that is sensitive to high temperatures or sharp temperature gradients. Sudden temperature rises can also damage a fuel assembly by creating pressure transients in pockets or restricted passages. Pressure buildups can be especially severe if the passages through which the pressure can relieve are small or are filled with water. Experience has shown, however, that after the initial reaction the action of water on heavy deposits in pockets or restricted passages may be retarded or even temporarily halted by the sodium hydroxide until it is dissolved into the water.

Careful consideration must be given to the control of the hydrogen gas released by the reaction of water with sodium or potassium. The reaction between hydrogen and oxygen is [17]

$$H_2 + \tfrac{1}{2}O_2 \rightarrow H_2O$$
$$\Delta H^\circ_{298} = -57.79 \text{ kcal/mole} \tag{7.4}$$

Hydrogen can react with oxygen in air with explosive violence that could cause damage to the fuel structure or the cleaning equipment.

Water cleaning was successfully used to remove NaK from fuel rods at EBR-I. The fuel rods were slowly lowered into water in a hot cell, and the reaction was controlled by regulating the rate at which the rods entered the water. This was possible with EBR-I fuel because of its simple shape, absence of internal flow passages, and low decay-heat generation.

Water has been used for cleaning sodium from subassemblies at the Sodium Reactor Experiment (SRE) [18]. The subassemblies are inserted in 3-in.-diameter by 24-ft-long cells that extend below the operating floor in the reactor building. The procedure is as follows: (1) a subassembly is inserted in a cell, (2) the cell is evacuated and filled with helium, (3) the cell is vented and slowly filled with water, (4) the cell is drained and filled with water a second time, and (5) the cell is drained and evacuated to dry the subassembly.

Experiments at Dounreay showed the feasibility of obtaining controlled NaK–water reactions using a mixture of soluble oil and water [19]. The oil tested was a dark, viscous, opaque liquid used for machine-tool lubrication. The solubility limit for water in the oil was about 2% by volume. The oil reacted slowly with NaK, giving off gas at a barely perceptible rate at temperatures up to 120°C (248°F). Between 80°C and 120°C (176°F and 248°F), a light fraction, principally water, distilled off, leaving a viscous oil that was completely inert to NaK. Mixtures of the oil and water up to the solubility limit of the water produced reasonable and controlled reaction rates when used for NaK cleaning.

7.4.2.1.2 CLEANING WITH STEAM. The sodium–steam reaction is [14]

$$Na + H_2O \rightarrow NaOH + \tfrac{1}{2}H_2$$
$$\Delta H^\circ_{298} = -45.7 \text{ kcal/mole} \tag{7.5}$$

The advantages of steam over water are that there is less likelihood of damage to the fuel assembly from a pressure excursion, the reaction rate can be regulated by controlled dilution of the steam flow with a suitable gas, and, since sodium is liquid at steam temperature, more effective cleaning is facilitated.

The comments on hydrogen in Sec. 7.4.2.1.1 apply to steam cleaning also. In addition, care must be taken to avoid condensation of steam with a resultant sodium–water reaction.

In selecting a cleaning process for Fermi fuel, APDA conducted steam cleaning tests on small mock-up specimens and full-size dummy fuel subassembly [20]. Preliminary tests on the mock-ups showed that steam cleaning followed by a water flush completely removed sodium from all surfaces except inaccessible locations, such as screw threads and press fit surfaces. In tests with the full-size dummy subassembly, the subassembly was first soaked in 750°F sodium and then drained with a nitrogen purge. This was followed by a 5-min purge of dry steam and a 15-min soaking period in tap water. The dummy subassembly was then disassembled. It was found to be free of metallic sodium. In a subsequent test a dummy subassembly was soaked in 750°F sodium and then purged with a high-velocity flow of nitrogen to blow off clinging sodium. The dummy was then cleaned with dry steam for 5 min, but the water-soaking step was omitted. Fifty-eight percent less sodium was found in the effluent, but the disassembled dummy subassembly disclosed a noticeable amount of metallic sodium in the space between the subassembly nozzle and its tight-fitting outer sleeve. The maximum temperature attained in the cleaning chamber after the subassembly was subjected to dry steam was 1110°F, a 390°F rise in 39 sec. The extent of corrosion of the dummy subassembly was insignificant.

Steam cleaning was the method selected for cleaning fuel assemblies at the Enrico Fermi plant. Forced-flow argon cooling is used to remove decay heat and some of the sodium from a fuel assembly while it is being transferred from a liquid-sodium environment to the steam-cleaning chamber. An interlock prevents withdrawal of the subassembly from the transfer-rotor storage tank until the argon flow has been established. The subassembly is pulled up into the cleaning machine by the steam-cleaning-machine gripper. During this operation the subassembly is cooled by argon flowing at the rate of 250 lb/hr. The argon is recirculated and cooled by means of a closed-loop heat-exchanger system to maintain the inlet temperature to the subassembly at about 260°F. The argon flows through the subassembly to the transfer-rotor tank, through an entrainment separator to a compressor, through a cooler to the cleaning chamber, and then through the gripper and subassembly.

When the subassembly is positioned in the cleaning machine, an argon bypass line around the isolation valve on the bottom of the cleaning chamber is opened, the cleaning machine and access tube valves are closed, and the machine is rotated to a position over the cut-up pool access tube. The cooling argon supply is switched from the recirculating system to the clean argon supply system, and the discharge line from the cleaning machine is opened to the waste liquid and gas systems. An automatic timer device is started, and, over a

period of 1 min, the stoichiometric amount of dry steam necessary to react the sodium on the subassembly is introduced into the argon. The ratio of argon to steam during the cleaning operation is controlled to assure a noncombustible mixture of argon and hydrogen in the cleaning effluent. Noncombustible mixtures are shown in Fig. 4.28 of Chap. 4. At the end of the first minute, the subassembly is being cooled by the steam and the argon supply is turned off. The subassembly is steamed for four additional minutes and then is rinsed with hot water. Then the cleaning machine is flooded with demineralized water, and the subassembly is rinsed for 12 min. The rinse water is drained from the chamber, and argon is admitted to break the vacuum. This ends the automatically timed cycle. The seal between the cleaning machine and the cut-up pool access tube is made and tested, the valves are opened, and the subassembly is lowered into the water-filled cut-up pool.

Nitrogen has been used with steam to clean sodium-covered equipment, and the process appears applicable to fuel subassemblies. The process, sometimes referred to as the moist-nitrogen process, achieves a controlled reaction rate between the steam and sodium through control of the amount of steam carried in the nitrogen. A high-velocity flow rate of the mixture assists the cleaning by removing molten sodium and reaction products.

7.4.2.1.3 CLEANING WITH ALCOHOL. The typical reaction between an alcohol and sodium is [14]

$$Na + CH_3OH \rightarrow NaOCH_3 + \tfrac{1}{2}H_2$$
$$\Delta H^\circ_{298} = -48.1 \text{ kcal/mole} \tag{7.6}$$

Methyl, ethyl, or propyl alcohol can be used. The sodium–alcohol reaction is less rapid than the sodium–water reaction, and those alcohols with the most carbon atoms per molecule react the slowest. Alcohols tend to limit the reaction rate by boiling, which absorbs the latent heat of vaporization and removes liquid from the region. Alcohol can be gradually diluted with water or steam as a final step in cleaning operation. It has the disadvantage that it is flammable. Being a liquid, alcohol increases the possibility of mechanical damage if pressure transients occur, and high temperatures can cause thermal cracking and coking of the alcohol. Care should be exercised in the manufacture and subsequent handling of an alcohol to control its water content since water increases the reaction rate. Testing experience indicates that it is advisable to keep the water content below 5 vol. %. In the cleaning of sodium, an alcohol containing large percentages of water presents a serious hazard because it couples the potential high-temperature sodium–water reaction with the flammability of alcohol. Suitable precautions must be taken with the hydrogen evolved to prevent a possible explosive combination with oxygen.

Experiments at Dounreay [19] have shown the feasibility of using a mixture of alcohol and Dowtherm A as a cleaning medium for NaK. Dowtherm A, the eutectic mixture of diphenyl (26.4%) and diphenyl oxide (73.6%), is an almost colorless liquid. It boils at 255°C (491°F) and has relatively good heat-transfer properties. It is inert to NaK below 100°C (212°F), but above this temperature a black film, possibly carbon, appears on the surface of the metal. Dowtherm can be steam-distilled and is miscible with alcohols in all proportions. Dowtherm–alcohol solutions react with NaK at a rate approximately proportional to the alcohol concentration in the range 0 to 30%, but the increase in reaction rate on further addition of alcohol beyond this concentration is minor. The reaction products show a high solubility in the alcoholic solution, and the black film formed at temperatures above 100°C (212°F) in Dowtherm disperses rapidly in the alcoholic mixture and does not inhibit its action. The alcohol employed to react with the NaK during cleaning should be chosen according to the surface temperature of the fuel element, ethyl below 80°C (176°F), amyl from 80°C (176°F) to 150°C (302°F), and decyl above 150°C (302°F).

The reaction rate of alcohol has also been controlled by using a mixture of two alcohols with different reaction rates, such as methyl and propyl alcohols. Another approach has been to use a mixture of an alcohol and kerosene.

7.4.2.2 Nonreactive Cleaning

7.4.2.2.1 CLEANING WITH AMMONIA. Liquid ammonia is one of the true solvents for sodium and therefore is a useful medium for removing sodium [14]. A solubility curve for sodium in ammonia is shown in Fig. 7.8. The pressures required for ammonia liquification (114 psig at 70°F) or the need for refrigeration generally limit the application of ammonia cleaning to small-scale experimental work. Over long periods of time, sodium will react with ammonia to form sodium amide by the following reaction:

$$Na + NH_3 \rightarrow NaNH_2 + \tfrac{1}{2}H_2 \qquad (7.7)$$

The reaction is slow and is catalyzed by the presence of iron, copper, zinc, or like materials. Above 300°C (572°F) the reaction proceeds rapidly.

Liquid ammonia is not a solvent for sodium oxide or hydroxide. Sodium oxide can be removed by adding 2 to 5% ammonium chloride to the liquid ammonia. Ammonium chloride reacts with sodium oxide to form sodium chloride, which is soluble to about 3 wt.% in ammonia. Ammonium chloride

reacts with sodium to release hydrogen; so it should be introduced only after the bulk of the sodium has been removed by the ammonia. Ammonia has been used successfully for cleaning both sodium and NaK. The characteristic deep blue color of sodium in liquid ammonia can be used as a convenient check on the completeness of the cleaning operation [22].

7.4.2.2.2 CLEANING WITH OIL. Cleaning fuel assemblies with oil consists in flushing the elements with a liquid hydrocarbon at sufficiently high temperatures and velocities to melt and remove the sodium. The sodium can then be removed from the oil by freezing the sodium and trapping the particles in a filter. The advantages of this cleaning system are that the oil serves as a coolant for the fuel, no reaction heat is generated, and the oil is compatible with a water decay system. Oil has the disadvantage that under prolonged high-temperature and radiation conditions hydrocarbons tend to break down and leave "coke" deposits. Since this cleaning method relies on a flushing action, the fuel-assembly configuration should allow fluid flow contact at all points or flow should be supplemented in some manner, such as by ultrasonic agitation. In the design of an oil-cleaning system, consideration should be given to the boiling and flash points of the oil and to fission-product contamination of oil. The related fuel-handling system should be designed to prevent oil from being carried back to the reactor systems.

APDA conducted a series of tests to determine the effectiveness of cleaning fuel subassemblies by means of oil flushing and ultrasonics [23]. Tests were also conducted to determine the compatibility of oils with sodium and radiation. The oils tested were mineral oils identified as Detergent Alkymer Bottoms Heavy (Standard Oil Co. of Indiana), hereafter referred to as Standard Oil and Kaydol (L. Sonneborn Sons, Inc.).

Two types of specimens were tested (Fig. 7.9), one to simulate the core portion of a subassembly and one to simulate the nozzle portion. The follow-

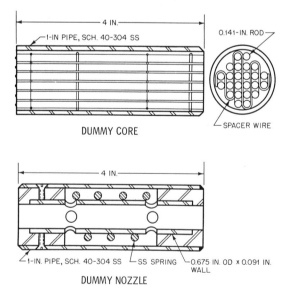

FIG. 7.9—Sodium cleaning-test specimens [23].

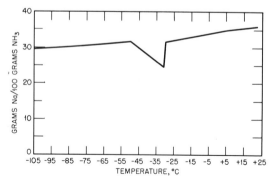

FIG. 7.8—Solubility of sodium in NH₃ [21].

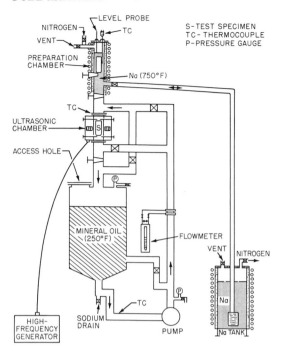

FIG. 7.10—Sodium cleaning test using ultrasonics and hydrocarbon flushing [23].

ing test procedure was used with the test equipment shown in Fig. 7.10: (1) the specimens were heated in sodium at 750°F for 4 hr, (2) some specimens were drained and then flushed for 15 min in oil at 250°F, (3) some specimens were drained, flushed for 10 min in 250°F oil, and then subjected to ultrasonic agitation in 250°F oil, and (4) the specimens were examined for evidence of residual sodium.

Visual observation indicated that: (1) Kaydol and Standard Oil both produced the same cleaning results; (2) extending specimen cooking time in sodium beyond 4 hr at temperatures up to 850°F produced no differences in cleaning results; (3) for the nozzle specimen oil flushing alone left small scattered spots of free sodium on outside surfaces and inner parts, whereas a combination of oil flushing and ultrasonic agitation left only the slightest trace of sodium on outside surfaces but did not remove pinpoint particles on inner parts; and (4) for the core specimen oil flushing alone left small scattered spots of free sodium on all visible surfaces, and a combination of oil flushing and ultrasonic agitation left no visible sodium residue on any part of the specimen. Chemical analysis of one specimen from each cleaning procedure showed that the effectiveness of the oil flushing was 64%. The effectiveness of the combination of oil flushing and ultrasonic agitation was 94%.

Both cleaning procedures minimized the explosive effects of sodium–water reactions resulting from immersion of the cleaned test specimens in water. The oil-flushed specimens showed mild to moderate bubbling, a little smoke, and a very brief burst of flame. Specimens cleaned by oil flushing and ultrasonic agitation produced only a mild bub-

bling, and no explosion, smoke, or flame. The oil film appeared to inhibit the reaction. Kaydol and Standard Oil in quantities of about 45 gal at 250°F to 280°F were found to be compatible with sodium (about 1/8 to 1/4 lb) at 400°F. They produced no chemical or physical reaction. The same quantity of Kaydol at 400°F also appeared compatible with 1/4 lb of sodium at 800°F.

APDA conducted irradiation tests on the Standard Oil Detergent Alkymer Bottoms Heavy to check polymerization and other property changes. Decolorized and nondecolorized oil were exposed to an accumulated dose of 1.0×10^9 rads in the Argonne high-level gamma-irradiation facility. [The Fermi core A subassembly maximum surface dose rate is 6×10^7 roentgens/hr at an operating power of 430 Mw(t) and two weeks decay time.] The test results were as follows: (1) both oil samples gave almost identical results, (2) the viscosity at 210°F increased from 5.96 to 9.19 centistokes, (3) the flash point changed from 340°F to 89°F, (4) there was no observed precipitate, i.e., tar or sludge, and (5) the NPA color for the (nondecolorized) oil dropped from 2 1/2 to 1.

Since these tests were performed, Standard Oil has developed a new fluid, the viscosity of which changes somewhat less than that of detergent Alkymer Bottoms Heavy on exposure to 1.0×10^9 rads. This fluid also has the property that its flash point increases, rather than decreases, on exposure to 10^9 rads.

7.4.2.2.3 CLEANING WITH MOLTEN METAL. Low-melting-point metals and metal alloys offer a potential means of removing sodium from fuel subassemblies by dissolving the molten sodium. Lead has been used at Dounreay for cleaning primary sodium from the outside of sealed lead-filled cans containing fuel subassemblies. Liquid metals offer the potential advantages of providing an efficient cooling medium for decay-heat removal and a compatible transition to a water decay pool. For effective cleaning the fuel subassembly configuration should allow contact between the cleaning metal and the subassembly surfaces. Flushing action or agitation will provide more-efficient cleaning action. A significant consideration is the effect of the dissolved sodium on the melting point of the cleaning metal. The means of disposal of the contaminated material should be factored into the evaluation of this type of cleaning.

7.4.2.2.4 VACUUM DISTILLATION. Sodium has been cleaned from dummy fuel subassemblies by vacuum distillation at the Fermi plant. The subassemblies were heated to 900°F to 1000°F in a vacuum chamber; then the chamber was evacuated to below 1 mm Hg absolute pressure. The sodium on the dummy subassemblies boiled off and was collected in a condenser outside the vacuum chamber. The process was very useful because it removed the sodium effectively, even from confined spaces inside the subassembly structure. However, the process does not lend itself to cleaning irradiated subassemblies where cooling is required to remove decay heat.

7.4.2.2.5 ULTRASONIC CLEANING. Any of the cleaning procedures that use a liquid cleaning medium lend themselves to the use of ultrasonic agitation to implement the cleaning. This approach utilizes ultrasonic vibrations in the liquid to create a cavitation effect on the surface being cleaned and implements removal of material adhering to the surface. This technique seems to be well adapted to an oil-cleaning system (Sec. 7.4.2.2.2) although its effectiveness is subject to the configuration of the fuel subassembly since transmission of the ultrasonic vibrations is reduced by metal barriers.

7.5 Fuel Decay Storage

Decay-heat levels are high in irradiated fast reactor fuel owing to the concentration of fission products that result from high enrichment and long residence time in the reactor. Consequently, decay storage is usually provided to reduce decay heat to a level suitable for safe handling and shipping. The decay time required before a fuel assembly can be safely placed in a shipping cask or disassembled in a hot cave will depend on the design of the fuel assembly and the shipping cask and may vary from 15 to 180 days. It may also be necessary to provide decay storage to permit accumulation of a sufficient number of fuel assemblies to provide an economical batch size for a processing facility. The economical batch size is dependent on process-plant cleanup cost, value of salvaged fuel, decay storage costs, fuel shipping facilities, etc. Decay

storage may be provided within the reactor vessel or in facilities outside the reactor vessel.

Fuel-disassembly facilities are required where comprehensive on-site inspection of irradiated fuel is desired. The extent of the facilities is, of course, a function of the degree of fuel disassembly required. Disassembly facilities are also required in instances where the core and blanket sections of a subassembly are to be shipped to different reprocessing locations or where it is desirable to reduce the amount of scrap subassembly hardware being shipped to a reprocessing plant.

7.5.1 DECAY STORAGE IN REACTOR VESSEL

Liquid-metal-cooled fast reactors can be designed to provide some decay storage space within the reactor vessel. This is practical because these reactors operate at low pressures which permit considerable latitude in the size and configuration of the design for the reactor vessel. A blanket of fertile material in this type of reactor is necessary for neutron economy. This blanket can also be used as an adequate neutron shield for irradiated fuel placed anywhere outside the blanket assembly. In the case of Fermi and EBR-II, a storage rotor (transfer rotor or transfer cask) has been provided to allow decay storage within the reactor vessel. Fermi and the APDA proposal for the PFFBR also

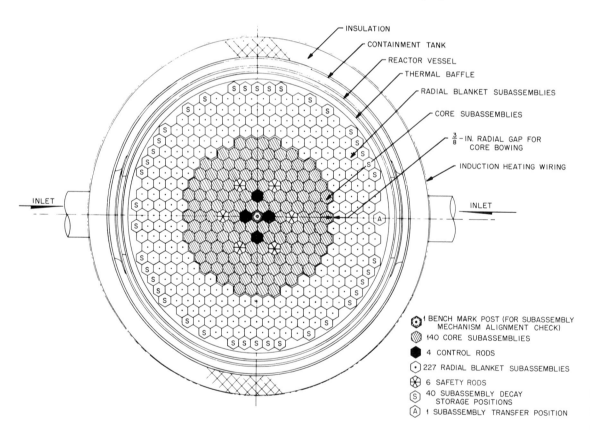

FIG. 7.11—PFFBR-reactor cross section showing decay storage in blanket area.

provide decay storage in the outer rows of the blanket (Fig. 7.11).

The chief advantages of decay storage within the reactor vessel are that no additional facilities are required for decay-heat removal, containment, or shielding and the down time required for refueling the reactor may be reduced because the removal of irradiated fuel need not be simultaneous with the introduction of new fuel. The chief disadvantages are the increase in size of the reactor vessel and the amount of fission products stored within the vessel.

7.5.2 DECAY STORAGE EXTERNAL TO REACTOR VESSEL

Decay storage external to the reactor vessel is prompted by the practical limitations on decay storage space available in a reactor vessel and the advantages of integrating an external storage facility with fuel inspection and shipping-cask loading facilities.

Some of the advantages of an external decay storage facility are (1) the facility can be sized to store large numbers of fuel assemblies to allow batch shipment for reprocessing, (2) the facility can be sized to permit complete unloading of the reactor to facilitate major repair work on the reactor complex, (3) external storage can be integrated with other on-site facilities, such as fuel inspection of fuel reprocessing, and (4) external storage facilities can be utilized for loading shipping casks.

Some of the disadvantages of an external decay storage facility are (1) the facility requires shielding and cooling, (2) if the facility is external to the containment building, containment considerations arise, (3) if the decay coolant is not compatible with the reactor coolant, a fuel-cleaning facility is required, and (4) space and cost.

7.5.3 FUEL DECAY STORAGE CONSIDERATIONS

7.5.3.1 Decay Storage Location

An examination of the decay curve for an irradiated fuel (Fig. 7.80) shows that a rapid decrease in gamma radiation occurs during the first hours and days after the fuel has been removed from the operating core. Since the reduction in gamma radiation is accompanied by a decrease in decay-heat generation, it is advantageous from both the shielding and cooling aspects to leave the fuel in the primary coolant for an initial decay period before removing it for final decay and shipment. This initial decay greatly reduces the cooling and shielding requirements for the equipment that transports irradiated fuel from the reactor.

In the Fermi reactor the transfer-rotor device (Fig. 7.59) that provides a step in the fuel-handling sequence from the reactor core to the cask car also provides fuel decay storage space. The rotor is contained in a tank attached to the reactor vessel, and the tank is filled with reactor-vessel sodium.

The normal fuel-handling sequence allows for storing 11 spent fuel assemblies in the rotor for two weeks before removing them to the cask car.

In addition to the rotor storage, certain positions in the outer row of the blanket array can also be used for fuel storage. EBR-II also has a provision (Fig. 7.48) for storing spent fuel assemblies in a storage rack (transfer rotor) under sodium within the reactor vessel. In this case the storage is in a rotary rack that is submerged in the primary sodium inside the primary tank.

The location of a fuel decay facility external to the reactor is determined primarily by the decay coolant selected and by space requirements. A location inside the containment building is attractive from the standpoint of containment and fuel handling. However, this is feasible only if space is available and if the decay coolant is compatible with the reactor coolant. Consequently, in fast reactor facilities with water decay pools, the hazards of water with sodium or NaK have dictated that the pools be located outside the containment building. However, decay storage in sodium, external to the reactor but inside the containment structure, has been considered in concept designs of fast reactors for both experimental and power applications.

7.5.3.2 Decay-heat Removal

A general overall review of means for removing decay heat is given in Sec. 7.3.2. Decay heat must be removed to protect irradiated fuel assemblies from high-temperature damage. Such damage can range from cladding failure to fuel-material melting. Some fuel assemblies with low heat generation and simple configuration will cool adequately in a still gas or air environment, whereas other assemblies with higher heat generation require forced-gas cooling or a liquid heat-transfer medium. Fuel assemblies stored in a reactor vessel can be readily cooled by the reactor coolant and the reactor shutdown heat-removal system. An external fuel decay storage facility, however, requires its own cooling system. The type of system depends in a great part on the decay coolant being used.

Coolant methods considered include forced and convection cooling. Gases considered range from inert gases for uncleaned fuel to air for cleaned fuel. The decay cooling of EBR-I fuel rods is an example of air cooling. The rods are first cleaned of NaK and then stored in a "rod farm" made up of tubes in the reactor building floor. Each rod is isolated in a steel tube where it is cooled by natural circulation of air within the tube.

Liquids considered for decay-heat removal include water, organics, such as oils and Dowtherms, and liquid metals and alloys, such as sodium and NaK. Water has seen considerable use. The advantages of water are that it is transparent, is stable in high gamma-radiation fields, and can be cleaned of fission products by well-established ion-exchange techniques. Another advantage is that present fuel reprocessing plants are prepared to receive and unload fuel from water-filled shipping casks. The use of a different decay coolant would require a transition of coolants either at the reactor site or at the reprocessing plant. Organics present the potential problem of decomposition under high-temperature and gamma-radiation conditions (Sec. 7.4.2.2.2).

A typical water-pool design can dissipate some heat from the pool surface and through the pool walls to the adjacent environment. However, where the decay-heat release exceeds this heat-dissipation rate, some form of heat exchanger is required, e.g., an external water-to-water heat exchanger, water-to-water heat exchangers in the pool, or a refrigeration type of heat exchanger.

The maximum acceptable pool-water temperature in the Fermi decay pools is 120°F because the ion-exchanger tanks for pool-water cleanup are submerged in the pools and the exchanger resins are limited to that maximum temperature. Heat removal is accomplished by service water circulated through stainless-steel plate coils supported underwater along the pool walls. Sufficient heat-exchange surface is installed for the normal decay-heat load, i.e., the maximum total decay heat anticipated, and the piping and connections are designed to accept additional plate coils in the event of a complete reactor unloading.

Solids considered for decay-heat removal systems include lead and aluminum—silicon. At Dounreay spent fuel assemblies are sealed in lead-lined cans, and the lead is melted to provide a heat-transfer medium. The lead, whether molten or solid, provides a good heat path from the fuel to the surface of the can where it can be more readily dissipated. In an APDA study of a 150-Mw plutonium-fueled fast breeder reactor plant, an aluminum—silicon casting (Al—Si) alloy was selected as a solid decay-heat transfer medium [24]. The APDA concept was to seal the fuel assembly in a can containing the Al—Si and melt the Al—Si alloy to obtain good contact with the fuel assembly and with the container wall. Upon freezing, the alloy provides a good heat-transfer path from the fuel assembly to the can. The alloy selected, Al—12% Si, is a standard aluminum casting eutectic that melts at 1200 to 1400°F. It has a density of 166 lb/cu ft, a thermal conductivity of 89 Btu/hr/ft/°F at 77°F, a latent heat of fusion of 167 Btu/lb, a specific heat of 23 Btu/lb/°F at 212°F, a coefficient of expansion of 11.9×10^{-6} from 68 to 572°F, and an emissivity of 0.035 to 0.07 at 77°F in air. As indicated in Sec. 7.9, Rapsodie uses a lead—antimony eutectic, 89% lead and 11% antimony, to can the subassemblies prior to transfer from the reactor building to the decay storage pool. The eutectic serves mainly as a good heat-transfer agent.

Reliability is of prime importance in a decay-heat removal system to avoid fuel damage or meltdown. A cooling system should have inherent reliability or equipment to back up the system if failures should occur. Where possible, cooling systems should be designed to utilize natural circulation effects to achieve reliability and minimize dependence on external power.

7.5.3.3 Criticality Control

Of prime importance in a fuel decay storage facility is assurance that the fuel will not be handled or stored in a manner that could create a critical assembly. A decay storage facility may frequently have sufficient fuel to achieve a critical assembly if the fuel assemblies are improperly arranged. Fuel-handling systems in decay facilities are typically devised to permit handling of only one fuel assembly at a time, and correct storage spacing is assured by the physical arrangement of the storage racks.

The Fermi fuel decay storage racks, for example, have storage positions on 14-in. centers, and the rack structure prevents insertion of a fuel assembly between these storage positions (Fig. 7.12). Fermi fuel assemblies are subcritical in water on 14-in. centers regardless of the array size. The fuel-handling equipment in the pools can handle only one fuel assembly at a time, and the handling equipment is interlocked so that fuel elements can be released only at designated storage or transfer positions. These precautions were taken to avoid the possibility of a critical grouping of fuel in the pools. At Dounreay fuel assemblies sealed in lead-filled cans are handled one at a time in the pools and are stored in 9-in. centers.

7.5.3.4 Decay-facility Shielding

A fuel decay facility has the same basic shielding problem the other areas in a reactor plant have. However, the problem of adequately shielding personnel may be somewhat complicated by the number of fuel assemblies stored, the size of the storage area dictated by critical spacing, and the mode of fuel handling. As with all radiation, the shielding problem is one of adequately shielding radiation-sensitive equipment components as well as personnel.

The amount of water shielding required in a given decay pool depends on the number of stored fuel assemblies, the source strength of the assemblies, the storage positions, the positions that individual assemblies will assume during handling, and inspection and cask loading in the pool. In pools where personnel have access to areas outside the pool walls at fuel elevations, the walls should be designed to keep radiation at personnel-tolerance levels.

7.5.3.5 Containment

A decay pool storage system should be designed and constructed to ensure satisfactory containment of radioactive fission products. If fission products escape into a water pool, some will escape from the water in gaseous form. Consequently it is necessary to control both pool-water leakage and also pool-surface ventilation to prevent radiation hazard to plant personnel or to the public.

At the Fermi Plant the water-leakage problem was approached by first providing a high-integrity pool liner. Stainless steel 304 of 3/16-in. thickness was selected for the liner on the basis of its corrosion resistance and structural strength. The pools are constructed with a 6-in. sand-filled space between the metal liner and the supporting concrete walls. Should a leak develop in the liner, the pool water would run into the sand space and from there through a drain to a monitored sump. This arrangement provides a double barrier between the pool

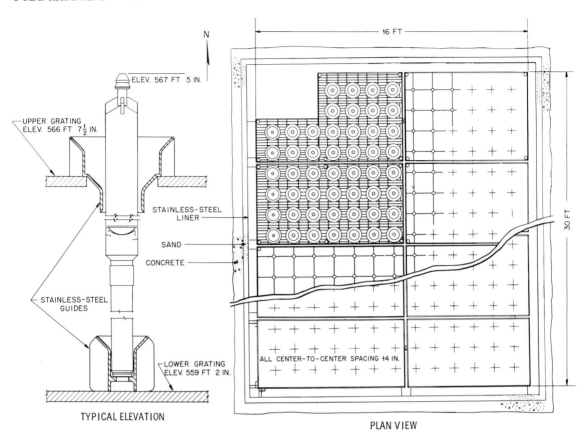

FIG. 7.12—Fermi fuel and repair building irradiated-subassembly decay storage pool.

water and the surrounding ground as well as a means of detecting pool leakage. Even if a simultaneous leak were to develop in the pool liner and the concrete pool walls, the high groundwater level would cause groundwater to flow from the outside through the concrete walls into the sand space and would thus prevent contaminated pool water from escaping to the ground.

At Fermi the pool-area ventilation system is a part of a ventilation exhaust system that services the fuel and repair building in which the pools are located. The air enters the pool area through dust filters and discharges from the area to an exhaust fan that, in turn, discharges to a waste-gas stack. Both pool areas have local radiation monitors, and the waste-gas stack air flow is monitored. Should radiation levels exceed permissible limits, the operators are alerted by alarms, and both pool areas can be isolated until the situation is corrected.

At Dounreay the decay pool is not covered by a building structure. The fuel elements are sealed in a lead-filled steel capsule in a manner that prevents escape of fission products. Consequently water or air contamination is not a problem.

7.5.3.6 Fuel-element Leakage

Fuel-cladding failures present a problem both in the reactor and in subsequent decay storage and shipment. The first indication of leakage is likely to occur when the fuel element is in the reactor core. Leakage in the core can be detected by cover gas or sodium radiation monitors. If a fuel element leaks while in a decay pool, the specific radioactivity of the pool water will increase, and the increase will be detected by radiation-monitoring equipment. If the leakage rate exceeds permissible limits, based on pool-water cleanup capacity or ventilation limitations, the leaking fuel element will have to be isolated.

Pool-water samples can be used to detect fuel leakage, but, when a number of fuel elements are stored in a decay pool, the question remains as to which fuel element or elements are leaking. At Fermi each fuel element is inserted into a sealed leaker test can immediately after the element is placed in the pool. After a fuel element has been in a leaker can for a week, a sample of the water in the can is checked for radioactivity. If the activity of the water [26] exceeds $5 \times 10^{-3} \, \mu c/cm^3$, the fuel element is classified as a leaker and is kept in a leaker can for its entire decay storage period. This activity is one-tenth the ORNL acceptance level for shipping-cask coolant-water activity. If the activity is below this level, the fuel element is removed from the can and stored in the decay pool.

Fuel leakage during decay storage does not present a problem at Dounreay because each fuel assembly is sealed in a lead-filled can before being placed in the decay pool. The fuel at Rapsodie is also canned. This approach sharply reduces requirements for pool-water cleanup and pool containment. As a result it was considered feasible to locate the decay pools outdoors at Dounreay.

7.5.3.7 Fuel Disassembly and Inspection

The on-site disassembly facilities required depend on the design of a fuel assembly and on the location and type of facility for reprocessing the irradiated fuel elements. Fuel elements of such fast power reactors as EBR-II and Enrico Fermi must be assembled into core subassemblies consisting of more than 100 fuel elements and containing both core and blanket material. Often the core and blanket materials are processed at different processing plants. It is desirable to ship the scrap hardware, i.e., support assemblies, flow nozzles, subassembly wrapper, and handling knob or bale, directly to the burial ground. Although disassembly of the fuel assembly is often performed on site, it, of course, could be performed at one of the processing plants, and the blanket elements could be reshipped to the appropriate processing facility.

Fuel assemblies may be disassembled under water or in a dry cave, depending on the decay-heat flux and the method used for decay storage. If a water pool is used for decay storage and inspection, underwater saws and other machine tools may be used for disassembly of the fuel subassemblies. The method used in handling fuel pins after disassembly should ensure that a subcritical array is maintained. Proper precautions should be taken in the collection of chips, shavings and particulates that are produced during the disassembly procedure. If the plant site has a dry cave facility and if the fuel is sufficiently decayed, the fuel assembly may be disassembled in the dry cave. It will be necessary, however, to provide special jigs and fixtures as well as the proper machine tools for disassembling the fuel assembly.

The low load factor and high cost of on-site fuel inspection and disassembly facilities suggest that whenever possible these facilities should be provided at the fuel-processing plant where higher load factors can be obtained. Except for first-time prototype power plants, on-site disassembly equipment may not be economically justified.

7.5.4 RADIOACTIVE-CONTAMINATION CONTROL IN DECAY POOLS

Radioactive materials that may collect in water decay pools must be removed. These materials are fission products that may get into the pools in the form of dissolved material, suspended particulates, and solids that collect on the pool walls or on submerged equipment.

The dissolved materials can be removed by circulating the pool water through ion exchangers. Filters in the circulating loop can be used to remove suspended particulates. Underwater vacuum-cleaning equipment, similar to the equipment used for cleaning swimming pools, can be used to remove solids that have settled onto the pool walls, floors, and equipment. Material picked up by the

vacuum equipment can be trapped in filters suitable for radioactive-waste disposal. A device for skimming the surface of the water is also necessary. Equipment of the type used for swimming pools is suitable if provisions are made for disposal of the trapped material.

Special attention should be directed to minimizing the release of radioactive materials into the pool. Fuel cutup equipment, for example, should be designed to trap the metal chips and keep the dispersion of particulates to a minimum. It is generally easier to trap chips and particulates at their source than to recover them after they have been dispersed in the pool. An underwater vacuum system with a hood positioned over the immediate vicinity of the cutter provides a means of catching particulates from a cutting operation.

Pools and contained equipment should be designed in a manner that facilitates cleaning [27]. One of the best materials from the standpoint of ease of decontamination is stainless steel. Glazed tile has been used for pool liners because its smooth surface facilitates cleaning; however, there have been instances where leakage has occurred through joints between tiles. Synthetic materials have been used successfully for pool liners, usually as a paint or fiberglass-reinforced coating applied over concrete. Some of the materials available have good leaktightness and decontamination properties, but they are generally limited to radiation doses [26] that do not exceed 10^9.

7.5.5 FERMI FUEL DECAY FACILITIES

The general arrangement of the building housing the decay facilities is shown in Figs. 6.65 and 6.66 of Chap. 6. Spent fuel is moved into the building in a cask car that runs on a north-south track. The fuel is deposited in an underfloor transfer tank filled with sodium. The fuel is next transferred to the cleaning chamber, where it is steam cleaned. It is then transferred to a water-filled tunnel that connects with the cutup pool.

Fuel assemblies are transported in the pools one at a time by a gripper mechanism mounted on a bridge that spans the narrow width of the pool and traverses the length of the pool. The mechanism grasps the handling head of a fuel assembly and raises it to a carrying position that clears the tops of the storage racks. The fuel assembly can be moved to any position in the pools for storage, testing, cutting, or cask loading. The gripper is constructed to assure a sufficient water-shield depth at all times, and the gripper and bridge equipment are provided with interlocks to protect against operator errors that might lead to damage to fuel assemblies or equipment. Underwater lights are attached to the gripper housings and illuminate the working area of the gripper. Movable underwater lights and television cameras are also provided for special viewing.

The cutup pool is 12 ft wide by 31 ft long by 30 ft deep. This pool contains a fuel leak-detector station, some storage racks, an ion-exchanger system for pool-water cleanup, a fuel-assembly cutup machine, a storage rack for cutup fuel, and space for loading a shipping cask. Space has also been provided for a fuel disassembly and inspection station. When a subassembly has been cleaned and deposited in the cutup pool, it is placed in a leaker test can, and the can is sealed. After a period of decay, a liquid sample is taken from the can and analyzed for fission products. If the concentration exceeds $5 \times 10^{-3} \mu c/cm^3$, the subassembly is classified as a leaker and is left in the can; the can is then transferred to the decay pool for decay storage. If the subassembly is not a leaker, it is removed from the can and transferred to the decay pool storage rack.

The decay pool is 17 ft wide by 31 ft long by 30 ft deep and is completely filled with decay storage racks that will accept 219 subassemblies, 77 of which will accept either a subassembly or a leaker can. The cutup pool contains a permanent storage rack that will accept 25 subassemblies or leaker cans. All the racks provide 14-in. center-to-center spacing of subassemblies. The total permanent storage capacity is 344 subassemblies. This is sufficient capacity to accommodate the normal storage of core and blanket subassemblies plus an additional complete core unloading. In the event a complete reactor unloading is required, temporary racks can be supported on top of the permanent racks to provide 513 additional storage spaces. All core subassemblies are, in any event, to be stored in the permanent racks; the temporary racks are to be used for blanket subassemblies only. The storage positions in the temporary racks would be on 14-in. centers but would be located at a higher elevation and midway between the positions in the permanent racks.

Spent subassemblies are stored in the decay pool for approximately 180 days, and then they are transferred back to the cutup pool. Blanket subassemblies are loaded directly into a shipping cask. Core subassemblies are transferred to the cutup machine, where they are positioned horizontally; two cuts are made to separate the fuel section from the axial blanket sections. This operation is required because the fuel and blanket portions may be reprocessed at different off-site locations. After the cutting operation the pieces are picked up by the bridge gripper and placed in a rack in a subcritical array until they can be loaded into a shipping cask.

Shipping casks are handled by the building crane. They are lowered to the bottom of the cutup pool through a removable hatch above the pool, and the entire operation is accomplished under water to ensure that the radiation level at the water surface will not exceed 0.75 mrem/hr. After the cask has been loaded, the cask cover is positioned and sealed. The cask is then hoisted above the pool surface and is rinsed with demineralized water that drains into the pool. After the cask dries, the building crane transports it to a railroad car located on the spur track inside the Fuel and Repair Building.

The depth of water in both the decay pool and the cutup pool is 30 ft. This depth satisfies the following shielding requirements: (1) the minimum depth of water above any subassembly located in either a permanent or a temporary storage rack should be 15 ft, (2) the minimum depth of water above one core subassembly in any vertical movement should be 11 ft, (3) the minimum depth of water above one core subassembly in a horizontal

position should be 13 ft. The depths given in (1) and (2) are the depths of water above the handling head of the subassemblies in a vertical position. The depth given in (3) is the minimum for core subassemblies in a horizontal position for cutting off the axial blankets in the cutup pool. The water shield limits the maximum radiation to 0.75 mrem/hr at the water surface. The level of activity in the decay pool and cutup pool water is kept below $8 \times 10^{-4} \mu c/cm^3$ by circulation of the water through ion exchangers which, for shielding purposes, are located underwater in the cutup pool. These exchangers can also service the liquid waste from the fuel-cleaning system.

The pools are lined with 3/16-in.-thick type 304 stainless steel. Between the liner and the concrete walls is a 6-in. layer of sand. This construction provides double containment and prevents the escape of contaminated water. The heat from the decaying subassemblies is removed by plate coolers suspended from the sides of the decay pool line. General service water is circulated through the plate coolers to maintain the pool-water temperature in the range of 90 to 100°F.

Figures 7.13 and 7.14 were prepared for a fuel-disassembly study by APDA. In the first panel of Fig. 7.13, the subassembly enters the disassembly station vertically after a six-month decay [28]. It is placed in a horizontal position in a cutup machine. The cutup machine cuts off the "telephone pole" lower support member, the handling plug, and the two axial blanket sections. The scrap pieces are placed in containers for shipping or placed in jigs for the decanning operation.

The second panel shows the decanning operation. Here a core section is placed in a decanning machine horizontally with the flats at an angle of 45° with the horizontal. A milling cutter or coarse grinding wheel traverses the length of the piece, cutting through the top corner of the can. The piece is then turned over 180° so that the opposite corner is exposed to the cutter. This corner likewise is cut through; now the can is loose in two sections. Using an extension gripper with a pliers head, the operator lifts away the can sections and places them in scrap containers. The fuel pins, still retained in the bird cage, can then be placed in the shipping container. Figure 7.14 shows the additional equipment required for disassembly to a gross inspection of pins. Supplemental forced cooling may be required in the cutup and decanning steps. Water is pumped through the flexible hose shown in panel 1 of Fig. 7.13 to cool the subassembly when it is horizontal.

After the subassemblies have been cut up and decanned, the next step requires the cutup machine to cut through the pin supports and the milling cutter to make transverse cuts along the outer faces of the bird cage. Pins from each row are lifted out individually and placed immediately in a special carrier rack to prevent inadvertent assembly of a critical mass. Selected pins are placed in a gauging fixture for inspection. An accurate length and diameter check is made with conventional dial gauges adapted for underwater use, and a gamma-radiation scan is performed. Certain pins may be sent to an off-site hot laboratory for metallurgical and radiochemical examinations. Equipment re-

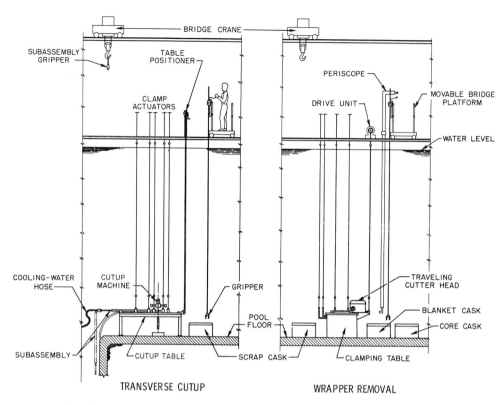

FIG. 7.13—Fermi subassembly cutup and wrapper–removal station for fuel decay facility [28].

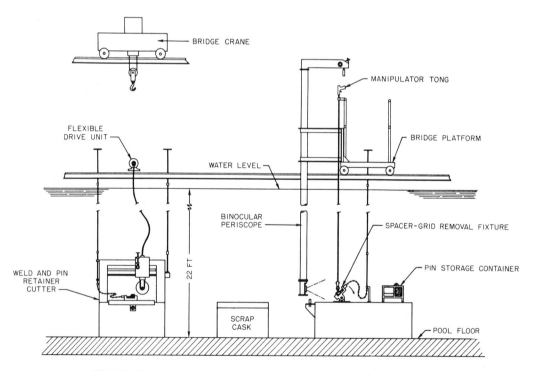

FIG. 7.14—Fermi subassembly core section dismantling station for fuel decay facility [28].

quired for pin disassembly and inspection includes a binocular eyepiece for the periscope, a wire-cutter attachment for the extension pliers, some additional fixture to hold the loose pin bundle during disassembly, storage racks (about 12 to 14), gauges and gauging fixtures for dimensional checks, and a gamma scanner.

7.6 Spent-fuel Shipping

Off-site processing of spent fuel raises the problems inherent in the shipping of high-level radioactive materials from a reactor site to a processing plant that may be a considerable distance from the reactor site. For example, Fermi fuel assemblies may be processed by Nuclear Fuel Services near Buffalo, N. Y. Shipping casks may cost up to several hundred thousand dollars. Single shipments may cost several thousands of dollars.

Because of the radioactive fission products and the fissionable materials contained in spent fuel, great care must be taken in all phases of the design, fabrication, and use of shipping casks. It is essential that every precaution be taken to preclude or minimize accidents that might result in a radiation hazard or a fission-product release. In particular, special attention should be directed to the prevention of a criticality or meltdown accident.

In the United States a license to transport fuel must be obtained from the USAEC together with approval of the shipping cask to be used. The USAEC has taken primary responsibility for developing adequate safety requirements. The regulation contained in Title 10, Code of Federal Regulations, Part 72 and its criteria for evaluating shipping casks have been used by the USAEC as its standard for approval of shipping casks [29]. The regulation contains requirements for criticality control, decay-heat removal, shielding, structural integrity, cask-contamination limits, and handling procedures. In additon to these regulations, some general criteria for the acceptance of shipping casks have been formulated by the Production Division of the USAEC and by individual processing plants. The International Atomic Energy Agency (IAEA) has established similar regulations, and the American Standards Association (ASA) has also prepared proposed standards.

The designer should include the USAEC regulations in his design criteria. He should consider possible accidents, failures, and such incidents as cask impact, fire, removal of material by an accident, mechanical failures, water immersion and leakage, fuel damage, vibration, acceleration, corrosion, and excess pressures and temperatures. Each condition should be analyzed and, if necessary, tested. The design should arrive at a cask that has the required integrity. The designer should aim toward reducing the number of shipments and toward increasing the life of the cask without jeopardizing any safety features.

7.6.1 CRITICALITY CONTROL [30]

The shipper may employ either mass control, geometry control, or poison control to keep within the prescribed limit of 0.9 of the effective neutron multiplication constant of the materials in their most reactive condition. In critical-mass determinations a credit may be taken for poisons built into the cask or fuel elements. In all other respects, however, the worst credible set of conditions should be assumed.

Fuel should be taken at its maximum reactivity; i.e., it should be treated as unirradiated fuel or, if it contains built-in poisons, as fuel irradiated to the point of greatest reactivity. The presence of an amount of hydrogenous material giving maximum reactivity should be assumed. Similarly, it should be assumed that the spacing between fuel elements is that which gives maximum reactivity, or it must be shown that the fuel elements cannot be arranged into a configuration more reactive than that for which the shipment is designed. Unless it can be established that meltdown of the fuel elements is impossible, the fuel should be considered as molten in the most reactive array. Where geometry control is employed, each controlling dimension should incorporate an allowance for defined uncertainties in experiment or calculation and, in addition, a safety factor. The applicant for a license should also demonstrate that shipments involving more than one cask will be safe from criticality based on interactions between casks.

Borated materials considered for criticality control include boron in aluminum, carbon steel, stainless steel, copper, and others.

7.6.2 DECAY-HEAT REMOVAL [30]

Either a liquid or a gaseous coolant is generally permitted by the regulations. However, liquids other than water may not be acceptable to the processing plants when such liquids could contaminate storage-basin water. Water will likely be the most used coolant since the loading of spent fuel into casks probably will be carried out under water at most power-reactor stations. Pressurizing the water to 50 psig and using materials of good conductivity increase the capacity of a cask and reduce the cost of transportation. For a spent-fuel load that liberates very little heat, an antifreeze may have to be used in the water. In that event, special arrangements would have to be made with the processing plants. If a liquid coolant is used, its maximum temperature should be restricted to 20°F below its boiling point at the highest elevation on the route. The temperature of the accessible surfaces of the cask should be limited to 180°F.

Coolant that is in contact with the fuel may not be circulated outside the cask shielding. A secondary coolant is required if heat sinks in the form of radiators separate from the cask are to be used. This requirement, together with another which states that the cooling system shall operate at approximately atmospheric pressure, probably will have the effect of limiting the use of gaseous coolants to casks holding only small amounts of fuel irradiated to a low level.

The use of fins for radiating heat should be considered. Section 7.10 presents methods for the analysis of fins.

An important part of the regulations pertaining to heat removal concerns the possible loss of coolant. The regulations acknowledge the inability to preclude the possible loss of coolant, and they establish criteria intended to minimize the damage that might result. In the event coolant is lost, no constituent in the cask, including fuel, cladding, and built-in poison, should reach a temperature greater than 200°F below its failure temperature. The failure temperature can be set at some radiation-release limit and can only be determined by test. The failure temperature should not be higher than the melting point of the fuel or cladding. Compliance would prevent criticality incidents that might otherwise occur if, for example, poison-containing spacers or fuel cladding should melt.

7.6.3 SHIELDING

Shipping casks should be shielded to meet regulations. For example, Ref. 30 states that gamma-radiation levels at any readily accessible surface of the cask must not exceed 200 mr/hr. For truck shipments a maximum level of 10 mr/hr at a distance of 1 m (3.28 ft) also applies. For rail shipments the level should not exceed 10 mr/hr at 3 m (9.84 ft).

Lead is frequently used for cask shielding. About 10 in. of lead should reduce the radiation level of an average fuel cooled 100 days below prescribed limits. A good bond is required between the lead and the surface material for heat transfer. In the studies described by Piper and Langhaar [31], it was found that lead bonded better to carbon steel than to stainless steel; thus carbon steel clad with stainless steel was used in the Savannah River cask design.

7.6.4 STRUCTURAL INTEGRITY [30]

Since the major safety problem is one resulting from a crash, the chief design consideration is to preserve the cask integrity during a crash. To meet specified tests (discussed below), the designers will usually provide some means of decelerating the cask to prescribed values. Crash shields and mounting methods that limit vibration and impact should be considered. A cask that is integral with a carrier that can take punishment provides one of the answers. The regulations [29] specify that it shall be assumed that a cover edge of the loaded cask traveling at 44 ft/sec (30-ft drop) will come in contact with a solid object. It must be shown that in this situation the cask will remain covered and intact and the fuel will not be rearranged into a more reactive configuration. It should not be required that there be no loss of coolant; the regulations on heat removal deal with that situation. The regulations also require a puncture test: the equivalent of a force 30 times the weight of the cask applied normal to the surface over any circular area 6 in. in diameter at a velocity of at least 16 m/sec (52.5 ft/sec) without exceeding the ultimate strength of the exterior cask material.

Possible leakage of water into the lead-filled section of the cask should be accounted for by safety devices that can blow water and steam but not lead.

The seals and the closure should be capable of withstanding the 150% hydrostatic pressure test. O-ring seals may be made of rubber or metal.

One-hour fire tests can be met by designing lead shielding so that with a lead expansion space the redistribution due to melting will not raise the radiation above acceptable limits or by insulating (wood or other material) the outside of the cask without reducing the normal heat-transfer effectiveness below prescribed limits.

7.6.5 CASK-CONTAMINATION LIMITS [30]

The regulations provide that a cask shall not be shipped if the surface beta−gamma activity exceeds 4000 dis/min/100 cm^2 or if the alpha activity exceeds 500 dis/min/100 cm^2. If a cask were shipped with contamination approaching the limits set in the regulations, additional decontamination would be required before it would be acceptable to the processor at most sites.

Surfaces of the cask that may become contaminated are generally made of series 300 stainless steel or some material that can be decontaminated readily by scrubbing with detergent and water. Carbon steel coated with a suitable paint can be decontaminated easily. One drawback to painted carbon steel, however, is the difficulty of decontaminating metal surfaces where the paint has been damaged.

Provision should be made for sampling the cask coolant. Samples are taken at the processing plant to determine coolant activity. Normal acceptance criteria limit the activity level of such samples to something less than 5×10^{-8} curies/cm^3. Any indication of activity level approaching this value might well indicate the existence of a ruptured fuel element.

7.6.6 OTHER CASK REQUIREMENTS

Shipping casks should be designed to facilitate underwater fuel handling at processing plants. When the cask is loaded in a pool at the reactor site, the requirements are much the same at the site as at the processing plant. The maximum weight of a shipping cask is limited by the handling facilities at both the reactor site and the processing plant. In general, cask weights up to 75 tons are reasonable for most facilities [30]. Such items as sampling and relief valves and expansion tanks should be recessed or protected from damage by steel guards. The processing plants desire that the bottom surface of the cask cover be free of projections so that it can be placed on the bottom of the fuel storage pool during unloading. The regulations specify that where there is a pressure-relief valve a filter should be provided to prevent, as far as possible, the release of particulate matter.

7.6.7 SHIPPING PROCEDURES [30]

United States regulations state that a license to transport fuel must be obtained from the AEC. Issuance of a license is considered on the basis of information submitted by the applicant, including engineering analyses of criticality, heat transfer, radiation shielding, structural integrity, control of contamination of shipping casks, and the handling procedures to be employed.

In addition to the technical and engineering criteria, the regulations specify requirements for labeling and describe the records that should be kept for the fuel. The AEC should be notified of any accidental criticality incident, major damage to the shipment, dispersal of fission products, or loss.

7.6.8 SHIPPING-CASK TESTING

A difficult problem in the design of a shipping cask is the reasonably accurate determination of the heat-transfer characteristics of the fuel and the cask. The limitations of calculations for this type of heat-transfer problem have prompted the use of test mockups using electrically heated dummy fuel assemblies [30, 32]. Temperature tests require around 20 hr to reach equilibrium temperature. Curves can be plotted of temperature vs. power input to determine cask heat dissipation at a fixed ambient.

Drop tests have been conducted by the AEC at Oak Ridge to determine the structural integrity of various case designs [33]. Of particular interest is the resistance to impact loadings that might result from a transportation accident. Since data on possible cask damage cannot be calculated with any degree of certainty, data are being obtained experimentally on small-scale models which should permit scale-up to actual cask sizes. All the cask models have an inner and outer steel shell and a lead-filled annulus [34]. In these tests the casks are instrumented. Compressometers indicate the maximum deflection in the cavity at impact, and accelerometers measure the deceleration at the location on the cask where they are attached. Inertia switches preset to function under a certain shock load are used to check the information obtained from the accelerometers. Strain gauges measure the strain at points of interest.

Casks have been dropped in various positions and from various heights. The data are being correlated to determine whether or not the results obtained from model testing can be satisfactorily scaled up to help in setting some of the important parameters in cask design.

Voids in lead shielding can be detected by checking volume vs. weight, by radiation penetration, and by ultrasonic calibration.

7.6.9 SHIPPING CASKS FABRICATED OR IN PROCESS

As of September 1962, approximately 111 fuel shipping casks had been fabricated or were in the process of being designed or fabricated by U.S. manufacturers [35]. These casks range from 5 tons to 125 tons. Seventy-seven of these are for U. S. Government facilities (AEC, Navy, Army, Air Force, and NASA). Twenty-five are for foreign facilities and nine are for private U. S. facilities.

This list does not include casks that have been made by operating contractors at major AEC installations. Truck shipments can handle up to 18 tons, depending on highway limitations. Rail shipments can probably exceed 125 tons. Crane capacity and dimensions are usually limiting for rail shipment. The decision whether to use rail or truck for shipments up to 18 tons is one of economics and insurance coverage.

In 1963 and 1964 the transportation of spent fuel from nuclear power reactors is expected to begin in appreciable volume [33]. Several firms are offering a complete fuel-transport service including cask rental, maintenance and inspection, arrangement and supervision of transportation, and the performance of regulatory paper work. The following descriptions encompasses only thermal reactor fuel for which experience is available.

7.6.9.1 Shipping Cask for Dresden and N.S. Savannah

Fuel-transport for the N.S. Savannah and for the Dresden nuclear plant is provided by the same 70-ton cask (Fig. 7.15) mounted on a specially designed railway car [33]. The cask contains six fuel cavities, eacy cavity capable of carrying four Dresden fuel assemblies or one N.S. Savannah fuel assembly. The 14-ft-high casks use an internal water-cooling system backed up by a secondary natural-convection water system. As added protection the cask can be pressurized [36]. The cask, weighing 75 tons loaded, sits in a well in the center of the railway car and is secured by a framework support.

7.6.9.2 Shipping Cask for Yankee [36]

Yankee spent fuel is transported in a 70-ton cask carried on a special railway car. An innovation in this cask is that its primary-water-system pumps are located in the head of the cask. The cask has a duplicate water cooling system and a standby power source, and it is designed to carry

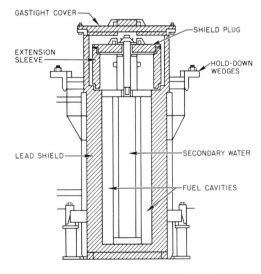

FIG. 7.15—Dresden shipping cask [36].

10 Yankee fuel elements per shipment and to dissipate 80 kw of heat.

7.6.9.3 Shipping Cask for Piqua and Elk River [36]

The shipping cask for spent fuel at Piqua and Elk River is a dry cask (Fig. 7.16). The conventional liquid coolant and cooling equipment was eliminated by developing a fuel-assembly basket capable of efficiently conducting decay heat to the cask's inner shell. From there the heat is conducted to cooling fins on the cask's outer shell. High heat-transfer efficiency was achieved by metallurgically bonding lead to the inner and outer shells of the cask.

The cask can carry 19 Piqua or Elk River fuel elements per shipment. Because of its compact design and simplified cooling concept, the cask is only 9 ft high by 4 ft in diameter; it weighs only 28 tons (32 tons loaded). The size, weight, and design are such that it can be hauled on a standard railway car.

7.6.9.4 Shipping Cask for WTR [37]

The shipping cask originally designed for the Westinghouse Test Reactor is a 15-ton cask designed to carry 19 WTR fuel elements after 90 days of fuel decay. It uses only noncirculating coolants and is designed to dissipate 8 kw of decay heat. The internal cavity of the cask is 16 1/4 in. in diameter by 55 in. deep. Criticality considerations led to the incorporation of a neutron poison in the fuel-element basket. The cask is transported on the highway on a trailer that incorporates auxiliary cooling equipment [36].

The ability of most shipping casks of this type to remove heat from spent fuel elements without the use of circulating coolants is severely limited by the gap formed between the lead shield and outer cask shell during cooling and solidification of the lead. A method of bridging this gap with flexible

metal fins was devised which improved the heat-dissipation qualities of the cask. Further enhancement of the heat-dissipation qualities of this cask was obtained by 4-in.-high by 1/4-in.-thick metal fins placed around the exterior of the cask. Experimental data were obtained which confirmed the exterior fin size as an optimum. These innovations permitted the cask to dissipate 8 kw of decay heat, within the AEC regulations.

Since water is used to bond the fuel elements thermally to the cask, the cask was designed to operate at a maximum pressure of 50 psig and comply with the ASME Boiler Code for unfired pressure vessels. Trunnions for lifting, rotating, and dumping were provided on the cask. A metal O-ring seal, which can be tested without pressurizing the cask, was used between the cover and cask. In addition, the top of the cask was designed to permit an extension to be added for shipment of longer fuel elements. This cask has been used to transport spent fuel elements between the WTR site and the National Reactor Testing Site in Idaho.

7.7 Fuel-handling-system Equipment

7.7.1 FUEL-HANDLING MACHINES

Fuel-handling machines may require combinations of the following motions: (1) raise gripper, (2) lower gripper, (3) rotate gripper, (4) actuate and disengage gripper, (5) sense fuel element, (6) lock gripper, (7) raise and lower offset arm, (8) move gripper radially on offset arm, (9) rotate offset arm. Methods of providing these motions are described in the following sections.

7.7.1.1 Raising and Lowering Grippers

7.7.1.1.1 SOLID SHAFTS. If a solid shaft is used to raise and lower the gripper, its length will determine the height of the fuel-handling machine. This, in turn, will influence the equipment-door size and may preclude movement of the cask car out of the reactor building whether the cask car refuels directly from the reactor, as at Dounreay, or from a transfer position, as at Fermi. Solid-shaft drives can be driven by rack and pinion, ball-nut screw (Fermi), or a regular lead screw. The solid shaft has the advantage of being able to push or pull, and it can get a positive indication of the latching motion. It has the disadvantage of requiring much greater headroom for straight probe, and it has additional sealing and mechanism requirements.

The drive shaft can be sealed by bellows or packing glands. Packing glands tend to bind on dry shafts. One method, if the fuel-handling machine is in permanently, is to tighten the seals against the shaft during nonrefueling and loosen them during the short refueling period when the leakage problem may not be as serious.

7.7.1.1.2 CABLE– OR CHAIN–OPERATED GRIPPER. Cable hoists, such as in the Fermi cask car, reduce the cask-car headroom requirements but require careful end design because the cables may also be required to activate and lock

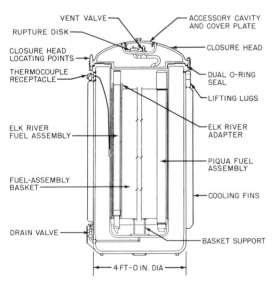

VENT VALVE

ACCESSORY CAVITY AND COVER PLATE

RUPTURE DISK

CLOSURE HEAD

CLOSURE HEAD LOCATING POINTS

THERMOCOUPLE RECEPTACLE

DUAL O-RING SEAL

LIFTING LUGS

ELK RIVER FUEL ASSEMBLY

ELK RIVER ADAPTER

PIQUA FUEL ASSEMBLY

FUEL-ASSEMBLY BASKET

COOLING FINS

DRAIN VALVE

BASKET SUPPORT

4 FT-0 IN. DIA

FIG. 7.16—Knapp mills design–dry cask for Piqua and Elk river fuel elements [36].

the gripper. The cable gripper requires little or no headroom; it can be totally enclosed in the cask. It has the disadvantage of being gravity actuated. You cannot push with it, and it is difficult or impossible to get a positive indication of latching motions or to know vertical position accurately. Problems of cable twist and stretch are also complications. A single cable permits the gripper to drop straight and to have a balanced pull on the subassembly, but it is difficult to actuate the gripper. A double cable provides actuation, but it is difficult to get the gripper to drop straight. A double-cable gripper can be made relatively fail safe even if one cable breaks.

Chain hoists, such as in the EBR-II cask car, reduce the headroom requirements and have the advantage of being able to push or pull. Section 7.9.3.4.7 contains details of the EBR-II chain drive.

7.7.1.1.3 TELESCOPING SHAFT. Telescoping shafts require little headroom but complicate sealing problems. Several telescoping shafts may be required to actuate and lock the gripper. These shafts have not been used in existing designs.

7.7.1.1.4 DIFFERENTIAL SCREW. If one screw is rotated within another, a saving of about 30% in headroom above a straight shaft can be obtained. Screws create problems similar to those of a telescoping shaft.

7.7.1.1.5 COMBINED RACK AND CHAIN DRIVE. A combination of a rack and chain drive, used at Dounreay (Sec. 7.9.2.4.1), can save headroom. The chain drive inside the rack tube can save the headroom required by the length of the subassembly plus the length of the gripper assembly below the tube rack. The chain is attached to the gripper carriage and can be driven independent from the rack.

7.7.1.2 Load Sensing

Fuel-handling machines should be equipped, where possible, with load-sensing devices that can initiate operations to stop a machine when the push or pull load exceeds certain limits or, in some cases, can indicate if the load is below prescribed values. Devices used may be counterbalanced weights, such as on the transfer arm at EBR-II, or strain gauges or other devices that measure the change in the strain of the machine. Devices can be incorporated, as at EBR-II, to actually limit the push–pull loads.

7.7.1.3 Drives

The following types of drives can be considered for fuel-handling machinery: (1) motor-driven ball-nut screw (Fermi), (2) motor-driven pinion driving a rack (Dounreay), (3) motor-driven worm gear driving a lead screw, (4) hermetically sealed drive using a harmonic motion transmitted through a thin diaphragm (United Shoe Machinery Corp. drive), (5) magnetic drive through a thin diaphragm, and (6) hydraulic drives. Each type of drive should be studied to determine which is best suited for the particular operation.

7.7.2 ROTATING-PLUG DRIVES

Several of the fuel schemes covered in this chapter include rotating plugs—double at Dounreay, EBR-II, and Rapsodie and single at Fermi. The drive for the concentric plug can be located on a platform external to the reactor; the drive for the eccentric, or inner, plug is mounted on the concentric plug.

The rotating plug or plugs serving as a machinery platform are also part of the operating-floor biological shield. With the machinery the total weight may reach 150 tons. The diameter over the bull gear, which is at the top periphery of each plug, may be over 10 ft, as in the case of Fermi. The drive, which may be a vertical or horizontally mounted unit, generally uses a gear-reduction unit with the pinion driving the bull gear to impart a rotation of approximately 1 rpm, with starting, stopping, and positioning velocities of about 0.1 rpm. The design criteria should include: (1) sufficient breakaway torque, (2) positioning accuracy, (3) ability to change torque, (4) flexibility to conform to the bull-gear geometry as it changes in dimension owing to temperature changes, gravity-load changes, and other loads, (5) braking as necessary to control positioning, (6) remote controls with readout and programming to repetitively produce some required position, and (7) interlocks to prevent malfunction.

7.7.3 TRANSFER-ROTOR MACHINERY

Transfer rotors may be used as intermediate storage positions (EBR-II and Fermi) between the reactor core and the cask car, or they may be used in the fuel-element storage building, as at Fermi, to store finned pots full of sodium prior to a turnaround with new fuel.

Transfer rotor design criteria should include: (1) an indexing mechanism that positions the designated storage position under the designated port, accounting for any possible shaft torsion, (2) a shaft strong in tension and in torsion with the rotor fully loaded and designed for possible accidents, including the dropping of a subassembly or a finned pot containing a subassembly, (3) a mode of attachment that will allow the shaft to be disengaged for examination and repair, (4) assured horizontal and vertical alignment during all conditions of operation of the transfer-rotor shaft and any adjacent parts, such as the tail bearing or shield material, and drive tubes, (5) assured alignment of the positions in the transfer-rotor basket, the plate that carries the fuel subassemblies, or pots containing the subassemblies, during all conditions of operation, and (6) transfer-rotor interlocks to prevent operation at any period other than during prescribed periods.

7.7.4 CASK CARS

Cask cars are used to transfer fuel subassemblies and other reactor subassemblies, such as control rods, to and from the reactor, examination pits, temporary storage racks, decay storage pools, and canning stations.

A cask car should be designed with the following criteria: (1) sufficient shielding to keep the radioactivity within tolerance for any condition of fuel loading, (2) sufficient cooling to remove the amount of decay heat required to keep the fuel temperature within design limits, (3) duplicate systems (blowers or pumps) with a self-contained power pack or connections by cable, (4) provisions to purge the car with inert gas, maintain the inert gas in the car, measure its impurity, and to dispose of it to storage or stack connections, (5) sufficient storage for spent and fresh subassemblies, (6) storage for exit port or other plugs, (7) storage for plug liners if these are needed, (8) provisions for remote or manual control, (9) provisions to drive the car on a track or a roadbed, (10) if equipped with a rotor, the car should have a rotor drive and an indexing mechanism, (11) provisions for connections to a data logger to keep track of all operations, (12) an interlock system with keys or cards to maintain a proper sequence of operations to preclude contamination of an improper operation or, if necessary, to reverse an operation, (13) adequate fuel-handling equipment, (14) automatically operated valves to seal the cask car fuel-access hole, (15) positioning devices to accurately align the cask over the refueling port, (16) provisions to prevent leakage of lubricants or other contaminants into the refueling port, (17) adequate seals to prevent leakage of contaminated cooling gas to the outside atmosphere, (18) a control panel for an operator at the cask car containing all necessary instruments, control systems, monitors, dams, and interlocks to operate the car in the manner prescribed, (19) provisions for seating and sealing connections between the cask car and the refueling port, either by a separate adapter valve or by a sealing flange lowered into position, or directly by lowering the cask on to the port flange, (20) provisions for sodium drainage, (21) shock absorbers to prevent damage in case of cask-car override, and (22) provisions for containment against any possible meltdown.

The capacity of a cask car depends on many factors, each of which requires evaluation. Among these factors are the following: (1) How many subassemblies can be safely handled? (2) As the number of subassemblies increases, the space requirements increase not only because of the number of units but also because of the additional cooling requirements, shielding requirements, and control and instrumentation requirements; the bulk of the cask car then becomes an important item and its cost, which also increases as a function of the number of subassemblies it handles, must be considered.

7.7.5 MACHINERY FOR STEAM CLEANING OF SUBASSEMBLIES

Steam-cleaning machinery can be a stationary unit into which a subassembly is inserted for cleaning, as at Fermi, or a portable unit with which the subassembly can be cleaned directly in the cask car or in a transit cask (coffin), as at EBR-II.

A stationary unit should incorporate: (1) lifting and traversing load-sensing devices or rotating devices for handling fuel subassemblies, (2) pro-

vision for connections to vacuum, inert gas, steam, and water supply, (3) provisions to automatically and positively seal off these supplies when necessary, (4) provisions to exhaust the waste gases and liquids, (5) provision for heating, (6) provision for cooling, (7) radiation shielding, (8) automatic control systems to operate the machine, (9) interlock and alarm systems to maintain proper sequence of operation and to preclude maloperation, (10) indexing mechanisms to locate the machine properly if such is necessary, (11) automatically operated shutoff valves to seal the cleaning machine, (12) means for cleaning and decontaminating the machine after a predetermined number of operations, (13) sufficient cooling and thorough cleaning, (14) accessibility at all times between any operation for inspection, maintenance, and repair, (15) corrosion resistance, (16) trouble-free operation under design pressures and temperatures, (17) backup cooling in case of normal cooling failure, and (18) means to prevent an explosion hazard.

A cleaning unit within the transit cask should provide items 2 through 18, plus a means for automatically or manually making and breaking connections to the transit cask at the cleaning station.

7.7.6 FUEL-DISASSEMBLY AND -INSPECTION MACHINERY

On-site inspection and disassembly may have to be done under water unless the decay storage is of sufficient duration to permit operations in a gas atmosphere. Disassembly operations may be partial or complete down to the fuel element. At Fermi (Figs. 7.13 and 7.14) the process consists of cutting the core section away from the end blanket sections, which are then sent to a different reprocessing point.

Some of the factors to be considered are: (1) radioactivity, (2) criticality control, (3) cooling during disassembly, (4) remotely operated machinery for performing operations under water or in an environmental gas subject to radiation, (5) maintenance of machinery, (6) controls for machinery, (7) removal of machining debris, (8) the design of the subassembly to accommodate disassembly, (9) handling equipment to handle the subassembly prior to and after the machining operation, and (10) viewing equipment.

It is probably good design practice to design the machinery for the intended purpose, fitting in standard parts where the design indicates this can be done.

7.8 Critical Machine Parts

There are certain critical parts in all fuel-handling equipment that require special design attention. These parts are grippers, bearings, seals, drives, drive shafts, and controls. Many features of the drives and drive shafts covered in Sec. 9.3, Chap. 9, are similar to fuel-handling-machine drives and drive shafts. Control features are covered in other sections of this chapter and in Chap. 9. This section will cover grippers, bearings, and seals, with particular emphasis on grippers.

7.8.1 GRIPPERS

The gripper, a key element in fuel handling, is that part of a fuel-handling mechanism which performs the function of latching on to a subassembly prior to picking it up for transport. It is also capable of delatching from the subassembly. Other names for grippers are grapple, grappling head, tongs, snout, lifter, and grab.

The following, which includes latching and delatching, lists other tasks the gripper may be called upon to perform, either independently or as part of an overall function of the fuel-handling machine: (1) latch and delatch, (2) lift and push, (3) self-align, (4) rotate, (5) translate, (6) lock fail safe in either latch or delatch position, (7) feed back indi-

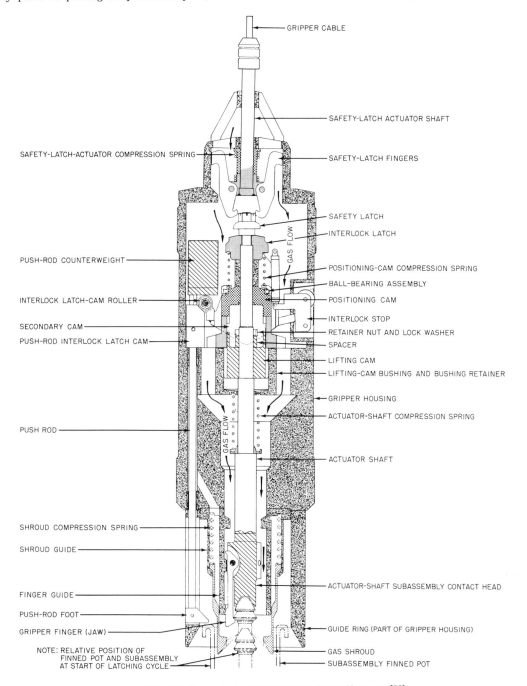

FIG. 7.17—Fermi steam-cleaning-station subassembly gripper [25].

cations to the control unit of latch, delatch, lock, or orientation, and (8) lock a subassembly into position. The gripper, a versatile tool, is used in the following types of operations: (1) fuel handling internal to the reactor, as at EBR-II and Fermi, (2) fuel transfer to and from the reactor and from and to a cask car and transfer to and from the cask car at canning stations, decay storage, or other points, and (3) fuel transfer at cleaning stations, examination cells, disassembly cells, shipping stations, and decay storage pools.

7.8.1.1 Design Criteria

A gripper should be able to perform repeatedly and, if necessary, do this in a sodium or sodium-vapor environment with the highest achievable reliability.

Gripper materials should be able to withstand the design loads, including impact, at the specified temperatures. Availability and cost of materials should generally be of secondary consideration since the amount of material involved in a gripper is not large. Gripper materials exposed to long-term irradiation greater than 10^{17} neutrons/cm^2 should withstand the irradiation without a reduction in reliability. The ease of fabrication, forming, machining, and hard surfacing should be of secondary consideration if the operations are necessary to produce a reliable product. The materials should be resistant to corrosion in the environmental sodium, sodium vapor, or inert gas at design temperatures, including the environmental contaminants.

7.8.1.2 Types of Gripper Operation

A gripper can be actuated by its own weight or by the weight of a fuel subassembly, or the pot can be used to actuate a cam, e.g., the steam-cleaning gripper at Fermi (Fig. 7.17). A gripper can be mechanically operated from a remote position, e.g., EBR-I and Fermi fuel handling machine grippers. A gripper can be electrically operated, with solenoids, transducers, and other electrically actuated devices used to provide motion or to feed back signals, or it can be pneumatically operated.

A gripper under sodium operates without lubricant. The materials should be chosen, as indicated in Sec. 7.8.1.1, to operate at the design temperatures, contact pressures, and sliding loads. The gripper should not impose an undue restriction to the flow of coolant. The parts that come in contact with the fuel subassembly and the moving parts that may come in contact with any other part of the gripper should be designed to prevent hang-up for any condition of operation. The gripper should operate through hollow tubes, holes, ports, and other entrances without hang-up.

The design should incorporate radii and fillets to minimize stress concentrations; pin clearances should prevent movements outside of tolerance but should be sufficient to provide low friction under all load conditions. Actuating forces should be built up gradually rather than abruptly. The gripper should be easy to disassemble for maintenance. Buildup of oxide or other solid contaminants

should be minimized by good drainage and a minimum of crevices.

A structural analysis of the gripper should be made for design conditions. The gripper should be subjected to lifetime tests at design conditions to determine friction and camming forces, contact stresses, pin stresses, spring stresses, possible hang-up forces, allowable overloads, failure stresses, and galling and bonding forces.

Generally, poor camming, galling, bonding, parts, such as pins, falling out of pin holes, pin bending, and stress cracking are the chief causes of failure. Lack of lubrication, high temperatures, and contaminant problems are contributory causes.

7.8.1.3 Gripper Description

The following sections describe the EBR-II fuel-handling-machine subassembly and control-rod gripper, the EBR-II cask car gripper, the basic AMF type gripper, the Dounreay cask-car (charge-machine) gripper, the Dounreay lidding-machine gripper, the Fermi offset handling-mechanism gripper, the Fermi cask-car gripper, the Fermi steam-cleaning gripper, the Rapsodie gripper, and miscellaneous grippers.

7.8.1.3.1 EBR-II GRIPPER. The EBR-II subassembly gripper [38] is a double-jaw cammed gripper, which utilizes a pin joint to support the fingers (Fig. 7.18). The fingers are cammed open and closed by a sliding sleeve.

The actuator drive shaft carries an outer sleeve, the lower portion of which is formed into an actuator cam which can close or open the gripper jaws. The mechanism drive shaft and gripper housing terminate in an actuator outer-sleeve guide, a guide pin, the gripper jaws, and the conical guide. A separate shaft, the indicator bar, is guided by the guide pin.

In operation the mechanism drive shaft is lowered, and the conical guide centers the gripper over the subassembly. The indicator bar (gripper sensing device) contacts the subassembly handling head and is driven upward as the gripper continues downward until the full down position is reached. The outer sleeve, which is attached to the actuator drive shaft, includes the gripper-jaw actuator cam as an integral part of the sleeve. The actuator cam operates in conjunction with camming surfaces on the gripper jaws to open, close, and lock the gripper jaws. The gripper jaws are attached to the gripper housing located on the lower end of this mechanism drive shaft. The conical guide is also an integral part of the gripper housing. The actuator drive shaft can now be operated, driving its outer sleeve with the actuator cam down and locking the gripper jaws below the handling head.

To be released, the subassembly must be bottomed or held in a fixed vertical position. The actuator shaft is then retracted; this action opens the gripper jaws. The orientation blade remains engaged to the subassembly slot holding the subassembly in a fixed vertical position. The mechanism drive shaft is then retracted vertically, and the gripper is removed from the subassembly.

The indicator bar performs two functions: it confirms whether or not a subassembly is present when the gripper jaws are closed and it confirms

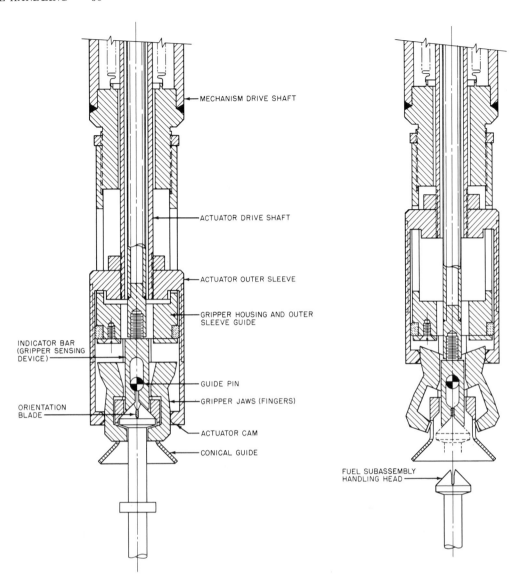

MECHANISM DRIVE SHAFT

ACTUATOR DRIVE SHAFT

ACTUATOR OUTER SLEEVE

GRIPPER HOUSING AND OUTER
SLEEVE GUIDE

INDICATOR BAR
(GRIPPER SENSING
DEVICE)

GUIDE PIN

ORIENTATION
BLADE

GRIPPER JAWS (FINGERS)

ACTUATOR CAM

CONICAL GUIDE

FUEL SUBASSEMBLY
HANDLING HEAD

FIG. 7.18—EBR-II gripper mechanism [38].

the separation of the gripper and the subassembly when the gripper is raised with jaws open.

The actuator cam performs four functions: closes the gripper jaws, keeps them locked in the closed position, opens the gripper jaws, and keeps them locked in an open position.

Proper orientation of the hexagonal subassemblies is obtained by means of an orientation blade in the gripper which engages a slot in the top of the subassembly handling head. The orientation blade is an integral part of the gripper housing. The gripper jaws cannot close unless the blade is properly engaged. Once the blade is engaged, the gripper can orient the subassembly into proper angularity by rotation of the mechanism.

The transfer arm operates in conjunction with the subassembly gripper mechanism as shown in Fig. 7.19 to transfer the subassembly to the storage

rack. This operation is described in detail in Sec. 7.9.3.

The gripper used in the cask car (Fig. 7.20) has jaws that are supported by balls that also function as pivots. The jaws are cammed open and closed by a sleeve that is actuated by the relative motion of the two link chains that raise and lower the gripper. These chains have special mating links that provide a rigid configuration that will transmit a downward force as the gripper is lowered. A third link chain is attached to a probe rod in the gripper. The probe rod performs three functions: maintains angular orientation of the subassembly by means of a blade, indicates vertical position of subassembly head in gripper, and performs an interlock function that prevents the gripper jaws from opening when a subassembly is being carried in the gripper.

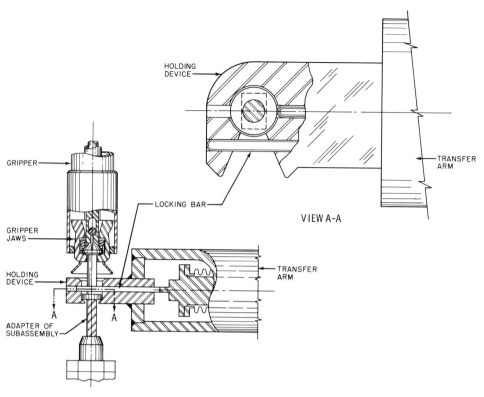

FIG. 7.19—EBR-II subassembly transfer arm [38].

7.8.1.3.2 AMF GRIPPER. The AMF gripper design was the forerunner of the Fermi and other fuel-handling grippers for fast reactors [39]. The gripper jaws are attached to the gripper housing by pins. The gripper incorporates a central indicator bar. Figure 7.21 shows the gripper indicator bar in contact with the top of the subassembly handling head. The gripper is shaped conically inside to guide over the subassembly. The camming surfaces, attached to the indicator bar, keep the jaws in an open position up to the point where the indicator bar touches the handling head. The indicator bar, in turn, is kept in proper position up to this point by the spring. As the gripper is lowered, the indicator bar compresses the spring, and the camming surfaces allow the jaws to close under the handling head self-aligning washer and lock the jaws into place. The weight of the subassembly also keeps the jaws closed. When the jaws have closed, as shown in Fig. 7.23, the limit switch at the upper end of the gripper stops the drive, and the toggle at dead center is locked when the lock drops in place. The gripper housing can now be elevated as a unit with the subassembly in place. Delatching is accomplished by a reverse process. The entire unit is driven down against a fixed surface to open the toggle and the jaws.

To operate under sodium, the limit switches would have to be above the reactor plug or hermetically sealed. The locking arrangement does not appear to be positive.

7.8.1.3.3 FERMI GRIPPER. The Fermi fuel-handling machine (Fig. 7.22), an offset handling mechanism (OHM), is so designed that it is imposible to delatch or release a subassembly in the carry position; i.e., it is necessary to seat the subassembly to complete the delatching operation [25]. Basically, the gripper has two parts: a retainer housing carrying four grapple fingers which hang freely from a collar and a cam collar which moves independently of the assembly and fingers. The assembly is fixed to the end of the offset arm. The cam collar is fixed to a latch-rod assembly through a latch-rod extension and a bell crank linkage which transmits motion of the cam cover to the latch rod assembly at right angles through the offset arm. The latch rod extends through the reciprocating tube terminating at its upper end above the overload plate assembly in a collar. The assembly and collar are located above the reactor rotating plug.

A spring-loaded slide plate with a key slot-shaped opening is fixed to the reciprocating assembly at the approximate level of the collar. The larger opening is sized to pass the collar, and the smaller opening is sized to clear the latch rod. In the delatched position, the collar partially penetrates the larger opening, holding the slide plate cocked.

During the latching sequence the OHM is driven down until the contact head of the gripper contacts the subassembly handling head. As the machine

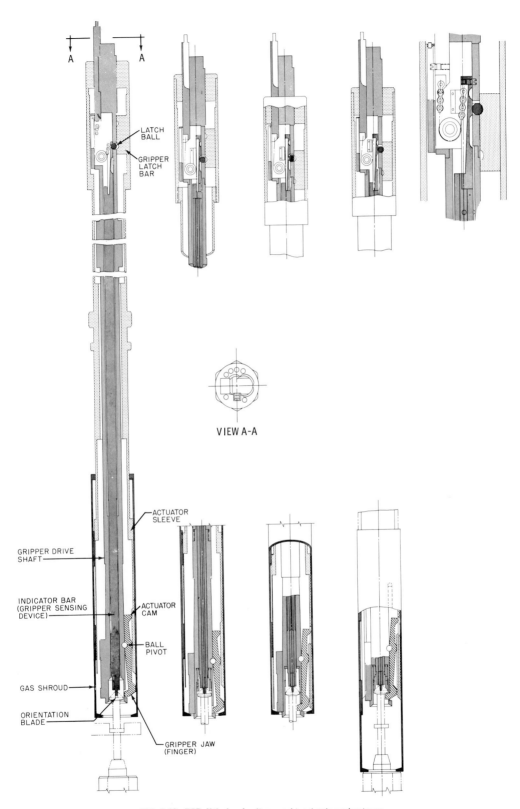

FIG. 7.20—EBR-II fuel-unloading-machine (cask-car) gripper.

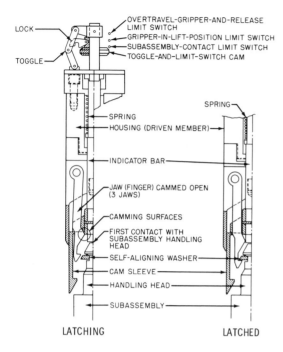

FIG. 7.21—AMF gripper [39].

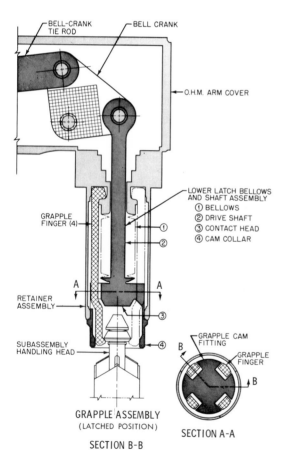

FIG. 7.22—Fermi offset handling-mechanism gripper [25].

continues to move down, the fingers are carried downward with respect to the cam collar causing them to be cammed inward under the proper subassembly handling head. At the upper end of the machine, the reciprocating tube carries the slide plate downward with respect to the latch rod. As the top of the slide plate clears the bottom of the latch-rod collar, the spring pulls the slide plate into the lock position, holding the latch rod–cam collar assembly in the latched position and maintaining the fingers closed. The subassembly can now be raised by raising the OHM.

It is necessary to seat the subassembly in its support plate location and drive the OHM down into the overtravel range to delatch. When the slide plate is clear of the latch-rod collar, the operator can energize a retracting solenoid, which pulls the slideplate back into the cocked position. With the solenoid energized, the OHM is driven up. The weight of the gripper assembly plus the force of a delatch assist spring keeps the contact head in contact with the subassembly handling head. As the reciprocating assembly moves up with respect to the latch-rod collar, the collar passes down into the larger opening again, holding the slide plate in the cocked position. This relative movement cams the grapple fingers open, and, as the OHM continues to drive up, the subassembly is left behind. Once the delatch motion is complete, the solenoid is deenergized. Design of the equipment is such that the slide plate cannot be retracted until the OHM has completed its downward stroke and the slide plate is clear of the latch-rod collar. Thus it is impossible to delatch unless the subassembly is seated so that the latch rod can push against it. It is not possible to drop a subassembly by accident.

FIG. 7.23—Fermi cask-car gripper.

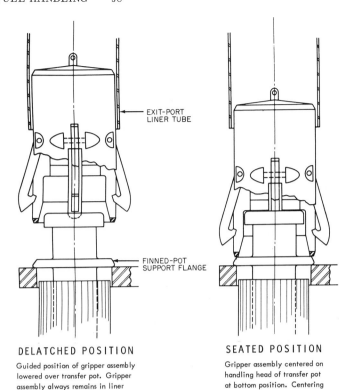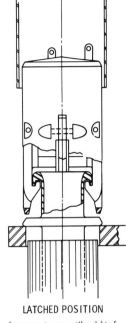

DELATCHED POSITION

Guided position of gripper assembly lowered over transfer pot. Gripper assembly always remains in liner tube. Jaws are spring loaded and will not close if gripper is raised in delatched position.

SEATED POSITION

Gripper assembly centered on handling head of transfer pot at bottom position. Centering skirt prevents pickup. Low-torque limit switch maintains taut cables at all times.

LATCHED POSITION

Jaws cannot open until weight of transfer pot is supported on support flange in cask-car rotor. Interlocks prevent delatch of rotor support unless the gripper is supporting the weight of the transfer pot.

EXIT-PORT LINER TUBE

FINNED-POT SUPPORT FLANGE

FIG. 7.24—Fermi cask-car gripper [25].

7.8.1.3.4 FERMI CASK-CAR GRIPPER. The Fermi cask-car gripper [25] is operated by two cables. The operation of the gripper is shown in Figs. 7.23 and 7.24.

7.8.1.3.5 FERMI STEAM-CLEANING-MACHINE GRIPPER. The Fermi steam-cleaning-machine gripper (Figs. 7.17 and 7.25) operates as a gravity unit with no external mechanical, electrical, hydraulic, or pneumatic actuating devices other than the cable. As the gripper is lowered by the gripper cable, the guide ring is lowered over the finned pot containing a subassembly. The push-rod foot then contacts the subassembly finned pot. The push rod attached to the foot travels in an upward direction carrying the push-rod interlock cam, which actuates the interlock latch-cam roller. The roller is attached to the interlock tube. The tube releases the interlock latch allowing the actuator shaft to move in a vertical direction. As the gas shroud is positioned over the top of the subassembly to prevent the coolant gas from escaping, the actuator-shaft subassembly conical contact head seats on the subassembly head. At this time the subassembly and the actuator shaft are in a fixed position and the gripper housing is moving downward relative to this fixed position. As the gripper housing continues to overtravel, the finger guide cams the fingers into a latched position as shown in the Fig. 7.17 latching sequence. As the gripper housing continues to travel, the lifting cam, the secondary cam, and the positioning cam operate as shown in Fig. 7.17 to vertically position the actuator shaft with respect to the gripper housing. The gripper housing is now moved in an upward vertical direction. The upward motion indexes the cams into the latched position. As this sequence is completed, the push-rod counterweight operates the interlock latch-cam roller moving the interlock tube onto the interlock latch and locking the actuator shaft relative to the gripper housing. The subassembly can now be moved into the cleaning station. For a subassembly to be disengaged, it must be in a stationary position resting at a fixed elevation, and the gripper housing must be overtravelled to index the positioning, secondary, and lifting cams into the unlatched position. The interlock-tube latching and unlatching is the same as described for picking up a subassembly.

The safety latch is provided to stop the drive in the event the subassembly is not properly latched in the gripper. If the cams are not properly engaged, the interlock tube cannot be fully engaged with this interlock latch. In this condition the interlock stop will not recess inside the gripper housing, and, when the gripper is raised, the interlock stop will create a sufficient friction force against the exit port to create an overload on the gripper-cable load-sensing device to stop the drive. A new latching cycle can be initiated by returning the subassembly to the initial fixed position. In the event that the recycling fails, the gripper-cable

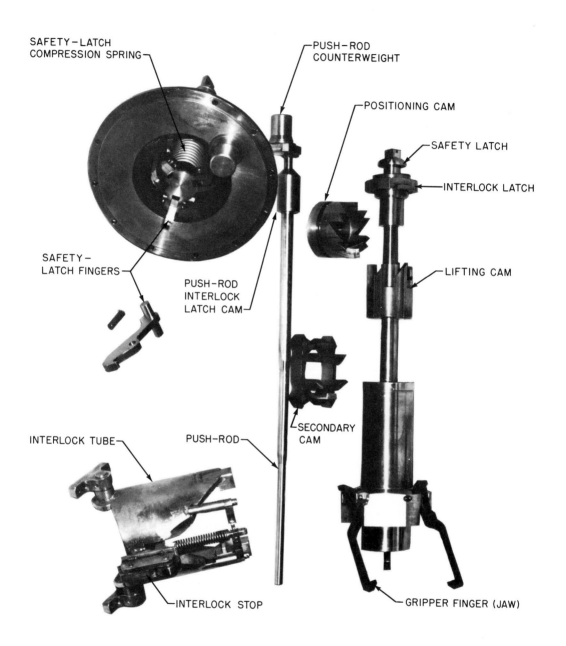

SAFETY–LATCH
COMPRESSION SPRING

PUSH–ROD
COUNTERWEIGHT

POSITIONING CAM

SAFETY LATCH

INTERLOCK LATCH

SAFETY–
LATCH FINGERS

PUSH–ROD
INTERLOCK
LATCH CAM

LIFTING CAM

SECONDARY
CAM

INTERLOCK TUBE

PUSH–ROD

INTERLOCK STOP

GRIPPER FINGER (JAW)

FIG. 7.25—Fermi steam-cleaning-machine gripper details [25].

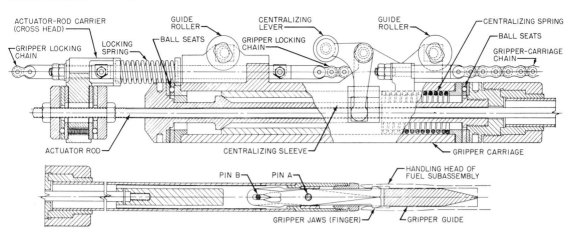

FIG. 7.26—Dounreay fuel-handling-machine gripper and gripper carriage [40].

sensing device can be overridden, and the cable load can be released. When the cable load is released, the preloaded safety-latch actuator spring will actuate the safety-latch fingers to engage the safety latch, thereby allowing the gripper to be moved as a unit with the subassembly engaged in a fail-safe mode.

7.8.1.3.6 DOUNREAY FUEL-HANDLING (CHARGE-MACHINE) GRIPPER.

The Dounreay fuel-handling-machine gripper (Fig. 7.26) is mounted on a vertical carriage driven by a chain anchored at the top and bottom of the carriage [40]. The operation of the chain and the rack tube are described in Sec. 7.9.2. A second chain, operating a push–pull actuator rod, is also attached to the bottom of the actuator-rod carrier and to the crosshead at the top of the actuator rods. The crosshead is loaded by the locking spring to maintain the gripper jaws in a normally open condition with the jaws locked in the subassembly. The second chain can move relative to the carriage carrying chain. The two opposed flat-plate gripper jaws are attached to the gripper carriage by means of a pin (pin A). The actuator rod is connected to another pin (pin B) and, by moving pin B up and down, it locks and unlocks the two jaws which operate internal to the fuel subassembly handling head (top fitting). The end of the gripper carriage carries a tapered gripper guide which aids in case of misalignment, guiding the gripper into the 5/16-in.-radius hole. There is no feeler rod which can feed back positive information as to whether a subassembly is or is not attached to the gripper.

The gripper carriage floats on ball seats, which help align the gripper to the subassembly. The entire carriage is automatically centralized by the centralizing spring as the carriage is raised; a roller and lever arrangement actuate the carriage sleeve.

7.8.1.3.7 DOUNREAY LIDDING-MACHINE GRIPPER.

The Dounreay lidding-machine gripper (Fig. 7.27) is a simple two-jaw gripper that operates with the jaws attached to a raising and lowering mechanism by means of a pin (pin A). The mechanism is raised and lowered by two levers. A third lever raises and lowers a pin (pin B) which actuates the opening and closing of the jaws. Cams operate the levers. The cams are mounted on a cam shaft driven by a worm wheel coupled hermetically to two level gears driven by a motor. The lidding machine is described in Sec. 7.9.2.4.3.

7.8.1.3.8 RAPSODIE FUEL-HANDLING-MACHINE (PRIMARY CASK-CAR) GRIPPER.

The Rapsodie fuel-handling gripper (Fig. 7.28) used on the primary cask car to refuel the reactor is an adaptation of the EBR-II and Fermi grippers [41]. It has four separate movements. There are three jaws (fingers) attached to the body of the gripper. The body of the gripper can be raised, lowered, and rotated. A gripper actuator cams the fingers open and closed. An indicator bar feeds back information as to the presence of the fuel subassembly handling head.

7.8.1.3.9 GRIPPERS FOR MISCELLANEOUS OPERATIONS.

Figures 7.29, 7.30, and 7.31 show several gripper designs that have been used in the handling of reactor elements.

The design shown in Fig. 7.29 consists of two pivoted gripper jaws locked by an advancing sleeve which is actuated by turning a nut. The nut can be turned manually or automatically. The gripper is unlocked by reversing the procedure. Figure 7.30 shows a slotted sleeve in which the members of the gripper act as a spring and snap shut after the gripper jaws have been forced over the reactor element handling head. The gripper jaws are unlocked by inserting an expander and forcing the jaws open. Figure 7.31 shows a ball-latch mechanism adaptable for wire-rope operation. When the hemispheric slotted hook is tilted, it releases the ball. When it is horizontal, it engages the ball.

7.8.2 BEARINGS

Fast reactor fuel-handling equipment may require bearings to perform at elevated temperatures in a liquid metal, in dry inert gas, or in inert gas containing a liquid-metal vapor. The temperatures

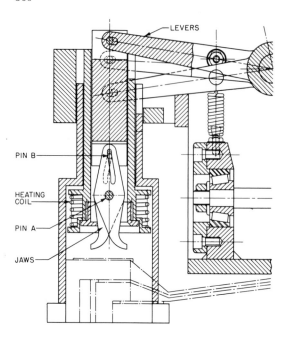

FIG. 7.27—Dounreay lidding-machine gripper [40].

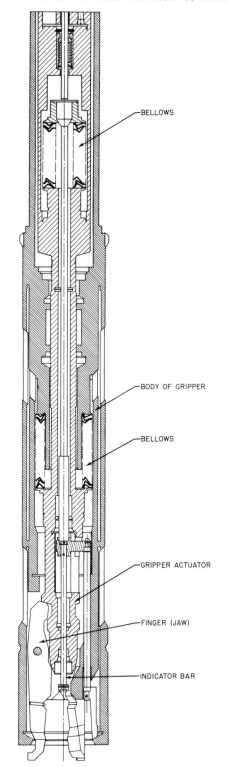

FIG. 7.28—Rapsodie primary cask-car gripper [41].

and nuclear considerations rule out conventional bearings and lubricants for many of these applications. The tendency for many metal combinations to gall or "self-weld" under load in such liquid metals as sodium or NaK has presented problems in material selection. Testing and operating experience, however, have provided some background on usable materials and practices. Some of this background is given in the following sections on wear, bearing materials, sleeve bearings, rolling-element bearings, and wear surfaces.

7.8.2.1 Wear

Metal-to-metal wear is the result of the mechanical interference of minute surface projections or asperities. As two surfaces in contact move past each other, these particles tend to interlock and develop a resistance to the motion. If the force is great enough, the projections will be deformed if the metal is ductile or broken off if it is brittle, and the resistance will be overcome. Repetitive cycling, impact loads, vibration, and fatigue promote wear. Hardness, toughness, and surface smoothness should promote wear resistance. Typical wear patterns include: (1) metal against metal with either sliding or rolling friction, (2) metal against nonmetal or an abrasive with either sliding or rolling friction and impacted or loose abrasive, and (3) metal against liquids or vapors, such as sodium, sodium vapor, inert gas and its contaminants, steam, and water.

7.8.2.2 Bearing Materials

There has been relatively little experience in the use of electrodeposited metal, sprayed metal, hot-dip castings, or ceramic, cermet, and refractory castings in liquid metals. Flame hardening and induction hardening are not generally applicable to

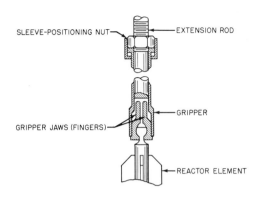

FIG. 7.29—Sleeve type gripper [42].

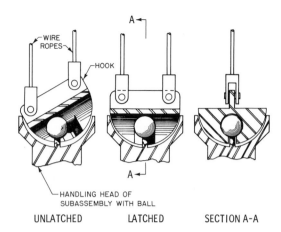

FIG. 7.31—Ball-latch-mechanism gripper [43].

stainless steel, which is a common material used in liquid-metal-cooled reactors. The following observations apply to bearings for liquid-metal applications: (1) contact surfaces should be as hard as possible, (2) the base metal under the contact surface should be hard, (3) surfaces should be highly finished, better than 10 μ in., (4) geometry may have considerable effect, (5) vibration may enhance diffusion bonding, (6) unit loads should be kept well below yield and side and line loadings should be avoided where possible (use end loading), and (7) surface oxide films, particularly those not induced by operation in sodium, may reduce diffusion bonding.

Nitriding of stainless steels has been one of the important methods used in fast reactors to improve their wear characteristics. The process must be carefully controlled, and light cuts should be used

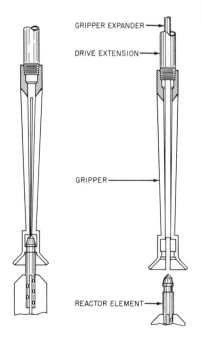

FIG. 7.30—Split sleeve gripper [43].

for final machining prior to nitriding. After the metal has been nitrided, it may be honed for final finish.

Hard facings (i.e., overlays applied by welding) have been used to provide hard surfaces. The facings are usually proprietary alloys with a cobalt base or nickel base or intermetallics. The nickel- and cobalt-base facings have been used more than intermetallic facings.

Contacting parts in which one surface bears on another should be designed to be compatible for the intended service to prevent galling and diffusion bonding or to reduce the effects of crevice corrosion or fretting corrosion. Loads should be spread over large surfaces to reduce pressures below diffusion-bonding limits.

Various approaches are used to overcome seizing and galling. Dissimilar materials can be used for mating surfaces, one surface soft and the other hard. In a soft—hard combination, the soft material usually wears in preference to the hard material. This approach works best where motion is repetitive and where conditions for diffusion bonding do not occur.

Another solution to the galling problem is to operate two hard surfaces against each other, in which case the friction and wear are usually less than for a soft—hard combination. This approach is worth investigating for cases where diffusion bonding may occur under steady-state loadings. The use of a lubricant between two hard surfaces, where this is possible, reduces both friction and wear. The possibility of incorporating into one of the surfaces a compatible solid lubricant is under exploration.

A series of tests conducted for APDA provided guides for the use of compatible bearing materials at Fermi [44]. In these tests the flat surface of a 1-in.-diameter sample was rotated under load against the flat surface of another sample. The tests were conducted under sodium at temperatures up to 1000°F and under loads up to 10,000 psi. Of 33 metal combinations tested, the best performance was observed from the following combinations: Inconel X vs. Inconel X, Stellite 6 vs. Colmonoy 6, Malcomized 347 stainless steel vs. 304 stainless steel, Stellite 6 vs. Stellite 6, and nitrided 347 stainless steel vs. nitrided 347 stainless steel.

Tests conducted by Pratt & Whitney Company, Inc., showed the following combinations to be promising: Kentanium 138a vs. Carboloy, 80 wt.% TiC and 20 wt.% Co vs. 91 wt.% WC and 9 wt.% Co, Stellite 6 (used in valve seats with 1200°F lithium) vs. Stellite 2, Stellite 6 (used in valve seats with 1200°F lithium) vs. Mo and 0.5 wt.% Ti, and 75 wt.% Mo and 25 wt.% CbC applied as a weld overlay on stainless steel.

Tests conducted by Battelle Memorial Institute showed the following combinations to have promise (the coefficient of kinetic friction is given in parentheses): molybdenum vs. molybdenum (0.42), TiC vs. Ti, tungsten vs. tungsten (0.39), TiC vs. TiC (0.30), Stellite 6 vs. hard chrome on stainless steel, and WC vs. WC (0.40).

7.8.2.3 Sleeve Bearings

Tests and equipment operation have shown the feasibility of sleeve-bearing applications in liquid metals. Several test programs [45, 46] have shown that liquid metals behave in accordance with established hydrodynamic principles in much the same manner as a conventional lubricant. In general, existing experience with sleeve bearings in liquid metals has been with larger clearances than are ordinarily used with conventional lubricants.

The sodium overflow pumps at Fermi have sleeve bearings with a Colmonoy 6 on both the shaft and the journal. The shaft is 3.607 in. in diameter, and the nominal diametral clearance in the bearing is 0.018 in. Two of these bearings remain submerged in sodium, and two are alternately submerged in sodium and exposed to argon. These bearings have been operated in service repeatedly at speeds from 0 to 830 rpm with satisfactory results.

The No. 1 primary sodium pump at Fermi has Colmonoy 6 vs. Colmonoy 6 in the sleeve bearings that operate in sodium. The No. 2 and 3 pumps have Colmonoy 5 journals vs. a Colmonoy 6 shaft. The shaft is 12.000 in. in diameter, and the nominal diametral clearance is 0.020 in. The pumps have seen extensive use up to 700 rpm in sodium during test-facility operation with satisfactory results.

The Fermi oscillator rod and drive shaft has three sleeve bearings and one conical bearing that operate in sodium. The two sleeve bearings on the drive shaft are 1 3/4 in. in diameter and have a nominal diametral clearance of 0.005 in. These bearings originally had Colmonoy 4 on the shaft and Ampco 22 sleeves. The sleeves wore excessively during testing and were changed to Stellite 6B. The top sleeve bearing on the rod is 2.100 in. in diameter and has a nominal diametral clearance of 0.006 in. The shaft is overlaid with Colmonoy 4 and the sleeve, with Colmonoy 70. These bearings are designed for speeds from 0.06 to 600 rpm. The lower bearing on the rod is a conical thrust bearing. The fixed male portion is Kennametal 95. The rotating female section is Kentanium 138a.

7.8.2.4 Rolling-element Bearings

The following are examples of the use of rolling-element bearings in liquid-metal environments. At Dounreay, the control-rod drives have ball screws that operate under NaK. The Dounreay oscillator rod has ball bearings and needle bearings that operate under NaK. The ball bearing is located at the lower end of the rod and has balls of approximately 3/16-in. diameter on approximately 5/8-in. pitch. The needle bearing is located at the upper end of the rod, and it has needle rollers on a pitch of approximately 3/4 in.

The EBR-II oscillator is a reciprocating type, and it employs two ball bushings that function under sodium. The bushings accommodate a maximum stroke of 8 in. and 0.05 to 120 cycles/min. The balls in the bushings are stainless steel, and the shaft is 440C stainless steel. The shaft is 3/4 in. in diameter, and the clearance between the shaft and the bushing balls is 0.0005 to 0.0015 in. This application has been successfully tested in sodium at 50 to 100 cycles/min for over 500,000 cycles.

7.8.2.5 Wear Surfaces

In addition to bearings, there are a number of other wear surfaces in reactor designs. These include surfaces on grippers, fuel supports, guides, load supports, face seals, and valve seats.

Following are some examples of the materials used at Fermi for specific applications: The hold-down fingers have Stellite 6 inlays where the fingers contact the nitrided 304 stainless steel heads of the fuel assemblies. The nitrided 304 stainless steel nozzles on the fuel and blanket assemblies are guided in holes of nitrided 347 stainless steel in the upper support plate and of Stellite 6B bushings in the lower support plate. The Fermi offset handling-mechanism gripper has fingers of Stellite 3 operated by a cam surface of Colmonoy 5. Guide pads of Stellite 6 on the offset handling mechanism offset arm slide under sodium against guide strips of Stellite 6B. The offset handling mechanism face seal, located in an argon-gas space, has Colmonoy 6 vs. Colmonoy 6. Ni-Resist was selected for several dry-argon areas because of its self-lubricating properties. Stellite was used for the seats in a number of valve applications for sodium service.

7.8.3 SEALS

The environmental conditions internal to the sodium-cooled fast reactor, combined with safety consideration, make mandatory the use of high-integrity seals for isolation of the reactor primary system from the external environment. Two major considerations are involved: preventing contamination of the sodium system with oxygen and other contaminants and preventing radioactive sodium vapor, argon, or any gaseous fission products from escaping the reactor through the fuel-handling equipment.

Seals are required for machines with rotary or reciprocating motion; the seals should, of course, be located at the point where the machine penetrates the reactor. The seals used for these applications should be leaktight, highly reliable, easily replaced or serviced, capable of being made or broken remotely or semi-remotely for maintenance, and as simple and inexpensive as possible. Such seals include the standard packing gland using square or chevron rings, the nested reciprocating metal bellows, the flexible diaphragm seal used in the Dounreay reactor, and other completely sealed units, such as the magnetic drive at Dounreay or harmonic drives.

7.8.3.1 Seals for Reciprocating Motions

Reciprocating motions, in general, are sealed either by packing glands or reciprocating metal bellows, as in Fermi and EBR-II. Dounreay has avoided bellows seals and has used nutating seals. Development of the E-span bellows has made possible reliable sealing of long-stroke reciprocating motions with large savings in overall compressed length of bellows as compared with the more familiar roll-formed bellows.

7.8.3.2 Seals for Rotary Motion

For rotary motion the packing gland, with or without gas bleed, can be used. Various forms of the rotary face seal are possible. Two versions of this seal are used in the Fermi reactor. The rotating shield plug uses a U type closure seal which is pressurized and depends on friction contact produced by deforming lubricated rubber lips against a flat face for sealing action. This seal has been used successfully on a 128-in.-diameter horizontal surface. Another type of rotary face seal is used in the Fermi offset handling mechanism to seal the azimuth tube motion. In this application it is not a true seal but acts more as a diffusion barrier. This seal is composed of two metal surfaces of Colmonoy lapped together. Provision is made for gas bleed through this seal, if required, to prevent leakage from the primary system.

7.8.3.3 Liquid-metal Seals

Fermi, EBR-II, Dounreay, and Rapsodie use variations of a liquid-metal seal. Fermi has provisions for a NaK dip seal that is molten at all times and forms a seal for the rotating shield plug. Dounreay, on the other hand, uses a sodium–mercury amalgam seal that is frozen during reactor operation and is liquid only during refueling operations. EBR-II uses a bismuth–tin alloy dip seal in both plugs. When the EBR-II seal is not fully molten, it is kept frozen on top and molten across the bottom of the dip seal. This seals off the gases that might leak through any imperfect bonding between the frozen alloy and the seal body. Rapsodie uses a tin–bismuth alloy to seal the plugs and an inflatable rubber seal outside the liquid seal.

7.8.3.4 Static Seals

Static seals are, in general, not as much of a problem as dynamic seals. The types most used are standard rubber or metal gaskets, packing glands, and rubber or metal O-rings. The primary difficulty in the selection of static seals is environment. For seals that must operate under sodium, stainless-steel O-rings are used. It is difficult to achieve a positive seal with metal O-rings because small irregularities in the groove are not easily filled in, and they form leakage paths. Proper

groove design and care in fabrication are necessary to achieve good seals with metal O-rings. Surface finish of the groove, in particular, is critical. Lapped surfaces are generally used. Where temperature and atmosphere permit, synthetic rubber or plastics, such as Teflon and nylon, can be used with good results and have the advantage of greater compressibility to assist in filling in irregularities in the sealing surfaces.

7.8.3.5 Maintenance

A major problem in designing seals for fuel-handling machinery is that of replacement or repair after the reactor has been in operation and the system has become radioactive. In some areas where a seal communicates directly with the primary system, e.g., the seal on refueling-port plugs, rather elaborate designs may be used to permit making and breaking such seals remotely to maintain system integrity. Similar problems are encountered when it is necessary to service or replace a major component. Seals should be located in accessible areas and in such a manner that replacement, if possible, be nonradioactive.

7.9 Description of Existing Fuel-handling Systems

7.9.1 INTRODUCTION

The fuel-handling cycles of the following reactor systems are described in the succeeding sections: UKAEA Dounreay Fast Reactor, ANL EBR-II, Enrico Fermi Atomic Power Plant, and the French AEC Rapsodie reactor. Each system is briefly described; a list of components and facilities used is included; the handling sequence is summarized; and finally the fuel-handling equipment is described in some detail. Table 7.1 lists the characteristics of each fuel-handling system.

7.9.2 DOUNREAY FUEL HANDLING

7.9.2.1 Fuel-handling-system Summary

The fuel cycle for Dounreay is shown in Fig. 7.32. The system employs double rotating plugs and two movable charge machines to insert and remove fuel from the reactor core. Before irradiated subassemblies are removed from the reactor building, they are sealed in cans that contain lead as a decay-heat transfer media. A shielded transit cask (interbuilding coffin) is used to move canned subassemblies, one at a time, out of the reactor building to a molten-lead bath where the lead in the can is melted and any NaK adhering to the can surface is removed. Canned subassemblies are stored in a water decay pool and are subsequently shipped to a reprocessing plant. New fuel subassemblies are placed in cans before their transfer to the reactor building to facilitate the handling operations in the reactor building.

7.9.2.2 List of Components

The main components of the Dounreay fuel-handling system are the reactor (Fig. 7.33), the charge

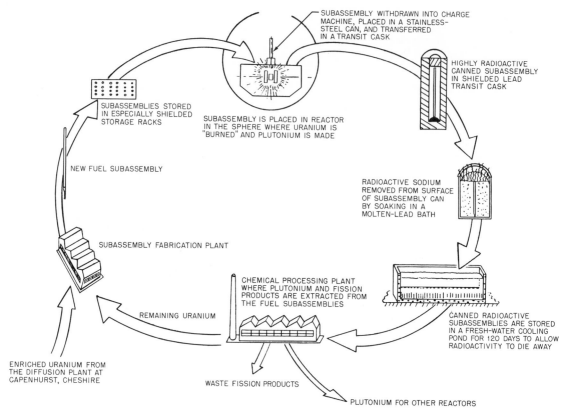

SUBASSEMBLY WITHDRAWN INTO CHARGE
MACHINE, PLACED IN A STAINLESS-
STEEL CAN, AND TRANSFERRED
IN A TRANSIT CASK

HIGHLY RADIOACTIVE
CANNED SUBASSEMBLY
IN SHIELDED LEAD
TRANSIT CASK

SUBASSEMBLIES STORED
IN ESPECIALLY SHIELDED
STORAGE RACKS

SUBASSEMBLY IS PLACED IN REACTOR
IN THE SPHERE WHERE URANIUM IS
"BURNED" AND PLUTONIUM IS MADE

NEW FUEL SUBASSEMBLY

RADIOACTIVE SODIUM
REMOVED FROM SURFACE
OF SUBASSEMBLY CAN
BY SOAKING IN A
MOLTEN-LEAD BATH

SUBASSEMBLY FABRICATION PLANT

CHEMICAL PROCESSING PLANT
WHERE PLUTONIUM AND FISSION
PRODUCTS ARE EXTRACTED FROM
THE FUEL SUBASSEMBLIES

REMAINING URANIUM

CANNED RADIOACTIVE
SUBASSEMBLIES ARE STORED
IN A FRESH-WATER COOLING
POND FOR 120 DAYS TO ALLOW
RADIOACTIVITY TO DIE AWAY

ENRICHED URANIUM FROM
THE DIFFUSION PLANT AT
CAPENHURST, CHESHIRE

WASTE FISSION PRODUCTS

PLUTONIUM FOR OTHER REACTORS

FIG. 7.32—Dounreay fuel-handling cycle [40].

machine (Figs. 7.34 and 7.35), hermetic coupling (Fig. 7.36), adapter valve and clamp (Fig. 7.37), canning station (Fig. 7.38), lidding machine (Fig. 7.39), transit cask (Fig. 7.40), lead bath (Fig. 7.41), pool cask car (Fig. 7.42), and cans and canning vessel (Figs. 7.43 and 7.44).

7.9.2.3   Fuel-handling Sequence

New fuel and blanket subassemblies are received from the fabricator by truck at the element storage building. The shipping containers are unloaded from the truck with a crane and are transported on a bogie to the new element storage area (Fig. 7.45). The fuel subassemblies are unloaded by hand from the shipping containers and stored in locked racks. The blanket subassemblies are unloaded by hand and stored in stacked wooden trays. Before a subassembly is transferred to the reactor building, it is placed in a lead-lined fuel subassembly can filled with nitrogen and sealed with a push-on lid. This operation is performed in a canning vessel in the new subassembly storage area. Canned subassemblies are placed, four at a time, in transit boxes. The boxes are raised by a crane to the air-lock platform and conveyed through the air lock into the reactor building by a transit cask trolley.

Inside the reactor building, the building crane lifts the transit box to the magazine end of the canning station, and the canned subassemblies are charged by hand into the magazine (Fig. 7.38). The

canned subassemblies in the magazine are charged singly into the shielded trolley inside the canning station which transfers the can to the lidding-machine position. The lidding machine removes and retains the can lid. The shielded trolley then transfers the can to the charge-machine position where the subassembly is extracted from the can and lifted into the charge machine. The empty can remains in the shielded trolley. The charge machine is moved by the building crane to the reactor, where it is positioned on the adapter valve that is temporarily mounted at a charge hole position on the inner rotating-shield plug. The inner rotating-shield plug is eccentric with an outer rotating-shield plug so that the charge hole can be moved over any core subassembly position (Fig. 7.33). The charge machine inserts the new subassembly into an empty core position. The rotating-shield plugs are repositioned to align the charge hole with the next irradiated subassembly to be removed, and the subassembly is lifted into the charge machine. Meanwhile, a second charge machine containing an irradiated subassembly has been returned to the canning station over the charge-machine position, and the subassembly is lowered into the empty can. The shielded trolley containing the can with the subassembly is returned to the lidding-machine position, where the can lid is brazed in place. The shielded trolley horizontally conveys the canned subassembly to a transit-cask (interbuilding coffin) position in the canning station, where the subassem-

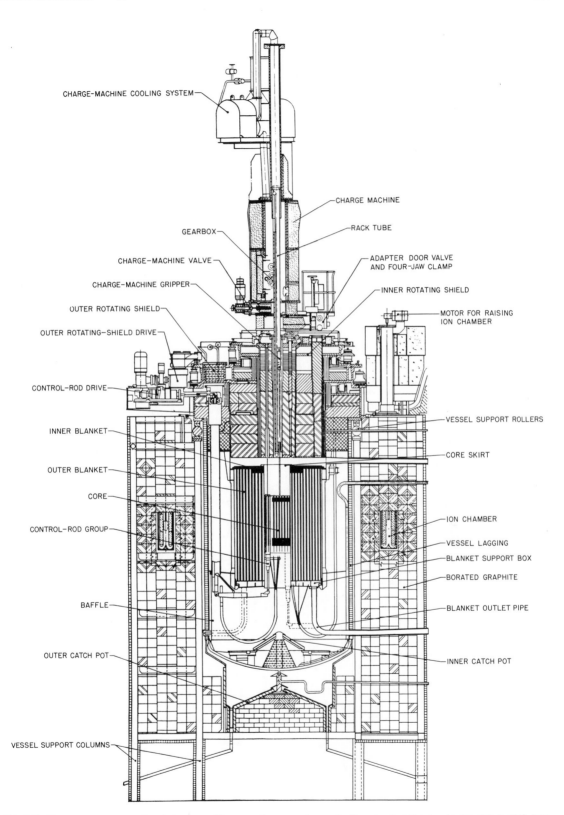

CHARGE-MACHINE COOLING SYSTEM

CHARGE MACHINE

GEARBOX

RACK TUBE

CHARGE-MACHINE VALVE

ADAPTER DOOR VALVE
AND FOUR-JAW CLAMP

CHARGE-MACHINE GRIPPER

INNER ROTATING SHIELD

OUTER ROTATING SHIELD

MOTOR FOR RAISING
ION CHAMBER

OUTER ROTATING-SHIELD DRIVE

CONTROL-ROD DRIVE

VESSEL SUPPORT ROLLERS

INNER BLANKET

CORE SKIRT

OUTER BLANKET

CORE

ION CHAMBER

CONTROL-ROD GROUP

VESSEL LAGGING

BLANKET SUPPORT BOX

BORATED GRAPHITE

BAFFLE

BLANKET OUTLET PIPE

OUTER CATCH POT

INNER CATCH POT

VESSEL SUPPORT COLUMNS

FIG. 7.33—Dounreay reactor vessel and charge-machine general arrangement. (From J. Tatlock et al., in Proceedings of the Symposium on the Dounreay Fast Reactor, London, Dec. 7, 1960, Institution of Mechanical Engineers, London, 1961.)

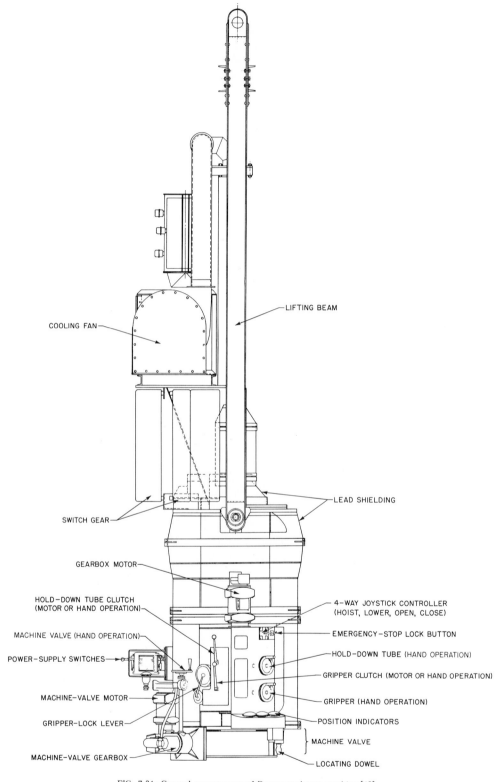

LIFTING BEAM

COOLING FAN

LEAD SHIELDING

SWITCH GEAR

GEARBOX MOTOR

HOLD-DOWN TUBE CLUTCH
(MOTOR OR HAND OPERATION)

4-WAY JOYSTICK CONTROLLER
(HOIST, LOWER, OPEN, CLOSE)

MACHINE VALVE (HAND OPERATION)

EMERGENCY-STOP LOCK BUTTON

POWER-SUPPLY SWITCHES

HOLD-DOWN TUBE (HAND OPERATION)

GRIPPER CLUTCH (MOTOR OR HAND OPERATION)

MACHINE-VALVE MOTOR

GRIPPER (HAND OPERATION)

GRIPPER-LOCK LEVER

POSITION INDICATORS

MACHINE VALVE

MACHINE-VALVE GEARBOX

LOCATING DOWEL

FIG. 7.34—General arrangement of Dounreay charge machine [40].

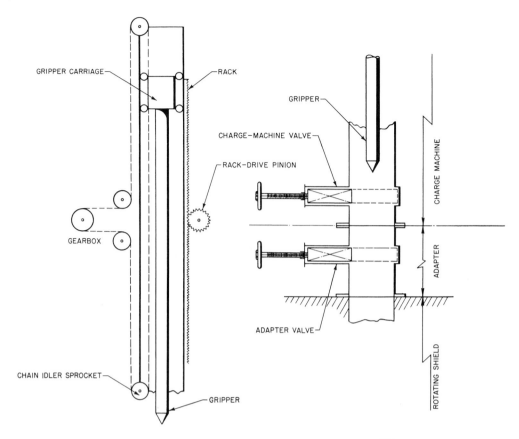

FIG. 7.35—Dounreay charge-machine arrangement diagram [40].

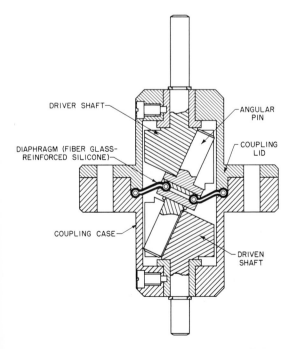

FIG. 7.36—Dounreay charge-machine hermetic coupling [40].

bly is raised vertically into a transit cask (Fig. 7.40).

The transit cask is returned to the air lock by the building crane; it passes through the air lock on the trolley and is carried by the 30-ton crane to the subassembly storage building. The 30-ton crane transports the cask to the lead-bath floor and positions the cask over a bath (Fig. 7.41). The canned subassembly is lowered into the bath, and the transit cask is returned to the canning station. The canned subassembly is immersed in the bath for approximately 1 hr to completely melt the lead in the can and to remove any NaK adhering to the outside of the can. The canned subassembly is removed from the lead bath by the pool cask car (Fig. 7.42). The pool cask car conveys the canned subassembly to the radioactive-subassembly decay storage pool and deposits it into one of the storage racks. The period of decay in the storage pool depends upon the degree of irradiation of the subassembly.

After decay the canned subassembly is removed from the pool, moved into the subassembly storage building by the pool cask car, and lowered into the subassembly off-loading bay. The cask car is moved away, and a shipping cask is positioned on top of the off-loading bay. The canned subassembly is raised into the shipping cask, which is then picked up by the 30-ton crane and lowered onto a

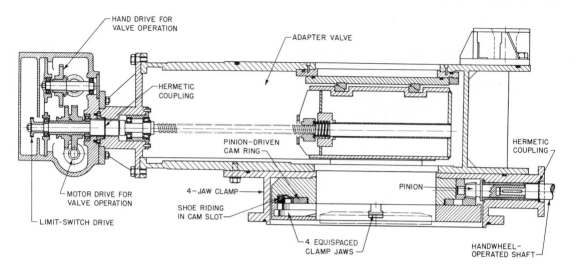

FIG. 7.37—Dounreay charge-machine adapter valve and clamp [40].

special road vehicle for transport to the fuel-reprocessing plant.

7.9.2.4 Fuel-handling Equipment

7.9.2.4.1 CHARGE MACHINE (FUEL-HANDLING MACHINE). Two identical charge machines are used for transporting new and irradiated subassemblies between the canning station and the reactor (Figs. 7.34 and 7.35). Each machine carries one fuel subassembly or one blanket subassembly. Both machines can be positioned and sealed directly to the two charge-machine transfer valves located over the canning station. An adapter valve is re-

quired to position a charge machine on the reactor plug, and only one machine at a time can be placed on the plug.

7.9.2.4.1.1 General Description. A diagrammatic sketch of the charge machine is shown in Fig. 7.35. The machine is 22 ft high and weighs 25 tons. The main working parts of the machine are the rack tube and rack-tube guide, the gripper and gripper carriage, the hold-down tube and carriage, the gearbox, the machine valve, and the cooling system.

The rack tube, hold-down tube, and gripper work on a telescopic arrangement, the rack tube being the

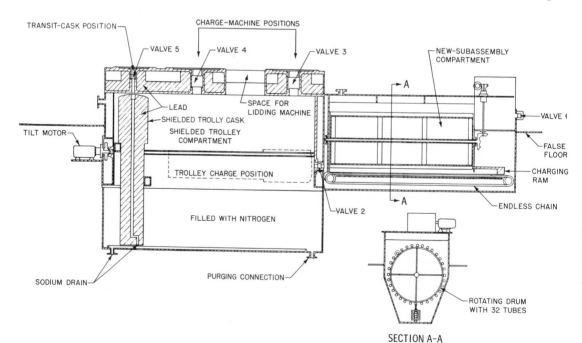

SECTION A-A

FIG. 7.38—Dounreay subassembly canning station [40].

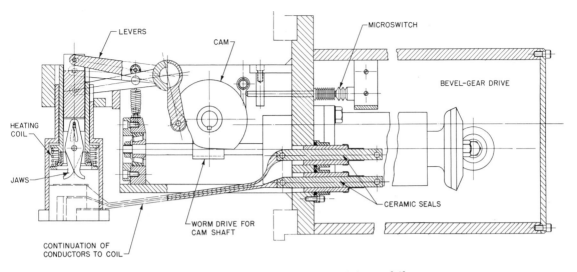

FIG. 7.39—Dounreay lidding-machine sectional elevation [40].

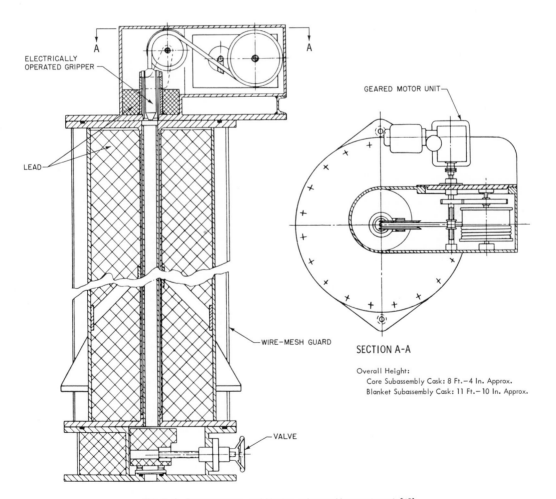

FIG. 7.40—Dounreay core- and blanket-subassembly transit cask [40].

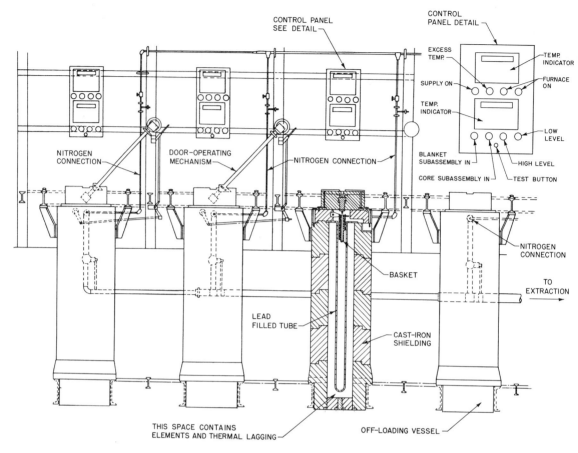

FIG. 7.41—Dounreay arrangement of lead baths and off-loading vessel [40].

outside member and the gripper the inside member. The function of the gripper is to lift the selected subassembly. In the fully extended position the complete gripper is below the rack tube. In the retracted position the gripper and subassembly are within the rack tube in the charge-machine body. The hold-down tube rests on the six subassemblies that surround the one being lifted and prevents them from being dislodged. A periscope is provided on the charge machine so a subassembly can be viewed through slots in the rack tube after it has been lifted from the core.

7.9.2.4.1.2 Rack Tube and Rack-tube Guide. The rack tube is 17 ft 7 in. long and is made of stainless steel. It is guided inside the rack-tube guide by rollers and is driven up and down by a pinion engaging the rack on the tube. At the bottom of its travel in the reactor, the lower end of the rack tube dips below the NaK surface. Slots have been provided in the lower portion of the tube to allow free flow of cooling nitrogen down the tube without bubbling nitrogen through the NaK.

7.9.2.4.1.3 Gripper and Gripper Carriage. The gripper, gripper carriage and jaws (Fig. 7.26) are 6 ft 1 3/8 in. long overall. The carriage, located

above the gripper, is guided inside the rack tube on three sets of rollers. The gripper is driven up and down by an endless chain. Different grippers are used for handling fuel and blanket subassemblies, and a bayonet socket is provided in the unit to facilitate changeover. Jaws operated by a push—pull rod engage the subassembly lifting head internally. When the gripper is handling core subassemblies, it is lowered a distance of 15 ft and enters a hole 0.54 in. in diameter in the top of the subassembly. The positional accuracy required at the gripper tip is 1 1/6 in. from a true vertical axis when the gripper is fully extended. Section 7.8.1.3.6 has detailed information on the gripper.

7.9.2.4.1.4 Hold-down Tube and Carriage. The hold-down tube and its carriage ride in the rack tube in the same way as the gripper and gripper carriage, but just below it. The tube fits over the gripper, and at the bottom of its travel it rests on the six elements surrounding the one to be lifted. The tube is left lowered while the gripper is raised to prevent the subassembly being removed from dislodging any adjacent subassemblies. The tube is raised and lowered by a chain drive, and it is arranged to follow any radial motion of the gripper. The hold-down tube is removed when the charge machine is handling blanket subassemblies.

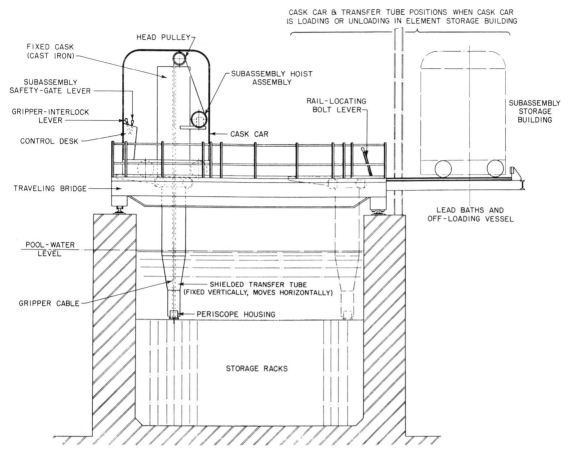

CASK CAR & TRANSFER TUBE POSITIONS WHEN CASK CAR
IS LOADING OR UNLOADING IN ELEMENT STORAGE BUILDING

FIXED CASK
(CAST IRON)

HEAD PULLEY

SUBASSEMBLY HOIST
ASSEMBLY

RAIL-LOCATING
BOLT LEVER

SUBASSEMBLY
STORAGE
BUILDING

SUBASSEMBLY
SAFETY-GATE LEVER

GRIPPER-INTERLOCK
LEVER

CONTROL DESK

CASK CAR

TRAVELING BRIDGE

LEAD BATHS AND
OFF-LOADING VESSEL

POOL-WATER
LEVEL

SHIELDED TRANSFER TUBE
(FIXED VERTICALLY, MOVES HORIZONTALLY)

GRIPPER CABLE

PERISCOPE HOUSING

STORAGE RACKS

FIG. 7.42—Dounreay pool cask car [40].

SECTION OF FUEL SUBASSEMBLY IN CAN SHOWING LEAD BEFORE MELTING

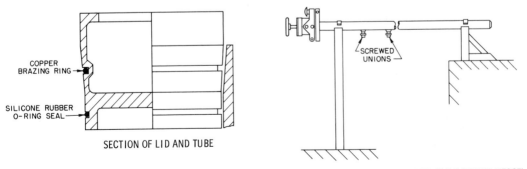

COPPER
BRAZING RING

SILICONE RUBBER
O-RING SEAL

SECTION OF LID AND TUBE

SCREWED
UNIONS

ARRANGEMENT OF NEW SUBASSEMBLY CANNING VESSEL

FIG. 7.43—Dounreay subassembly can and canning vessel [40].

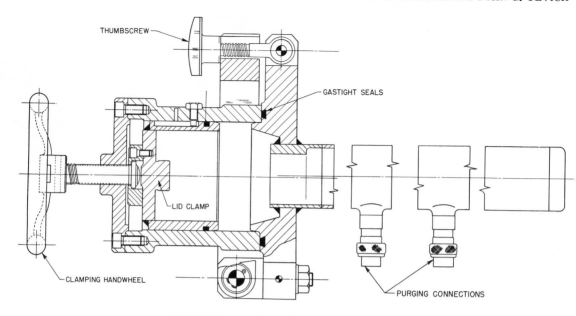

FIG. 7.44—Dounreay subassembly canning vessel details [40].

7.9.2.4.1.5 Gearbox. The machine gearbox actuates the rack tube, gripper carriage, hold-down tube, and gripper-release mechanism. All drives into parts of the machine that may contain radioactive gases have hermetically sealed couplings (Fig. 7.36). When the gripper tube is driven to within 5 ft of the core, the gripper tube and hold-down tube are changed from power to hand operation to avoid damage that could occur from misalignment of the entering subassembly.

7.9.2.4.1.6 Machine Valves. The charge-machine valve is shown in Fig. 7.46. It is normally bolted to the bottom of the fuel-handling machine

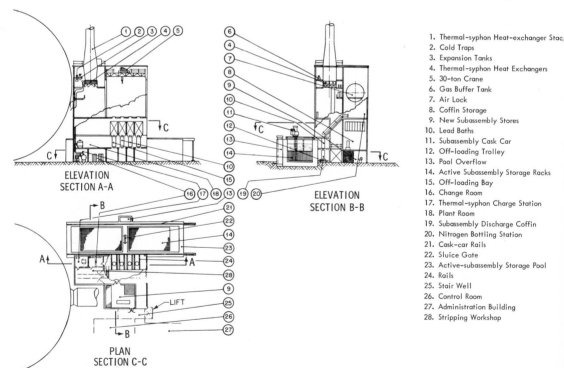

1. Thermal-syphon Heat-exchanger Stac
2. Cold Traps
3. Expansion Tanks
4. Thermal-syphon Heat Exchangers
5. 30-ton Crane
6. Gas Buffer Tank
7. Air Lock
8. Coffin Storage
9. New Subassembly Stores
10. Lead Baths
11. Subassembly Cask Car
12. Off-loading Trolley
13. Pool Overflow
14. Active Subassembly Storage Racks
15. Off-loading Bay
16. Change Room
17. Thermal-syphon Charge Station
18. Plant Room
19. Subassembly Discharge Coffin
20. Nitrogen Bottling Station
21. Cask-car Rails
22. Sluice Gate
23. Active-subassembly Storage Pool
24. Rails
25. Stair Well
26. Control Room
27. Administration Building
28. Stripping Workshop

FIG. 7.45—Dounreay subassembly storage building and pool [40].

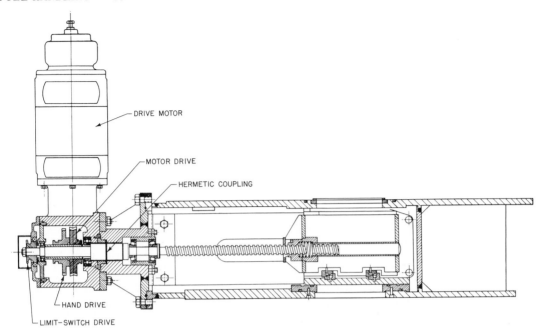

FIG. 7.46—Dounreay charge-machine valve [40].

and is designed to seal off the machine interior from the atmosphere. It contains a lead-filled sliding door operated by a motor drive. When the valve is closed, a wedging action forces down the bottom face of the door to complete two O-ring seals. Two dowels on the lower side of the valve structure align the valve when it is positioned on the adapter valve (described below).

7.9.2.4.1.7 Cooling System. The maximum heat generated from an irradiated core subassembly is about 2.5 kw for the first several cores. Forced convection cooling is provided to maintain safe temperatures. Two d-c motor-driven centrifugal fans, arranged in parallel, circulate 350 cu ft/min of argon down the inside of the rack tube, over the subassembly, and up into the body of the machine, from which it is drawn through a heat exchanger back to the input side of the fans. The two fans are designed to operate normally under half load, but, in the event of an electrical or mechanical failure of one fan, the remaining motor will automatically come up to full speed. Two axial-flow fans draw air over the argon heat exchanger for final heat rejection to the atmosphere.

7.9.2.4.2 ADAPTER VALVE. The function of the adapter valve is to maintain the argon atmosphere above the core during removal of the charge-hole plug and during charge and discharge operations (Fig. 7.33). The adapter valve, designed to seal to the charging hole, contains a sliding valve similar to the charge-machine valve (Fig. 7.37). At the beginning of a charge–discharge operation, the adapter valve is positioned and sealed over the charge hole. The plug is removed into a cask, and a liner tube is lowered from a cask into the charge hole. The charge machine is then positioned and

sealed on top of the adapter valve. Air is purged from between the adapter valve and the machine valve, and both valves are opened. The charge machine may then be used to insert and remove elements from the reactor. Whenever the charge machine is to be removed from the reactor, the adapter valve is closed to maintain the argon atmosphere in the reactor. The adapter valve is also used with the special-equipment handling casks.

7.9.2.4.3 CANNING STATION. The canning station is located inside the reactor building (Fig. 7.38). The station is used for the following functions: (1) to introduce new subassemblies into the charge machines, (2) to remove irradiated subassemblies from the charge machines, (3) to can and seal irradiated subassemblies in lead-lined subassembly cans, (4) to transfer canned irradiated subassemblies to transit casks, and (5) to maintain an argon atmosphere during transfers to the charge machines to avoid introducing oxygen into the reactor.

The canning station consists of two gastight compartments, one called the new subassembly compartment and the other called the shielded-trolley compartment. The two compartments are built in line and are joined by a valve.

7.9.2.4.3.1 New-subassembly Compartment. The new-subassembly compartment contains a horizontal-drum magazine with 32 tubes around its circumference. Each tube will accept one new subassembly contained in a lead-lined element can. The center of the magazine contains a neutron-absorbing material to assure subcriticality under all conditions. The magazine is motor driven and automatically aligned. Identification of subassemblies is by visual inspection through a window in the compartment. New canned subassemblies are loaded into the magazine by hand one at a time through a gastight valve (Valve 1). A manually operated ram is mounted so that it enters the bottom tube of the magazine and pushes a canned new subassembly through the connecting valve into the shielded-trolley compartment.

7.9.2.4.3.2 Shielded-trolley Compartment. The shielded-trolley compartment contains a shielded cask mounted on trunnions on a trolley so that it can be moved the length of the compartment and can be pivoted to either a horizontal or a vertical position. In the horizontal position the cask can be positioned in line with the bottom magazine tube so that the ram can push a canned new subassembly into the cask. In the vertical position the cask can be positioned under any one of three shielded transfer valves (Valves 3, 4, and 5) or under a lidding machine, all located in the top of the shielded-trolley compartment.

7.9.2.4.3.3 Shielded Transfer Valves. Two of the shielded transfer valves accommodate charge machines and the third one is for a transit cask. The shielded-trolley compartment is reinforced to carry the combined weights of two charge machines (25 tons each) and a transit cask (7 tons) during subassembly charge and discharge operations.

7.9.2.4.3.4 Lidding Machine. The lidding machine is installed between the two charge-machine transfer valves (Fig. 7.38). The machine remotely handles and brazes subassembly can lids (Fig. 7.39). The machine removes and retains the lid from a new subassembly can. When the can is returned with an irradiated subassembly, the machine replaces the lid and seals the can by brazing the lid in place.

7.9.2.4.3.5 Canning-station Operating Sequence. The operating sequence of the canning station is as follows. The two compartments are isolated by closing the connecting valve, Valve 2 in Fig. 7.38. The new subassembly compartment is purged of argon and filled with air. The loading valve (Valve 1) is opened, and canned new subassemblies are loaded one at a time into the magazine. When the magazine is full, the loading valve is closed, and the compartment is purged of air and filled with argon. The shielded trolley cask is then moved to its horizontal position in line with the valve that connects with the compartment (Valve 2). This valve is opened, and a canned new subassembly is pushed into the trolley cask with the ram. The trolley cask is rotated to the vertical position and moved to the lidding-machine position, where the can lid is removed. The cask is then moved under a transfer-valve position that is occupied by an empty charge machine, and the valve on the canning station and the valve on the charge machine are opened. The charge machine gripper is lowered, and the subassembly is lifted into the charge machine leaving the can behind. The valves are closed, and the valve interspace is purged. The charge machine is then moved to the reactor, and the trolley cask is moved to the transfer valve where the other charge machine containing an irradiated subassembly is positioned. The machine

and compartment valves are opened, and the irradiated subassembly is lowered into the can. Then the valves are closed, and the trolley cask is moved to the lidding machine, where the can lid is inserted and brazed in place. The trolley cask is moved under the transit-cask position, the transit cask and compartment valves are opened, and the canned irradiated subassembly is lifted into the transit cask. The valves are then closed.

7.9.2.4.4 TRANSIT CASKS. Two types of subassembly transit casks are provided, one for fuel and one for blanket subassemblies (Fig. 7.40). In construction, the two types are similar except that fuel-subassembly casks are 8 ft 4 in. high and weigh 7 tons and blanket subassembly casks are 11 ft 10 in. high and weigh 8 1/2 tons. Six casks are provided in all, three of each type. The purpose of the casks is to shield the canned irradiated subassemblies during transit from the canning station to the lead baths. At a later stage the casks are used to shield canned irradiated subassemblies in transit between the off-loading bay and the chemical processing plant. There is a valve at the lower end of each cask which seals off the inside of the cask from the atmosphere. The top of the cask is sealed by the operating head, which contains an electrically operated gripper and hoist mechanism.

Several special casks are required for operations directly related to fuel handling. A cask is required to handle the charge-hole plug, and another is required for the charge-hole liner. Another cask, somewhat like the charging machine, is used to remove the oscillator rod, boron rod, neutron source, and makeup piece from the inner rotating-shield plug prior to rotating the plugs.

7.9.2.4.5 LEAD BATHS. Three lead-bath stations are provided (Fig. 7.41). Each station consists of a central vertical mild-steel 6-in.-ID tube, sealed at the bottom, open at the top, and surrounded by heating elements and thermal lagging. The whole is surrounded by an annular cast-iron radiation shield composed of stepped blocks. The external dimensions are 3 ft 6 in. (diameter) by 12 ft (height). The shielding is completed by a sliding shield door that is fitted inside the uppermost shield block above the open end of the tube. The central tube contains lead that is maintained at a temperature of 360°C (680°F).

A canned irradiated subassembly is transported to a lead bath in a transit cask. The can is transferred to the lead bath and is immersed for about 1 hr to assure complete melting of the lead inside the can and removal of any NaK that may be adhering to the outside of the can. Lead fumes and any "dirty" nitrogen that may be contained in the bath atmosphere are drawn off by an exhaust system and discharged through a fan into the thermal-siphon stack. The can is removed from the lead bath by the pool cask-car machine and transferred to the decay pool.

7.9.2.4.6 POOL CASK CAR. The function of the pool cask car is to transfer canned irradiated subassemblies from the lead baths to the storage pool and to remove canned decayed subassemblies from the pool. The cask car is used in conjunction with a traveling bridge and a shielded transfer tube (Fig. 7.42). The traveling bridge has two pairs of rails. The outer pair of rails carries the cask car; the inner pair carries the shield tube. The bridge is arranged to travel the length of the pool. The cask car and shield tube travel on the bridge. When operating over the pool, the cask car and shielded transfer tube are locked together, but, when a subassembly is being picked up from the lead bath or deposited in the off-load bay, the cask car is moved off the bridge onto the rails over the selected bath or bay, leaving the shielded transfer tube on the bridge.

The cask car consists primarily of an annular cast-iron radiation shield, 3 ft in outer diameter, 1 ft 4 1/2 in. thick, and 10 ft high, mounted in an enclosed steel frame running on wheels. The cask car has a cable hoist that raises and lowers a gripper. The hoist is electrically driven through a torque-limiting clutch, and it contains a position indicator and zone interlocks. The gripper contains three spring-loaded jaws that close on the top of an element can. Normally the jaws are held in the closed position by springs; they are opened by the operation of a nitrogen-actuated bellows and plunger in the gripper. Interlocks prevent the gripper from being opened unless it is within 3 in. of the top of a subassembly in the lead baths or pool.

The hoist cable comes out of the top of the radiation shield and passes over a pulley which is carried on a pivoted arm equipped with a load-sensing device that indicates when the gripper is carrying a subassembly. The device also stops the hoist motor if the cable goes slack during lowering. A safety gate is provided at the underside of the element shield to prevent accidental release of the subassembly during transit between lead baths and pool. All main controls, e.g., bridge, car, hoist, grapple, safety gate, and shield-tube lock, are situated on a control desk in the cask car.

The shielded transfer tube is made of cast iron and runs on wheels on the inner pair of rails on the bridge. It has a machined step that mates with a recess in the bottom of the cask-car shielding to provide positive location between the two. An interlock locks the step and recess together when the cask car is operating over the pool.

The cask car is positioned approximately over a pool storage position by visual alignment with markings on the bridge and pool wall. Final alignment with a storage rack tube is accomplished with a periscope. The periscope is in two parts; the upper section is fixed to the cask car, and the lower section is attached to the shielded transfer tube. Its object end is positioned 9 in. from the center line of the tube shield, and the operator can line up the tube shield with the desired storage rack tube by visually sighting the adjacent tube.

7.9.2.4.7 DECAY STORAGE POOL.
The decay storage pool is divided into two halves, connected by a central sluice gate (Fig. 7.45). Each half is approximately 23 ft wide, 48 ft long, and 20 ft deep. The normal depth of water is 16 ft 6 in. The storage racks located in the pool consist of 9 ft 6 3/4 in. lengths of 2 1/2-in.-ID mild-steel tube, supported vertically on the bottom of the pool on a framework of angle iron. In each half of the pool there are 1456 tubes arranged on a 9-in. square lattice. Twelve slots, each 10 in. long, are cut in the walls of each tube at different heights in three groups of four to permit free circulation of water around the elements. The water supply to the pool is taken from the domestic water system. Portable pumps may be connected to the installed piping to remove water from the pools. Hold-up tanks facilitate monitoring of this water before it is discharged into the plant's hot drain system.

7.9.2.4.8 OFF-LOADING BAY.
The off-loading bay, which is situated alongside the lead baths, consists of a cast-iron shield surrounding a subassembly support (Fig. 7.41). The shield and upper door are of the same dimensions as a lead bath. A "cooled" subassembly, destined for the chemical processing plant, is lifted from the pool by the pool cask car and deposited in the support bracket in the off-load vessel. The cask car is then moved, and a transit cask is placed over the vessel. The subassembly is lifted into the cask by the cask gripper and hoist, and the shield door and cask valve are closed. The cask is then lifted by the 30-ton crane and loaded onto a road vehicle for transport to the chemical processing plant.

7.9.2.4.9 NEW-SUBASSEMBLY RECEIVING AND STORAGE.
Fuel subassemblies are received from the fabricator in shipping containers that hold six subassemblies each. The shipping container is composed of six horizontal stainless-steel tubes supported in a steel framework. Each tube has an access door with a lock. Blanket subassemblies are received in shipping containers that hold sixteen subassemblies each. The blanket subassembly shipping container is made of a steel I beam with supports for eight subassemblies on each side of the web. The I beam is enclosed with plywood sides and steel ends.

The subassemblies are unloaded and stored in the subassembly storage area. Fuel subassemblies are stored in horizontal racks made of 2-in.-ID steel tubing. Each rack consists of 20 tubes, one above the other, on 2 3/4 in. centers. There are 19 racks, spaced 10 3/4 in. apart, providing storage for 380 fuel elements. The racks have locked doors, each door providing access to four tubes. Blanket subassemblies are stored in racks consisting of wooden trays arranged to stack one upon the other. Each tray carries 26 subassemblies. A total storage space for 624 blanket subassemblies is provided.

A fuel-subassembly can is 66 in. long. It has an inner diameter of 1.715 in. and a wall thickness of 0.08 in. (Fig. 7.43). The can is made of stainless steel lined with lead that is melted when an irradiated subassembly is canned. The melted lead provides a good thermal bond to transfer decay heat from the subassembly to the larger heat-transfer surface of the can. The open end of each can is externally grooved to accept a gripper and internally shaped to accept a stainless-steel lid. The lid has grooves for a silicone rubber O-ring seal and a copper brazing ring. External fins, located just below the gripper grooves at the open end of the can, provide a means of location in other vessels. The bottom end of each can is sealed and has a conical shape. Blanket-subassembly cans differ from fuel-subassembly cans in that they are 108 in. long and contain a smaller volume of lead to accommodate the larger element.

The canning vessel is a horizontal vessel, 8 ft 11 in. long and 2 in. in inside diameter. The vessel is sealed at one end and carries a hinged vessel closure with a can-lid pusher at the other (Figs. 7.43 and 7.44). The following procedure is used to can a subassembly. A can is inserted in the vessel, a subassembly is placed in the can, and a lid is inserted in the lid pusher. The lid clamp is closed, and the vessel and can are evacuated and filled with nitrogen. The can lid is then pushed into the can to form an O-ring seal, sealing the subassembly in the can.

7.9.3 EBR-II FUEL HANDLING

7.9.3.1 Fuel-handling System

The fuel cycle for EBR-II is shown in Fig. 7.47. The reprocessing shown in the cycle diagram is accomplished in an on-site facility located adjacent to the reactor building. A description of the reprocessing is not included in this book.

The EBR-II fuel-handling system uses double rotating plugs carrying a fixed handling machine to insert and remove fuel from the reactor core. The system includes a storage rack to provide necessary decay storage for fuel before it is removed from the primary sodium. Fuel is removed from the primary sodium by a cask car. Fuel is transported from the reactor building to the reprocessing facility in an interbuilding coffin, which also serves as a cleaning chamber. The cask car and the coffin both carry one subassembly at a time and cool the subassembly with forced argon flow.

7.9.3.2 List of Components

The main components in the EBR-II fuel-handling system are the rotating plugs (Fig. 7.48), the gripper mechanism (Fig. 7.48), the subassembly hold-down (Figs. 7.48 and 7.49), the transfer arm (Figs. 7.19 and 7.48), the storage rack (Fig. 7.48), the exit port (Fig. 7.48), the cask car (Figs. 7.48 and 7.50 to 7.52), and the subassembly basin (Fig. 7.53).

7.9.3.3 Fuel-handling Sequence

The general arrangement of the principal components of the fuel-handling system is shown in Fig. 7.48. The sequence is described in the following paragraphs. (See also Fig. 7.2.)

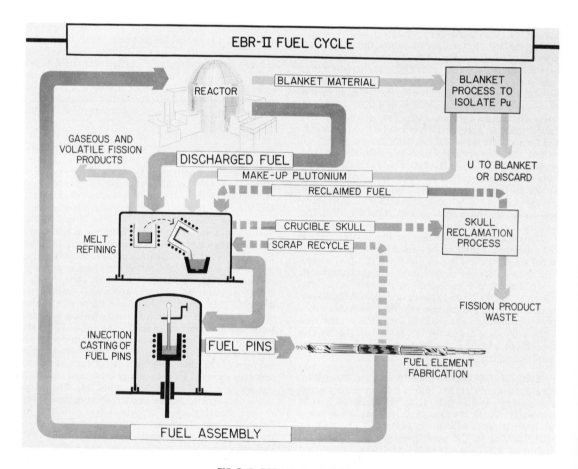

FIG. 7.47—EBR-II fuel cycle [38].

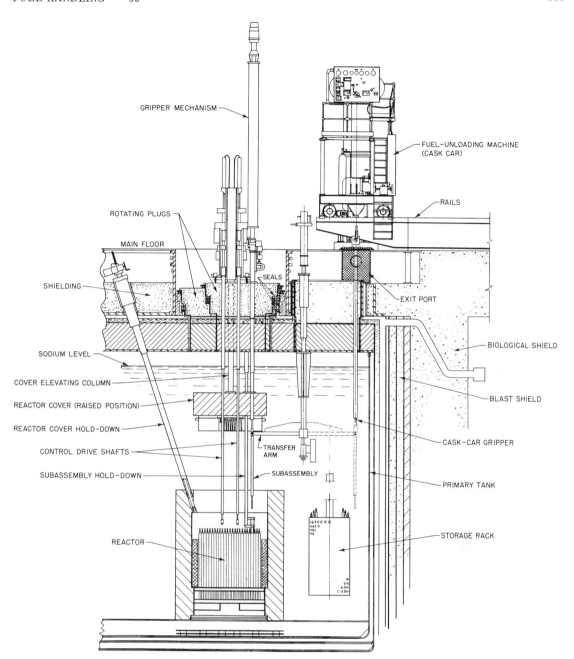

FIG. 7.48—EBR-II principal fuel-handling components [38].

After the reactor is shut down, the 12 control rods are released from their individual control-rod drive mechanisms. The three equally-spaced reactor cover hold-down mechanisms which clamp the cover to the reactor tank are then released (Fig. 7.48). Clamping is accomplished by a tube that slides over a fixed rod secured to the reactor-vessel flange. Sliding the clamping tubes upward provides clearance between the reactor-vessel cover and the tubes permitting the cover to be raised by the two elevating columns. The columns are raised by two synchronized electric-motor-driven lifting mechanisms located on the small rotating plug. In the raised position the reactor cover (about 13 tons) engages pins extending from the underside of the small rotating plug which prevent it from swinging during plug rotation. The cover is raised 9 ft 8 in. to provide clearance below it for removal of subassemblies from the reactor. The control drive mechanisms are then raised 3 in. to clear the subassembly handling heads. The reactor is now prepared for unloading a subassembly.

The following operations are performed with the reactor shutdown. The rotating-shield plugs are

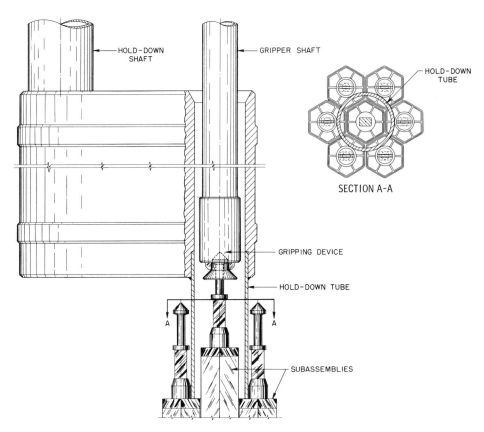

FIG. 7.49—EBR-II subassembly hold-down [38].

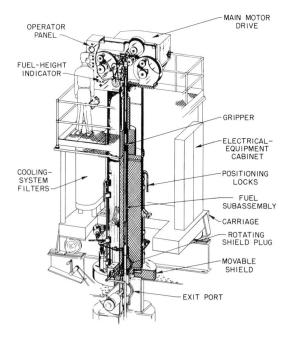

FIG. 7.50—EBR-II fuel-unloading machine (cask car) general arrangement [38].

rotated, after melting the seals, to align the gripper mechanism with the desired subassembly position in the core. The gripper mechanism is driven down, and the subassembly is engaged. The irradiated subassembly is lifted free of the core. The subassembly hold-down prevents adjacent subassemblies from being dislodged during this operation. The rotating-shield plugs are rotated to bring the subassembly to the transfer arm pick-up arm position, as shown in Fig. 7.48. The subassembly is deposited in the transfer arm by the gripper mechanism. The transfer arm is then rotated to a position over the storage rack, as shown in phantom in Fig. 7.48. The storage rack is raised to accept the subassembly after having been properly oriented. The transfer arm is rotated away from the rack, leaving the subassembly in the rack. The storage rack is lowered back to the position shown in Fig. 7.48.

The following operations can be performed with the reactor in operation. The storage rack is rotated and raised to give the transfer arm access to the subassembly that is to be removed. The transfer arm is rotated into position so that the arm is under the subassembly head. The rack is lowered to its down position, leaving the subassembly in the transfer arm. The transfer arm is rotated to the position under the exit port above which the cask car is positioned. The cask-car gripper is

FIG. 7.51—EBR-II fuel-unloading machine (cask car).

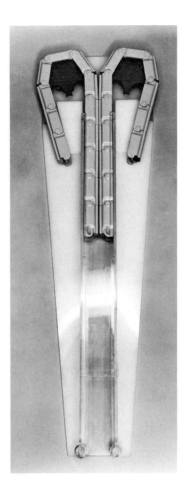

FIG. 7.52—Model of EBR-II cask-car gripper-actuator linkage.

lowered to engage the subassembly handling head, and the subassembly is raised out of the sodium into a shielded container in the cask car. Most of the sodium is blown off by the argon circulating system. The cask-car valve and the exit-port valve are closed, and the space between the valves is purged of argon. The cask car can now be moved from the transfer port.

The cask car is moved on rails to a station that positions it over the interbuilding coffin, and the space between the valves is purged with argon. The subassembly is lowered into the coffin and released. The coffin is lifted by the containment-building crane and placed on a self-propelled dolly inside the equipment air lock (Fig. 7.54 and Fig. 6.29 of Chap. 6). The coffin dolly is moved to the other end of the air lock, where the coffin is removed vertically by a fixed hoist through a hatch and placed on a self-propelled interbuilding cart. The coffin is moved into the fuel-cycle facility, where the subassembly is cleaned in the coffin. The coffin is deposited through a hatch onto a fuel-cycle cart by the building crane and is transferred under the fuel-cycle facility disassembly cell (air cell). The subassembly is then moved from the coffin to the disassembly cell as the first step in on-site fuel reprocessing.

The interbuilding coffin has a self-contained argon cooling system to cool subassemblies in transit. New subassemblies are loaded into the reactor by reversing the handling cycle described above, with the exceptions that new subassemblies are not cleaned and they are preheated before being immersed in the sodium in the primary tank.

7.9.3.4 Fuel-handling Equipment

All operations involved in the fuel-handling cycle include provision for maintaining a "known" angular orientation of the subassembly. Three locations on the subassembly provide this orientation control: (1) The cone-shaped adapter is slotted and engages a blade in the gripper mechanisms; (2) the section below the collar is rectangular and engages the slotted adapter of the transfer arm; and (3) the bottom adapters of the subassemblies are slotted and engage orientation bars in the reactor grid and the storage rack. Each of these orientation controls on the subassemblies is in the same plane. Control of angular orientation, as well as knowledge of angular orientation, is maintained at all times during the fuel-handling cycle.

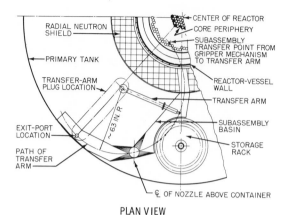

PLAN VIEW

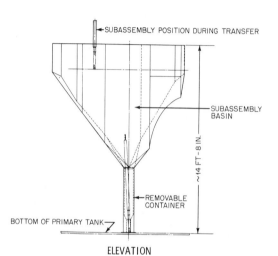

ELEVATION

FIG. 7.53—EBR-II subassembly basin [38].

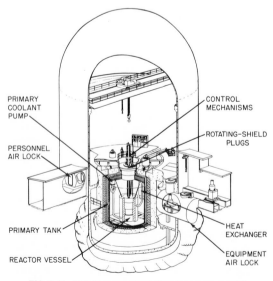

FIG. 7.54—EBR-II arrangement of major equipment [38].

7.9.3.4.1 ROTATING-SHIELD PLUGS. There are two rotating-shield plugs; the smaller plug is located eccentrically inside the larger plug (Fig. 7.48). The smaller plug carries the control drives, the cover-elevating columns, the gripper mechanism, and the subassembly hold-down. The plugs can be rotated to align the gripper mechanism with any subassembly position in the reactor or with the transfer arm. Both shield plugs are supported by ball bearings and rotated by a motor-driven gear drive.

The plugs are sealed around their periphery by a combination molten—frozen seal employing a bismuth—tin alloy. The bismuth—tin alloy is contained in a trough around the plug, and a baffle fastened to the plug dips into the liquid metal. During reactor operation the upper portion of the seal is frozen and the lower region is maintained in a molten state. The frozen upper region prevents seal metal loss in the event of a large pressure differential across the seal, and the molten lower region prevents leakage. The entire seal is melted to permit rotation of the plugs.

7.9.3.4.2 GRIPPER MECHANISM. The gripper mechanism is an electromechanical device used to insert or to extract subassemblies from the reactor vessel (Fig. 7.48). It is mounted on the inner rotating-shield plug and extends into the sodium in the primary tank. A subassembly is removed from the reactor by rotating the rotating plugs and gripper head to the proper position for the particular subassembly to be removed. (There is an angular position for each of these three units for each lattice position in the reactor.) The hold-down mechanism is lowered over the subassembly to be removed. It contacts and spreads the six adjacent subassemblies, prevents them from moving as the subassembly is removed, and acts as a guide for the gripper mechanism.

The gripper head is lowered (through the hold-down tube) and grips the adapter on the subassembly, and the orientation blade between the gripper jaws engages the slot in the conical shaped head. The subassembly is then lifted out of the core. The gripping mechanism is moved vertically by an electrically driven screw drive, and the gripper jaws are motor operated. Interlocks prevent the opening of the gripper jaws except when the gripper head is in the upper plenum chamber of the reactor or at the transfer point between the gripper and the transfer arm. After the subassembly has been raised out of the reactor, the hold-down tube is raised around the suspended subassembly to act as a support during movement of the two rotating plugs. The plugs are rotated to the transfer point, and the gripper head is rotated to the transfer angle. The transfer arm is rotated to engage the subassembly, and the gripper deposits the subassembly in the transfer arm. The hold-down is lowered to clear the subassembly. A new subassembly is inserted into the core by reversing the procedure.

The gripper-mechanism shaft that extends through the plug is sealed with a compression type packing gland. The packing gland is mounted on a standpipe that bolts to the small plug. The packing gland is enclosed in a separate housing for ease of installation and maintenance. It consists of two sets of four standard-form asbestos split rings. Each ring is 0.5 in. square in cross section and contains a graphite lubricant. The two sets of rings are separated by a metallic spacer; this provides a gap for bleed-in of argon gas to reduce the leakage rate, if necessary. When the gripper mechanism is not in use, a motor-driven pressure plate is driven down to exert a uniform compressive force on the packing to tightly seal the shaft. Prior to either rotation or translation of the shaft, the pressure plate is driven up to reduce the amount of compression in the packing. An important design feature of the gripper mechanism is the force-limiting function that controls the push and pull force applied to a subassembly during fuel handling. The device used to effect force limiting is complicated because it must differentiate between the force applied on the subassembly by the mechanism and the force required to move the gripper shaft. The latter force has two components: the friction between shaft and packing gland (variable) and the weight of the shaft. A friction-compensator device is employed to allow differentiation between these two components. The design allows a wide adjustable range of force-limiting settings (approximately 400 to 4000 lb).

The gripper (Fig. 7.18), which engages the subassembly handling head, and the two gripper bellows, one of which provides the sodium seal between the main shaft and the jaw-actuating shaft and the other between the jaw-actuating shaft and the sensing-rod shaft, were tested in sodium at 800°F. The test cycle consisted in lowering the gripper into a tank of sodium, closing the jaws over the handling head of a simulated subassembly, raising the subassembly, lowering it, releasing the gripper jaw, and raising the gripper. This operation was performed for about 15,000 cycles. Upon conclusion of the test, the gripper-jaw assembly was removed and inspected. It was found to be in satisfactory condition with insignificant evidence of wear. The gripper bellows were cycled through a 2.25-in. stroke (design value) while submerged in the 800°F sodium. The bellows developed a small leak (noted by a loss in pressure within the vessel) after 9540 cycles. This performance was considered adequate since the test was estimated to represent at least 20 years of normal operation in EBR-II.

7.9.3.4.3 SUBASSEMBLY HOLD-DOWN TUBE AND DRIVE. The hold-down tube and drive is an electromechanical device that works in conjunction with the gripper (Figs. 7.48 and 7.49). The device is mounted on the small rotating-shield plug and extends into the sodium in the primary tank. During the removal of a subassembly from the reactor vessel, the hold-down tube contacts the six adjacent subassemblies, spreads them slightly, and prevents them from moving as the subassembly is removed. The hold-down tube also acts as a guide funnel for the subassembly during the loading sequence. After the subassembly has been raised out of the reactor, the hold-down tube serves as a guide for the subassembly while the plugs are being rotated. The hold-down is driven up and down by an electrically driven screw. The shaft is sealed with a packing seal of the same type described for the gripper mechanism in Sec. 7.9.3.4.2.

7.9.3.4.4 TRANSFER ARM. The transfer arm transfers subassemblies back and forth from the gripper to the storage rack and from the storage rack to the cask car, or from the gripper directly to the cask car (Figs. 7.19 and 7.48). The arm is attached to a shaft that extends through the operating floor. The transfer arm is manually operated and electrically interlocked. The arm rotates through a horizontal arc of about 180°; thus it can be positioned under the gripper or the cask car or over any one of the three concentric rows in the storage rack. Subassemblies are supported by a slotted seat that accepts the subassembly adapter head. A locking bar secures the head in the seat (Fig. 7.19).

The counterbalancing of the arm, together with manual operation, gives the operator a "feel" that provides several checkpoints: (1) the operator can feel the contact of the arm and a subassembly at the transfer positions, (2) he cannot move a subassembly with the arm if it is still held by the gripper or hold-down sleeve, and (3) he cannot move a subassembly from the storage rack if the rack has not been lowered to clear the subassembly.

7.9.3.4.5 STORAGE RACK. The storage rack is a tank-shaped structure providing 75 storage locations in three concentric rows (Fig. 7.48). The rack is suspended from a shaft extending from a drive mechanism mounted on the operating floor. The rack is completely submerged in the primary tank sodium to assure natural convection cooling of spent subassemblies stored in the rack. The storage rack can be rotated as well as raised and lowered in the primary tank. When a subassembly is being transferred from the transfer arm to the storage rack, the arm is first rotated to position the subassembly over a row in the rack. Then the rack is rotated to bring an empty location under the subassembly. Elevating the storage rack inserts the subassembly into a storage location. At the end of the upward movement, the subassembly head is lifted free from the transfer-arm seat.

A transfer-indicating device is used to assure proper vertical movement of the storage rack. This is a sensing rod extending vertically from the operating floor directly to the transfer position. It is actuated by the subassembly handling head, which will be raised if the storage-rack position is already occupied or if the storage-rack lifting mechanism accidentally over travels. In either case the transfer-indicating device acts as an electrical safety stop. An additional check exists here. As long as the subassembly is held jointly by the storage rack and the transfer arm, the transfer arm cannot be moved. After the subassembly transfer the transfer arm is rotated to a neutral position, and the storage rack is lowered. The storage-rack shaft is sealed with a compression type packing gland of the same design as the seal described for the gripper mechanism.

7.9.3.4.6 EXIT PORT. The exit port provides access to the inside of the primary tank for fuel handling (Fig. 7.48). It forms the link between the transfer arm inside the primary tank and the cask car, which operates on the main floor. The exit port is basically a large manually operated valve, normally closed, which is opened for fuel unloading.

It has provisions for argon-gas purging during the fuel-transfer operations.

7.9.3.4.7 CASK CAR. The cask car (Figs. 7.48, 7.50, and 7.51) is an electromechanical device that transfers fuel subassemblies from the transfer arm inside the primary tank to the interbuilding coffin outside the primary tank. The cask car is shielded and is mounted on a set of tracks with internal mechanisms including a gripping device and a drive unit that moves the car between the exit port and the interbuilding coffin location. Provisions are included to circulate argon gas through the subassembly from an external argon system. The argon-gas circulating system removes excess sodium from the subassembly and cools the spent fuel during the transfer. The shielded portion of the cask car has a retractable shield ring at the bottom. This ring has a 2 1/2-in. vertical travel so that it can be lowered to match the exit port or the interbuilding coffin and avoid a shielding gap during fuel transfer.

The gripper is raised and lowered by two special link chains (Fig. 7.52) arranged to provide a rigid configuration that will transmit a downward force as the gripper is lowered. Actuation of the gripper jaws is accomplished by the relative movement of the link chains. The chains are driven up or down by sprocket wheels and are stored on single-width drums provided with negator springs to maintain a constant take-up tension. The mating link chains between the drive sprockets and the gripper accept a third and smaller link chain that passes through the center of the mating-chain configuration. The third chain provides an indication of the position of the probe rod within the gripper. All position indications and operating controls are located on the panel on the top platform of the cask car.

The cask car is used in the following manner. An irradiated subassembly is removed from the storage rack by the transfer arm and aligned directly under the exit port. The cask car is positioned over and sealed to the transfer port. The gripping device is lowered through the exit port to the level of the transfer arm to engage the subassembly. The transfer arm is rotated free of the subassembly, and the subassembly is lifted by the gripper into the shielded cask car. The car is then moved to a position over the interbuilding coffin, and the subassembly is lowered into the coffin. The reverse procedure is employed to load a new subassembly into the primary tank. Purging, heating, and cooling are accomplished by the argon system.

7.9.3.4.8 INTERBUILDING COFFIN. The interbuilding coffin is a portable sealed and shielded vessel with an integral argon-gas cooling system (Fig. 7.54 and Fig. 6.29 of Chap. 6). The blower units on the coffin are battery powered to ensure continuous operation in the event of transport difficulties or power failure during transit to the fuel-cycle facility. The interbuilding coffin has provisions for removing the sodium adhering to the subassemblies. The sodium can be removed while a subassembly is still in the coffin by steam and water from the fuel-cycle facility. The effluent from the cleaning operation is piped directly to the sodium disposal unit in the fuel-cycle facility.

The cask car inserts a subassembly into the interbuilding coffin. The coffin is then lifted by the rotary bridge crane and placed on a dolly inside the equipment air lock. After passing through the air lock, the coffin is lifted through a hatch onto a self-propelled interbuilding cart in the entrance to the fuel-cycle facility where the subassembly is cleaned. The coffin is then propelled to a hatch, lifted by the facility building crane, and lowered onto a fuel-cycle cart, which is then propelled to a position under the fuel-cycle facility air cell.

The same equipment is employed to transfer a subassembly from the fuel-cycle facility to the primary tank. Sufficient fission-product heat is generated in the reprocessed fuel subassembly to require forced convection cooling during its return to the reactor. This requirement indicated the advisability of a single system that could accomplish fuel-subassembly transfer in both directions.

7.9.3.4.9 SUBASSEMBLY BASIN. Although virtually no possibility exists that a subassembly could be dropped accidentally within the primary tank during transfer operations, a subassembly basin has been incorporated to provide additional safety. The function of this basin (Fig. 7.53) is to guide a dropped subassembly into a position in which it will be adequately cooled by natural convection until retrieved. The system has been tested by deliberately dropping a number of dummy subassemblies from various positions (within the range covered by the basin) to ensure that the subassembly comes to rest in the correct position and with the correct (vertical) attitude. Actual retrievals through the primary tank access plug directly above the subassembly position were not made since retrieval gear will not be devised unless this unanticipated accident actually occurs.

7.9.3.5 Fuel-handling Control and Interlocks

Fuel handling is accomplished semi-automatically. The operator supplies the intelligence by initiating instructions relating to the sequence of operations to be performed. Interlock circuits provide information to the operator indicating the next operation to be performed, but the operator initiates the operation. Preventive control is provided to preclude the operator's initiating the wrong operation (the system will only respond to the correct instructions). The fuel-handling center is the primary control point for fuel-handling operations. With the exception of the transfer arm, all mechanisms constituting the fuel-handling system are controlled and supervised by an operator at the fuel-handling center. The transfer arm is manually operated; however, its operation is limited to the appropriate motions in the fuel-transfer cycle by electromechanical interlocks. The position of the transfer arm is transmitted to the fuel-handling center. The circuitry for fuel-handling operations is interlocked with the reactor control system to prevent fuel-handling operations unless the reactor is shut down and the reactor control system is locked out. Conversely, reactor operation is prevented unless the fuel-handling control system is shut down and locked out.

The fuel-handling center is comprised of a main operating panel, punched-card reader, card punch, alarm lights, log count-rate recorder, scaler and scaler timer, and miscellaneous controls and indicators. The fuel-handling control system performs two distinct functions: it controls operation of the various components in the system and it prepares a record of certain operations performed (data gathering).

7.9.3.5.1 CONTROL OF COMPONENT OPERATIONS. Repetitive, identical motions for a given operating sequence are controlled by conventional circuits utilizing limit switches, push buttons, and other devices. Motions that are a function of the point of origin or destination of a subassembly are performed in response to a numerical position-control system. These latter functions include angular position of the rotating-shield plugs, gripper, and storage rack; storage-rack vertical positioning; and supervision of transfer-arm position. The major components of the numerical position control are a card reader and card-reader storage, plug- and gripper-position encoders, translators, digital subtractors, digital position indicators, digital-to-analog converters, motor controllers, drive-motor units, and an output card punch. A rotating-plug command coordinate, which is punched on an input card in decimal form, is converted to binary-coded decimal and is stored as such when the card is inserted in the card reader. The actual position of the plug, encoded in binary-coded decimal, is subtracted from the command input by the subtractor, and an error signal is developed that causes the motor controller to drive the motor in the proper direction to reduce the error. When the actual position coincides with the command position, the drive is deenergized, and the brake is set. Figure 7.55 is the format for the punched card layout. Figure 7.56 is a block diagram of the numerical position-control system.

Four different types of input cards are used during subassembly transfers. Each type is used for a particular transfer operation and is identified by color (Fig. 7.55).

Color Code

W - White   B - Blue
Y - Yellow   R - Red
G - Green   X - Punch in Cols.

Col No's.	Type of Data		"Refueler to Basket" Card		"Basket to Core" Card		"Core to Basket" Card		"Basket to Refueler" Card	
		Input or Output	I	O	I	O	I	O	I	O
		Color	B	W	G	W	R	W	Y	W
1	Type of Operation No.		1	1	2	2	3	3	4	4
2–3	Sequential Order No.		X	X	X	X	X	X	X	X
4–8	Fuel Element No.		X	X	X	X	X	X	X	X
7	Basket Coord.	Ring No.	X	X	X	X				
10–11	Basket Coord.	Angle No.	X	X	X	X				
12–16	Date & Time			X		X		X		X
17–19	Core Location No.				X	X	X	X		
20–24	Large Plug Angle				X	X	X	X		
25–29	Small Plug Angle				X	X	X	X		
30–32	Gripper Angle				X	X	X	X		
33	Basket Coord.	Ring No.					X	X	X	X
34–35	Basket Coord.	Angle No.					X	X	X	X
36–59										
60–62	Repeat Basket Coord.		X		X					
63–67	Repeat Large Plug Angle				X		X			
68–72	Repeat Small Plug Angle				X		X			
73–75	Repeat Gripper Angle				X		X			
76–78	Repeat Basket Coord.						X		X	

FIG. 7.55—EBR-II fuel-handling punched-card layout format.

Prior to transfer operations the following information is supplied to the system on the input punched cards: (1) type of transfer; (2) card serial number; (3) subassembly identification; (4) core location (row, sector, and number); and (5) storage rack, rotating plug, and gripper angular coordinates. The approximate accuracy and resolution of the numerical positioning system are summarized below. The combined positions can place the subassembly gripper with an accuracy of about 1/64 in.

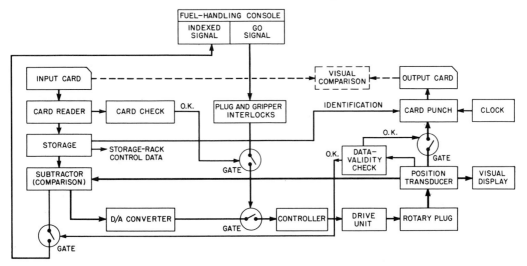

FIG. 7.56—EBR-II fuel-handling numerical positioning system [38].

Mechanism	Positioning accuracy	System resolution
Large rotating plug	$\pm 5 \times 10^{-5}$ revolution	1.0×10^{-5} revolution
Small rotating plug	$\pm 5 \times 10^{-5}$ revolution	1.0×10^{-5} revolution
Gripper (angular position)	$\pm 1 \times 10^{-3}$ revolution	5×10^{-4} revolution

The storage-rack elevation and rotation drives are controlled in an on—off fashion to effect indexing at certain discrete points, including any of the 75 holes in the storage rack (basket). The accuracy of indexing is determined by limit-switch settings and other mechanical devices. The transfer-arm positions over the storage rack are supervised but are not controlled by the system. The numerical position-control system utilizes digital position data throughout with one exception, i.e., conversion to analog data is made in the circuits controlling drive-motor speed.

Several measures are taken to enhance reliability and eliminate errors. Coordinate information is punched in duplicate on the input cards. The two sets of data are automatically checked for agreement before the system takes action. If there is no agreement, the positioning system cannot start. Parity checking and redundancy checking techniques are employed where appropriate in the position transducer data-handling circuits. And finally, each input card is punched with a serial number, which is automatically checked for proper sequence.

7.9.3.5.2 DATA GATHERING. A permanent record of operations regulated by the numerical position-control system is made on punched output cards. The output cards are automatically punched as the mechanisms are indexed in response to the input cards. The information punched should correspond to that on the input cards except that the cards are also punched to record the date and time. Thus a permanent record of actual performance is available and can be checked against the input cards at any time.

7.9.4 FERMI FUEL HANDLING

7.9.4.1 Fuel-handling System

The on-site portion of the Fermi plant fuel-cycle flow diagram is shown in Fig. 7.57. The fuel is reprocessed in an off-site reprocessing facility.

The Fermi fuel-handling system employs a single rotating plug with a fixed fuel-handling machine to insert and remove fuel from the reactor core. The handling machine rotates around its vertical axis. The machine is also called an offset handling mechanism. The plug and machine can be rotated to bring the gripper over any position in the reactor core.

The system includes a transfer rotor to provide some decay storage for fuel before it is removed from the primary sodium. Fuel is removed from the primary sodium by a cask car that can transport 11 subassemblies at a time to a fuel facility outside the reactor building. There the subassemblies are cleaned, stored in a decay pool, and subsequently shipped to an off-site reprocessing facility.

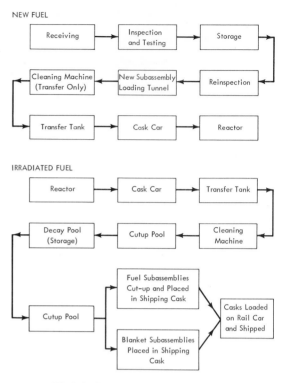

FIG. 7.57—Fermi fuel-cycle flow diagram [25].

7.9.4.2 List of Components and Facilities

The main components and facilities in the Fermi fuel-handling system are a rotating-shield plug (Figs. 4.34 and 4.36 of Chap. 4), an offset handling mechanism (Fig. 7.58), a transfer-rotor machine (Fig. 7.59), a cask car (Figs. 7.60 to 7.62), the fuel and repair building (Figs. 6.65 and 6.66 of Chap. 6), and the decay pool storage rack (Fig. 7.12).

7.9.4.3 Fuel-handling Sequence

The arrangement of the components in the fuel-handling system in the reactor building is shown in Fig. 11.52 of Chap. 11. The fuel-handling sequence is discussed in the following paragraphs.

The following steps must be taken before the cask car can be moved into the reactor building for fuel handling: (1) the reactor is shut down and the safety rods are inserted into the core; (2) the primary sodium flow is reduced to a level where the hydraulic forces on the fuel subassemblies and the safety and operating control-rod lower guide tubes are well below those required to unseat them; (3) the safety and control rods are delatched in the core; (4) the safety- and control-rod drive extensions are raised to clear the subassemblies; (5) the hold-down plate is raised to its "up" position to clear the subassemblies. The reactor-building equipment door is then opened and the cask car is moved into the building. The equipment door is closed and sealed, and the cask car is connected and sealed to the reactor-vessel exit port. Fuel-

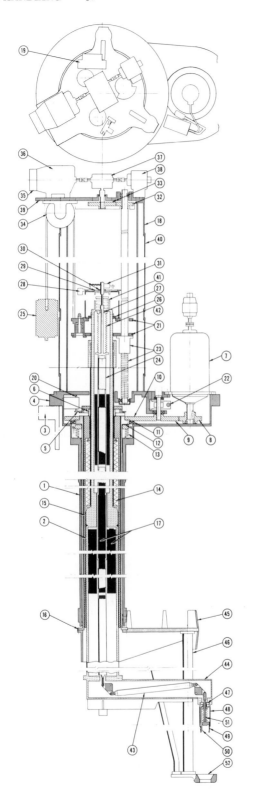

1 Housing Pipe
2 Reciprocating Tube
3 Shield Basket
4 Azimuth Housing
5 Ring Gear (Analog-to-digital Converter)
6 Backup Packing Seal
7 Azimuth Drive Motor-gear Reducer
8 Azimuth Drive Pinion
9 Azimuth Idler Gear
10 Azimuth Gear (Driven)
11 Azimuth Bearing
12 Rotating Face Seal
13 Face-seal Bellows
14 Reciprocating Bellows Assembly
15 Elevation Bearing Pipe
16 Azimuth Bearing Pipe
17 Powdered Shielding
18 Frame-elevation Housing
19 Analog-to-digital Converter
20 Drive Shaft (Analog to Digital)
21 Overload Plate Assembly
22 Azimuth Brake
23 Ball Screw and Ball Nut
24 Latch-tube Assembly
25 Counterweight Assembly
26 Elevation Bearing
27 Latch-rod Guide Bushing
28 Latch-closed Limit Switch
29 Latch-slide Plate
30 Latch-rod Collar
31 Slide-plate Retracting Solenoid
32 Ball-screw Drive Gear
33 Vertical Drive Pinion
34 Counterweight Pulley (3)
35 Motor Brake
36 Elevation Drive Motor
37 Gear Reducer
38 Elevation Selsyn Transmitter
39 Top Plate-elevation Housing
40 Frame-elevation Housing Cover Plate
41 Latch-rod Counterbalance Spring
42 Latch-rod Bellow Seals (Upper)
43 Bell-crank Linkage
44 Offset Arm and Gripper Assembly
45 Stabilizer Plate
46 Stabilizer Guide Bars
47 Gripper-finger Retainer Collar
48 Gripper Housing
49 Cam
50 Gripper Finger
51 Latch-rod Extension
52 Stabilizer Foot

FIG. 7.58--Fermi offset handling mechanism [25].

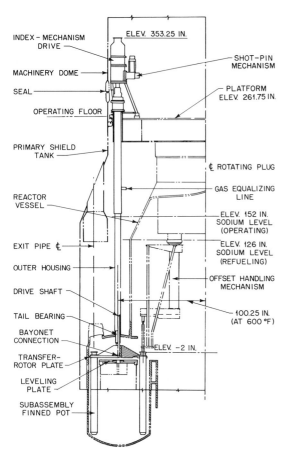

FIG. 7.59—Fermi transfer-rotor assembly [25].

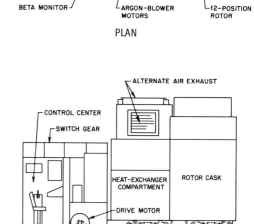

PLAN

ELEVATION

FIG. 7.60—Fermi cask car [25].

transfer operations from the cask car to the reactor vessel may now proceed.

After the preparations described are completed, the following fuel-handling sequence is used to transfer subassemblies from the cask car to the reactor vessel. The shield plug in the exit port is lifted into the cask car by the cask-car gripper and hoist and is deposited in one of the 12 positions in the cask-car rotor. The transfer rotor is rotated to bring an empty position under the exit port, and a finned pot containing a new subassembly is lowered from the cask car into the empty transfer-rotor position. The transfer rotor is rotated to bring a finned pot with a spent subassembly under the exit port, and the finned pot containing the spent subassembly is lifted into the cask car and deposited in the cask-car rotor position just vacated. This procedure is repeated until all the spent subassemblies in the transfer rotor have been exchanged for new subassemblies from the cask car. At the end of the transfer, one of the 12 transfer-rotor positions has an empty finned pot to accommodate the transfer operations from the transfer rotor to the core. The exit-port shield plug is then lowered from the cask car back into the exit port, and the port is sealed. The cask car is disconnected from the exit port, the equipment door is opened, and the cask car is moved to the fuel and repair building. The equip-

ment door is closed and sealed in preparation for the next step in the fuel-handling sequence.

The preparations listed above also apply to fuel-handling inside the reactor vessel except that the cask car is to be removed from the containment building and both the equipment door and the exit port are to be closed and sealed before fuel-handling proceeds in the core.

The following fuel-handling sequence is used to transfer subassemblies from the transfer rotor to the core. The transfer rotor is rotated to locate the empty finned pot under the offset-handling-mechanism (OHM) deposit position. The plug and OHM are rotated to position the OHM gripper over the core or blanket subassembly to be removed, and the OHM gripper is lowered to engage the subassembly and withdraw it from the reactor lattice. The plug and OHM are rotated to position the subassembly over the empty finned pot in the transfer rotor, and the spent subassembly is lowered and deposited into the empty finned pot. The empty OHM gripper is raised to the full ''up'' position, and the transfer rotor is rotated to position the next new subassembly under the OHM gripper. The OHM gripper is lowered to engage the new subassembly, and the subassembly is raised. The plug and OHM are then rotated to place the fresh subassembly over the empty position in the reactor lattice, and

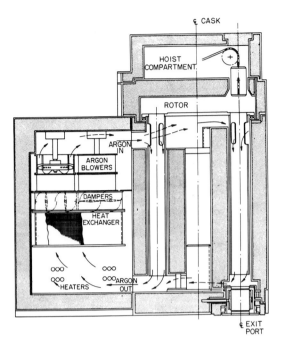

FIG. 7.61—Section through center of Fermi cask car [25].

the subassembly is lowered into the reactor lattice (the OHM will automatically reduce the rate of core subassembly insertion to 1 ft/min during the last 3 ft of travel). The gripper is delatched and raised to full "up" position, leaving the subassembly in place in the reactor lattice. The above procedure is repeated until all the new subassemblies have been transferred to the reactor and the spent subassemblies have been placed in the transfer rotor for initial decay where they will remain until

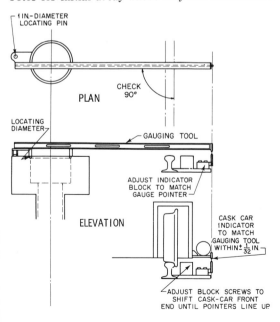

FIG. 7.62—Method of positioning Fermi cask car over exit port [25].

the following shutdown. After transfer is completed, the plug and OHM are rotated to the reactor operating position (hold-down directly over its support columns ready for lowering; OHM gripper near the transfer-rotor deposit point), and the OHM gripper is lowered to the storage position.

If more than 11 subassemblies in the reactor are to be exchanged, the cask car will make two trips. Some of the subassembly storage positions provided at the outer edge of the radial blanket will be used, and the loading data will be properly recorded.

The sequence for handling spent fuel outside the containment building is described below (reference is made to Figs. 6.65 and 6.66 of Chap. 6). The cask car is moved to the fuel and repair building and sealed to the access tube at the cask-car unloading-station transfer tank. The access-tube shield plug is raised into the cask car and stored in the cask-car rotor. The finned pots containing the spent subassemblies are lowered one at a time into the cask-car unloading-station transfer rotor. After all the spent subassemblies have been transferred out of the cask car, the access-tube plug is lowered into the access tube, the tube is sealed, the cask-car valve is sealed, the interspace is purged, and the car is moved to its storage location.

After a decay period of one to two weeks, the spent subassemblies are cleaned and transferred to the water decay pool by the sequence described below. The rotor of the cask-car unloading station (transfer-rotor storage tank) is rotated to position the desired subassembly under the cleaning-chamber port. The cleaning chamber is positioned and sealed to the port, and then it is purged and filled with argon. The cleaning-chamber valve and port valve are opened, and the cleaning-chamber gripper is lowered to grasp the subassembly. The subassembly is lifted from the finned pot into the cleaning chamber (cooling is maintained by a continuous argon flow through the subassembly), and the cleaning-chamber valve and port valve are closed. The chamber is positioned and sealed over the cutup-pool port. Sodium is cleaned from the subassembly by a steam-cleaning step followed by a water rinse; then the cleaning-chamber valve and cutup-pool valve are opened, and the subassembly is lowered into an underwater cart that transports it through a tunnel into the cutup pool. The spent subassembly is removed from the underwater transfer cart by the pool bridge and gripper and is deposited in a leaker can. The subassembly is sealed in the can for a test period, and the water in the can is sampled to determine if the subassembly is leaking fission products. If the subassembly does not present a leakage problem, it is removed from the can and transferred through an underwater tunnel to the adjacent decay pool, where it is placed in a decay storage rack. If the subassembly leakage is unacceptable, it is left in a leaker can during decay storage. When the subassembly has decayed sufficiently, it is returned to the cutup pool where, after it has been cut up into core and blanket sections, it is loaded under water into a shipping cask. After the shipping casks are loaded, they are removed from the cutup pool by the building crane and loaded on a railroad car for shipment offsite.

New fuel is handled in the following sequence. Subassemblies are received in the new-fuel receiving area (area B in Fig. 6.65 of Chap. 6). They are unloaded from the shipping containers, inspected, and stored. Before reactor loading a subassembly is reinspected and then inserted into the new subassembly loading tunnel on to a self-propelled cart. The subassembly is moved to a position under the cleaning-chamber loading-tunnel port and is raised into the cleaning chamber where it is isolated and preheated in an argon atmosphere. The cleaning chamber is positioned and sealed over the cask-car unloading-station transfer tank, and the subassembly is lowered into an empty finned pot in the transfer tank. The remainder of the handling sequence to the reactor is the reverse of the sequence previously described for spent fuel.

7.9.4.4 Fuel-handling Equipment

The following are descriptions of the principal pieces of equipment of the Fermi fuel-handling system.

7.9.4.4.1 ROTATING-SHIELD PLUG. The rotating-shield plug, shown in Figs. 4.34 and 4.36 of Chap. 4, serves as an integral part of the biological shield and as a part of the subassembly-handling equipment. It consists of a 1 1/32-in.-thick stainless-steel cylindrical shell containing layers of shielding materials and insulation. The plug has a 12-in.-thick carbon-steel cover plate that carries the hold-down assembly, the control drives, and the offset handling equipment. The deflection of the cover plate is limited to 0.015 in. to ensure that the offset handling mechanism is vertical to within 0.5 min of arc. The 150-ton dead-weight load of the plug and machinery is transmitted to the reactor-vessel plug-container flange through the load-carrying ring and the ball-bearing assembly shown in Fig. 4.36 of Chap. 4. The plug gear is integral with the load carrying ring. The intermediate race of the double-row ball bearing provides for differential thermal expansion between the carbon-steel load-carrying ring and the stainless-steel plug-container flange. Molybdenum disulfide was selected as the lubricant. The seal between the rotating plug and the plug container is achieved with a silicone rubber seal. The center of the seal is supplied with clean argon gas at approximately 2 psi above system pressure. This pressure seats the lips of the seal on the rotating seal ring and assures that any leakage is into the vessel rather than out. Provision is made for a NaK dip seal to act in conjunction with the closure seal in the event that sodium vapor in this area develops into a problem. All bolted covers and flanges are sealed with rubber O-rings and gaskets.

A 3-in. hole is provided through the center of the plug for alignment purposes, and three 6-in. holes are provided for removing the lower control-rod guide tubes and handling the beryllium section of the source. All four holes contain shielding plugs during plant operation.

7.9.4.4.2 OFFSET HANDLING MECHANISM. The offset handling mechanism (OHM) is used to transfer fuel and blanket subassemblies from the transfer rotor to the reactor lattice and vice versa. It is also used to handle the safety and control rods, thermal-shield bars, and the antimony section of the neutron source, when replacement of these items is required. The OHM is shown in Fig. 7.58. The center of the OHM is located approximately 36 in. from the center of rotation of the plug.

Structurally, the machine is made up of four concentric tubes, an elevation drive unit, an azimuth drive unit, seals, and shielding. The four tubes are, respectively, the housing tube, azimuth bearing tube, elevation bearing tube, and the reciprocating tube. The various parts of the machine are described below. Numbers in parenthesis refer to part numbers on Fig. 7.58.

7.9.4.4.2.1 Stationary Members. The stationary portion of the machine consists of the elevation housing (18), which houses the vertical drive assembly, above the top of the rotating plug and the azimuth housing pipe assembly below the top of the rotating plug.

7.9.4.4.2.2 Rotating Members. The major parts of the azimuth assembly are the azimuth drive assembly, azimuth bearing pipe, elevation bearing pipe, stabilizer assembly, and reciprocating assembly.

The azimuth assembly, except the drive, is supported on a combination thrust radial azimuth bearing (11), which is mounted on the azimuth housing (4). The azimuth bearing inner race carries the azimuth bearing pipe (16) and the elevation bearing pipe (15), which are pinned together at their upper ends and rotate as a unit. Also fixed to the inner race of the azimuth bearing is the azimuth gear (10). The lower end of the azimuth bearing pipe is supported radially by a journal type wear ring at the lower end of the housing pipe. A rotating face seal (12) permits rotation of the azimuth bearing pipe with respect to the stationary housing pipe (1) isolating the primary-system cover gas from the machinery-dome atmosphere.

The stabilizer assembly, consisting of the stabilizer plate (45), stabilizer guides (46), and stabilizer bottom plate or foot (52), is bolted to the azimuth bearing pipe. The foot is designed to prevent overload damage. It guides the offset arm during its vertical travel and provides lateral stabilization of the offset arm under load.

The azimuth drive consists of a motor-gear reducer (7) and drive gear train which terminate in the azimuth gear. A brake on the azimuth idler gear (9) stops the machine positively when the drive-motor power is off. This provides fail-safe operation.

7.9.4.4.2.3 Reciprocating Members. The reciprocating assembly consists of the reciprocating tube, offset arm-gripper assembly, overload plate assembly, and counterweight assembly. The reciprocating assembly is supported and aligned at the upper end of the reciprocating tube (2) by a radial-thrust bearing (26), which is mounted in the overload plate assembly (21).

The entire reciprocating complex is supported and driven by ball screws (23) through ball nuts that are fixed to the bottom plate of the overload plate assembly. The counterweight assembly (25) is also attached to the overload plate assembly by cables; it balances the weight of the reciprocating assembly.

The ball screws are driven by a motor-gear reducer (36 and 37) through a drive pinion (33). A fail-safe motor brake (35) which is "on" when drive-motor power is "off" assures that the reciprocating assembly will stop and remain in position in the event of power failure. Locking-worm construction of the gear reducer in combination with the counterweight assembly further assures positive stopping of the reciprocating assembly if power fails. In addition, the counterweight reduces drive-motor power requirements.

A stainless-steel bellows (14) effects a positive seal between the primary-system cover gas and the machinery-dome atmosphere but permits the reciprocating assembly to move vertically relative to the rest of the machine. The bellows is backed up by a packing seal (6), which keeps leakage to a minimum in the event of a bellows failure.

The offset arm and gripper assembly (44) is fixed to the lower end of the reciprocating tube and travels between the stabilizer guide bars (46). The guide bars prevent the reciprocating assembly from rotating with respect to the rest of the machine during vertical travel. A hole in the stabilizer foot (52) guides the subassemblies as they are inserted in, or withdrawn from, their positions in the support plates. The stabilizer foot also prevents excessive side sway of the subassemblies during the carry operation. The stabilizer foot is designed to break away in the event of excess internal lateral load.

7.9.4.4.2.4 Gripper Design and Operation. The OHM latch plate is so designed that it is impossible to delatch or release a subassembly in the carry position, i.e., it is necessary to seat the subassembly to complete the delatching operation. Basically, the gripper consists of a housing (48) carrying four fingers (50), which hang freely from the gripper-finger retainer independently of the housing and fingers. The housing is fixed to the end of a latch-rod assembly (24) through a latch-rod extension (51) and a bell-crank linkage (43) which transmits motion of the cam to the latch-rod assembly at right angles through the offset arm. The latch rod extends through the reciprocating tube terminating at its upper end above the overload plate assembly in a latch-rod collar (30).

A spring-loaded latch slide plate (29) with a key-slot-shaped opening is fixed to the reciprocating assembly at the approximate level of the collar. The larger opening is sized to pass the collar, and the smaller opening clears the latch rod. In the delatched position the collar partially penetrates the larger opening, holding the slide plate cocked. During the latching sequence the OHM is driven down until the latch rod—cam assembly contacts the subassembly handling head. As the machine continues to move down, the fingers are carried downward with respect to the cam, causing them to be cammed inward under the proper subassembly handling head. At the upper end of the machine, the reciprocating tube carries the slide plate downward with respect to the latch rod. As the top of the slide plate clears the bottom of the latch-rod collar, the spring pulls the slide plate into the lock

position, holding the latch rod—cam assembly in the latched position and maintaining the fingers closed. The subassembly can now be raised by driving the OHM up.

It is necessary to seat the subassembly in its support-plate location and drive the OHM down into the overtravel range as in latching to delatch. When the slide plate is clear of the latch-rod collar, the operator can energize the latch-plate retracting solenoid (31), which pulls the slide plate back into the cocked position. With the solenoid energized, the OHM is driven up. The weight of the latch-rod assembly plus the force of a delatch assist spring keeps the latch rod in contact with the subassembly handling head. As the reciprocating assembly moves up with respect to the latch-rod collar, the collar passes down into the larger opening again, holding the slide plate in the cocked position. This relative movement cams the gripper fingers open, and, as the OHM continues to drive up, the subassembly is left behind. Once the delatch motion is complete, the solenoid is deenergized. Design of the equipment is such that the slide plate cannot be retracted until the OHM has completed its downward stroke and the slide plate is clear of the latch-rod collar, which makes it impossible to delatch unless the subassembly is seated such that the latch rod can push against it.

Because core and blanket subassemblies are square, they must be oriented in angular position to insert them into the reactor. So that the OHM gripper design could be kept as simple as possible, provision for orienting the subassemblies was designed into the subassembly rather than providing for rotation of the gripper. The self-orientation feature of the subassembly consists of specially designed cams located at the top and bottom of the subassembly. These cams serve to rotate a subassembly into proper angular alignment for insertion into its lattice position.

7.9.4.4.2.5 Seals. The rotating face seal and primary bellows seals have been described. The seals internal to the machine are metal O-rings. Compressible O-rings are used to seal the azimuth housing flange to the shield-basket flange and the shield-basket flange to the rotating-plug cover plate.

7.9.4.4.2.6 Shielding. Where necessary, voids in the machine have been filled with shielding material to reduce neutron and gamma radiation levels at the top of the rotating plug. The shield basket (3) in which the OHM is installed is shielded with layers of stainless steel plate (not shown) and canned borated graphite in the same manner as the rest of the rotating plug. Gaps between the basket and the penetration in the plug proper have been adjusted to give optimum shielding protection while providing as large a clearance gap as possible for installation and differential expansion. This gap is stepped in accordance with established practice to reduce streaming.

Voids in the reciprocating tube and latch-rod assembly are filled with a powdered shielding mixture of iron, graphite, and boron carbide. The housing tube is stepped to reduce streaming, and voids in the azimuth housing are filled with steel plate.

Design stroke of the OHM is 106 in. plus 1 in. overtravel at each end. Normal operating stroke is 102 in. The OHM is designed to exert a maximum force of 1500 lb at the gripper, either pushing or pulling. Normal working forces are much less than this (100 to 600 lb). The overload plate assembly settings are 600 to 800 lb.

7.9.4.4.3 SWEEP ARM. At the start of fuel-handling operations, after the hold-down mechanism is raised and prior to rotation of the plug, a sweep arm will traverse the region above the handling heads of core and inner radial-blanket subassemblies.

This sweep arm is operated from the top of the rotating-shield plug and passes through the central guide-tube access penetration. The sweep arm is designed to be collapsed and retracted following its use so that the hold-down mechanism can be located above the core and inner radial-blanket region.

The purpose of the sweep arm is to confirm that no subassembly is inadvertently protruding above its design position.

7.9.4.4.4 TRANSFER ROTOR. The transfer-rotor assembly is shown in Fig. 7.59. This component consists of a rotary drive unit with indexing equipment, a vertical drive shaft to provide the rotary motions, and a large rotating disk at the bottom of the drive shaft in which the finned pots containing the subassemblies are stored. The device serves a twofold purpose. First, the rotor disk provides temporary storage for 11 irradiated core subassemblies between unloadings. Second, the rotor diverts subassemblies horizontally out from under the offset handling-mechanism port so that they can be raised vertically upward into a cask car. A low sodium flow is maintained to the transfer rotor, through connections from the blanket plenum, for removing decay heat from stored subassemblies.

7.9.4.4.5 CASK CAR. The main function of the cask car is to transfer core and blanket subassemblies between the exit port of the reactor and the unloading station of the fuel and repair building. The total travel distance on a special covered wide-gauge track is approximately 125 ft (Fig. 7.60). Radiation and heat-generation data given in Sec. 7.9.4.4.5.2 are based on a full load of central core subassemblies irradiated to 1% and 6% burnup.

7.9.4.4.5.1 Description of Equipment. The cask car consists of three main components: a vertical 12-position cask and rotor, a shielded heat exchanger, and a control cab. The nominal overall dimensions are: 10 ft wide by 13 ft high by approximately 22 ft long. The total weight is 200 tons, the main load being supported on two four-wheel trucks. The car is self-propelled by an electric motor drive, is equipped with brakes, and is provided with heavy-duty hydraulic snubbers mounted fore and aft to assure uniform and positive stops at each end of the car travel.

The upper part of the cask and rotor section has been constructed with an intermediate shield and houses the hoisting mechanism. The interme-

diate shield below the hoisting mechanism area provides an area of reduced radiation activity for maintenance on the cable and hoist equipment. The gripper hoist is supported by two cables and is motor driven by grooved drums that are locked together following the initial cable adjustment. The latch—delatch operation of the gripper jaws is accomplished by a motor-actuated idler, which provides the differential movement of the cables and is compensated to hold a fixed gripper eleva-tion. The hoisting speed is 20 ft/min; travel time in each direction is 1 1/2 min.

Because of the heat-transfer requirements for removing decay heat from irradiated fuel, the sub-assemblies are contained in finned transfer pots filled with sodium; argon is used as the cover gas. The weights of the heaviest items to be handled by the hoist equipment are: (1) finned transfer pot filled with sodium, 230 lb, (2) core subassembly, sodium, and finned pot, 347 lb; (3) blanket subas-sembly, sodium, finned pot, 400 lb; and (4) exit-port shielding plug, 800 lb. The safety rod, shim rod, neutron source, and the oscillator-rod assembly all have lower handling weights than the core and blanket subassemblies and are handled in special trans-fer pots without fins and of reduced size.

The fuel-storage rotor of the cask car con-sists of 11 guide tubes, 9 in. in diameter and sized to receive the 8 1/2-in.-OD transfer-pot flanges. A twelfth position is used for storing the exit-port shielding plug during the fuel trans-fer. Argon for cooling enters the vertical guide tubes at the top and exits at the bottom; the gas stream sweeps the finned section of the trans-fer pots. An axial-vane blower circulates 6500 cu ft/min of argon at approximately 6-in. H_2O pressure to the cask and rotor to cool the 11 transfer pots continuously during the irradiated-fuel transfer. Fuel subassembly temperatures are monitored by 11 thermocouples extending upward from the floor of the car into the argon stream directly below the transfer pots. These gas temperatures, when interpreted in terms of finned-pot heat-transfer performance, pro-vide an approximate fuel temperature. Any seri-ous deviations in temperature can be readily ob-served from the log of the automatic temperature recorder provided for this purpose. The bulk temperatures of the argon entering and leaving the heat exchanger are also automatically re-corded to demonstrate adequate heat-exchanger performance.

The heat-exchanger compartment is lead shield-ed for Na^{24} activity in the sodium vapor which may be deposited in the heat exchanger. The shielding encloses the argon-to-air heat exchanger, two argon blowers with remotely operated louver dampers, and four 25-kw electric resistance heaters (Fig. 7.61). The air blowers and the automatic tempera-ture-control dampers are located external to the shielded compartment. All the stainless-steel tubing was ultrasonic, hydrostatic, and mass-spectrometer tested before assembly, to assure a high degree of integrity in the argon-to-air heat exchanger. All tube-to-tube sheet welds were care-fully examined, and all flange seals were machined for accurate fit. After complete assembly the unit was again mass-spectrometer tested to demon-strate a completely tight system.

The forward part of the cab carries the electrical switchgear for all the motors, heaters, and control devices; the beta monitor and compressor; the cask-car propulsion motor; and assorted recording equipment. The operator's station consists of one bench panel and two wall panels fitted with flush-mounted recorders, indicators, monitors, gauges, and alarm lights. The bench panel carries the switches for controlling all the equipment on the cask car.

7.9.4.4.5.2 Design Data. The transfer cask car is sized to handle 11 new fuel subassemblies and 11 irradiated subassemblies in each cycle. This corresponds to the 11-subassembly decay storage capacity of the reactor transfer rotor. The irradiated subassemblies that are transferred from the reactor core to the transfer rotor will remain in the transfer rotor for decay until the next refueling operation. The length of the decay period is a function of fuel burnup and reactor power level. For cask-car design the decay periods in the transfer rotor were designated as one week for reactor operation at less than 1 at.% burnup and two weeks for operation at 6 at.% burnup. For added safety and flexibility of operation, the cooling capacity requirements were based on a full complement of 11 central core subassemblies.

Studies of the core subassemblies and finned transfer pot show that 19% of the total decay heat is released in the cask shield and 81% at the fins of the transfer pots. The cooling-capacity requirements as originally designed for 300-Mw reactor operation with a 91 subassembly core (or 430 Mw with a 130 subassembly core), based on central core subassemblies only, are as follows:

Burnup, at. %	Decay time, weeks	Decay heat in terms of power before shutdown (P/P_0)	Heat generation per subassembly, kw	Total heat generation 11 subassemblies, kw	81% of heat generation, total kw
1	1	0.002	8.2	90.2	73.0
6	2	0.0015	6.15	67.65	54.8

The cooling capacity of the cask car has a nominal rating of 100 kw. For 200-Mw(t) reactor operation, there is substantial overcapacity.

The design requirements for the cask-car housing and the heat exchanger are primarily for gamma shielding and structural support. The bulk of the shielding material consists of lead poured between 1/2-in. steel plates. With an internal surface temperature of 360°F and an ambient room temperature of 100°F, the calculated external surface temperature is 200°F. The resulting heat losses during the new-fuel preheating period are calculated to be 70,000 Btu/hr, and, during the irradiated-fuel transfer, 80,000 Btu/hr. Although the surface temperature of 200°F is higher than normal power-plant practice, the advantages of the additional cooling capacity and of free access for inspection and maintenance outweigh the benefits of placing thermal insulation over the entire exterior surface.

7.9.4.4.5.3 Shielding and Monitoring. The gamma shielding of the irradiated subassemblies in the cask-car storage space consists of a minimum of 14 in. of lead integrally poured between two 1/2-in. steel walls. At the front end of the cask car, the lead is partially replaced by 8 1/8 in. of depleted uranium to meet the clearance requirements of the primary shield tank. The maximum radiation dose rate at any part of the cask car during normal operation is 7.5 mrem/hr. This station is approximately 15 ft away from the cask proper and 6 ft away from the nearest wall of the shielded heat exchanger. The cask-car operator is assisted by a helper whose duties consist mainly of lining up the exit port with the cask car, removing the floor shield and directing the crane operator, making floor-to-cask car connections, directing purging operations, and standing by as a temporary operator. His standby position is approximately 15 to 20 ft from the shielded cask except for short periods of inspection and during the final exit-port closure procedure.

Although the activity of the argon gas within the cask car will decay to a low level during the one- to two-week interval between loadings, it will gradually build up during refueling as a result of mixing with the exit-port cover gas. The A^{41} activity of the cover gas in the exit port has been calculated to be 2.4 μc/cm^3, and the Na^{24} activity, 0.05 curies/cm^3. Because of the low concentration of Na^{24} in the saturated argon (8.1 × 10^{-5} curies in one cask-car volume), it is the A^{41} that controls for considerations of maximum permissible leakage. The entire cask car, including the heat exchanger, exit-port valve, and operating-shaft penetrations, has been specified to have a maximum leak rate of less than 0.05 standard cu ft/hr at operating temperatures and pressures. For complete mixing of the room atmosphere, based on the reactor-building volume above the operating floor, the above leak rate will not cause the building environment activity to exceed the occupational environment tolerance of 2 × 10^{-6} μc/cm^3 for a two- to four-hr unloading period. For personnel safety a monitoring system for radioactive gas has been provided to continuously read and record the activity at seven potential leak areas on the cask car. Gas samples at each of the seven areas are monitored for beta activity, and the instruments are calibrated to sound an alarm when the leak rate at any one area exceeds the prescribed limits.

7.9.4.4.5.4 Cask-car Alignment with Exit Port. The reactor exit-port standpipe, which extends vertically from the transfer-rotor tank to the operating floor above, has been designed to be free standing and is permitted to float with temperature. At the maximum operating temperature and at the refueling temperature, the horizontal and vertical positions vary owing to the expansion of the stainless steel. The cask-car alignment with the exit port to take care of expansion is accomplished by adjustable rail stops and a car-centering gauge. Figure 7.62 shows the centering gauge in position over the exit port and indicates the method of adjusting the index point adjacent to the rail before the cask car moves over the exit port. The centering tool is removed, and an index pointer on the cask car is then aligned with the pointer on the floor in both the east−west and north−south directions. The index point on the cask car is initially set by a male−female checking template that periodically serves to check the centering gauge.

The locating pin on the floor sealing flange fits into a hole on the bottom of the cask-car flange in such a way that the combined clearances will ensure against any possibility of restraining the free movement of the fuel exit port beyond the safe allowable force and moment values. An adjustable guide is provided outside the wheel flanges to adjust the alignment of the cask car in the direction normal to the rails. The front end of the cask car can thus be shifted to match the position of the fuel exit port.

Vertical movement of the top flange of the fuel exit port during refueling results from the heating effects of the hot irradiated fuel that passes through the length of the exit standpipe. The heavy sealing ring on the underside of the cask car mates and seals with the exit-port flange by means of a double O-ring seal. It seals in the down position owing to its own weight of approximately 1 ton and is raised to the travel position by three motor-driven linear actuators. The sealing-flange weight is supported on the exit-port access tube well within the allowable design loading for this component.

7.9.4.4.5.5 Cask-car Operation. The refueling of the reactor is a scheduled operation with the reactor down and all the system interlocks in effect. Before the cask-car hoist can be made operative to remove the exit-port seal and shield plug, the equipment door must be closed and bolted to register a monitor seal pressure of 5 psig. Following the purging and pressure testing of the space between the ball valve of the cask car and the exit-port shield plug, the operator obtains instructions from the main control room to proceed. An intercom provides continuous contact with the main-control-room operator. The cask-car alarm signals are also fed back to the control room and must therefore be properly corrected before a clear signal will be given to continue operation.

All the cask-car controls are located within reach of the operator's position in the control cab. All the recording instruments; monitoring gauges; pressure, temperature, and flow gauges; and all the position indicators, including alarm signals, are conveniently located for the operator's information. The argon valve station for the exit port below floor is located at a station outside the cask car and is operated by the cask-car operator's assistant.

The actual refueling procedure is performed as a one-for-one exchange, starting with the lowering of a new fuel subassembly into the transfer rotor of the reactor and followed by the hoisting of an irradiated subassembly into the cask car. The fuel exchange from the transfer rotor into the core of the reactor begins after cask-car unloading has been completed, the exit port sealed, the cask-car vehicle moved out of the reactor building, and the equipment door closed and sealed.

The complete cycle time for loading 11 new fuel subassemblies into the cask car, moving the car from the fuel and repair building into the reactor building, purging the seal area, and exchanging 11 subassemblies at the transfer rotor is approximately 24 hr. It takes about 12 more hours to exchange spent and fresh subassemblies in the reactor.

7.9.4.4.5.6 Cask-car Unloading Station. The cask-car unloading station (transfer-rotor storage tank) is a sodium-filled jacketed storage tank within which there is a transfer rotor capable of holding 22 finned pots in sockets spaced 19 in. apart around its outer periphery (Figs. 6.65 and 6.66 of Chap. 6). The tank is equipped with an access port to the cleaning chamber and another to the cask-car unloading station. The tank is 13 ft in diameter and 12 ft high; it is constructed of 9/16-in.-thick carbon steel and carries an ASME code stamp. The design conditions are 0 to 68 psia at 650°F; normal operating conditions are 15 to 20 psia at 450°F. The tank can hold 67,500 lb of sodium and is equipped with a cold trap and plugging indicator which provide a means of maintaining and checking the sodium oxide level.

The heat released in the transfer tank by the decay of irradiated subassemblies is removed by a closed-loop nitrogen cooling system, which is capable of handling 22 subassemblies at 8 kw of decay heat per subassembly. Nitrogen is recirculated through shielded ducts, a nitrogen-to-water heat exchanger, a dual-fan arrangement located in an accessible space in the fuel and repair building, and then to a shroud around the transfer tank. Each fan has full capacity; one fan is connected to emergency power and the other has provisions for connections to emergency power. A moisture detector is installed in the duct immediately downstream from the nitrogen-to-water heat exchanger. If moisture is detected, the water supply to the cooling coils will automatically shut off, and an alarm will sound in the control room.

7.9.4.4.6 STEAM-CLEANING MACHINE. An irradiated subassembly to be cleaned is transferred inside the transfer tank from the cask-car unloading port to the cleaning-machine port. The cleaning machine is connected to the port, the space between the cleaning-machine valve and the port valve is purged with argon, the seal is tested, the valves are opened, and the cleaning-machine gripper is lowered and latched onto the subassembly.

Cooling of the irradiated subassembly is provided by a flow of argon through the subassembly prior to its withdrawal from the sodium. An interlock prevents withdrawal of the subassembly from the transfer tank until the argon flow is established. The subassembly is pulled up into the cleaning machine by the gripper. During this operation the subassembly is cooled by argon passing through it at the rate of 250 lb/hr. The argon is recirculated and cooled by a closed-loop heat-exchanger system to maintain the subassembly inlet temperature at about 260°F. The argon flows through the subassembly to the transfer tank, through an entrainment separator to a compressor, through a cooler to the cleaning chamber, and then through the gripper and subassembly.

When the subassembly is positioned in the cleaning machine, an argon bypass line around the isolation valve on the bottom of the cleaning chamber is opened, the cleaning-machine and access-tube valves are closed, and the machine is rotated to a position over the cutup-pool access tube. The cooling argon supply is switched from the recirculating system to the clean argon supply system, and the discharge line from the cleaning machine is opened to the waste-liquid and -gas systems. An automatic timer device is started, and, over a period of 1 min, the stoichiometric amount of dry steam necessary to react the sodium on the subassembly is introduced into the argon flow. At the end of the first minute, the subassembly is being cooled by the steam and the argon supply is turned off. The subassembly is steamed for four additional minutes and then rinsed by hot water. Then the cleaning machine is flooded with demineralized water, and the subassembly is rinsed for 12 min. The rinse water is drained from the chamber, and argon is admitted to the chamber to break the vacuum. This ends the automatically timed cycle. The inflatable seal between the cleaning machine and the cutup-pool access tube is made and tested, the valves are opened, and the subassembly is lowered into the water-filled cutup-pool.

7.9.4.4.7 CUTUP AND DECAY POOLS. Upon completion of the cleaning operation, the irradiated subassembly is deposited in an underwater transfer car and transferred to the cutup pool. It is then moved with handling devices on the cutup-pool bridge and is inserted into a leaker can. The leaker can is fitted with a flanged and gasketed top. After a period of decay, a liquid sample is taken from the can and analyzed for fission products. If the concentration exceeds $5 \times 10^{-3} \, \mu c/cm^3$, the subassembly is left in the leaker can for the entire decay period. If the subassembly proves to be a nonleaker, it is removed from the leaker can. The subassembly, either in or out of a leaker can, is then transferred by the cutup-pool bridge and an underwater transfer car from the cutup pool through the pool isolation valve to the decay pool. The decay-pool bridge gripper positions the subassembly in the underwater storage rack.

The permanent storage rack consists of a single tier that provides spaces for 344 subassemblies on a noncritical spacing of 14 in., as shown in Fig. 7.12. This is sufficient capacity to accommodate the normal storage of core and blanket subassemblies plus an additional complete core subassembly unloading. In the event a complete reactor unloading is required, temporary racks could be procured which could be supported on top of the permanent rack to provide 513 additional storage spaces. All core subassemblies will, in any event, be stored in the permanent rack, and the temporary rack will be used for blanket subassemblies only. The storage positions in the temporary rack will be on the same spacing as the permanent rack but will be located midway between the positions in the permanent rack.

The subassemblies are stored in the decay pool for a period of approximately 180 days. After the decay period the subassemblies are transferred by the decay-pool bridge and the underwater transfer car through the pool isolation valve back to the cutup pool. Blanket subassemblies are loaded directly into a shipping cask. Core subassemblies are transferred to the cutup machine, where they are placed in a horizontal position, and two cuts are made to separate the fuel section from the axial blanket sections. The design of the core subassembly provides an adequate space between the fuel section and the axial blanket sections to allow these cuts to be made without risk of cutting into the fuel pins or the blanket rods. The cutup step is

necessary because the fuel and blanket material may be reprocessed at different off-site locations. After the fuel section has been separated from the blanket sections, the pieces are stored in a rack in a subcritical array until they are loaded into a shipping cask. Section 7.5 has additional details on decay storage.

7.9.4.4.8 NEW-FUEL HANDLING AND STORAGE FACILITIES. New-fuel handling and storage facilities comprise a loading dock, fuel receiving room, subassembly inspection station, storage vault, transfer tunnel, and tunnel transfer car. The facilities are situated in the northeast corner of the fuel and repair building.

The new-fuel flow diagram is shown in Fig. 7.57. Fuel-subassembly shipments are made by truck transport and are received at the fuel and repair building loading dock. The subassembly shipping container is transferred from the dock to the adjoining receiving room by a motor-propelled cart. In the receiving room the subassemblies are removed from the reusable shipping containers and inspected. Each core subassembly shipping container holds one core subassembly. Each blanket subassembly shipping container holds as many as three blanket subassemblies. Subassemblies are handled in the receiving and storage areas by a manually operated subassembly handling cart, which is capable of handling only one subassembly at a time. Administrative procedures assure that subassemblies are always stored either in a shipping container or in the storage vault, both of which provide a subcritical array of subassemblies under all conceivable conditions.

After the subassemblies have been removed from the shipping containers, they are transferred to the new-fuel inspection station, where they receive a visual inspection and are checked for weight, dimensions, and air-flow pressure drop. This inspection is performed to confirm the inspection made by the fabricator, to make sure the subassemblies were not damaged in shipment, and to assure that the subassemblies are dimensionally and physically correct. The subassemblies are identified by serial number, and the inspection data for each subassembly are recorded on individual data sheets.

Following inspection the subassemblies are transferred by the subassembly handling cart to the adjoining new-fuel storage vault, where they are stored in individual tubes suspended below the operating floor. The new-fuel storage vault is a room containing 209 sleeves embedded in the floor in a 19-row by 11-row array in a 14 in. square pattern. The vault is divided by the floor into a lower compartment and an access area above. The top of each sleeve is covered and fits flush with the floor. Storage tubes are fitted into the floor sleeves. Positive spacing of the storage tube is assured by the design of the sleeves. The atmosphere within the storage vault is controlled to maintain the temperature at $70°F \pm 2°F$ and the relative humidity at a maximum of 40%. Air is circulated from the lower compartment of the storage vault through perforations in the sleeves to the upper compartment and back to the lower compartment. Dust filters are provided on the air inlet.

The upper compartment is approximately 17 ft wide by 25 ft long by 18 ft high. The room has a steel door that normally is locked; the room is accessible only to authorized personnel. The lower compartment is approximately 16 ft wide by 24 ft long by 13 ft high. Walls below grade are water-proofed, and a drain is provided in the floor. There would be no danger of criticality, however, even if the vault were completely or partially flooded. There is no normal access to the lower compart-ment space.

When they are needed in the reactor, subassem-blies are transferred from the storage vault by the handling cart to the new-subassembly loading tunnel. The new-subassembly loading tunnel is immediately adjacent to the transfer tank. This tank represents a strong gamma source when it contains irradiated fuel. The tunnel has therefore been constructed of reinforced concrete to assure that the dose rate does not exceed 0.75 mrem/hr at the outside walls. The access port to the new-subassembly loading tunnel is located in the fuel-receiving room and is equipped with a plug that is interlocked with a radiation monitor so that the plug cannot be removed unless the radiation level in the tunnel is 200 mrem/hr or less.

A remotely operated car in the new-subassembly loading tunnel transfers the new subassembly from the access port through the tunnel to a position under the cleaning-machine port. When the cleaning machine is ready, the subassembly is lifted from the loading tunnel through the port into the cleaning machine. Interlocks are provided that prevent mal-operation in every step from this point until the spent fuel is returned to the cutup pool. The cleaning machine acts primarily as a transfer unit when handling new fuel since no cleaning is per-formed on the new subassemblies.

After the new subassembly is positioned in the cleaning machine, the valve on the port is closed. The floor of the cleaning-machine chamber has three subassembly ports: one from the new-sub-assembly loading tunnel to the chamber, a second from the chamber to the transfer tank, and the third from the chamber to the cutup pool. The cleaning-machine chamber is mounted on a hinged support that allows rotation over any of the three access ports. Argon, steam, and water-service systems are connected to the machine. Interlocks prevent the accidental introduction of water or steam into the cleaning machine when it is posi-tioned over the port to the transfer tank. The cleaning machine is rotated to a position over the port between the cleaning chamber and the transfer tank. The air atmosphere in the cleaning machine is purged with argon, the cleaning-machine heaters are turned on, and argon heated to 450°F is circu-lated through the subassembly to preheat it before it is deposited in the sodium-filled transfer tank.

The cleaning machine is connected to the trans-fer tank, the air in the space between the valve on the bottom of the cleaning machine and the valve on the access port is purged with argon, and the seal is checked. The two valves are opened, and the new subassembly is lowered into a sodium-filled finned pot submerged in a pool of sodium in the transfer tank. The transfer-tank sodium pool, which is covered with an argon blanket, is main-tained at an operating temperature of 400°F to 450°F by thermostatically controlled electrical heaters. The tank appurtenances include a plugging indicator and cold trap. Prior to insertion of a subassembly, a plugging run is made on the sodium in the tank to protect against the possibility of plugging a subassembly with sodium oxide. The tank is also equipped with a pressure-relief system that is vented to the waste-gas system.

Thirty-three finned pots are available. In addi-tion, special pots for handling the antimony section of the neutron source for the safety and control rods have also been provided. The fuel-handling finned pots are made of type 304 stainless steel, schedule 40 pipe, approximately 96 in. in length. They have a minimum inside diameter of 3.690 in. and weigh approximately 190 lb. Their outer wall surface is extended with 64 equally spaced fins that are re-sistance welded to the pipe. These fins are also of 304 stainless steel and are 0.035 in. thick, 1 1/2 in. wide, and 87 in. long.

The special pots for the control and safety rods and for the antimony section of the neutron source have no fins since only a very small heat-removal capacity is needed. They are dimensionally compat-ible, however, for use in the cask car and transfer rotor. A fuel subassembly cannot be placed in a special pot because inside dimensions are such as to allow only the smaller special components to fit. A special gripper and other provisions have been made so that cleaning of transfer pots can be accomplished in the cleaning chamber.

After depositing the subassembly in the finned pot, the cleaning-machine gripper is retracted, and the access-port valve is closed. The transfer-tank rotor is then rotated, and the new subassembly is positioned under the access port from the cask-car unloading station. Subsequent operations involve loading the subassembly into the car and transfer-ring it to the rotor in the reactor vessel.

7.9.4.5 Controls and Interlocks

Extensive automatic program controls, inter-locks, and data logging devices are provided so that the sequence of operations can be controlled posi-tively from the time a subassembly enters the fuel-handling cycle until it returns to the cutup pool. Administrative procedures also provide a double check on the status of every subassembly in the system. All the foregoing activities, except the interchange of subassemblies between the cask car and the reactor-vessel transfer rotor, are carried out in the fuel and repair building. Each operation in this building has been designed to prevent the accumulation of a critical array of new or spent fuel and to provide continuous cooling of spent fuel so that fuel melting cannot occur.

A key interlock system has been designed to assure that the proper sequence of operations is followed during the preparation of the reactor for fuel loading and then for the return to normal operating conditions. The interlocks provided make it impossible for the operator to perform other than in the proper sequence.

The key interlock assemblies have a key-oper-ated lock bolt and, in some of the units, a solenoid-operated latch-bar release unit. A push button is used to energize the solenoid that lifts the latch bar out of a slot in the lock bolt, permitting the lock bolt to be moved by the key from its latched position. The design of the assembly is such that the key must be in the lock before the lock bolt can be moved. In addition, the key must be in a vertical position before it can be removed from the lock. The transfer-position key-interlock assembly is a special two-key unit. Both keys must be inserted before the lock bolt can be moved. Only one key can be removed at any one time.

Each solenoid key-release unit has one or more switch contacts in series with the push button and the solenoid. Each contact in the series, including the push button, must be closed before the solenoid can be energized. A white indicating lamp is connected in parallel with the push button and solenoid. This lamp is illuminated when all series-connected contacts (except the push button) are closed, and thus it provides an indication that the solenoid may be energized by depressing the push button.

A mimic bus mounted on the front of the panel serves to remind the operator of the correct operating sequence. Figure 9.53, Chap. 9, is a schematic diagram of the key-interlock system. The solid lines in Fig. 9.53 are used to indicate the shutdown sequence. The dotted lines indicate the start-up sequence.

7.9.4.6 Data Logging System and Subassembly Accountability

Two complete sets of automatic logging equipment have been provided to ensure that proper accounting of the core and blanket subassemblies is accomplished at all times. This equipment consists of programmers to receive input signals that indicate the position of the fuel-handling equipment and a Flexowriter to log the information.

One of the data loggers is located in the fuel and repair building to log all operations of the steam-cleaning machine, the sodium-filled transfer tank, and the cask car while it is in the fuel and repair building. A separate data logger is located in the main control room to log all operations of the transfer rotor, rotating-shield plug, offset handling mechanism, and the cask car while it is in the reactor building. The data-logger systems compare the operation performed with the desired operation as shown on the program tape. Any error will be annunciated in the main control room for both loggers or in the fuel and repair building for the logger located therein and will prevent operation of the offset handling mechanism (OHM) gripper until the data-logger error circuit is released. This is an administrative function. The OHM gripper will not release unless both data loggers are in service.

In addition to the permanent record of all core- and blanket-subassembly movements, which is provided by the data logger on perforated tape, a set of accountability cards is also maintained by the operator as various steps are accomplished. Each subassembly has its own card. The cards are 5 in. by 8 in. preprinted cardboard and contain loading or charging information on the front side and discharging information on the reverse side. The amount of filing space, sources of error, and confusion are reduced by keeping the number of accountability card types to a total of three. The cards record the results of all gauging tests and inspections; the exact position the subassemblies occupy in the storage vault, transfer tank, cask car, transfer rotor, reactor vessel cutup pool, and decay pool; the date and time when various operations and transfers are performed; and the final shipping data including the date and shipping-cask number.

7.9.5 RAPSODIE FUEL HANDLING

7.9.5.1 Fuel-handling System

The fuel-handling system at Rapsodie [41] utilizes a double rotating plug in the reactor. A primary cask car moved into position over the reactor for refueling transfers the spent subassembly to an examination cell or a canning station located in a transfer compartment. A secondary cask car moves the subassembly out of the reactor building into the decay pool area. New plutonium fuel is stored in a shielded area, canned, and brought into the reactor by the reverse of this procedure. Figure 7.63 shows the complete fuel-handling cycle. Figures in Chap. 11 show details of the reactor assembly and the rotating plugs.

7.9.5.2 List of Components and Facilities

The main components and facilities in the Rapsodie fuel-handing system are reactor fuel-handling port (Fig. 7.64), primary cask car (Fig. 7.65), primary cask-car gripper (Fig. 7.28), examination cell (Fig. 7.66), canning station (Fig. 7.67), temporary storage pit with transfer rotor (Fig. 7.63), decanning station (Fig. 7.69), secondary cask car (Fig. 7.70), decay storage pool with entrance and exit transfer arms and traveling bridge (Fig. 7.68), and new-fuel storage building with radioactive and nonradioactive subassembly storage areas and handling equipment (Fig. 7.71).

The transfer compartment in the reactor containment building serves as a transfer point from one cask car to another. A fuel-storage and component-repair building is connected to the reactor containment building by an air lock.

7.9.5.3 Fuel-handling Sequence

The following is the sequence of fuel handling (Fig. 7.63).

Radioactive new fuel is brought into a new-fuel storage cell by a transfer car. All handling of the subassembly is automatic (Fig. 7.71). A traveling bridge stores and removes each subassembly. Prior to transfer to the reactor cask, the subassembly is canned in a lead alloy. An underground transfer car removes the subassembly and positions it under the secondary cask car; the same transfer car can also remove nonradioactive subassemblies from a separate nonradioactive storage room. The secondary cask car (Fig. 7.70) transfers the subassembly into the reactor building.

The secondary cask car deposits the subassembly in the decanning station, which is located in the transfer compartment. Here the lead alloy is heated by induction heating (Fig. 7.69). The primary cask car (Fig. 7.65) removes the subassembly from the decanning station to a point over the reactor handling

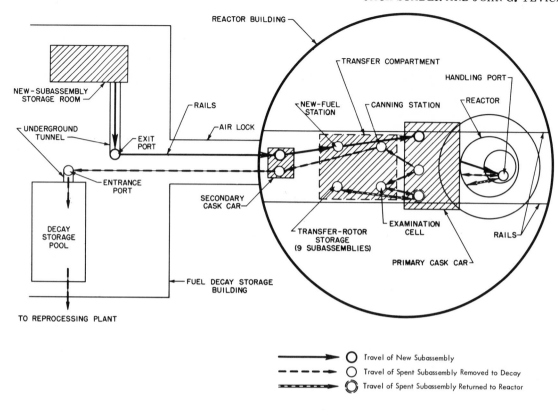

FIG. 7.63—Rapsodie fuel-handling cycle [41].

port (Fig. 7.64), which is located in the reactor eccentric rotating plug. The primary cask-car gripper (Fig. 7.28) transfers the subassembly into the reactor. After burnup the primary cask-car gripper transfers the subassembly into the primary cask-car transfer rotor. The primary cask car deposits the irradiated subassembly in an examination cell (Fig. 7.66). The primary cask car removes the subassembly and redeposits it in the canning station (7.67) in a lead-alloy bath. The secondary cask car removes the canned subassembly from the canning station and out of the reactor building.

The secondary cask car transfers the canned subassembly to the decay storage pool entrance port (Fig. 7.68). A carriage transfers the subassembly through the subassembly decay pool entrance port to the decay pool. The traveling bridge stores the canned subassembly in a storage position. After sufficient decay time the traveling bridge transfers the subassembly to an exit port. A removal cask car removes the canned subassembly to a fuel-processing plant.

7.9.5.4 Fuel Handling in the Primary Cask Car

7.9.5.4.1 FUEL-HANDLING PORT. The handling port (Fig. 7.64) located in the small eccentric rotating plug provides access for the gripper of the primary handling cask car to any subassembly in the reactor. Argon at 150°C (302°F) is provided to the cask car for cooling or preheating subassemblies when they are above the level of the

reactor sodium. A vertical fixed tube is a part of the small rotating plug. This tube immersed in sodium limits the volume of radioactive argon that can escape into the cask car at the start of handling operations.

A retainer tube located inside the fixed tube can occupy two positions, a high position during operation of the reactor or rotation of the plug and a low position during fuel handling. During fuel handling the retainer tube is in contact with the handling head of the six subassemblies adjacent to the subassembly being removed, and it keeps them in position. The tube also provides a flow passage for the gas coolant. The retainer tube is normally pulled upward by a spring. It is pushed toward the lower part of the fixed tube by the lowering of the primary cask-car handling mechanism. In the low position a group of springs acting on the retainer tube provide a force of 100 to 200 kg (220 to 440 lb) on the heads of the adjacent subassemblies. The position of this tube is controlled by a rotating potentiometer. Above the handling port there is a shield ring that assures a gastight fitting between the primary cask car and the handling port. This ring consists of two principal parts, a low assembly, which surrounds the mechanism of the retainer tube, and a high assembly, which is placed in position prior to the start of handling operations. During reactor operation this assembly is replaced by a leaktight shield plug. The plug for the handling port is removed by the primary cask. This plug is heated electrically to avoid sodium condensation on the surfaces. Leaktightness of the primary cask con-

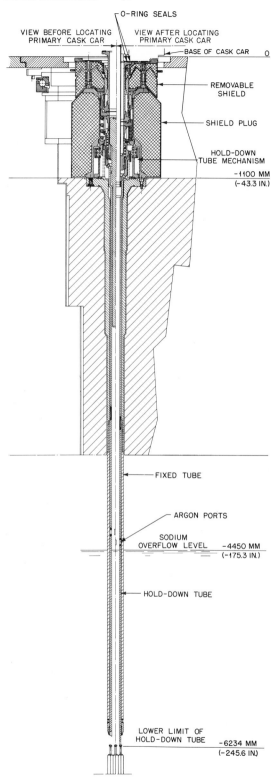

FIG. 7.64—Rapsodie reactor fuel-handling port [41].

nection to the handling port is obtained by two O-rings located above the shield ring at a -40-mm (-1.57 in.) level. The cask-car mechanism is guided

by a tube in the upper part of the port which is lowered from the primary cask. This tube channels the flow of cooling gas during refueling.

7.9.5.4.2 OTHER PORTS. Three other ports are located in the rotating plug to allow for the handling and transfer of subassemblies within the reactor. The rotating plugs are not turned and the control rods are kept connected during this operation. Special handling machines or even the primary cask car may be used for these ports.

7.9.5.4.3 PRIMARY CASK CAR. The primary cask car (Fig. 7.65) contains a gripper that is used for the removal of the subassemblies. The gripper is fixed at the end of a rigid shaft that makes possible the use of a controlled force on a subassembly during its insertion into the reactor. The cask car is approximately 40.2 ft (12.250 m) high, 24.6 ft (7.5 m) long, and 20.5 ft (6.25 m) wide. It is made of two vertical cylinders, the body of the cask car containing a transfer rotor and a long vertical shaft. The two assemblies have separate atmospheres to prevent the radioactive argon in the body of the cask car from leaking into the inert nonradioactive argon in the nonshielded vertical shaft. The cask car can have a vertical movement of 4.92 in. (125 mm) from +3.35 in. to -1.57 in. (+85 mm to -40 mm). This is made possible by four hydraulic jacks. The assembly is mounted on two carriages to provide for longitudinal and transverse movements (the main carriage provides longitudinal movements). A control cab is located on the main carriage. A heat-transfer loop carried on the transverse carriage can cool two irradiated subassemblies at 2 kw each without exceeding a 450°C (842°F) fuel-pin sheath temperature. This same circuit can be used for heating new subassemblies to approximately 150°C (302°F). The primary cask car is shielded sufficiently to protect personnel working in the reactor containment building.

7.9.5.4.3.1 Main Carriage. The main carriage is made up of a chassis mounted on four wheels; two of the wheels are connected to electric-motor drives. The carriage has two speeds, 1.97 and 0.079 in./sec (0.050 and 0.002 m/sec). The carriage is stopped by means of two hydraulic brakes applied to the rails. Laterally this carriage is guided by two systems of three rollers mounted in a triangle bearing on the rail flanges.

7.9.5.4.3.2 Transverse Carriage. The transverse carriage has a rigid frame. Movement of the carriage perpendicular to the main carriage is on four idler wheels. Two pinion gears drive two racks integral with the main carriage. A manually controlled electric motor provides speeds of 0.0175 m/sec (0.69 in./sec) and 0.00875 m/sec (0.34 in./sec). The alignment and the braking are similar to their counterparts in the main carriage. The transverse carriage supports the cask itself and assures its alignment during vertical movement.

7.9.5.4.3.3 Cask Body. The internal walls of the cask body are of stainless-steel welded plate; the external walls are of a lesser alloy. The cask body is 4.9 ft (1.5 m) in diameter, 8.2 ft (2.5 m) high,

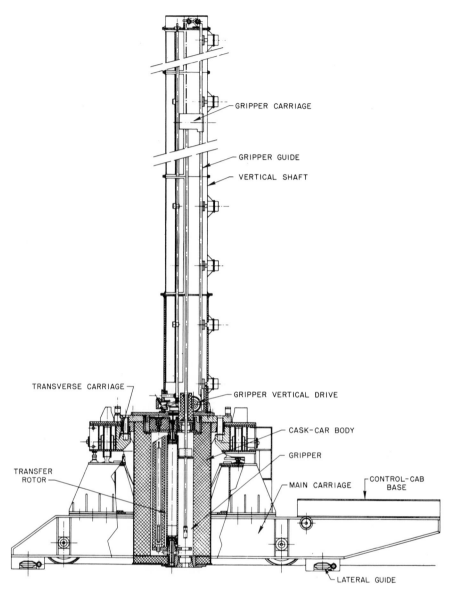

FIG. 7.65—Rapsodie primary cask car [41].

and weighs 41.8 short tons (38 metric tons). A lead shield is located between the two walls. The entrance holes for the gripper can be closed by two electrically controlled valves, which can also be operated manually. The upper cover plate of the cask is made of two special plugs, which, after the removal of the vertical shaft, provide for the removal of the subassemblies contained in the transfer rotor.

7.9.5.4.3.4 Transfer Rotor. The transfer rotor in the cask car is mounted on two bearings. The transfer rotor is driven by a manually controlled electric motor located external to the cask body. The rotation is at two speeds of 1.25 rpm and 0.0625 rpm. The rotor is equipped with a position indicator that transmits the position indications to the cask-car control cab. There are five rotor positions for:

(1) shutoff of the vertical shaft, (2) handling port plugs, (3) guide tube of the cask car, (4) new subassembly, and (5) irradiated subassembly. These positions are designed for proper cooling and heating.

7.9.5.4.3.5 Gripper. The gripper assembly (Fig. 7.28) consists of the gripper and those mechanisms which close, open, and rotate the gripper. The gripper has three fingers; a feeler rod determines the presence of a subassembly within the fingers. There are three speeds in a vertical direction, 3.94, 0.394, and 0.0394 in./sec (10, 1, and 0.1 cm/sec). Rotation is 60°, which allows for unlocking control-rod guide tubes, as previously described. The electric drives and mechanical transmissions are integral with the carriage, which moves vertically with the gripper drive shaft in the vertical shaft.

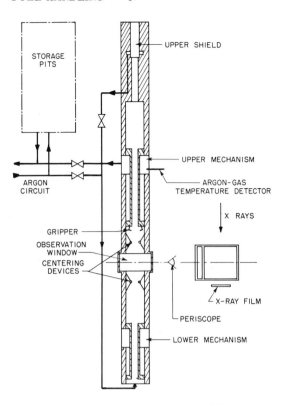

FIG. 7.66—Rapsodie examination cell [41].

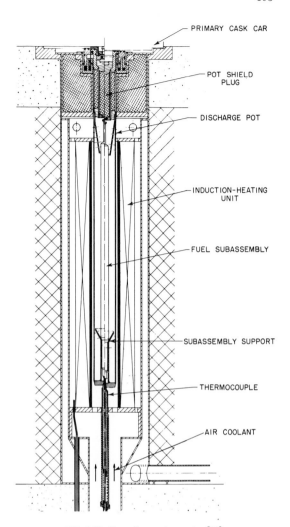

FIG. 7.67—Rapsodie canning station [41].

7.9.5.4.3.6 Vertical Shaft. The vertical shaft encloses the manual safety controls, the gripper interlocks, the mechanisms necessary for alignment and movement of the carriage, and the counterweights for the gripper. The framework of the casing is made of four cylindrical plates 28.4 in. (720 mm) in diameter tied together by bolted flanges. The lower cylinder is located on top of the cask body. The assembly is leaktight. The gripper moves in the vertical shaft through an upper cylinder hole containing scraping segments and argon preheating inlets which provide an argon blast to remove traces of liquid sodium. The hole can be covered when the vertical cask is removed.

7.9.5.4.3.7 Heat-transfer Loop. The transverse carriage carries the heat-transfer loop used to cool or heat the subassemblies in the cask car or in the fuel-handling port in the reactor plug. The loop can be used to heat the body of the cask car to 100°C (212°F), to purge the space between the cask car and the port plugs, and to supply argon at the proper pressure.

7.9.5.4.3.8 Control Cab. The control cab, located on the main carriage, has the necessary instrumentation and controls to indicate the status of the mechanical equipment in the cask car, the status of the heat-transport circuit, and the pressures and temperatures in the entrance and exit of the body of the cask car. The operator in the control cab can perform all the necessary handling functions. He receives authorization from the control room to proceed with operations. It is possible in case of

emergency to stop all movements from the control room.

7.9.5.4.3.9 Positioning of Cask Car. The cask car can be placed over the rotating plugs without interfering with the rotation of the two plugs. The alignment between the axis of the gripper and the axis of the handling port is within 0.019 in. (0.5 mm). An optical apparatus is used to align the cask car with the handling port. A television camera is also used for visual control. One receiver is in the control cab, and another is in the control room.

7.9.5.5 Secondary Handling

7.9.5.5.1 TRANSFER COMPARTMENT. Since the primary cask car is at all times within the containment building, the transfer of subassemblies and other equipment from the containment building is by means of a secondary handling system. This means that there must be a link between the primary cask car and a secondary cask car. This link is a transfer compartment. Two pits are located in the

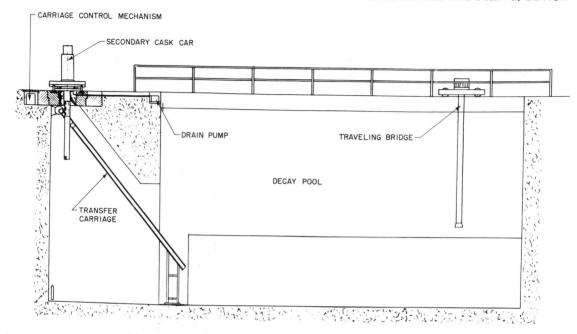

FIG. 7.68—Rapsodie fuel building decay pool—vertical elevation [41].

transfer compartment, one for charging new fuel (decanning station) and one for discharging spent fuel (a canning station). An examination cell in the transfer compartment is used for examining new and irradiated subassemblies. A storage pit that can accept nine new or irradiated subassemblies is provided. Only the primary cask car can be used over the examination cell and the storage pit.

After their removal from the reactor, the subassemblies are canned in discharge pots containing an alloy of lead. The secondary cask car then removes the subassembly from the canning station. In a similar fashion the secondary cask car brings new subassemblies to the decanning station in a charging pot filled with an alloy of lead. After the alloy has been melted, the primary cask car removes the subassembly for installation in the reactor.

7.9.5.5.1.1 Canning Station and Discharge Pots. The canning station (Fig. 7.67) is closed off at the top with a removable gastight slab. Cooling air enters a central annulus at the bottom, passes up the annulus and through an external annulus, and leaves at the bottom. The long central portion of the canning station has an annulus of induction coils for heating and melting the alloy and keeping it in a molten state. The flange located in the upper part of the station carries the discharge pot, which consists of a tube closed at the top by a shield plug. The bottom of the pot contains a conical section for supporting the subassembly. The upper flange at the top of the pot forms a seal between the primary cask car and the pot. The alloy used in the pot is a eutectic of lead and antimony, 89wt.% lead and 11wt.% antimony. This alloy forms a compound with the sodium that does not react with air. It forms a good thermal bond with the subassembly, and, owing to its good heat conductivity and heat capacity, the pot can remain without cooling for 50 min with fuel not exceeding 450°C (842°F). The eutectic is solidified by cooling after the insertion of the subassembly. The alloy also forms a gamma shield. The lead—antimony alloy is preferred to pure lead because the alloy shrinks less during cooling.

7.9.5.5.1.2 Decanning Station and Charging Pots. The decanning station (Fig. 7.69) is identical with the canning station. Preheating by induction raises the subassembly temperature to above 150°C (302°F). The charging pots are smaller in diameter than the discharge pots and do not need a bond between the assembly and the alloy.

7.9.5.5.1.3 Examination Cell. The examination cell (Fig. 7.66) is designed to allow the examination of any type of subassembly, new or irradiated. It is designed to remove 2 kw of heat and to contain contamination that may result from a leaky subassembly. The cell is used to check the exterior dimensions of a subassembly or fuel pin and to radiographically examine a fuel pin. The cell is gastight. A translation and rotation mechanism located in the cell provides a means of viewing, through an observation window, the upper 15.8 in. (400 mm) of a subassembly. A second mechanism located above the first grips the handling head and positions the subassembly so that the lower part of the subassembly, including the nozzle, can be viewed. Located between the two mechanisms are the examination window, examination apparatus, and centering rollers that serve as a subassembly alignment guide. A periscope with a magnification of 6 is used to observe the subassembly through the observation window. The distance between the objective and the point being observed is 3.94 ft (1.2 m). The assembly has a 300-kv X-ray machine and a light intensifier.

7.9.5.5.1.4 Temporary Storage Pits. These pits, each a gastight shell 27.6 in. (700 mm) in diameter, contain a transfer rotor with nine positions. Each position is automatically cooled by argon before the introduction of a subassembly. A mechanism with a double jaw orients the subassembly.

7.9.5.5.2 SECONDARY CASK CAR. The use of a canning station permits the design of a simple secondary cask car (Fig. 7.70) without gastight joints and without cooling circuits. It consists of a cylinder of lead shielding contained in a carbon-steel tank into which is placed a discharge pot or a charge pot. An automatic cable gripper handles the pots. The assembly is mounted on an automated four-wheeled carriage traversing a track from the containment building to the decay storage pool. The secondary cask car is 9 ft (2.75 m) long, 4.9 ft (1.5 m) wide, and 9.8 ft (3 m) high. The car weighs approximately 20 metric tons (22 short tons).

7.9.5.6 General Principles for the Control of Mechanical Handling

7.9.5.6.1 INTRODUCTION. For each handling sequence a program called the handling program precisely defines movements of elements in the reactor building as well as in the containment building. This program is transmitted to the radioactive building control room, the regular control room, the control cabs of all cask cars, and the control section for the transfer compartment. The transmission of the program to each of these locations is necessary since there is no automatic remote control from one to the other. The operations are divided into a number of handling cycles no one of which can be started without authorization from the affected control room. Each supervisor has permanent control of the sequence of operations and can intervene to stop any operation not conforming with the program.

7.9.5.6.2 HANDLING SAFETY. The program of inserting a subassembly or removing a control rod is done in accordance with two principal safety rules:

1. The first is related to the number of fuel subassemblies that can be placed into the reactor. If N is the number of fuel subassemblies within the containment building, then

$$N = n_1 + n_2 - 1 \qquad (7.8)$$

where n_1 is the number of fuel subassemblies that can produce criticality without control rods and n_2 is the number of fuel subassemblies equal in reactivity to the total negative reactivity of the control rods. This rule imposes a detailed surveillance of the movements of various subassemblies or control rods in Rapsodie. This is done by means of an accounting system based on punched cards.

2. The movement of subassemblies must be automatically stopped or the removal of a control rod must be stopped and that movement reversed when the rate of increase of the multiplication coefficient exceeds a given value. This is done whatever the position of the control rods. The

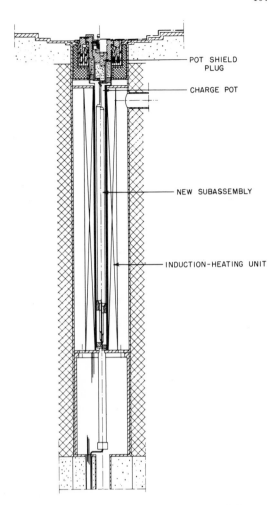

FIG. 7.69—Rapsodie new fuel decanning station [41].

threshold is fixed at a minimum of one subassembly below the critical point.

7.9.5.6.3 SAFETY DURING CONTROL-ROD REMOVAL. In addition to the rules stated above, the program for the removal of control rods has taken into account the following: (1) it must be impossible to remove more than one rod at a time and (2) there must be verification of the state of the reactor. This latter is done by raising the control rods prior to their removal to test the divergence of the reactor.

7.9.5.6.4 ACCOUNTING OF SUBASSEMBLIES AND CONTROL RODS. Each subassembly or each control rod is furnished with two cards, A and B. The first code on the card defines the nature of the subassembly, i.e., whether it is fuel, blanket, or reflector, regulating rod, safety rod, or other element; the type of nozzle; its radioactivity; and its serial number. The following seven codes serve to record on card A all the movements of the subassembly in the radioactive building: (1) the date of entrance into the building, (2) the number of its position in the storage room, (3) the date it left the storage room, (4) results of the dimensional

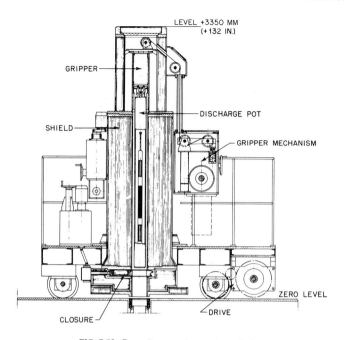

FIG. 7.70—Rapsodie secondary cask car [41].

inspection, (5) the date it was placed in the decay pool, (6) the date it left the pool and its destination, and (7) the rate of burnup. The second card, card B, contains data relative to its transfer into the containment building: (1) the date of entrance into the containment building, (2) the date it was placed in the reactor, (3) the number of its position in the reactor, and (4) the rate of burnup of the subassem-

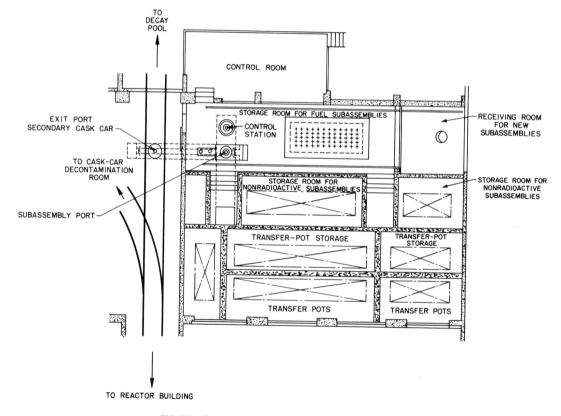

FIG. 7.71—Rapsodie new-fuel storage building, plan view [41].

bly in the zone corresponding to its location when it is placed in the reactor and again when it is removed from the reactor. An element may have more than one B card if it is removed from the reactor and then returned.

7.10 Analysis and Tests

7.10.1 DECAY HEAT [47]

A reliable and yet not overly conservative estimate of the total decay heating from existing compilations on decay heating is needed for fuel-handling heat-transfer analysis. Decay heating could be calculated from the existing data on fission-product distribution and known decay schemes of the individual nuclides, but it would be very difficult to duplicate some of the previous efforts that have gone into this problem, such as the work for fast fission reported in Ref. 48 by Blomeke and Todd. Recommended decay-heat correlations were obtained by Dillon and Burris, comparing Refs. 48 and 49 with Way–Wigner data (Ref. 50). The recommended correlations are:

Decay time, sec		Recommended decay-heating correlations
From	To	
0	10	Assume a constant value of 0.065 watt of total decay power per watt of prior operating power
10	3600	Use Way-Wigner times 2
3600	1.3×10^7	Reference 49
1.3×10^7	2.6×10^7	Reference 49, with an appropriate factor to take into account the fact that the empirical curves only fit the calculated data ±50%

The following are the reasons for these recommendations. Reference 49 was calculated for a fast (about 1-Mev) fission-spectrum yield assuming that the nuclear charge of a nuclide originating directly in fission is about three beta decays from the stable isotope of the chain. It was also assumed that there was a 100% yield for the first nuclide of reasonably long half-life along a given mass-decay chain. Nuclides with half-lives shorter than 1 hr were, in general, not considered.

Reference 48 used all the known fission-product yield to make the calculations as precise as possible. If individual yields were not known, they were estimated in the best manner available to make the total yields for a given mass consistent. A rather generalized decay scheme was assumed which allowed for four beta decays and also allowed for neutron capture in the fission-product spectrum. Since these calculations were carried out by a machine, independent yields of the individual fission-product nuclides could be taken into account with very little difficulty. The results on total decay heating were presented in the form of graphs for various thermal flux levels varying from 10^{12} to 10^{15} neutron/cm^2/sec. Even in a thermal flux over this large range, the heating values remained the same.

For a visual comparison of Refs. 48 and 49, the heating values were plotted against the decay time for a large range of irradiation times. Way-

Wigner heating is also included in Figs. 7.72 to 7.75 for 10^5 to 10^8 sec, inclusive. The following was used for Way–Wigner:

$$\frac{P}{P_0} = 0.065\left[t^{-0.2} - (t + t_0)^{-0.2}\right] \quad (7.9)$$

where t and t_0 are the decay and irradiation times in seconds, respectively. An examination of the curves immediately reveals a discrepancy between Ref. 50 and Ref. 51 for decay times from 1 hr to 1 week. This difference could be attributed to the difference in the fission-product spectrum between fast and slow fission. A comparison of the two fission-product distributions, fast and thermal, for a given mass number reveals very little difference except for those cases where the absolute yield is very small. This factor cannot contribute to the large difference between Refs. 48 and 49. Although the effect of fast fission contributes a difference to the overall heating, the difference should certainly be less than a factor of 2.

Reference 48 takes into account the independent yields of the individual nuclides for a given mass chain wereas Ref. 49 assigns the total yield to the first nuclide in a decay chain. From this one would expect Ref. 49 values to be higher than Ref. 48 since, if the total yield were assigned to the first member in a decay chain, more beta decay energy would be realized. The error by doing this is not large since for a given mass chain the first members in a decay chain will usually have a half-life short compared to 1 hr, and hence their effect

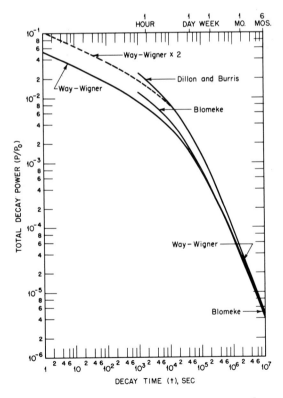

FIG. 7.72—Decay-heat correlation (irradiation time, 10^5 sec) [48-50].

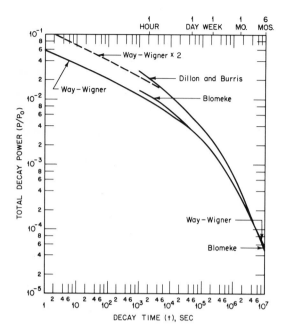

FIG. 7.73—Decay-heat correlation (irradiation time, 10^6 sec) [48–50].

would be negligible in about three half-lives (which is less than 1 hr). Reference 49 not accounting for the nuclides whose half-lives were shorter than 1 hr would certainly, according to Ref. 48, overcompensate the assumption of assigning the complete yield to the first member in a decay chain.

The values given in Ref. 49 are conservative on the high side, particularly for short times. The original experimental work of Day and Cannon, Borst, and Brady and Turkevich as reported by Way–Wigner [50] for the most part lie between the data of Refs. 48 and 49. Reference 49 data agree reasonably well with the experimental data of Ref. 51. In view of the experimental results, it would seem

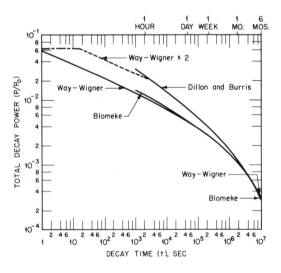

FIG. 7.74—Decay-heat correlation (irradiation time, 10^7 sec) [48–50].

reasonable to assume that Ref. 49 should give a good representation of conservative heat estimates.

Immediately after shutdown the decay heat for a reactor that has been operating for a long time is about 6.5%, or 13 Mev out of 200 Mev per fission. As can be seen from Figs. 7.72 to 7.75, if a constant value of 0.065 is assumed for the first 10 sec and Way–Wigner times 2 for the period of 10 sec to 1 hr, the curves blend fairly well with the data of Ref. 49. These values are undoubtedly conservative, but, for this critical period of high decay heat, they represent a reasonable compromise.

Another reason for choosing this conservative approach is that Ref. 48 results for short decay times ($0 < t < 10^4$ sec) do not account for many of the short-lived fission products with large decay energies. When Ref. 49 equations are used for times exceeding 150 hr, the decay heating values should be increased by 50% to take into account the error in fitting the calculated data to the empirical equation made up to fit the calculated curve.

7.10.2 DECAY-HEAT VALUES USED IN HEAT-TRANSFER ANALYSES [52]

When the fuel subassemblies are handled separately, some of the gamma rays escape from the subassemblies and are absorbed in the material surrounding the subassembly. Reference 53 estimates the gamma-energy escape to be about 10% of the total energy released (20% of the gamma energy). Reference 54 reports that the escaping gammas account for about 12% of the total decay heat one day after shutdown and 9.0% of the total 100 days after shutdown. For calculation of decay heat in subassemblies, an allowance of 10% can be used for gamma energy escaping from the subassembly. Where a group of subassemblies are adjacent to each other, the value of decay heat not escaping can be raised 10%. The decay-heat values that can be used in calculations for the period of 10 to 3600 sec, one region of interest, can be obtained from the following:

$$\frac{P}{P_0} = (2.0) \times (0.9) \times 0.065 \left[t^{-0.2} - \left(t + t_0 \right)^{-0.2} \right] \quad (7.10)$$

where P = decay heat produced in subassembly
P_0 = heat generation in subassembly during operation
2.0 = factor to account for spread in Way–Wigner data
0.9 = factor to account for escaping gammas
t = time after shutdown, sec
t_0 = time of operation at P_0 power, sec

A plot of the Way–Wigner correlation is given in Fig. 7.76. The decay heat varies with the operating power (P_0) of the subassembly and the time at the operating power (t_0). These quantities (P_0 and t_0) depend on the location of the subassembly in the reactor. For a fixed burnup limitation, t_0 is inversely proportional to P_0. Owing to the radial heat-flux gradient in the core, the coolest core subassembly may operate at a power as low as one-half the power of the hottest core subassembly. To reach equivalent burnup, the coolest core subassembly may remain in operation, for the example

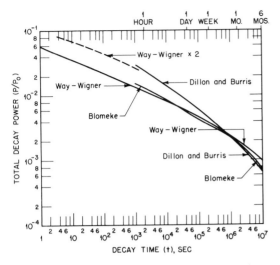

FIG. 7.75—Decay-heat correlation (irradiation time, 10^8 sec) [48-50].

The last factor is a ratio generally known, and

$$t_0 = \frac{\text{Mw(t) years of burnup}}{\text{Reactor power, Mw(t)}} \times \frac{31.536 \times 10^6 \text{ sec}}{\text{year}}$$

The power generated in the axial blankets can be neglected since it is a small portion of the core power. The power generated in the radial blankets includes the heat from the plutonium, assuming the maximum amount of plutonium buildup allowable. If the variation of heat flux along the length of the subassembly is desired, the distribution of decay-heat generation can be assumed to be approximately the same as the heat-generation distribution during operation.

7.10.3 HEAT TRANSFER FROM SPENT FUEL AND BLANKET SUBASSEMBLIES [52]

7.10.3.1 Introduction

Spent fuel and blanket subassemblies are generally removed from the reactor through an inert gas. The heat generation due to the radioactive decay of fission products, although small at the time of the transfer, is still sufficiently large to require provisions for cooling the subassembly in the gas. Heat-transfer analyses determine the critical temperatures for conditions of natural convection. Such analyses set the basis for forced-convection cooling requirements. An important consideration is loss of forced-convection cooling. Will the subassembly overheat or possibly melt if the blower or power supply fail? If melting occurs while the subassembly is being lifted out of the primary-system sodium, cleanup is expensive and time-consuming. If melting occurs outside the reactor, it still presents a difficult cleanup job that might delay the normal unloading schedule by tying up the transfer equipment. The transfer equipment should be designed

chosen, about twice as long as a hot core subassembly.

Decay-heat generation increases with increasing t_0 and decreases with decreasing P_0. A check should be made to determine whether a subassembly operating at the center of the core or one at the edge of the core would be generating more decay heat at a given time after shutdown since the handling equipment should be designed to handle the hottest subassembly. For short times after shutdown, the effect of t_0 on decay-heat generation is small, but, at large times after shutdown, the effect is more important for the hottest core subassembly.

$$P_0 = \frac{\text{Core power, Btu/hr}}{\text{No. of subassemblies}} \times \frac{\text{power in hottest subassembly}}{\text{power in average subassembly}}$$

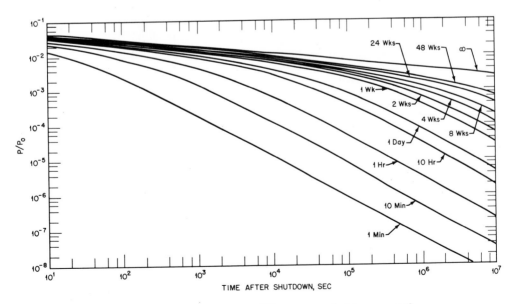

FIG. 7.76—Decay-heat generation rates [50]. $P/P_0 = 0.065[t^{-0.2} - (t + t_0)^{-0.2}]$.

for possible loss of normal cooling supply. Most of the transfer operations take place in a relatively short time (on the order of minutes). The cooling systems should be capable of continuous heat removal in the event of a failure of the transfer equipment.

The heat-transfer capability of a subassembly can be improved by an extended heat-transfer surface area. One method is to provide a finned pot for the subassembly with a liquid-metal bond. Another method is to can the subassembly in a bath of metal and let the bath solidify. The heat is transferred from the subassembly to the extended surface area through the liquid-metal or solid-metal bond.

Heat transfer analyses of the transfer of a subassembly from a reactor include: (1) steady-state heat transfer from the subassembly in an extended-surface medium to a gas, (2) steady-state heat transfer from the subassembly to a gas, and (3) heat transfer from the subassembly when it is insufficiently cooled. The following sections describe the calculations, results, and conclusions for the conditions listed when a finned pot containing liquid sodium is used. The analyses may be used to estimate temperatures of spent fuel and blanket subassemblies for several conditions encountered in their transfer from the reactor. No factors for uncertainty have been included. A number of assumptions are made to simplify the analysis. If it is desired to design very close to design limitations, more refined analyses are necessary, and they should be supplemented by tests duplicating operating conditions. The analyses can also be useful for subassemblies canned in solid metal.

7.10.3.2 *Steady-state Heat Transfer to Gas from a Subassembly in a Sodium-filled Finned Pot*

A schematic diagram of a subassembly in a sodium-filled finned pot is given in Fig. 7.77. The heat transfer from the subassembly to the gas on the outside of the finned pot is determined by making an assumption as to the mode of heat transmission within the pot. Heat transfer from the subassembly to the wall of the pot will probably be a combination of conduction radially through the sodium and free convection of the sodium. Such an analysis, including both these modes simultaneously, is cumbersome and is not justified because of other uncertainties in the calculation.

A preliminary analysis can be made with the simplest and most pessimistic assumption of only radial conduction. Heat then would be transferred from only that section of the fins adjacent to the core section of the subassembly. A second analysis can be made assuming natural convection of sodium up through the subassembly and down the space between the subassembly and wall of the finned pot. With this second analysis, the entire length of fins is utilized, and, as may be expected, the analysis shows that more heat is transferred for the same maximum sodium temperature. These two methods are presented separately in the following sections.

7.10.3.2.1 RADIAL CONDUCTION THROUGH SODIUM. The temperature drop through the sub-

assembly can be determined if an apparent conductivity of the mixture of fuel elements and sodium is known. For an infinitely long square rod with uniform internal heat generation and uniform surface temperature, the temperature drop from the center to the surface is given by Ref. 55 as

$$\theta_0 = \frac{0.59 \, q''' a^2}{2 k_a} \qquad (7.11)$$

where θ_0 = maximum temperature drop, °F
  q''' = volumetric heat generation, Btu/hr/cu ft
  a = (side of square/2), ft
  k_a = apparent thermal conductivity, Btu/hr/ft/°F

The apparent thermal conductivity, k_a, can be calculated by a procedure similar to that used in Ref. 55.

The temperature drops through the subassembly wall, through the sodium between the subassembly and finned pot, and through the pot wall can be calculated by the usual conduction formula, using an average thickness for the sodium. The equation for these calculations is

$$\theta = \frac{q'' s}{k} \qquad (7.12)$$

where q'' = heat flux, Btu/hr/sq ft
  s = thickness, ft
  k = thermal conductivity, Btu/hr/ft/°F

The heat transfer from the finned surface to the gas is a combination of free convection and radia-

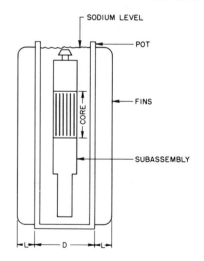

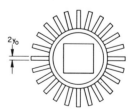

FIG. 7.77—Finned pot for transferring spent subassemblies [52].

tion. Equations describing heat transfer from straight fins of rectangular profile have been derived in Ref. 55. With the same nomenclature as Jakob [55] used, the heat transferred from one side of a fin is

$$q_0' = \theta_0 \left[hky_0 \left(1 - n^2 \right) \right]^{\frac{1}{2}} \qquad (7.13)$$

where q_0' = heat transferred from one side of fin per unit length, Btu/hr/ft

θ_0 = temperature excess of root of fin over ambient, °F

h = film heat-transfer coefficient, Btu/ hr/sq ft

k = thermal conductivity of fin, Btu/hr/ ft/°F

y_0 = 1/2 thickness of fin, ft

L = width of fin, ft

n = $1/\cosh \left[\left(h/ky_0 \right)^{\frac{1}{2}} L \right]$

The assumptions made in the above derivation are that the film heat-transfer coefficient, h, and thermal conductivity, k, are constant. The validity of assuming a constant h will be discussed later. The assumption of constant k is valid for stainless steel since k does not vary much over the temperature range of interest (500 to 1500°F).

The total heat q' transferred from the finned surface per foot of length is the sum of the heat transferred from the fins and the heat transferred from the pot surface between fins or

$$q' = 2N \left(q_0' + q_p' \right) \qquad (7.14)$$

where N = number of fins

q' = total heat transferred per unit length, Btu/hr/ft

q_p' = heat transferred from 1/2 the space between fins, Btu/hr/ft

The heat transferred from the surface area between fins is calculated by the usual convection equation

$$q_p' = hC\theta_0 \qquad (7.15)$$

where C is 1/2 the distance between roots of fins and θ_0 is the temperature excess of root of fin above environment temperature (°F). The use of θ_0 in Eq. 7.15 assumes that there is no variation in pipe-wall temperature between a point that has no fin attached and one that does. This is a good approximation since natural-convection film coefficients are very low relative to the metal conductivity. To calculate the heat transferred from the fin tube, q', for a given temperature excess, θ_0, you must estimate the film heat-transfer coefficient. As mentioned previously, heat transfer by radiation as well as convection must be considered. At high surface temperatures (1500°F), the radiation coefficient may be several times the free-convection coefficient. The coefficients can be calculated separately and then added for the combined effect. Natural-convection heat transfer from a plane vertical plate to a gas can be determined from empirical relations. However, free convection between parallel planes at substantially the same temperature presents a different problem. As long as the fins are far enough apart that the boundary

layer on one surface does not interfere with the boundary layer on an adjacent surface, these empirical relations for a plane surface are valid [55]. The minimum spacing between fins can be chosen so that the assumption of noninterference of boundary layers can be made. Thus the free-convection heat-transfer film coefficient for turbulent flow is, from Ref. 55,

$$Nu = 0.129 \left(Gr \times Pr \right)^{\frac{1}{3}} \qquad (7.16)$$

where Nu = Nusselt number = hD_e/k

Gr = Grashof number = $D_e^3 \rho^2 g\beta\theta/\mu^2$

Pr = Prandtl number = $c_p \mu/k$

D_e = characteristic length = height of vertical surface, ft

k = thermal conductivity of gas, Btu/hr/ ft/°F

ρ = density of gas, lb/cu ft

g = gravitational constant = 4.18×10^8 ft/hr²

β = coefficient of thermal expansion of gas, cu ft/cu ft/°F (1/°F)

θ = temperature excess of surface above environment temperature, °F

μ = absolute viscosity of gas, lb/ft/hr

c_p = specific heat of gas at constant pressure, Btu/lb/°F

For argon, if values of physical properties at 300°K are substituted, Eq. 7.16 becomes

$$h_c = 0.135 \theta^{\frac{1}{3}} \qquad (7.17)$$

The heat transferred by radiation is given in Ref. 56 as

$$q = \sigma F_e F_A A \left(T_1^4 - T_2^4 \right) \qquad (7.18)$$

where q = heat transferred, Btu/hr

F_e = factor to account for emissivity and relative position of emitting and absorbing surfaces

F_A = factor to account for geometry of emitting and absorbing surfaces

A = heat-transfer surface area of finned tube

T_1, T_2 = absolute temperature of emitting and absorbing surfaces, respectively, °R

σ = Stefan–Boltzmann constant = 0.174 $\times 10^{-8}$ Btu/hr/sq ft/°F⁴

It can be assumed that the enclosed body (finned pot) is small compared with the enclosing body (room). From Ref. 56 for the above configuration, F_e is equal to the emissivity of the emitting body. The emissivity depends on the condition of the surface of the emitting body. In general, a smooth, silvery surface has a low emissivity, and a rough, dark surface has a high emissivity. When the finned pot is lifted out of the sodium, it probably will have a thin film of sodium clinging to it which will give the surface a low emissivity. If the gas environment is not saturated with sodium vapor, the sodium film may be vaporized and thus expose the steel surface, which then would have a higher emissivity. The emissivity of a steel rod lifted out of a sodium bath into a helium atmosphere is about 0.1. After about 15 min the sodium film vaporizes, leaving only a residue of sodium oxide and other contaminants on the surface. For this surface condition the emissivity is about 0.5. In the transfer of subassemblies from a sodium bath, the gas space may be saturated with sodium vapor since it will be over a sodium surface at all times. Therefore, for the finned-pot heat-transfer calculation, the sodium film can be assumed to remain on the surface of the pot, with an emissivity of 0.1.

The calculation of F_A, the geometry factor, is not as simple. It may be calculated by procedures given in Ref. 57 or 58. However, the other uncertainties of the calculation make a detailed calculation of F_A unwarranted. Instead, F_A can be assumed to be 1.0 by the following reasoning. The longitudinal fins on the round tube form diverging boundaries for radiation waves traveling radially from the pot. The emissivity (and absorptivity) of the fin surface is low (0.1); therefore the reflectivity of the surface is high. Waves leaving the fin at the root will be reflected several times but will eventually get out of the space between the fins and be absorbed by the walls of the room. Even the small portion of the energy that is absorbed by the fin for each reflection improves the efficiency of heat transfer from the fins since it is a mechanism by which heat is transferred from the root to the tip of the fin. Another assumption made is that the walls of the room are at the same temperature as the gas environment in the room. The environment temperature, T_e, may be substituted for the wall temperature, T_2, in Eq. 7.18. With this assumption, Eq. 7.18 becomes

$$\frac{q}{A} = 0.174 \times 0.1 \times 1.0 \left[\left(\frac{T_1}{100}\right)^4 - \left(\frac{T_e}{100}\right)^4 \right]$$

or   (7.19)

$$q'' = 0.0174 \left[\left(\frac{T_1}{100}\right)^4 - \left(\frac{T_e}{100}\right)^4 \right]$$

By definition, the heat-transfer coefficient due to radiation, h_r, is

$$h_r = \frac{q''}{(T_1 - T_e)} = \frac{q''}{\theta} \qquad (7.20)$$

When Eq. 7.19 is substituted into Eq. 7.20,

$$h_r = 0.0174 \frac{(T_1/100)^4 - (T_e/100)^4}{\theta} \qquad (7.21)$$

The coefficients for convection and radiation as a function of temperature excess of the surface over environment are plotted in Fig. 7.78 for an environment temperature of 550°F. Below a surface temperature of 1000°F ($\theta = 450°F$), the radiation coefficient is about the same magnitude as the convection coefficient. However, for surface temperatures above 1000°F, the radiation coefficient becomes much more important. Over the temperature range 100°F to 1000°F, the coefficients vary by a factor of about 2.0, exclusive of the variation due to the change of physical properties of the gas with temperature. At a mean gas-film temperature of 1000°F and a surface temperature of 1450°F, the convection film coefficient, h_c, would be about 35% lower than the value given in Fig. 7.78. However, for a first approximation, this effect can be neglect-

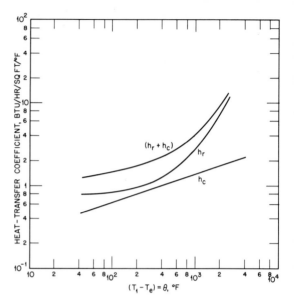

FIG. 7.78—Heat-transfer coefficients from a vertical surface to still argon [52]. Convection coefficient, $h_c = 0.135\theta^{1/3}$; radiation

$$\text{coefficient, } h_r = \frac{0.0174 \left[\left(\frac{T_1}{100}\right)^4 - \left(\frac{T_e}{100}\right)^4 \right]}{T_1 - T_e}.$$

ed. Variations in the density and coefficient of volume expansion of argon with temperature are given in Fig. 7.79. Additional physical properties of argon are given in Chap. 4. The total coefficient, for a first approximation, can be constant over the finned surface at the value of $\theta = \theta_0$. The coefficient used may be high, but it probably will be within experimental accuracy.

The rate of heat transfer is affected by any variation in fin dimensions for a given fin tip. In general, the larger the fin surface area, the greater the heat transfer. The maximum fin-tip diameter is usually set by transfer-equipment limitations. The size of the subassembly limits the inside diameter of the pot. The thickness of the fin may vary; nominal thicknesses are 1/16 in. or 1/8 in. Stainless steel is generally selected as the fin and pot material since it is used in sodium. The minimum space between fins can be selected so that boundary layers of gas on opposite sides of the space do not interfere with each other. Most heat transfer will be obtained from a finned pot with the minimum

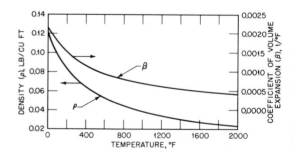

FIG. 7.79—Thermal properties of argon at atmospheric pressure [52].

size tube, maximum fin-tip diameter, minimum fin thickness, and maximum number of fins.

A Fermi core subassembly normally is removed with 6 to 8 kw of decay heat and temperatures limited to prevent fuel distortion. A central core subassembly can generate 69,500 Btu/hr (20.3 kw) in a sodium-filled finned pot without exceeding 1600°F in the subassembly. This assumes a prior operation at 200 Mw(t) and an argon ambient of 500°F. From Fig. 7.80 this corresponds to about 2 hr of decay time prior to removal.

7.10.3.2.2 FREE CONVECTION OF THE SODIUM INSIDE THE FINNED POT. The pessimistic assumption of conduction only from the subassembly to the finned tube results in decay periods for the core subassembly longer than may be warranted. A more realistic analysis can be made assuming free convection inside the pot. The assumptions used for heat transfer from the finned surface are the same. The heat transferred by free convection inside the pot is determined by the circulation rate of sodium. It can be assumed that the change in heat generation with time is slow and that steady-state conditions exist at any instant after shutdown. The problem is one of balancing the thermal head available with the friction head loss in the free-convection circuit. The thermal head available depends on the cooling of the downcomer, which, in turn, depends on the temperature gradient in the downcomer leg. The problem can be solved with a semianalytical approach.

The friction loss through the convection loop as a function of mass flow can be determined. If laminar flow is assumed, the friction loss (in pounds per square inch) is given by

$$\Delta P = \frac{32\mu L V}{3600 g D_e^2} \qquad (7.22)$$

where μ = absolute viscosity, lb/ft/hr
$\quad\;\; L$ = length of flow path, ft
$\quad\;\; V$ = velocity, ft/sec
$\quad\;\; g$ = gravitational constant = 32.2 ft/sec^2
$\quad\;\; D_e$ = equivalent diameter of flow path, ft

According to the continuity equation,

$$w = \bar{\rho}_n V_n A_n = \bar{\rho}_c V_c A_c \qquad (7.23)$$

where w = mass flow rate, lb/hr
$\quad\quad\quad\; \bar{\rho}$ = average density, lb/cu ft
$\quad\quad\quad\; A$ = cross-sectional area, sq ft
subscript n = any section
subscript c = core section

Rearranging Eq. 7.23,

$$V_n = \frac{w}{\bar{\rho}_n A_n} \qquad (7.24)$$

The calculation of pressure drop for the large number of calculations to be made is simplified by assuming that

$$\bar{\rho}_n = \bar{\rho}_c$$

Thus,

$$V_n = \frac{w}{\bar{\rho}_c A_n}$$

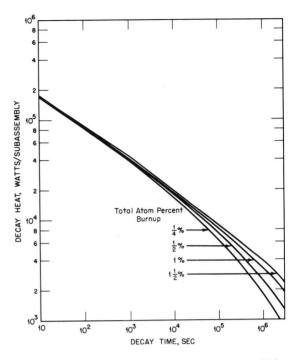

FIG. 7.80—Decay heating for Fermi central core subassembly [52]. Subassembly power during 200 Mw operation = 2.42 Mw for central subassembly: Power from zero to 10 sec, $H_{0-10} = 1.578 \times 10^5$ watts.

and the pressure drop in any section is

$$\Delta P_n = \left(\frac{32}{3600^2}\frac{\mu}{g}\right)\frac{w}{\bar{\rho}_c}\left(\frac{L}{AD_e^2}\right)_n \qquad (7.25)$$

The total pressure drop around the loop is

$$\Delta P = \sum_1^n \Delta P_n = 7.66 \times 10^{-8}\frac{\mu w}{\bar{\rho}_c}\sum_1^n\left(\frac{L}{AD_e^2}\right)_n \qquad (7.26)$$

The quantity L/AD_e^2 should be evaluated for each section of flow path. The flow path inside the core subassembly (up-flow leg) can be divided into $n-2$ sections, similar to Fig. 7.81. The flow path outside the subassembly (down-flow leg) can be divided into two sections, one adjacent to the square tube section and one adjacent to the round support section. The result is

$$\Delta P = \frac{k_1 w}{\bar{\rho}_c} \qquad (7.27)$$

where the constant $k_1 = 7.66 \times 10^{-8}\mu\sum_1^n\left[L/(AD_e^2)\right]_n$. The net thermal head is

$$H = H_D - H_U \qquad (7.28)$$

where H = thermal head, psi
subscript D = down-flow leg
subscript U = up-flow leg

In general,

$$H = \int \rho\, dx$$

A schematic diagram of the convection loop is shown in Fig. 7.82. For the up-flow leg the sodium temperature is assumed constant above and below

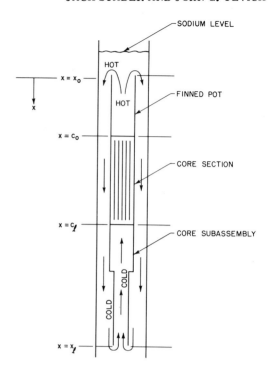

FIG. 7.82—Schematic diagram of convection loop [52].

the core section. The sodium temperature through the core is assumed to vary linearly with the distance x. The up-flow thermal head is

$$H_U = \int_{x_l}^{c_l} \rho_l \, dx + \int_{c_l}^{c_0} \rho \, dx + \int_{c_0}^{x_0} \rho_0 \, dx \qquad (7.29)$$

The first and third terms contain constant-density values of ρ_l and ρ_0, respectively. In the second term, ρ varies with x. It can be assumed that the density of liquid sodium varies linearly with temperature in the range of interest, and from this it can be shown that ρ varies linearly with x. This is a good approximation, as seen from Fig. 7.83. Therefore

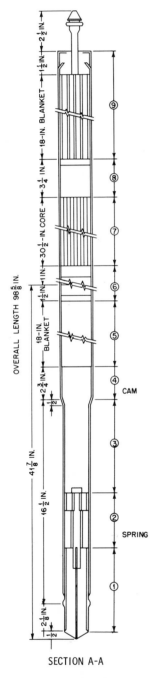

FIG. 7.81—Fermi type core subassembly [52]. Circled numbers indicate sections used in pressure-drop analysis.

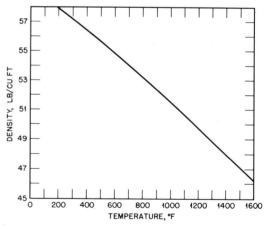

FIG. 7.83—Density of sodium [52].

for the second term an average density can be used, and Eq. 7.29 becomes

$$H_U = \rho_l(x_l - c_l) + \frac{(\rho_l + \rho_0)(c_l - c_0)}{2} + \rho_0(c_0 - x_0) \quad (7.30)$$

For the down-flow leg

$$H_D = \int_{x_0}^{x_l} \rho \, dx$$

Since the heat transfer from the down-flow leg is not constant over the entire length, a linear relation between ρ and x cannot be assumed over the entire length. Therefore the head is calculated over lengths short enough to allow the assumption of a linear relation. Four intervals should be sufficient to give

$$H_D = \sum_{n=1}^{4} \frac{1}{2} (\rho_n + \rho_{n-1})(x_n - x_{n-1}) \quad (7.31)$$

The densities are determined from the sodium temperature distribution in the down-flow leg. It can be assumed that there is no heat transfer between the up-flow leg and the down-flow leg. This assumption is adequate since in the upper portion of the pot heat transfer would be from the up-flow to down-flow leg, and in the lower portion, from the down-flow to the up-flow leg. The net effect on the circulation rate, and therefore the heat transfer from the pot to the gas, should not be large.

The heat transfer from the finned surface, q', at any temperature excess, θ, is given by Eqs. 7.13, 7.14, and 7.15. A plot of q' vs. θ can be made once the pot size and environment conditions have been selected. Such a plot is given in Fig. 7.84 for a 7.5-in.-diameter pot. If sufficiently short intervals are chosen, q' may be assumed to vary linearly with θ,

$$q' = a + b\theta \quad (7.32)$$

where a and b are constants.

The differential equation for heat flow from the finned surface to the gas is

$$dq = -q' \, dx \quad (7.33)$$

The differential equation for sodium temperature rise is

$$dq = wc_p \, d\theta \quad (7.34)$$

Substituting Eq. 7.32 into 7.33 and equating Eqs. 7.33 and 7.34,

$$wc_p \, d\theta = -(a + b\theta) \, dx$$

Separating variables and integrating over an interval $i = 0$ to $i = 1$,

$$-\int_{\theta_0}^{\theta_1} \left(\frac{1}{a + b\theta} \right) d\theta = \frac{1}{wc_p} \int_{x_0}^{x_1} dx$$

which, when integrated, gives

$$\frac{1}{b} \ln \left(\frac{a + b\theta_0}{a + b\theta_1} \right) = (x_1 - x_0) \left(\frac{1}{wc_p} \right)$$

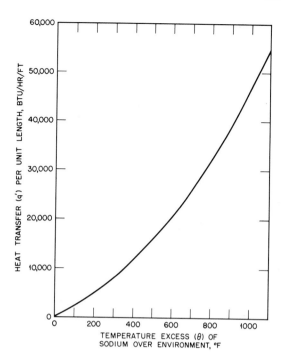

FIG. 7.84—Heat transfer from a finned surface [52]. Fin-tip diameter, 7.5 in.; fin-root diameter, 4.5 in.; fin thickness, 0.125 in.; No. of fins, 57; argon temperature, 500°F.

Substituting $b = (q'_0 - q'_1)/(\theta_0 - \theta_1)$ from Eq. 7.32 gives

$$x_1 - x_0 = wc_p \left(\frac{\theta_0 - \theta_1}{q'_0 - q'_1} \right) \left(\ln \frac{q'_0}{q'_1} \right)$$

and, in general

$$x_i - x_{i-1} = wc_p \left(\frac{\theta_{i-1} - \theta_i}{q'_{i-1} - q'_i} \right) \left(\ln \frac{q'_{i-1}}{q'_i} \right) \quad (7.35)$$

Equation 7.35 can be solved by selecting values of θ and q' at intervals sufficiently short that the distance between may be assumed to be a straight line and by assuming a value for w. A θ vs. x curve can be plotted and used to calculate the thermal head, H, in Eq. 7.28. In the equilibrium condition H is equal to Eq. 7.27. The calculation is repeated until a value of w is found which satisfies Eqs. 7.35 and 7.27. The total heat released from the finned pot is

$$q = wc_p(\theta_0 - \theta_l) \quad (7.36)$$

The heat transfer from various sized finned pots vs. maximum sodium temperature in the pot can be plotted. The plot for Fermi is given in Fig. 7.85. The heat transferred at Fermi from a 7.5-in.-OD pot with a maximum temperature of 1600°F is 185,000 Btu/hr (54.2 kw). The value calculated by assuming radial conduction within the pot was only 69,500 Btu/hr for the same conditions.

The two largest areas of uncertainty are the emissivity of the fin surface and the effect of fin geometry on radiant-energy transfer. The emissivity was assumed on the low side. The heat transfer

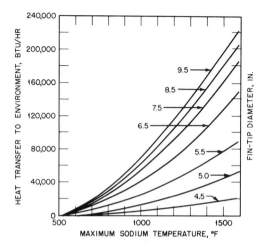

FIG. 7.85—Heat transfer from a finned vertical cylinder to argon at 500°F assuming natural convection of sodium in the pot [52]. Fin material, stainless steel; fin thickness, 0.125 in.; No. of fins, 57; spacing, 0.123 in.

should be more than that calculated. The factor (F_A) of 1.0 to account for geometry in the radiation equation is optimistic and introduces a possibility that the heat transfer will be less than calculated. If the finned pot is in a close-fitting tube instead of a large room, the heat transfer will probably be less than calculated. If the finned pot is enclosed by a close-fitting tube filled with argon instead of a large room as assumed, the emissivity of the absorber becomes important to the calculation of radiant-energy transfer. The emissivity factor, F_e, of the radiation equation may be only one-half the value used in the calculation. Also, if the pot is in a close-fitting tube, the method of removing the heat from the argon environment should be examined since it may affect heat transfer from the finned pot to the environment. Since the calculations assume free convection inside the pot, the convection flow path must be assured in the design to obtain the heat transfer indicated. This requires that the subassembly be submerged in sodium and free access maintained to the ends of the subassembly.

7.10.3.3 Steady-state Heat Transfer from a Subassembly to Gas

To determine the heat transfer from a bare subassembly in a gas atmosphere, you first determine the degree of free convection of the gas through the subassembly. Experiments conducted by ANL on their EBR-II fuel subassembly (described in Sec. 7.10.4) indicate that there will be very little convection through the subassembly. The EBR-II subassembly has about the same pin size and spacing as the Fermi subassembly. However, the core section is only about one-half as long, and the cross section is a hexagon about 2.2 in. across flats.

A calculation of gas convection through the Fermi subassembly indicates that the amount of heat transferred from the Fermi subassembly by natural convection through the subassembly is small and that the process is primarily by radiation and conduction through the assembly. The tempera-

ture drop through the subassembly can be calculated with an apparent thermal conductivity. Equation 7.11 can be used for this calculation. Radiation within the assembly should be included in the calculation of apparent thermal conductivity. The heat transferred from the surface of the subassembly to the gas can be obtained by the correlation for free convection from a vertical surface for turbulent flow given by Eq. 7.16. With these relations the heat transfer from a fuel subassembly for various maximum fuel-alloy temperatures can be calculated.

Two considerations that may affect the calculations are emissivity and end losses. An emissivity of 0.1 for sodium-covered surfaces can be used. Emissivity values with no sodium film present can be obtained from Refs. 59 to 64. The accuracy of using emissivity as noted is probably within a factor of 2.

If the calculations are used in conjunction with Fig. 7.80, the time after shutdown at which a core or blanket subassembly may be handled in a gas without exceeding a specified maximum temperature can be found. Figure 7.80 gives the maximum heat output. The average heat output per subassembly is equal to this value divided by the ratio of the maximum to average axial heat flux.

7.10.3.4 Temperature Increase of a Core Subassembly When Insufficiently Cooled

Certain operations may require the removal of a subassembly from a sodium bath to an inert atmosphere. If the process convection cooling should fail, how long would it take for the subassembly to reach a critical temperature? The critical temperature may be assumed to be the melting point of the fuel. A similiar problem arises when a finned pot containing a subassembly is removed from a sodium bath into an inert atmosphere. It is necessary to determine the time for the finned pot and subassembly to reach a critical temperature if forced convection should fail. The critical temperature in this case is the boiling point of sodium, 1618°F. A conservative assumption can be made that the heat generation is constant for the duration of the transient. The transient times considered are usually short enough that the decay-heat generation will not decrease appreciably. The assumption becomes more valid for transients starting at longer times after shutdown. A second conservative assumption, with a subassembly in gas, is that all the heat generated within the subassembly is used to raise the temperature of the subassembly material. For short times after shutdown, the heat generation is much greater that the amount of heat lost from the subassembly. The assumption becomes less valid for longer times after shutdown, but the solution is adequate for extended periods up to a time when the heat generation in the subassembly is still a ratio of four or five to that which the subassembly can dissipate to the environmental gas.

When a subassembly is submerged in a sodium-filled finned pot, the heat transfer from the pot is a large fraction of the total heat generated, and an average heat loss from the subassembly during the transient should be included. For preliminary design calculations an assumption can also be made that the temperature throughout the unit is uniform. For short-term transients measured in minutes this assumption is adequate. Free convection should be considered for long-term transients. It is estimated that the value thus obtained is the minimum heat transferred; the maximum may be three times that value.

With the above assumptions, the temperature rise of the subassembly can be calculated from the basic heat-storage equation,

$$(p - q)\Delta t = \rho c_p v \Delta T \qquad (7.37)$$

where p = decay heat generation, Btu/hr
q = heat loss to environment, Btu/hr
Δt = time interval, hr
ρ = density, lb/cu ft
c_p = specific heat at constant pressure, Btu/lb/°F
v = volume, cu ft
ΔT = temperature rise of material, °F

For the bare subassembly in a gas, $q = 0$ and the heat-capacity terms, ρ, c_p, and v, are for the fuel alloy only. The initial temperature is the steady-state temperature in the finned pot immediately prior to removal of the subassembly. The calculated time interval is a minimum. The maximum time interval may be 1.5 times that calculated. For the subassembly in a finned pot, the heat-capacity terms include finned pot, sodium, and the complete subassembly. The time interval is estimated to be accurate within a factor of 1.5.

7.10.4 DECAY-HEAT COOLING REQUIREMENTS OF SPENT EBR-II FUEL SUBASSEMBLIES

EBR-II subassemblies, after about 1% burnup of the fuel, decay in the primary tank storage rack for about two weeks. At the end of the two weeks, the subassemblies generate about 2300 watts of decay heat. An electrically heated model of a reference-design fuel subassembly (see Figs. 11.43 through 11.45, Chap. 11, for the fuel subassembly design) was constructed to simulate the decay heat after removal from the storage rack at the end of the two weeks. A ceramic-insulated nichrome resistance wire was inserted the length of the fuel, 14.25 in., into a fuel tube that was closed at one end and had a spiral rib welded on. Groups of 18 tubes wired in series constituted a single circuit. There were five such circuits, each controlled by an autotransformer and monitored by an ammeter and voltmeter. One tube was controlled by its own autotransformer. In all, 21 thermocouples were welded to various tubes to facilitate vertical and transverse temperature surveys of the tube-surface temperatures. The 91 elements were inserted in a reference hexagonal subassembly tube and mounted in a vertical position. Provision was made for metering a blast of cooling air or argon gas into the bottom of the assembly.

The first test consisted in a determination of the heat dissipation from the assembly in air without forced cooling. At a power of 261 watts, 11% of expected power, the hottest element (Fig. 7.86)

reached a temperature of 530°C (986°F). A 30-in.-high stack was attached to the top of the assembly to determine whether or not the chimney effect would enhance the cooling. There was no detectable difference. Air at the rate of 9.41 standard cu ft/min was introduced into the bottom of the assembly, and the power was adjusted to 2330 watts. Under these conditions a maximum tube-surface temperature of 563°C (1045°F) was recorded. The air outlet temperature was 444°C (831°F), indicating an air-temperature rise of 422°C (760°F). This amount of air and temperature rise accounted for 90% of the heat input. With a heat input of 2265 watts and an argon-gas flow of 12.2 standard cu ft/min, a maximum temperature of 536°C (997°F) was recorded. The argon outlet temperature was 453°C (797°F). This amount of argon and temperature rise accounted for 96.5% of the heat input.

7.10.4.1 EBR-II Subassembly Temperature with Loss of Coolant

Calculations were made to determine the rate of temperature rise in a subassembly if the coolant-gas flow should fail. It was assumed that the subassembly was perfectly insulated. The rate of temperature rise vs. the subassembly temperature is shown in Fig. 7.87. The cooling tests described were run on a section of the subassembly containing only the fuel section. In practice the cooling gas must flow through the entire subassembly, including the fuel section, upper and lower blanket sections, and the upper and lower attachments. Pressure drop vs. flow data for air were obtained on a complete subassembly. From these data the pressure drop of argon gas was calculated. Figure 7.88 shows the pressure drop vs. the flow of coolant gas.

It was concluded that forced-gas cooling of the fuel subassembly is necessary from the time that it is removed from the reactor sodium until the individual fuel pins are separated. A flow of 15 standard cu ft/min of argon gas at room temperature and at a pressure of about 3 in. H_2O should maintain a maximum temperature below 1100°F. The high temperature attained in a very short time following cessation of coolant-gas flow emphasizes the need for a reliable gas system.

7.10.4.2 Cooling of EBR-II Pin Bundle Without Hexagonal Can

During fuel disassembly the hexagonal tube is removed from around the cluster of fuel pins, axial gas flow is no longer possible, and cross-flow gas cooling through the cluster becomes necessary. The cooling requirements of this configuration were determined as follows: 91 electrically heated fuel tubes were removed from the hexagonal can, and the hexagonal cluster was supported horizontally in air. With no forced cooling the hottest tube achieved a temperature of 570°C (1058°F) with a power input of only 490 watts (21% of the expected decay heat power). The cluster was next supported in a perforated half-hexagonal tube to which was attached a manifold so that cooling air could be forced into the bottom and sides of the bundle. With 2200 watts heat input (95% of the expected decay

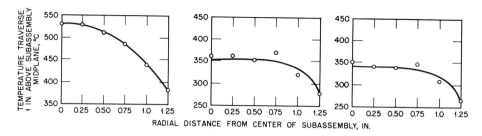

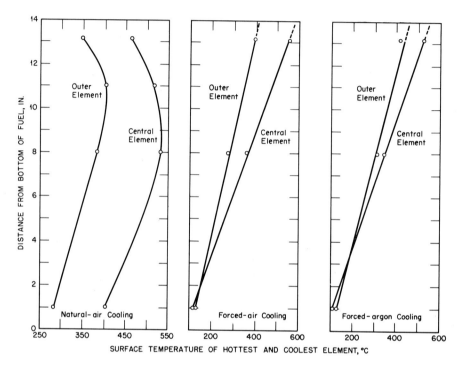

FIG. 7.86—Dissipation of simulated decay heat generated in EBR–II core subassembly [65].

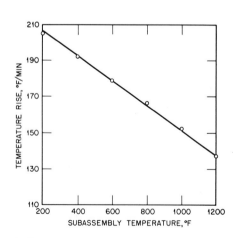

FIG. 7.87—Rate of temperature rise in EBR–II subassembly with no cooling and 2330 watts decay heat [66].

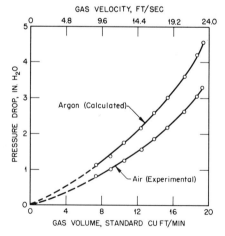

FIG. 7.88—Pressure drop vs. cooling gas flow in full-scale EBR–II model fuel subassembly [66].

heat power) and a cooling flow of 9.62 standard cu ft/min, a maximum fuel tube temperature of 645°C (1193°F) was recorded. A calculated 13.4 standard cu ft/min would be required to maintain this temperature with argon as the coolant while the individual pins are being removed from the cluster. A single element, laid flat upon a table, was heated electrically at a rate corresponding to the decay heat developed in an irradiated fuel element. Under these conditions the surface temperature was 225°C (437°F); no external cooling was required.

7.10.5 FERMI CASK-CAR COOLING

The Fermi cask car described in Sec. 7.9.4.4.5 contains 11 finned-pot storage positions. Each finned pot containing a subassembly is filled with sodium. The heat from the irradiated fuel subassemblies is removed by forced convection of argon gas through an argon–air heat exchanger. The subassemblies are stored in the cask-car fuel storage rotor (Fig. 7.61). The rotor consists of 11 guide tubes, 9 in. in diameter and sized to recieve 8 1/2-in.-OD finned pots.

Argon enters the guide tubes at the top, passes downward along the fuel subassemblies, crosses the bottom of the cask, and enters the argon–air heat exchanger from the bottom; the argon flows in the tubes and the air flows around the outside of the tubes. The argon flow area can be considered as composed of two flow areas: the area between the fins and the area outside the fins. Because of the large difference in hydraulic resistance of these two portions of the flow area, the mean gas velocities in these two areas are different. For the first approximation the heat-transfer coefficient can be assumed to be governed by the gas velocity between the fins. It can also be assumed that the mixing of the two flows is sufficient for the local gas temperature to be considered the mixed mean temperature of the two flows.

Figure 7.89 illustrates the division of the total flow area into two flow areas. The dashed circle, which is the envelope of the fin tips, is taken as the boundary between the two flow areas. The hydraulic diameter, D_e, for flow area A is (4 × flow area)/(actual wetted perimeter). The hydraulic diameter for flow area B is taken as twice the spacing of the annular passage. The gas-transport properties used are: c_p (specific heat), Btu/lb/°F; ρ (density at pressure and temperature), lb/cu ft; k (thermal conductivity at average gas temperature), Btu/sec/°F/ft; and μ (absolute viscosity at average gas temperature), lb/ft/sec. The properties of k and μ for argon are for 300°F average gas temperature. Higher gas temperatures are encountered in some operations, but the effect of increased k and μ with gas temperature is small compared to the uncertainties in the heat-rejection values. The procedure is described for a weight-flow, w, through area A. The average gas velocity, v, between the fins is $w/\rho a$, where ρ is the density of the argon at the gas temperature.

The Nusselt number heat-transfer relation used is [63]

$$Nu = \frac{hD_e}{k} = 0.023 \, Re^{0.8} Pr^{0.4} \qquad (7.38)$$

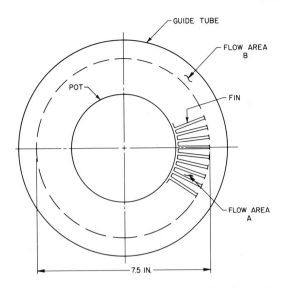

FIG. 7.89—Division of gas-flow area around a finned pot in the Fermi cask-car guide tube [67].

where $Pr = \mu \, c_p/k$ (Prandtl number) and $Re = D_e v \rho/\mu$ (Reynold's number).

The fin effectiveness, φ, is a convection factor that can be applied to account for a mean temperature difference less than the temperature difference between the fin base and the ambient gas. The fin effectiveness is defined as

$$\varphi = \frac{1}{\theta_b} \frac{\int_{A_f} \theta \, dA_f}{A_f} \qquad (7.39)$$

where θ_b is the temperature difference between fin base and ambient gas and A_f is the area of the finned surface.

The second term on the right is the mean temperature difference θ_m; therefore $\theta_m = \varphi \theta_b$. The heat output per subassembly is

$$Q = hA_b\theta_b + hA_f\theta_m = h(A_b\theta_b + A_f\varphi\theta_b)$$
$$= h\theta_b(A_b + \varphi A_f) \qquad (7.40)$$

or

$$\theta_b = \frac{Q}{h(A_b + \varphi A_f)}$$

where Q = heat output per subassembly
  h = heat transfer coefficient determined from the Nusselt number, assumed to be approximately the same for the base-pot surface as for the fin
  A_b = area of base-pot surface not covered by fins

A conservative assumption can be made that the effective length of the finned pot for the transfer of heat consists of the section from the bottom of the core to the top of the sodium in the pot. For the

Fermi pot this is approximately 50 in. vs. a heat-producing length in the core of 30.5 in.

The total flow past the pot, i.e., sum of the flows through areas A and B, is obtained from the assumption that the pressure drops, Δp, through both areas must be the same. Since $\Delta p \sim V^{1.8}/D_e^{1.2}$, equating the pressure drop gives

$$\frac{V_A}{V_B} = \left(\frac{D_{eA}}{D_{eB}}\right)^{\frac{2}{3}}$$

and the total weight flow past the pot is

$$W = w \left[1 + \frac{B}{A}\left(\frac{D_{eB}}{D_{eA}}\right)^{\frac{2}{3}}\right] \qquad (7.41)$$

where A and B are the flow areas shown in Fig. 7.89, w is the assumed weight flow through area A, and D_{eA} and D_{eB} are the hydraulic diameters of areas A and B, respectively.

Assuming mixing of the two flows, the temperature rise of the gas is

$$\Delta T_g = \frac{Q}{Wc_p} \qquad (7.42)$$

where Q = heat output, Btu/sec
W = total flow (from Eq. 7.41), lb/sec
c_p = specific heat, Btu/lb/°F

The pot surface temperature for an inlet gas temperature T_g is

$$T_w = T_g + \Delta T_g + \theta_b \qquad (7.43)$$

where ΔT_g is determined from Eq. 7.42 and θ_b from Eq. 7.40.

The temperature difference ΔT_f between the fuel and the pot-wall surface can be estimated using the thermal conductivity of sodium. An effective conductivity equal to twice the thermal conductivity value (owing to natural circulation of the sodium within the pot) can be computed. Hence the maximum fuel temperature is

$$T_{f\max} = T_w + \Delta T_f \qquad (7.44)$$

where T_w is obtained from Eq. 7.43.

The friction pressure drop Δp in the cask-car fuel and storage rotor can be calculated on a single cross-sectional area for the argon flow rather than on two separate areas. The equivalent diameter D_e is

$$D_e = \frac{4(A + B)}{P}$$

where $(A + B)$ is total cross-sectional flow area and P is the total wetted perimeter. The friction pressure drop Δp is

$$\Delta p = 4f\frac{L}{D_e}\frac{\rho v^2}{2g} \qquad (7.45)$$

where $f = 0.046/Re^{0.2}$ i.e., the Fanning friction factor [66]
L = length of pot, ft
g = 32.2 ft/sec^2

The velocity $v = W/(A + B)$. Substituting this term in Eq. 7.45 gives the resulting pressure drop

$$\Delta p = 4f\frac{L}{D_e}\frac{\rho W^2}{2g(A + B)^2} \qquad (7.46)$$

where W is obtained from Eq. 7.41.

Gas may be bypassed through such sections as the clearance gap between the rotor and the shielded sides of the cask containing the rotor. The bypass is calculated by means of the conventional Δp relation.

The total pressure drop from the entrance to the exit of the cask coolant system should include: (1) pressure loss in plenums, (2) entrance and exit losses, (3) momentum loss due to heating of the flow, (4) friction pressure loss, (5) turn losses, and (6) pressure loss across heat-exchanger bundle.

The mean temperature (°F) of the mixed gas flows entering the heat exchanger is

$$T'_g = T_g + \frac{Q'}{W'c_p} \qquad (7.47)$$

where Q' is the total cask heat loss in Btu/sec, W' is total gas flow in lb/sec, and c_p is the specific heat in Btu/lb/°F.

The volume flow (cu ft/min) at the blower inlet is

$$V = \frac{W''}{\rho} \qquad (7.48)$$

where W'' is the total flow in lb/min and ρ is the density of the gas in lb/cu ft.

The resistance curve for the system drawn through the fan characteristic curve gives the fan operating point, which determines the fan requirements.

The argon-to-air heat exchanger is sized to dissipate Q' heat with a gas outlet temperature below T_g. A cross-flow tube-bank design is used as an example with the argon gas flowing through the tubes and cooling air flowing across the tubes.

1. The heat-exchanger nomenclature is:

	Unit	Symbol
Inside tube diameter	in.	D_i
Tube-wall thickness	in.	t
Tube spacing (equilateral pitch)	in.	S
Number of tube banks		m
Number of tubes per bank		n
Tube length	in.	L
Heat-exchanger length in air-flow direction	in.	L_A
Heat-exchanger length in direction at right angles to air flow	in.	w

2. The heat-exchanger performance should be calculated for:

Argon gas inlet temperature	°F	T_{Ai}
Argon gas outlet temperature	°F	T_{Ao}
Argon gas weight flow	lb/sec	W_A
Cooling-air weight flow	lb/sec	W_a
Cooling-air inlet temperature	°F	T_{ai}
Cooling-air outlet temperature	°F	T_{ao}
Average specific heat of argon	Btu/lb/°F	c_{pA}
Average specific heat of air	Btu/lb/°F	c_{Pa}

Convection heat-transfer coefficient, argon side	Btu/sec/sq ft/°F	h_A
Convection heat-transfer coefficient, air side	Btu/sec/sq ft/°F	h_a
Overall heat-transfer coefficient	Btu/sec/sq ft/°F	U
Thermal conductivity of argon	Btu/sec/°F/ft	k_A
Thermal conductivity of air	Btu/sec/°F/ft	k_a
Viscosity of argon	lb (mass)/ft/sec	μ_A
Viscosity of air	lb (mass)/ft/sec	μ_a
Average argon density	lb (mass)/cu ft	ρ_A
Average air density	lb (mass)/cu ft	ρ_a
Average argon velocity through the tubes of the tube bank	ft/sec	v_A
Average air velocity between the tubes of the tube bank	ft/sec	v_a
Mass velocity of argon ($\rho_A v_A$)	lb/sec/sq ft	G_A
Mass velocity of air ($\rho_a v_a$)	lb/sec/sq ft	G_a

3. The basic heat-transfer and friction relations are:

For the argon gas flow [63]

$$Nu_A = \frac{h_A D_i}{k_A} = 0.023 \, Re_A^{0.8} \, Pr_A^{0.4} \quad (7.49)$$

where

$$Re_A = \frac{D_i G_A}{\mu_A}$$

$$Pr_A = \left(\frac{c_p \mu}{k}\right)_A$$

The pressure drop in the tubes is

$$\Delta p_A = 4f \frac{L}{D_i} \frac{G_A^2}{2\rho_A g} \quad (7.50)$$

where f = Fanning friction factor = $0.046/Re_A^{0.2}$
g = 32.2 (lb-m) ft/(lb-f)/sec^2

For air flow the Nusselt number is [63]

$$Nu_a = \frac{h_a D_0}{k_a} = 0.30 \, Re_a^{0.60} = 0.30 \left(\frac{D_0 G_a}{\mu_a}\right)^{0.60} \quad (7.51)$$

The air pressure drop across the tube bank is [63]

$$\Delta p_a = \frac{4 m f G_a^2}{2 \rho_a g} \quad (7.52)$$

where

$$f = 0.34 \, Re_a^{-0.15} = 0.34 \left(\frac{D_0 G_a}{\mu_a}\right)^{-0.15}$$

The overall heat-transfer coefficient, U, is determined from

$$\frac{1}{U} = \frac{1}{h_A} + \frac{1}{h_a}$$

neglecting the conductivity of the tubes. Equating the heat transfer on the air side to the heat transfer on the argon side,

$$W_a c_{pa}(T_{ao} - T_{ai}) = W_A c_{pA}(T_{Ai} - T_{Ao})$$

results in the following relation:

$$\frac{W_a c_{pa}}{W_A c_{pA}} = \frac{T_{Ai} - T_{Ao}}{T_{Ao} - T_{ai}} = Z \quad (7.53)$$

where Z is the heat-capacity rate ratio.

The heating effectiveness η_h is defined [63]

$$\eta_h = \frac{T_{ao} - T_{ai}}{T_{Ai} - T_{ai}} \quad (7.54)$$

and

$$Z\eta_h = \frac{T_{Ai} - T_{Ao}}{T_{Ai} - T_{ai}} \quad (7.55)$$

The value of η_h can be obtained from [63]. Knowing Z, η_h, T_{ai}, and T_{Ai}, one can obtain

$$T_{Ao} = T_{Ai} - Z\eta_h(T_{Ai} - T_{ai}) \quad (7.56)$$

The cooling-air-circuit pressure-drop losses include: (1) turning losses in ducts near the inlet and the outlet of heat exchanger, (2) sudden enlargement loss in the duct at the heat exchanger inlet, and (3) loss of some fraction of the dynamic heat exiting from the fan outlet annulus into the duct.

References

1. Civilian Power Reactor Program, Part I, Summary of Technical and Economic Status as of 1959, USAEC Report TID-8516, 1960.
2. Civilian Power Reactor Program, Part III, Status Report on Pressurized Water Reactors as of 1959, USAEC Report TID-8518 (Bk 2), 1960.
3. A Plutonium-Fueled Fast Breeder Atomic Power Plant, USAEC Report APDA-129, Atomic Power Development Associates, Inc., Apr. 2, 1959.
4. L. E. Minnick, Highlights of Operating Experience During 1962 at Yankee Atomic Electric Company Plant, Proceedings of the 25th Annual Meeting of American Power Conference, Chicago, Ill., p. 234, Illinois Institute of Technology, 1963.
5. C. B. Zitek, Highlights of Operating Experience During 1962 at Dresden Nuclear Power Station, Proceedings of the 25th Annual Meeting of American Power Conference, Chicago, Ill., p. 238, Illinois Institute of Technology, 1963.
6. Duquesne Light Company, Shippingport Atomic Power Station, Power Station Department Monthly Operating Report, January 1963.
7. P. A. Fleger et al., Shippingport Atomic Power Station Operating Experience, Developments and Future Plans, Proceedings of U.S.–Japan Atomic Industrial Forums Joint Conference on Nuclear Power, pp. 41–69, Japan Atomic Industrial Forum, Tokyo, 1963.
8. A. Amorosi and J. G. Yevick, Capital Costs Reduced for Fast Breeders, Nucleonics, 19(2):64–65 (February 1961).
9. S. McLain et al., Methods of Replacing Fuel in Heterogeneous Reactors, Nuclear Engineering and Science Congress, Dec. 12–16, 1955, Cleveland, Ohio, Vol. 1, Problems in Nuclear Energy, pp. 267–277, Pergamon Press, New York, 1957.
10. Reactor Development Program Progress Report, USAEC Report ANL-6683, Argonne National Laboratory, p. 18, January 1963.
11. Reactor Development Program Progress Report, USAEC Report ANL-6698, Argonne National Laboratory, pp. 25–26, February 1963.
12. A. Smaardyk et al., FARET, A Fast Reactor Facility, Trans. Am. Nucl. Soc., 5(2):435–436 (November 1962).
13. Reactor Development Program Progress Report, USAEC Report ANL-6509, Argonne National Laboratory, p. 26, January 1962.
14. C. R. Jackson (Ed.), Liquid-Metals Handbook, Sodium–NaK Supplement, 3rd ed., USAEC Report TID-5277, pp. 10–12, 21, 126, and 265, July 1955.
15. S. C. Furman, Metal–Water Reactions, V, The Kinetics of Metal–Water Reactions—Low Pressure Studies, USAEC Report GEAP-3208, General Electric Company, July 31, 1959.
16. P. B. Longton, Reactions of Sodium with Water Vapor, British Report IGR-TN/C-418, December 1956.
17. J. H. Perry, Chemical Engineers' Handbook, 3rd ed., p. 239, McGraw-Hill Book Company, Inc., New York, 1950.
18. D. E. Bloomfield to E. C. Kovacic, Review of Information Received to Date on Methods of Removing Sodium from Components, APDA Memo, Atomic Power Development Associates, Inc., p. 5, May 14, 1959.
19. K. Q. Bagley, J. L. Bramman, and M. F. Finlan, The Removal of Sodium and Sodium/Potassium Alloy from Irradiated Fast-Reactor Fuel Elements, IGD Memorandum 041, United Kingdom

Atomic Energy Authority Industrial Group, Technical Memorandum, pp. 4 and 6.

20. R. H. Costello to R. H. Jones, Report on Steam Cleaning Test of Dummy Fuel Element Subassemblies, APDA Test Memo No. 3, Atomic Power Development Associates, Inc., Sept. 23, 1958, and Oct. 21, 1958.

21. M. Sittig, Sodium, Its Manufacture, Properties and Uses, Reinhold Publishing Corp., New York, 1956.

22. H. W. Alter and P. A. McManus, Sodium Mass Transfer III, The Application of Liquid Ammonia As a Sodium Cleaning Agent, USAEC Report GEAP-4006, General Electric Company, April 1962.

23. Z. R. Kanaan and C. R. Nash, Removal of Sodium from Core Subassemblies with White Oil and Ultrasonics, APDA-142, Atomic Power Development Associates, Inc., March 1961.

24. 150-Mw Plutonium-Fueled Fast Breeder Atomic Power Plant, APDA-136, Atomic Power Development Associates, Inc., March 1960.

25. Enrico Fermi Atomic Power Plant, Technical Information Hazard Summary Report, Power Reactor Development Company, Detroit, Mich., June 1961.

26. R. F. Mantey and J. G. Feldes, Shielding and Waste Disposal Aspects of the Fuel Cleaning and Storage System at the Enrico Fermi Plant, Trans. Am. Nucl. Soc., 3:354 (1960).

27. W. R. Casto, Fuel-Element Handling, Nucl. Safety, 2(2):7-10 (December 1960).

28. C. R. Nash, Status Report on Facility for Fuel Element Decay and Radioactive Equipment Repair, APDA Memorandum, Atomic Power Development Associates, Inc., Aug. 21, 1958.

29. Atomic Energy Commission, Protection Against Radiation in the Shipments of Irradiated Fuel Elements, Title 10, Code of Federal Regulations, Part 72, Federal Register, p. 2142, Mar. 5, 1963.

30. W. L. Albrecht, Shipment of Spent Fuel Elements, Nucl. Safety, 2(1):3-7 (September 1960).

31. W. H. Piper and J. H. Langhaar, 70-ton Shipping Cask for the Savannah River Plant, Design and Fabrication, USAEC Report DP-357, E. I. du Pont de Nemours and Company, Inc., January 1959.

32. Neil Ritchey, Transportation of Spent Fuel, Proceedings of Annual Conference of Atomic Industrial Forum, p. 229, Atomic Industrial Forum, New York, 1960.

33. Transportation of Irradiated Fuel, Reactor Fuel Process., 6(1): 3-4, (January 1963).

34. Chemical Technology Division Annual Progress Report for Period Ending June 30, 1962, USAEC Report ORNL-3314, Oak Ridge National Laboratory, Sept. 21, 1962.

35. Forum Memo to Members, Shipping Casks for Spent Fuel, pp. 7-16, Atomic Industrial Forum, Inc., New York, September 1962.

36. Power Reactor Spent Fuel Transport Services Taking Shape, Nucleonics, 20(10):26-27 (October 1962).

37. E. C. Lusk, H. M. Epstein, R. J. Eiber, and J. E. Gates, Containers for the Shipment of Spent Reactor Fuel Elements, Trans. Am. Nucl. Soc., 5(2):361-362 (November 1962).

38. L. J. Koch et al., Experimental Breeder Reactor II (EBR-II) Hazard Summary Report, USAEC Report ANL 5719, Argonne National Laboratory, May 1947, and Addendum, USAEC Report ANL-5719(Add.), January 1964.

39. J. A. Bolton and P. T. Calabretta, How to Load Solid Fuel Reactors, Nucleonics, 13(6):52-55 (June 1955).

40. Fast Reactor Descriptive Manual, British Report IG-Report-170(D), Vol. 2, Section A.9.

41. C. P. Zaleski and L. Vautrey, La Reacteur Rapide Surregenerateur, Vols. 1 and 2, Commissariat, a l'Energie Atomique, France, Oct. 23, 1961.

42. L. G. Soderholm, Control Rod Gripper Design, Design News, pp. 30-31, May 8, 1961.

43. P. F. Shaw, Control Elements for Sodium Graphite Reactors, Power Reactor Technol., 5 (4):74 and 75 (September 1962).

44. D. O. Leeser and R. C. Williams, Evaluation of Material Wear and Self-Welding in Sodium-Cooled Reactor Systems, USAEC

Report APDA-126, Atomic Power Development Associates, Inc., August 1958.

45. H. Apkarian, Investigation of Liquid Metal Lubricated Bearings, USAEC Report R50GL231, General Electric Company, November 1950.

46. G. R. Fox and E. Schnetzer, Low Viscosity Bearing Stability Investigation, AEC-NASA Bearing Conference, Washington, D. C., July 24-25, 1962, General Electric Flight Propulsion Laboratory Department.

47. E. Garelis to W. J. McCarthy, Decay Heating, APDA Memo, Atomic Power Development Associates, Inc., Mar. 26, 1958.

48. J. O. Blomeke and M. F. Todd, Uranium-235 Fission-Product Production as a Function of Thermal Neutron Flux, Irradiation Time, and Decay Time, USAEC Report ORNL-2127, Oak Ridge National Laboratory, 1957-1958.

49. L. Burris, Jr., and I. G. Dillon, Estimation of Fission Product Spectra in Discharged Fuel from Fast Reactors, USAEC Report ANL-5742, Argonne National Laboratory, July 1957.

50. K. Way and E. P. Wigner, Rate of Decay of Fission Products, Radiochemical Studies: The Fission Products, Book 1, Paper 43, p. 436, National Nuclear Energy Series, McGraw-Hill Book Company, 1951.

51. S. Untermeyer and J. T. Weills, Heat Generation in Irradiated Uranium, USAEC Report ANL-4790, Argonne National Laboratory, February 1952.

52. L. L. Kintner, Heat Transfer From Spent Fuel and Blanket Subassembly During Transfer From Reactor to Decay Storage Facility, APDA Technical Memo. No. 2, Atomic Power Development Associates, Inc., May 15, 1957.

53. D. R. Patterson and R. J. Schiltz, The Determination of Heat Generation in Irradiated Uranium, prepared for use in School of Nuclear Science and Engineering at Argonne National Laboratory, August 1955.

54. W. C. Francis and L. L. Marsden, Gamma Intensity and Heating From Spent MTR Fuel Elements, paper presented at American Nuclear Society Meeting June 6-8, 1956.

55. Max Jakob, Heat Transfer, Vol. 1, John Wiley & Sons, Inc., New York, 1949.

56. A. I. Brown and S. M. Marco, Introduction to Heat Transfer, McGraw-Hill Book Company, Inc., New York, 1942.

57. H. C. Hottel, Radiant Heat Transmission, Mech. Eng., 52(7): 699 (July 1930).

58. F. C. Hooper and I. S. Juhasz, Direct Graphical Evaluation of Radiation Form Factor, Paper No. 52-F-19, American Society of Mechanical Engineers, 1952.

59. M. Fischenden and O. A. Saunders, The Calculation of Heat Transmission, Her Majesty's Stationery Office, London, 1932.

60. F. A. Brooks, Solar Energy and Its Use for Heating Water in California, Bulletin 602, College of Agriculture, University of California, 1936.

61. N. W. Snyder, J. T. Fier, and R. V. Dunkle, Total Normal Emissivity Measurements on Aircraft Materials Between 100 and 800°F, Trans. Am. Soc. Mech. Engrs., 77:1011-1019 (1955).

62. H. Schmidt and E. Furthman, Ueber die Gesamtstrahlung fester Koerper, Mitt. K. W. Inst. Eisenforsch, Abh. 109, Dusseldorf, 1928.

63. W. H. McAdams, Heat Transmission, 3rd ed., McGraw-Hill Book Company, Inc., New York, 1954.

64. Frank Kreith, Principles of Heat Transfer, International Textbook Co., Scranton, Pa., 1958.

65. Reactor Engineering Division Quarterly Report, July, August, September 1955, Section II, USAEC Report ANL-5511, Argonne National Laboratory, January 1956.

66. Reactor Engineering Division Quarterly Report, October, November, December 1955, Section I, USAEC Report, ANL-5561, Argonne National Laboratory, April 1956.

67. Final Design Report on the Fuel Handling Cask Car for the Enrico Fermi Atomic Power Plant, Report GNEC-89, General Nuclear Engineering Corporation, Feb. 27, 1959.

CHAPTER 8

Shielding

H. E. HUNGERFORD, Ph.D.
Professor of Nuclear Engineering
Purdue University, Lafayette, Indiana
with contributions from R. F. MANTEY, Philadelphia Electric Co.

Contents

This chapter on shielding of fast reactors was prepared as a guide in the design, fabrication, construction, testing, and operation of fast reactor power plants. It presents little theory, leaving this to the quoted references. The chapter should give the user a broad knowledge of the many facets of shielding for fast reactors. The chapter encompasses material available in the literature as well as material hitherto unpublished.

In general, the chapter's contents fall into five categories: (1) basic shielding considerations and principles, material requirements, environmental effects, design criteria, and effect of coolant, (2) shield calculations, (3) test programs, (4) nuclear data and mathematical aids, and (5) a description of fast reactor power-plant shields.

No compilation of data and methods is ever complete. Admittedly many areas are discussed only sketchily. For more information the reader is referred to the general shielding information contained in the <u>Reactor Handbook</u>, 2nd ed., Vol. I,

1960, and Vol. III, Part B, 1962, Interscience Publishers, Inc. The references contained at the end of this chapter will also allow the reader to pursue any given subject more thoroughly.

8.1 General Shielding Considerations

Shielding a reactor involves problems dealing with the intrinsic behavior of neutrons and gamma rays in their passage through matter. As a rule of thumb, the best neutron shields are built of light materials; the best gamma-ray shields are made of heavy materials. The selection of the right material depends upon many considerations, e.g., type of reactor, reactor power, location of shield, physical environment of material (temperature, atmosphere, radiation intensities), physical, chemical, and nuclear characteristics of the material, and cost and availability of the material.

8.1.1 NEUTRON SHIELDS

The main purpose of a shield is to protect people, equipment, and structures from the harmful effects of nuclear radiations. The shield moderates and absorbs neutrons and gamma rays, the two most important types of radiation from a shielding standpoint. Neutrons are born with high energies, i.e., in the million electron volt range. The most efficient way to capture neutrons is to first slow them down (moderate them) since neutron capture is much more probable at low (thermal) energies. Materials of low atomic weight moderate neutrons more rapidly than heavy materials because during elastic collisions the nuclei of light atoms are able to absorb the neutron energy by recoil. Heavy atoms do not recoil much and therefore do not moderate neutrons very rapidly. Light materials are called moderators. The moderating materials in order of moderating efficiency are hydrogen, beryllium, lithium, boron, and carbon. Hydrogen is the best moderator since it can, during one collision, reduce the energy of a fast neutron to the thermal range. From a purely nuclear viewpoint, hydrogenous materials make the best shields.

Beryllium and carbon are good moderators but have almost no capture ability. Materials with high capture cross sections, such as boron, are added to capture the thermalized neutrons. High-atomic-weight elements by their ability to produce inelastic collisions exhibit good fast-neutron attenuating characteristics. Inelastic scattering turns high-energy neutrons into intermediate-energy neutrons. During inelastic scattering a neutron is captured by a nucleus; a very short time later another neutron of lower energy is emitted together with a gamma ray. The sum of the energies of the emitted neutron and gamma ray is equal to the energy of the original neutron. (These reactions have a lower energy limit.) Heavy materials do not usually have good attenuation properties for neutrons of intermediate energy.

8.1.2 GAMMA-RAY SHIELDS

Gamma rays, a form of electromagnetic radiation, are absorbed within materials mainly by interaction with the electrons surrounding the nucleus of atoms. Heavy elements make the best gamma-ray shields because the electron density within a material is proportional to the atomic number, Z. High-Z materials are also materials of high atomic weight, e.g., iron, copper, lead, and uranium.

8.1.3 FAST REACTOR CHARACTERISTICS

In a fast reactor the chain reaction proceeds at high neutron energies (0.1 to 0.5 Mev). This energy range is considered high for a reactor spectrum but is considered intermediate from a shielding standpoint. Cores of fast reactors are small. As a result the neutron leakage from a fast reactor core not only is large but also is of much higher energy than from a thermal reactor.

8.1.4 MODERATION OF NEUTRONS IN A FAST BREEDER REACTOR

The average energy of fission in a fast reactor should be kept high to maintain a high breeding ratio. Materials that have a high moderating ratio, and thus tend to degrade the neutron-energy spectrum in the core to lower energies, should not be used.

The moderating ratio, P_m, of a material can be shown to be inversely proportional to its atomic weight, A. Thus

$$P_m = \frac{\sigma_s}{\sigma_c}\xi \simeq \frac{\sigma_s}{\sigma_c}\left(\frac{6}{3A+2}\right) \qquad \text{(for } A > 3\text{)}$$

where σ_s is the scattering cross section, σ_c is the capture cross section, and ξ is the average logarithmic energy decrement per collision. The value of ξ for good moderating materials (hydrogen, beryllium, carbon) ranges from 1.0 to 0.15. For heavy materials it is less than 0.05.

8.1.5 RELATION OF CORE MATERIALS TO NEUTRON LEAKAGE IN A FAST BREEDER REACTOR

For a fast breeder, where it is desirable to have as little moderation as possible within the core,

P_m should be small. Materials that make the best neutron shields are usually excluded from the core to keep P_m small. The result is that 30 to 50% of all neutrons generated may leak out into the blanket or shield. A fast reactor should be designed to exclude the possibility of the sudden introduction of moderating materials into the reactor core to avoid large reactivity changes.

8.1.6 SHIELDING PENALTY IN A FAST REACTOR DUE TO LACK OF MODERATION

Because of the lack of moderation, there is a shielding penalty attached to a fast reactor which is not present with a thermal reactor. The flux of neutrons escaping the core of a fast reactor is of both high intensity and high energy. This condition exists because materials used in a fast reactor are chosen to be of medium or high atomic weight to keep moderations by neutrons during elastic collisions to a minimum. Also, inelastic scattering becomes important as a moderating process. This process may degrade the effective fast-neutron energy some 10% or more. In contrast, very little inelastic scattering takes place in a thermal reactor. Below the inelastic scattering threshold (< 0.1 Mev) for the medium-weight and heavy elements, there is very little moderation in a fast reactor. Neutrons captured in the blanket which produce fission add very little more to the high-energy groups. The effect of all this in a fast reactor is to produce a leakage spectrum containing very few neutrons of high energy or low energy but one rich in neutrons of intermediate energies. The shield for a fast reactor, which is placed outside the core and blanket region, should be designed to absorb the intermediate-energy neutrons.

Figure 8.1 shows the neutron-energy spectrum in the core and at the outer edge of the blanket region of the Enrico Fermi Reactor [1] and in the center of the EBR-I core [2]. Of the neutrons es-

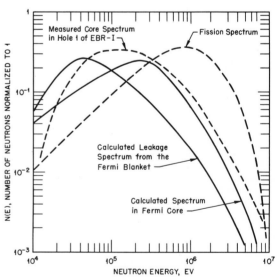

FIG. 8.1—Neutron spectra in Fermi reactor and in EBR-I core [3, 4].

caping the core and blanket of these reactors, there are almost no very low energy neutrons and relatively few extremely high energy neutrons. The great bulk of neutrons leaking from a fast reactor have energies in the range of 10 to 500 kev. This makes shielding against them a difficult task.

8.1.7 FAST REACTOR SHIELDS

Neutron shielding of a fast power reactor is generally accomplished as follows: A protective layer of heavy material, such as stainless steel, is used inside the reactor vessel to protect the vessel against radiation damage from the high-energy component of the escaping flux. As an alternate to the use of heavy material, a light material can be used in conjunction with a high capture agent, for example, boron in canned graphite. A good moderating material, together with a strong neutron absorber, is used outside the vessel. Graphite with a few per cent by weight of boron satisfies these requirements and makes an excellent shield material. To reduce expense, concrete or other low-cost materials are generally used in low-intensity regions to complete the shielding.

The use of water and other hydrogenous liquids as shields is generally precluded for two reasons: (1) the possibility that the liquid will be introduced into the reactor where it will act as a moderator and (2) the possibility that the liquid will be introduced into the coolant system where it will react with the sodium and liberate excess energy and contaminating reaction products.

Gamma-ray shielding is accomplished by the use of lead, steel, or other heavy elements. In a fast breeder reactor the blanket serves to shield out most of the core gammas. Any steel layer around the blanket will absorb a large part of the captured gamma radiations produced within it and within the blanket. Shield design is influenced by the amount of heat produced by gamma rays within the various parts of the shield.

Another consideration in shielding is the relative importance of neutrons and gamma rays in particular locations. The amount of neutron leakage from the primary shield is an important consideration. On the other hand, the gamma flux excaping from the primary shield is not of overriding importance because of the intense gamma activity from the radioactive primary coolant outside the shield.

8.1.8 EFFECT OF LIQUID-METAL COOLANTS ON SHIELDING

One of the large penalties resulting from the use of liquid-metal coolants in power reactors is the high activation of the coolant. Other stringent design conditions for fast reactors, such as high temperatures, tend to increase the difficulties in designing proper shielding for the coolant system. The use of liquid-metal coolants adds to the amount of biological shielding required and complicates the heating problems within the shield.

8.2 Fast Reactor Shield-material Considerations

8.2.1 GENERAL ENVIRONMENTAL CONSIDERATIONS

As the general technology of power reactors progresses, the trend is toward systems that operate at higher temperatures and efficiencies. One of the areas affected by these demands for high temperature is that of materials. Fast reactor shield materials may be required to perform satisfactorily in high radiation fields, under high temperatures, in undesirable environments, and under high mechanical stresses. Materials used should be capable of withstanding high temperatures and high radiation fields while retaining their strength and structural and shielding properties.

8.2.2 ECONOMIC AND TECHNICAL CONSIDERATIONS

In the electric-power field nuclear plants are designed as economically as possible. Shield materials considered for use under high-temperature high-radiation conditions should be commercially available, easily fabricated, and economically feasible. Where a shield material is also used as a structural member, its structural properties must be considered.

The deleterious effects of heat on common materials are well known. For instance, at elevated temperatures metals may undergo phase changes that lead to loss of strength, creepage, and warpage or to loss of ductility and to embrittlement. At high temperatures many materials decompose, are transformed to a liquid state, react chemically with their environment, or change in some other way which is undesirable from a shielding point of view. Under high-temperature conditions nonmetallic materials may also exhibit general loss of strength, changes in crystalline structure, or loss of the bonds between components if the material is a mixture. These materials may also exhibit other properties, such as spalling or crumbling, under extreme environmental conditions.

8.2.3 CRITERIA GOVERNING THE CHOICE OF MATERIALS FOR FAST REACTORS

There are several general criteria governing the choice of materials for use as shields in fast reactors. Among these are the following: The material should exhibit continued shielding effectiveness over long periods of time. The material should maintain structural integrity under prescribed environmental conditions for prescribed periods of operation. Radiation over the expected life of the material should not harmfully change its properties. The material should be inert to the action of molten sodium or other coolant. If it is not, it must be protected from physical contact with the coolant. The prescribed heat conductivity and expansion characteristics of the material should be maintained for the life of the plant.

8.2.4 ENVIRONMENTAL EFFECTS

8.2.4.1 Temperature Effects

Increased temperatures mechanically weaken materials. In metals this phenomenon is demonstrated by a constantly progressing loss of tensile strength, an increase in ductility, and a tendency to warp and creep. This weakening of material also occurs if the metal undergoes a change of state which produces new mechanical properties. Most stainless steels, for instance, lose up to 80% of their original (room-temperature) tensile strength when subjected to temperatures of 1500°F for long periods of time. Type-304 stainless steel under the same conditions may lose 95% or more of its creep strength [5, 6].

High temperatures can cause materials that are chemically inert at low temperatures to react with their environment, with adjacent materials, or, in the case of some mixtures or alloys, with some constituent of its own composition. Metals may react with nitrogen in the air and become nitrided. Oxidation at elevated temperatures is a problem with a great number of metals and nonmetals. Materials containing hydrated water molecules lose their water under heating. Impurities in a material may help catalyze reactions with the environment or with the adjacent material. The presence of water vapor in the atmosphere at elevated temperature can cause ionic bonds between dissimilar metals to separate. This separation results in electrolytic action, which is the start of corrosion. The presence of water vapor at high temperatures may result in deleterious chemical actions in materials.

Ordinary concrete, which is an excellent neutron-shield material because of its water content and relatively high density, has from 8 to 15% of hydration at normal temperatures. This water,

under natural environmental conditions, is retained in the concrete for periods of 20 to 50 years; even after 50 years as much as half the original water may still remain. Heating the concrete increases the molecular vibrations in the crystals of the material, which breaks the hydrated-water-molecule bond; the water begins to come off at a temperature of about 150°F. Concrete held at the boiling point of water dehydrates at quite a rapid rate, and the extent of dehydration is pronounced. As the water of hydration is removed, a general but moderate loss of strength occurs. Concrete can be heated up to about 350°F without any further appreciable changes if water retention is unimportant. From 350°F to about 500°F, there is a slow loss of structural properties. As the temperature is increased beyond 500°F, this decrease in strength becomes more pronounced until at 1000°F spalling begins [7]. If the concrete is held for very long periods of time at these temperatures, crumbling may result. Figure 8.2 shows water retention properties of ordinary concrete as a function of temperature. Temperature effects on heavy concrete are, in general, more severe than on ordinary concrete [8].

8.2.4.2 Radiation-damage Effects

In shield design radiation-damage effects to materials should be carefully evaluated. During moderation and radiation capture the shield material is damaged. Collision between a fast neutron and an atom transfers energy from the neutron to the atom. This causes the atom to move from its normal position. If the motion is great enough to break the atom permanently out of its position, a local change of properties occurs. When enough changes of any given property occur to make that change of property general throughout a large region of the material, damage is said to have occurred. The extent of damage to a given material depends on many factors, e.g., type and energy of the radiation (in reactor-shield design one is primarily concerned with neutrons and gamma radiation), radiation flux (neutrons/cm^2/sec or photons/cm^2/sec), duration of the exposure to radiation, and temperature of material.

The temperature of the material undergoing irradiation is important because in some materials damage caused by radiation at low temperatures can be partially or wholly self-annealed at higher temperatures.

Existing information on radiation damage to shield materials in fast reactor environments is meager. Much of the available data have been obtained from materials used in thermal reactors, which have relatively few high-energy neutron-flux components. Considerably more information is needed on the behavior of fast reactor materials in radiation fields and in temperature environments typical of fast reactors.

8.2.4.3 Radiation Damage to Stainless Steel

Stainless steel is used in sodium-cooled fast reactor vessels as a construction material and as internal shielding. One of the primary functions of internal shielding is to reduce the damaging neutron flux on the reactor-vessel wall. The damaging

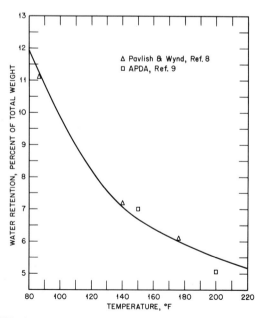

FIG. 8.2—Water-retention properties of ordinary concrete as a function of temperature.

flux consists mainly of neutrons whose energies are above 0.1 Mev. This shield is usually a loose-fitting shield that can adjust to temperature changes due to nuclear-radiation absorption. Since it has no other function, stresses and changes in its properties due to radiation damage are relatively unimportant.

The thickness of the steel shielding depends upon the total integrated fast flux the reactor-vessel wall is designed to withstand. This total integrated fast flux (nvt) design value must be based on the available experimental data for the particular steel. In the mid 1950's there were no firm data on the elevated-temperature exposure limit of stainless steel. Experimental data gained from examination of the EBR-I core after the core meltdown of November 1956 indicated that stainless steel can take a fast-neutron exposure of at least 6×10^{22} neutrons/cm^2 without harmful effects [10].

8.3 Radiation Effects in Graphite

8.3.1 MECHANISM OF WIGNER ENERGY STORAGE AND RELEASE

Graphite, used extensively in fast reactor shields, undergoes severe changes in its crystalline structure when irradiated by neutrons at temperatures below 200°C. During collisions with graphite atoms, neutrons have the ability to knock the atoms from their bound locations in the graphite hexagonal crystal structure into metastable interstitial positions. Because of the forces interacting between atoms of the crystal, the interstitial position represents a state of higher potential energy of the atom (i.e., an atom in this state has absorbed energy). Increased thermal agitation of the atoms can upset this metastable equilibrium, and the atom may return to its original (or to another) crystal location, liberating the stored energy as heat. If the stored-energy content surpasses a certain value,* a release of energy can, under certain conditions, become autocatalytic; that is, the release may become self-sustaining until such time as the energy content again falls below a fixed value. Figure 8.3 shows typical stored-energy release spectra in graphite as a function of temperature when the graphite has been irradiated at 30°C. Some experimental values of the stored-energy content and release rates of this energy in graphite reactors are shown in Table 8.1. The sudden release of a large amount of stored energy raises the temperature of the graphite [11, 13, 14]. In the case of Britain's Windscale Reactor, this temperature rise in the graphite moderator caused the fuel to melt, which, in turn, resulted in a release of fission products. A sudden release of a large amount of energy in graphite is being used as a shield may result in unduly high temperatures if the heat release can not be readily reversed.

8.3.2 CONDITIONS UNDER WHICH ENERGY IS STORED AND RELEASED

Experiments indicate that Wigner energy may be stored in graphite up to a certain saturation value, which depends upon the irradiation flux and the irradiation temperature. The buildup of stored energy E may be represented by an equation of the form $E = E_{sat}(1 - e^{-\lambda' t})$, where λ' is a time constant of the annealing relaxation. The conditions under which stored energy may be released are essentially (1) that long-time irradiation take place at a low temperature (below 200°C) and (2) that thereafter a mechanism be present to raise the temperature of the graphite sufficiently high to dissipate the metastable states of the displaced atoms. Annealing (or soaking) of the graphite at a temperature higher than the irradiation temperature will eventually cause much of the stored energy to be released. The rate of energy release and the amount finally released depends upon the annealing temperature compared to the irradiation temperature and the ability of the heat accumulated to propagate itself through the material.

Experiments indicate that graphite subject to low-temperature irradiation (30°C) followed by annealing at a temperature of 200°C produces the sharpest release rates. This gives rise to temperature gradients on the order of 0.25°C per sec-

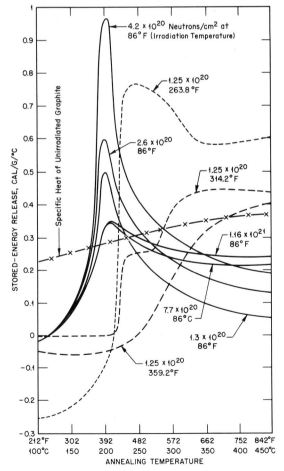

FIG. 8.3—Stored-energy release spectra in graphite at various irradiation temperatures [11, 12]. Note: cal/g/°C × 1,000 = Btu/lb/°F.

*The natural heat capacity (specific heat) of the material. Because of metastable equilibrium the Wigner energy storage value can exceed the specific heat.

Table 8.1—Wigner Energy Content, Release Rates, and Temperature Rises
in Graphite Reactors*†

Reactor	Date of stored-energy release	Irradiation temperature, °C	Irradiation exposure, neutrons/cm²/sec	Max. stored‡ energy released, cal/g	Maximum release rate, cal/g/°C	Maximum temperature rise, °C
BEPO	1958	120 (?)	5×10^{20} (?)	95	0.35	∼200
ORNL X-10	1958	30	1.5×10^{20} (?)	32§	0.6	∼220
Brookhaven Graphite Reactor	1953	55	1.7×10^{20}	50		∼240

* Data of table constructed from material in Refs. 13 and 14.
† Question marks in parenthesis indicate adjacent value is uncertain.
‡ These figures do not coincide with total energy content.
§ National Bureau of Standards measurements on total energy content gave 160 cal/g for samples taken just before the release was initiated.

ond in large masses of graphite. Under these conditions energy is being liberated at the rate of 0.75 cal/sec/g (or about 3 watts per gram of graphite).

Complete annealing occurs only at high temperatures. Experiments indicate that annealing at 800°C for 3 hr causes graphite irradiated at 30°C to lose about half its stored energy. The temperature must be increased to 1800°C to ensure complete removal of the stored energy.

8.3.3 SPONTANEOUS WIGNER ENERGY RELEASE

When the stored energy exceeds a certain value in graphite, a spontaneous release of energy may occur [15]. There must be a large heat input by means of conduction or convection to start the release. The heat liberated by the release raises the local temperature, which, in turn, triggers more atoms to release their energy. When this process builds up to the point where enough heat is being generated by the release to sustain the release mechanism without the use of external heat, the reaction becomes autocatalytic and will continue until the total stored-energy content falls below a fixed value or until such time as the rate of release falls below the value of the specific heat. At this point the reaction becomes self-quenching, and no more stored energy will be released without the addition of heat.

8.3.4 FORMULAS TO ESTIMATE WIGNER ENERGY STORAGE AND RELEASE IN GRAPHITE* [13, 14]

8.3.4.1 Total Stored-energy Content, $E_s'(x)$, At Point x After Irradiation Time t_{ir} at 30°C

$$E_s'(x) = 1.09 \times 10^{-8} \sqrt{\phi_0 t_{ir}} \exp(-x/2\lambda) \quad (8.1)$$

where $E_s'(x)$ = total stored-energy content, cal/g, at point x in a graphite shield

---

*These are empirical formulas based upon United States and British energy-storage data which will give order-of-magnitude estimates of energy release [16].

ϕ_0 = neutron flux incident on graphite shield, neutrons/cm²/sec
λ = relaxation length of neutrons through the shield, cm
t_{ir} = irradiation time, sec
x = distance in shield, cm

8.3.4.2 Residual Stored Energy $E_r'(x)$ at Point x at Temperature T_{ir} with Annealing at Temperature T_A

$$E_r'(x) = 1.09 \times 10^{-8} B \sqrt{(\phi_0 t_{ir})} \exp[-0.0103(T_{ir} - 30)] \quad (8.2)$$

where $E_r'(x)$ = residual stored energy at distance x in graphite shield after anneal at temperature T_A, cal/g
$B = \left(1 - 0.00145 T_A + 4.95 \times 10^{-7} T_A^2\right) e^{-x/2\lambda}$
T_A = temperature of anneal, °C
T_{ir} = irradiation temperature, °C

8.3.4.3 Total Residual Stored Energy, E_{tot}

$$E_{tot} = 2E_r'(0) \rho a \lambda \{1 - \exp[-d/(2\lambda)]\} \quad (8.3)$$

where E_{tot} = total energy release, cal
$E_r'(0)$ = $E_r'(x)$ evaluated at x = 0
ρ = graphite density, g/cm³
a = surface area of a (cylindrical) layer of graphite, cm², which is exposed to the radiation
d = thickness of graphite layer, cm

8.3.4.4 Relaxation Rate of Release of Stored Energy, F(t)

$$F(t) = \{t[\ln(\nu t) - 1]\}^{-1} \quad (8.4)$$

where $F(t)$ = relaxation release rate, sec⁻¹
t = time after start of release, sec
ν = collision constant, 7.5×10^{13} sec⁻¹ for graphite

Condition: $\nu t > 1$

8.3.4.5 Rate of Temperature Rise dT/dt (sudden release)

$$\frac{dT(t,x)}{dt} = E_r'(x) F(t) \left[c_p \left(1 - \frac{k}{c_p \nu \rho x} \right) \right]^{-1} \quad (8.5)$$

where $dT(t,x)/dt$ = temperature gradient, °C/sec
c_p = specific heat of graphite, cal/g/ °C

k = thermal conductivity of graphite, cal/sec/cm/°C

The velocity of propagation of the temperature wave, v, cm/sec is given by

$$v^2 = \left(\frac{k}{\tau \rho c_p}\right)\left[\left(\frac{T_f - T}{T - T_{ir} + 1}\right)\right] \qquad (8.6)$$

where T_f = final expected temperature to be reached, °C

$T = T_{ir} + 1.51 \times 10^{-7} t_r^2$ °C

t = time after initiation of release, sec

τ = average time, sec, for reaction to increase by the factor $e = 2.718$

Typical measured values of τ are as follows:

X-10 Pile at ORNL: 635 sec

BEPO: 540 sec

These values will vary with the amount of energy released.

8.3.5 GROWTH AND SHRINKAGE OF GRAPHITE UNDER IRRADIATION

The small amount of available data on graphite growth and shrinkage under irradiation [14] indicates that low-temperature irradiation produces growth and high-temperature irradiation produces shrinkage. A summary of British data is shown in Fig. 8.4.

8.3.6 EFFECT OF RADIATION ON THE OXIDATION RATE OF GRAPHITE

Available data indicate that the rate of oxidation of graphite [14] at 300°C is increased by factors of 5 or 6 when the graphite is exposed to 4×10^{20} neutrons/cm^2. There is evidence that at higher temperatures this effect tends to be annealed out.

8.3.7 EFFECTS OF RADIATION ON THERMAL CONDUCTIVITY OF GRAPHITE

The thermal conductivity of graphite [11] decreases significantly when graphite is irradiated under room-temperature conditions. The ratio of the initial to the final thermal conductivity with temperature and integrated flux is shown in Fig. 8.5. High temperature has an annealing effect, and the ratio of initial to final thermal conductivity decreases with increase in temperature. The same general annealing effect is true regarding many other physical properties of graphite.

8.4 Fast Reactor Shield Design Criteria

The first step in any reactor shield design is to establish the design criteria. These include the radiation sources and their strengths and the limitations imposed on radiation intensities in various parts of the reactor plant.

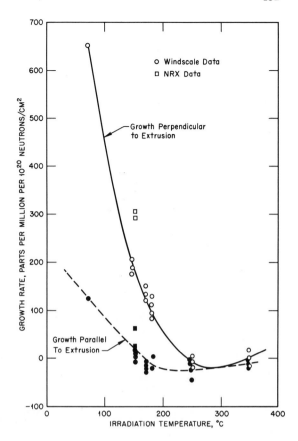

FIG. 8.4—Growth and shrinkage of Acheson-R coke graphite as a function of temperature per 10^{20} neutrons/cm^2/sec [14]. Note: 1.8°C + 32 = °F.

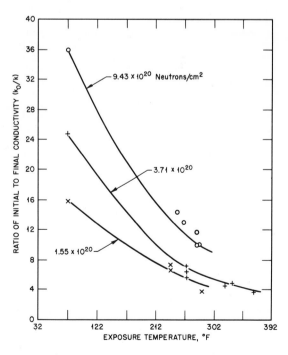

FIG. 8.5—Thermal conductivity of graphite under various neutron exposures as a function of temperature [11].

Limitations that must be considered in any design are those imposed by the following: (1) allowed biological dose rates; (2) effects of nuclear heating; (3) neutron-induced activation of components or equipment; (4) radiation damage effects; (5) mechanical criteria, e.g., necessary expansion movement and structural limitations; and (6) environment, i.e., temperature and atmosphere.

Shield design criteria for the Fermi reactor are given later in this chapter in Table 8.85.

8.4.1 BIOLOGICAL LIMITATIONS

Biological limitations for the protection of plant workers and the public are established by law; they are contained in Title 10, Code of Federal Regulations, Part 20 [17]. These limitations are operational limits as distinguished from design limits. Design limits, however, should be established on the basis of the operating limits. The law allows whole-body dose for plant workers of 5.0 rem per year or a total of 1.25 rem in any calendar quarter. The corresponding weekly dose of about 100 mrem can be translated into an hourly rate of 2.5 mrem/hr based on a 40-hr week. The yearly permissible radiation accumulated dose for the general population is 0.5 rem.

The law allows a maximum permissible design leakage from any biological shield at locations where there will be continuous personnel access of no more than 2.5 mrem/hr of both neutron and gamma radiation. In limited-access areas (where entry can be controlled by supervision), it may be desirable for economic or other reasons to establish the dose-rate level in accordance with the expected time of occupancy of the area so that the operating limits are not exceeded. Controlled areas must be supervised by the plant health physicist or other authorized persons.

Some of the reactor plants being designed at this time are using shield design limits that are one-third to one-tenth the permissible level for radiation workers. The radiation effectiveness of a shield may decrease with time whereas in many cases the top operating power of reactors may increase with time. Another justifiable reason for establishing a low dose-rate radiation limit is that the permissible radiation limits set by law may be lowered, and any increase in shielding after the plant has been built is expensive and difficult to add.

8.4.2 HEATING EFFECTS IN MATERIALS

Radiation absorbed in materials appears as heat. This heat raises the temperature of the material and may create steep temperature gradients that lead to severe stresses. Concrete is especially vulnerable since internal cracking and void formation may result (Sec. 8.2). The nuclear-heat flux that will produce a temperature rise of no more than $10°F$ in a concrete shield is about the upper limit to which concrete should be exposed unless the shield is extremely thick. This limit in terms of energy flux is about 4×10^{10} Mev/cm^2/sec; in terms of heat flux it is 20 Btu/hr/sq ft. It can be shown by the analytic methods of Sec. 8.6.8 that above this limit stresses may develop which are

severe enough to cause cracking of the concrete (see Fig. 8.36). Limitations on the temperature due to internal heat generation determine the amount and type of cooling required in a shield. Heat generation in shields is discussed in more detail in Secs. 8.6.6 and 8.6.7.

8.4.3 ACTIVATION LIMITS

Material exposed to a thermal-neutron flux of 1×10^4 neutrons/cm^2/sec will not become significantly radioactive, and the material can be handled safely without resorting to special techniques if the thermal-neutron capture cross section for the material is no greater than 1 to 2 barns. If there are materials that need protection from neutron irradiation because of handling or access problems, a limitation on the thermal flux such as the 10^4 value should be established. For those materials with larger cross sections, the limit is correspondingly lower.

8.4.4 RADIATION–DAMAGE–EFFECT LIMITS

A brief discussion of the mechanism of radiation damage is given in Secs. 8.2 and 8.3. Organic materials suffer radiation damage more easily than other classes of materials. Metals and metallic oxides are the least susceptible to radiation damage. The approximate limits, which hold for most materials, above which radiation damage becomes noticeable are given in Table 8.2. These figures do not include damage by fission products.

8.4.5 MECHANICAL LIMITATIONS

It may be necessary in assessing the physical needs of a plant or reactor system to limit radiation intensities for purely mechanical reasons. Heating effects due to radiation absorption which may not be harmful to a material per se may be harmful because of expansion and the resulting external strains upon other parts of the system. Particular values for the limiting heat flux should be generated for each individual system on the basis of analysis of preliminary conceptual designs.

Structural and load limitations in the plant should be assessed to make sure that heating, temperature rises, expansion, and radiation effects do not change the physical characteristics of the structure. It may be necessary to limit radiation fluxes and temperatures in certain areas.

Table 8.2—Approximate Limits of Exposure Before Harmful* Radiation Effects Set in

Material	Fast-neutron exposure, neutrons/cm^2	Gamma-ray exposure, rads
Water, oils	10^{15}	10^8
Paraffins	$10^{14} - 10^{15}$	$10^7 - 10^8$
Lucite	$\sim 5 \times 10^{14}$	$\sim 5 \times 10^7$
Rubber	10^{14}	10^7
Polystyrene	5×10^{15}	$\sim 5 \times 10^8$
Stainless steel	$> 10^{22}$	10^{15}
Concrete	$\sim 10^{19}$	10^{12}

* Average 25% damage limits.

8.4.6 ENVIRONMENTAL LIMITATIONS

Most materials should be used with care under severe radiation and temperature conditions. Shields are safety devices and are to be treated as such. The right ambient temperature, the proper cooling requirements, and the proper gas atmosphere in a region where a shield is to be located should be specified along with radiation limitations. The presence of water vapor is to be avoided since water is a catalyst for corrosion reactions. Many materials require an inert atmosphere.

8.5 Effect of Coolant on Shield Design

8.5.1 GENERAL

The neutron-induced activation of the primary liquid-metal coolant of a fast reactor presents some shielding design problems. In fact, the shielding for the primary coolant may determine the size of the plant rather than the neutron shielding for the reactor proper. In some instances common shielding materials cannot be used because of the added high-temperature consideration. Most of the present-day fast reactors use either sodium or a sodium-potassium alloy (NaK) as the reactor coolant. Studies of advanced fast reactor concepts and systems have called for other coolants, such as mercury or lithium. Chapter 2 has detailed information on coolants.

Since irradiated liquid-metal coolants usually emit copious amounts of gamma radiation, the nuclear characteristics of the radioactive coolant are important. Some nuclear characteristics that influence the shield design are the specific activity of the coolant (usually expressed in $\mu c/cm^3$), the number of photons per disintegration, the energy of the decay gamma rays, and the half-life of the decay gamma rays.

The specific activity of sodium in a fast reactor is so high that thick biological shields are required. The size and the location of the sodium source are two other important considerations. If a large sodium source is in close proximity to the shield, the internal heat generation in the shield may require an extensive ventilation system to cool the shield. With concrete shields steel thermal shielding may be required to decrease the high incident gamma-radiation flux to protect the concrete. Heat generation due to radioactive sources is discussed in Sec. 8.6.

8.5.2 PRIMARY-SYSTEM SODIUM-COOLANT ACTIVATION

When sodium coolant passes through a reactor, it becomes radioactive by neutron capture. The activation of the coolant is dependent upon the magnitude of the neutron flux, the time of exposure of the coolant in the neutron flux, the half-life of the particular radioactive isotope, and the activation cross section for the reaction. With all other factors in reactor systems being equal, the activation of the coolant is a function of the nuclear cross section. The specific activity of sodium in a fast

reactor may be much less than it would be in a sodium-cooled thermal reactor since the activation cross section decreases with increases in neutron energy. In the Fermi fast reactor, the median energy of the core neutrons is about 0.3 Mev as compared to near-thermal energies for neutrons in a sodium-cooled graphite reactor.

If the coolant passes j times through a reactor that has an average flux ($\bar{\phi}$) neutrons/cm^2/sec, the activity [$S_V(t)$] in dis/cm^2/sec as a function of time (t) in sec from the start of the jth cycle is given by [18]

$$S_V(t) = S_{Vj} \exp(-\lambda' t)$$

where

$$S_{Vj} =$$

$$\frac{\lambda'\bar{\phi}\Sigma_c\left\{1-\exp\left[-(\bar{\phi}\Sigma_c t'/N)\right]\right\}\left\{1-\exp\left[-(j+1)(\bar{\phi}\Sigma_c t'N^{-1}+\lambda' t_c)\right]\right\}}{(\bar{\phi}\Sigma_c N^{-1}+\lambda')\left\{1-\exp\left[-(\bar{\phi}\Sigma_c t'N^{-1})-\lambda' t_c\right]\right\}} \tag{8.7}$$

At saturation the activity is for $\lambda' t_c \ll 1$ and $\bar{\phi}\sigma \ll \lambda'$

$$S_{V_{sat}} = \frac{\bar{\phi}\Sigma_c t'}{t_c} = \frac{\bar{\phi}\Sigma_c V_0}{V_{t_c}} \quad \begin{matrix}\text{(simple series-flow}\\ \text{circuit only)}\end{matrix} \tag{8.8}$$

In Eqs. 8.7 and 8.8, the symbols have the following meanings:

S_{V_j} = the activity after j cycles, dis/cm^3/sec
λ' = the radioactive decay constant, sec^{-1}
Σ_c = $N\sigma_c$ the macroscopic capture cross section at the average energy of capture, cm^{-1}
σ_c = average microscopic cross section, cm^2/atom
N = the number of coolant nuclei per cubic centimeter
t_c = the time for a complete cycle, sec
t' = the time in the activating flux per cycle, sec
V_0 = the volume of coolant in the activating flux, cm^3
V_{t_c} = the total circulating volume of coolant, cm^3

8.5.2.1 $Na^{23}(n,\gamma)Na^{24}$ Reaction

Sodium becomes radioactive by the capture of a neutron according to the reaction:

$$Na^{23} + n \rightarrow Na^{24*} + \gamma$$
$$\underset{15.1\ hr}{\big\lfloor\!\!\longrightarrow}\ Mg^{24} + \beta^- + 2\gamma$$

The Na^{24*} compound nucleus decays with a half-life of 15 hr by emission of a beta ray to Mg^{24}. The asterisk (*) indicates an excited (or unstable) state. Two gamma rays with energies of 1.38 Mev and 2.76 Mev, respectively, are emitted with each disintegration. When Na^{23} captures a neutron to form a compound nucleus, high-energy prompt (capture) gamma rays are also emitted instantaneously.

These prompt gamma rays have a spectrum of energies, the highest energy being about 6 Mev. On the average there are about two prompt photons per neutron capture.

8.5.2.2 $Na^{23}(n, 2n)Na^{22}$ Reaction

The production of Na^{22} may become significant in a fast reactor. The threshold for this $(n, 2n)$ reaction is about 11.7 Mev. Since the cross section is very low (of the order 6 μ barns averaged over the fission spectrum), a good supply of high-energy fission neutrons is required to produce any appreciable amount. The Na^{22} decays by positron emission and has a half-life of 2.6 years. A 1.26-Mev gamma ray is emitted per disintegration. The complete reaction is

$$Na^{23} + n \rightarrow Na^{24*} + \gamma \xrightarrow{\text{inst.}} Na^{22*} + 2n$$
$$\downarrow \text{2.6 year}$$
$$Na^{22} + \beta^+ + \gamma$$

The asterisk (*) indicates an excited (or unstable) state. The Na^{22} production in a fast reactor will be roughly a factor of 10^5 lower than the Na^{24} production. However, since Na^{22} has such a long half-life, its activity can be significant from a dose level or shielding standpoint during maintenance or equipment servicing long after the Na^{24} isotope has decayed to a negligible value. After approximately 16 half-lives the Na^{24} activity is reduced to a sufficiently low value that Na^{22} becomes the predominate radioactive isotope (neglecting any impurities in sodium). Some shielding is therefore necessary for large sources of activated sodium long after the Na^{24} has decayed, e.g., around radioactive-sodium storage tanks. At the Fermi plant the shield walls around the radioactive-sodium storage tanks are 2.5-ft-thick ordinary concrete walls. Shielding for equipment handling fresh Na^{24} at Fermi requires a 6-ft-thickness of concrete.

Table 8.3 is a resume of the nuclear properties of Na^{22} and Na^{24}.

8.5.3 ACTIVATION OF SODIUM IMPURITIES

The activation of impurities in natural sodium must be considered in shield design. The equations used to calculate the activation are similar to Eqs. 8.7 and 8.8, except that the macroscopic capture cross section (Σ_c) and the number of atoms per cubic centimeter (N) must be calculated on the basis of the impurity concentrations. Typical impurities found in sodium are listed in Chap. 2. An example of the specific activity of sodium and its impurities as a function of decay time is shown in Fig. 8.6,

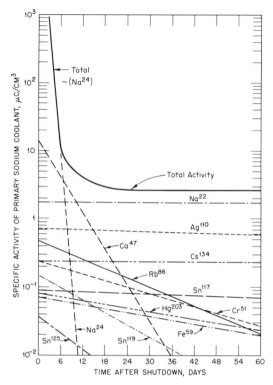

FIG. 8.6—Decay of sodium primary coolant and its impurities as a function of time from operation at a reaction power of 300 Mw [3].

which was based on a list of impurities in Table 1 of Ref. 3.* These curves indicate that the activation of impurities in sodium can be significant. The impurity concentrations in most reactor-grade sodium are, in general, significantly below those shown in Fig. 8.6. For example, the calcium-impurity concentration, which was taken as 450 ppm for the calculation in Fig. 8.6, is reduced to less than 5 ppm in the Fermi reactor.

8.5.4 SODIUM-ACTIVATION VALUES FOR VARIOUS REACTORS [3, 19-21]

The estimated or measured primary coolant sodium specific activity for various fast reactors is given in Table 8.4. The secondary sodium coolant in the Fermi reactor flows outside the reactor containment building to the steam generator. Its activity at a reactor power of 300 Mw is 6.0×10^{-11} curies/cm^3. In EBR-II the secondary sodium coolant activity is 5.4×10^{-8} curies/cm^3 at 62.5 Mw(t) reactor power. In Table 8.4 the specific activity refers to the usual standard disintegration rate. For Na^{24}, where there are two photons per disintegration, the total gamma emission rate (in photons/cm^3/sec) of coolant is twice the specific activity in curies times 3.7×10^{10}.

Examples of sodium-activation calculations by multigroup methods are shown for EBR-II in Tables

Table 8.3—Nuclear Properties of Radioactive Sodium [22]

	Na^{22}	Na^{24}
Photons per disintegration	1	2
Energy per photon, Mev	1.28	1.38; 2.76
Half-life	2.6 year	15 hr
Typical activity, when used as primary coolant for fast reactors, $\mu c/g/Mw(t)$	0.0015	50

*Figure 8.6 shows the results of calculations of the neutron-induced activity in commercial-grade sodium in the Fermi reactor when operated at a power of 500 Mw.

Table 8.4–Specific Activity of Primary Coolant for Various Fast Reactors
at Full Power and Per Megawatt of Power [22]

	Reactor power, Mw	Specific activity			
		Curies/cm^3		Curies/cm^3/Mw (t)	
		Na^{24}	Na^{22}	Na^{24}	Na^{22}
Fermi	300	3.0×10^{-2}	1.0×10^{-6}	1.0×10^{-4}	3.3×10^{-9}
Dounreay	60	3.5×10^{-3}	3.5×10^{-6}	0.58×10^{-4}	58.0×10^{-9}
EBR-I	1.4	2.5×10^{-6}		0.02×10^{-4}	
EBR-II	62.5	1.4×10^{-3}		0.23×10^{-4}	

8.5 and 8.6. Table 8.5 gives the relative absorption rate by energy groups, and Table 8.6 gives the absolute absorption by regions at full power.

8.5.5 METHOD OF CALCULATING THE ALLOWABLE LIMIT OF SPECIFIC ACTIVITY OF SECONDARY SODIUM COOLANT

8.5.5.1 Establishing the Design Criterion

The most common method of establishing a limit on secondary sodium activity is to specify limits for personnel access to the secondary sodium equipment. The allowable specific activity of the secondary sodium coolant will thus depend upon the biologically permissible levels accepted for personnel working in the area of the secondary coolant equipment. The usual procedure is to establish a limiting gamma-ray dose rate at the surface of the largest piece of accessible equipment in the secondary coolant system.

The location of the intermediate heat exchanger with respect to the reactor may have an appreciable effect on the overall plant shield system. In some reactor systems the primary neutron shielding is designed to reduce the neutron flux at all points to biologically permissible levels (of the order to 10 to 100 neutrons/cm^2/sec). In other designs it may not be necessary to do this since there may be no need for personnel access. In these designs neutron shielding sufficient to prevent significant activation of the secondary coolant under full-power operation is provided. The neutron-flux level in the compartment requiring access for maintenance should be of the order of 1×10^4 neutrons/cm^2/sec to prevent

activation [3]. This number was established on the basis of calculations using the methods developed in the following sections.

There are other methods of establishing limitations on the activation of the secondary coolant. For instance, one might want to establish a criterion based on the toxicity or radioactive contamination of the air in the area containing the system which would result should a fire, leak, or explosion expose the coolant to the environment. (This method is not normally used because it is too restrictive and is based upon abnormal conditions.)

The technique outlined in the following section is valid for the toxicity method as well as the neutron-flux method.

8.5.5.2 Establishing the Limit of Allowable Specific Activity in the Secondary Coolant

Once the biologically permissible radiation levels at the surface of the largest piece of equipment have been established, it is necessary to determine the limiting activity in the secondary coolant system. If there is only one gamma ray emitted per disintegration, the maximum coolant activity [S_V (max.)] that can be contained within a very large container for a limiting surface dose rate is

$$S_V(\text{max.}) = 2\mu(E)D_s/C(E) \quad \text{dis/cm}^3/\text{sec} \quad (8.9)$$

where $\mu(E)$ = gamma-ray linear absorption coefficient in the coolant for the gamma ray of energy E, cm^{-1}
D_s = limiting dose rate, r/hr

Table 8.5–Relative Neutron Absorption by Sodium in the EBR-II by Energy Groups [19]

Energy group	Energy range, Mev	Relative neutron absorption in the central core and blanket regions	Relative neutron absorption in the neutron primary shield and outer vessel regions
1 – 2	0.4979 – 10	0.0494	
3 – 4	0.1832 – 0.4979	0.0470	
5 – 6	0.0674 – 0.1832	0.0360	0.000013
7 – 8	0.00912 – 0.0674	0.0134	0.000050
9 – 10	$300 – 9120 \times 10^{-6}$	0.0004	0.000072
11 – 12	$43 – 300 \times 10^{-6}$	0.000003	0.00887
13 – 14	$22 – 43 \times 10^{-6}$		0.00591
15 – 16	$9 – 22 \times 10^{-6}$		0.0109
17 – 18	$0.7 – 9 \times 10^{-6}$		0.0571
19 – 20	$0.0 – 0.7 \times 10^{-6}$		0.7708
Total in region		0.1463	0.8537
Combined total		1.000	

Table 8.6—Neutron Absorption by the Primary-Coolant Sodium
of EBR-II at a Power of 62.5 Mw (t)

Region	Sodium activation, %	Absorptions/sec	Activity, $\mu c/cm^3/sec$
Core	7.1	9.3×10^{14}	103
Rod	6.6	8.6×10^{14}	95
Inner blanket	7.5	9.8×10^{14}	108
Outer blanket	6.5	8.5×10^{14}	95
Vessel	37.4	4.9×10^{15}	536
Neutron shield	34.9	4.6×10^{15}	503
Total		1.31×10^{16} *	1440

* Corresponds to an energy absorption rate of 2.2×10^8 Mev/cm³/sec.

$C(E)$ = conversion factor at energy E, r/hr per gamma/cm²/sec

Equation 8.9 must be modified for a sodium coolant. Since two gamma rays are emitted during each disintegration of the Na^{24} atom and since both contribute to the dose rate, the dose rate is made up of two components D_1 and D_2

$$D_s = D_1 + D_2$$

Thus the limiting specific activity of the secondary coolant is

$$S_V(\text{max.}) = \frac{2\mu_1\mu_2 D_s}{\mu_2 C_1 + \mu_1 C_2} \qquad (8.10)$$

where μ_1 = gamma absorption coefficient in the coolant at energy E_1, cm⁻¹
μ_2 = gamma absorption coefficient in the coolant at energy E_2, cm⁻¹
C_1 = conversion factor, r/hr per gamma/cm²/sec for energy E_1
C_2 = conversion factor, r/hr per gamma/cm²/sec for energy E_2

Table 8.7 gives the values of μ_1, μ_2, C_1, and C_2 for Na^{24} gammas at various sodium temperatures.

When a coolant such as mercury is used, there may be an arbitrary number n of radioactive isotopes of the coolant material, all of which contribute significantly to the total radiation. For coolants such as mercury, the formulas can be extended as

follows: The total activity S_v is the sum of the activity from the n isotopes,

$$S_V = \sum_{i=1}^{n} S_{Vi}f_i = S_{V1} \sum_{1}^{n} f_i \qquad (8.11)$$

Here S_{V1} is usually chosen as the isotope contributing the largest amount of activity. The values of f_i are calculated from the fractional amounts of activation

$$f_i = N_i\sigma_i/N_1\sigma_1 \qquad (8.12)$$

where N_i represents the number of nuclei per cubic centimeter of coolant for each isotope i and σ_i represents the corresponding activation cross section for each isotope. The activity of the isotope contributing the largest amount is

$$S_{V1} = D_s\left(\sum_{0}^{n} A_{n+1}f_1\right)^{-1} \qquad (8.13)$$

where

$$A_i = \sum_{j=1}^{n} \frac{a(\gamma)_{ij} C_{ij}}{2\mu_{ij}} \qquad (8.14)$$

In the above relations the quantities D_s, C, and μ are the same as previously defined. The $a(\dot{\gamma})$ values are the fractional gamma-ray yields for each isotope; the first subscript refers to the isotope number and the second refers to the gamma-ray number.

The subscript n takes on a value equal to the number of gamma rays associated with the ith isotope.

8.5.6 MAXIMUM ALLOWABLE NEUTRON FLUX FOR THE SECONDARY SODIUM COOLANT ACTIVITY

The maximum allowable neutron flux at the secondary coolant compartment can be estimated after the value of S_V has been established. The specific activity at equilibrium can be approximated by the relation

$$S_V(\text{max.}) = \Sigma_c(\overline{E})\, \phi(\overline{E})_{\lim}(t/t_c) \qquad (8.15)$$

where $\phi_{\lim}(\overline{E})$ = limiting neutron flux in energy range $\overline{E}$, neutrons/cm²/sec
$\overline{E}$ = the dominant neutron energy, electron volts
$\Sigma_c(\overline{E})$ = sodium neutron-capture macroscopic cross section at neutron energy $\overline{E}$, cm⁻¹
t = time of exposure of secondary sodium in neutron flux during one cycle, sec
t_c = cycle time for secondary sodium coolant, sec

For the limiting flux in the region where the coolant will be activated to be established, enough preliminary calculation should have been carried

Table 8.7—Values of Absorption Coefficients [22] and Dose-Rate Conversion Factors for Na^{22}

Sodium temperature, °F	i	Gamma-ray energy, Mev	μ_i, cm⁻¹	C_i, r/hr per gammas/cm²/sec
300	1	1.38	0.0476	2.35×10^{-6}
	2	2.76	0.0327	4.18×10^{-6}
600	1	1.38	0.0456	2.35×10^{-6}
	2	2.76	0.0312	4.18×10^{-6}
900	1	1.38	0.0438	2.35×10^{-6}
	2	2.76	0.0300	4.18×10^{-6}
1200	1	1.38	0.0416	2.35×10^{-6}
	2	2.76	0.0284	4.18×10^{-6}
1500	1	1.38	0.0384	2.35×10^{-6}
	2	2.76	0.0284	4.18×10^{-6}

out on the overall plant shielding to make possible an estimate of the dominant neutron energy in the region of exposure of the secondary coolant since the activation cross section is energy dependent. If Σ_c is assumed to follow a $1/v$ law of neutron-velocity dependence, the cross section is given by the expression

$$\Sigma_c(\bar{E}) = 0.158\,\Sigma_c(th)(\bar{E})^{-\frac{1}{2}} \qquad (8.16)$$

where $\Sigma_c(th)$ is the macroscopic thermal capture cross section in cm^{-1} and $0.158 = \sqrt{0.025}$, where $0.025 = E(th)$.

If Eqs. 8.15 and 8.16 are combined, the limiting value of the neutron flux at the dominant energy E is given by

$$\phi(E)_{\text{lim}} = 6.33\,S_V(\text{max.})(\bar{E})^{\frac{1}{2}}\,t_c\,[\Sigma_c(th)\,t]^{-1} \qquad (8.17)$$

where

$$\Sigma_c(th) = \sigma_c(th)N_0\,\rho/A \qquad (8.18)$$

in which $\sigma_c(th)$ = thermal capture cross section for the coolant, cm^2/atom
N_0 = Avogadro's number, atoms/mole
ρ = density of the coolant, g/cm^3
A = atomic weight of coolant, g/mole

and where $S_V(\text{max.})$ has been previously calculated using Eq. 8.9, 8.10, or 8.11, whichever is applicable.

8.6 Shield Calculations

8.6.1 *METHODS FOR CALCULATING NEUTRON ATTENUATION*

It is not the purpose of this chapter to present detailed descriptions of the methods used to calculate the attenuation of neutrons through shields. The theory of neutron diffusion through material media is well developed in the literature [23-30] as are the derivations of the equations from the theory. One or more of the following methods are adaptable to hand or machine calculations for fast reactor shields: (1) transport theory (a) hand calculations, one energy group; (b) machine calculations, two or more energy groups; (2) diffusion theory (a) hand calculations, one to six energy groups; (b) machine calculations, three energy groups and up; (3) age theory, hand calculations; (4) Bethe—Tonks—Hurwitz method, hand or machine calculations; (5) removal theory, hand calculations, also machine calculations in combination with multigroup diffusion theory; (6) modified straight-ahead approximation to diffusion theory, hand or machine calculations; (7) Monte Carlo method, machine calculation; and (8) stochastic process methods, machine calculation.

The fundamental physics of neutron diffusion is embodied in transport theory. All other theories and methods are approximations or modifications of transport theory. The basic transport-theory equations do not lend themselves easily to rigorous analytical solutions. Simplifying assumptions and approaches are made first, and out of these come

the various methods listed above and briefly described below.

In every type of calculation, a model of the reactor and its shield is decided upon, and the various components and material configurations are given their appropriate assignments in the model. The actual calculation follows one of two courses of action. One technique is to solve the reactor criticality equations for the model assumed. This results in the development of a neutron source within the core and blanket. The resulting fluxes are then computed through the shield regions. This technique is applied mainly to machine computations using transport or diffusion theory, in which the calculations are solved using several neutron-energy groups and in which the effect of each group on the other groups is taken into account. The other technique is to define a leakage source of neutrons into the shield region, possibly by means of one of the methods listed. This leakage source becomes the primary source for the neutron-attenuation calculations within the shield material. The calculations can use any one of the above-mentioned methods of computation, either hand or machine. Table 8.8 summarizes some of the basic equations of the various methods.

8.6.2 *APPLICABILITY OF SEVERAL METHODS TO NEUTRON-SHIELDING CALCULATIONS*

8.6.2.1 *Transport Theory*

The methods developed using pure transport theory are usually confined to relatively simple geometries. Even these involve some degree of approximation. The transport equation is a mathematical description of the neutron behavior within an arbitrary, infinitesimal volume element in a medium, which takes into account the energies and directions of all neutrons entering and leaving the volume element as well as neutrons undergoing collision, absorption, or birth within the volume element. Solution of this equation leads to flux and current distributions within the medium. If hand calculations are to be performed, the neutron energy must be monoenergetic. Machine calculations invariably use simplifying assumptions and numerical integrations. However, where the method can be used, even with these penalties if they are not too limiting, the results yielded are the most accurate. Machine codes available* include those written for Carlson's S_n method [31] and the NIOBE multigroup method [32, 33]. Machine calculations using transport theory are time consuming and expensive.

One form of the transport equation known as the Boltzmann transport equation has been solved using what is known as the moments method [34]. In this method the solution is given in terms of a Legendre polynomial expansion; the coefficients of each term

---

*Readers interested in descriptions of the various reactor and shielding codes available may write to Argonne Code Center, Argonne National Laboratory, 9700 South Cass Avenue, Argonne, Ill., and to Radiation Shielding Information Center, Oak Ridge National Laboratory, P. O. Box X, Oak Ridge, Tenn.

Table 8.8—Some Neutron-Transmission Equations and Their Solutions Suitable for Hand Calculations

Method	Fundamental equations and solutions	Subsidiary equations
Age theory	$\nabla^2 q(\mathbf{r},u) = \partial q(\mathbf{r},u)/\partial \tau(u)$ Slab solution in two media: $q(u,x) = (4\tau_0)^{-1/2} \int_{x_0}^{x'} p(u) \exp\left[-(x-x')^2\right] q(u',x') \, dx$	$p(u) = \exp\left[-\int_{u_0}^{u} Q(u)\,\Sigma_a(u)\,du\right]$ $\tau(u) = \int_{u_0}^{u} Q(u)\,D(u)\,du$ $\phi(u,x) = q(u,x)\,Q(u)$ $Q(u) = \left[\xi\,\Sigma_s(u) + \gamma\,\Sigma_a(u)\right]^{-1}$
Bethe–Tonks–Hurwitz	$\nabla^2 q(\mathbf{r},u) = \partial q(\mathbf{r},u)/\partial \tau(u)$ Slab solution in one medium: $q(u,x) = \sqrt{2}\,(Mu)^{-1/2}\,\Sigma_s(u)\,K_M \exp\left(-\dfrac{uM\Psi_M}{2}\right)$	$j(u,x) = \int_{x}^{\infty} \dfrac{\partial q(u,x)}{\partial u}\,dx$
Transport theory	$v\left[\nabla\cdot\mathbf{\Omega} + \Sigma_T\right]\Psi(\mathbf{r},u,\mathbf{\Omega}) =$ $S(\mathbf{r},u,\mathbf{\Omega}) + cv\Sigma_T \int \Psi(\mathbf{r},u,\mathbf{\Omega}')\,f(\mathbf{\Omega},\mathbf{\Omega}')\,d\mathbf{\Omega}'$ Point isotropic source solution in infinite medium: $\phi(r,u) = S_0\,\Sigma_T/4\pi r \left\{\dfrac{\partial K_0}{\partial c}\exp\left[-(K_0 r)\right]\right.$ $\left. + \int_0^{'} g(c,m)\exp\left[-(r/m)\right]\,dm\right\}$	$g(c,m) = \left[(1 - mc\tanh^{-1}m)^2 - (\tfrac{1}{2}\pi mc)^2\right]^{-1}$ $= \sum_{n=0}^{\infty}(-1)^n\,a_n\,E_n(r)$ $E_n(r) = r^{n-1}\int_r^{\infty} e^{-u}\,du/u^n$ $K_0 = \tanh(K_0/c)$ $c = \Sigma_s/\Sigma_T$
Modified straight-ahead approximation to diffusion theory	$D_{ij}\nabla^2\phi_{ij}(r,\bar{u}_i) - \Sigma_{ic}\,\phi_i(r,\bar{u}_i) - \Sigma_{i,in}\,\phi_i(r,\bar{u}_i)$ $+\,\Sigma_{i,in}\,\phi_i(r,\bar{u}_i) + S(\delta r_0) = 0$ Solution in one medium: $\phi_j(r,u_i) = \phi_j(r,u_0)\,G(r,r_0)\exp\left(-\sum_{i=1}^{n_j}\alpha_i K_j \Delta r_i\right)$	$\Delta u_j = \sum_{i=j}^{n_j}\alpha_i\,\Delta u_i \qquad n_i = \Delta u_i/\xi$ $\bar{u}_i = \dfrac{u_{i-1}+u_i}{2} \qquad T = \sum_{i=j}^{n_j}\alpha_i\,\Delta r_i$ $\Delta r_i = f_i\,\Delta u_i/\xi\,\Sigma_{is} \qquad K_i = \sqrt{3\Sigma_{is}(\Sigma_{ic}+\Sigma_{i,in})}$ $u_{jf} = u_{jo} + \Delta u_j \qquad f_i = \dfrac{1}{4}\left[\dfrac{(1+\overline{\cos\theta})(2n_i+1)+2}{n_i+1}\right]$
Diffusion theory, one group	$D\nabla^2\phi(r,u) - \Sigma_a\,\phi(r,u) + S_0 = 0$ Finite slab solution in one medium: $\phi(x,u) = A\left(\exp\left[-(Kx)\right] - \exp\left\{-[K(2T-x)]\right\}\right)$	$A = \left(2K\,D(u)\,\{1 + \exp[-(2KT)]\}\right)^{-1}$ $j(u,x) = -D\,\dfrac{\partial\phi(x,u)}{\delta x}$

Note:

a_n	= coefficients of exponential integrals	u_{jo}	= initial lethargy for neutron group j
c	= average number of particles departing from a point of collision for every collision suffered	u_{jf}	= final lethargy for neutron group j
$D(u)$	= diffusion coefficient at lethargy u	v	= neutron velocity corresponding to a given lethargy u
D_{ij}	= diffusion coefficient in ith lethargy region for the jth group of neutrons	x	= space coordinate in slab geometry
$E_n(r)$	= exponential integrals	x_0	= initial location (or source location), medium 1
$f(\mathbf{\Omega},\mathbf{\Omega}')$	= fraction of neutrons scattering into solid angle $d\Omega$ about $\mathbf{\Omega}$ following collisions by neutrons traveling in direction $\mathbf{\Omega}'$	x'	= location of space point in medium 2 (age-theory equations)
f_i	= average straight-ahead distance traveled per collision in the ith lethargy region	α_i	= end-correction coefficients
$g,\,m$	= complex quantities related to the attenuation characteristics of the medium	γ	= absorption constant per collision
		δ	= Kronecker delta function
$G(r,r_0)$	= geometric factor depending upon points $r,\,r_0$	Δu_i	= width of lethargy region i
$j(u,x)$	= neutron current of lethargy u at point x	Δu_j	= total lethargy change for neutron group j
K_M	= coefficient in Bethe–Tonks–Hurwitz equation	θ	= scattering angle in the center-of-mass system
M	= atomic mass of scattering material	K_0	= attenuation constant in the medium
n_i	= number of collisions in the ith lethargy region	K_i	= attenuation coefficient for the ith lethargy region
n_j	= number of regions into which thickness T is divided for the jth neutron group	ξ	= average logarithmic energy decrement per collision
$p(u)$	= resonance escape probability for neutrons of lethargy u	$\Sigma_a,\,\Sigma_c,\,\Sigma_s,$ $\Sigma_T,\,\Sigma_{in}$	= absorption, capture, scattering, total, and inelastic cross section (macroscopic)
$q(\mathbf{r},u)$	= slowing-down density at space point r and lethargy u	$\tau(u)$	= neutron age to lethargy u, (cm^2)
$Q(u)$	= variable depending upon scattering and absorption properties of a medium	τ_0	= initial age
$\mathbf{r},\,r$	= space coordinates	$\phi(r,u)$	= neutron flux per unit lethargy u at distance r from the source
$S(r,u,\mathbf{\Omega}),$ $S,\,S(\delta r_0)$	= neutron source terms	$\phi(u,x)$	= neutron flux per unit lethargy of lethargy u at distance x from the origin
T	= thickness of material through which neutrons are traveling	$\phi_{ij}(r,\bar{u}_i)$	= neutron flux per unit lethargy in the ith lethargy region for the jth group of neutrons
u	= lethargy of neutron	$\mathbf{\Omega}$	= direction of travel of neutrons
u'	= lethargy of neutron at point x in medium 1	$\mathbf{\Omega}'$	= direction of travel of neutrons before a collision
$\bar{u}_i$	= average lethargy in the ith lethargy region	$\Psi(\mathbf{r},u,\mathbf{\Omega}')$	= number of neutrons per cubic centimeter per unit of lethargy at space point $\mathbf{r}$ traveling in a unit solid angle about the direction $\mathbf{\Omega}$
		Ψ_M	= coefficient of the exponent in Bethe–Tonks–Hurwitz equation
		$'$	= quantity of lower lethargy than the unprimed quantity (in modified straight-ahead approximation equations)

of this expansion are known as moments, or spatial moments. These moments are related to the neutron density and hence to the scalar flux at all points in the medium.

The approximations in the use of transport-theory methods come about because the integral appearing in the differential equation (Table 8.8) cannot be evaluated exactly.

8.6.2.2 Diffusion Theory

This theory, which is probably one of the most popular methods used today to calculate fast reactor shields, solves an elementary differential equation known as the diffusion equation, which is derivable from Fick's law of neutron diffusion. Fick's law is a mathematical statement which says that the net neutron current from a region is directly proportional to the gradient of the neutron flux in the region; it assumes isotropic scattering at all points in the medium. Hand calculations may be made with this method if the neutron spectrum can be adequately described by division into a few energy groups. There are literally dozens of machine codes available for computation using many neutron-energy groups. In or near the reactor core, diffusion theory agrees well with experimental results if the nuclear constants are chosen properly. Diffusion theory will give quite good results with thin shields. As one proceeds outward through the shield, diffusion theory becomes less and less reliable. The theory gives optimistic values of attenuation for thick shields and thus should not be used to find thick-shield leakage.

8.6.2.3 Age Theory [24, 26, 35, 36]

This theory provides a handy method that can be adapted to hand or machine calculation wherever a continuous slowing-down model is applicable. Age theory is a modification of transport or diffusion theory in which the neutron slowing-down density at any point within a medium is describable in terms of a parameter τ, the Fermi age or neutron age. This quantity is not actually a time unit as the name might imply but is a direct measure of the average distance a neutron of some given initial energy will travel before it slows down past a prescribed lower energy. The theory attempts to take into consideration the energy degradation suffered by neutrons in their passage through material. To use the age theory, the designer must make several assumptions. One is that energy degradation is a continuous process rather than a step function, which it actually is. Another is that scattering is isotropic and that neutron capture in the medium is small. Age theory works well only for small distances from the initial source. It works best where the logarithmic energy decrement (Sec. 8.1) is small. It is inaccurate if the age τ is not well known or if the nuclear cross sections of the material are rapidly changing (such as in a resonance region). It also gives optimistic flux values for thick shields. Its value lies mainly in allowing an evaluation of the neutron-energy distribution within a shield without too much difficulty.

8.6.2.4 Bethe–Tonks–Hurwitz (BTH) Method [28]

The BTH method is an extension of age theory in which the parameters are adjusted according to the variation of the cross section. A variable slowing-down density is assumed over the region. This method can be easily adapted to a machine method in which the primary-neutron distribution is divided into groups and there are numerous shield regions.

8.6.2.5 Removal Theory

Removal theory as practiced at Oak Ridge National Laboratory is adaptable mainly to hydrogenous materials. However, by careful definition of the removal source, one can adapt the method to nonhydrogenous materials. This method utilizes a point-to-point attenuation kernel and is based on the experimental observation that only the most energetic neutrons from a source penetrate hydrogenous materials and the farther they penetrate, the more energetic they have to be to reach the point in question. The overall process of shield penetration results in a spectrum hardening and in the removal of the lower energy neutrons from the beam. One can thus define a removal cross section which accounts for the removal of the lower energy neutrons from the beam by scattering or absorption. The attenuation of neutrons at some distance r from the source is proportional to $\exp(-\Sigma_R r)$, where Σ_R is the removal cross section. Integration of the point kernel over the total source yields the flux of fast neutrons at the reception point. Removal theory, in combination with diffusion theory, can be used to define the behavior of the fast-neutron energy groups through a material. The method is adaptable to hand or machine calculations. Removal cross sections have values roughly two-thirds the values of the total cross sections of materials at 8 Mev. Experimental and estimated removal cross sections are tabulated in Tables 8.72 to 8.74.

8.6.2.6 Modified Straight-ahead Approximation to Diffusion Theory [37]

In this method the neutron diffusion is assumed to be in one direction (straight ahead), with appropriate corrections for scatter in other directions. The primary-neutron distribution is divided into groups, and the diffusion of each group followed through finite lethargy regions is related to distances in the shield. For each lethargy region the average neutron cross section and attenuation constant characteristic of the region is used. The method is adaptable to hand or machine calculations, and its main worth lies in the ease with which neutron-energy distributions in a material can be obtained. It has most of the failings and limitations of diffusion theory.

8.6.2.7 Monte Carlo Theory [38-42]

The Monte Carlo method is a statistical method developed using the physics of the transport equa-

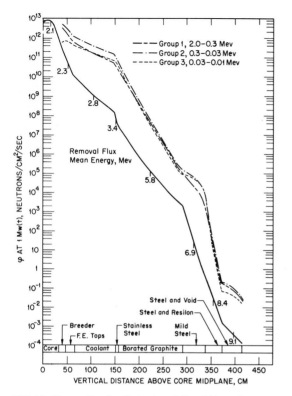

FIG. 8.7—Neutron-flux distribution from 0.01 to 2 Mev in Dounreay shield vertically above core center [20].

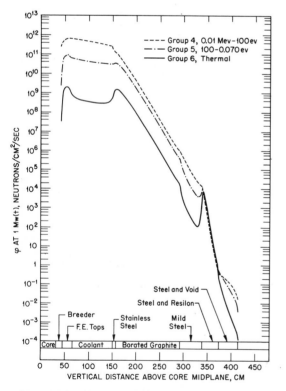

FIG. 8.8—Neutron-flux distribution from thermal to 0.01 Mev in Dounreay shield vertically above core center [20].

tion. A good review of the basic concepts of the Monte Carlo technique is given in Ref. 42. In this technique the history of each neutron, assuming random motion, is followed through the material. When enough neutron histories have been followed, the spatial and energy distribution of the neutrons within the material can be obtained. The intensity at any point in the material is then compared with the original intensity. This method yields accurate answers if sufficient statistics are collected. But the number of case histories that must be collected to give reliable statistics for moderate penetrations of a shield is above 100,000 unless some technique is used to extend the reliability to a lower number of histories. Such techniques as doubling or Russian Roulette significantly reduce the number of case histories that must be obtained. In any event the method is time consuming and expensive and is not easily adaptable to complex geometries.

8.6.2.8 Stochastic Method [43]

Neutron diffusion may be treated as a random-motion or stochastic process in which the physics of random motion is adopted. This method requires the calculation of neutron probability distributions by use of statistical equations similar to those involved in the theories of molecular diffusion or Brownian motion. This method has not had much use to date because of the difficulty in applying the basic equations to particular geometries.

8.6.3 METHODS AVAILABLE FOR CALCULATING GAMMA-RAY ATTENUATION

The fundamental equation for the calculation of the transmission of gamma rays through shields is the gamma-transport equation [23]. This equation is similar in many respects to the neutron-transport equation, but, because of certain properties of gamma-rays, it can be solved with less difficulty. Moments-method solutions of gamma-ray penetration in infinite media for several materials are well known [23, 44]. For most shielding calculations, however, an approximation called Lambert's law is valid if it is used in conjunction with the concept of buildup (Sec. 8.6.5). This is in essence a point-kernel approach. The semi-infinite-slab geometry form of this equation for gamma rays of a single energy is

$$\Gamma(x) = \Gamma' B(\mu x) \exp(-\mu x) \quad \text{gammas/cm}^2/\text{sec} \quad (8.19)$$

where
Γ' = the incident gamma-ray intensity, gammas/cm^2/sec
$\Gamma(x)$ = the intensity at point x, cm, within the slab, gammas/cm^2/sec
μ = the linear absorption coefficient for the material, cm^{-1}
$B(\mu x)$ = the buildup function

Specific formulas for gamma-ray attenuation in various shield geometries are given by Rockwell [18].

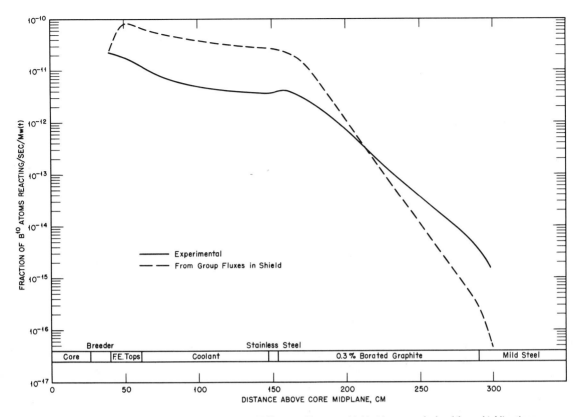

FIG. 8.9—Comparison of experimental reaction rate of B$^{10}(n, \alpha)$ in Dounreay shield with curve calculated from shielding theory.

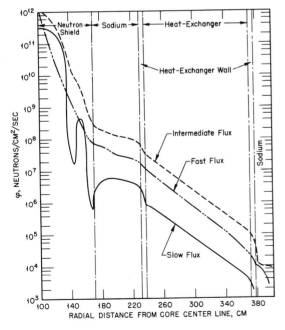

FIG. 8.10—Three-group radial neutron flux with 3% borated (graphite) neutron shield and unborated heat-exchanger wall of EBR-II [19].

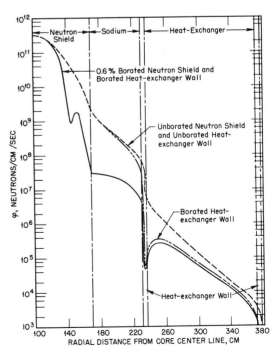

FIG. 8.11—EBR-II slow-flux radial distribution [19].

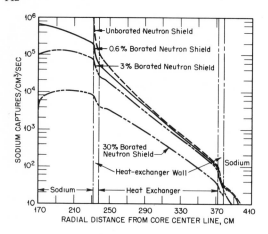

FIG. 8.12—Total sodium capture rate with unborated heat exchanger wall of EBR-II [19].

8.6.4 NEUTRON AND GAMMA-RAY DISTRIBUTIONS IN FAST REACTOR SHIELDS

This section presents, in the form of figures, the results of calculations and experiments on various fast reactor shields. It is suggested that, if the reader consults Chap. 11 for background information on the reactors involved and reads Secs. 8.16, 8.17 and 8.18 of this chapter on shield descriptions before he examines the following figures, the information exhibited in these figures will have more meaning for him.

8.6.4.1 Dounreay Fast Reactor Shield Calculations

Figures 8.7 and 8.8 give the vertical distribution of the calculated neutron flux through the top shield. Figure 8.9 shows a comparison of the calculated and experimental detector responses through the shield.

8.6.4.2 EBR-II Shield Calculations [19]

Figures 8.10 to 8.13 give the results of calculations for the EBR-II primary side shield.

8.6.4.3 Enrico Fermi Shield Calculations [45-49]

Figures 8.14 to 8.29 show the results of gamma-ray and neutron attenuation calculations in the Fermi reactor primary shields.

8.6.5 GAMMA-RAY BUILDUP FUNCTION $B(E, \mu t)$ [23, 44, 50]

The buildup function is in the nature of an energy-dependent correction function that must be applied to gamma-ray calculations if the gamma-ray source is not narrow-beam or is not collimated in any way. Figure 8.30 shows the arrangements of the apparatus for a narrow-beam and for a broad-

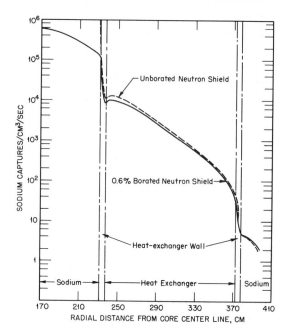

FIG. 8.13—Total sodium capture rate with borated heat-exchanger wall of EBR-II [19].

beam gamma-ray experiment. The experiment points out the need for a buildup function. The buildup function accounts for the increased intensity at the detector due to scattering and consequent change of direction of the radiation within the shield. The buildup is a direct function of the number of

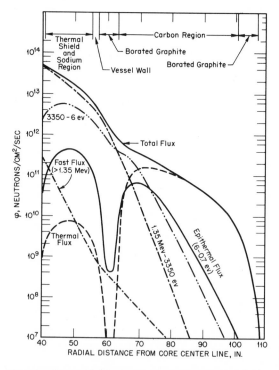

FIG. 8.14—Neutron fluxes at reactor center line in Fermi primary (side) shield [uranium-metal core at 500 Mw(t)] [45, 46].

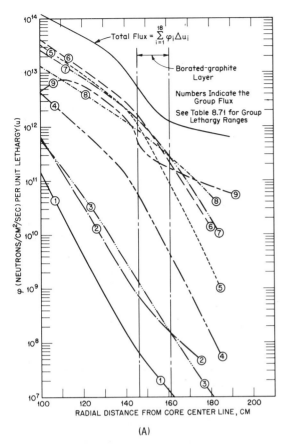

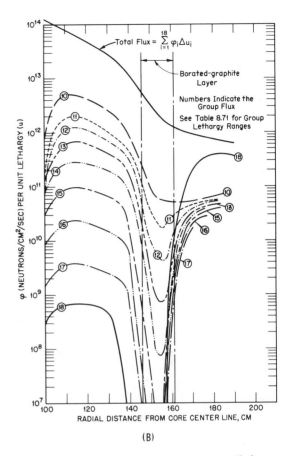

(A)   (B)

FIG. 8.15—Normalized multigroup neutron-flux distribution at core midplane through Fermi thermal shield and inner layer of borated

graphite [(UO$_2$–PuO$_2$–stainless-steel core at 500 Mw(t)] [46]. (A) Groups 1 to 9. (B) Groups 10 to 18.

scatterings and mean free paths (thickness) traversed by the primary beam in the material. The buildup function is calculated by comparing an exact calculation of the gamma intensity at various distances from the source [44] with the undeflected component [Eq. 8.19 with $B(\mu x)$ set equal to unity]. The buildup function may be expressed as a dose buildup, an energy (flux) buildup, or an energy-absorption buildup.

8.6.5.1 Gamma-ray Buildup Factors

The gamma-ray buildup function may be expressed as a sum of exponentials, as a polynominal, or as a combination of these. Two expressions for an infinite medium are

$$B(E,\mu x) = a_1 \exp(-a_1\mu x) + a_2 \exp(-a_2\mu x) \quad (8.20)$$

$$B(E,\mu x) = 1 + \beta_1\mu x + \beta_2(\mu x)^2 + \beta_3(\mu x)^3 + \cdots \quad (8.21)$$

In these equations E is the initial gamma-ray energy, μ is the linear absorption coefficient at energy E, and x is the distance into the material. Values of a_1, a_2, and a_i for several materials are given on pp. 416–423 of Ref. 18.

For many materials the buildup approximation given by the first two terms of Eq. 8.21 is adequate

to describe the buildup, and β_1 can be set equal to unity. For lead the value $\beta_1 = 1/2$ is often used. In general, the coefficients β_i must be found from experimental or calculated buildup data. Gamma-ray

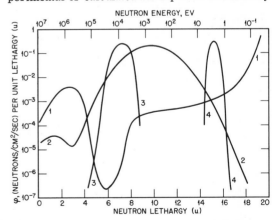

FIG. 8.16—Normalized neutron spectra at various locations in the Fermi primary shield [1]. Curve 1: graphite shield 40 in. from reactor vessel wall at core center line elevation; 20-group diffusion theory method. Curve 2: base of rotating plug; straight-ahead approximation. Curve 3: top of rotating plug, 7 ft of boron steel; BTH approximation. Curve 4: top of rotating plug, 7 ft of borated graphite; straight-ahead approximation.

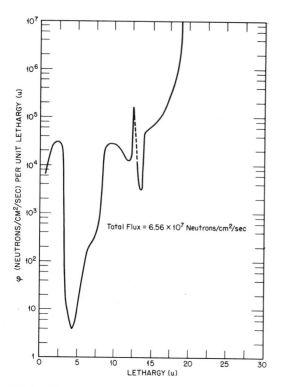

FIG. 8.17—Neutron-energy spectrum 3.74 ft into Fermi shield (along south radial line 102 in. above horizontal center line of core) [49]. Twenty-group diffusion-theory results.

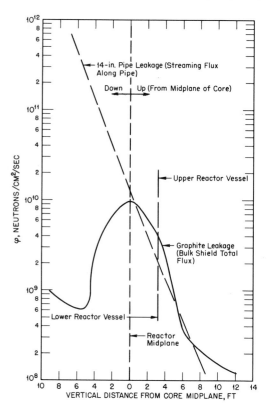

FIG. 8.19—Neutron flux near 14-in. pipe in Fermi graphite shield [3].

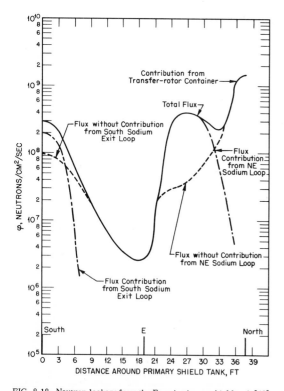

FIG. 8.18—Neutron leakage from the Fermi primary shield tank [49]. Note: Flux distribution is not in the plane of the core center line but represents on one plane a composite picture of the areas of greatest neutron leakage.

buildup curves for various materials are presented in Sec. 8.12.

8.6.5.2 Neutron Buildup Factors

The concept of buildup in neutron attenuation is used only with removal theory. It is possible to define spatially dependent removal cross sections that include the effect of buildup so that it need not appear explicitly. Whereas gamma-ray buildup factors may be of the order of hundreds, neutron buildup factors hardly ever exceed 3 or 4. Neutron buildup factors [51] may be approximated as

$$B(\Sigma_r x) = 1 \qquad (x \leq 1/\Sigma_r) \qquad (8.22)$$

$$B(\Sigma_r x) \cong \Sigma_r x \quad (1/\Sigma \leq x \leq 8/\Sigma_r) \qquad (8.23)$$

and for water thicknesses greater than 2 ft, the following holds:

$$B(\Sigma_r x) \cong 3 + 0.2\Sigma_r x \quad (x \geq 8/\Sigma_r) \qquad (8.24)$$

In the above equations Σ_r is the macroscopic removal cross section.

8.6.5.3 Gamma-ray Multilayer Buildup Factors

The use of buildup factors for multilayer shields in various combinations is discussed on pp. 8-10 of Ref. 18 and on pp. 223-226 of Ref. 23. To ap-

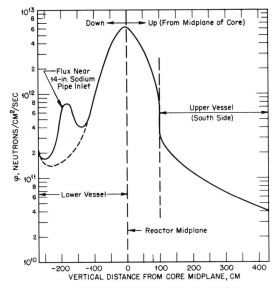

FIG. 8.20—Total vertical neutron-flux distribution at the interface between the Fermi reactor vessel and the inner borated-graphite shield [49].

proximate the total buildup in a multilayer shield, convert the total thickness of the shield to an equivalent shield thickness using the material of greatest abundance* in the shield, through the relationship $B(\mu_1 x')$, where

$$\mu_1 x' = \sum_{1}^{n} \mu_i x_i \qquad (8.25)$$

*If the outermost material is a heavy material (steel, lead, etc.) several mean free paths thick, the buildup factor may be calculated on the equivalent thickness of the outermost rather than the most abundant material.

and represents the number of mean free paths in the equivalent shield, the μ's are the linear absorption coefficients of the materials in the shield, the x's are the thicknesses of these materials, the subscript 1 refers to the material of greatest abundance, and the other subscripts refer to other materials in the shield. Further information on multilayer buildup factors can be found in Ref. 50, pp. 120-122.

8.6.5.4 Gamma-ray Finite Buildup Factors

Calculations made using infinite-media buildup factors are slightly on the conservative side. If a heating or other calculation based upon an infinite-medium buildup factor presents physical structure or support problems because of the unexpectedly high temperature rises, expansions, or stresses created, it is permissible to correct to a finite-medium buildup factor. In thin shields utilizing light materials (water, concrete, etc.), a correction factor of 0.7 may be used. In thick light-material shields for most energies, a correction factor of 0.8 may be used safely. Finite buildup factors for heavy materials, such as lead, are only a few per cent less than the infinite-medium buildup factors. For further information on this subject see pp. 179-181 of Ref. 23 or Ref. 50.

8.6.6 NUCLEAR-HEAT GENERATION IN SHIELDS

8.6.6.1 General Discussion

Nuclear heating is a phenomenon encountered in all types of reactors. The effects of nuclear heating should be evaluated. Large nuclear-heat generation rates and cooling requirements, combined with high temperatures, may have a significant effect upon the choice and the configuration of

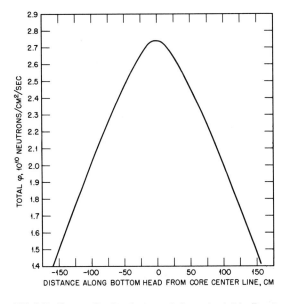

FIG. 8.21—Neutron-flux distribution at the bottom head of the Fermi reactor vessel [49].

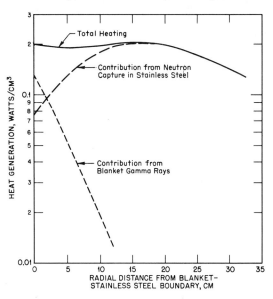

FIG. 8.22—Heat generation in Fermi stainless-steel thermal shield [48]. Note: watts/cm^3 × 9.67 × 10^4 = Btu/hr/cu ft.

shield materials, total cooling requirements, support arrangement, and design allowances for expansion and movement.

Heating in a material due to nuclear-radiation absorption is a complex problem and is beyond the scope of this volume. The exact spatial distribution of radiation heating, with due consideration for the points of scatter and the subsequent capture of the radiation, and the methods and formulas are presented in Chap. 2.7 of Ref. 52 and Chap. 13 of Ref. 50. If one is interested in the overall effect using some simplifying assumptions that produce somewhat conservative results, the formulas in the following sections may be used.

8.6.6.2 Heat Generation Due to Neutron Capture

If the simplifying assumption is made that the gamma, alpha, or beta radiation emitted during neutron capture is absorbed at once and the heat is released at the point of capture, the heating in a cubic centimeter of material, $H_n(r)$, at point r due to the capture of neutrons of known energy can be found by the following formula:

$$H_n(r) = 1.6 \times 10^{-13} \Sigma_c(r) E_B \phi_n(r) \quad \text{watts/cm}^3 \quad (8.26)$$

where $\phi_n(r)$ = total neutron flux at point r, neutrons/cm^2/sec
r = the spatial coordinates of the point under consideration, cm
E_B = binding energy of the neutron, Mev
$\Sigma_c(r)$ = macroscopic neutron-capture cross section, cm^{-1}

8.6.6.3 Heat Generation Due to Elastic Scattering of Neutrons

The heat produced by elastic scattering in any cubic centimeter of material is due to the energy absorbed by the nucleus of an atom during the collision. This energy appears first as recoil energy of the nucleus and finally as thermal motion. This heat (watt/cm^3) can be calculated from

$$H_n(r) = 1.6 \times 10^{-13} \Sigma_s(r) E_0 \phi_n [1 - \exp(-\xi)] \quad (8.27)$$

where $\Sigma_s(r)$ = macroscopic elastic-scattering cross section, cm^{-1} [at point r averaged over the energy spectrum]
E_0 = average neutron energy before collision, Mev
ξ = average logarithmic energy decrement per collision

8.6.6.4 Heat Generation Due to Inelastic Scattering of Neutrons

Inelastic scattering will produce heat in the shield by the exchange of a neutron for another of lower energy. The energy left behind as a gamma ray eventually appears as heat. Assuming the gamma ray is absorbed at the point of emission, the formula for the heat thus produced is

$$H_n(r) = 1.6 \times 10^{-13} \Sigma_{in}(r) \phi_n(r)(E_0 - E_1) \quad (8.28)$$

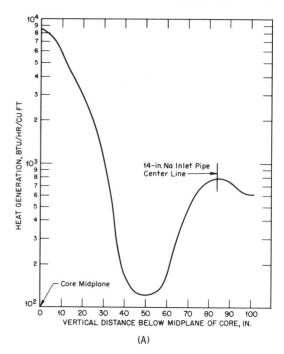

(A)

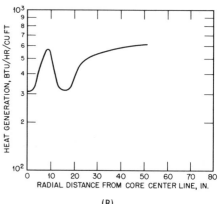

(B)

FIG. 8.23—(A) Heat generation in Fermi stainless-steel lower reactor vessel (excluding bottom head). (B) Heat generation in bottom head.

where E_0 = the average energy of the incident neutrons
$\Sigma_{in}(r)$ = the macroscopic inelastic-scattering cross section, cm^{-1}
E_1 = the average energy of the reemitted neutrons, Mev

8.6.6.5 Total Neutron Heating

The total rate of heating $H_{ntot}(r)$ due to the passage of neutrons through a material is simply the sum of the rates from Eqs. 8.26, 8.27, and 8.28. To find the integrated heating rate due to neutron capture throughout the shield, integrate each value of heating over the shield. For several neutron-energy groups, the total heating rate is the sum of the heating for each group.

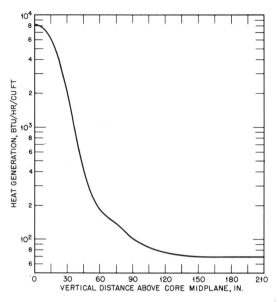

FIG. 8.24—Heat generation in Fermi stainless-steel upper vessel [3].

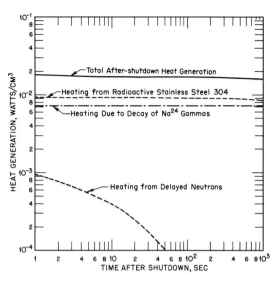

FIG. 8.26—Decay heating in stainless-steel thermal shield of Fermi lower reactor vessel at core center line 1 sec to 15 min after shutdown (from Fermi data). Note: watts/cm³ × 9.67 × 10⁴ = Btu/ hr/cu ft.

8.6.6.6 Heat Generation Due to Gamma-ray Absorption in Thin Shields

Gamma rays of those energies associated with nuclear reactors interact with matter by three main processes: (1) Compton scattering, (2) photoelectric effect, and (3) pair production. In the first process, which is predominant over most of the

energy range 0.5 to 10 Mev, a gamma ray is scattered from an electron in one of the shells or orbits surrounding the nucleus (actually absorbed

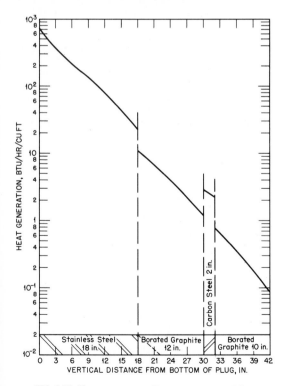

FIG. 8.25—Heat generation in Fermi rotating plug [3].

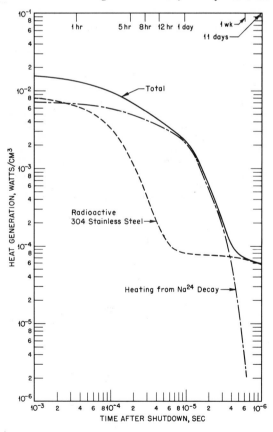

FIG. 8.27—Decay heating in stainless-steel thermal shield of Fermi reactor-vessel wall at reactor center line 15 min to 11 days after shutdown (from Fermi data). Note: watts/cm³ × 9.67 × 10⁴ = Btu/hr/cu ft.

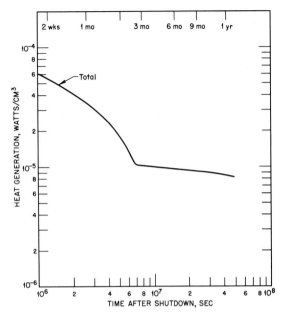

FIG. 8.28—Decay heating in stainless-steel thermal shield of Fermi lower reactor vessel at reactor center line 11 days to 1 year after shutdown (from Fermi data). Note: watts/cm^3 × 9.67 × 10^4 = Btu/hr/cu ft.

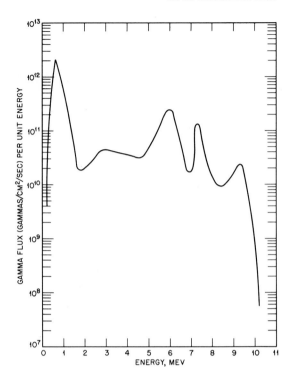

FIG. 8.29—Gamma-ray-energy spectrum at Fermi reactor-vessel wall [3].

and reemitted). The scattered (or reemitted) gamma ray is usually of much lower energy, depending upon the angle of scatter. It is subsequently absorbed by the second process at a short distance away. The second process takes place at low gamma-ray energies. In this process a gamma-ray photon is absorbed by an orbital electron. The electron is subsequently ejected from its orbital position, and the heat of its recoil is absorbed by the shield material when it is stopped. In the third process gamma rays of energies over 1.02 Mev may be absorbed in an electron in such a way that an electron—positron pair, each with energy 0.51 Mev or greater, is created. The energy produced when these particles are stopped appears as heat.

This process takes place mainly at high energy in high-atomic-number materials.

The interaction between gamma radiation and a material results in an energy transfer that heats the material. The energy-absorption coefficient, μ_e/ρ, is a measure of the fraction of the total gamma-ray energy that is converted into heat in the shield at the point of absorption. Values of the gamma-ray-absorption coefficients for some materials (expressed in square centimeters per gram) are given in Sec. 8.12. The linear energy-absorption coefficient, μ_e, is obtained by multiplying the energy-absorption coefficient μ_e/ρ by the material

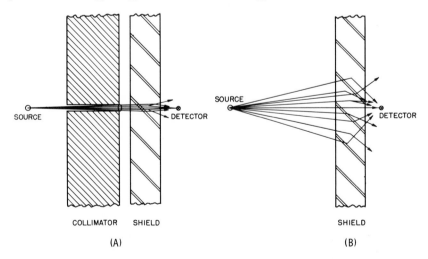

FIG. 8.30—Narrow- and broad-beam gamma-ray transmission through a shield. (A) Narrow beam. (B) Broad beam.

density. For shields thin enough to allow most of the scattered radiation from Compton scattering to escape (i.e., a thickness less than $1/\mu_e$), the volumetric gamma heating for each gamma energy, $H_\gamma(E_\gamma, r)$, is given by the relation

$$
\begin{aligned}
H_\gamma(E_\gamma, r) &= \mu_e \Gamma(r) E_\gamma && \text{Mev/cm}^3/\text{sec} \\
&= 1.6 \times 10^{-13} \mu_e \Gamma E_\gamma && \text{watts/cm}^3 && (8.29)\\
&= 1.55 \times 10^{-8} \mu_e \Gamma E_\gamma && \text{Btu/hr/cu ft}
\end{aligned}
$$

where μ_e = linear energy-absorption cross section, cm^{-1}
$\Gamma(r)$ = gamma-ray flux, gammas/cm^2/sec
E_γ = gamma-ray energy, Mev

8.6.6.7 Heat Generation Due to Gamma-ray Absorption in Thick Shields

If the shield is thick and the exact distribution of the heat is not required, then the Compton-scattered gamma ray can be assumed to be absorbed at the point of emission, and the heating formula that can be applied to each gamma-ray energy is

$$
\begin{aligned}
H_\gamma(E_\gamma, r) &= \mu \Gamma(r) E_\gamma && \text{Mev/cm}^3/\text{sec} \\
&= 1.6 \times 10^{-13} \mu \Gamma(r) E_\gamma && \text{watts/cm}^3 && (8.30)\\
&= 1.55 \times 10^{-8} \mu \Gamma(r) E_\gamma && \text{Btu/hr/cu ft}
\end{aligned}
$$

where μ is the linear absorption coefficient.

8.6.6.8 Total Heating Due to Gamma-ray Absorption

Calculations using Eqs. 8.29 and 8.30 should be repeated for every different gamma-ray energy, summed for the total heating, and integrated over the entire shield.

8.6.6.9 Useful Approximation of Total Nuclear Heating

One can get an overestimate (but usually a fairly reliable upper limit) of the total heating in the shield by assuming that the shield is thick enough to absorb all the incident radiation. With this assumption the total heating in the shield is

Neutron heating:

$$
H_n = 1.6 \times 10^{-13} \overline{\phi}_n E_B a \quad \text{watts} \qquad (8.31)
$$

Gamma heating:

$$
H_\gamma = 1.6 \times 10^{-13} \overline{\Gamma} \overline{E}_\gamma a \quad \text{watts} \qquad (8.32)
$$

$$
\overline{\Gamma} = \sum_i^n \overline{\Gamma}_i
$$

where $\overline{\phi}_n$ and $\overline{\Gamma}$ = the average values for the neutron and gamma-ray fluxes
$\overline{\Gamma}_i$ = the average gamma flux for the ith gamma ray

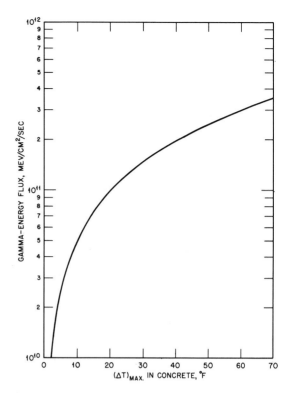

FIG. 8.31—Maximum temperature difference in concrete as a function of incident gamma-energy flux [53].

E_B = the binding energy for the main neutron-capture reaction, Mev
a = the total shield area upon which these fluxes are incident, cm^2

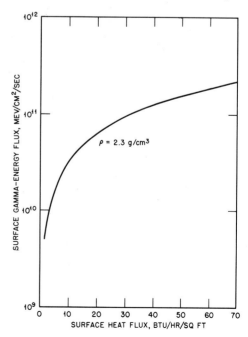

FIG. 8.32—Total gamma heat generation per unit area of concrete face [53].

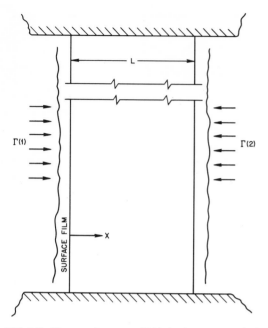

FIG. 8.33—Diagram of concrete shield showing gamma-radiation sources on both sides [53].

$\bar{E}_\gamma$ = the average energy per photon, Mev, where $\bar{E}_\gamma$ is

$$\bar{E}_\gamma = \sum_i E_{\gamma i} f_i \qquad (8.33)$$

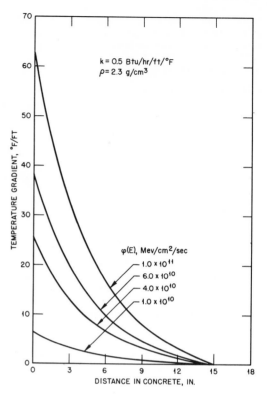

FIG. 8.35—Temperature gradient as a function of distance into a 30-in. concrete shield for various incident gamma-energy fluxes [53].

where $E_{\gamma i}$ is the energy of the ith gamma ray and f_i is the fractional yield of the ith gamma ray per disintegration.

8.6.7 TEMPERATURE RISE IN A SHIELD DUE TO GAMMA HEATING [48, 53]

8.6.7.1 Shield with Gamma-ray Source on One Side

From a simple analytical model, the temperature rise in a biological shield can be calculated

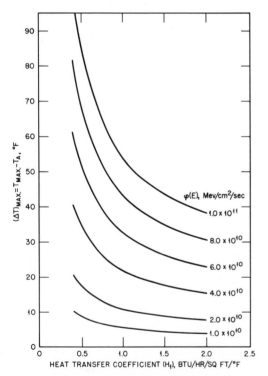

FIG. 8-34—Maximum temperature difference between concrete and ambient temperature as a function of surface-film heat-transfer coefficient for various gamma-energy fluxes [53].

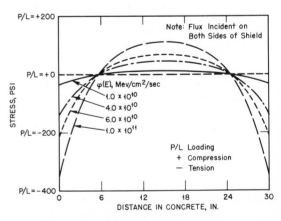

FIG. 8.36—Thermal stress in a 30-in. concrete shield for various incident gamma-energy fluxes [53].

as a function of the gamma-ray flux, Γ, incident on one face of the shield. The heat-conduction equation, assuming steady-state conditions and using slab geometry, is

$$-k\frac{d^2 T(x)}{dx^2} \doteq H_\gamma(x) \qquad (8.34)$$

where $T(x)$ = the temperature at point, x, °F
   $H_\gamma(x)$ = the gamma heating at point x, Btu/hr/cu ft
   x = distance in the shield, ft
   k = thermal conductivity of shield material, Btu/hr/°F/ft

The heat source can be represented by the equation

$$H_\gamma(x) = H_0 \exp(-x/\lambda) \qquad (8.35)$$

where*

H_0 = $1.55 \times 10^{-8} \mu_e \Gamma E_\gamma$, thin shield, Btu/cu ft

= $1.55 \times 10^{-8} \mu \Gamma E_\gamma$, thick shield, Btu/hr/cu ft (8.36)

where μ_e = linear energy-absorption coefficient at energy E_γ, cm^{-1}
   μ = linear mass-absorption coefficient at energy E_γ, cm^{-1}
   Γ = gamma-ray flux, gammas/cm^2/sec
   $\lambda = 1/\mu$ = relaxation length for gamma-ray heating [in Eq. 8.35, λ should be expressed in feet; to convert: λ ft = $(30.5)^{-1}\lambda$ cm]
   E_γ = gamma-ray energy, Mev

The boundary conditions are:

$$T(x) = T_0 \qquad \text{at } x = 0$$
$$dT(x)/dx = 0 \qquad \text{at } x = \infty$$

Using the boundary conditions and solving for the constants, the final equation for the temperature as a function of distance x in the shield is

$$T(x) = T_0 + (H_0 \lambda^2/k)[1 - \exp(-x/\lambda)] \qquad (8.37)$$

The maximum temperature rise in °F in the thin shield is

$$\Delta T_{\text{max.}} = H_0 \lambda^2/k = 1.55 \times 10^{-8} \mu_e \lambda^2 E_\gamma \Gamma/k \qquad (8.38)$$

For a thick shield, μ_e of Eq. 8.38 is replaced by μ. Figure 8.31 shows the maximum temperature rise in an ordinary concrete shield as a function of incident gamma-energy flux, $E_\gamma \Gamma$, from a radioactive Na^{24} source.

It is also possible to correlate the heat generation, $H(x)$ in Btu/hr/cu ft, in the shield with the gamma-ray flux incident on the shield surface. It

can be shown that replacing th thickness of the shield as the upper limit of integration by infinity results in only a very slight conservatism. Thus the heat flux absorbed per unit area of shield face, Q, is

$$Q = \int_0^\infty H(x)\, dx = H_0 \lambda \quad \text{Btu/hr/sq ft} \qquad (8.39)$$

where $H(x)$ is given by Eq. 8.35.

For thick shields the incident flux ΓE_γ and the absorbed flux $H_0 \lambda$ are the same. This can be seen by comparing $1.55 \times 10^{-8}\Gamma E_\gamma$ with $Q = H_0 \lambda$. When μ is expressed in ft^{-1}, these expressions are equal.

The total gamma heat generation per unit area of concrete shield surface as a function of gamma-ray energy fluxes is shown in Fig. 8.32.

8.6.7.2 Shield with Gamma-ray Sources on Both Sides

Often there are radioactive-coolant pipes and radioactive equipment on both sides of a shield. The purpose of a secondary concrete shield wall (Sec. 8.18) which separates the reactor compartment from the liquid-sodium secondary coolant circuit is to absorb neutrons and thus prevent significant activation of the secondary sodium coolant and associated equipment. The position of the secondary shield may be such that there are large primary-sodium-coolant gamma-radiation sources of approximately equal intensity on both sides of the concrete wall. Steel thermal shielding may be necessary on both sides of the concrete wall to protect the concrete from excessive gamma radiation.

The heat-source equation for equal gamma-radiation sources on both sides of a shield wall L ft thick, as shown in Fig. 8.33, is

$$H(x) \doteq H_0 \exp(-x/\lambda) + H_0 \exp[-(L-x)/\lambda] \quad \text{Btu/hr/cu ft}$$
$$(8.40)$$

For steady-state conditions and slab geometry, the heat-conduction is given by Eq. 8.34. If the sources on each side of the wall are different, the factor H_0 in the second term of Eq. 8.40 should be changed to H_0'. When this is done, Eqs. 8.41, 8.42, and 8.43 should be modified. The boundary conditions are

$$\frac{dT(x)}{dx} = 0 \qquad \text{at } x = L/2$$

$$k\frac{dT(0)}{dx} = H_1[T(0) - T_a]$$

where H_1 is the surface coefficient of heat transfer in Btu/hr/sq ft/°F and T_a is the ambient temperature on both sides of the wall in °F.

From the above model the temperature distribution in °F in the concrete is

$$T(x) = T_a + H_0 \lambda \left\{ \frac{[1 - \exp(-L/\lambda)]}{H_1} + \frac{\lambda}{k}\left[1 + \exp\left(-\frac{L}{\lambda}\right)\right.\right.$$
$$\left.\left. - \exp\left(-\frac{x}{\lambda}\right) - \exp\left(-\frac{L-x}{\lambda}\right)\right]\right\} \qquad (8.41)$$

---

*It is convenient to keep parts of this expression in metric units. Thus μ_e and H_0 should be expressed in terms of cm^{-1}, Γ, in gammas/cm^2/sec, and E_γ, in Mev. The conversion from metric to English units is

$$H_0 = 1.60 \times 10^{-13} \mu_e \Gamma E_\gamma \text{ watt/cm}^3 \times 9.6 \times 10^4 \ \frac{\text{Btu/hr/cu ft}}{\text{watt/cm}^3}$$

$$= 1.55 \times 10^{-8} \mu_e \Gamma E_\gamma \text{ Btu/hr/cu ft}$$

The maximum temperature rise is at a point in the center of the shield and is given by the relation

$$(\Delta T)_{max.} = \frac{H_0 \lambda^2}{k} [1 + \exp(-L/\lambda) - 2 \exp(-L/2\lambda)]$$

$$(8.42)$$

where all quantities are measured in English units. The maximum temperature difference between the concrete shield and ambient temperature as a function of the surface-film heat-transfer coefficient, H_1, for various gamma-energy fluxes is given in Fig. 8.34. Values for H_1 can be found in Chaps. 2, 4, and 6 and in the literature for natural convection from a vertical surface to air. In these evaluations a conservative value for the thermal conductivity of concrete of 0.50 Btu/hr/ft/°F and a conservative shield thickness of 30 in. is used. If a thermal shield (of steel) is used and if it is located close to the concrete shield, then the heat flux from the thermal shield must be taken into account. Also, cross heat radiation between the concrete wall and its protective (steel) shield must be considered.

In the simple analytical model being used as an example, the temperature gradient is maximum at the surface and decreases to zero at the center of the shield. The equation for the temperature gradient at a distance x ft in the shield is

$$\frac{dT(x)}{dx} = \frac{H_0 \lambda}{k} \left\{ \exp(-x/\lambda) - \exp[-(L - x)/\lambda] \right\} \quad (8.43)$$

Figure 8.35 shows the gradient in a concrete shield for various incident gamma-energy fluxes.

The temperature distribution in a concrete shield gives rise to tensile stresses in the outer edges of the shield and to compressive stresses in the interior parts. Concrete shield walls may support restraining loads in addition to their own weight. In these instances the increase in loading will place more of the wall in compression and reduce the amount in tension. As the allowable radiation flux on the surface is increased, the temperature difference will increase; consequently thermal stresses in the concrete will increase.

8.6.8 THERMAL STRESSES IN A SHIELD DUE TO NUCLEAR-RADIATION ABSORPTION [53, 54]

Chapter 3 covers thermal stresses due to radiation heating effects; therefore the subject will be treated only superficially here.

The thermal stress $\sigma(x)$ in pounds per square inch (psi) at point x in a shield wall which is due to the absorption of radiation can be represented by the equation

$$\sigma(x) = \frac{\zeta \overline{E}}{1 - \gamma} \Delta T(x) + \sigma_0 \qquad (8.44)$$

where

$$\Delta T(x) = \frac{H_0 \lambda^2}{k} \left\{ 1 + \exp(-L/\lambda) - \exp(-x/\lambda) \right.$$

$$\left. - \exp[-(L - x)/\lambda] \right\} \quad °F$$

and the average stress, σ_0, is given by $\sigma_0 = \sigma_0'/144$, where

$$\sigma_0' = \frac{P}{L} - \left\{ \frac{\overline{E} H_0 \lambda^2}{[Lk(1 - \gamma)]} \right\} \left[L - 2\lambda - (L + 2\lambda) \exp(-L/\lambda) \right]$$

$$(8.45)$$

where P = total restraining load of wall at the stress point considered, lb/ft
P/L = unit wall loading, psf
$\overline{E}'$ = modulus of elasticity of concrete, psf
      = 144 $\overline{E}$, with $\overline{E}$ in psi
ζ = linear coefficient of thermal expansion for concrete, in./in./°F
H_0 = the initial heating rate at shield surface, Btu/hr/cu ft
γ = Poisson's ratio for concrete
λ = relaxation length for gamma-ray heating, ft

Figure 8.36 shows the thermal-stress distribution in a typical concrete shield for various incident gamma-energy fluxes. In this example the following values were used: $E = 3.0 \times 10^6$ psi, $\zeta = 6.0 \times 10^{-6}$ in./in./°F, and $\gamma = 0.14$.

As the total loading, P/L, increases in magnitude, the amount of wall in tension decreases. Since a portion of the concrete shield wall is in tension, reinforcing steel should be added to prevent cracks from opening in the concrete which may give rise to neutron streaming and thus reduce the shielding effectiveness.

8.7 Ducts and Voids in a Shield

8.7.1 GENERAL CONSIDERATIONS FOR EMPTY DUCTS AND VOIDS

One of the most serious problems a shield designer must face is radiation streaming through ducts and voids in a shield. The problem becomes acute in shields for large fast power reactors because (1) the high operating temperatures require greater clearances for expansion and movement of component parts than do low-temperature or low-power reactors; (2) the instrumentation, control, and fueling access passages through the shield may be more numerous; and (3) the access passages "see" larger percentages of the core than they do in smaller size reactors.

8.7.2 METHODS FOR COMPUTING THE STREAMING CURRENTS THROUGH EMPTY DUCTS AND SLOTTED VOIDS

8.7.2.1 Geometric Methods

The available literature on radiation streaming is meager. In the early and mid 1950's, some experimental work was done on measuring radiation streaming in ducts and voids [56-60]. Simple geometric and phenomenological approaches to duct streaming were developed from these and other experiments. These approaches were found to be more or less successful with simple geometries, but they failed when complex geometries were involved. After an inactive period of several years, there has been renewed interest in the field [61-64].

Some work on voids and ducts encountered in fallout-shelter entranceways (Ref. 65, pages 179-193 and 266-291) is largely inapplicable to small ducts and voids. Perhaps the best-known equations for duct-streaming calculations are the purely geometric formulas found in Chap. 8 of Ref. 18. Many of these formulas give conservative results. Meager data on streaming existed at the time these formulas were developed, and arbitrary factors were used to account for such items as source distribution and scattering within the void. The formulas are, however, fairly simple to apply, and shielding developed using them is adequate. A summary of these formulas is given in Table 8.9. For more information about them the reader is referred to Ref. 18.

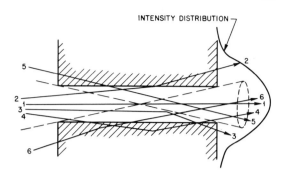

FIG. 8.37—Paths through ducts in a shield [51].

8.7.2.2 Empirical Methods

The experimentally measured attenuation of radiations through ducts and voids at Oak Ridge National Laboratory (ORNL), Massachusetts Institute of Technology (MIT), and Brookhaven National Laboratory (BNL) has led to the development of empirical formulas that are satisfactory in many instances. These formulas are geometric in nature; variable parameters have been evaluated from the

experiments to make the equations "work." They fit, more or less, over a range of duct sizes and lengths. These formulas are also summarized in Table 8.9 and in Chap. 8 of Ref. 18.

8.7.2.3 Analytical Methods

Reference 55 discusses the fundamental physics of the duct streaming of neutrons. It considers the six types of radiation streaming shown in Fig. 8.37.

Table 8.9—Summary of Geometric and Phenomenological Equations for Estimating the Streaming of Neutrons and Gamma Rays Through Empty Ducts, Slots, and Annuli* [18, 29, 50]

Streaming passage	Fast neutron†	Thermal neutron†	Gamma ray†
Rectangular slot or gap	Cosine emission: $$\phi(Z) = 20\phi_0 \left(\frac{L}{Z}\right)^2$$ provided $Z \gg L$ $Z > d$	Cosine emission: $$\phi(Z) = 20\phi_0 \left(\frac{L}{Z}\right)^2$$ provided $Z \gg L$ $Z > d$	Isotropic emission:‡ $$\phi(Z) = \frac{1}{2}\phi_0 \left(\frac{L}{Z}\right)$$ Cosine emission:§ $$\phi(Z) = \frac{2\phi_0}{\pi} \left(\frac{L}{Z}\right)$$ Fermi-distribution emission:⊕ $$\phi(Z) = \frac{\phi_0}{\sqrt{2}} \left(\frac{L}{Z}\right)$$
Straight cylindrical duct	Cosine emission: $$\phi(Z) = \frac{1}{2}\phi_0 \left(\frac{R}{Z}\right)^2$$	Cosine emission: $$\phi_1(Z) = \frac{1}{2}\phi_0 \left(\frac{R}{Z}\right)^2 \left\{1 + \frac{4R\,\alpha(th)_2}{[1 - \alpha(th)_1]\,Z}\right\}$$ Isotropic emission: $$\phi_1(Z) = \frac{1}{2}\phi_0 \left(\frac{R}{Z}\right)^2 \left[\frac{1}{1 - \alpha(th)_1}\right]$$	Isotropic emission: $$\phi(Z) = \frac{1}{2}\phi_0 \left(\frac{R}{Z}\right)^2$$ Cosine emission: $$\phi(Z) = \phi_0 \left(\frac{R}{Z}\right)^2$$ Fermi-distribution emission: $$\phi(Z) = \frac{4}{3} \left(\frac{R}{Z}\right)^2$$
Bent cylindrical ducts with n sections	Cosine emission: $$\phi(Z) = \frac{1}{2}\phi_0 \left(\frac{R_1}{Z_1}\right)^2 \left[\frac{R_2}{2Z_2}\frac{\alpha(f)}{\sin\theta_1}\right] \times \left[\frac{1}{2}\left(\frac{R_3}{Z_3}\right)^2 \frac{\alpha(f)}{\sin\theta_2}\right] \cdots \left[\frac{1}{2}\left(\frac{R_n}{Z_n}\right)^2 \frac{\alpha(f)}{\sin\theta_{n-1}}\right]$$	Cosine emission: $\phi_1(Z)$ is given above $$\phi_2(Z) = \frac{1}{6}\phi_1(Z)\left(\frac{R_2}{Z_2}\right)^2 \csc\theta_1$$ $$\phi_3(Z) = \frac{1}{6}\phi_2(Z)\left(\frac{R_3}{Z_3}\right)^2 \csc\theta_2$$ $$\vdots$$ $$\phi_n(Z) = \frac{1}{6}\phi_{n-1}(Z)\left(\frac{R_n}{Z_n}\right)^2 \csc\theta_{n-1}$$	

Table 8.9—Summary of Geometric and Phenomenological Equations for Estimating the Streaming of Neutrons and Gamma Rays Through Empty Ducts, Slots, and Annuli[*] [18, 29, 50] (continued)

Streaming passage	Fast neutron[†]	Thermal neutron[†]	Gamma ray[†]
Straight annular ducts	$\phi(Z) = \dfrac{10\phi_0 M_1}{Z^2}$ $M_1 = \left(2R_o^2 - R_i^2\right)\cos^{-1}\left(\dfrac{R_i}{R_o}\right) - R_i\sqrt{(R_o^2 - R_i^2)}$	$\phi(Z) = \dfrac{10\phi_0 M_1}{Z^2}$ M_1 given in column 1	Isotropic emission: $\phi(Z) = \dfrac{\phi_0 M_1}{2\pi Z^2}$ Cosine emission: $\phi(Z) = \dfrac{\phi_0 M_1}{\pi Z^2}$ Fermi-distribution emission: $\phi(Z) = \dfrac{1.27\phi_0 M_1}{\pi Z^2}$ M_1 given in column 1
Annular ducts with several (n) sections at right angles to each other	$\phi(Z) = 10\phi_0 \displaystyle\prod_1^n \left(\dfrac{M_1}{Z_n^2}\right)^n$ $M_1 = \left[2R_o^2 - R_j^2\right]\cos^{-1}\left(\dfrac{R_j}{R_o}\right) - R_j\left(R_o^2 - R_j^2\right)^{1/2}$	$\phi(Z) = 10\phi_0 \displaystyle\prod_1^n \left(\dfrac{M_1}{Z_n^2}\right)^n$ M_1 given in column 1	

* It is appropriate that users of these formulas be cognizant of the warning given in Rockwell [18], p. 261: "These formulas are based on meagre data over a narrow range of conditions. They are approximations and do not in all cases merge smoothly from one geometry to another. They should not be used without an understanding of their origin and limitations as described in (Chapter 8 of Ref. 18) . . . ."

† Note: $\phi(Z)$ = neutron or gamma-ray streaming flux from the end of a duct, gap, or annulus of total length Z, neutrons/cm^2/sec, or gammas per cm^2/sec

   $\phi_j(Z)$ = neutron flux at the end of the jth section of a multiple-section duct $(j = 1,2,3, \ldots , n)$

   Z = length of streaming passage

   Z_j = length of jth section of streaming passage having multiple sections $(j = 1,2,3, \ldots , n)$

   ϕ_0 = neutron or gamma-ray flux at entrance to streaming passage

   d = width of rectangular gap or slot

   L = thickness of rectangular gap or slot

   R = radius of circular cylindrical duct

   R_j = radius of the jth section of a multiple-section duct $(j = 1,2,3, \ldots , n)$

   R_i = inner radius of a circular annular passage

   R_o = outer radius of circular annular passage

   θ_j = angle between the jth and $(j + 1)$ section of a bent duct or annulus

   $\alpha(f)$ = fast-neutron reflection coefficient or albedo for the duct wall material

   $\alpha(\text{th})_1$ = thermal-neutron albedo for the duct wall material for isotropic emission: $\alpha(\text{th})_1 \cong 1 - 2.48\sqrt{(\sigma_c/\sigma_t)}$

   $\alpha(\text{th})_2$ = thermal-neutron albedo for the duct wall material for cosine emission: $\alpha(\text{th})_2 \cong 1 - 2.31\sqrt{(\sigma_c/\sigma_t)}$

   M_1 = streaming area in a circular annular duct from any given source position

‡ Equation for nondirectional detector. For directional detector, multiply $\phi(Z)$ by $2/\pi$.

§ Equation for nondirectional detector. For directional detector, multiply $\phi(Z)$ by $\pi/4$.

⊕ Equation for nondirectional detector. For directional detector, multiply $\phi(Z)$ by $\sqrt{1.5}$.

Although there is much to be desired in the interpretation and in the range of application of the formulas developed in Ref. 55, the formulas give more reasonable values of the streaming currents than do other methods. The formulas have been reworked and are presented in the following sections.

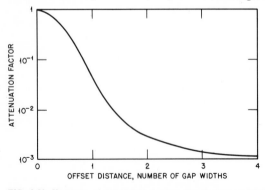

FIG. 8.38—Variation of attenuation in a gap as a function of offset distance [56].

8.7.3 NEUTRON STREAMING IN A STRAIGHT CYLINDRICAL DUCT

The streaming currents from a cylindrical duct of Z-cm length and L-cm radius are given by the modified Fisher formulas below.

8.7.3.1 Direct Streaming Current, J_d, at Duct Exit

$$J_d = \frac{\pi\Phi L^2}{Z^2}\left[1 + \left(\frac{L}{Z}\right)^2\right] \quad \text{neutrons/cm}^2\text{/sec} \quad (8.46)$$

where Φ is the vector flux at the duct entrance in neutrons/cm²/sec/steradian and ϕ is the scalar flux at the duct entrance in neutrons/cm²/sec. In an isotropic medium the general relation between the vector flux Φ and the scalar flux ϕ is

$$\phi \geq 4\pi\Phi \quad \text{neutrons/cm}^2/\text{sec} \qquad (8.47)$$

Equation 8.47 combined with Eq. 8.46 leads to the following overestimation for the direct-streaming current:

$$J_d = \frac{1}{4}\left(\frac{L}{Z}\right)^2 \phi \left[1 + \left(\frac{L}{Z}\right)^2\right] \qquad (8.48)$$

At the entrance to a duct, the vector flux becomes distorted, and the expression for the vector flux becomes

$$\Phi = \frac{\phi}{8\pi}\left[\frac{(1 + a_1)(1 - \beta_1)}{1 - a_1\beta_1}\right] \qquad (8.49)$$

where the neutron-reflection coefficients* a_1 and β_1 can be approximated if $\sqrt{\Sigma_c/\Sigma_t} \ll 1$:

$$a_1 = \left[1 - (2/\sqrt{3})\left(\sqrt{\Sigma_{c_1}/\Sigma_{t_1}}\right)\right]\left[1 + (2/\sqrt{3})\left(\sqrt{\Sigma_{c_1}/\Sigma_{t_1}}\right)\right]^{-1}$$

$$= 1 + \sum_1^\infty (-1)^n x_1^n \quad \left(\text{where } x_1 = 2\sqrt{\Sigma_{c_1}}/\sqrt{3\Sigma_{t_1}}\right)$$

$$(8.50)$$

---

*See also Sec. 8.8.3 for more information on neutron-reflection coefficients. The reader is referred to Ref. 27, pp. 129-136, and to Ref. 29, pp. 192-197.

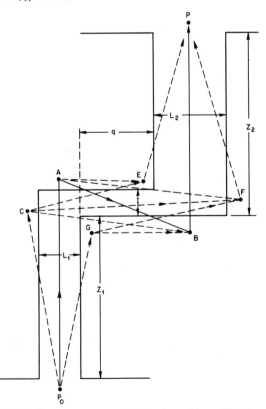

FIG. 8.39—Neutron-streaming paths through an offset gap [3, 55].

$$\beta_1 = \left[1 - (2/\sqrt{3})\left(\sqrt{\Sigma_{c_2}/\Sigma_{t_2}}\right)\right]\left[1 + (2\sqrt{3})\left(\sqrt{\Sigma_{c_2}/\Sigma_{t_2}}\right)\right]^{-1}$$

$$= 1 + \sum_1^\infty (-1)^n x_2^n \quad \left(\text{where } x_2 = 2\sqrt{\Sigma_{c_2}}/\sqrt{3\Sigma_{t_2}}\right)$$

$$(8.51)$$

where Σ_c and Σ_t are the macroscopic capture and total cross sections, respectively, and the subscripts 1 and 2 refer to the source medium and the duct wall medium, respectively. A more accurate expression for J_d than that given by Eq. 8.46 is

$$J_d = \frac{\phi}{8}\left(\frac{L}{Z}\right)^2 \left[\frac{(1 + a_1)(1 - \beta_1)}{1 - a_1\beta}\right]\left[1 + \left(\frac{L}{Z}\right)^2\right] \qquad (8.52)$$

8.7.3.2 Once-Scattered Streaming Current at Duct Exit †

$$J_s \cong 2\pi\Phi\left(\frac{\Sigma_s}{\Sigma_c\Sigma_t}\right)\left(\frac{L^2}{Z^3}\right) = \frac{\phi}{2}\left(\frac{\Sigma_s}{\Sigma_c\Sigma_t}\right)\left(\frac{L^2}{Z^3}\right)$$
$$\text{neutrons/cm}^2/\text{sec}$$

If the ratio of the macroscopic scattering cross section to the total cross section, Σ_s/Σ_t, is very near to unity, the above equation can be simplified

$$J_s \cong \frac{\phi}{2\Sigma_c}\frac{L^2}{Z^3} = \frac{\phi}{2}\frac{1}{\Sigma_c Z}\left(\frac{L}{Z}\right)^2 \qquad (8.53)$$

8.7.3.3 Total Streaming Current at Duct Exit

If it is assumed that the contribution from diffuse scattering is small, the total neutron streaming current is

$$J_{\text{tot}} = J_d + J_s \quad \text{neutrons/cm}^2/\text{sec}$$

$$= \pi\Phi\left(\frac{L}{Z}\right)^2\left[1 + \left(\frac{L}{Z}\right)^2 + \frac{2\Sigma_s}{\Sigma_c\Sigma_t Z}\right]$$

$$\cong \frac{\phi}{4}\left(\frac{L}{Z}\right)^2\left[1 + \left(\frac{L}{Z}\right)^2 + \frac{2}{\Sigma_c Z}\right] \qquad (8.54)$$

8.7.3.4 Range of Usefulness

Fisher's formulas should be highly reliable within the ranges

$$Z \leq 4/\kappa = 4/\sqrt{3\Sigma_c\Sigma_s}$$
$$L \leq 1/(2\Sigma_t) \qquad (8.55)$$

where $\kappa = \sqrt{3\Sigma_c\Sigma_s}$.

Outside these ranges Fisher states that the scattered-flux contribution becomes less reliable.

---

† This expression overestimates the once-scattered current; however, it neglects the multiple-scattered current, and therefore, since the error of estimation tends to offset the error of omission, the expression should be reasonably accurate.

However, since the scattered portion of the beam is usually less than the direct portion by a factor of ~ 10, the range of usefulness of the formulas can be extended by the same factor. A suggested range for fair accuracy is

$$Z \leq 20/\kappa = 20/\sqrt{3\,\Sigma_c \Sigma_s}$$
$$L \leq 5/\Sigma_t \tag{8.56}$$

Outside this range the equations become much less accurate.

8.7.4 NEUTRON STREAMING IN RECTANGULAR GAPS OR SLOTS

The modified Fisher formulas for a slot of depth Z, width L, and length $10L$ are given below.

8.7.4.1 Direct Streaming Current, J_d, from Slot Exit

$$J_d = \frac{\pi}{2}\,\frac{L}{Z}\,\Phi\left[1 + \left(\frac{L}{Z}\right)^2\right] \quad \text{neutrons/cm}^2/\text{sec}$$

$$\cong \frac{\phi}{8}\,\frac{L}{Z} \tag{8.57}$$

8.7.4.2 Scattered Streaming, J_s, from Slot Exit

$$J_s = \frac{\Phi}{2}\,\frac{\Sigma_s}{\Sigma_t}\left(\frac{L}{Z}\right)^2\left(\ln\frac{Z}{2L} + 2\right) \quad \text{neutrons/cm}^2/\text{sec}$$

$$\cong \frac{\phi}{8\pi}\left(\frac{L}{Z}\right)^2\left(\ln\frac{Z}{2L} + 2\right) \tag{8.58}$$

8.7.4.3 Slot-exit Streaming Current, J_p, from Penetration of the Base of the Shield into the Slot

In the case of the slot, a third source, J_p, of the streaming current becomes important: those neutrons leaking into the base of the slot through the shield and those neutrons leaving the slot through the shield at the top (Fig. 8.37, paths 2, 3, 5, and 6). This component is given by

$$J_p = \frac{\pi}{2}\,\Phi\,\frac{\Sigma_s}{\Sigma_c \Sigma_t}\,\frac{L}{Z^2} \quad \text{neutrons/cm}^2/\text{sec}$$

$$\leq \frac{\phi}{8}\,\frac{\Sigma_s}{\Sigma_c \Sigma_t}\,\frac{L}{Z^2} \cong \frac{\phi}{8}\,\frac{1}{\Sigma_c Z}\,\frac{L}{Z} \tag{8.59}$$

8.7.4.4 Total Neutron Streaming Current, J_{tot}, from This Slot

$$J_{\text{tot}} = J_d + J_s + J_p \quad \text{neutrons/cm}^2/\text{sec}$$

$$= \frac{\pi}{2}\,\Phi\,\frac{L}{Z}\left[1 + \left(\frac{L}{Z}\right)^2 + \frac{\Sigma_s}{\pi\Sigma_t}\,\frac{L}{Z}\ln\left(\frac{Z}{2L}+2\right) + \frac{\Sigma_s}{\Sigma_t \Sigma_c Z}\right]$$

$$\cong \frac{\phi}{8}\,\frac{L}{Z}\left[1 + \left(\frac{L}{Z}\right)^2 + \frac{L}{\pi Z}\left(\ln\frac{Z}{2L}+2\right) + \frac{1}{\Sigma_c Z}\right]$$

$$\tag{8.60}$$

In practice, $L \ll Z$ and $(L/Z)^2$ can be neglected, giving

$$J_{tot} \cong (\phi/8)(L/Z)[1 + (1/\Sigma_c Z)]$$

8.7.5 NEUTRON STREAMING THROUGH AN ANNULAR GAP

The modified Fisher formulas for an annulus of length Z, gap width L, inner radius R, and outer radius $R + L$ are given below.

8.7.5.1 Direct Streaming Current, J_d, from End of Annulus

$$J_d = 8\left(\frac{2}{3}\right)^{1/2}\frac{L^{3/2}R^{1/2}}{Z^2}\,\Phi \quad \text{neutrons/cm}^2/\text{sec}$$

$$= \frac{2\phi}{\pi}\left(\frac{2}{3}\right)^{1/2}\left(\frac{L^{3/2}R^{1/2}}{Z^2}\right) \tag{8.61}$$

8.7.5.2 Streaming Current at End of Annulus Due to Scattering from Inner Wall

$$J_{s1} = \frac{4}{15}\,\frac{\Phi}{\sqrt{2}}\,\frac{\Sigma_s}{\Sigma_t}\,\frac{L^{3/2}R^{1/2}}{\Sigma_c Z^3} \quad \text{neutrons/cm}^2/\text{sec}$$

$$\cong \frac{\phi}{15\pi\sqrt{2}}\,\frac{L^{3/2}R^{1/2}}{\Sigma_c Z^3} \tag{8.62}$$

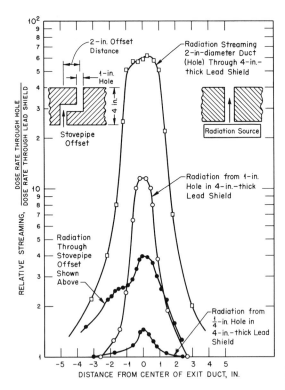

FIG. 8.40—Gamma-ray streaming through a duct (BNL experiments) [54, 56].

8.7.5.3 Streaming Current at End of Annulus Due to Scattering from Outer Wall

$$J_{s2} = \frac{12\Phi}{5\sqrt{2}} \frac{\Sigma_s}{\Sigma_t} \frac{L^{3/2}R^{1/2}}{\Sigma_c Z^3} \quad \text{neutrons/cm}^2/\text{sec}$$

$$\cong \frac{3\phi}{5\pi\sqrt{2}} \frac{L^{3/2}R^{1/2}}{\Sigma_c Z^3} \tag{8.63}$$

8.7.5.4 Total Streaming Current from End of Annular Duct

$$J_{\text{tot}} = J_d + J_{s1} + J_{s2} \quad \text{neutrons/cm}^2/\text{sec}$$

$$= 4\sqrt{2}\,\Phi \frac{L^{3/2}R^{1/2}}{Z^2} \left(\frac{2}{3} + \frac{\Sigma_s}{3\Sigma_t\Sigma_c Z} \right)$$

$$\cong \frac{\sqrt{2}\,\phi}{\pi} \frac{L^{3/2}R^{1/2}}{Z^2} \left(\frac{2}{3} + \frac{1}{3\Sigma_c Z} \right) \tag{8.64}$$

8.7.5.5 Range of Validity of the Annulus Equations

The equations are valid for $R < Z$. If $R > Z$ the gap formulas must be used. For $R \sim Z$ an extrapolation between the two cases is necessary.

8.7.6 STREAMING CURRENTS FROM COAXIAL ANNULI

In many instances several concentric annuli exist. The contribution to the streaming current from any one annulus made by any of the others can be estimated as follows: Let an annulus of length Z, inner radius R_0, and width L_0 be the annulus receiving a streaming current from an adjacent annulus with inner radius R_1 and width L_1. (All the units are in centimeters.) Then the streaming contribution J_{co} from the second annulus to the first annulus is

$$J_{co} = \frac{16\sqrt{2}}{3\pi} \left(\frac{\Phi\Sigma_s}{\Sigma_t} \right) \left[R_1 L_1^{5/2} \left(R_0^{1/2} Z^3 \right)^{-1} \right] K_0(x)$$

$$\qquad\qquad\qquad\qquad\qquad\quad \text{neutrons/cm}^2/\text{sec}$$

$$\cong \frac{4\sqrt{2}\,\phi}{3\pi^2} \frac{R_1 L_1^{5/2}}{R_0^{1/2} Z^3} K_0(x) \tag{8.65}$$

where x is $\sqrt{3\Sigma_s\Sigma_c}\,|R_0 - R_1|$ and $K_0(x)$ is a Bessel function of the second kind of order 0. This current exists in addition to the primary streaming current.

8.7.7 NEUTRON STREAMING FROM STEPPED GAPS OR OFFSETS

Experimental data provide information on the attenuation of a neutron beam that may be obtained when an offset is introduced into the streaming path. Figure 8.38 shows the variation in attenuation as a function of the offset distance [29, 56].

The modified Fisher formulas for a stepped gap are given below (all units are in centimeters). Consider neutrons incident upon the entrance channel of depth Z_1, width L_1, and length equal to or greater than $10L$. They scatter around an offset of length q and width l into the exit channel of length Z_2 and width L_2. The exit channel is thus displaced from the entrance channel a distance q. The streaming currents go from the entrance channel mainly by one of three scattering paths, as shown in Fig. 8.39. The step function, p, in the formulas is an addition to the Fisher formulas.

8.7.7.1 Streaming Current at the End of Path $P_0 ABP$

The streaming current J_{21} at the end of the path $P_0 ABP$ (see Fig. 8.39) is given by

$$J_{21} = \frac{\sqrt{3}\,p}{16\pi^2} \frac{L_1}{L_2} \frac{\sqrt{\Sigma_s}}{\sqrt{\Sigma_c}} \frac{(\Sigma_s L_2)^2}{\Sigma_t Z_2} J_1 \quad \text{neutrons/cm}^2/\text{sec}$$

$$\tag{8.66}$$

In Eq. 8.66 p is the offset function given by

$$p = \frac{\Sigma_t\lambda^2}{q} \exp(-y) \cong \frac{\lambda}{q} \exp(-y) \quad (q > 0) \tag{8.67}$$

where

$$y = 2\left[1 + \frac{1}{4}(2q + L_1 + L_2)^2 (2\lambda + l)^{-2} \right]^{1/2} - \sqrt{5}$$

and J_1 is given by Eq. 8.60. The quantity p may be set equal to unity under two conditions: (1) if $q \approx \lambda$ and if l, L_1, and $L_2 \ll \lambda$; or (2) if $q \approx \lambda$ and if $l = L_1 + L_2 \approx \lambda$. There is no restriction on the sign $(\pm)$ of y.

8.7.7.2 Streaming Current, J_{22}, at the End of Paths Similar to $P_0 CEP$, $P_0 CFP$, $P_0 QBP$, $P_0 GFP$, and $P_0 CBP$ (Fig. 8.39)

$$J_{22} = \frac{G\phi_1 p}{\sqrt{3}} \frac{\Sigma_s}{\Sigma_t} \frac{L_2}{Z_2} \quad \text{neutrons/cm}^2/\text{sec} \tag{8.68}$$

where ϕ_1 and G are given by

$$\phi_1 = (\phi/16)(L_1/Z_1)^2 \quad \text{neutrons/cm}^2/\text{sec} \tag{8.69}$$

$$G = 0.30 - 0.017\lambda\Sigma_t \tag{8.70}$$

and ϕ is the scalar flux at the entrance to the first leg.

8.7.7.3 Streaming Current, J_{23}, at the End of Paths Similar to $P_0 AEP$ and $P_0 AFP$

$$J_{23} = \frac{cpJ_1}{\sqrt{3}} \left(\frac{\Sigma_s}{\Sigma_t} \right)^2 \frac{\sqrt{\Sigma_s}}{\sqrt{\Sigma_c}} \frac{L_1 L_2}{Z_2^2} \quad \text{neutrons/cm}^2/\text{sec}$$

$$\tag{8.71}$$

where $c = 0.16 - 0.01\lambda\Sigma_t$ and $\Sigma_t = \Sigma_s + \Sigma_c$.

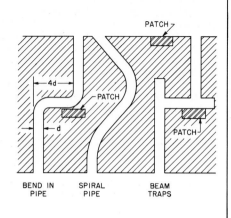

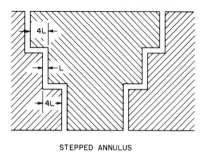

PREVENTION OF STREAMING IN
EMPTY PIPES AND DUCTS

PREVENTION OF STREAMING IN
ANNULI AROUND A PLUG

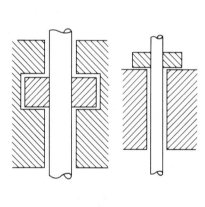

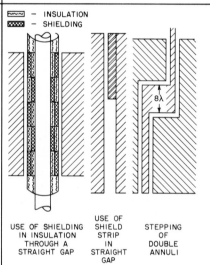

USE OF RING SHIELDS OR DONUTS
TO PREVENT STREAMING AROUND
LIQUID-FILLED PIPES

FIG. 8.41—Methods of reducing streaming in voids and gaps [3, 51].

8.7.7.4 Total Streaming Current, J_2, at the Exit of the Stepped Gaps

$$J_2 = J_{21} + J_{22} + J_{23} \quad \text{neutrons/cm}^2/\text{sec}$$

$$= \sqrt{3}\, p\, \frac{L_2}{Z_2}\, \frac{\sqrt{\Sigma_s}}{\sqrt{\Sigma_c}} \left[J_1 L_1 \left(\frac{\Sigma_s}{16\pi^2} + \frac{c}{3 Z_2} \right) + \frac{2\phi_1 G}{3} \right]$$

$$(8.72)$$

8.7.7.5 Range of Application of the Stepped-gap Formulas

For Eq. 8.67 to be valid, the following conditions must prevail:

$$q - L_1 > |L_1 - L_2| \qquad \lambda \geq L_1 + L_2$$

The equation for J_{22} becomes inaccurate if the limits $1 < \lambda \Sigma_t < 5$ are exceeded.

8.7.8 NEUTRON STREAMING FROM A STEPPED ANNULUS

The modified Fisher formulas for the stepped annulus are given below (Fig. 8.39 applies).

8.7.8.1 Current, J_{21}, from Streaming Along Paths Similar to $P_0\, ABP$

$$J_{21} = \frac{p J_1}{20 \sqrt{3}}\, \frac{R_1}{R_2}\, \frac{L_1}{L_2}\, \frac{\sqrt{\Sigma_s}}{\sqrt{\Sigma_c}}\, \frac{\Sigma_s L_2^{5/2} R_3^{1/2}}{Z_2^2} \quad \text{neutrons/cm}^2/\text{sec}$$

$$(8.73)$$

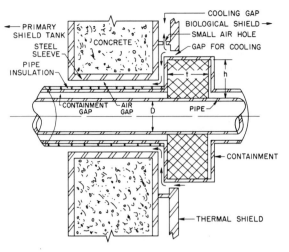

FIG. 8.42—Design concept of a sodium-filled-pipe penetration showing steel sleeve shielding and donut in thermal-shield area.

where $R_3 = \frac{1}{2}(R_1 + R_2)$, J_1 is given by Eq. 8.64, and p is given by Eq. 8.67. R_1 and R_2 refer to the inner radius of the first and second legs of the stepped annulus, respectively.

8.7.8.2 Current, J_{22}, from Streaming Along Other Paths

$$J_{22} = \frac{pF}{2\pi\sqrt{3}} \frac{\sqrt{\Sigma_s}}{\sqrt{\Sigma_c}} \frac{R_3^{3/2} L_2^{3/2}}{R_2 Z_2^2} \left(\phi_1 + \frac{2R_1}{R_2} \frac{L_1}{Z_1} J_1'' \right)$$

$$\text{neutrons/cm}^2/\text{sec} \quad (8.74)$$

where

$$\phi_1 \cong \frac{4\sqrt{2}}{3\pi} \frac{L_1^{5/2} R_1^{1/2}}{Z_1^3} \phi \quad \text{neutrons/cm}^2/\text{sec} \quad (8.75)$$

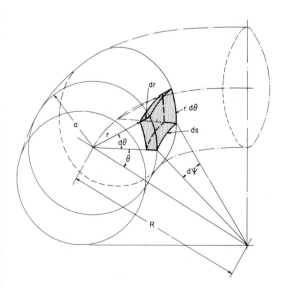

FIG. 8.43—The volume element, $r \, dr \, d\theta \, ds$.

J_1'' is given by Eq. 8.64, p is given by Eq. 8.67, ϕ is the flux at the entrance to the first leg, and $F = 2.4 - 0.15 \, \Sigma_t \lambda$.

8.7.8.3 Total Streaming Current from a Stepped Annulus

$$J_2 = J_{21} + J_{22} \quad \text{neutrons/cm}^2/\text{sec}$$

$$\cong \frac{p}{2} \left(\frac{\Sigma_s}{3\Sigma_c} \right)^{1/2} \frac{R_3^{1/2} L_2^{3/2}}{Z_2^2} \left[\frac{R_1 L_1}{R_2} \left(\frac{2FJ_1''}{\pi Z_2} + \frac{\Sigma_s J_1''}{10} \right) \right.$$

$$\left. + \frac{FR_3 \phi_1}{\pi R_2} \right] \quad (8.76)$$

8.7.8.4 Range of Validity of Stepped-annuli Streaming Equations

The region of validity of the equations for this case is the same as that for the stepped offset. In addition, the current J_{22} becomes inaccurate outside the range $1 < \Sigma_t \lambda < 5$.

8.7.9 BENDS IN DUCTS AND SLOTTED GAPS

8.7.9.1 Ducts with One Bend

Given a duct of radius L which has a leg of length Z and a second leg of length Z_2, at the end of the first leg and at an angle θ with the first leg, Fisher's method yields for the streaming current J_2 out of the end of the second leg

$$J_2 \cong J_1 \left(L^3 \Sigma_s^3 W / \Sigma_t^2 Z_2^2 \right) \cong J_1 \left(\Sigma_s L^3 / Z_2^2 \right) W$$

$$\text{neutrons/cm}^2/\text{sec} \quad (8.77)$$

where J_1 is the current at the end of the first leg as calculated by Eq. 8.54, and

$$W = (0.15 + 0.026 \, \Sigma_t \lambda) - (0.08 + 0.004 \, \Sigma_t \lambda) \cos\theta \quad (8.78)$$

8.7.9.2 Ducts with More than One Bend

For this case Eq. 8.77 may be applied as many times as there are bends.

8.7.9.3 Straight Gaps with One Bend

If two slots of width L and length greater than $10L$ are joined at an angle θ to each other, where the depths of the two legs of the offset are Z_1 and Z_2, respectively, the streaming current J_2 out of the end of the second leg is

$$J_2 \cong \left(J_1 \Sigma_s^3 L^2 Y / \Sigma_t^2 Z_2 \right) \cong J_1 Y \left(\Sigma_s L^2 / Z_2 \right)$$

$$\text{neutrons/cm}^2/\text{sec} \quad (8.79)$$

where J_1 is the streaming current at the end of the first leg as calculated by Eq. 8.60 and

$$Y = (0.015 + 0.023\,\Sigma_t\,\lambda) - (0.009 + 0.0016\,\Sigma_t\,\lambda)\cos\theta$$
$$(8.80)$$

8.7.9.4 Gaps with More than One Bend

For n bends Eq. 8.79 may be applied n times. Equations 8.77 and 8.79 are unsatisfactory as θ approaches 0 or π, or if $L < 1/\Sigma_t$ or Z_2 becomes very small.

8.7.10 GAMMA-RAY STREAMING IN DUCTS AND GAPS

The streaming of gamma rays through ducts is treated by geometric methods in Chap. 8 of Ref. 18. Some experimental results are presented in the reference. Figure 8.40 shows the effect of holes of various sizes on reactor gamma radiation through a 4-in. lead slab (as measured in water behind the slab at BNL) (see Table 8.9).

A more basic treatment of gamma-ray streaming through ducts is given by Fisher's formulas [55]. Fisher's formulas as presented above can be used for gamma-ray streaming if the following transformations are used:

$\phi \rightarrow \Gamma$, gammas/cm^2/sec

$\Sigma_t \rightarrow \mu$, cm^{-1} (linear-absorption coefficient)

$\Sigma_c \rightarrow \mu_e$, cm^{-1} (linear-energy-absorption coefficient)

$\Sigma_s \rightarrow \mu_s = \mu - \mu_e$ cm^{-1} (linear-scattering coefficient)

Extreme caution must be used in applying these transformations. Scattered gamma rays lose a good portion of their energy. The scattered portion of the streaming current from long straight ducts and slots, with $L/Z \ll 1$, will have a gamma-ray energy 80 to 90% of that of the primary beam because only gamma rays involved in small-angle scattering survive to the end of the duct. Therefore, choice of the values of μ, μ_s, and μ_e, as well as the conversion to biological dose rates, must reflect the lowered energy.

The total exit current from stepped or bent ducts and annuli will have been scattered at least twice inside the void. Thus the values of μ, μ_s, and μ_e must reflect the degraded energy. As a rule of thumb, for original gamma-ray energies of 1 Mev and above, take the energy of the scattered radiation to be 0.25 Mev. For initial gamma-ray energies below 1 Mev, take the scattered energy to be about one-fourth the initial energy. Conversion to dose rates must also reflect this energy degradation.

8.7.11 METHODS OF REDUCING STREAMING IN VOIDS AND DUCTS

It is usually impossible to eliminate all voids in a shield design, but it is possible to design in such a way that the streaming from all voids is considerably reduced, provided the shielding is

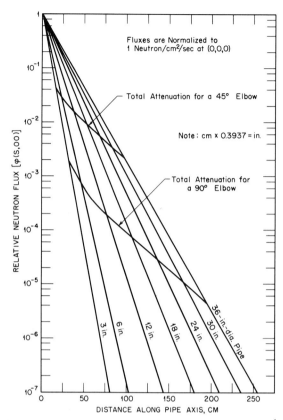

FIG. 8.44—Attenuation of thermal neutrons along the axis of a sodium-filled long-bend pipe elbow as a function of distance along the axis for various pipe diameters [66].

accounted for in the mechanical design. Such steps as the following can be taken singly or in combination to reduce streaming [3]: (1) reduce all clearances for expansion and motion to reasonable minimum values; (2) spiral or bend ducts and empty pipes where possible, or offset the gap; (3) make the offset distance four times as large as the average gap width, and, if the radiation intensity has to be reduced by more than a factor of 10^5, use two offsets; (4) make certain that collar or donut shields used around pipes to reduce streaming in annular gaps have radial dimensions three to four times the gap width and have an axial dimension of about five relaxation lengths; (5) separate double annuli at the offsets by a thickness of at least eight relaxation lengths; and (6) use a checkerboard pattern of insulation and shielding around an insulated pipe to reduce the effective gap (see Fig. 8.78). Some of the above ideas are illustrated in Fig. 8.41. The penetration details of a sodium-filled pipe passing through a secondary shield wall are shown in Fig. 8.42. (See Figs. 8.106, 8.110, 8.112, and 8.114 for examples of how some of these methods are employed.)

8.7.12 NEUTRON STREAMING THROUGH LIQUID-METAL-FILLED PIPES AND DUCTS

A problem in fast sodium-cooled reactor design is the streaming of neutrons through the coolant in

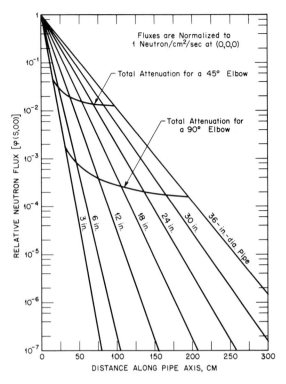

FIG. 8.45—Attenuation of 1-Mev neutrons along the axis of a sodium-filled long-bend pipe elbow for various pipe diameters [66].

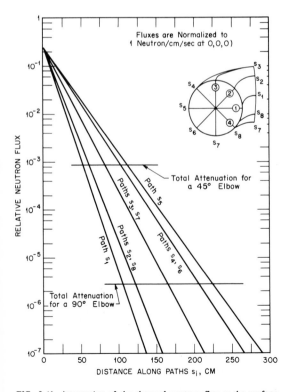

FIG. 8.46—Attenuation of the thermal-neutron flux on the surface of a sodium-filled long-bend 30-in. pipe elbow along the paths s_1 to s_8 [66].

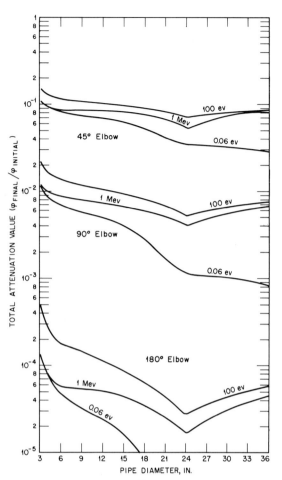

FIG. 8.47—Total axial neutron attenuation in sodium-filled short-bend pipe elbows as a function of pipe diameter [66].

pipes which penetrate the shield [66]. Formulas for estimating the streaming of monoenergetic neutrons through liquid-metal-filled pipes are given below.

8.7.12.1 Short Straight Duct of Length L and Radius a

The neutron flux at any point (r, z) in the duct is given by

$$\phi(r, z) = J_0(\omega r)[\phi_1 \exp(-\beta_0 z) + \phi_2 \exp(\beta_0 z)]$$

$$\text{neutrons/cm}^2/\text{sec} \qquad (8.81)$$

where
z = distance down the duct, cm
r = radial distance from the duct axis, cm
$J_0(\omega r)$ = Bessel function of the first kind of order 0
ϕ_1 and ϕ_2 = constants (see below)
$\omega = 2.405/(a + d)$, cm^{-1}
a = radius of duct
d = extrapolation distance, cm

The parameters β and κ depend upon the nuclear characteristics of the coolant.

$$\beta_0^2 = \kappa^2 + \omega^2, \text{ cm}^{-2}$$
$$\kappa^2 = 3\Sigma_s \Sigma_c, \text{ cm}^{-2} \qquad (8.82)$$

The constants ϕ_1 and ϕ_2 are found by simultaneously solving the following two equations:

$$\phi_1 + \phi_2 = \phi_0$$

$$\phi_1 \exp(-\beta_0 L) + \phi_2 \exp(\beta_0 L)$$
$$= \beta_0 d [\phi_1 \exp(-\beta_0 L) - \phi_2 \exp(\beta_0 L)] \qquad (8.83)$$

where ϕ_0 is the neutron flux at the duct entrance.

The neutron current, I_Z, parallel to the axis of the duct is given by

$$I_Z(r,z) = \frac{\beta_0}{3\Sigma_s} J_0(\omega r) \left(\phi_1 e^{-\beta z} - \phi_2 e^{\beta z}\right)$$
$$\text{neutrons/cm}^2/\text{sec} \quad (8.84)$$

The neutron current, I_r, in the radial direction is given by

$$I_r(r,z) = \left(\frac{\omega}{3\Sigma_s}\right) J_1(\omega r) \left(\phi_1 e^{-\beta z} + \phi_2 e^{\beta z}\right)$$
$$\text{neutrons/cm}^2/\text{sec} \quad (8.85)$$

where $J_1(\omega r)$ is Bessel's function of first kind and first order.

8.7.12.2 Long Straight Ducts

The neutron flux at any point (r,z) is given by

$$\phi(r,z) = \phi_0 J_0(\omega r) \exp(-\beta_0 z) \quad \text{neutrons/cm}^2/\text{sec} \quad (8.86)$$

The current motion parallel to the axis is given by

$$I_Z(r,z) = [\beta_0 \phi_0 /(3\Sigma_s)] J_0(\omega r) \exp(-\beta_0 z)$$
$$\text{neutrons/cm}^2/\text{sec} \quad (8.87)$$

The current motion in the radial direction is given by

$$I_r(r,z) = [\omega \phi_0 /(3\Sigma_s)] J_1(\omega r) \exp(-\beta_0 z)$$
$$\text{neutrons/cm}^2/\text{sec} \quad (8.88)$$

8.7.12.3 Bends in Ducts or Pipe

The coordinates of any point in a pipe bend are given by the variables r, in the radial direction, and Ψ, the angle of turning or bending of the pipe (see Fig. 8.43). The neutron flux at any point (r, Ψ) is then

$$\phi(r, \Psi) = \phi_0 J_0(\omega r) \exp(-\beta_1 \Psi) \quad \text{neutrons/cm}^2/\text{sec} \quad (8.89)$$

Alternately, where Ψ is expressed in terms of the radius of curvature, R, of the pipe bend, the flux is expressed in terms of s (the distance measured along the pipe axis), r, and θ (the angular deviation of the point from the plane of the bend)

$$\phi(s,r,\theta) = \phi_0 J_0(\omega r) \exp\left(-\frac{\beta_1 s}{R}\right) \text{ neutrons/cm}^2/\text{sec} \quad (8.90)$$

where $s = R\Psi$, cm

$$\beta_1^2 = (\omega^2 + \kappa^2) R^2$$

Along the pipe axis for $r = \theta = 0$ the flux is

$$\phi(s,0,0) = \phi_0 \exp(-\beta_1 s/R) \quad \text{neutrons/cm}^2/\text{sec} \quad (8.91)$$

The neutron-current motion parallel to the axis in a pipe bend is given by

$$\mathbf{J}_s(s,r,\theta) = \frac{\mathbf{s}_1 \phi_0 \beta_1}{3\Sigma_s} \frac{J_0(\omega r)}{R - r\cos\theta} \exp\left(-\frac{\beta_1 s}{R}\right) \quad (8.92)$$

The neutron-current motion in the radial direction is given by

$$\mathbf{J}_r(s,r,\theta) = \frac{\mathbf{r}_1 \phi_0}{3\Sigma_s} \left[\omega J_1(\omega r) + \frac{\beta_1 s \cos\theta J_0(\omega r)}{R(R - r\cos\theta)}\right] \exp\left(-\frac{\beta_1 s}{R}\right)$$
$$(8.93)$$

The neutron-current (swirl) motion in the θ direction is given by

$$\mathbf{J}_\theta = -\mathbf{\theta}_1 \frac{\beta_1 \phi_0 s \sin\theta J_0(\omega r)}{3\Sigma_s R(R - r\cos\theta)} \exp\left(-\frac{\beta_1 s}{R}\right) \quad (8.94)$$

In the above quantities $\mathbf{s}_1$, $\mathbf{r}_1$ and $\mathbf{\theta}_1$ are unit vectors in the s, r, and θ directions, respectively.

Figure 8.44 shows the attenuation along the axis of standard long-bend sodium-filled pipe elbows of various sizes for thermal neutrons. Figure 8.45 shows the same data for 1-Mev neutrons.

In Fig. 8.46 the attenuation of the thermal flux along various surface paths on a 30-in.-diameter sodium-filled pipe bend is shown. The total attenuation of the neutron intensity which can be expected in pipes of various diameters with bends of 45°, 90°, and 180° is shown in Fig. 8.47 for short-bend pipes and in Fig. 8.48 for long-bend pipes.

8.7.13 NEUTRON ENERGY STREAMING THROUGH MATERIALS

Certain materials, notably iron, have energy regions in the cross-section distribution within which the value of the total cross section is very low compared with the value in surrounding energy regions. There are two notable regions in iron; the largest is at 25 kev, and the other is at 84 kev. The energy "holes" in the cross section can give rise to the streaming through the material of neutrons at or close to the hole energy. An approximate calculation of the streaming flux of neutrons of energy

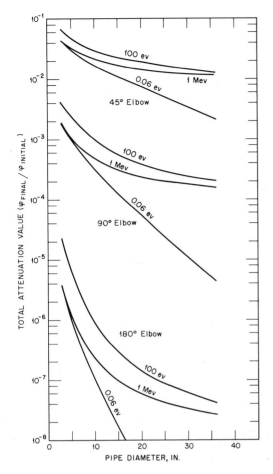

TOTAL ATTENUATION VALUE ($\varphi_{FINAL}/\varphi_{INITIAL}$)

100 ev

0.06 ev   1 Mev

45° Elbow

100 ev

1 Mev

0.06 ev

90° Elbow

180° Elbow

100 ev

1 Mev

0.06 ev

PIPE DIAMETER, IN.

FIG. 8.48—Total axial neutron attenuation in sodium-filled long-bend pipe elbows as a function of pipe diameter [66].

E_s through an iron thickness d cm is as follows [3, 18]. Let the energy range of neutrons incident upon an iron shield be between E_{th} (thermal neutrons) and E_0 (fast neutrons). If E_s is the energy at which the neutron cross-section hole exists and if the half width of this hole is ϵ, the fraction f_1 of all the incident neutrons with energy E_s passing through the material is given by

$$f_1 = \frac{\int_{E_s - \epsilon + \Delta E'}^{E_s + \epsilon + \Delta E} \phi(E)\, dE}{\int_{E_{th}}^{E_0} \phi(E)\, dE} = \frac{1}{N_1} \int_{E_s - \epsilon + \Delta E'}^{E_s + \epsilon + \Delta E} \phi(E)\, dE$$

(8.95)

where $\phi(E)$ is the energy-distribution spectrum of the incident neutrons and N_1 is the total number of incident neutrons. The neutrons not streaming through the material lie above the range $E_s + \epsilon + \Delta E$ or below $E_s - \epsilon + \Delta E'$. The term ΔE in the upper limit makes allowance for those neutrons slowing down from energy $E_s + \Delta E$ to energy $E_s + \epsilon$ during travel through the material; and $\Delta E'$ in the lower limit makes allowance for those neutrons slowing

past $E_s - \epsilon$ from $E_s - \epsilon + \Delta E'$. The terms ΔE and $\Delta E'$ can be calculated by the equations

$$\Delta E = E_s \xi \bar{\Sigma}_s d \qquad (8.96)$$

$$\Delta E' = E_s \xi \Sigma_s(E_s) d \qquad (8.97)$$

where ξ = the logarithmic energy decrement per collision in the material (Sec. 8.1.4)

$\bar{\Sigma}_s$ = the average macroscopic scattering cross section in the energy regions adjacent to the hole

$\Sigma_s(E_s)$ = the scattering cross section value at E_s

d = the slab thickness

The fraction f_2 of neutrons of other energies passing through the material is given by

$$f_2 = \frac{1}{N_1}\left[\int_{E_{th}}^{E_s - \epsilon + \Delta E'} \phi(E)\, dE + \int_{E_s + \epsilon + \Delta E}^{E_0} \phi(E)\, dE\right]$$

$$= 1 - f_1 \qquad (8.98)$$

where E_{th} is the lower energy limit and E_0 is the upper energy limit of the neutron-energy distribution.

In slab geometry the neutron-streaming flux, ϕ_s, from the material accounting for absorption is

$$\phi_s = \phi_s(\text{through hole}) + \phi_s(\text{other energies})$$

$$\phi_s = \phi_0[f_1 \exp(-\kappa_s d) + f_2 \exp(-\kappa_{av} d)]$$

$$= \phi_0\{\exp(-\kappa_{av} d) + f_1[\exp(-\kappa_s d) - \exp(-\kappa_{av} d)]\}$$

(8.99)

where $\kappa_s = \sqrt{(3\Sigma_s \Sigma_c)}$ and ϕ_0 = total flux incident on the slab.

$$\kappa_{av} = \sqrt{(3\Sigma_s \Sigma_c)_{av}} = \sqrt{3\Sigma_s/E_0} \int_{E_{th}}^{E_0} \left[\Sigma_c(E)\right]^{1/2} dE$$

(8.100)

The attenuation coefficient κ_{av} may be replaced by $1/\lambda$, where λ is the typical relaxation length of the neutrons in the material.*

If ϕ is the emergent flux due to κ_{av} (no streaming), then the buildup $B(\kappa d)$ of the flux through the shield due to energy streaming is given by

$$B(\kappa d) = \frac{\phi_s}{\phi} = 1 + f_1\{\exp[(\kappa_{av} - \kappa_s)d] - 1\} \quad (8.101)$$

where $\phi = \phi_0 \exp(-\kappa_{av}d)$.

8.8 Radiation Scattering

Radiation scattered in air from structures must be considered in the development of structures and

---

*If the neutron-energy spectrum within the slab lies between the limits E_1 and E_2 (where $E_{th} \leq E_1 < E_2 \leq E_0$), a more accurate evaluation of κ_{av} is made by substituting the limits E_1 and E_2 in Eq. 8.100 for E_{th} and E_0, respectively.

of procedures for remote-maintenance operations connected with power reactors and propulsion reactors. Scattered radiation must be considered also in the study and development of procedures for emergency evacuation from nuclear accidents of various sorts. Under certain circumstances scattered-radiation effects are as important to a design as direct-radiation effects. A complete discussion of the subject is beyond the scope of this volume; however, some aspects important to shielding are discussed.

8.8.1 NEUTRON SCATTERING IN AIR

There is a limited amount of experimental data available on the air scattering of neutrons (Ref. 68, pp. 188-208, and Ref. 71). Some theoretical studies have been made on the behavior of scattered neutron radiation, based upon the integration over all space of the integral form of the Boltzmann transport equation. The mathematical formulation to determine the angular distribution and energy spectrum of air-scattered neutrons for the idealized case of a monoenergetic point source of neutrons in air, assuming single isotropic scattering, is as follows:

Let a nondirectional detector be placed at the origin of the coordinate system, and let a monoenergetic anisotropic point source of neutrons emitting $S_0(-\Omega)$ neutrons/sec/steradian at energy E_0 about the direction $-\Omega$ be placed at a distance r_0 from the detector in the direction Ω_0. Let r' be the position coordinates of an element of volume in air which is scattering radiation in the direction $-\Omega$ from the source to the detector (Fig. 8.49). Then the angular flux, $\Psi(0,E,\Omega)$, reaching the detector at energy E about the negative direction $-\Omega$ at the origin is given by the following generalized expression:

$$\Psi_\phi(0,E,\Omega) = \int q(\mathbf{r}',E,-\Omega) \exp\left[-\int_0^{r'} \Sigma_t(\mathbf{r}'',\Omega,E)\,dr''\right]$$

$$\times \left[\delta(\Omega',\Omega)\,dr'\right]/(r'^2)\Bigg]$$

$$(8.102)$$

where $\qquad\qquad \Omega =$ a unit vector

$\Psi_\phi(0,E,\Omega) =$ neutrons/cm^2/sec per unit energy at energy E per steradian about the negative direction $-\Omega$ at the origin

$\Sigma_t(\mathbf{r},E) =$ the macroscopic total cross section at position $\mathbf{r}$ and at energy E, (cm^{-1})

$q(\mathbf{r},E,-\Omega) =$ the source term: neutrons/cm^3/sec per unit energy at E per steradian about direction $-\Omega$ at position $\mathbf{r}'$

$dr' = r'^2\,d\Omega'\,dr'$

$\delta(\Omega',\Omega) = 0$ (if $\Omega' \neq \Omega$)

$$\int_{\Omega'} \delta(\Omega',\Omega)\,d\Omega = 1$$

In the particular case of interest here, with a point source $S_0(-\Omega)$ as defined above, the source term $q(\mathbf{r}',E,-\Omega)$ is given by

$$q(\mathbf{r}',E,-\Omega) = \frac{S_0(-\Omega)\,\delta(\Omega_0,\Omega')\,\delta(\mathbf{r}_0-\mathbf{r}')\,\delta(E_0-E)}{(r')^2}$$

$$+ \int_{E''}\int_{\Omega''} \Sigma_s(\mathbf{r}',E'')\,q(\mathbf{r}',E'',\Omega'')$$

$$\times f(E,E'',-\Omega,\Omega'')\,dE''\,d\Omega''$$

where $\qquad S_0(-\Omega) =$ the point-source strength, particles/sec/steradian about the direction $-\Omega$

$E_0 =$ the source energy

$r_0 =$ the radial distance to the point source

$\Omega_0 =$ the direction to the point source from the origin

$\delta(r_0-r') =$ the Dirac delta function

$\Sigma_s(\mathbf{r}',E'') =$ the macroscopic scattering cross section at position $\mathbf{r}'$ and at energy E'', cm^{-1}

$f(E,E'',-\Omega,\Omega'')dE''d\Omega'' =$ the probability of scattering from a direction Ω'' at energy E'' into the solid angle $d\Omega''$ about the direction $-\Omega$ and into the energy interval between E and $E+dE''$

(The first term on the right of the equation represents the source-term contribution from unscattered neutrons and the second term is the contribution from scattered neutrons.) Substituting in Eq. 8.102,

$$\Psi_\phi(0,E,\Omega) = \frac{S_0(-\Omega)\,\delta(\Omega_0,\Omega)\,\delta(E_0-E)}{r_0^2}$$

$$\times \exp\left[-\int_0^{r_0} \Sigma_t(\mathbf{r}'\,\Omega,E)\,dr'\right]$$

$$+ \int_{\substack{all\\space}}\int_{E''}\int_{\Omega''} \Sigma_t(\mathbf{r}',E'')\,q(\mathbf{r}',E'',-\Omega'')$$

$$\times \frac{\Sigma_s(\mathbf{r}',E'')}{\Sigma_t(\mathbf{r}',E'')}\,f(E,E'',-\Omega,\Omega'')$$

$$\times \exp\left[-\int_0^{r'} \Sigma_t(\mathbf{r}''\,\Omega',E)\,dr''\right]\frac{\delta(\Omega',\Omega)}{(r')^2}$$

$$\times dr'\,dE''\,d\Omega''$$

$$(8.103)$$

The first term on the right of Eq. 8.103 is the contribution from the direct unscattered beam, Ψ_D, and the second term is the contribution from the scattered radiation, Ψ_s.

The function f in Ψ_s can be easily associated with the differential scattering cross section. If it is assumed that inelastic scattering can be neglected and if it is assumed there are m nuclear species in the transport medium with which the

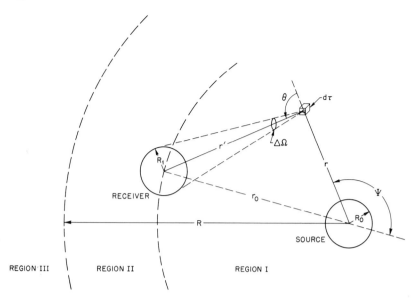

FIG. 8.49—Geometry of source and receiver for single scattering of radiation in air.

neutrons can make an elastic-scattering collision, then f is given by

$$f(E, E'', -\Omega, \Omega'') = \frac{\sum\limits_{n=1}^{m} \dfrac{d\Sigma_s^n(r', E'', -\Omega \cdot \Omega'', E')}{d\Omega}}{\Sigma_s^n(r', E'')} \delta(E' - E)$$

$$\times \frac{\Sigma_s^n(r', E'')}{\Sigma_s(r', E'')} \qquad (8.104)$$

where $\Sigma_s^n(r', E'') =$ the contribution to the macroscopic scattering cross section from the nth nuclear species at position r' and energy E''

$\Sigma_s(r', E'') =$ the total macroscopic scattering cross section at position r' and energy E''

$d\Sigma_s^n(r', E'', -\Omega \cdot \Omega'', E')/d\Omega =$ the differential macroscopic scattering cross section contributed by nth nuclear species at position r' for scattering from a direction Ω'' with energy E'' into a unit solid angle about direction $-\Omega$ with resultant energy E'

The ratio of the differential scattering cross section, $d\Sigma_s^n/d\Omega$, to the scattering cross section, Σ_s^n, for the nth nuclear species, assuming isotropic scattering, may be shown to be

$$\frac{d\Sigma_s^n(r', E'', -\Omega' \cdot \Omega'', E')/d\Omega}{\Sigma_s^n(r', E'')} = \frac{1}{4\pi A_n}\left[-2\Omega' \cdot \Omega'' + B \right.$$

$$\left. + \frac{(\Omega' \cdot \Omega'')^2}{B} \right]$$

$$(8.105)$$

where $A_n =$ the atomic weight of the nth nuclear species

$B = \left| \left[A_n^2 - 1 + (\Omega' \cdot \Omega'')^2 \right]^{\frac{1}{2}} \right|$

$E' = E'' \left[(-\Omega' \cdot \Omega'' + B)/(1 + A_n) \right]^2$

The exponential term in ϕ_s can be computed straight forward as

$$\exp\left[-\int_0^r \Sigma_t(r''\Omega', E)\, dr'' \right] = \exp\left[-\Sigma_t(E) |r| \right]$$

For the total flux incident on a detector located at the origin, ϕ_T (neutrons/cm²/sec), the expression for $\phi(0, E, \Omega)$, given by Eq. 8.103, must be integrated over all energies E that lie between the

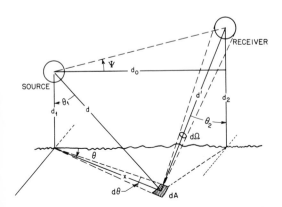

FIG. 8.50—Geometry of source and receiver for ground scattering of radiation.

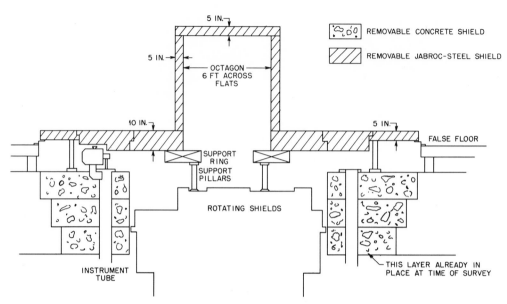

FIG. 8.51—Arrangement of removable shield system on top of the Dounreay fast reactor [79].

source energy and some cutoff energy and over all solid angles Ω,

$$\phi_T(\mathbf{r} = 0) = \int_{\Omega} \int_{E} \phi(0, E, \Omega) \, dE \, d\Omega$$

The results for a monoenergetic point source can also be integrated to make up any arbitrary source distribution in space and energy (Ref. 168).

The direct-beam term, Ψ_D, in Eq. 8.103 can be calculated directly. However, the integral term for

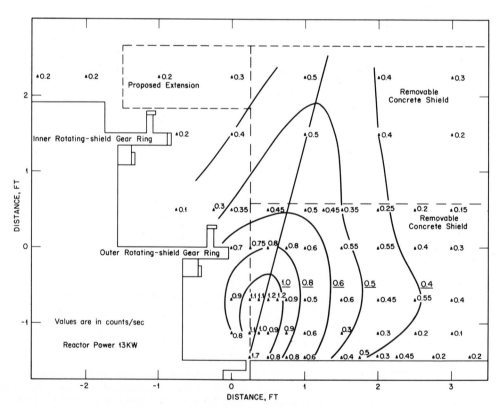

FIG. 8.52—Fast-neutron flux contours on top of Dounreay fast reactor [79].

the scattered radiation, Ψ_s, cannot be solved analytically. To evaluate this term, one must perform the integrations numerically. For this reason hand calculations are not usually practical unless simplifying approximations can be introduced[69]. The problem is usually programmed for an electronic computer. The method of solution usually used is to divide space up into a finite series of volume elements, each of which becomes a scattering source. The integrals of Eqs. 8.102 and 8.103 are replaced by appropriate summations. The computer calculates angles, directions, energy losses, distances, and attenuation values of the flux reaching the detector from each of these volume-element sources. Reference 72 describes a moments-method solution, and Refs. 67, 70, and 73 describe Monte Carlo solutions. Additional information on the scattering of neutrons in air will be found in Chap. 1 of Ref. 26 and on pp. 116-122 of Ref. 29.

8.8.2 GAMMA-RAY SCATTERING IN AIR
[68, 69]

8.8.2.1 Compton Scattering and the Klein-Nishina Formula

The main gamma-ray scattering process that occurs in the energy ranges usually encountered in shielding calculations is Compton (or incoherent) scattering (Ref. 23, pp. 117-122). In this process the orbital electrons around the nucleus interact with the gamma ray. The gamma-ray photon loses a definite amount of energy, according to the magnitude of the angle of scattering. The energy after scattering, a', of a photon of initial energy a'' which has scattered through the angle θ is

$$a' = \frac{a''}{1 + a''(1 - \cos\theta)} = \frac{a''}{1 + 2a''\sin^2(\theta/2)} \quad (8.106)$$

where a'' and a' are measured in units of mc^2:

$$a'' = h\nu/mc^2 \quad \text{(where } 1\ mc^2 = 0.51\ \text{Mev)}$$

and $h\nu$ is the energy of the gamma ray in ergs.

The Compton differential-scattering cross section per electron, $d\sigma_s/d\Omega$, is given by the Klein-Nishina formula

$$\left(\frac{d\sigma_s}{d\Omega}\right)_{\theta, a''} = \frac{d^2}{2}\left[\frac{1}{1 + 2a''\sin^2(\theta/2)}\right]^2 \left\{1 + \cos^2\theta \right.$$

$$\left. + \frac{[2a''\sin^2(\theta/2)]^2}{1 + 2a''\sin^2(\theta/2)}\right\} \quad \text{cm}^2/\text{electron}$$

$$(8.107)$$

where $(d\sigma_s/d\Omega)_{\theta, a''}$ = the probability per electron that a photon of initial energy a'' will be scattered through an angle θ into a solid angle $d\Omega$, cm^2/electron
$d = e^2/m_0 c^2$, the classical electron radius
= 2.82×10^{-13} cm

Equation 8.107 is derived for free electrons. This approximation is valid for bound electrons in a material if the loss in gamma-ray energy, $a'' - a'$, is large compared to the binding energy of an electron, i.e., for initial photon energies above about 200 kev* for scattering in air and light materials. For the macroscopic Compton differential-scattering cross section for a material, $d\Sigma_s/d\Omega$, Eq. 8.107 should be multiplied by the electron density, η, per cubic centimeter in the material.

$$(d\Sigma_s/d\Omega)_{\theta, a''} = \eta\,(d\sigma_s/d\Omega)_{\theta, a''} \quad \text{cm}^{-1}$$

where $\eta = 6.03 \times 10^{23}\rho(Z/A)$, electrons/cm^3
ρ = density of the scattering material, g/cm^3
Z = atomic number of the scattering material
A = atomic weight of the scattering material

8.8.2.2 Transport-equation Solutions

Air scattering of gamma rays may be described in terms of the Boltzmann transport equation whose solution follows that given by Eq. 8.102. In this application the quantity Σ_t of Eq. 8.102 is replaced by μ, the total gamma-ray absorption coefficient; and $d\Sigma_s/d\Omega$ is replaced by $\eta\,d\sigma_s/d\Omega$, where η is the electron density in the material (electrons/cm^3) and where $d\sigma_s/d\Omega$ is given by Eq. 8.107. Discussions of transport solutions may be found in Ref. 74.

8.8.2.3 Approximate Solution (After Plesset) [69]

If a number of simplifications are made, a solution of the air-scattering problem can be arrived at on the basis of Lambert's law (Sec. 8.6.3). Here isotropic emission is assumed. Let S_0 be the isotropic source strength (photons/sec) of a source located a distance r_0 from the detector. All photons are assumed to have energy E_0. The source is assumed spherical and has a radius R_0. The nondirectional detector has a radius R_1. The scattered flux of gamma radiation received at the detector (Fig. 8.49) from all elements of volume in air at a distance r from the source and r' from the detector is given by

$$\Gamma_s(r', a') = \frac{S_0\,\eta\,B(\mu'r')}{2}$$

$$\times \int_{R_0}^{\infty}\int_0^{\pi} \frac{\exp\left\{-[\mu(a'')r + \mu'(a')r']\right\}}{r'^2}$$

$$\times \left(\frac{d\sigma_s}{d\Omega}\right)_{\theta, a''} d\Omega\, dr\, \sin\Psi\, d\Psi \quad (8.108)$$

where

η = the electron density of the air, electrons/cm^3
$\mu(a'')$ = the linear-absorption coefficient of the initial gamma-ray energy in air

* This equation is valid for all energies in hydrogen. For high-z materials coherent scattering is important, and the Klein–Nishina formula is not valid below about 0.6 Mev for iron, 1.0 Mev for lead, and 3.0 Mev for uranium.

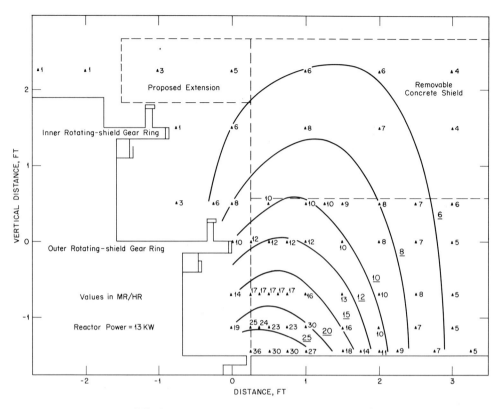

FIG. 8.53—Gamma-flux contours on top of Dounreay fast reactor [79].

$\mu'(a')$ = the linear-absorption coefficient for the scattered gamma-ray energy

a'', a' = the energies of the initial and scattered gamma rays, respectively, expressed in units of mc^2

$(d\sigma_s/d\Omega)_{\theta,\,a''}$ = the differential scattering cross section for given energy and scattering angle

$B(\mu'r')$ = the buildup term accounting for multiple scattering

Ψ = the original angle of emission with respect to the source-receiver axis (see Fig. 8.49)

The value of $d\sigma_s/d\Omega$ is given by the Klein–Nishina differential scattering formula (Eq. 8.107). The relation between r and r' is given by

$$r'^2 = r_0^2 + r^2 + 2rr_0 \cos\Psi \qquad (8.109)$$

An analytic solution to Eq. 8.108 is not possible. Numerical methods are used. In one method all space is divided into a large number of volume elements; the distances r and r' and the angles Ψ and θ are computed for each volume element. From these values the scattering cross section for each volume element $d\sigma_s/d\Omega$ is evaluated, and the energy degradation for each scattering angle is computed. From these values μ and μ' are found, and the flux contributions from each volume element are deter-

mined. The total flux is then found by adding in the direct component

$$\Gamma_{\text{dir}} = \frac{S_0\,\eta\,\exp\left[-\mu(a'')(r_0 - R_0)\right]}{4\pi(r_0 - R_0)^2} \qquad (8.110)$$

An analytic approximation for the solution to Eq. 8.108 which will yield an order-of-magnitude estimate in air can be found as follows: Divide space into three regions about the source. Region I consists of all scattering volume elements at distance r_1 within a sphere of radius r_0 drawn about the source such that $r_1 < r_0$. Next, a sphere of radius R is drawn about the source (see Fig. 8.49) such that

$$R > r_0$$
$$\exp(-\mu'R) \geqq 0.5 \qquad (8.111)$$

for all μ' at radius R. Region II consists of all those volume elements at distance r_2 located between spheres such that $r_0 \leqq r_2 \leqq R$. Region III consists of all those volume elements $r_3 > R$ outside the sphere of radius R. The total scattered flux, Γ_s, is then the sum of the scattered components

$$\Gamma_s = \Gamma_{\text{I}} + \Gamma_{\text{II}} + \Gamma_{\text{III}}$$

8.8.2.3.1 REGION I. In region I the scattered flux is assumed to come predominantly from scattering at angles between $\pi/2$ and $\pi/8$; thus the value of $d\sigma_s/d\Omega$ can conservatively be chosen at $\pi/4$ and $\pi/8$ to represent scattering in the whole region.* The contribution from region I is thus

$$
\Gamma_I = \frac{S_0\,\eta}{r_0}\left(\frac{d\sigma_s}{d\Omega}\bigg|_{\alpha'',\,\pi/4}\left\{\frac{\pi^2}{8} - \left[\sum_1^n \frac{1}{(2n-1)^2}\left(\frac{R_0}{r_0}\right)^{2n-1}\right]\right\}\right.
$$

$$
+ \frac{d\sigma_s}{d\Omega}\bigg|_{\alpha'',\,\pi/8}\left\{0.3471 - \left[\frac{0.293\,r_0}{r_0 + R_0}\right]\right.
$$

$$
+ \frac{0.0429\,r_0^2\,(3R_0 + r_0)}{(r_0 + R_0)^3}
$$

$$
\left.\left.+ \frac{0.0112\,r_0^3\left(2R_0^2 - 5R_0 r_0 + r_0^2\right)}{(r_0 + R_0)^5}\right]\right\}\right)
$$

$$
\text{photons/cm}^2\text{/sec} \qquad (8.112)
$$

The dominant energy of the scattered radiation is given by

$$
\alpha' = \alpha''/(1 + 0.293\,\alpha'') \quad \text{(units of } mc^2) \quad (8.113)
$$

8.8.2.3.2 REGION II. In region II the major portion of the radiation reaching the detector comes from scattering near the angle $\pi/2$. Therefore the value of $d\sigma_s/d\Omega$ evaluated at $\pi/2$ may be conservatively used to represent scattering from the region. In this event the radiation flux reaching the detector is

$$
\Gamma_{II} = \frac{S_0\,\eta}{r_0}\left(\frac{d\sigma_s}{d\Omega}\right)_{\pi/2,\,\alpha''}\left\{\frac{\pi^2}{8} - \left[\sum_1^\infty \frac{1}{(2n-1)^2}\left(\frac{r_0}{R}\right)^{2n-1}\right]\right\}
$$

$$
(8.114)
$$

with the dominant energy of scattered radiation given by

$$
\alpha' = \alpha''/(1 + \alpha'') \quad \text{(units of } mc^2) \quad (8.115)
$$

8.8.2.3.3 REGION III. In the outer region all the radiation is assumed to be scattered through the angle π to reach the detector. In this event $r' \cong r$, and the scattered radiation reaching the detector from this region is given by

$$
\Gamma_{III} = \frac{S_0\,\eta}{2R}\left(\frac{d\sigma_s}{d\Omega}\right)_{\pi,\,\alpha''} E_2(\gamma R) \qquad (8.116)
$$

where $E_2(\gamma R)$ is an exponential integral defined in Sec. 8.21.2 and where

$$
\gamma = (\mu + \mu') \quad \text{cm}^{-1} \qquad (8.117)
$$

The predominant energy of the scattered radiation is given by

$$
\alpha' = \alpha''/(1 + 2\alpha'') \quad \text{(units of } mc^2) \qquad (8.118)
$$

---

*Plesset ignores the contribution from scattering angles less than $\pi/4$, assuming in his problem that a shield would remove this contribution. The second term in the large parentheses of Eq. 8.112 represents this contribution, developed using Plesset's method. Here the dominant scattering angle was assumed to be near $\pi/8$.

Equations 8.110, 8.112, 8.114, and 8.116 must be summed to obtain the total flux reaching the detector. Note that in these equations no buildup is used on the scattered beam to account for multiple scattering. These calculations are sufficiently conservative that a buildup function need not be included.

It should also be noted that the scattering from the various elemental components making up air should be summed over all components to yield the total radiation at the detector.

8.8.2.4 Importance of Multiply Scattered Radiation

Radiation reaching the detector which has traveled more than one mean free path in air from the first scattering center will have a high probability of being scattered more than once [69]. This multiply scattered radiation will affect the intensity at the detector if the source-detector distance is large compared with radius R defined by Eq. 8.111. At very large distances the multiply scattered component becomes dominant. For $r_0 > R$ an approximate solution may be found by the method outlined on pp. 318 and 319 of Ref. 18. Rigorous transport-equation solutions and Monte Carlo methods have multiple-scattering effects automatically incorporated into their solutions.

8.8.3 GROUND AND STRUCTURE SCATTERING OF NEUTRONS AND NEUTRON ALBEDO

8.8.3.1 Neutron Albedo or Reflection Coefficients

The common method of treating neutron scattering from a surface involves the use of a reflection coefficient or albedo, which is either the ratio of the reflected flux to the incident flux or the ratio of the reflected energy or dose to the incident energy or dose. Flux albedos are also called number albedos. Number albedos are given by Eqs. 8.50 and 8.51. Bethe [75] shows the reflection coefficient a for neutrons incident normal to a surface to be given by

$$
a = \Sigma_s\left[2\Sigma_a + \Sigma_s + 2\sqrt{\Sigma_a(\Sigma_s + \Sigma_a)}\right]^{-1} \quad (8.119)
$$

Fermi [76] shows that for thermal neutrons incident at an angle θ with the normal upon a semi-infinite slab the reflection coefficient is given by

$$
a_{\text{th}} = \left[\sqrt{(\Sigma_t/\Sigma_s)} - 1\right]\left[\sqrt{(\Sigma_t/\Sigma_s)} + \sqrt{3}\cos\theta\right]^{-1} \quad (8.120)
$$

The energy albedo a_E is shown by Plesset [69] for neutrons incident normal to weakly absorbing media to be given by

$$
a_E = \left[1 + (m/M) + \sqrt{(2m/M)}\right]^{-1} \quad (m \ll M) \quad (8.121)
$$

and by

$$
a_E = \left[1 + P(m/M) + \sqrt{P^2(m/M)^2 + 2P(m/M)}\right]^{-1} \quad (8.122)
$$

Table 8.10–Characteristics of Some Important Spontaneous-fission Neutron Sources [22]

Source	Half-life (spontaneous fission)	Half-life (alpha decay)	Alphas per fission	Neutrons per fission	Neutrons/sec/g
U^{232}	$8 \times 10^{13} y$	$74 y$	1.1×10^{12} 6.5×10^{12} after aging. With 1.9-year half-life		
Pu^{236}	$3.5 \times 10^9 y$	$2.7 y$	1.3×10^9	1.9	3.1×10^4
U^{238}	$8.3 \times 10^{15} y$	$4.51 \times 10^9 y$	1.8×10^6		
Pu^{238}	$4.9 \times 10^{10} y$	$89.6 y$	5.5×10^8	2.0	2.3×10^3
Pu^{240}	$1.3 \times 10^{11} y$	$6600 y$	1.9×10^7	2.1	7.0×10^2
Pu^{242}	$7.2 \times 10^{10} y$	$3.8 \times 10^5 y$	1.9×10^5	2.3	1.8×10^9
Cm^{242}	$8.2 \times 10^6 y$	$162.5 d$	1.6×10^7	2.3	1.0×10^7
Cm^{244}	$1.4 \times 10^7 y$	$18.4 y$	7.6×10^5	2.6	2.6×10^{12}
Cf^{252}	$66 y$	$2.2 y$	30		
Cf^{254}	$60 d$	$60 d$	0	3.5	

where m = mass of the neutron
M = isotropic mass of scattering medium

$$P = [1 + (m/M)]^2 [1 - (m/M)]^{-1} \qquad (8.123)$$

Experimental values of the neutron-dose albedos [77] for concrete and water are: water, 0.08; concrete, 0.12. The number albedo for neutrons usually falls in the range 0.4 to 0.7. Reference 65, p. 277, reports a value of 0.675 for Pu–Be neutrons scattered from concrete.

8.8.3.2 *Flux of Ground-scattered Radiation Reaching Detector*

The flux ϕ_g of neutrons reaching the detector after being scattered by the ground (or a surface) can be computed by a method similar to that of Plesset [69]. A detector located at a height d_2 above the ground (Fig. 8.50) receives ground-scattered neutrons from a source emitting S_0 neutrons/sec placed at a height d_1 above the ground and at a projected distance d_0 from the detector. If the source is assumed to be point isotropic, then the ground-scattered flux ϕ_g is calculated as follows:

$$\phi_g = \frac{aS_0 d_1}{8\pi^2}$$

$$\times \int_0^\infty \int_0^{2\pi} \frac{x\,dx\,d\theta}{(d_1^2+x^2)^{3/2}(x^2+d_0^2 \sec^2 \Psi + 2d_0 x \sec \Psi \cos\theta + x^2 + d_2^2)}$$

$$\text{neutrons/cm}^2/\text{sec} \qquad (8.124)$$

where a = number albedo for the ground material
x = distance on scattering plane from perpendicular projection of source location to reflecting area $x\,dx\,d\theta$, cm
θ = polar angle of the scattering element from the source–detector axis
$\Psi = \tan^{-1}[(d_2 - d_1)/d_0]$ = constant

This integral may be evaluated by numerical integration techniques. Scattering from a finite surface may be found by converting the scattering area to an equivalent disk of radius R and replacing the infinite upper limit on the first integral sign in Eq. 8.124 by the limit R.

The energy flux, ϕ_E (Mev/sec/cm2), reaching the detector may be found by (1) replacing the source S_0 by its energy equivalent $S_0 E_n$, where E_n is the kinetic energy (Mev/neutron), and (2) by replacing a by a_E (Eq. 8.121).

8.8.3.3 *Approximate Method for Calculating Neutron Scattering from a Finite Surface*

Given a scattering surface of area A, at a distance d (Fig. 8.50) from a source emitting S_0 neutrons/sec, if the square of the distance from the scattering surface to the source is large compared with the scattering area, then the total number of neutrons reaching A is

$$J \cong (S_0 A \cos\theta_1)/(4\pi d^2) \quad \text{neutrons/sec} \qquad (8.125)$$

where θ_1 is the angle of incidence from the normal.

If the scatterer has a thickness z, the total number of scattering events within it (assuming isotropic scattering) is given by

$$N_1 \cong J\Sigma_s \int_0^z \exp(-x'/\lambda)\,dx' = J\Sigma_s \lambda[1 - \exp(-z/\lambda)]$$

$$\text{neutrons/sec} \qquad (8.126)$$

where x' = depth into material from scattering surface, cm, Σ_s = macroscopic scattering cross section, cm^{-1}, and λ = relaxation length of neutrons in the scatterer, cm. Conservatively, all the scattered neutrons emerge from the scatterer. N_1 then represents the total scattering source. The detector is located at a distance d' from the scattering source (this distance is large compared with the largest dimension of the scatterer); then the scattered flux reaching the detector is simply

$$\phi_{\text{scatt}} \cong N/4\pi d'^2) \quad \text{neutrons/cm}^2/\text{sec} \qquad (8.127)$$

If the detection point is near the scattering surface, the scattering surface may be thought of as a radiating source of radius $R = \sqrt{(A/\pi)}$ with a specific unit surface strength $N_s = N_1/A$ neutrons/cm^2/sec. The flux reaching the detector is then

$$\phi_{scatt} = \frac{N_s \cos\theta_2}{2} \ln\left[\sqrt{1 + (R/d')^2}\right] \quad \text{neutrons/cm}^2/\text{sec}$$

(8.128)

where θ_2 is the reflected angle, measured from the normal.

8.8.4 GROUND AND STRUCTURE SCATTERING OF GAMMA RAYS AND GAMMA-RAY ALBEDO

8.8.4.1 Reflection Coefficients for Gamma Rays

When a beam of gamma rays strikes a material surface, a certain amount of energy from the beam is transferred to the medium; the remainder is either transmitted through the medium or reflected back from the surface. The energy-reflection coefficient, R_E, for gamma rays is defined as

$$R_E = \Gamma_s E_s / \Gamma_i E_i \quad (8.129)$$

evaluated at the surface. The number-reflection coefficient is given by

$$R_n = \Gamma_s / \Gamma_i \quad (8.130)$$

where $\Gamma_s E_s$ is the energy flux of the scattered beam, $\Gamma_i E_i$ is the energy flux of the incident beam, Γ_s is the scattered-gamma flux, and Γ_i is the incident-gamma flux. Plesset [69] shows that, if the backscattered intensity is due mainly to single scattering, these quantities become

$$R_E = \pi d^2 \int_0^{-1} \frac{1}{[1 + a_0(1 - \mu)]^3}$$

$$\times \left\{ 1 + \mu^2 + \frac{[a_0(1 - \mu)]^2}{1 + a_0(1 - \mu)} \right\} \frac{\mu \, d\mu}{[\sigma(a_1) - \sigma(a_0)\mu]}$$

(8.131)

$$R_N = \pi d^2 \int_0^{-1} \frac{1}{[1 + a_0(1 - \mu)]^2}$$

$$\times \left\{ 1 + \mu^2 + \frac{[a_0(1 - \mu)]^2}{1 + a_0(1 - \mu)} \right\} \frac{\mu \, d\mu}{[\sigma(a_1) - \sigma(a_0)\mu]}$$

(8.132)

where $\mu = \cos\theta$, where θ = angle of scattering
  a_0 = the incident-gamma-ray energy, units of mc^2
  a_1 = the average energy of the backscattered gamma rays
  $\sigma(a_0)$ = the Compton scattering cross section at energy a_0, cm^2/electron
  $\sigma(a_1)$ = the Compton scattering cross section at energy a_1, cm^2/electron
  d = the classical electron radius, e^2/mc^2, cm

These integrals can be evaluated numerically. Gamma-ray albedos, or reflection coefficients, have been measured experimentally [77]. A value of the dose albedo for Co^{60} gamma rays reflected off concrete has been measured to be 0.04. This corresponds to a number albedo of 0.2 and to an energy albedo of about 0.03. Calculated values for the energy albedo for gamma rays reflected at various angles from iron as a function of the incident angle are given in Ref. 78.

8.8.4.2 Calculation of Ground and Structure Scattering

An accurate calculation of ground-scattered radiation can be made with Eq. 8.124, the value of a being calculated according to Eq. 8.132. The quantity ϕ_g in this case is the particle flux of gamma photons. This can be converted into energy or dose quantities if appropriate conversions are used.

A simplified approach to the calculation of the gamma radiation scattered from a thin finite scatterer is given in Ref. 29. If multiple scattering is neglected, the photon flux reaching a point at a distance d_2 from the scattering surface after scattering through the angle θ is given by

$$\phi_{scatt} = [S_0 \eta A z \sigma(\theta)] [4\pi r^2 (d')^2]^{-1} \quad \text{gammas/cm}^2/\text{sec}$$

(8.133)

where S_0 = source emission rate, gammas/sec
  η = electron density in scatterer, electrons/cm^3
  A = surface area of scatterer [small compared to r^2 and $(d')^2$]
  z = thickness of scatterer (less than one gamma-ray relaxation length)
  $\sigma(\theta)$ = differential cross section for Compton scattering through angle θ
  r = distance of scatterer from source
  d' = distance of scatterer from detector

8.9 Material Activation

8.9.1 THIN MATERIALS

A thin material containing N_i atoms/cm^3 of the ith kind when placed in a neutron flux ϕ_{oj} of energy j will have a rate of formation of corresponding radioactive atoms, $d\eta_{ij}/dt$, according to the basic law

$$d\eta_{ij}/dt = \Sigma_{cij}\phi_{oj} - \eta_{ij}\lambda_i \quad (8.134)$$

where η_{ij} = the number of radioactive atoms per cubic centimeter responding to the isotope i and energy j
  Σ_{cij} = the macroscopic neutron-capture cross section for isotope i in the material and energy j, cm^{-1}, = $N_i \sigma_{cij}$
  λ_i = the radioactive decay constant, sec^{-1}, for the radioactive atoms η_{ij}
  ϕ_{oj} = incident-neutron flux of energy j, neutrons/cm^2/sec

After a time t_1 in a constant flux ϕ_0 and at a time t_2 after the end of the irradiation period, the number of radioactive nuclei per cubic centimeter formed is

$$\eta_{ij}(t) = (\Sigma_{cij}\phi_{oj}/\lambda_i)[1 - \exp(-\lambda_i t_1)]\exp(-\lambda_i t_2)$$

$$\text{atoms/cm}^3 \quad (8.135)$$

The equilibrium (or saturated) activity after infinite reactor operating time at $t_2 = 0$ is given by

$$\eta_{ij}(\text{sat}) = \Sigma_{ij}\phi_{oj}/\lambda_i \quad \text{atoms/cm}^3 \quad (8.136)$$

The rate of radioactive decay of the radioactive isotope is just $\eta_{ij}\lambda_i$ dis/sec/cm^3, and the specific curie activity is

$$S_{Vcij}(t) = \eta_{ij}(t)\lambda_i/3.7 \times 10^{10} \quad \text{curies/cm}^3 \quad (8.137)$$

The value of Σ_{cij} may be calculated from

$$\Sigma_{cij} = N_0\sigma_{ij}\rho_i/A_i \quad \text{cm}^{-1} \quad (8.138)$$

where σ_{ij} = the microscopic cross section at energy j of the ith kind of atom, cm^2/atom
N_0 = Avogadro's number, atoms/mole
ρ_i = density of the ith kind of isotope in the total material, g/cm^3
A_i = the atomic weight of the ith atom

The total activity in the material after time t summed over all isotopes, materials, and energies is

$$S_{Vc}(t) = \sum_{ij} S_{Vcij}(t) \quad \text{curies/cm}^3 \quad (8.139)$$

8.9.2 THICK MATERIALS

For thick materials the neutron flux at any point x in the material can be assumed to be

$$\phi_j(x) = \phi_{oj}\exp(-\kappa x) \quad \text{neutrons/cm}^2/\text{sec} \quad (8.140)$$

where κ is the characteristic neutron-attenuation coefficient of the material. In thick materials the activation in various parts of the material varies with the flux in the material. The average activation requires an averaging of the flux over the material thickness x, with the aid of Eq. 8.140.

$$\overline{\phi}_j = (\phi_{oj}/x)\int_0^x e^{-\kappa x'}dx' = \frac{\phi_{oj}}{\kappa x}(1 - e^{-\kappa x})$$

$$\text{neutrons/cm}^2/\text{sec} \quad (8.141)$$

8.9.3 MATERIAL ACTIVATION IN FAST REACTORS

Exact evaluation of the induced activity in materials within and around a fast reactor is made difficult because (1) the energy distribution of the neutrons within the materials is often not well known and (2) the cross sections for activation of

the material for all the energy regions j are not well known. The most accurate method to evaluate induced activity is to use the results of multigroup transport or diffusion theory problems for the flux values. Make certain the best available cross sections have been used in the problem. For an energy region ΔE, the total flux ϕ_j in the region is given by

$$\phi_j = \int_{\Delta E} \phi_j(E)\,dE \quad \text{neutrons/cm}^2/\text{sec} \quad (8.142)$$

where $\phi_j(E)$ is the flux per unit energy. A similar equation is used when $\phi_j(\mu)$ is the flux per unit lethargy. The integration is then over the lethargy range Δu.

8.10 Shield Test Programs for Fast Reactors

8.10.1 PURPOSE OF A SHIELD TEST PROGRAM

The correct evaluation of the safety and performance of a reactor and its auxiliary systems can only be made by testing. Moreover, it is only through testing that ideas for improving the concept or design arise. The shield systems for each area of a reactor plant are usually designed with both safety and economy in mind. How well the shield designer has succeeded can only be ascertained through testing the performance of the shields.

Some of the detailed purposes of a shield test program are (1) to check the condition of each shield as built to ensure that no large voids, cracks, or imperfections are contained within it, (2) to determine, as needed, radiation levels and energy spectra within and outside shields during operating and shutdown conditions of the reactor, (3) to determine the nuclear performance of critical shields within special areas of the reactor plant to evaluate their shield adequacy, (4) to verify by measurements the calculations that determined the size and material of the shields, and (5) to test the shield design at annular gaps around pipes and plugs and at other void spaces through which radiation might leak.

8.10.2 TYPICAL SHIELD TEST PROGRAM

The test program should cover all the shields in the reactor plant. It can be separated into a program for shields within and around the reactor building and a program for the shields for auxiliary buildings and equipment.

8.10.2.1 Types of Measurements

The tests should include, as appropriate, the following types of measurements: neutron-flux measurements, neutron-energy-spectra measurements, gamma-ray dose-rate measurements, and gamma-ray spectral measurements. The neutron-

Table 8.11–Photoneutron Sources [22]

Sources	Half-life	Gamma energy, Mev	Neutron energy, Mev	Standard yield, 10^4 neutrons/sec/g
Na^{24} + Be	15.1 h	2.76	0.83	13
Na^{24} + D_2O	15.1 h	2.76	0.22	27
Ga^{72} + Be	14.1 h	1.87, 2.21, 2.51	(0.78)	5
Y^{88} + Be	87 d	1.9, 2.8	0.158 ± 0.005	10
In^{116} + Be	54 m	1.8, 2.1	0.30	0.82
Sb^{124} + Be	60 d	1.7	0.024 ± 0.003	19
La^{140} + Be	40 d	2.50	0.62	0.3
RdTh + D_2O	1.90 y	2.62 (ThC")	0.197 ± 0.010	9.5
MsTh + Be	6.7 y	1.80, 2.62	0.827 ± 0.030	3.5
MsTh + D_2O	6.7 y	2.62 (ThC")	0.197 ± 0.010	9.5
Ra + Be	1622 y	1.69, 1.75, 1.82, 2.09, 2.20, 2.42	0.7 max.	3.0
Ra + D_2O	1622 y	2.42	0.1	0.1

flux measurements should include measurements for fast neutrons, resonant and epithermal neutrons, and thermal neutrons. Subsequent analysis of the data requires that careful calibration techniques be used.

Thermal-neutron measurements may be taken by one or all of the following techniques where applicable: gold foil measurements, 2.7-day half-life; indium foil measurements, 54-min half-life; U^{235} foil measurements; BF_3 proportional-counter measurements; U^{235} fission-counter measurements; and other techniques, such as cadmium ratios.

Resonance- and epithermal-neutron measurements may be made by covering thermal detectors with appropriate layers of cadmium, B^{10}, or other strong thermal-neutron absorbers.

Threshold detectors may be used to aid in determining neutron spectra. Threshold detectors are foils or counters that respond only to neutrons above a certain threshold energy. For example, a fast-fission (or U^{238}) counter responds effectively only to neutrons that have energies above 1.5 Mev. Threshold measurements may be made with the following detectors: Pu^{240}, 0.5 Mev and above; P^{31}, 1.0 Mev and above; U^{238}, 1.5 Mev and above; S^{32}, 3 Mev and above; Al^{27}, 5 Mev and above; Mg^{24}, 6 Mev and above; and U^{234}, 0.3 Mev and above.

Accurate gamma-ray measurements may be made with a calibrated scintillation detector or ionization chamber mounted on a device for holding it in the desired location. Associated electronic gear may be mounted on a portable cart. For some of the tests, portable health physics survey instruments may provide sufficient accuracy. A gamma-ray spectral analysis at each point of measurement may be made by feeding the scintillation detector output signal into a multichannel analyzer. The decision as to whether to use a scintillation detector, ionization chamber, or a portable instrument depends mainly on the use to which the results of the measurements are to be put. A simple "go" or "no-go" type answer does not require complicated instrumentation or experimental procedures. Any contemplated analytic use of the data in checking the actual performance of the shield, however, requires careful procedures and the best possible measurements and measuring devices.

Table 8.12–(α, n) Reaction Sources [22]

Sources	Half-life	Maximum neutron energy, Mev	Average neutron energy, Mev	Yield per curie, 10^6 neutrons/sec
Po^{210}-Li	138.40 d	1.32	0.48	0.05
Po^{210}-Be	138.40 d	10.87	4.2	2.5
RaDEF-Ge	19.4 y	10.87	4.5	2.5
Ra-Be	1622 y	13.08	3.9	15
Em^{222}-Be	3.825 d	13.08		15
Pu^{239}-Be	24,400 y	10.74	4.5	0.064 (per g)
Ac^{227}-Be	21.8 y	12.79	4.6	
Po^{208}-Be	2.93 y	10.71		
$RaBeF_4$	1622 y	13.08		2.53
Po^{210}-B	138.40 d	B^{10} 6.29, B^{11} 4.48		0.6
Ra-B	1622 y	B^{10} 8.58, B^{11} 7.25		7
Po^{210}-F	138.40 d	2.8	1.4	0.2
Po^{210}-Na	138.40 d	4.45		0.04
Am^{241}-Be	462 y			
Cm^{242}-Be	162.5 d			
Mock fission	138.40 d	10.87	1.6	0.4

Table 8.13—Threshold Detectors [22]

Detector	Reaction	Product	Half-life	Approximate threshold energy, Mev	Effective reaction cross sections for fission neutrons, mb
Np^{237}	(n,f)	Many	Many	0.2	1450
In^{115}	$(n,n'\gamma)$	In^{115m}	4.5 h	0.45	~300
Ba^{137}	$(n,n'\gamma)$	Ba^{137m}	2.6 m	0.60	~60
U^{238}	(n,f)	Many	Many	0.7	590
Th^{232}	(n,f)	Many	Many	1.3	140
S^{32}	(n,p)	P^{32}	14.3 d	1.7	285
P^{31}	(n,p)	Si^{31}	2.6 h	1.8	120
Al^{27}	(n,p)	Mg^{27}	10 m	2.6	25
Si^{28}	(n,p)	Al^{28}	2.27 m	4.4	45
Fe^{56}	(n,p)	Mn^{56}	2.6 h	5.0	18.5
Mg^{24}	(n,p)	Na^{24}	15.06 h	6.3	39
Al^{27}	(n,α)	Na^{24}	15.06 h	6.5	0.6
Cu^{63}	$(n,2n)$	Cu^{62}	10 m	11.4	20
C^{12}	$(n,2n)$	C^{11}	20.5 m	20	6

8.10.2.2 Tests Within the Reactor Building

Shield tests within the reactor building may be separated into the following categories according to the reactor power available: preoperational tests (zero power), low-power tests (0 to 0.01% of operating power), intermediate-power tests (0.01 to 10% of power), high-power tests (10 to 100% of power).

The preoperational tests can be conducted with small portable neutron and gamma sources. The source strength depends on the thickness and type of shield to be tested. Tests include: (1) measurement of the integrity of shield walls (concrete shield walls in particular), (2) measurement of the effectiveness of shield walls against neutrons, and (3) gross check on the adequacy of shielding of gaps and annuli through shield walls (penetrations).

The low-power tests primarily check radiation distributions within the reactor and shield. They are an indispensable aid to the proper evaluation of shield performance. The following neutron-flux measurements can be made within the reactor: within the core, within the blanket, and within the coolant channels. These measurements require special fuel and blanket subassemblies designed

Table 8.14—Special Materials Used in Fast Reactor Shields [22]

Material	Reactor plant	Use	Special property
Uranium	Fermi	Cask-car shield for spent fuel subassemblies	Dense enough for use in restricted space
Boron carbide	EBR-I	Top-access-hole shield	Efficient neutron absorption
Permali (Jabroc)	DFR	Top shield	Effective hydrogen shield
Steel imbedded in graphite	EBR-II	Rotating plug	Increased X-ray attenuation with neutron thermalization
Boron steel	EBR-II	Heat-exchanger shield	Thermal-flux depressant to prevent secondary sodium activation
Boron steel	Fermi	Rotating plug, operating floor	In rotating plug, reduces streaming near access penetrations; in floor used in certain areas near annuli for increased neutron shielding effectiveness
Iron oxide	PFFBR	Main heat-absorbing shield	Fairly cheap, can take high temperature differentials
Steel and paraffin	BR-5	Neutron and gamma shield above rotating plug	Effective combination shield to catch streaming fluxes around plug
Calcium borate	Fermi	Primary sodium pipe shields	Can take high temperatures, also has some insulating property
Serpentine aggregate	Fermi	Stationary plugs in operating floor	Does not lose water at high temperature
Serpentine concrete	Fermi	Operating floor in high-temperature areas	Serpentine retains its water content at high temperatures
Resilon	DFR	Rotating plug	Effective neutron absorber and is radiation resistant

Table 8.15—Typical Shield Material Costs (1962) [22]

Material	Unit	Material cost per unit, $	Fabricated cost per unit, $	Installed cost per unit, $
Concrete, ordinary	1 cu yd	14.00		115.00
Concrete, magnetite	1 cu yd	100.00		270.00
Concrete, ferrophosphorus	1 cu yd	200.00		300.00
Concrete, limonite	1 cu yd	110.00		100.00
Concrete, barytes	1 cu yd	130.00		295.00
Concrete, serpentine	1 cu yd	20.00		125.00
Concrete blocks, solid	1 block (8 in. × 8 in. × 12 in.)	1.09		
Serpentine aggregate	1 ton	35.00		60.00
B^{10}, elemental	1 g	6.50		
Boron carbide*	1 lb	7.00		
Carbon steel, plate	1 ton	160.00	350	
Stainless steel	1 ton	1000.00	1500	
Boron steel[†]	1 ton	1750.00	1250	
Boron stainless steel[†]	1 ton	2500.00	3000-5000	
Boral[‡]	1 sq ft × $\frac{1}{4}$ in.	12.00		
Paraffin	1 lb	0.10		
Calcium borate (Sigma K)	1 lb	0.55		0.67
Lead	1 lb	0.45	1	
Graphite, plain, reactor grade	1 cu ft	92.00		
Graphite, borated, reactor grade	1 cu ft	1% B, 140.00 5% B, 207.00		
Shot, plain steel	1 ton	460.00		
Shot, borated steel[†]	1 ton	1500.00		
Lead-filled epoxy resin	1 lb	4.00		
Sand; trap rock	1 cu yd	2.00		
Earth fill	1 cu yd	0.72		
Ferroboron	1 lb	0.85		
Masonite	1 sheet (4 ft × 8 ft × $\frac{1}{2}$ in.)	10.00		

* Reactor grade. Commercial grade costs about $3.50/lb.

[†] Prices of boron steel and boron stainless steel are high because they include the cost of cleaning and relining the furnace after filling the order for boron steel. Most U.S. suppliers will only sell boron steel in furnace lots.

[‡] This price includes only 16 to 30% B_4C in an aluminum matrix sandwiched between two sheets of aluminum.

and built for holding foils and for sampling, and they may require experimental tubes designed and built into the reactor vessel. The following neutron-flux measurements can be made outside the reactor vessel: at reactor—shield interface, if possible; above vessel plug; and within detector tubes above the top shield.

The intermediate-power tests check the radiation leakage through the primary reactor shields, and, together with the lower-power tests, are needed in the shield performance evaluation. At the same time an evaluation of the performance of reactor regulating and safety detectors can be made. Any defects in the primary shield system

Table 8.16—Concrete Costs at the MTR*

Description	Unit	Average unit costs of materials, $			
		1953 (actual)		1962 (estimated)[†‡]	
		Direct	Total	Direct	Total
Ordinary concrete building foundations	1 cu yd	119.82	199.47	198	329
Ordinary concrete walls	1 cu yd	97.16	170.34	160	281
Barytes concrete shield	1 cu yd				
Conventional pour		142.41	193.25	235	319
Prepacked method		150.58	188.41	248	311
Average costs		147.74	190.09	244	315
Ordinary concrete, average of all types of pours	1 cu yd	80.71	141.03	133	233
Barytes shielding blocks	1 block[§]	2.17		3.58	

* Cost data from H. A. Ohlgren, Ref. 82.

[†] Estimated from data in Ref. 83.

[‡] Private communication, V. Lomuller, Atomic Power Development Associates.

[§] Block size: 4 in. × 8 in. × 16 in. Price includes materials, manufacturing, and delivery.

Table 8.17—Cost of Shielding Items Incurred at the Enrico Fermi Atomic Power Plant
(Courtesy Power Reactor Development Company)

Item	Unit	Unit cost, $	Total costs, $		
			Direct*	Indirect†	Total‡
Reactor-building operating-floor slab:					
Concrete	1 cu yd	30.00	19,500	1,560	21,060
Reinforcing steel	1 ton	350.00	17,500	1,400	18,900
Steel-plate shielding	1 ton	500.00	225,000	18,025	243,025
Total costs			262,000	20,985	282,985
Secondary shield wall:					
Prepacked concrete	1 cu yd	45.00	84,000	6,730	90,730
Reinforcing steel	1 ton	365.00	29,200	2,340	31,540
Shield wall plates and pipe sleeves	1 ton	800.00	200,000	16,020	216,020
Miscellaneous			8,000	640	8,640
Total			321,200	25,730	346,930
Primary shield (graphite):					
Graphite, plain and borated§	1 cu ft	153.00	1,375,000	103,000	1,478,000
Graphite, installation	1 cu ft	57.00	513,000	39,000	552,000
Miscellaneous labor			128,000	14,000	142,000
Miscellaneous material			157,000	18,000	175,000
Lower tub graphite, plain and borated	1 cu ft	51.00	33,000	3,000	36,000
Lower tub graphite, installation	1 cu ft	8.00	5,000	1,000	6,000
Primary shield tank			119,000	21,000	140,000
Primary shield tank accessories			45,000	4,000	49,000
Total			2,375,000	203,000	2,578,000
Rotating plug shield:					
Plug shell, drive and index system			512,000	89,395	601,395
Plug shielding (steel, plain and borated graphite, cans, etc.)			250,000	20,025	270,025
Installation			12,000	960	12,960
Total			774,000	110,380	884,380
Calcium borate pipe shields:					
Calcium borate material	1 lb	0.67	230,000	22,400	252,400
Calcium borate donuts			40,000	3,200	43,200
Valve-shaft streaming shields			10,000	800	10,800
Total			280,000	26,400	306,400
Fuel- and repair-building concrete shields:					
Concrete	1 cu yd	20.00	160,000	12,815	172,815
Form work	1 sq ft	1.10	99,000	7,930	106,930
Reinforcing steel	1 ton	260.00	117,000	9,370	126,370
Total			376,000	30,115	406,115
Steam-generator building concrete shield:					
Concrete	1 cu yd	25.00	45,000	3,605	48,605
Reinforcing steel	1 ton	275.00	33,000	2,645	35,645
Forms	1 sq ft	1.50	45,000	3,605	48,605
Total			123,000	9,855	132,855
Control-building shielding:					
40-in. concrete shield walls	1 sq ft	7.00	35,000	2,805	37,805
4-in. concrete roofing (with support structure)	1 sq ft	1.50	5,250	420	5,670
Total			40,250	3,225	43,475
Sodium service building:					
Concrete (incl. finish)	1 cu yd	23.60	33,000	2,645	35,645
Reinforcing steel	1 ton	240.00	24,000	1,920	25,920
Form work	1 sq ft	1.50	25,500	2,045	27,545
Miscellaneous steel shields			7,500	600	8,100
Knock-out concrete-block walls	1 cu yd	60.00	3,000	240	3,240
Total			93,000	7,450	100,450
Inert-gas-facility shields:					
Below-grade concrete	1 cu yd	30.00	6,000	480	6,480
Above-grade concrete	1 cu yd	35.00	18,000	1,440	19,440
Form work	1 sq ft	1.50	13,500	1,080	14,580
Reinforcing steel	1 ton	250.00	15,000	1,200	16,200
Steel shield sleeves			1,000	80	1,080
Total			53,500	4,280	57,780

*Direct costs given in "Second Semiannual Financial Report of Power Reactor Development Company as of June 30, 1959." Submitted to the USAEC pursuant to construction permit CPPR-4.

†Indirect costs prorated from overall indirect cost figures given in financial report cited above.

‡Sum of previous two columns.

§Block size: 6 in. × 6 in. Cost per block is $15.00 to $19.00. Graphite costs were incurred later than 1959. Figures reflect cost of removal of unsatisfactory material and reinstallation. Original installation costs totaled about $860,000.

Table 8.18—Cost of Prepacked Limonite Concrete Shielding at Fermi [85]

Item	Shield volume, cu yd	Cost per cu yd, $	Total cost, $
Limonite aggregate, including freight		18.00	6804
Conventional aggregate and mixing costs		23.00	8694
Placement of ordinary aggregate		18.00	6904
Placement of light and and heavy aggregate		59.00	22,302
Testing and control during pouring		3.00	1,134
Unit cost of in-place shield	378	62.00	23,436
Indirect cost		4.97	1,879
Total cost		66.97	25,315

will show up, and steps can be taken to correct the deficiencies prior to full operation.

Neutron-flux measurements should be taken within neutron-detector tubes, within surveillance or sampling tubes, on the surface of primary side shield, on the shield over the top of the reactor, and on the biological shield. Neutron spectral measurements may be made within or on surveillance tubes, detector tubes, surface of primary shield, if possible, and biological shield, if possible. Gamma-ray dose measurements should be made within the detector tubes. Gamma-ray spectral measurements may be made within the detector tube. A check of sodium activity should be performed.

The purpose of the high-power tests is to measure actual radiation conditions. Shield weaknesses that failed to show up under the lower-power tests may be found in these tests. The performance of many of the shields cannot be checked until reactor powers close to design are achieved. This is especially true of shields around the coolant systems of sodium-cooled reactors. The high-power tests

Table 8.19—Typical Costs of Various Steels*

Item	Condition†	Material cost,‡ $/lb	
		1960	1962 (Est.)
Carbon steel	H-R	0.0733	0.0858
1095 carbon spring steel		0.470	0.550
1095 carbon spring steel, blue finish		0.495	0.579
304 stainless steel	H-R	0.5076	0.5939
304 stainless steel	H-R,A	0.5425	0.6347
304 stainless steel	H-R,A,P	0.570	0.670
316 stainless steel	H-R	0.7852	0.9187
316 stainless steel	H-R,A	0.8025	0.9389
316 stainless steel	H-R,A,P	0.830	0.970
347 stainless steel	H-R	0.7152	0.8368
347 stainless steel	H-R,A	0.7325	0.8750
347 stainless steel	H-R,A,P	0.740	0.866

* PRDC Project price data: 1/2-in. steel plates, 10-ton order, minimum.

† Abbreviations: H-R, hot-rolled; A, annealed (or heat treated); and P, pickled.

‡ FOB prices, do not include freight charges.

should repeat any unsatisfactory intermediate-power neutron-flux measurements. These measurements are used as a check on the performance of the shields since they yield leakage rates that can be compared with the design values. Such measurements include a survey of the surface of primary shield, a survey of the surface of sodium-filled-pipe shields, a space radiation survey within the equipment compartment, a space radiation survey above the operating floor, and a survey of the biological shield. Neutron spectral measurements may be made within the reactor compartment. The following gamma-ray dose measurements should be made: a survey above the shield on top of the reactor, a space survey within the equipment compartment, a survey of radiation through the operating floor, and a survey of radiation directly outside the reactor building (or biological shield). Sodium-activity measurements should include the Na^{24} activity in the primary and secondary coolant systems, the Na^{22} activity in the primary system, and the impurity activity in the primary system, including natural impurities and fission-product contamination. Maintenance access is evaluated by measurements of steel activity within the equipment compartment or within any area where the neutron flux is 10^3 neutrons/ cm^2/sec or higher.

8.10.2.3 Tests Within the Service Buildings

These tests can be divided into preoperational tests and operational tests.

The word "operational" refers to the condition of a given system during the time of operation of the reactor or during its normal use.

Preoperational tests should include gross tests of service-building shields and tests of the adequacy of the shielding to stop radiation streaming in ducts and penetrations of these shields. These tests are designed to show up design or construction weaknesses in the shield so that remedial steps may be taken prior to nuclear operation.

Operational tests should include radiation surveys of the habitable areas within and around the service buildings, i.e., unlimited-access areas and limited-access areas; and measurement of the radioactive source levels of the various service systems, i.e., primary sodium coolant, secondary sodium coolant,* primary inert-gas system, including samples from the above reactor and handling system, waste-gas system, reactor-building ventilation systems, and waste liquid and other service systems. The operational tests serve the dual purposes of checking the actual performance of the auxiliary shields against predicted performance and evaluating limits of accessibility for maintenance.

8.10.3 SHIELD SURVEY OF DOUNREAY FAST REACTOR

A portion of the Dounreay fast reactor shield test program is described in Ref. 79. Fast-neutron and gamma-ray dose rates were measured on top

*The activity of the primary and secondary coolants will normally be lower in auxiliary process and storage loops than in the main reactor systems.

of the reactor rotating shields and in the reactor well. These tests were conducted to determine the adequacy of the removable shielding system that had been designed to supplement the permanent shield during the generation of power. Previous radiation measurements had shown that there was considerable streaming through a region between the fixed shield in the top of the reactor vessel and the radial graphite shield. As a result, a removable shield system was devised. The detailed arrangement of the removable shield system is shown in Fig. 8.51 (the overall shielding is shown in Chap. 11). These shields are described in detail in Sec. 8.16).

A radiation survey was made in the reactor well on a vertical plane containing the reactor central vertical axis. Measurements were also made around the circumference of the reactor-vessel flange to check the angular distribution of radiation; no important variation in flux with angular position was found.

The neutron monitor used was of the polyethylene knock-on-proton type, and the **gamma-ray** monitor used was an ionization chamber. The reactor power during this radiation survey was 13 kw(t). At this power level, which was about 0.02% of full power, the dose rates on top of the rotating shield plug were too small to measure reliably. The measurements in the well around the vessel could be measured satisfactorily.

The results of the radiation survey are shown in Figs. 8.52 and 8.53. These measurements demonstrate that radiation streaming through a gap or through an area of reduced shielding can be significant.

8.10.4 ENRICO FERMI ATOMIC POWER PLANT SHIELD TEST PROGRAM

The Fermi plant shield test program [46, 80] follows the general plan outlined in Sec. 8.10. The measurements for in-reactor portions of the program are coordinated with the reactor-plant experimental program, which began in late 1962 and has continued to the date of this writing. As of this time no results are available.*

8.10.5 SHIELD SURVEYS FOR OTHER FAST REACTORS

As described in Sec. 8.14, the gamma-radiation level at the surface of the original EBR-I biological side shield was about 100 to 200 mr/hr at about 70% of full power. A 30-in.-thick belt of concrete had to be added to this shield to reduce the dose rate to an acceptable level [4].

8.10.6 MISCELLANEOUS DATA OF INTEREST IN A SHIELD TEST PROGRAM

Information regarding emission energies, yields, and half-life periods of various types of neutron sources is given in Tables 8.10 to 8.12. Data of

interest concerning threshold detectors is given in Table 8.13.

8.11 Fast Reactor Shield Materials

8.11.1 GENERAL CONSIDERATIONS

The materials used in land-based fast power reactor shields are generally common, inexpensive materials, such as steel; graphite, plain and borated; concrete, ordinary and heavy; gravel; lead; earth; and sand. There are locations where more expensive materials have been used because of requirements for their special properties. Table 8.14 lists special materials used in existing or planned fast power reactors. Materials of special interest to spacecraft reactor shields, such as certain high-neutron-absorbing rare earths and hydrides and borohydrides, are not discussed here. For information on these, the reader is referred to Ref. 81.

8.11.2 COST OF MATERIALS

Table 8.15 lists the costs of common shield materials as of early 1962. Lists of shield material and placement (or fabrication) costs such as are given in Table 8.15 should be used only as guides or for rough estimates. The cost of materials, freight, labor, and use of equipment varies so widely from region to region in the United States that costs typical for one area may be much too high or low for another area. Table 8.16 lists some actual concrete costs at the MTR in 1953 [82] and the corresponding estimated 1962 costs [83]. Table 8.17 lists some shielding costs [84] at the Enrico Fermi plant incurred through June 30, 1959. Table 8.18 gives a cost analysis [85] of a small amount

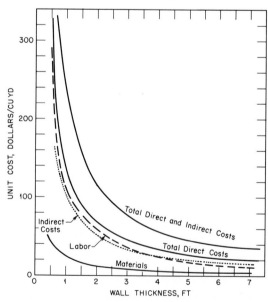

FIG. 8.54—Unit-cost trends (1962) of reinforced-concrete walls as a function of wall thickness [83].

---

*Note added in proof: Preliminary tests made before operation at power levels up to 1 Mw indicate that the shields are performing adequately.

Table 8.20—Physical and Mechanical Properties of Commercial
Graphite and Carbon*

Property	Graphite	Carbon
Density, g/cm³	1.56	1.55
Porosity, %	30	23
Specific heat, cal/g/°C		
At 25°C	0.172	0.17
At 127°C	0.237	0.24
At 327°C	0.336	0.34
At 527°C	0.395	0.40
At 727°C	0.428	0.43
Mean thermal-expansion coefficient, per °C†		
Extruded, parallel to axis		
At 20°C	$\sim 2.3 \times 10^{-6}$	
At 750°C	$\sim 4.4 \times 10^{-6}$	
Extruded, perpendicular to axis		
At 20°C	$\sim 5.7 \times 10^{-6}$	
At 750°C	$\sim 7.7 \times 10^{-6}$	
21-750°C (av)	$\sim 5.2 \times 10^{-6}$	$\sim 2.3 \times 10^{-6}$
Mean thermal conductivity, cal/sec/cm/°C		
At room temperature	0.334	0.0124
At 300°C	0.27	
At 500°C	0.21	
At 700°C	0.17	
At 1100°C	0.13	
Electrical resistivity, ohm-cm	0.000914	0.00406
Melting point, °C	3650‡	3650‡
Boiling point, °C	4200	4200
Vapor pressure, atm		
At 1500°C	$\sim 10^{-11}$	$\sim 10^{-11}$
At 3000°C	~ 0.01	~ 0.01
Heat of vaporization, cal/g	11,917	11,917
Tensile strength, psi	900	1,100
Compressive strength, psi	3,100	6,300
Flexural strength, psi	1,650	3,000
Crushing strength, psi	10,500	8,320
Elastic modulus, psi	1.35×10^{6}	1.7×10^{6}
Moh hardness	1-2	1-2§
Creep rate at 2500°C, %/hr		
Under stress of 1600 psi	0.1-0.2	
2800 psi	0.4	
4000 psi	1.0	

* Data compiled from Refs. 86 and 88 through 91.
† Data are for graphite brick and carbon brick. Values quoted are for measurements parallel to the extrusion where applicable.
‡ Sublimation point
§ Carbon is usually harder than the same quality graphite.

of limonite concrete shielding used at Fermi. Some typical 1960 costs of steel (material only) are given in Table 8.19. The variation of concrete-shield costs with thickness is given in Fig. 8.54.

8.11.3 PROPERTIES OF MATERIALS

This section is not intended to duplicate the complete materials data presented in the Reactor Handbook and other sources. The materials considered here are collected in one place with other fast reactor shielding information mainly as a convenience for the users of this volume. Nuclear properties are not given if they are easily available elsewhere or if there are no new values to be reported.

Common materials whose properties are given in this section are graphite; steels; concrete; gravel shield mix; earth and sand shields; and lead.

New materials discussed in this section are serpentine aggregate and concrete, calcium borate,

powder shield mix, lead-filled epoxy resin, and Permali.

8.11.4 GRAPHITE

Graphite has been used extensively and successfully as a moderator material in many types of reactors. The British have used graphite as a moderator in all their CO_2-cooled production and power reactors. The large Hanford water-cooled plutonium-production reactors have graphite moderators. The Sodium Reactor Experiment (SRE) and the Hallam reactor (Atomics International) are graphite moderated and sodium cooled. Brookhaven and ORNL have air-cooled graphite-moderated research reactors. In fact, the first reactor built used graphite as a moderator. A large store of knowledge has been accumulated on graphite under a wide range of temperatures and irradiation conditions.

Because graphite is a good moderator, it is a good shield material for slowing down and capturing

Table 8.21—Physical and Mechanical Properties of Reactor Grades of Graphite[*]

Property	AGOT	AGHT	TSP	GBF	CS-312
Density at 20°C, g/cm³	1.70	1.61-1.65	1.70	1.70	1.70
Specific heat, cal/g/°C					
At 25°C	0.172	0.172	0.172	0.172	0.172
At 127°C	0.237	0.237	0.237	0.237	0.237
At 327°C	0.336	0.336	0.336	0.336	0.336
At 527°C	0.395	0.395	0.395	0.395	0.395
At 727°C	0.428	0.428	0.428	0.428	0.428
Thermal-expansion coefficient, per °C					
At 20°C					
Axial	1.4×10^{-6}		1.4×10^{-6}	1.4×10^{-6}	1.6×10^{-3}
Transverse	2.7×10^{-6}		2.7×10^{-6}	2.7×10^{-6}	3.1×10^{-3}
Thermal conductivity at 20°C, cal/sec/cm/°C					
Axial	0.413		0.413	0.413	0.36
Transverse	0.31		0.31	0.31	0.27
Electrical resistivity, ohm-cm					
Axial	0.00076	0.0008	0.00076	0.00076	0.00089
Transverse	0.00102	0.00105-0.00125	0.00102	0.00102	0.0012
Melting point, °C	3650[†]	3650[†]	3650[†]	3650[†]	3650[†]
Boiling point, °C	4200	4200	4200	4200	4200
Vapor pressure, atm					
At 1500°C	$\sim 10^{-11}$	$\sim 10^{-11}$	$\sim 10^{-11}$	$\sim 10^{-11}$	$\sim 10^{-11}$
At 3000°C	~ 0.01	~ 0.01	~ 0.01	~ 0.01	~ 0.01
Heat of vaporization, cal/g	11,917	11,917	11,917	11,917	11,917
Tensile strength at 20°C, psi					
Axial	1400	2200	1400	1400	1400
Transverse	1400	600	1400	1400	1400
Compressive strength[‡]					
At 20°C, psi	6,000		6,000	6,000	6,000
Flexural strength[‡]					
At 20°C, psi	2100		2100	2100	2100
Stress to produce a creep rate of 0.1%/hr at 2500°C, psi		2200			
Elastic modulus, psi					
Axial	1.5×10^6		1.5×10^6	1.5×10^6	1.5×10^6
Transverse	1.1×10^6		1.1×10^6	1.1×10^6	1.1×10^6

[*] Data compiled from Refs. 86, 89, and 92.
[†] Sublimation point.
[‡] Data valid for both axial and transverse directions.

Table 8.22—Physical and Mechanical Properties of Karbate Impervious Graphite and Carbon[*][†]

Property	Impervious graphite	Impervious carbon
Density, g/cm³	1.91	1.76
Porosity, %	0.70	2
Specific heat at 25°C, cal/g/°C	0.17	0.2
Mean thermal-expansion coefficient, at 20°C, per °C	4.1×10^{-6}	5.0×10^{-6}
Mean thermal conductivity at 20°C, cal/sec/cm/°C	0.355	0.0124
Electrical resistivity, ohm-cm	0.00091	0.0041
Melting point, °C	3650[‡]	3650[‡]
Boiling point, °C	4200	4200
Vapor pressure, atm		
at 1500°C	$\sim 10^{-11}$	$\sim 10^{-11}$
at 3000°C	~ 0.01	~ 0.01
Heat of vaporization, cal/g	11,917	11,917
Tensile strength, psi	2500	1800
Compressive strength, psi	9000	10,000
Flexural strength, psi	4700	4400
Elastic modulus, psi	2.2×10^6	2.8×10^6
Moh hardness	1-2[§]	1-2[§]

[*] Data compiled from Refs. 3, 86, and 88 to 91.
[†] Karbate is a trade name of The National Carbon Company. Values are given for the brick form, and data are measured parallel to the extrusion.
[‡] Sublimation point.
[§] Carbon is usually harder than the same quality graphite.

fast neutrons when impregnated with a capture agent, such as boron or boron carbide. Graphite impregnated with B^{10} makes a very effective neutron-capture medium, not only for thermal neutrons, but also for neutrons of much higher energy.

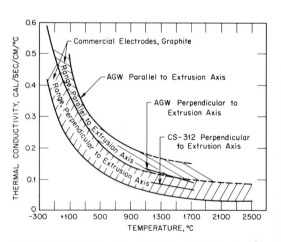

FIG. 8.55—Typical thermal conductivities of various graphites. Note: cal/sec/cm/°C × 241.90 = Btu/hr/ft/°F. (Submitted by Battelle Memorial Institute, Sept. 1, 1952.)

Table 8.23—Chemical Composition of Various Grades of Artificial Graphite*

Grade of graphite	C, wt.%	Impurities, ppm						
		B	Al	Ca	Ti	Fe	V	Ash
AGX†	99.63	1.3	20	2000	50	40	70	1500
C-18†	99.70	1.0	10	1200	35	100	200	1200
	99.73							1500
AGHT‡	99.75			500	100	100	100	700
								1700
AGOT‡	99.88	0.5		100	100	100	100	350
				200				700
CS‡	99.92	0.5§				100		350
								700

* Data taken from Refs. 86 and 92.
† Typical commercial grade.
‡ Reactor-grade graphite.
§ Grade CS-312.

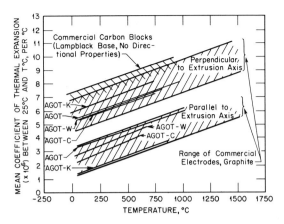

FIG. 8.56—Thermal-expansion coefficients of various graphites. (Submitted by Battelle Memorial Institute, Sept. 1, 1952.)

Graphite has sufficient mechanical strength to support itself, can withstand high temperatures and high neutron fluxes, and has good thermal-conductivity and low thermal-expansion properties [87]. From a shielding standpoint the density of graphite should be at least 100 lb/cu ft (1.6 g/cm³), which is easily obtainable. A good graphite can be cut into various shapes with commercially available cutting tools.

8.11.4.1 Types of Graphite for Shields

The physical properties of graphite are dependent upon the raw materials used and upon the temperature at which it is formed.

Natural graphite, obtained from earth deposits, has a high impurity content (about 10% of contaminants or greater). It cannot be used as a shield material in high-temperature areas because of excessive oxidation. Many of the impurities act as catalysts and accelerate oxidation.

Commercial graphites are usually considered to be manufactured carbon products that have been heated to about 2750°F. Some grades of this material are difficult to machine. Commercial graphite has a low thermal conductivity. It can be used as a shield material in low-temperature areas in an oxygen-free atmosphere. The impurity content is such as to prevent its use in high-temperature areas, i.e., above 300°F. Degassing and general

deterioration can be a severe problem at higher temperatures.

Artificial graphite is manufactured from petroleum and coal derivatives held with a pitch binder and graphitized at temperatures of the order of 4500 to 5400°F. Reactor-grade graphites are high-purity artificial graphites.

In high-temperature areas a graphite and borated-graphite shield should be constructed of reactor-grade graphites [93]. Oxidation is minimized and the release of volatiles is controlled if the graphite is held in a dry inert-gas atmosphere and out-gassed, if possible, before use at or above the operational temperature [94].

8.11.4.2 Properties of Graphite

The physical and mechanical properties of reactor-grade and commercial graphite are shown in Tables 8.20 and 8.21. Physical properties of impervious graphite are given in Table 8.22. Typical thermal conductivities of various graphites are given in Fig. 8.55. One means of identifying a good grade of graphite (graphite properly graphitized) is by its thermal conductivity. A poor graphite has a thermal conductivity near that of carbon [95]. Table 8.23 gives the elemental compositions of various grades of artificial graphite. Thermal expansion coefficients of various graphites are shown in Fig. 8.56.

Table 8.24—Composition of Several Types of Carbon and Alloy Steels*

Steel SAE number or type	Composition,† wt.%									
	Fe	C	Mn	P	S	Si	Ni	Cr	Mo	V
1095	98.36–98.71	0.9–1.05	0.30–0.50	0.04 (max.)	0.05 (max.)					
1330	97.34–98.84	0.28–0.33	1.60–1.90	0.04 (max.)	0.04 (max.)	0.20–0.35				
3115	96.64–97.54	0.13–0.18	0.40–0.60	0.04 (max.)	0.04 (max.)	0.20–0.35	1.10–1.40	0.55–0.75		
4023	98.42–98.82	0.20–0.25	0.70–0.90	0.04 (max.)	0.20–0.35					
4620	96.40–97.25	0.17–0.22	0.45–0.65	0.04 (max.)	0.04 (max.)	0.20–0.35	1.65–2.00		0.20–0.30	
6120	97.45–98.05	0.17–0.22	0.70–0.90	0.04 (max.)	0.04 (max.)	0.20–0.35		0.70–0.90		0.10 (min.)
8630	96.79–97.79	0.28–0.33	0.70–0.90	0.04 (max.)	0.04 (max.)	0.20–0.35	0.40–0.70	0.40–0.60	0.15–0.25	
E 9310	93.77–95.14	0.08–0.13	0.45–0.65	0.025 (max.)	0.025 (max.)	0.20–0.35	3.00–3.50	1.00–1.40	0.08–0.15	

* From T. Layman (Ed.), *Metals Handbook*, p. 307, 1948 edition, American Society for Metals, Cleveland, Ohio, 1948.
† Cobalt content varies usually between 0 and 0.2%, depending on the nature of the raw material used. Steels that utilize scrap materials usually have a higher cobalt content than virgin steels.

Table 8.25—Physical and Mechanical Properties of Selected Carbon and Alloy Steels[a]

Property	Value or Description							
	1095	1330	3115	4023	4620	6120	8630	E 9310
Density,[b] g/cm^3	7.83			7.86		7.84		7.85
Specific heat,[c] cal/g/°C								
50–100°C	0.116			0.116		0.118		0.117
450–500°C	0.152			0.158		0.157		0.159
Thermal conductivity,[d] cal/sec/cm/°C								
At 0°C	0.108			0.124		0.116		0.079
At 100°C	0.107			0.122		0.111		0.081
At 500°C	0.086			0.094		0.085		0.080
Thermal-expansion coefficient, per °C								
20°–100°C	11.1×10^{-6e}	8.8×10^{-6f}	11.8×10^{-6g}			12.2×10^{-6h}		
20°–500°C	13.6×10^{-6e}	13.1×10^{-6f}	14.0×10^{-6g}			14.1×10^{-6h}		
Electrical resistivity,[i] μohm-cm								
At 20°C	19.6			16.9		21.0		28.0
At 400°C	54.0			48.7		51.7		57.2
Tensile strength, psi				120,000[j]				174,000[k]
Hot rolled	130,000 (min.)							
Cold drawn	90,000–115,000	113,000	93,000		98,000	108,000	119,000	
Annealed	95,250	97,000[l]	86,000[l]		88,000[l]	93,000[l]	98,000[l]	
Forged		150,000–154,000[m]						
Elongation, % in 2 in.				20[n]				
Hot rolled	5							
Cold drawn	10–20	15	21		18	18	13	
Annealed	13	21[l]	23[l]		23[l]	22[l]	16[l]	
Forged		18.0–18.9[m]						
Yield point, psi				85,000[n]				150,000[k]
Hot rolled	71,500 (min.)							
Cold drawn	80,000–100,000	93,000	78,000		83,000	91,000	111,000	
Annealed	38,250	83,000[l]	71,000[l]		73,000[l]	75,000[l]	86,000[l]	
Forged		135,000–139,000						
Brinell hardness								
Hot rolled			134–170	140–170		140–170		269
Cold drawn	201–235	235	179–296[o]	170–196	197	187–228	241	
Annealed	192	197[l]	174[l]		179	187[l]	197	207–217
Forged								
Rockwell hardness					~C 37[j]			C 37–40[p]
Working temperatures,[q] °F	1250–1650	1500–2300	1425–2200	1425–2250	1425–2200	1425–2250	1500–2250	1525–2200

[a] Data compiled from Refs. 5 and 99.

[b] Exact densities of specific types of carbon and alloy steels are not available. The densities quoted are those for a specific composition nearest to the composition of the type given. The range of densities for all types of carbon and alloy steels is from 7.79 to 7.92 g/cm^3.

[c] The specific heats for specific types of steels are not available. The values quoted are for specific compositions nearest to the type given. The range of specific heats is 0.114 to 0.119 for carbon and low alloy steels and 0.098 to 0.124 for high alloy steels.

[d] The thermal conductivities of specific types of steels are not available. The values quoted are for specific compositions nearest to the type given. The range of thermal conductivities for most carbon steels is from about 0.11 cal/sec/cm/°C at low temperatures to 0.09 at high temperatures. Alloy steels run slightly less, from 0.08 to 0.1 cal/sec/cm/°C at low temperatures to 0.08 to 0.09 at high temperatures.

[e] Annealed condition.

[f] Value quoted for 1340 steel, which has carbon content 0.05 to 0.1% higher than 1330 steel.

[g] Quenched and tempered condition. Value quoted for type 3140, which has slightly different carbon and manganese composition.

[h] Annealed. Value quoted for type 6150, which has a carbon content lower by 0.3%.

[i] Values quoted for composition nearest type given.

[j] Value given for 7/8-in. rod quenched in oil at 1700°F.

[k] Heated 8 hr at 1700°F, box quenched.

[l] Cold drawn and annealed.

[m] Quenched.

[n] Pseudo-carburized and quenched.

[o] Average, 187.

[p] Heated 8 hr at 1700°F, fire cooled, quenched at 1450°F in oil (1-in.-diameter rods).

[q] Quenching temperatures are lowest 50 to 200° of range given. Normalizing and annealing temperatures are in middle of range. Forging temperatures are at top 300° of range.

When graphite is heated, gases are given off, including CH_4, H_2, CO, and CO_2. The amount given off is dependent upon the temperature and upon the amount and type of impurities. The evolution of gases can be minimized by using a high-purity reactor-grade graphite. It has been reported [96] also that the gas evolution can be appreciably re-duced by a high-temperature halogen treatment of the graphite.

8.11.4.3 Radiation Damage to Graphite

Radiation damage to graphite is very dependent upon the integrated neutron flux (nvt) and upon

Table 8.26—Composition of Several Types of Stainless Steel [22]

Steel SAE number	Composition,* wt.%								
	Fe	C	Cr	Ni	Mn	Si	Mo	Nb	N_2
201	67.60–73.60	0.15 (max.)	16.0–18.0	3.5–5.5	5.5–7.5	1.00 (max.)			0.25 (max.)
301	70.85–74.85	0.15 (max.)	16.0–18.0	6.00–8.00	2.00 (max.)	1.00 (max.)			
302	67.85–71.85	0.15 (max.)	17.00–19.00	8.00–10.00	2.00 (max.)	1.00 (max.)			
304	64.92–70.92	0.08 (max.)	18.00–20.00	8.00–12.00	2.00 (max.)	1.00 (max.)			
316	61.92–68.92	0.08 (max.)	16.00–18.00	10.00–14.00	2.00 (max.)	1.00 (max.)	2.00–3.00		
317	57.92–64.92	0.08 (max.)	18.00–20.00	11.00–15.00	2.00 (max.)	1.00 (max.)	3.00–4.00		
347	65.12–70.12	0.08 (max.)	17.00–19.00	9.00–12.00	2.00 (max.)	1.00 (max.)		<0.8[†]	
410	83.85–85.85	0.15 (max.)	11.50–13.50	0.50 (max.)	1.00 (max.)	1.00 (max.)			
430	79.38–83.38	0.12 (max.)	14.00–18.00	0.50 (max.)	1.00 (max.)	1.00 (max.)			
440A	78.00–80.15	0.60–0.75[‡]	16.00–18.00	0.50 (max.)	1.00 (max.)	1.00 (max.)	0.75 (max.)		

* Cobalt content varies usually between 0 and 0.2%, depending on the nature of the raw material used. Steels that utilize scrap materials usually have a higher cobalt content than virgin steels.

† Niobium content is 10 times minimum carbon content.

‡ 440B steel has a carbon content in the range 0.75 to 0.95%; 440C steel has carbon content in range 0.95 to 1.20%.

temperature. Some radiation effects in graphite are discussed in Sec. 8.3.

8.11.5 STEELS AND STAINLESS STEELS

8.11.5.1 Iron and Carbon Steels

One of the most versatile materials from a nuclear engineering standpoint is steel. It can be used for structural and shielding purposes. It is widely used as a thermal shield material to absorb gamma radiation selectively so that the heat produced can be removed easily and without harming or damaging other parts of the shield or reactor system. Boron may be added to steel to enhance the neutron shielding capability of steel. Ordinary steel does not by itself make a particularly good neutron shield, except at low neutron energies. Inelastic scattering in iron will degrade high-energy neutrons into lower energy regions; in some of these regions neutron-energy streaming (Sec. 8.7.13) may occur. Steel and ordinary concrete used together compete quite successfully with heavy concretes on a cost and overall-performance basis.

Table 8.24 gives the composition of several types of steel. Table 8.25 lists the physical and mechanical properties of steel.

8.11.5.2 Stainless Steel

Stainless steel is a corrosion-resistant steel that has neutron-shielding and -attenuation properties superior of those of ordinary steel, in addition to its gamma-shielding characteristics. Stainless steel is an excellent attenuator for high-energy neutrons because of its inelastic properties. The presence of nickel in stainless steel improves the slowing-down properties of steel. Stainless steel can be used in high-temperature regions and under many conditions where other metals cannot be used. Stainless steel forms an alloy with molten uranium. Manganese in stainless steel makes it extremely radioactive under neutron irradiation. Because of the long half-life of Co^{60}, the presence of cobalt to an extent greater than a few tenths of

1% in stainless steel is undesirable from a handling and maintenance viewpoint in parts that are exposed to strong neutron bombardment. Stainless steel will endure integrated neutron fluxes of over 3×10^{22} neutrons/cm^2 without harmful changes in its physical properties [100]. The compositions of several types of stainless steel are given in Table 8.26. Table 8.27 lists their physical and mechanical properties.

8.11.5.3 Boron Stainless Steel

The addition of boron in small amounts (up to 2 wt.%) enhances the neutron-attenuating capability of steels. Physical and mechanical properties of boron steel are given in Table 8.28, and those of boron stainless steels are given in Table 8.29.

8.11.6 CONCRETE

Concrete [86, 101] is a universally used shield material for stationary power reactors. Almost any kind of concrete can be used for reactor shields; the exact type will depend upon the design of the reactor. Where thickness is not a factor, ordinary concrete is cheap and effective, especially when used in conjunction with steel or other heavy material. High-density concretes are desirable when thin shields are needed.

Ordinary concrete is, in general, the cheapest material. Where space is not a limitation and where strength is important, ordinary concrete fills the bill more adequately than special concretes [3].

8.11.6.1 High-density Concretes

The neutron- and gamma-shielding properties of concrete are improved if high density is attained. This can be accomplished by the use of high-density aggregates. The following aggregates (among others) make good high-density concretes: barytes, limonite, and magnetite.

8.11.6.2 Boron-containing Concretes

Boron increases the neutron-shielding effectiveness of concretes, especially for low-energy neu-

Table 8.27—Physical and Mechanical Properties of Selected Wrought Stainless Steels[a]

Property	Stainless Steel 201	301	304	316	317	347	410	440
Type[b]	A	A	A	A	A	A	M	M
Density at 20°C, g/cm³	7.75	7.93	7.90	7.98	7.9	7.98	7.75	7.68
Specific heat, 20°-100°C, cal/g/°C	0.12	0.118	0.12	0.118	0.12	0.118	0.11	0.11
Thermal conductivity, cal/sec/cm/°C								
At 20°C						~0.036		
At 100°C		0.039	0.039	0.039	0.039	0.038		
At 500°C		0.051	0.051	0.051	0.051	0.053	0.0595	0.058
							0.069	
Thermal-expansion coefficient, per °C								
20°-100°C	16.6×10^{-6}	16.6×10^{-6}	$17.5 \times 10^{-6\,c}$	$16.0 \times 10^{-6\,c}$	16.6×10^{-6}	$16.7 \times 10^{-6\,c}$	$9.9 \times 10^{-6\,c}$	$10.1 \times 10^{-6\,c}$
20°-870°C	20.3×10^{-6}	19.8×10^{-6}	$18.4 \times 10^{-6\,d}$	$17.5 \times 10^{-6\,d}$	19.3×10^{-6}	$18.5 \times 10^{-6\,d}$	11.5×10^{-6}	$10.6 \times 10^{-6\,f}$
Electrical resistivity, μohm-cm								
At 20°C	69	72	72	74	74	73	57.0	60
At 650°C			116	116			108.7	
Magnetic permeability, annealed	1.02 (max.)	1.02	1.02	1.02	1.02	1.02	Magnetic	Magnetic
Melting range, °C		1400-1420	L, 1508[g] S, 1425	1370-1400	1370-1400	1399-1427	1480-1510	1370-1510 1370-1482[h]
Annealing temp., °C	1010-1093	1010-1120	1010-1120	1080-1120	1080-1175	1065-1120	650-675	730-790
Hardening temperature, °C	h	h	h	h	h	h	950-995	1010-1065
Forging temperature,[i] °C	1260-930	1260-930	1260-930	1260-1150	1400-1150	1260-980	1150-900	1150-1040[p] 1175-1040[p] 1205-1040[h,p]
Stress-relieving temperature, °C		205-400	205-400	205-400				150-425[j]
Tensile strength, psi								
Cold rolled		100,000-180,000	110,000-125,000	90,000[k]		100,000[k]	100,000 (min.)[l]	115,000-125,000[k]
Annealed, 70°F		80,000-90,000	87,000	80,000-90,000	75,000[m]	90,000-95,000	65,000-89,000	105,000-110,000
Annealed, 1000°F		58,000	58,000	67,500		61,500	44,500	
Yield strength,[n] psi								
Annealed	40,000	35,000-45,000	30,000-35,000	30,000-40,000	30,000	35,000-40,000	35,000-40,000	60,000-65,000
Cold rolled		50,000-150,000	75,000-95,000	60,000[k]		65,000[k]	85,000[l]	90,000-100,000[k]
Elongation, % in 2 in.								
Annealed	40	55-60	50-60	50-60	40	45-50	25-35	14-20
Cold rolled		10-50	25-60	45[k]		40[k]	17[l]	7-12[k]
Elastic modulus,[o] psi	29×10^6	29×10^6	29×10^6	29×10^6	29×10^6	29×10^6	29×10^6	30×10^6
Creep strength at 1000°F, psi								
1% flow in 10,000 hr		19,000	19,000	24,000	24,000	32,000	12,000	
1% flow in 100,000 hr		13,000	13,000	15,000	15,000	27,000	11,000	
Brinell hardness								
Cold rolled		190-330		190[k]		212[k]	205[l]	240-260[k]
Annealed	210 (max.)	135-185	150	150	200 (max.)	160	150-155	215-230
Rockwell hardness								
Cold rolled							B94[l]	B99, C23, C24[p]
Annealed	B95	B-90 (max.)	B-80	B78-85	B-95 (max.)	B-85	B80-82	B95-97
Maximum operating temperature, continuous service, °F	1550	1700	1700	1700	1700	1700	1300	1400

[a] Data compiled from Refs. 5, 88, 99, 102.
[b] Abbreviations: A, austenitic; M, martensitic.
[c] Temperature range 0° to 100°C.
[d] Temperature range 0° to 538°C.
[e] Temperature range 20° to 704°C.
[f] Temperature range 0° to 316°C.
[g] Abbreviations: L, liquidus; S, solidus.
[h] Hardenable only by cold rolling.

[i] First temperature given is starting temperature.
[j] Tempering range.
[k] Annealed and cold drawn.
[l] Tempered and cold drawn.
[m] Value quoted for ultimate strength.
[n] Yield strengths given for 0.2% offset condition.
[o] Annealed condition.
[p] Values respectively for types 440A, 440B, and 440C.

trons. Boron in concrete also acts as a suppressor of secondary (capture) gamma rays. Use of more than 1% boron usually retards the setting properties. Boron may be added to concretes as aggregates, e.g., colemanite, pyrex glass, boron frits; as boron cements; and directly in the mix water. The compositions and densities of two types of pyrex-borated concretes are given in Table 8.30.

8.11.6.3 Composition of Concretes

Table 8.31 summarizes the compositions of several types of ordinary and heavy concretes. The elemental compositions of ordinary concretes are given in Table 8.32, and those of several types of heavy concretes is given in Tables 8.33 to 8.35.

Table 8.28—Physical Properties of Boron Steels[*][†]

Property	Boron content, wt.%			
	2	3	4	5
Thermal expansion over range 20-100°C (10^{-6} per °C)	10.0	10.0	9.5	
Specific gravity (20°C)	7.72	7.44	7.36	
Specific heat, cal/g/°C	0.110	0.124	0.125	
Thermal conductivity (c.g.s. units at 70-100°C)	≈ 0.096			
Machinability	Easy, similar to cast iron	Good, normal methods	Stiff, carbide tools needed	Unma-chinable
Available forms	Forged and rolled bar and plate, extruded tubes		Castings	

[*] From B. T. Price, C. C. Horton, and K. T. Spenney, *Radiation Shielding*, Pergamon Press, New York, 1957.

[†] These steels are covered by British Patent Application No. 34872/55. The data are reproduced by permission of Messrs. Hadfields Ltd., Sheffield. The steels contain a maximum of 0.1% of cobalt and 0.5% of manganese.

8.11.6.4 Physical and Mechanical Properties

A summary of the physical properties of ordinary concrete is given Table 8.36. These properties are typical and will vary with the exact composition. The properties of common heavy concretes are given in Table 8.37 (limonite and magnetite concretes) and Table 8.38 (barytes concrete).

8.11.6.4.1 DENSITY. Density is a large factor in the shielding ability of concretes. It varies from a low of 130 lb/cu ft for certain types of ordinary concrete to a high of 300 lb/cu ft for steel-loaded concretes. In any shield design, once a density has been decided on, uniformity in the mix and in the pour is very important for good shielding characteristics. The density of ordinary concretes can be increased slightly without harming the mix formula by the addition of a few per cent of washed heavy aggregate.

8.11.6.4.2 COMPRESSIVE STRENGTH. Ordinary concrete using well-known mixing and placement methods gives the best all-around strength properties. Suitable strength properties for shields

Table 8.29—Physical and Mechanical Properties of Boron Stainless Steels [86]

Material designation	Boron content, wt.%	Condition[a]	Tensile strength, psi	Yield point 0.2% offset, psi	Reduction in area, %	Elongation, %	Hardness, Rockwell A
N-270	0.3	H-R	92,800	55,200	44		51
		A	89,200	31,300	49		45
N-268	0.8	H-R	108,800	67,500	33		58
		A	99,100	39,000	33		53
N-263	1.6	H-R	118,300	78,000	19		62
		A	102,200	52,700	26		55
N-272	2.4	H-R	108,000	63,200	20		62
		A	105,700	39,600	21		59
SS-1[b]	1.44 to 2	Cast	51,000	30,200	0	0.9	
SS-2[c]	1.0	I-M	95,800	54,700	13	18.0	
SS-3[d]	1.5	V-M	100,000	70,000	8	8.3	
SS-4[e]	0.3	V-M	92,800	55,200	44	29.0	
SS-5	0.3	H-R	104,100	85,500	46		63
		A	85,200	33,400	32		53
SS-6	0.7	H-R	111,300	84,000	32		65
		A	98,200	38,100	42		57
SS-7	1.2	H-R	112,000	82,100	34		65
		A	89,500	31,900	37		57
SS-8	1.7	H-R	112,300	79,500	28		65
		A	112,100	43,800	23		59

[a] Abbreviations as follows: A, annealed; H-R, hot rolled; I-M, induction melted; and V-M, vacuum melted.

[b] An 18-8 SS made by Electric Steel Foundry Co.; tested by Argonne National Laboratory.

[c] Made by Superior Steel Division, Copperweld Corp.; 18% Cr, 11% Ni, 0.08% C.

[d] 304 SS with added boron.

[e] Made by Universal-Cyclops Steel Corporation, tested by Knolls Atomic Power Laboratory; 18% Ni, 15% Cr.

Table 8.30—Compositions and Densities of
Pyrex-Borated Concretes [103]

Material	Composition, wt.%	
	Portland-pyrex concrete	Portland-limonite-iron-pyrex concrete
Coarse aggregate	46.55*	41.4†
Fine aggregate	27.78*	32.8†
Iron content		62.78‡
Pyrex glass	1.25	0.7
Portland cement	18.37*	12.3
Water§	6.05	12.8
Density, g/cm³	2.39	3.60

* The cement:sand:gravel proportions were reported as 1:2:3.

† No details of the grading of the aggregates were reported.

‡ This is the total iron content reported and is all contained in the aggregates. No breakdown of the amount of steel scrap and amount of limonite aggregate used is given although it is estimated that about 35% of the total aggregate was steel scrap.

§ This is the water added only. The fixed water in the aggregates is included in the aggregate percentages. Fixed-water content in ordinary concrete runs from 5 to 8% of total weight; in limonite concrete it is around 10%.

can be obtained through the use of aggregates. In general, strength must be sacrificed somewhat to obtain high density or high water content in concretes. A good quality Portland concrete has a 90-day compressive strength of 3500 to 6000 psi. Iron-ore-aggregate concretes have compressive strength of 5500 to 6500 psi if conventional placement is used. Pressure-grouted and other prepacked methods give strengths of 3500 to 5000 psi for iron-aggregate concretes. Barytes concretes have strengths ranging from 3500 to 5000 psi.

8.11.6.4.3 THERMAL CONDUCTIVITY. The thermal conductivity of ordinary concrete varies between 0.2 and 1 Btu/hr/ft/°F, depending on the mix. In general, heavy aggregates added to concretes increase their conductivity. Barytes concrete has a conductivity of around 1 Btu/hr/ft/°F. Iron-ore-aggregate concretes have conductivities ranging from 1.2 to 3 Btu/hr/ft/°F. High-density concrete made with steel shot may have conductivity as high as 9 Btu/hr/ft/°F. Steel reinforcement may increase the thermal conductivity by as much as 1 Btu/hr/ft/°F.

8.11.6.4.4 HYDROGEN CONTENT. Hydrogen occurs in concrete mainly in the form of fixed water and small amounts of organic impurities. The main shielding effectiveness of concrete for neutrons is due to the water content of concrete. Ordinary concretes used for neutron shields should have a fixed hydrogen content of at least 0.5 wt.% hydrogen [29]. A minimum water content in concrete shields used in high-temperature areas (above 100°C) should be guaranteed by design. The concrete should be protected against loss of water by cooling or other means.

8.11.6.4.5 DEHYDRATION. Ordinary concrete will retain its water content for long periods of time. Dehydration is so slow at ordinary temperatures that many concretes still retain half of their original water content after periods of 20 to 30 years. Heat and radiation accelerate the dehydration pro-

cess. At temperatures above 200° F dehydration is noticeable, and above 600°F it becomes very rapid. Concretes used as shields should not be exposed to constant temperatures of over 200°F. Figure 8.2 shows how the water content of concrete varies with temperature. Figures 8.57 through 8.65 [106] show the results of measurements and calculations of the effect of water loss at various temperatures on the attenuation properties of a 4-ft shield made of ordinary concrete and ferrophosphorous concrete. Figures 8.57 and 8.61 are particularly significant in that the anticipated increases in neutron flux can be readily found from the curves if the water content before and after the water loss is known. If the water content is originally 18 lb/cu ft and reduces to 12 lb/cu ft, the fast flux (Fig. 8.57) will increase by the factor $0.018/0.0034 = 5.3$. This data can be roughly extrapolated to other thicknesses by the equation

$$R_\phi = (\phi/\phi_0)^{x/4} \qquad (8.143)$$

where R_ϕ = increase in neutron flux
  ϕ = flux after water loss, neutrons/cm²/sec
  ϕ_0 = flux before water loss, neutrons/cm²/sec
  x = thickness of the shield, ft

If the water content is not known but the densities of an ordinary concrete shield are known before and after water loss, the rise in the neutron leakage through the shield can be calculated roughly by

$$R_\phi = \phi/\phi_0 = \exp[0.0195 + x(\rho_0 - \rho)] \qquad (8.144)$$

where ρ_0 = density of shield before water loss, lb/cu ft
  ρ = density of shield after water loss, lb/cu ft
  x = shield thickness, ft

The constant in the exponent of Eq. 8.144 can be changed as follows for various heavy concretes: ferrophosphorus, 0.0284; magnetite, 0.024; limonite, 0.0208; barytes, 0.0227. It should be remembered that the above equations should be used only as guides; they may be typical of all concretes of a given type but may not necessarily represent any given concrete shield since the exact values of the constants depend strongly on the exact constituent makeup of a given concrete.

8.11.6.5 Nuclear Properties

8.11.6.5.1 RADIATION DISTRIBUTIONS IN CONCRETE SHIELDS. Radiation distributions in 4-ft concrete slabs are shown in Figs. 8.58 through 8.60 and 8.62 through 8.65. The radiation distributions in the ORNL X-10 Pile shield (barytes concrete and ordinary concrete) are shown in Fig. 8.66; those in the National Research Experimental Reactor (NRX) shield (ordinary concrete) are shown in Fig. 8.67; and those in the BEPO shield (barytes concrete) are shown in Fig. 8.68. The ORNL X-10 Pile 7-ft concrete shield consists of 5 ft of barytes—

Table 8.31—Summary of Concrete Compositions [101]

Concrete	Symbol*	Density (ρ) g/cm³	lb/cu ft	Water	Cement	Aggregate	Steel punchings	Total	Reference
ORDINARY									
1	01	2.33	145						16
2a	02a	2.30	144	260	318	3300 (sand and gravel)		3878	16
2b	02b	2.20	137						16
3 ORNL	03	2.39	149						4
4 NBS	04	2.35	147						8
5 Harwell	05	2.50	156						2
6 APDA	06	1.30	80	0.231	0.256	0.513 (Volume fractions)			11
7 APDA	07	2.09	130	373	525	2032 950 (serpentine) (sand)		3887	11
0 HW1	0-HW1	2.33	145						14
0 HW2	0-HW2	2.26	141						14
FERROPHOSPHORUS									
1a	FP-a	4.68	292	383	730	4070 2710 (coarse) (fine)		7893	10
1b	FP-b	4.57	285						10
HW1 Hanford	FP-HW1	4.82	301						13
HW3 Hanford	FP-HW3	4.67	292						13
BARYTES									
1a	BA-a	3.50	219						16
1b	BA-b	3.39	212						16
H Harwell	BA-H	2.575	160						2
Haydite ORNL, X-10	BAHA	2.35	147	10.0	16.3	46.4 27.3 (Barytes) (Haydite)	(Wt.%)		5
Haydite ORNL, X-10	BAHA-d	2.28	142						5
OR ORNL	BA-OR	3.30	206	383	468	4711		5562	18
MAGNETITE									
1a EBWR	M-a	3.55	222	330	875	2623 2160 (coarse) (fine)		5988	7, 10
1b ANL, EBWR	M-b	3.45	215						7, 10
1c ANL, EBWR	M-c	3.62	226	330	875	2700 2200		6105	7, 10
HW1 Hanford	M-HW1	3.29	205						17
HW2 Hanford	M-HW2	3.27	204						17
ILMENITE									
1a New York ore	I-1a	3.50	219	330	875	4695		5900	12
1b New York ore	I-1b	3.40	212						12
2a Swedish ore	I-2a	3.76	235	330	875	5140		6345	12
2b Swedish ore	I-2b	3.66	228						12
NRU Chalk River	I-NRU	3.49	218						15
NRUe Chalk River	I-NRUe	3.44	215						15
MAGNETITE AND STEEL									
a ANL; EBWR	MS-a	4.70	293	340	940	1846	4800	7926	7, 10
b ANL; EBWR	MS-b	4.60	287				4800		7, 10
c ANL; EBWR	MS-c	4.73	296	340	940	1900	4800	7980	7, 10
LIMONITE AND STEEL									
1a ANL, CP-5	LS-a	4.54	284	347	980	1661	4680	7668	9
1b ANL, CP-5	LS-b	4.44	277						9
1c ANL, CP-5	LS-c	4.65	290	347	980	1825	4680	7832	1
2a BNL	LS-BRa	4.16	260	296	940	1684	4100	7020	3
2b BNL	LS-BRb	4.08	255						3
2c BNL	LS-BRc	4.28	267	296	940	1880	4100	7216	3
HW1 Hanford	LS-HW1	4.23	264						6
HW2 Hanford	LS-HW2	4.14	258						6

* a Indicates 100% water retention.
  b Indicates 50% water retention.
  c Indicates 100% water retention including free moisture in mix.

d Average composition of four sample cores.
e Composition after two years.
HW1 As cured concrete.

HW2 Heated to 100° C.
HW3 Heated to 320° C.

References

1. G. A. Anderson, private communication.
2. A. F. Avery et al., Methods of Calculation for Use in the Design of Shields for Power Reactors, British Report AERE-R-3216, February 1960.
3. C. R. Binner et al., High Density Concrete Shielding, pp. 12-13, USAEC Report HFK-1, Feb. 15, 1957.
4. E. P. Blizard and J. M. Miller, Radiation Attenuation Characteristics of Structural Concrete, p. 2, USAEC Report ORNL-2193, Aug. 29, 1958.
5. T. V. Blosser et al., A Study of the Nuclear and Physical Properties of the ORNL Graphite Reactor Shield, pp. 5-8, USAEC Report ORNL-2195, Sept. 8, 1958.
6. W. L. Bunch, Attenuation Properties of High Density Portland Cement Concretes as a Function of Temperature, p. 39, USAEC Report HW-54656, Jan. 22, 1958.
7. The Experimental Boiling Water Reactor, p. 60, USAEC Report ANL-5607, May 1957.
8. G. W. Grodstein, X-ray Attenuation Coefficients from 10 kev to 100 Mev, p. 50, NBS Circular 583, Apr. 30, 1957.
9. E. E. Hamer, private communication.
10. E. E. Hamer, Reactor Handbook, Rev. Ed., Tables 7.1-4.1, 7.1-4.2, Interscience Publishers, New York, 1960.
11. H. E. Hungerford et al., New Shielding Materials for High-temperature Application, Nucl. Sci. Eng., 6:401-404 (November 1959).
12. C. Palache et al., The System of Mineralogy, Vol. 1, p. 537, John Wiley & Sons, Inc., New York, 1951.
13. E. G. Peterson, Shielding Properties of Ferrophosphorus Concrete as a Function of Temperature, pp. 43-44, 62, USAEC Report HW-64774, July 15, 1960.
14. E. G. Peterson, Shielding Properties of Ordinary Concrete as a Function of Temperature, p. 24, USAEC Report HW-65572, Aug. 2, 1960.
15. J. M. Robson, The Attenuation of Neutrons by the Side Shield of the NRU Reactor, pp. 15-16, Canadian Report CRP-860, October 1959.
16. J. F. Hogerton and R. C. Grass, The Reactor Handbook. Vol. I, Physics, pp. 674, 725-727, USAEC Report AECD-3645, March 1955.
17. D. E. Wood, The Effect of Temperature on the Neutron Attenuation of Magnetite Concrete, p. 16, USAEC Report HW-58497, Dec. 11, 1958.
18. W. J. Grantham, Jr., Barytes Concrete for Radiation Shielding: Mix Criteria and Attenuation Characteristics, p. 44, USAEC Report ORNL-3130, July 25, 1961.

Table 8.32—Summary of the Elemental Compositions of Ordinary Concretes [101]

Element	Concrete composition, g of element/cm³ of concrete									
	01	02-a	02-b	03	04	05	06	07	0-HW1	0-HW2
H	0.00484	0.023	0.0115	0.020	0.013	0.022	0.034	0.033	0.015	0.007
O in water	0.0384	0.183	0.0915	0.159	0.103	1.231	0.793	1.075	1.057	0.995
in mix	1.1106	1.037		0.980	1.062					
B							0.010	0.002		
C	0.130		0.0023	0.118		0.008		0.002		
Na		0.0368			0.040	0.029		0.008	0.041	
Mg	0.00486	0.005		0.057	0.006	0.002	0.003	0.281	0.085	
Al	0.0119	0.078		0.085	0.107	0.131	0.025	0.040	0.137	
Si	0.438	0.775		0.342	0.737	0.63	0.417	0.435	0.487	
P				0.007				trace	0.002	
S	0.00192			0.007	0.003	0.0037			0.002	
Cl								trace		
K		0.0299		0.004	0.045	0.025		0.008	0.015	
Ca	0.581	0.100		0.582	0.194	0.242	0.001	0.141	0.295	
Ti						0.017		trace	0.011	
Mn								trace		
Fe				0.003		0.045		trace	0.003	
Ni	0.00726	0.032		0.026	0.029	0.122	0.013	0.064	0.178	
Cu								0.002		
Density, g/cm³	2.33	2.30	2.20	2.39	2.35	2.50	1.30	2.09	2.33	2.26

haydite concrete sandwiched between two 1-ft thicknesses of ordinary concrete.

8.11.6.5.2 NUCLEAR CONSTANTS. Neutron cross sections of interest and capture gamma-ray spectra for elements found in concrete are given in Table 8.39. Neutron constants for the concretes listed in Table 8.31 are presented in Table 8.40. The capture gamma-ray spectra data for this same group of concretes is given in Table 8.41. The linear mass- and energy-absorption coefficients in these concretes for various photon energies are listed in Tables 8.42 and 8.43. The effective atomic numbers for determining gamma-ray buildup fac-

Table 8.33—Summary of the Elemental Compositions of Heavy Concretes [101]

Element	Concrete composition, g of element/cm³ of concrete									
	FP-a	FP-b	FP-HW1	FP-HW3	BA-a	BA-b	BA-H	BAHA	BAHA-d	BA-OR
H in water	0.0234	0.0117	0.021	0.004	0.0243	0.0122	0.007	0.026	0.0298	0.036
in ore									0.0045	
O in water	0.201	0.100	0.322	0.191	0.195	0.0975	0.710	0.209	1.084	0.291
in ore	0.041				0.872			0.494		
in cement	0.154				0.118			0.138		0.971
C	0.0023			0.004			0.0233			
Mg in ore			0.006						0.0441	
in cement	0.0047					0.00385		0.0046		0.0099
Al in ore			0.009				0.0123	0.0546	0.0565	
in cement	0.0187					0.0137		0.0161		0.0066
Si in ore	0.0796		0.090				0.180	0.308	0.232	
in cement	0.0515					0.0352		0.0414		0.139
P	0.967			1.049						
S				0.004			0.180	0.144	0.0094	0.287
Ca in ore			0.203			0.0203	0.148	0.109	0.209	0.135
in cement	0.197					0.147		0.172		
Ti				0.042						
V				0.084						
Cr	0.0023			0.084						
Mn	0.117			0.013						
Fe in ore	2.808		2.823		0.151		0.595	0.0107	0.0338	0.277
in cement	0.014				0.0091					
Ni			0.017							
Cu			0.008							
Mo			0.042							
Ba					1.551	0.718	0.618	0.577	1.20	
Density, g/cm³	4.68	4.57	4.82	4.67	3.50	3.39	2.575	2.35	2.28	3.30

Table 8.34—Summary of the Elemental Compositions of Heavy Concretes [101]

Element	Concrete composition, g of element/cm³ of concrete										
	M-a	M-b	M-c	M-HW1	M-HW2	I-1a	I-1b	I-2a	I-2b	I-NRU	I-NRUe
H in water	0.0219	0.0110	0.0219	0.015	0.0128	0.0219	0.0110	0.0219	0.0110	0.0115	0.0093
in ore			0.0076								
O in water	0.174	0.087	0.174			0.174	0.087	0.174	0.087		
in ore	0.826	0.826	0.887	1.279	1.261	0.981		0.989		1.212	1.272
in cement	0.187	0.187	0.187			0.187		0.187			
C										0.0185	0.0148
Mg in ore		0.0172		0.184			0.267		0.0148	0.0527	0.0571
in cement		0.0062					0.0062		0.0062		
Al in ore		0.0752								0.0743	0.0416
in cement		0.0218					0.0218		0.0218		
Si in ore		0.0670		0.129						0.121	0.0664
in cement		0.0561					0.0560		0.0560		
P		0.0006									
S		0.0037									
Ca in ore		0.0071							0.0012	0.112	0.102
in cement		0.233		0.0220			0.233		0.233		
Ti		0.0959					0.955		0.959	0.508	0.649
V		0.0062									
Cr		0.0030									
Mn		0.0024					0.0225		0.0302		
Fe in ore		1.730		1.460			0.560		1.049	1.38	1.309
in cement		0.0145					0.0145		0.0145		
Density, g/cm³	3.55	3.45	3.62	3.29	3.27	3.50	3.40	3.76	3.66	3.49	3.44

tors in concretes are given for several types of concrete in Table 8.44. (See Sec. 8.12 for buildup factors.)

8.11.6.5.3 RELAXATION LENGTHS. The relaxation length of fast neutrons from a fission source passing through high-density concretes will vary from between 6 to 9 cm. For ordinary concretes it is between 10 and 13 cm. For very high energy neutrons from particle accelerators, the relaxation lengths may be as high as 35 cm. The density of a particular concrete has considerable bearing on the relaxation length. The geometry-free relaxation length may be taken approximately equal to the reciprocal of the macroscopic removal cross section. Prompt-fission gammas have, on the average, a macroscopic absorption cross section of 0.09 cm⁻¹ in ordinary concrete. This corresponds to a

Table 8.35—Summary of the Elemental Compositions of Heavy Concretes with Steel Punchings [101]

Element	Concrete composition, g of element/cm³ of concrete										
	MS-a	MS-b	MS-c	LS-a	LS-b	LS-c	LS-BRa	LS-BRb	LS-BRc	LS-HW1	LS-HW2
H in water	0.0225	0.0112	0.0225	0.0232	0.0116	0.0232	0.0196	0.0098	0.0196	0.028	0.018
in ore			0.0036			0.0125			0.0130		
O in water	0.179	0.089	0.179	0.183	0.091	0.183	0.156	0.078	0.156		
in ore	0.334	0.334	0.363	0.247	0.247	0.346	0.322	0.322	0.425	0.806	0.726
in cement	0.200	0.200	0.200	0.210	0.210	0.210	0.201	0.201	0.201		
Mg in ore		0.0125						0.0036			
in cement		0.0071			0.0071			0.0065			
Al in ore		0.0237			0.0029			0.0095		0.039	
in cement		0.0231			0.0234			0.0231			
Si in ore		0.0107			0.126			0.0362		0.078	
in cement		0.0605			0.0629			0.0605			
P		0.006			0.0005						
S		0.0018									
Ca in ore		0.0047									
in cement		0.251			0.262			0.251		0.250	
Ti		0.0676						0.0006			
V		0.0042									
Cr		0.0018									
Mn		0.0018			0.0053			0.0024			
Fe in ore		0.631			0.590			0.625		3.030	
in cement		0.0154			0.0160			0.0154			
in steel		2.846			2.779			2.432			
Density, g/cm³	4.70	4.60	4.73	4.54	4.44	4.65	4.16	4.08	4.28	4.23	4.14

Table 8.36—Typical Physical and Mechanical
Properties of Ordinary
Concrete [22]

Property	Value
Density, g/cm^3	
Range	2.2 – 2.4
Average	2.3
Specific heat, Btu/lb/°F	0.156
Thermal conductivity, Btu/hr/ft/°F	
Not reinforced	0.5
Reinforced	1 – 2
Tensile strength, psi	300 – 450
Compressive strength, psi	
7 days	3000
28 days	5500

relaxation length of 11 cm. Fission-product gamma rays have an average attenuation length of about 6 cm in ordinary concrete. Capture gamma rays from steel have a relaxation length in ordinary concrete of 19 cm. High-density concrete considerably improves these properties. Table 8.39 gives the capture gamma-ray spectra of concretes.

8.11.6.5.4 HEAT GENERATION. Radiation-induced heating in concrete (Sec. 8.2.4.1) must be kept to a minimum to avoid local high temperatures that could dehydrate the concrete or cause cracking. An energy flux of 4×10^{10} Mev/cm^2/sec (of either neutrons or gamma-rays) produces a temperature rise of the order of 10 °F in ordinary concrete. This corresponds to a heat-generation rate of 0.6 to 1.0 mw/cm^3 (about 6 to 10 Btu/hr/cu ft), depending somewhat on the energy content of each gamma photon or neutron as well as on the density of the material. For information on methods of calculating

heating in concrete and associated effects see Secs. 8.6.6 to 8.6.8.

8.11.6.5.5 RADIATION DAMAGE. There exist no appreciable reliable data on radiation damage to concrete. Small specimens that have been irradiated show some gas evolution, presumably mostly water vapor and small amounts of dissociated hydrogen and oxygen. Compressive strength appears to change. It increases for ordinary concrete and decreases for MgO concrete. Radioactivity builds up under irradiation. From a design standpoint there are apparently no serious radiation-damage effects in concrete under reasonably high radiation fields other than the loss of water. Some damage was observed during the running of the ANL Borax-I tests: some of the concrete lining in the reactor pit was found to be crumbled. Hanging thick steel plate over the deteriorated spot stopped further crumbling [112]. Some British data on concrete irradiation are shown in Table 8.45; see also Ref. 81, p. 1104.

8.11.6.6 Quality Control and Placement of Concrete for Shields

The following rules, if adhered to during construction of concrete shields, will help to ensure the integrity of the shield: (1) the ore aggregate should be sound and free from deleterious materials, which may retard setting or have poor strength or aging properties, (2) the aggregate should be uniform as to size and shape of the recommended grades, and (3) the aggregates should be washed to remove rock dust, dirt, wood particles, and other foreign particles.

Table 8.37—Physical and Mechanical Properties of Limonite and Magnetite High-Density Concrete* [86,104]

Property	Age, days	Limonite (conventional)	Magnetite (conventional)	Limonite-iron		Limonite-magnetite	
				Conventional	Prepacked	Conventional	Prepacked
Density, g/cm^3							
Wet		2.96	3.41	4.27	4.37	3.44	3.43
Hardened				4.3-4.5[†]	4.37	3.58	3.43
Specific heat, cal/g/°C				0.166[†]	0.18	0.205	0.20
Thermal-expansion coefficient, per °C				6.8×10^{-6}[†]	1.07×10^{-5}	1.0×10^{-5}	0.9×10^{-5}
Thermal conductivity, Btu/hr/°F/ft				1.6-2.1[†]	2.75	1.54	1.36
Void volume, %					3.3	1.3	
Compressive strength, psi	7	4120	4610	4800[‡]	2210	3930	2830
	28	5870	6060	5580	3260	5550	4000
	90				3400	6540	4880
Bond strength, psi	28				930	650	820
Length change, psi (dimensional stability)	7	0.017	0.004	0.014	0.004	0.006	0.004
	28	0.016	0.007	0.019	0.004	0.008	0.004
	90				0.013	-.019	0.020
Elastic modulus, 10^6 psi (at 1000-psi stress)	7	3.78	7.45	5.90	4.28	4.31	3.98
	28	4.42	8.33	6.90	5.83	4.83	4.74
	90				4.69	4.82	3.33
Rupture modulus, psi	28	700	925	650	410	700	460
	90				280	630	430

* Values given are averaged over various tested specimens of varying compositions. The words "conventional" and "prepacked" refer to the method of placement of the aggregate.

† Values quoted are for the Brookhaven Graphite Pile Shield. Other values are from University of Washington data or Corps of Engineers NPD Laboratories.

‡ Value quoted for Brookhaven concrete. University of Washington data gives a value of 3710 psi [104].

Table 8.38—Physical and Mechanical Properties of Barytes and Barytes-limonite Concretes [105]

Property	Barytes concrete	Barytes-limonite concrete
Density, g/cm^3	3.5	3.25
Specific heat, cal/g/°C		0.15
At 122°F	0.123	
At 392°F	0.150	
Termal conductivity, Btu/hr/ft/°F		0.9
At 122°F	0.926	
At 212°F	0.997	
At 392°F	0.866	
At 482°F	0.745	
Compressive strength, psi		3750*
Age 28 days	3600	
Age 112 days	4200	
Shear strength, psi	845	800
Expension upon setting, in./in.		~10^{-3}
After 2 to 3 days	8 × 10^{-4}	
After 28 days	5 × 10^{-4}	

*Age 7 days.

High-density aggregates may settle out of the concrete during the settling period unless special placement methods (such as puddling or prepacking) are used. This is especially true of steel shot.

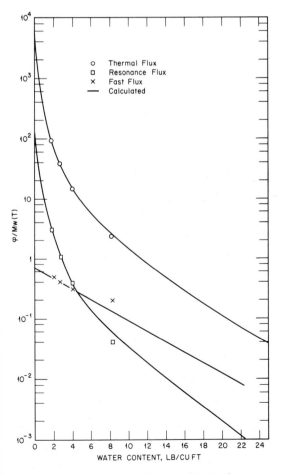

FIG. 8.57—Increase in neutron leakage as a function of water content (based on a thickness of 48 in. of ordinary concrete) [107].

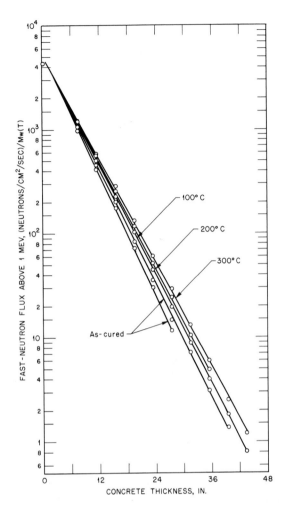

FIG. 8.58—Fast-neutron-flux distribution in ordinary concrete at various temperatures [107].

Shields made with ordinary concretes can be poured or pumped into forms by conventional methods. High-density or other special shielding concretes usually require special placement techniques to produce uniform homogeneous shields. Two methods are recommended: puddling, wherein layers of mortar and aggregate are placed alternately in the forms and then rodded or puddled together; and prepacking the aggregate, wherein the aggregates are laid uniformly in special forms and a grout is pumped into the void spaces. The prepacked method gives greater assurance that there will be no large voids and that the aggregate will be uniformly distributed.

Impurities in the aggregates or other ingredients in concrete may seriously affect the setting, aging, and physical and nuclear characteristics of concretes. Undesirable materials (such as opal in barite and clay in iron ore) produce deleterious effects on the setting characteristics, which, in turn, affect the aging and strength properties (see also Sec. 8.11.6.2).

Debris and dirt particles in unwashed aggregate may cause concrete to crack upon settling and

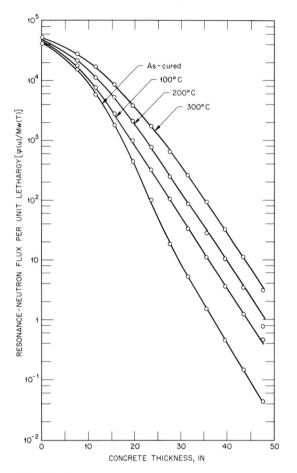

FIG. 8.59—Resonance-neutron-flux distribution in ordinary concrete at various temperatures [107].

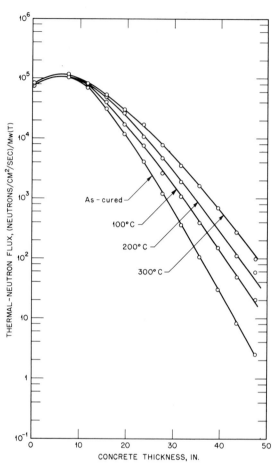

FIG. 8.60—Thermal-neutron-flux distribution in ordinary concrete at various temperatures [107].

crumble with age. Gas pockets formed by extreme heat generation during the setting process may create voids that weaken the concrete and decrease its shielding value.

8.11.7 GRAVEL, SAND, AND EARTH SHIELDS

8.11.7.1 Gravel Shields

For gamma-ray shielding the use of gravel shields is satisfactory in locations where size is not a factor but cost is. Ordinary tamped gravel can be expected to have an overall reliable density of about 90 lb/cu ft. Since gravel contains much the same elements as ordinary concrete, the thickness of a gravel shield will run about 1.7 times that of an equivalent concrete shield.

Loose gravel is not recommended for neutron shielding if space is a limitation. Gravel with enough limonite, serpentine, or other water-bearing aggregate to give 12 lb of water per cubic foot is suitable as a substitute for concrete where such can be properly used.

A special gravel shield mix [113] has been developed that has a density comparable with ordinary concrete. This gravel mix can be used in high rad-

iation areas where the gamma heat generation would be sufficiently high to crack ordinary concrete if there were no protective steel thermal shield. Such a case may be encountered in the design of a shield for spent core subassemblies removed from a fast reactor power plant after only a short decay time. The fission-product gamma rays from the spent fuel subassemblies may generate considerable heat in the shield. This heat generation in a concrete shield could result in a temperature distribution that would cause cracking and reduce shielding effectiveness.

Steel thermal shielding can be added to protect the concrete, but this is expensive. The substitution of a gravel mixture with the same density as ordinary concrete would circumvent the thermal-stress problems associated with an all-concrete shield wall in high radiation areas.

Table 8.46 shows a special gravel shield mix [85] which gives a minimum dry density of 145 lb/cu ft if properly placed. This mix was used at the Fermi plant in the spent-subassembly cleaning-room shield, where the surface radiation from the subassemblies at the time of cleaning is greater than 10^6 curies. The materials were mixed to a uniform color with just enough water so that the material began to glisten. The water was added to

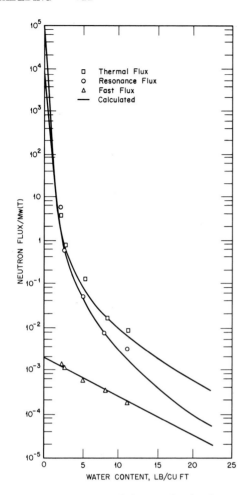

FIG. 8.61—Increase in neutron leakage as a function of water content (based on a thickness of 48 in. of ferrophosphorus concrete) [106].

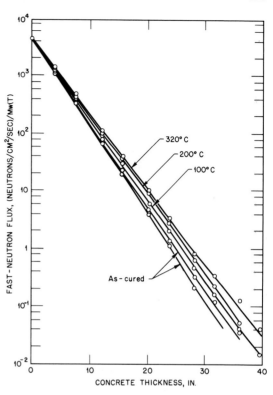

FIG. 8.62—Fast-neutron-flux distribution in ferrophosphorus concrete at various temperatures [106].

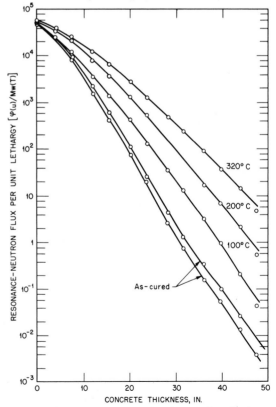

FIG. 8.63—Resonance-neutron-flux distribution in ferrophosphorus concrete at various temperatures [106].

aid compaction to the proper density. The coarse-limonite graduation is shown in Table 8.47. The use of limonite aggregate results in a density comparable to that of ordinary concrete. The materials can be mixed at a ready-mix plant in a manner similar to conventional concrete mixing. The special mix can be discharged directly from a ready-mix truck to the point of deposit and can be compacted with a Jackson vibrator or equivalent in layers not more than 12 in. thick. Density determinations can be obtained during compaction to ensure a minimum density. If greater density is required, increase compaction with the Jackson vibrator. The estimated cost for the in-place gravel shield at the Enrico Fermi plant was about $62.00 per cubic yard. This included a limonite aggregate cost of $18.00 per cubic yard (1 cu yard of limonite aggregate weighs about 1950 lb).

Experimental measurements in gravel have been made [114] in the Aerospace Systems Test Reactor (ASTR) facility with top soil and crushed limestone gravel having a density of about 96 lb/cu ft. The fast-neutron dose attenuation in this gravel is shown in Fig. 8.69; the attenuation of thermal neutrons in this gravel is shown in Fig. 8.70; and

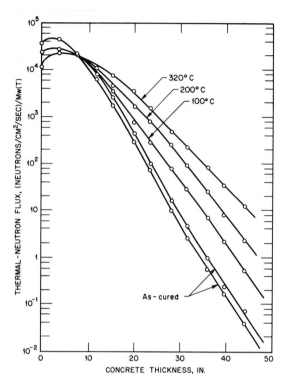

FIG. 8.64—Thermal-neutron-flux distribution in ferrophosphorus concrete at various temperatures [106].

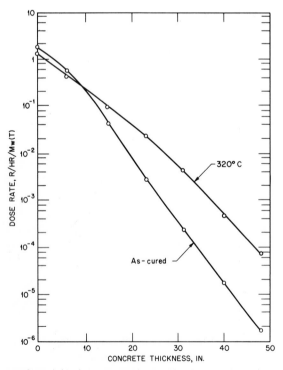

FIG. 8.65—Gamma-ray dose rate in ferrophosphorus concrete at various temperatures [106].

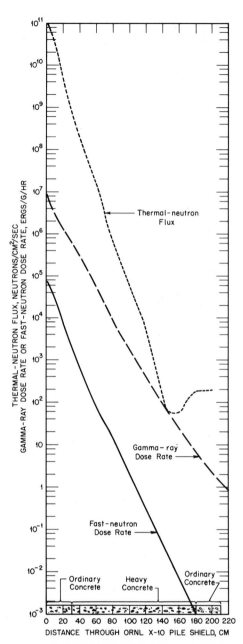

FIG. 8.66—Radiation distributions in the ORNL X-10 pile concrete shield at a power of 3500 kw(t) [108, 111].

the reactor gamma-ray attenuation curves are shown in Fig. 8.71. These curves show the fast-neutron relaxation length in this gravel to be about 24 cm and the reactor gamma-ray relaxation length to be about 28 cm.

8.11.7.2 Sand Shields

Moist sand can be used for gamma-ray shielding in place of gravel, provided it is used where there is no opportunity for the sand to shift or move from its original position. It will have roughly

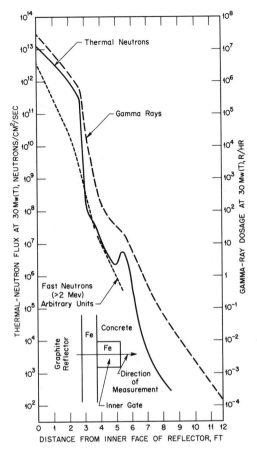

FIG. 8.67—Observed radiation intensities in the reflector and shield of the heavy-water NRX Reactor [109].

the same nuclear characteristics as gravel. Sand for use as a neutron shield should be used only in closed containers and should have a minimum moisture content of 5 wt.%.

The ASTR experiments mentioned above yielded information regarding the attenuation of nuclear radiation in wet and dry sand (Figs. 8.69, 8.70, and 8.71). The relaxation lengths of interest which may be deduced from these measurements are:

	Wet sand	Dry sand
Fast neutrons	15 cm	22 cm
Gamma rays	25 cm	32 cm

8.11.7.3 Earth Shields

Below-grade radiation protection may be acquired through the use of earth shields. Since dry earth may have a density of only 70 lb/cu ft, the earth-shield equivalent to a concrete gamma-ray shield is 2.5 times as thick. Earth with a great deal of clay in it may be taken to be equivalent to a gravel shield if the earth is always kept moist. Earth should not be used as neutron shielding if it is not enclosed within forms because

neutrons will be absorbed in it and may cause it to become an uncontrolled source (albeit small) of radioactivity.

From experimental measurements (Figs. 8.69, 8.70, and 8.71) of the nuclear radiation attenuation through clay and through a mixture of 72% top soil, 8% moisture, and 20% crushed gravel, the following relaxation lengths can be inferred:

	Clay	Top soil–gravel mixture
Fast neutrons	15 cm	17 cm
Gamma rays	34 cm	31 cm

8.11.8 SERPENTINE ROCK AND SERPENTINE CONCRETE

8.11.8.1 Serpentine Aggregate

Serpentine rock [115] is a mineral of asbestos having a fairly extensive distribution throughout the world.* It is essentially a hydrous magnesium silicate with the formula $3MgO \cdot 2SiO_2 \cdot 2H_2O$. The water of hydration in serpentine amounts to about 13.5 wt.%. A remarkable characteristic of this

* Only about 25% of that found in the western United States is suitable for shield use without extensive processing to remove the asbestos fiber [116].

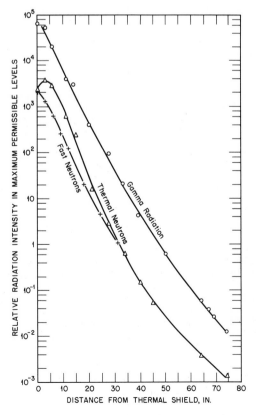

FIG. 8.68—Neutron and gamma intensities in the barytes concrete shield of the BEPO Reactor at a power of 6.3 Mw(t) [110].

Table 8.39—Tabulation of Elemental Data for Concretes [101]

Elements	Cross-section data[a]				Capture gamma-ray spectra, photons/100 captures[b]						
	σ_a, barns	σ_s, barns	σ_r, barns[c]	σ_T, barns[d]	1 Mev	2 Mev	3 Mev	4 Mev	6 Mev	8 Mev	10 Mev
H	0.33	99[e]	1.00	2.0		100					
B	755	4	0.97	1.7				110	28	6	0.8
C	0.003	4.8	0.72	1.5				100			
O	0.002	4.2	0.92	2.0							
Na	0.515	4.0	(1.14)	2.5	96	127	187	70	31		
Mg	0.063	3.6	(1.18)	2.0			28	72	10	3.3	0.57
Al	0.230	1.4	1.31	2.5	236	195	69	62	19	19	
Si	0.16	1.7	(1.30)	2.5	100	63	30	89	11	4.1	0.1
P	0.20	5	(1.39)	2.5	290	97	55	98	27	7.2	
S	0.52	1.1	(1.41)	2.5	70	32	72	70	44	6.5	
Cl	33.8	16	1.2	2.5	49	85	41	47	55	24	
K	2.07	1.5	(1.51)	3.0	100	81	57	106	37	4.7	
Ca	0.44	3.2	(1.52)	2.5	14	191	77	85	64	1.8	
Ti	5.8	4	(1.61)	3.0	54	160	16	24	78	1.3	0.2
V	5.00	5	(1.64)	3.0	83	132	11.4	21	67	16	
Cr	3.1	3.0	(1.64)	3.5	85	41	21	12	23	39	6.4
Mn	13.2	2.3	(1.67)	3.5	125	91	60	50	34	17	
Fe	2.53	11	1.98	3.0	75	60	27	23	25	38	2.1
Ni	4.6	17.5	1.89	3.0	84	40	23	23	34	62	0.8
Cu	3.77	3.6	(1.88)	3.5	68	47	26	30	27	43	
Zn	1.1	7.2	2.04	3.5	156	93	67	48	29	16	1
Mo	2.7	7	(2.21)	4.5	137	18		84	26	3	0.03
Ba	1.2	8	(2.69)	5.5				75	14	1.4	0.1

[a] 2200 m/sec.

[b] Troubetzkoy,,E., and H. Goldstein, *A Compilation of Information on Gamma Ray Spectra Resulting from Thermal Neutron Capture*, USAEC Report ORNL-2094, Jan. 18, 1961. See also Table 8.41.

[c] Parentheses around removal cross sections indicate that the value is emprical rather than experimental.

[d] Estimated value for 1 to 10 Mev.

[e] All hydrogen present is assumed to be in the form of water. The transport cross section for water is 2.083 cm^{-1}. Therefore, it was necessary to assign σ_s for hydrogen this value in order to obtain the required result.

molecule is that it has the ability to retain its water of crystallization under very much higher temperatures than is normally the case with hydrated molecules. The rock has a lump density of between 2.55 and 2.65 g/cm^3 (160 to 165 lb/cu ft). It can be piled loosely to a density of from 80 to 110 lb/cu ft. It can be easily crushed and tamped to a density of about 130 lb/cu ft. The crystalline asbestos chaff has to be removed before this latter density can be obtained. Table 8.48 shows the typical chemical analysis of serpentine rock; Table 8.49 gives the corresponding elemental analysis and Table 8.50 gives the general physical data on the material.

High-temperature tests were conducted on the material at Johns-Manville laboratories for periods varying from a few hours to over six weeks (1000 hr) [118]. The results of these tests indicate that once the free water (which runs about 1% of the total weight) has been driven off, the remaining water (about 12.5%) is released at a very slow rate up to temperatures of over 950°F. At 1000°F the dehydration is rather rapid. These results indicate that somewhere between 950 and 1000°F the bond between the water molecule and the remainder of the molecule is broken. The tests prove that the material can be taken up to at least 900°F without losing the hydrated water. Figure 8.72 is a summary of the Johns-Manville high-temperature data.

8.11.8.2 Dry Packed Serpentine as a Shield Material

Graded serpentine aggregate can be used as a dry-fill shield material for some high-temperature

areas where both neutron and gamma-ray shielding are required. Densities of the order of 130 lb/cu ft have been attained with a two-grade mixture, a coarse aggregate and a fine aggregate in the proper portions. The primary reason for the selection of a dry-filled serpentine-rock material is that it retains its neutron-shielding effectiveness at temperatures up to at least 800°F and has sufficient density to serve as a good gamma shield in areas where it is not practical to use serpentine concrete. Such an application is the use of dry-packed serpentine in the intermediate heat exchanger plugs (IHX plugs) and primary sodium-pump plugs that penetrate the biological-shield floor of the Enrico Fermi plant, as shown in Fig. 8.73. The serpentine rock used consisted of two grades, a 70 wt.% coarse mixture and a 30 wt.% fine rock mixture. The coarse mixture was graded so that all would pass through a 1/2-in.-mesh screen and be retained on a 10-mesh screen. The fine mixture was graded so that all would pass through a 30-mesh screen. The dry-fill was tamped with a pneumatic jack to a minimum density of 130 lb/cu ft. The IHX tank contains high-temperature radioactive sodium with a gamma-radiation background of the order 10^4 r/hr at the base of the plug at full power.

8.11.8.3 Serpentine Concrete

Serpentine aggregate can be used as an aggregate in concrete.* Table 8.51 gives a typical

---

*Recently Hanford has had success in grinding the aggregate into a sand and using it as a sand for the mix [116].

Table 8.40—Neutron Constants for Concretes [101]

Concrete	Density, ρ g/cm^3	σ_r, cm^{-1} calc.	σ_r, cm^{-1} exptl.	$1/\lambda$, cm^{-1} exptl.	σ_t, cm^{-1} calc.	σ_a, cm^{-1} calc.	D_{th}, cm	κ_{th_1}, cm^{-1}
01	2.33	0.0740	0.083*	0.090	0.149	0.0059	0.968	0.0778
02-a	2.30	0.0849			0.174	0.0094	0.484	0.139
02-b	2.20	0.0748			0.154	0.0074	0.749	0.0993
03	2.39	0.0837	0.086		0.168	0.0097	0.512	0.137
04	2.35	0.0793			0.162	0.0086	0.688	0.112
05	2.50	0.0833			0.179	0.0187	0.485	0.196
06	1.30	0.0611			0.126	0.380	0.406	0.968
07	2.09	0.0836			0.168	0.0850	0.378	0.474
0-HW1	2.33	0.0781	0.078	0.083	0.156	0.0129	0.629	0.143
0-HW2	2.26	0.0712	0.0735	0.078	0.142	0.0115	0.926	0.112
FP-a	4.68	0.125	0.15*		0.216	0.0924	0.344	0.518
FP-b	4.57	0.115			0.195	0.0903	0.463	0.442
FP-HW1	4.82	0.125	0.131	0.139	0.216	0.0902	0.358	0.502
FP-HW3	4.67	0.111	0.128	0.136	0.187	0.0872	0.585	0.386
BA-a	3.50	0.0926		0.125	0.188	0.0197	0.440	0.212
BA-b	3.39	0.0817			0.165	0.0176	0.667	0.162
BA-H	2.575	0.0643			0.125	0.0220	0.912	0.155
BAHA	2.35	0.0770			0.155	0.0128	0.421	0.174
BAHA-d	2.28	0.0773		0.098	0.158	0.0111	0.412	0.164
BA-OR	3.30	0.0985	0.0993		0.199	0.0224	0.334	0.259
M-a	3.55	0.106			0.198	0.0553	0.393	0.375
M-b	3.45	0.0966			0.179	0.0534	0.540	0.314
M-c	3.62	0.133			0.212	0.0566	0.330	0.414
M-HW1	3.29	0.0984		0.114	0.186	0.0402	0.482	0.289
M-HW2	3.27	0.0965		0.105	0.182	0.0398	0.517	0.277
I-1a	3.50	0.107			0.209	0.0848	0.419	0.450
I-1b	3.40	0.098			0.190	0.0829	0.592	0.374
I-2a	3.76	0.111			0.213	0.0975	0.401	0.493
I-2b	3.66	0.107			0.193	0.0956	0.557	0.414
I-NRU	3.49	0.0990			0.188	0.0699	0.536	0.361
I-NRUe	3.44	0.0983		0.075	0.187	0.0766	0.579	0.364
MS-a	4.70	0.124			0.213	0.0953	0.337	0.532
MS-b	4.60	0.114			0.193	0.0933	0.445	0.458
MS-c	4.73	0.127			0.220	0.0959	0.313	0.554
LS-a	4.54	0.121	0.114*		0.207	0.0888	0.340	0.511
LS-b	4.44	0.111			0.187	0.0868	0.445	0.437
LS-c	4.65	0.132			0.230	0.0910	0.268	0.583
LS-BRa	4.16	0.110			0.191	0.0800	0.382	0.458
LS-BRb	4.08	0.102			0.173	0.0783	0.502	0.395
LS-BRc	4.28	0.122		0.159	0.214	0.0823	0.290	0.532
LS-HW1	4.23	0.118	0.128		0.208	0.0800	0.316	0.503
LS-HW2	4.14	0.110	0.119		0.190	0.0782	0.396	0.445

*ANL Shield Facility (collimated beam).

chemical analysis of serpentine concrete; the corresponding elemental analysis is given in Table 8.49. Tests carried out [119] using a fairly large serpentine aggregate from small sizes up to about 1 in. and sand instead of the fine material indicate that compressive strengths of from 1500 to 2500 psi are attainable. The tests indicate that the densities attainable are on the order of 130 to 140 lb/cu ft, which is quite comparable with ordinary concrete.

Experimental data [122] on the thermal expansion of serpentine concrete is plotted as a function of temperature in Fig. 8.74. On the same plot are some experimental measurements made on stainless steel. At the boiling point of water, expansion of serpentine and stainless steel appears to be the same. The expansion of the serpentine concrete seems to be fairly erratic at high temperatures.

Sieve analyses for the fine and coarse serpentine aggregates used in the concrete for the Fermi plant are given in Table 8.52. The results of slump, moisture, density, shrinkage, and other tests are presented in Table 8.53.

The calculated nuclear properties of serpentine are given in Table 8.54 (see also Tables 8.39, 8.42, and 8.43). Note that from a neutron removal standpoint serpentine-aggregate concrete is about as good as concrete of comparable density.

8.11.9 CALCIUM BORATE*

8.11.9.1 General Description

Calcium borate [115] is the name applied to a number of borated calcium minerals, including hydrated calcium borate ($CaO \cdot 3B_2O_3 \cdot 2H_2O$), colemanite ($Ca_2B_6O_{11} \cdot 5H_2O$), and Gerstley borate, a mixture of the calcium minerals ulexite ($NaCaB_5O_9 \cdot 8H_2O$) and colemanite. The borated calcium minerals listed above are combined within a matrix of asbestos. The product has a boron content of about 12 wt.% and a density of around 70 lb/cu ft. It is pressed into 4- by 8-ft sheets and can be

---

*This product marketed by Johns-Manville under the trade name Sigma K.

Table 8.41—Gamma-ray Spectra from Thermal-neutron Capture in Concretes [101]

Concrete	Σ_a, cm^{-1} (calc.)	Photons per neutron capture						
		1 Mev	2 Mev	3 Mev	4 Mev	6 Mev	8 Mev	10 Mev
01	0.0059	0.355	1.29	0.676	0.715	0.408	0.0332	0.0003
02-a	0.0094	0.546	0.533	0.739	0.447	0.143	0.0542	0.0004
02-b	0.0074	0.694	0.678	0.668	0.569	0.182	0.0689	0.0005
03	0.0097	0.374	0.911	0.751	0.483	0.284	0.0514	0.0003
04	0.0086	0.675	0.765	0.694	0.595	0.218	0.0618	0.0004
05	0.0187	0.781	0.796	0.611	0.435	0.277	0.127	0.0006
06	0.380	0.0047	0.0032	0.0171	1.08	0.275	0.0593	0.0078
07	0.0850	0.0477	0.0475	0.0916	1.00	0.261	0.0017	0.0071
0-HW1	0.0129	0.636	0.813	0.584	0.420	0.270	0.151	0.0010
0-HW2	0.0115	0.713	0.912	0.533	0.471	0.302	0.169	0.0011
FP-a	0.0924	0.871	0.655	0.373	0.302	0.258	0.312	0.0016
FP-b	0.0903	0.890	0.670	0.359	0.308	0.264	0.319	0.0016
FP-HW1	0.0902	0.873	0.669	0.309	0.283	0.284	0.320	0.0036
FP-HW3	0.0872	0.903	0.692	0.286	0.293	0.294	0.331	0.0037
BA-a	0.0197	0.279	0.274	0.426	0.483	0.204	0.0920	0.0008
BA-b	0.0176	0.313	0.307	0.357	0.541	0.229	0.103	0.0009
BA-H	0.0220	0.576	0.511	0.323	0.372	0.224	0.257	0.0016
BAHA	0.0128	0.244	0.391	0.635	0.442	0.176	0.0278	0.0004
BAHAd	0.0111	0.195	0.344	0.618	0.374	0.139	0.0413	0.0005
BA-OR	0.0224	0.330	0.298	0.477	0.383	0.184	0.126	0.0009
M-a	0.0553	0.676	0.721	0.325	0.240	0.304	0.296	0.0020
M-b	0.0534	0.700	0.747	0.301	0.249	0.315	0.307	0.0020
M-c	0.0566	0.660	0.704	0.341	0.235	0.297	0.289	0.0019
M-HW1	0.0402	0.698	0.615	0.338	0.247	0.244	0.337	0.0019
M-HW2	0.0398	0.705	0.621	0.332	0.249	0.246	0.340	0.0019
I-1a	0.0848	0.568	1.34	0.242	0.250	0.636	0.0783	0.0018
I-1b	0.0829	0.581	1.37	0.225	0.256	0.650	0.0801	0.0019
I-2a	0.0975	0.599	1.25	0.248	0.248	0.588	0.116	0.0018
I-2b	0.0956	0.611	1.27	0.234	0.253	0.600	0.118	0.0019
I-NRU	0.0699	0.632	1.07	0.246	0.240	0.496	0.189	0.0020
I-NRUe	0.0766	0.618	1.15	0.229	0.239	0.540	0.165	0.0020
MS-a	0.0953	0.705	0.647	0.304	0.234	0.271	0.339	0.0020
MS-b	0.0933	0.723	0.661	0.290	0.239	0.277	0.346	0.0020
MS-c	0.0959	0.701	0.643	0.309	0.232	0.269	0.337	0.0020
LS-a	0.0888	0.713	0.600	0.315	0.237	0.245	0.352	0.0019
LS-b	0.0868	0.729	0.614	0.299	0.243	0.251	0.360	0.0020
LS-c	0.0910	0.696	0.585	0.332	0.231	0.239	0.344	0.0019
LS-BRa	0.0800	0.712	0.603	0.313	0.236	0.246	0.354	0.0020
LS-BRb	0.0783	0.728	0.616	0.298	0.241	0.252	0.362	0.0020
LS-BRc	0.0823	0.693	0.586	0.332	0.229	0.240	0.345	0.0019
LS-HW1	0.0800	0.695	0.589	0.324	0.230	0.241	0.339	0.0019
LS-HW2	0.0782	0.711	0.602	0.309	0.235	0.247	0.357	0.0020

ordered in various thicknesses from 1/2 in. up to about 2 1/2 in. Though the material is slightly brittle, it can be easily fabricated; it handles somewhat like plaster board. It can be cut and sawed rather easily into shapes and is strong enough to support its own weight. Tests on this material indicate that it will withstand temperatures to 1800°F with less than 3% shrinkage. At 1000°F the measured shrinkage is about 0.5% after 24 hr. It has successfully undergone a great number of temperature-cycling tests. Results of these tests indicate that when the material is properly calcined, no cracks develop or spalling or crumbling take place under expected operating conditions. When freshly made, this material contains about 7 wt. % of moisture, but, after firing at about 1000°F, it loses most of this, retaining only about 2% of the total weight. The rupture modulus of the material in shear is reported to be higher than 400 psi.

8.11.9.2 Composition and Properties

Typical chemical analyses of calcium borate shield material are given in Tables 8.55 and 8.56.

These are taken from a sample having a density of about 71 lb/cu ft. Table 8.57 lists the measured physical properties of the material [123].

8.11.9.3 Temperature Effects

This material withstands high temperatures well [124]. Caution must be observed in using the material under high rates of change of temperature. Improperly developed material may crack in places parallel to its wide surfaces. Figures 8.75 to 8.77 show temperature effects on water retention, thermal conductivity, and shrinkage of the material.

8.11.9.4 Irradiation Tests

This material has undergone extensive neutron-irradiation tests and has withstood a total integrated flux of over 2×10^{20} neutrons/cm^2 without showing any loss of strength. Table 8.58 gives the results of pre- and postirradiation tests on dimensional changes and compressive strength. These samples prepared by Johns-Manville were cylinders 1 in. in diameter and 7/8 in. high. Six of these were put

Table 8.42—Total Gamma-ray Linear Attenuation Coefficients (cm^{-1}) of Concretes [101]

Concrete	Density, g/cm^3	Photon energy								
		0.5 Mev	1 Mev	2 Mev	3 Mev	4 Mev	5 Mev	6 Mev	8 Mev	10 Mev
01	2.33	0.2033	0.1482	0.1042	0.0851	0.0743	0.0675	0.0630	0.0570	0.0539
02-a	2.30	0.2017	0.1473	0.1034	0.0841	0.0732	0.0663	0.0615	0.0554	0.0520
02-b	2.20	0.1917	0.1400	0.0983	0.0801	0.0697	0.0632	0.0587	0.0529	0.0497
03	2.39	0.2095	0.1527	0.1074	0.0877	0.0766	0.0696	0.0649	0.0588	0.0556
04	2.35	0.2040	0.1489	0.1046	0.0852	0.0744	0.0674	0.0627	0.0566	0.0533
05	2.50	0.2188	0.1596	0.1122	0.0916	0.0801	0.0728	0.0679	0.0615	0.0581
06	1.30	0.1154	0.0843	0.0591	0.0479	0.0415	0.0374	0.0346	0.0309	0.0288
07	2.09	0.1841	0.1343	0.0943	0.0768	0.0668	0.0605	0.0561	0.0506	0.0474
0-HW1	2.33	0.2025	0.1476	0.1038	0.0849	0.0744	0.0677	0.0632	0.0575	0.0545
0-HW2	2.26	0.1957	0.1426	0.1004	0.0821	0.0720	0.0656	0.0613	0.0588	0.0529
FP-a	4.68	0.3946	0.2851	0.2024	0.1697	0.1529	0.1430	0.1371	0.1304	0.1280
FP-b	4.57	0.3839	0.2773	0.1969	0.1653	0.1491	0.1397	0.1341	0.1277	0.1256
FP-HW1	4.82	0.4058	0.2930	0.2080	0.1747	0.1576	0.1477	0.1418	0.1351	0.1329
FP-HW3	4.67	0.3915	0.2825	0.2007	0.1688	0.1526	0.1432	0.1377	0.1316	0.1297
BA-a	3.50	0.3168	0.2142	0.1517	0.1295	0.1187	0.1130	0.1097	0.1066	0.1064
BA-b	3.39	0.3054	0.2058	0.1459	0.1248	0.1147	0.1094	0.1065	0.1038	0.1038
BA-H	2.57	0.2265	0.1569	0.1112	0.0941	0.0856	0.0809	0.0781	0.0752	0.0745
BAHA	2.35	0.2108	0.1470	0.1038	0.0869	0.0782	0.0731	0.0698	0.0661	0.0647
BAHA-d	2.28	0.2038	0.1425	0.1005	0.0838	0.0751	0.0699	0.0666	0.0627	0.0610
BA-OR	3.30	0.2964	0.2030	0.1436	0.1217	0.1107	0.1047	0.1010	0.0972	0.0963
M-a	3.55	0.3027	0.2192	0.1550	0.1290	0.1150	0.1066	0.1014	0.0950	0.0922
M-b	3.45	0.2932	0.2132	0.1502	0.1251	0.1117	0.1036	0.0987	0.0927	0.0900
M-c	3.62	0.3093	0.2240	0.1684	0.1317	0.1174	0.1087	0.1033	0.0967	0.0937
M-HW1	3.29	0.2809	0.2037	0.1439	0.1192	0.1059	0.0977	0.0926	0.0863	0.0833
M-HW2	3.27	0.2789	0.2022	0.1429	0.1184	0.1052	0.0971	0.0921	0.0958	0.0828
I-1a	3.50	0.2997	0.2173	0.1535	0.1271	0.1129	0.1042	0.0987	0.0919	0.0886
I-1b	3.40	0.2902	0.2103	0.1486	0.1233	0.1096	0.1012	0.0960	0.0895	0.0864
I-2a	3.76	0.3193	0.2312	0.1635	0.1361	0.1214	0.1126	0.1071	0.1005	0.0975
I-2b	3.66	0.3090	0.2236	0.1582	0.1319	0.1178	0.1093	0.1042	0.0979	0.0951
I-NRU	3.49	0.2965	0.2147	0.1518	0.1263	0.1126	0.1043	0.0992	0.0930	0.0902
I-NRUe	3.44	0.2909	0.2106	0.1490	0.1241	0.1108	0.1028	0.0978	0.0919	0.0892
MS-a	4.70	0.3957	0.2855	0.2027	0.1706	0.1542	0.1446	0.1391	0.1328	0.1308
MS-b	4.60	0.3860	0.2783	0.1977	0.1666	0.1507	0.1416	0.1363	0.1304	0.1286
MS-c	4.73	0.3989	0.2878	0.2043	0.1719	0.1553	0.1456	0.1400	0.1336	0.1315
LS-a	4.54	0.3827	0.2761	0.1960	0.1650	0.1490	0.1398	0.1344	0.1283	0.1263
LS-b	4.44	0.3727	0.2688	0.1909	0.1609	0.1455	0.1367	0.1316	0.1258	0.1241
LS-c	4.65	0.3935	0.2840	0.2015	0.1694	0.1528	0.1432	0.1375	0.1310	0.1288
LS-BRa	4.16	0.3511	0.2533	0.1798	0.1513	0.1365	0.1280	0.1230	0.1173	0.1154
LS-BRb	4.08	0.3426	0.2471	0.1755	0.1478	0.1336	0.1253	0.1206	0.1152	0.1135
LS-BRc	4.28	0.3623	0.2615	0.1855	0.1558	0.1405	0.1315	0.1262	0.1201	0.1179
LS-HW1	4.23	0.3578	0.2583	0.1833	0.1539	0.1387	0.1298	0.1246	0.1185	0.1164
LS-HW2	4.14	0.3492	0.2519	0.1788	0.1503	0.1357	0.1271	0.1221	0.1164	0.1144

in an aluminum capsule, sealed, and sent to the MTR for irradiation. After irradiation these samples were taken to the hot caves at Battelle Memorial Institute for the postirradiation measurements.

8.11.9.5 Nuclear Data

On the basis of the known experimental data and of generally available cross-section data, the nuclear properties of calcium borate were calculated. They are given in Table 8.59.

8.11.9.6 Calcium Borate Pipe Shields

Calcium borate material is being used as a shield material for 30-in.-diameter pipe shields at the Fermi plant [45, 46, 115]. It is also being used in ring shields or donuts, which fit on pipes to block streaming passages. Figure 8.110 is a view of a 30-in. pipe shield, showing the construction details of the calcium borate, and Fig. 8.111 is a photograph of one of the shields during construction. Four donut or ring shields are used in

this design to prevent neutron streaming in the gaps along the side of the pipes. Figure 8.78 shows the use of calcium borate and insulation staggered around the pipe to provide reduced gap space for streaming.

8.11.10 A GRAPHITE–BORON CARBIDE– IRON SHOT SHIELD MIX

A shielding mixture was developed for use in the annular areas within and around the Fermi reactor safety-rod drive mechanism [126]. It was desirable to obtain a material that would meet the following specifications: (1) serve as both a good neutron and gamma radiation shield, (2) be in powder form so that it could be compacted in small annular gaps, (3) withstand a temperature of 1000°F and maintain its shielding effectiveness over the life of the plant, and (4) have a minimum density of about 1.80 g/cm^3. The shielding material consists of a mixture of graphite, boron carbide, and iron shot as shown in Table 8.60. As developed for the Fermi plant application, the graphite (Great Lakes Carbon Corporation, grade 1036 or equiva-

Table 8.43—Gamma-ray Energy-absorption Linear Attenuation Coefficients (cm^{-1}) of Concretes [101]

Concrete	Density, g/cm^3	Photon energy								
		0.5 Mev	1 Mev	2 Mev	3 Mev	4 Mev	5 Mev	6 Mev	8 Mev	10 Mev
01	2.33	0.0694	0.0650	0.0558	0.0507	0.0477	0.0456	0.0444	0.0428	0.0423
02-a	2.30	0.0684	0.0644	0.0551	0.0499	0.0466	0.0443	0.0429	0.0410	0.0403
02-b	2.20	0.0650	0.0612	0.0524	0.0475	0.0444	0.0423	0.0410	0.0392	0.0386
03	2.39	0.0716	0.0670	0.0575	0.0523	0.0492	0.0470	0.0458	0.0441	0.0437
04	2.35	0.0693	0.0651	0.0558	0.0506	0.0475	0.0452	0.0439	0.0422	0.0415
05	2.50	0.0746	0.0699	0.0600	0.0546	0.0513	0.0491	0.0478	0.0461	0.0456
06	1.30	0.0391	0.0369	0.0315	0.0283	0.0263	0.0249	0.0239	0.0227	0.0222
07	2.09	0.0627	0.0589	0.0504	0.0456	0.0426	0.0406	0.0393	0.0376	0.0370
0-HW1	2.33	0.0691	0.0647	0.0556	0.0507	0.0478	0.0458	0.0447	0.0432	0.0429
0-HW2	2.26	0.0668	0.0625	0.0537	0.0490	0.0463	0.0444	0.0434	0.0420	0.0417
FP-a	4.68	0.1382	0.1251	0.1096	0.1040	0.1020	0.1015	0.1020	0.1035	0.1067
FP-b	4.75	0.1345	0.1217	0.1068	0.1014	0.0996	0.0993	0.0999	0.1015	0.1048
FP-HW1	4.82	0.1424	0.1286	0.1127	0.1072	0.1054	0.1051	0.1057	0.1075	0.1110
FP-HW3	4.67	0.1375	0.1240	0.1088	0.1038	0.1022	0.1022	0.1029	0.1049	0.1085
BA-a	3.50	0.1263	0.0978	0.0840	0.0813	0.0815	0.0825	0.0839	0.0869	0.0905
BA-b	3.39	0.1224	0.0941	0.0809	0.0786	0.0790	0.0802	0.0817	0.0848	0.0885
BA-H	2.57	0.0862	0.0705	0.0610	0.0585	0.0580	0.0583	0.0590	0.0605	0.0626
BAHA	2.35	0.0790	0.0659	0.0566	0.0534	0.0522	0.0517	0.0518	0.0522	0.0535
BAHA-d	2.28	0.0762	0.0639	0.0547	0.0514	0.0499	0.0493	0.0491	0.0492	0.0502
BA-OR	3.30	0.1153	0.0920	0.0791	0.0758	0.0752	0.0756	0.0764	0.0783	0.0811
M-a	3.55	0.1055	0.0962	0.0837	0.0784	0.0759	0.0746	0.0743	0.0742	0.0756
M-b	3.45	0.1022	0.0932	0.0811	0.0761	0.0738	0.0727	0.0724	0.0725	0.0740
M-c	3.62	0.1077	0.0984	0.0855	0.0800	0.0773	0.0760	0.0756	0.0754	0.0768
M-HW1	3.29	0.0976	0.0894	0.0776	0.0722	0.0695	0.0680	0.0674	0.0669	0.0678
M-HW2	3.27	0.0969	0.0888	0.0771	0.0717	0.0691	0.0676	0.0670	0.0665	0.0675
I-1a	3.50	0.1041	0.0955	0.0828	0.0770	0.0741	0.0725	0.0718	0.0712	0.0722
I-1b	3.40	0.1009	0.0924	0.0802	0.0747	0.0720	0.0705	0.0700	0.0695	0.0705
I-2a	3.76	0.1114	0.1016	0.0884	0.0828	0.0801	0.0789	0.0786	0.0785	0.0801
I-2b	3.66	0.1079	0.0982	0.0855	0.0803	0.0779	0.0768	0.0766	0.0767	0.0783
I-NRU	3.49	0.1033	0.0943	0.0820	0.0767	0.0743	0.0731	0.0727	0.0726	0.0740
I-NRUe	3.44	0.1015	0.0925	0.0805	0.0755	0.0732	0.0721	0.0718	0.0719	0.0733
MS-a	4.70	0.1392	0.1253	0.1100	0.1048	0.1032	0.1032	0.1039	0.1058	0.1095
MS-b	4.60	0.1359	0.1221	0.1073	0.1025	0.1011	0.1012	0.1020	0.1041	0.1078
MS-c	4.73	0.1403	0.1263	0.1108	0.1056	0.1039	0.1038	0.1045	0.1064	0.1100
LS-a	4.54	0.1345	0.1211	0.1063	0.1013	0.0997	0.0996	0.1004	0.1022	0.1057
LS-b	4.44	0.1311	0.1179	0.1036	0.0989	0.0975	0.0976	0.0984	0.1004	0.1039
LS-c	4.65	0.1382	0.1246	0.1092	0.1039	0.1021	0.1018	0.1024	0.1041	0.1075
LS-BRa	4.16	0.1234	0.1112	0.0975	0.0928	0.0913	0.0912	0.0918	0.0933	0.0964
LS-BRb	4.08	0.1205	0.1085	0.0952	0.0908	0.0895	0.0894	0.0901	0.0918	0.0950
LS-BRc	4.28	0.1272	0.1148	0.1006	0.0956	0.0938	0.0935	0.0940	0.0953	0.0984
LS-HW1	4.23	0.1257	0.1134	0.0993	0.0944	0.0926	0.0923	0.0927	0.0941	0.0971
LS-HW2	4.14	0.1227	0.1106	0.0970	0.0923	0.0907	0.0905	0.0910	0.0925	0.0956

lent) was graded as 80 ± 5% through No. 4 and retained on No. 20 mesh. The graphite flour (Great Lakes Carbon Corporation, grade 1008 or equivalent) was graded as 55 ± 5% through No. 200 mesh. The chilled iron shot was Metals Disintegrating Company's Grade S-110 or equivalent, and the boron carbide was Norbide high-purity technical-grade boron carbide (325°F), 25 μ, or equivalent.

The theoretical maximum density of the mixture is 2.06 g/cm^3 (128.5 lb/cu ft). The material should be mixed and blended in small batches to a homogeneous mixture of the proportions specified. Samples should be taken periodically during the blending process, and a sample should be taken of the final mixture. A sieve analysis should be run and compared with a control sample to assure adequate blending before installation of the mixture. Considerable care should be taken in blending and in handling the blended mixture since the mixture is very susceptible to segregation. Vibration, either during installation or during subsequent handling, is to be avoided. Tests indicate a strong tendency of the mixture to segregate when it is subjected to vibration; therefore the mixture should be compacted by a jolting technique (not by vibration). The mixture should be sealed from an oxidizing atmosphere. Off-gassing in an inert atmosphere is desirable after the mixture has been placed. If it cannot be off-gassed, enough space should be allowed for off-gassing during operation. The mixture should not be used where there are likely to be strong vibrations that might cause segregation. The calculated nuclear properties of the shielding mixture are given in Table 8.61.

8.11.11 LEAD

Lead is probably one of the most common gamma shield materials used where there are space limitations. It is not a structural material and may require the use of steel linings. Temperature is often a limiting factor in its use. The material is also relatively expensive as compared to other shield materials. Because of its gamma-ray-absorption effectiveness, it can be used to best advantage wherever there is a thickness limitation. The chem-

Table 8.44—Effective Atomic Numbers for Determining the Buildup Factors for Concretes [101]

Concrete symbol	Density, g/cm³	Type	Effective atomic number	Reference
01	2.33	Ordinary	12	J. R. Hogerton and R. C. Grass, *The Reactor Handbook, Vol I, Physics*, p. 674. USAEC Report AECD-3645, March 1955.
04	2.35	Ordinary	11	G. W. Grodstein, *X-Ray Attenuation Coefficients from 10 kev to 100 Mev.*, p. 50, NBS Circular 583, Apr. 30, 1957.
0-HW1	2.33	Ordinary	12	E. C. Peterson, *Shielding Properties of Ordinary Concrete as a Function of Temperature*, p. 24, USAEC Report HW-65572, Aug. 2, 1960.
FP-a	4.68	Ferrophosphorus	21	E. E. Hamer, personal communication.
FP-HW1	4.82	Ferrophosphorus	21	E. G. Peterson, *Shielding Properties of Ferrophosphorus Concrete as a Function of Temperature*, pp. 43-44, USAEC Report HW-64774, July 15, 1960.
BA-a	3.50	Barytes	27	J. R. Hogerton and R. C. Grass, *The Reactor Handbook, Vol I, Physics*, p. 674, USAEC Report, AECD-3645, March 1955.
BA-OR	3.30	Barytes	25	W. J. Grantham, Jr., *Barytes Concrete for Radiation Shielding: Mix Criteria and Attenuation Characteristics*, p. 44, USAEC Report ORNL-3130, July 25, 1961.
M-a	3.55	Magnetite	17	*The Experimental Boiling Water Reactor*, p. 60, USAEC Report ANL-5607, May 1957.
M-HW1	3.29	Magnetite	17	D. E. Wood, *The Effect of Temperature on the Neutron Attenuation of Magnetite Concrete*, p. 16, USAEC Report HW-58497, Dec. 11, 1958.
I-NRUe	3.44	Ilmenite	18	J. M. Robson, *The Attenuation of Neutrons by the Side Shield of the NRU Reactor*, pp. 15-16, Canadian Report CRP-860, October 1959.
MS-a	4.70	Magnetite and Steel	22	*The Experimental Boiling Water Reactor*, p. 60, USAEC Report ANL-5607, May 1957.
LS-HW1	4.23	Limonite and Steel	21	W. L. Bunch, *Attenuation Properties of High Density Portland Cement Concretes as a Function of Temperature*, p. 39, USAEC Report HW-54656, Jan. 22, 1958.

ical compositions of several types of commercially available lead are given in Table 8.62. The physical and mechanical properties of lead are given in Table 8.63.

8.11.12 LEAD-FILLED EPOXY RESIN

Lead-filled epoxy resins [129, 130] can be used in low radiation fields in areas where both shielding and sealing properties are required (or shield blocks may be cast, as needed). The resin comes as a liquid. It is mixed with a hardening agent, poured into a mold, and allowed to cure overnight. Directions for its use and its properties are given in Table 8.64. Most epoxy resins and other plastic materials have temperature limitations and should not be used at temperatures higher than those recommended by the manufacturer. These limits will in general lie within the range 200 to 300°F.

8.11.13 PERMALI*

Permali [131, 132] is a resin-impregnated plywood with a density of 1.34 g/cm³. It has better shielding characteristics than water. There are two basic types made for shielding. The first is Permali N, made from wood veneers that have been vacuum impregnated with a creosol formaldehyde synthetic resin and subsequently bonded under heat and pressure (2000 psi) until a specific gravity approaching 1.34 is attained. An epoxy-boron coating can be applied between the laminations, if desired. In this application the boron is not uniformly distributed. A second type, Permali JN, is made by impregnating selected wood veneers with a soluble solution of boron; the laminations are coated with a film of phenolic glue and bonded together under

*Known in England by the trade name Jabroc.

Table 8.45—Effects of Irradiation on the Properties of Concrete*†

Block	Irradiation time, months	Thermal flux, 10¹² neutrons/cm²/sec	Integrated thermal flux, neutrons/cm²	Total rate of energy deposition, watts/cm²	Weight loss, %	Rupture stress, psi
Q	2	1.1	0.5	0.011	2	1073
R	2	1.1	0.5	0.011	2.1	1076
S	6	1.2	1.6	0.012	2.4	918
T	6	1.2	1.6	0.012	2.6	810
U	12	1.3	3	0.013	2.2	810
V	12	1.3	3	0.013	2.6	940
W	24	1.4	7	0.014		734
X	24	1.4	7	0.014		627

*From B. T. Price, C. C. Horton, and K. T. Spinney, *Radiation Shielding*, Pergamon Press, New York, 1957.
†Observations by A. W. Chisholm-Batten.

Table 8.46—Special Gravel Shield Mix* [85]

Material	Dry-weight content		
	Weight %	Weight lb/cu yd	Weight lb/cu ft
Sand	39.75	1567	58.0
Stone	15.00	591	21.9
Coarse limonite	45.00	1774	65.7
Kaolin	0.25	9.85	0.37
Plastiment	12 fluid oz/cu yd		
Wet weight	160.6 lb/cu ft		
Dry weight	146.0 lb/cu ft		
Moisture content	10%		

* This mix was developed by Toledo Testing Laboratory under the direction of Commonwealth Associates, Inc., Enrico Fermi Power Plant architect-engineer.

heat and pressure. The manufacturer does not specify what boron contents can be obtained. It may be surmised, however, that, with the proper solution, boron contents up to 2 or 3 wt. % are possible. Neutron-attenuation experiments with this material show it to have an attenuating ability similar to Lucite. Its gamma-ray properties are also presumably similar to Lucite.

The properties of Permali are given in Table 8.65 and the cost data are given in Table 8.66. This material is being used for top-floor shielding at Dounreay (Figs. 8.51 and 8.79), the outer face of the shield for Reactor G2 at Marcoule, France, and on a chimney type refueling machine for the AGR at Windscale, England.

8.12 Nuclear Data for Fast Reactor Shielding Calculations

8.12.1 DISCUSSION

The nuclear data presented here are not intended to be complete; they are the data of most interest and use to a fast reactor shield designer. Admittedly the material presented is selective; however, more extensive sources are suggested for the reader who does not find what he needs in these pages. A small amount of nuclear data is presented in Sec. 8.11 in connection with the discussion of properties of specific materials.

Table 8.47—Coarse-limonite Gradation for Gravel Shield Mix [85]

	%
Total passing 2 1/2-in. screen	100
2-in. screen	95.8
1 1/2-in. screen	89.6
1-in. screen	73.2
3/4-in. screen	52.8
1/2-in. screen	25.1
3/8-in. screen	7.3
No. 4 sieve	0.50
Specific gravity	3.31

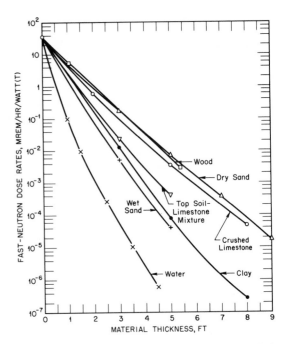

FIG. 8.69—Fast-neutron dose rates as a function of material thickness [114].

8.12.2 GENERAL NUCLEAR CONSTANTS

The following nuclear constants are given in Tables 8.67 and 8.68: atomic numbers, atomic weights, densities, and atomic densities of the elements [81] (Table 8.67) and molecular densities of compounds found in shielding materials and atomic densities of hydrogen in the compounds (Table 8.68).

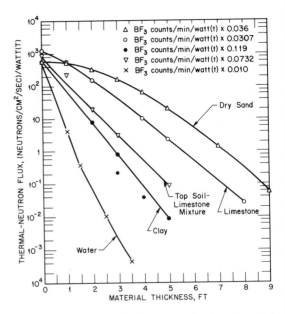

FIG. 8.70—Thermal-neutron fluxes as a function of material thickness [114].

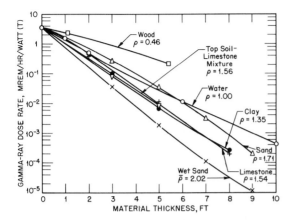

FIG. 8.71—Gamma-ray dose rates as a function of material thickness [114].

For expanded tables on nuclear constants, the following references are suggested: general atomic parameters, Ref. 133; atomic masses and binding energies, Ref. 133; fission-product decay schemes, Ref. 134; decay schemes of the elements, Refs. 52, 133, and 135; general reactor constants, Ref. 136.

8.12.3 NEUTRON CROSS SECTIONS

8.12.3.1 Multigroup Diffusion Cross Sections

Neutron cross sections especially developed for multigroup fast reactor diffusion calculations are given in Tables 8.69 to 8.71.

In addition capture cross sections are given as a function of neutron energy in Figs. 8.80 to 8.86: Ar^{41}, Fig. 8.80; B^{10}, Fig. 8.81; carbon, Fig. 8.82; sodium, Fig. 8.83; stainless steel, Fig. 8.84; boron steel, Fig. 8.85; and iron, Fig. 8.86.

8.12.3.2 Removal Cross Sections

Neutron-removal cross sections [140, 141] are presented in Tables 8.72 to 8.74.

8.12.3.3 Cross-section References

For other neutron cross section data, see the following references: total cross sections, Ref. 142; (n, p), (n, α), $(n, 2n)$ cross sections, Ref. 81; total, scattering, and miscellaneous cross sections, Ref. 143; and other multigroup cross sections, Refs. 137 and 144.

8.12.4 GAMMA-RAY ABSORPTION COEFFICIENTS

Selected mass-absorption coefficients at various energies are given in Table 8.75 (mass-absorption coefficients) and Table 8.76 (energy-absorption coefficients).

Figure 8.87 shows how the mass-absorption coefficient for ordinary concrete varies as a function of energy.

Table 8.48—Chemical Analysis of Serpentine Rock*

Compound	Composition, wt. %
MgO	40.0
SiO₂	39.3
H₂O†	12.2
FeO	3.8
Fe₂O₃	2.1
Al₂O₃	1.5
CaO	0.61
NiO	0.39
Cr₂O₃	0.35
K₂O	0.18
Na₂O	0.10
TiO₂	0.05
Cl‡	0.01 – 0.1
P₂O₅	Trace
ZrO₂	Trace
Mn₂O₃	Trace

* Analysis carried out by Johns-Manville [117].

† Water content varies slightly. This value represents a minimum.

‡ As $MgCl_2$ or $NaCl$.

8.12.5 GAMMA RAYS FROM INELASTIC SCATTERING

Table 8.77 presents data on the emission of gamma rays by inelastic scattering of neutrons from various elements [23, 136].

8.12.6 GAMMA RAYS FROM NEUTRON CAPTURE

Table 8.78 summarizes the emission data on gamma rays from neutron capture [148, 149, 150] in elements.

Table 8.49—Elemental Composition of Serpentine Rock and Concrete [3]

Element	Composition, wt. %	
	Serpentine rock	Serpentine concrete*
O	50.1	51.2
Mg	24.2	13.5
Si	18.3	20.9
Fe	4.4	3.1
H	1.4	1.6
Al	0.7	1.9
Ca	0.3	6.8
Ni	0.2	0.1
Cr	0.2	0.1
K	0.1	0.4
Na		0.4
Ti	< 0.1	Trace
Cl		Trace
P		Trace
Zr	Trace	Trace
Mn		Trace
C		0.1

* Gradation as given in Table 8.47.

Table 8.50—Physical Properties of Serpentine Rock and
Serpentine Concrete[a]

Property	Serpentine rock	Serpentine concrete[b]
Density, g/cm^3		2.06 - 2.2
Lump	2.60 - 2.65	
Loose material	1.3 - 1.6	
Dry, rodded	1.58	
Fine aggregate, tamped	2.08	
Density, lb/cu ft		130 - 140
Lump	160 - 165	
Loose material	80 - 100	
Dry, rodded	98.6	
Fine aggregate, tamped	130	
Thermal conductivity, Btu/hr/sq ft/°F/in.	3.0 at 125°F	∼6
Coefficient of expansion, per °F	15×10^{-6}	$\sim 18 \times 10^{-6}$
Water content, [c] wt. %	13.5	
Wet		16.8[e]
After heating at 300°F, 5 hr[d]		14.9[e]
After heating at 300°F, 10 hr[d]		13.9[e]
Shrinkage, average linear, %	∼0	< 0.05
Volume, %		< 0.13
Compressive strength, psi		1900 - 2300[f]

[a] Data supplied by Johns-Manville, The Toledo Testing Laboratory, and Alco Products, Inc. [119, 120].

[b] Concrete composition given in Table 8.49.

[c] See Fig. 8.82.

[d] Cycled in 1-hr intervals and allowed to cool between cycles.

[e] This value includes the water taken up by the cement plus the water content of the serpentine aggregate.

[f] Preliminary tests with concrete having a greater serpentine-concentration or with concrete made only from fine aggregate showed compression strength of only 670 psi or less.

8.12.7 GAMMA-RAY BUILDUP [44, 101]

The following gamma-ray buildup data are presented: Table 8.79, gamma-ray dose buildup factors for various materials from a point isotropic source; Table 8.80, gamma-ray dose buildup factors for various materials from a plane monodirectional source; Table 8.81, gamma-ray energy buildup factors for various materials from a point isotropic source; and Table 8.82, gamma-ray energy buildup factors for various materials from a plane monodirectional source.

The following gamma-ray dose buildup data in concretes are presented: Fig. 8.88, fission-product gamma-ray dose buildup factors in ordinary concrete (point isotropic source); Fig. 8.89, point

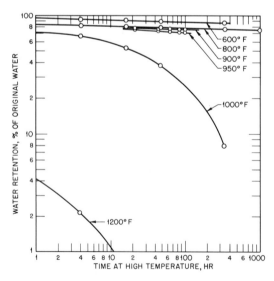

FIG. 8.72—Retention of water in serpentine rock and concrete as a function of time at various temperatures [115].

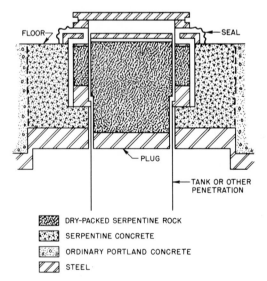

FIG. 8.73—Sketch showing the use of serpentine rock and serpentine concrete in the biological-shield floor of the Fermi plant [121].

Table 8.51—Typical Analysis of Serpentine Concrete [119]

Material	Amount required for 1 cu yd		Dry material	
	Wt., lb	Vol., cu ft	Vol, %	Wt. %
Serpentine	2032	12.51	51.5	54.5
Sand	956	5.83	23.9	25.8
Cement	525*	2.68	11.1	14.2
Water	373	5.98	13.5	5.5
Plastiment	1.39†			

* 5.5 bags cement.

† 4 oz. per bag cement.

isotropic dose buildup factors in ordinary concrete for Na^{24} decay gamma rays; Fig. 8.90, point isotropic dose buildup factors in ordinary concrete for various gamma-ray energies; Fig. 8.91, point isotropic dose buildup factors in ferrophosphorus concrete for various gamma-ray energies; Fig. 8.92, point isotropic dose buildup factors in magnetite concrete for various gamma-ray energies; Fig. 8.93, point isotropic dose buildup factors in barytes concrete for various gamma-ray energies.

8.12.8 FISSION-PRODUCT DECAY RATES

After shutdown gamma-energy release rates and fission-product heat-generation rates are given in Figs. 8.94 and 8.95.

8.12.9 REFERENCES FOR NUCLEAR DATA

For more information on nuclear parameters and constants, the reader is referred to Refs. 52, 133 to 136, 142, and 152.

8.13 Description of Fast Reactor Shields

The primary neutron-absorbing shields for existing and planned fast power reactors are com-

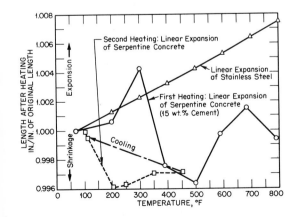

FIG. 8.74—Thermal expansion of serpentine concrete and steel as a function of temperature [115].

Table 8.52—Sieve Analysis of Fine and Coarse Serpentine Aggregate for Concrete Mixture Shown in Table 8.51 and Properties of the Aggregate [119]

Screen or sieve size	Per cent passing through sieve	
	Fine Aggregate	Coarse aggregate
No. 100 sieve	1.92	
No. 550 sieve	12.68	
No. 30 sieve	47.74	
No. 16 sieve	84.01	
No. 8 sieve	97.50	
No. 4 sieve	100.00	2.72
$3/8$-in. screen		15.02
$1/2$-in. screen		24.91
$3/4$-in. screen		41.91
1-in. screen		72.75
$1\frac{1}{2}$-in. screen		100.00
Specific gravity	2.604	2.60
Lb/cu ft, dry, rodded		100.0
Fineness modulus, %	2.56	
Decantation loss, %	1.22	
Organic material	Less than standard	

posed of nonhydrogenous materials, with one important exception, BR-5, which has a water shield. The use of shield plugs, either rotating or fixed, is common. Beyond these similarities, the shields are many and varied and do not share many common characteristics.

Factors that affect the choice of shield structure and materials are as follows:

1. Purpose of reactor: Feasibility experiments and short-time projects will not require criteria as demanding as those of permanent facilities.

2. Arrangement of components: Depending upon how the various reactor components and systems are arranged, the shield may be either unitized or compartmentalized. In the unitized shield the whole shield is wrapped around the reactor vessel; there is little or no shield outside this region. In a compartmentalized shield system, the protective needs of each individual area are studied, and the shield is developed to fit the need. Compartmentalized shields are more flexible to mechanical-design requirements and are more popular in power-reactor design than unitized shields.

3. Choice of coolant: The type of coolant selected will have a bearing on the type of shield selected. Fast reactors develop higher power densities within their cores than do thermal reactors and are designed to operate at higher temperatures. High-temperature high-efficiency operation is made possible by a liquid-metal coolant. There is a penalty involved in the use of liquid-metal coolants, however; they become highly radioactive, and shielding the primary coolant system is a necessity. This shielding may be more extensive and expensive than the neutron shield around the reactor. The effect of coolants on shield design are discussed in Sec. 8.5. Properties of coolants are discussed in Chap. 2.

4. Temperature and radiation conditions: Temperature and radiation environments around a reactor and its various components influence the types of materials which can be used (Sec. 8.4), which, in turn, influences the type of structure required to hold the shield.

Table 8.53—Results of Tests on Serpentine Concrete [119]

Property	Sample number	Test Batch Specimen		
		Batch S-2	Batch S-3*	Batch S-4
Yield, cu ft		26.98	27.01	27.01
Slump, in.		1.25	1.75	1.75
Air content, %		1.3	1.5	1.9
Wet density, lb/cu ft	1	142.67	142.88	143.10
	2	142.67	142.30	143.10
	3	142.18	142.80	143.10
	4	142.67	142.69	143.20
	5	142.81	143.10	143.20
	6	143.12	143.10	142.57
Dry density, lb/cu ft				
After heating for five	1	135.47	131.79	135.87
1-hr cycles to 500°F†	2	134.21	132.14	135.01
	3	134.30	132.30	135.01
After heating for ten	4	132.33	129.63	133.32
1-hr cycles to 500°F†	5	131.46	130.29	132.67
	6	133.03	130.62	132.43
Moisture loss during	1	5.05	7.76	5.05
cycling, wt. %	2	5.93	7.14	5.65
	3	5.54	7.35	5.65
	4	7.25	9.15	6.90
	5	7.95	8.95	7.35
	6	7.05	8.72	7.11
Linear shrinkage	1	0.021	0.062	0.017
upon cycling, %	2	0.012	0.066	0.013
	3	0.012	0.071	0.013
	4	0.034	0.123	0.025
	5	0.029	0.126	0.033
	6	0.033	0.151	0.033
Volumetric shrinkage	1	0.055	0.158	0.065
upon cycling, %	2	0.035	0.197	0.050
	3	0.055	0.191	0.050
	4	0.107	0.304	0.069
	5	0.099	0.279	0.094
	6	0.114	0.308	0.101
Compressive strength	1	2246	1910	2320
after cycling, psi	2	2335	1923	2228
	3	2246	1923	2109
	4	2228	2023	2295
	5	2317	2016	2361
	6	2299	2003	2216
Compressive strength before cycling, psi	Average	2520	2282	2484

*Batch S-3 tests indicate that this batch had properties inferior to the other test batches. The only difference between the batches is that during the moist curing period the humidity control was less for this batch.

†Specimens were dried to a constant weight at 130°F before undergoing the heat-cycling tests. In each batch three specimens were given a five cycle test during which they were heated to 500°F for 1 hr per cycle and allowed to cool between cycles. The other three specimens were cycled ten times.

5. Types and uses of shields: The shield for fast breeder reactors starts with the breeder blanket. The blanket acts as both a reflector and a neutron-capture medium, keeping neutron leakage from the blanket to a minimum. Because core materials for fast reactors are selected with the purpose of keeping neutron energies as high as possible and because nonhydrogenous materials are generally used in the vicinity of the core, the dominant energy of neutrons leaking into the external shield is high, and they must be moderated before being captured (Sec. 8.1). The shield material chosen for the external shield is generally a moderator and is used in conjunction with a capture agent. This shield is the prime neutron-absorbing shield. Heat-absorbing or thermal shields are employed to reduce the gamma-ray heating in sensitive areas of the shield system. Often thermal shields are employed within, or adjacent to, the reactor vessel to reduce the intensity of core and blanket gamma rays. The nuclear heating in a shield can be controlled in this manner. Internal thermal shields are usually composed of steel or stainless-steel plates paced to allow passage of a coolant between or around them. Any heavy material will suffice as a heat-absorbing shield, but steel is cheaper and more abundant than other heavy materials. The Russian BR-5 employs a copper container as the thermal shield. The main heat-absorbing material may be in the form of iron oxide used external to the reactor.

Table 8.54—Calculated Nuclear Properties of Serpentine
Rock and Serpentine Concrete*

Nuclear Property	Serpentine rock[†]	Serpentine concrete[†]
Macroscopic thermal-neutron capture cross sections, cm^{-1}	0.0115	0.0434
Average macrosoopic scattering cross section, cm^{-1}	1.01	1.03
Removal cross section, cm^{-1}	0.097	0.092
Gamma-ray mass-absorption coefficients, cm^2/g		
At 0.5 Mev	0.0880	0.0884
At 1 Mev	0.0638	0.0644
At 3 Mev	0.0367	0.0367
At 6 Mev	0.0268	0.0269

* From H.E. Hungerford, R.F. Mantey, and L.P. Van Maele, *Nucl. Sci. Eng.*, 6:396 (November 1959).
[†] Neutron cross sections taken at a density of 130 lb/cu ft.

Table 8.55—Typical Chemical Analysis of Calcium
Borate Shield Material*

Compound	Composition, Wt. %
B_2O_3	35.7
CaO	24.1
SiO_2	12.2
H_2O[†]	11.2
Na_2O	6.6
MgO	3.4
CO_2	2.9
FeO	2.5
Al_2O_3	1.3
Others	0.3

* This analysis was taken from a sample of density 71 lb/cu ft supplied by Johns-Manville [117].
[†] Water content varies. After firing, most of this water is lost.

In some fast reactor designs, equipment is protected by an intermediate neutron-absorbing secondary shield. Neutron-flux levels outside this shield are low enough to prevent serious activation of materials, but they are biologically too high. Such shields add flexibility to the overall plant design.

Biological shields for fast reactors, like those for most other stationary reactors, are composed mainly of concrete, concrete and steel, or heavy concrete. The problems are those of high temperatures and access to the reactor. Radiation-streaming problems and high temperatures usually call for the use of special materials and methods of design around access holes, penetrations, ducts, pipes, and plugs. Shields for these areas should consist of the most effective materials for the job, the costs involved being a secondary consideration.

Detailed descriptions of the shield systems for six existing fast reactors and one design study reactor are described in Secs. 8.14 through 8.20. Some comparisons of the overall characteristics of some existing and planned fast reactors are given in Table 8.83. Some detailed comparisons of the shield systems for various existing and planned reactors are given in Table 8.84.

8.14 EBR-I Shield System

8.14.1 PURPOSE OF REACTOR

The Experimental Breeder Reactor (EBR-I), located at the National Reactor Testing Station in Idaho, was designed and built to demonstrate and promote the fast-neutron breeder reactor concept [2, 4, 156]. It is a sodium–potassium alloy (NaK) cooled reactor with a total thermal power of about 1.4 Mw. The reactor core and inner natural-uranium blanket are cooled by NaK. The outer movable blanket is aircooled. Figure 8.96 shows the concrete biological shield surrounding the reactor vessel. The outer blanket (Chap. 11) also serves as a part of the overall shield system.

8.14.2 SHIELD DESIGN CRITERIA

The shield is designed to reduce the neutron and gamma-ray intensities to permissible levels (7.5 mrem/hr).

8.14.3 SIDE SHIELD

The side shield of the EBR-I consists of an 18-in. graphite reflector, a 4-in. iron thermal shield, and originally a 6-ft outer concrete shield. The concrete density is 150 lb/cu ft. At a reactor power of 1 Mw, the gamma-ray dose rate at the surface of the 6-ft concrete shield was of the order 100 to 200 mr/hr; therefore a belt of concrete 30 in. thick and 6.5 ft high was added to the original shield. This reduced the dose rate at the shield surface to 1 to 5 mr/hr.

8.14.4 BOTTOM SHIELDING

A hole in the concrete shield for access to the elevator room below the reactor is loosely plugged by 5 ft of iron shield. Neutrons and gamma rays streaming into the elevator room from around the edges of the shield are not a serious problem since the elevator room has limited access.

8.14.5 TOP SHIELDING

A 3.5-ft-diameter 10.5-ft-deep hole in the concrete shield above the reactor forms the access through which fuel and blanket rods are inserted and removed. This hole is partially filled with a series of 10 steel plates and spacers for shield purposes; the control and safety rods pass through

Table 8.56—Elemental Composition of
Calcium Borate [3]

Element	Composition, Wt. %
O	53.9
Ca	17.2
B	11.1
Si	5.7
Na	4.9
Mg	2.1
Fe	1.9
C	1.2
H	1.2
Al	0.7

Table 8.57—Physical Properties of Calcium Borate
Shield Material*

Property	Value or description
Apperance	Calcium borate shield material in the shape of pressed board 4 ft x 8 ft in thicknesses up to 2 in. It is off-white in color, has a chalky feel, is brittle, and has a slightly grainy structure
Density, 20°C	
G/cm³	1.12 - 1.20
Lb/cu ft	70 - 75
Thermal conductivity, Btu/hr/sq ft/°F/in.	
At 400°F	1.70
At 500°F	1.73
At 600°F	1.76
At 800°F	1.82
Thermal-expansion coefficient, per °F	
Parallel to grain	6.4×10^{-6}†
Perpendicular to grain	14×10^{-6}†
Compressive strength, psi	800 - 950
Shear rupture modulus, psi	390
Moisture retention, wt. %	
Unfired	7.3
After firing 24 hr at:	
400°F	3.7
600°F	2.7
800°F	2.4
1000°F	2.2
Linear shrinkage, %	
At 400°F	0.44
At 500°F	0.55
At 600°F	0.58
At 800°F	0.81
At 1000°F (length)	0.64 - 0.86
At 1000°F (width)	0.49 - 0.69
At 1000°F (thickness)	1.00 - 1.13
Boron content, wt. %	10 - 12

* Except where noted, all measurements of these properties were
made by Johns-Manville [123].
† Preliminary measurements by H. E. Hungerford.

the plates and spacers. The rod extensions have
boron carbide and steel shielding.

8.14.6 COOLANT-SYSTEM SHIELDING

The NaK alloy of the primary coolant system is
radioactive, and it is shielded with 3 ft of concrete.
The NaK activity at full power was measured to be
2.5 μc/cm³.

8.15 USSR Fast Reactor BR-5 Shield System

8.15.1 REACTOR DESCRIPTION

A description of this reactor is given in Chap.
11 and in Refs. 157 and 158.

8.15.2 SHIELD SYSTEM

The BR-5 side shield is the same as that in the
BR-2 reactor. Unlike other sodium-cooled fast

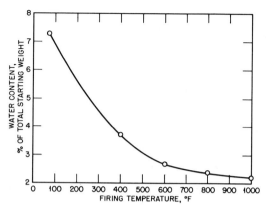

FIG. 8.75—Water retention of calcium borate shield material as a
function of temperature [121].

reactors in existence, water is used for shielding.
The shield system is designed to reduce the radiation level to about one-half the normal biological
radiation dose.* The general shield arrangement
for the BR-5 reactor is shown in Chap. 11.

8.15.3 SIDE SHIELD

Surrounding the reactor core is a removable
nickel reflector 15 cm thick and a stationary reflector assembled from 3.5-cm-diameter uranium
rods encased in stainless-steel cans. These layers
serve also as shields to reduce the intensity of the
core-leakage radiation. A 15-cm-thick copper layer
surrounds the uranium shield and acts as a container for the reactor. The copper, nickel, and the
uranium shields are placed inside a cylindrical tank
of water. The water side shield is 50 cm thick.
Outside this is a 40-cm cast-iron thermal shield
that completely surrounds the tank. The outermost
part of the side shield consists of a 110-cm layer
of heavy concrete containing limonite, 4.2 g/cm³
density.

---

*Normal biological-dose design value is not specified.

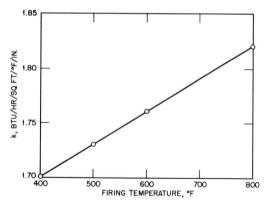

FIG. 8.76—Thermal conductivity of calcium borate shield material
as a function of temperature [121].

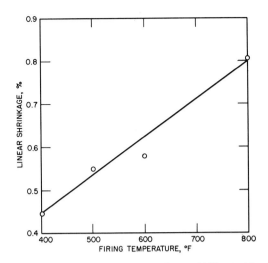

FIG. 8.77—Linear shrinkage in calcium borate shield material as a function of temperature [121].

8.15.4 UPPER BIOLOGICAL SHIELD

The upper biological shield can be divided into three regions: (1) an inner region including the rotating access plug, (2) the region over the water tank outside the reactor vessel, and (3) the top-hat shield above the rotating plugs.

Inner-shield region: Directly above the core is a 30-cm-thick stainless-steel reflector. The shielding above this consists of an 80-cm-thick layer of boron carbide, a rotating steel plug 120 cm thick, and the upper removable top hat. Surrounding the stainless-steel reflector and boron carbide shield and directly above the nickel reflectors is an annular reflector-shield of stainless steel through which the reflector control elements pass. This shield reduces the streaming into the annular passage directly above, which contains the control cables.

Upper shield outside the reactor container: The shield above the water tank consists of the 40-cm-thick cast-iron thermal shield and the 110-cm-thick heavy-concrete shield. The thin portion of the top-hat shield completes this shielding.

Top-hat biological shield: The removable top-hat shield consists of a hat-shaped cylinder of shielding made from laminated layers of iron and paraffin located directly over the rotating plugs, with a thinner brim extending outward over the heavy-concrete shield. The central cylinder is about 140 cm thick and 150 cm in diameter. The thinner portion has a thickness of 25 cm and a diameter of about 3.5 m. It is supported directly on the top surface of the heavy-concrete biological shield.

8.15.5 LOWER SHIELD

The lower shield consists of a 20-cm-thick layer of water and a 40-cm-thick layer of cast iron. Underneath the reactor is a shielded room that contains some sodium test-loop equipment. This room is inaccessible during reactor operation but may be entered during shutdown periods by means of a maze entranceway through the concrete biological shield.

Table 8.58—Pre- and Postirradiation Requirements for Calcium Borate Shield Material Specimens*

Property	Specimen No.	Specimen type	Preirradiation measurements[†]	Postirradiation measurements[‡]	Change in value under irradiation,	Change in value, %
Density, g/cm^3	3	Gerstley borate	1.321			
	4	Gerstley borate	1.361			
	5	Colemanite	1.218			
	6	Colemanite	1.243			
Average height, in.	3	Gerstley borate	0.778	0.803	+ 0.025	+ 3.21
	4	Gerstley borate	0.808	0.826	+ 0.018	+ 2.23
	5	Colemanite	0.853	0.861	+ 0.008	+ 0.94
	6	Colemanite	0.841	0.866	+ 0.025	+ 2.97
Average diameter, in.	3	Gerstley borate	1.026	1.029	+ 0.003	+ 0.29
	4	Gerstley borate	1.013	1.027	+ 0.014	+ 1.38
	5	Colemanite	1.006	1.020	+ 0.014	+ 1.39
	6	Colemanite	1.017	1.014	− 0.003	− 0.29
Crushing strength, §psi	7,8		770, 940		No significant change	
	3	Gerstley borate		795		

*Specimens were prepared and encapsulated by Johns-Manville. Each specimen was approximately 1 in. in diameter and 7/8 in. high. The capsule was made of aluminum and measured 6 in. long by 1 1/8 in. in diameter. Capsule was irradiated in position A27NE of the MTR to an integrated flux of 2.4×10^{20} neutrons/cm^2 under an irradiation flux of about 8×10^{13} neutrons/cm^2/sec. Ambient temperature during irradiation was 100 to 110°F. Post irradiation measurements were made by Battelle Memorial Institute in their hot caves. Samples 1 and 2 were light density and crumbled upon irradiation.

†Measurements by Johns-Manville [125].

‡Measurements by Battelle Memorial Institute [125].

§ Sample 3 was selected for the postirradiation crusing strength test. Samples 7 and 8 were taken from the same block as sample 3 to give a direct comparison. All samples were loaded with a 50-lb dead weight.

Table 8.59—Calculated Nuclear Properties of Calcium Borate [3,45]

Nuclear Property	With 11% H_2O	With 3.7% H_2O*	With 0% H_2O[†]
Thermal-neutron macroscopic capture cross section, cm^{-1}	9.02	9.02	9.02
Average scattering macroscopic cross section, cm^{-1}	0.476	0.241	0.109
Removal cross section, cm^{-1}	0.0708	0.0394	0.0351
Gamma-ray mass absorption coefficient, cm^2/g at:			
At 0.5 Mev	0.0873	0.0859	0.0852
At 1 Mev	0.0635	0.0625	0.0620
At 3 Mev	0.0392	0.0387	0.0384
At 6 Mev	0.0270	0.0267	0.0265

* Corresponds to a loss of two-thirds of the original water content.

[†] High temperatures will eventually drive virtually all water out of material.

8.15.6 MISCELLANEOUS SHIELDS

Equipment and pipelines of the primary circuit are placed in shielded hermetically sealed boxes attached to the reactor.

8.15.7 HEAT GENERATION IN NICKEL AND URANIUM REFLECTOR SHIELDS

About 130 kw of heat is produced in the nickel shield (movable reflector), and 800 kw is produced in the outer uranium shield (stationary reflector).

8.16 Shield System for the Dounreay Fast Reactor

8.16.1 GENERAL CONSIDERATIONS AND PURPOSE

The Dounreay Fast Breeder Reactor [20, 160] is a NaK-cooled reactor with a design heat output of 72 Mw. The shield system (Chap. 11) is divided into four main sections: (1) the vessel annulus shield and the rotating shields about the reactor, (2) the radial shield interposed between the reactor vessel and the primary heat exchangers, (3) the biological shield enclosing the primary heat-exchanger vault, and (4) supplementary removable shielding on top of the whole reactor area.

8.16.2 ROTATING-SHIELD SYSTEM

The shield system above the core is designed so that the element-charge machines can reach any core or blanket element through one of two holes. This is made possible by having the shield in three sections. The inner two sections form a double plug; the sections rotate one within the other. An outer section is fixed next to the inside wall of the vessel; it forms the vessel annular shield. The outer rotating shield is fitted with an 18-in.-diameter plug that can be removed for access to control-rod mechanisms, coolant trace heaters, and coolant thermocouples. The inner rotating shield has three plugs; two of these are 9 in. in diameter and can be removed to permit handling of core and blanket elements. The core-charge plug fits inside another 33-in.-diameter plug in the inner rotating shield and is constructed so that it can be taken out to permit removal of the entire core-support matrix.

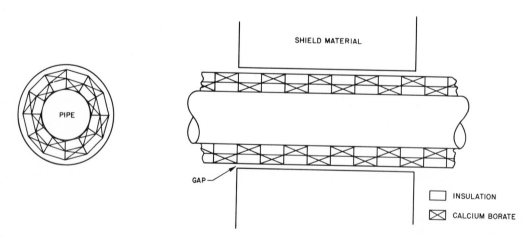

FIG. 8.78—Illustration of the method of applying calcium borate shield material and insulation on a pipe to reduce neutron streaming around the pipe [121].

Table 8.60—Composition of Powder Shield Material

Material	Wt.%
Boron carbide	9
Iron shot	34
Graphite	
Grade 1036	37
Grade 1008	20

All the plugs are stepped to reduce radiation streaming.

The radiation-shielding material in the rotating shields consists of blocks of 0.3% borated graphite, mild-steel plates, and laminations of Resilon. Resilon is a hydrogenous shielding material made of resin bonded with glass fiber. The graphite and the Resilon moderate and absorb neutrons, and the steel acts as a gamma shield. The lower parts of both the rotating shields, i.e., the 33-in.-diameter plug and two charge plugs, contain a 54-in.-thick layer of borated graphite. In the outer rotating shield, an annulus of mild-steel plate 7 1/2 in. thick surrounds the upper 18 in. of graphite. This is covered by a 3-in.-thick layer of aluminum foil to reflect heat. In the inner shield there are a 16-in.-thick layer of mild-steel above the graphite, a 3-in.-thick layer of aluminum foil, and a free space approximately 10 in. thick. The 33-in.-diameter plug has 18 in. of mild-steel shielding above the graphite followed by 14 in. of alternate steel and Resilon laminations. This is covered by 3 in. of Rocksil insulation (rock-fiber insulating material resistant to radiation damage). The shielding in the 33-in. plug is penetrated by the 10 control-rod position indicators, 3 boron rods, a neutron source, and the oscillator access holes. There is a 6-in. free space above the Rocksil. The core and breeder charge plugs are filled with 43 in. of mild steel above the graphite.

8.16.3 REACTOR-VESSEL ANNULUS SHIELDING

The space between the upper plate of the vessel annulus and the level of the vessel step is filled with stainless-steel punchings. With stainless steel there is no magnetic interference in the operation of the control-rod magnetic limit switches. Ten

Table 8.61—Calculated Nuclear Properties of Graphite-boron Carbide-iron Shot Mix [3]

Property	Value
Macroscopic thermal-neutron capture cross section, cm^{-1}	5.88
Average macroscopic scattering cross section, cm^{-1}	0.237
Removal cross section, cm^{-1}	0.0557
Gamma-ray mass-absorption coefficients, cm^2/g	
At 0.5 Mev	0.0855
At 1 Mev	0.0620
At 3 Mev	0.0364
At 6 Mev	0.0269

inches of mild-steel plate is laid above the punchings, and the space around the 4-in. pipe for the control-rod drive is filled with borated graphite.

8.16.4 BORATED-GRAPHITE SHIELD

The purpose of the borated-graphite side shield is to reduce the high-intensity neutron flux from the reactor to a level at which there is no neutron-induced radioactivity in the heat-exchanger vault. A plain graphite ring within the shield provides thermal-neutron fluxes for reactor-power measurement. The graphite is 4 ft 2 in. thick and extends over a height of 24 ft from just above the vessel step to a point 4 ft below the vessel, i.e., to the bottom of the outer catchpot. The boron content of the graphite lies between 0.2 and 0.4 wt.%. There is no graphite below the vessel, but the Pyrobor (a plastic containing boron carbide) beneath the outer catchpot serves as a neutron shield. The graphite is contained in a mild-steel casing and is in a nitrogen atmosphere to prevent excessive oxidation at the elevated temperatures expected (about 200°C). It is built up around the vessel between the inner and outer ring of supports and is penetrated by holes for the primary sodium inlet and outlet and other pipes. Twelve vertical holes evenly spaced around the vessel contain the reactor-power-measuring ion chambers. The ion chambers themselves are located in an annular ring of quality B pile graphite about the center of the vessel. The cross section of the ring is rectangular, 48 in. high by 41 in. wide. The midplane of the ring coincides with the horizontal center line of the core. A 1-in.-thick boundary of 5% borated graphite on the inner edge of the plain graphite prevents thermal neutrons from leaking back to the vessel. On the outside of the annulus, an 8-in. boundary of 5% borated graphite prevents thermal neutrons from leaking into the heat-exchanger vault.

8.16.5 CONCRETE VAULT

The concrete vault shown in Chap. 11 consists of a bowl of concrete within a 5-ft-thick spherical shell, which provides a lower floor with an inside diameter of 54 ft. The outside diameter of the vertical walls is 88 ft. The overall height of the vault is 45 ft. This vault is fitted with a cover or roof of concrete 5.5 ft thick. A hole in the center of the roof 23 ft across allows access to the top of the rotating shields. The vault is designed to reduce the radiation level from the core and the primary circuits to three times the maximum permissible level (or about 22.5 mrem/hr) at the outside of the vault. The concrete is a mix of one part cement to 6.23 parts aggregate, with a water to cement ratio of 0.46. The aggregate is washed sand and a natural gravel not exceeding 1 1/2 in. in size for the walls and 3/4 in. for the roof. The minimum dry density of the concrete is 145 lb/cu ft. The concrete is reinforced with mild-steel and has a total weight of 9,000 tons. Direct streaming of radiation from the core is avoided by arranging the center lines of all the pipe liners that pass through

Table 8.62—Chemical Composition of Commercial Lead[*][†]

Type	Chemical composition, wt. %								
	Pb (min.)	Ag	Cu	Sn (max.)	Fe (max.)	As + Sb + Sn (max.)	Zn (max.)	Bi (max.)	Other
Corroding lead	99.94	0.0015[‡]	0.0015[‡]		0.002	Sb + Sn 0.0095 (max.)	0.0015	0.05	As, 0.0015 (max.)
Chemical lead	99.90	0.002 - 0.020	0.040 - 0.080		0.002	0.002	0.001	0.005	
Acid lead	99.90	0.002	0.040 - 0.080		0.002	0.002	0.001	0.025	
Copper lead	99.85	0.020	0.040 - 0.080		0.002	0.015	0.002	0.10	
Desilverized lead A	99.85	0.002	0.0025		0.002	0.015	0.002	0.15	
Desilverized lead B	99.73	0.002	0.0025		0.002	0.015	0.002	0.25	
Undesilverized lead	99.93	0.002	0.04		0.002	0.015	0.002	0.005	
Calcium lead	99.8	0.002 - 0.02	0.02 - 0.10	0.005				0.005	Co, 0.023 - 0.033
Tellurium lead	99.8 +		0.06						Te, 0.05

[*] Data compiled from Ref. 99.
[†] Compositions are maximum, unless range is given or minimum value is specified.
[‡] Ag + Cu, 0.0025 (max.).

the vault walls tangential to a 5-ft radius from the center of the vault. In the walls of the vault there are four openings, 17 ft by 14 ft, which are filled with concrete blocks so that they can be removed if access is ever required. The blocks are stepped so that shielding is not impaired.

Table 8.63—General Physical and Mechanical Properties of Commercially Pure Lead and Chemical Lead[*]

Property	Commercially pure lead	Chemical lead
Apperance	Soft, heavy metal, malleable and ductile; color, gray.	
Density at 20°C, g/cm³	11.340	Rolled, 11.36 Cast, 11.34
Specific heat, g-cal/g/°C	0.0309	0.0309
Thermal-expansion coefficient, °C		
At 20°C	29.1×10^{-6}	
At 17 to 100°C	.	29.3×10^{-6}
Thermal conductivity, cal/sec/cm/°C	0.083[†]	0.081[‡]
Electrical resistivity, μohm	20.65	20.648
Melting point, °C	327.4	325.6
Boiling point, °C	1740	
Heat of fusion, g-cal/g	5.89	
Heat of vaporization, g-cal/g	204.6	
Volume change on fusion, %	3.6	
Vapor pressure, atm		
At 988°C	0.0013	
At 1168°C	0.013	
At 1418°C	0.13	
Tensile strength, psi	2380 - 2630	1800 - 2000
Yield strength, psi	1180 - 1320	800
Shear strength, psi		1825
Ultimate strength		1700 - 3000
Elongation, %	52 - 57[§]	30 - 47
Elastic modulus, psi	2.56×10^{6}	2×10^{6}
Stress to produce a creep rate of 1% per year, psi	200	
Hardness, Brinell		4 - 5.5
Rockwell	75 - 78	

[*] Data compiled from Refs. 5,52,90,99,127, and 128.
[†] At 20°C.
[‡] At 100°C.
[§] Value given for 2-in. length. For 8-in. length the value is 27 to 29%.

Table 8.64—Lead-Filled Epoxy Resin [130]

Characteristics:	EPOCAST 11C, a lead-filled epoxy resin, has been developed as a room-temperature setting resin capable of shielding against many of the harmful radiations emanating from radioactive sources. Its high density makes EPOCAST 11C a good ballast material in boat hulls. As a casting resin it will reproduce faithfully the shapes and configurations of the mold in which it is cast.
Mixing proportions:	To 100 parts by weight (pbw) EPOCAST 11C add 1.5 pbw Hardener 988. Stir thoroughly until the hardener has been fully and completely dispersed.
Pot life:	Approximately 60 min for 1-lb mass.
Curing:	Cure overnight at room temperatures of 70 to 80°F.
Handling:	Lead compounds are poisonous, and personnel handling EPOCAST 11C should clean hands carefully after working with material.

Properties:	Density	6.5 g/cm^3
	Flexural strength at 76°F	5,700 psi
	Flexural strength at 150°F	4,500 psi
	Compressive strength at room temperature	10,000 psi
	Shore "D" at 76°F	77
	Viscosity at 75°F	78,000 centipoise

Packaging:	1-qt Unit	1-gal Unit
	10 lb EPOCAST 11C	40 lb EPOCAST 11C
	0.15 lb Hardener 988	0.6 lb Hardener 988
	10.15 lb net weight	40.6 lb net weight

8.16.6 REMOVABLE SHIELDING AROUND VESSEL

The space above the graphite between the vessel and the edge of the concrete in the center of the vault roof is filled with removable concrete blocks. The blocks are encased in mild steel and are varied in shape so as to fit around and behind the various pipes and obstructions in the area. The blocks do not have to be moved each time the reactor is shut down and are regarded as a fixed part of the shield. They extend to the level of the top of the vault roof. Above this there is a removable shield (see Fig. 8.51) made up of alternate 1/2-in.-thick laminates of Jabroc and mild-steel encased in steel. Jabroc* is a hydrogenous neutron-shielding material made of wood bonded with resin. This shield is designed to cover the whole of the reactor area as far as the outer limit of the well. It rests on pillars standing on the inner rotating shield under the removable concrete shield. The control and access mechanisms above the rotating-shield area are encased within a 5-in.-thick octagonal shell of the material. The outer region of the rotating shields is surmounted by blocks 10 in. thick laid horizontally. This 10-in.-thick portion is continued outwards to about half way across the well; beyond this the thickness is reduced to 5 in.

8.17 EBR-II Shield System

8.17.1 PLANT DESCRIPTION AND PURPOSE

The Argonne Experimental Breeder Reactor (EBR-II) [19, 159, 161-164] is an unmoderated, heterogenous, sodium-cooled reactor plant with a power output of 62.5 Mw of heat, which is converted to 20 Mw of electricity through a conventional steam system. The EBR-II is an integrated nuclear power plant; that is, it includes a complete fuel-processing and fuel-element-fabrication facility in addition to the reactor, the heat-transfer systems, and a stream-electric plant. The plant is located at the National Reactor Testing Station in Idaho. The EBR-II reactor building, including general shielding and equipment layout, is shown in Chap. 11.

8.17.2 REACTOR DESCRIPTION

The EBR-II complex, including the coolant system, the control and safety drive system, the fuel-handling system, and other associated components, is located within a double-walled primary tank 26 ft in diameter and 26 ft deep. The tank is full of sodium, which acts as the reactor coolant. Chapter 11 shows the reactor with its primary shield, the fuel-handling system, and associated shield above the reactor.

The reactor core consists of fuel rods containing U^{235} clad in stainless steel. The core is surrounded by blanket rods of depleted uranium. Control of the reactor is achieved by the motion of the fuel. The core and blanket rods are contained within the reactor vessel. The neutron shield, which is located between the blanket and the primary sodium, lies partly inside and partly outside the reactor vessel.

8.17.3 SHIELD DESCRIPTION

There are two main shields in the EBR-II reactor: a primary neutron-absorbing shield and a biological shield. The neutron shield, located immediately outside the blanket, serves to reduce the neutron-flux leakage into the large pool of sodium

---

*The British trade name for Permali.

Table 8.65—Composition, Physical, Mechanical, and Nuclear Properties
of Permali [131]

Quantity	Type 5*	Type 6†
Elemental composition, wt.%		
H	6.08	
C	58.50	
N	0.37	
O	35.05	
Density, g/cm^3	1.30-1.34	
Specific heat, cal/g/°C	0.4	
Thermal conductivity, cal/sec/cm/°C		
Parallel to laminations		
With grain	56.0×10^{-4}	
Across grain	3.6×10^{-4}	
Perpendicular to laminations	3.4×10^{-4}	
Linear coefficient of thermal Expansion, per °C		
Parallel to laminations		15×10^{-6}
With grain	8×10^{-6}	
Across grain	69×10^{-6}	
Perpendicular to laminations	113×10^{-6}	113×10^{-6}
Rockwell Hardness, H scale	90-100	
Compressive strength, psi		
Parallel to laminations	17,000	26,000
Perpendicular to laminations	17,000	40,000
Tensile strength with grain, psi	30,000	15,000
Flexural strength, psi		
With grain	32,500	
Lengthwise		18,000
Crosswise		15,000
Shear strength, psi		
Parallel to laminations		2,700
With grain	2,500	
Across grain	4,500	
Perpendicular to laminations	7,000	7,200
Bonding strength, (Cond. A) lb	2,000	18,000
Izod impact strength, ft-lb/in. of notch		
Perpendicular to face, with grain	5.4	3.4
Perpendicular to edge, with grain	5.0	1.6
Modulus of elasticity, psi	2.5×10^6	2.0×10^6
Average dielectric strength, kv/in. (RMS 60 cycle)		
Perpendicular to laminations		
1-in. thickness		
25°C	127	
90°C	111	
2-in. thickness		
25°C	96	
90°C	80	
Parallel to liminations		
1-in. between electrodes		
25°C	76	
90°C	64	
2-in. between electrodes		
25°C	110	
90°C	94	
6-in. between electrodes		
25°C	208	
90°C	184	
Dielectric constant, 60 cycles	4.5	
Power factor, %		
60 cycles	1.9	
1 kc	3.0	
1 Mc	5.0	
Maximum continuous operating temperature, °C	105	
Maximum intermittent operating temperature, °C	150	

Table 8.65—Composition, Physical, Mechanical, and Nuclear Properties
of Pemali [131] (continued)

Quantity	Type 5*	Type 6[†]
Water absorption in 24 hr, wt.%		
1/2-in. thickness	1	
1-in. thickness	3/4	
Neutron relaxation length,[‡] cm	7.8	

*Type 5: Grains in all layers of the lamination run parallel with each other.

[†] Type 6: Grains in alternate layers of the lamination run perpendicular to each other.

[‡] Experimental results at Chatillon, France. Other experiments indicate that the material has nuclear properties similar to Plexiglass.

in the primary tank, keeping activation of the coolant and system components to a minimum. It also serves to some extent as a reflector, conserving neutrons for breeding gains. The biological shield around the sodium tank is intended to keep radiation levels at accessible locations around the reactor within acceptable limits.

8.17.4 NEUTRON SHIELD

8.17.4.1 Breeder Blanket as a Shield

The neutron shield is located partially inside the reactor vessel and partly outside, as shown in Fig. 8.97, all within the sodium-filled primary tank. The 21.3-in. blanket region reduces the neutron leakage to the graphite layers immediately outboard of it. Thus, in addition to its prime func-

Table 8.66—Cost, Manufacturing, and Delivery Data
for Permali [132]

Quantity	Value or Description
Cost data (1961):	
Approximate unit cost, $/lb	1.00
Panels,* $/sq ft	
1/4 in.	2.25
1/2 in.	3.60
1 in.	6.00
1 1/2 in.	9.00
2 in.	12.30
Fabrication tolerances, in.	
Length and width	± 0.125
Thickness, per in.	± 0.0078
Sizes of panels	
Common size[†]	
Dimensions, in.	46 × 20
Area, sq in.	920
Largest size[‡]	
Length, in.	108
Width, in.	54
Area, sq. in.	5000
Thickness of panels available, in.	
Standard thicknesses	3/16 - 2
Special-order thicknesses	2 1/16 - 6
Delivery time, weeks	
Standard panels	2 - 5
Special panels	8 - 10

* Add 20% for orders under 16 sq ft; add 10% for orders between 16 and 36 sq ft.

[†] Any dimensions whose area adds to no greater than 920 sq ft is considered a standard size.

[‡] Present equipment does not allow maximum length and maximum width at the same time. The maximum area is controlling.

tion of breeding plutonium, it acts as the innermost portion of the shield.

8.17.4.2 Primary Graphite Shield

The activation of reactor-system components in the sodium tank (pumps and heat exchangers) is kept within prescribed limits by a shield between the outer blanket and the sodium. This shield moderates and absorbs most of the neutrons that escape from the blanket before they get into the primary tank. Radially there are seven rows of 4-in.-thick graphite blocks, two inside the reactor vessel. The fourth and sixth rows contain 3% boron carbide. Boron carbide has been omitted in the areas immediately adjacent to the neutron-detecting instruments to permit a meaningful response (Fig. 8.98). The graphite shield is divided into an inner section, located within the reactor vessel, and an outer section, located outside of the reactor vessel and held within two concentric steel retainer shells, as shown in Fig. 8.99.

Inner graphite radial shield: The inner graphite shield consists of plain (unborated) graphite blocks assembled in cans 41.5 in. long and 4-7/16 in. square. The graphite blocks are 18 in. long and 4-1/8 in. square. The cans are designed to withstand an internal pressure of 50 psig. The cans are placed in two staggered layers around an inner stainless-steel retaining shell separating the graphite region from the blanket. Steel spacer shells erected between layers and between the outer layer and the reactor-vessel wall, as well as clearances allowed between adjacent cans, permit the sodium coolant to pass through the inner-shield region, removing the heat generated in the graphite. Staggering of the cans prevents neutron streaming. Specially shaped cans are used around the primary sodium coolant inlet and outlet lines to the reactor vessel. Total graphite thickness in the inner shield is 8-1/4 in.

Outer graphite radial shield: This shield is composed of five layers of graphite-filled cans, which have the same cross section as the inner cans and are 13 ft long. These layers are erected in a staggered array between the inner and outer retaining shells, as shown in Fig. 8.99. The inner-layer cans and the middle layer are filled with plain (unborated) graphite. The other layers are filled with 3% borated graphite, except in those areas immediately adjacent to neutron detectors. Clearance between the cans allows sodium coolant to pass through the shield. The total graphite thickness of the outer graphite shield is 20-5/8 in., of which 12-3/8 in. is borated.

8.17.4.3 Bottom Shielding

The bottom shield is located just under the reactor vessel, between the reactor vessel and the primary tank. The shield here consists of two 1/2-in. 3% boron-steel plates placed 3 in. apart just above the tank floor.

8.17.4.4 Reactor-vessel Top-cover Graphite Shield

This shield, located just above the top of the upper blanket (Fig. 8.97) consists of six staggered layers of stainless-steel cans filled with either 3% borated graphite, or boron carbide, to a total shield thickness of 24-3/4 in. Because of the many holes required in the top shield to allow control- and safety-rod access to the reactor, the shapes of cans adjacent to these holes are complex. These cans are filled with boron carbide to reduce streaming. Cooling is provided by a flow of sodium between the cans.

8.17.5 BIOLOGICAL TOP SHIELD

The top shield functions both as a neutron-absorbing shield and as a biological shield. This shield, shown in Chap. 11, consists partly of a large amount of sodium in the pool above the reactor. It was found necessary to keep the shield above the sodium as thin as possible because of the many penetrating rods, access holes, and other equipment that had to be kept short in length for operating efficiency and because the shield thickness affects the building height. Access to the region above the reactor was an important consideration in its design. Originally the basic material chosen for the shield above the sodium was heavy concrete. Temperature limitations precluded its use. The material finally specified was a combination of graphite and steel. A convenient and economical form for these materials is a mixture of steel shot and plain-graphite granules. The total thickness of the top shield is approximately 7 ft 7-3/4 in., which includes a 3-ft steel–graphite shield topped by a 37-in. shield of heavy concrete, a 6-in. insulation layer, and a 6-in. gap.

8.17.6 ROTATING-PLUG SHIELDS (BIOLOGICAL)

A 7-1/2-ft-thick double rotating plug, located directly over the reactor within the top shielding (Chap. 11), provides access to the reactor for the control mechanism, subassembly gripper mechanism, and vessel top-cover lifting device. The shielding in the plugs is in the same configuration as that in the top shield outside. The bottom stainless-steel plates of the plug are 1-1/2 in. thick to carry the weight of the shielding within. The top-cover plate (which carries the fuel-handling and control equipment) is 2 in. thick. The lower 3 ft of shielding within the plugs was originally specified

to be laminated steel and graphite layers; however, the high cost of fabricating the complex shapes for steel and graphite within the plugs around the many penetrations led to a change in this region to the steel-shot and powdered-graphite mixture now in use.

The total thickness of the top plug would be more than adequate shielding if it were solid; but, because of the limited amount of the shielding space available and the many penetrations, there is the possibility of streaming through the annuli. Additional shielding may be added if operating experience proves it necessary.

8.17.7 RADIAL BIOLOGICAL SHIELD

The radial shield beyond the sodium tank (Fig. 8.100) is 6 ft of ordinary concrete. The concrete is reinforced with continuous steel hoops made of reinforcing rods to withstand pressures up to 75 psig. Structural columns within the biological shield are set back 2 in. from the inner face of the shield to avoid lateral loading should the concrete tend to move outward for any reason.

8.17.8 BLAST SHIELD

A 2-ft-thick blast shield (Fig. 8.100) is located between the primary tank and the biological shielding. This shielding is designed to protect the biological shield and building structure from the effects of an incident within the primary tank. It consists of three layers of shock-absorbing material located within four concentric steel cylinders with 3/8-in. to 1/2-in. thick walls. The inner layer of the blast shield consists of 8-3/4 in. of vermiculite concrete; the central layer is 8-1/4 in. of aerated concrete; and the outer layer is an 8-in. thickness of celotex. Besides acting as a blast shield, this shield serves to reduce the gamma-ray heat generation in the biological shield, mainly because of the presence of the 1-3/8 to 1-3/4 in. of steel.

8.17.9 NUCLEAR HEAT GENERATION WITHIN THE BIOLOGICAL SHIELD AND COOLING REQUIREMENTS

A total of 43,000 Btu/hr of heat has to be removed by the shield cooling system [163]. It consists almost entirely of the heat lost from the primary system; the heating in the shield due to neutron and gamma-ray absorption is only about 15,000 Btu/hr. An air-cooling system of 15,000 cfm capacity with a maximum air velocity of approximately 30 ft/sec is required. For reliability there are auxiliary power supplies to the exhaust blowers and coolers. Because of the large heat capacity of the system, interruption of the cooling system is not critical.

The shield cooling system is part of the building ventilation system; the air is exhausted from the building through the shield cooling system. The system operates at a pressure slightly below that of the building atmosphere, which provides in-leakage and also simplifies certain areas in the

FIG. 8.79—Permali N being placed in shielding floor of Dounreay reactor. (Courtesy Permali, Inc.)

shield which cannot be connected to a closed-circulation system. The top structure and shield plugs are cooled by air drawn from the building atmosphere. The radial shield and the structure below the primary tank are cooled primarily by recirculated air. Air from the building is drawn into the primary system through ducts in the rotating plugs and primary top structure and is then circulated around the top cover of the primary tank and through ducts in the biological shield into exhaust blowers. It joins air that has circulated through the radial shield and bottom-shield air space. The air flow is then routed either to the exhaust stack in the process plant or through coolers.

8.17.10 INTERMEDIATE-HEAT-EXCHANGER SHIELD

The intermediate heat exchanger is located within the primary tank and is subject to neutron irradiation. So that the secondary sodium (which is pumped outside the reactor building) will not become too highly activated, neutron shielding is used around the heat exchanger. This shield consists of a 1.5% boron-steel jacket 2-3/8 in. thick. An access plug in the heat-exchanger tank has shielding approximately equivalent to that in the large rotating plugs.

8.17.11 FUEL-TRANSFER SHIELDING

The transfer of spent fuel from the reactor is accomplished in two steps. The fuel or blanket subassemblies are first transferred from the reactor to the storage basket by means of the transfer arm (Chap. 7). When the element is ready for processing, a shielded cask car is moved over the storage-basket exit port and the subassembly is taken from the basket by the cask-car gripper and pulled into the cask car. The cask-car shielding consists of 13-1/2 in. of lead at midplane, which reduces the radiation intensity to no more than 4 mr/hr at the surface. The cask car is shown diagrammatically in Chap. 7.

8.18 Shield System for Enrico Fermi Fast Breeder Reactor

8.18.1 PURPOSE AND DESIGN CRITERIA

8.18.1.1 Biological-shield Criteria

Each shielded area of the Fermi plant is protected by a shield, or a system of several shields, that has been designed to accomplish a certain

Table 8.67—Atomic Numbers, Atomic Weights, Densities, and Atomic Densities of the Elements [81*]

Element	Symbol	Atomic number, Z	Atomic weight, A	Density at 20°C, g/cm^3	Atomic density, N, 10^{22} atoms/cm^{2a}
Actinium	Ac	89	227		
Aluminum	Al	13	26.98	2.699	6.03
Americium	Am	95	(243)		
Antimony	Sb	51	121.76	6.618	3.27
Argon	A	18	39.944	1.6626×10^{-3b}	0.00251
Arsenic	As	33	74.91	5.73	4.61
Astatine	At	85	(211)		
Barium	Ba	56	137.36	3.78	1.66
Berkelium	Bk	97	(245)		
Beryllium	Be	4	9.013	1.84	12.30
Bismuth	Bi	83	209.00	9.747	2.81
Boron	B	5	10.82	2.54^c	14.14^c
Bromine	Br	35	79.916	3.12	2.35
Cadmium	Cd	48	112.41	8.648	4.63
Calcium	Ca	20	40.08	1.54	2.31
Californium	Cf	98	(248)		
Carbon	C	6	12.011	2.25^d	11.28^d
Cerium	Ce	58	140.13	6.9	2.97
Cesium	Cs	55	132.91	1.873	0.849
Chlorine	Cl	17	35.457	3.24×10^{-3e}	0.0055
Chromium	Cr	24	52.01	6.92	8.01
Cobalt	Co	27	58.94	8.92	9.11
Copper	Cu	29	63.54	8.9326	8.47
Curium	Cm	96	(245)		
Dysprosium	Dy	66	162.51	8.45	3.17
Einstenium	E	99	(255)		
Erbium	Er	68	167.27	4.77^f	1.72^f
Europium	Eu	63	152.0	5.24	2.08
Fermium	Fm	100	(252)		
Fluorine	F	9	19.00	1.69×10^{-3g}	0.00536
Francium	Fr	87	(223)		
Gadolinium	Gd	64	157.26	7.95	3.04
Gallium	Ga	31	69.72	5.903	5.10
Germanium	Ge	32	72.60	5.46	4.53
Gold	Au	79	197.0	19.296	5.90
Hafnium	Hf	72	178.58	11.4	3.84
Helium	He	2	4.003	0.1785×10^{-3h}	0.00269
Holmium	Ho	67	164.94	8.76	3.20
Hydrogen	H	1	1.0080	8.987×10^{-5i}	0.00537
Indium	In	49	114.82	7.28	3.82
Iodine	I	53	126.91	4.94	2.34
Iridium	Ir	77	192.2	22.42	7.03
Iron	Fe	26	55.85	7.87	8.49
Krypton	Kr	36	83.8	3.488×10^{-3j}	0.00251^j
Lanthanum	La	57	138.92	6.15	2.67
Lead	Pb	82	207.21	11.342	3.30
Lithium	Li	3	6.940	0.534	4.63
Lutetium	Lu	71	174.99	9.24	3.18
Magnesium	Mg	12	24.32	1.741	4.31
Manganese	Mn	25	54.94	7.42	8.13
Mendelevium	Mv	101	(256)		
Mercury	Hg	80	200.61	13.546	4.07
Molybdenum	Mo	42	95.95	10.2	6.40
Neodymium	Nd	60	144.27	6.96	2.91
Neon	Ne	10	20.183	0.8387×10^{-3k}	0.025
Neptunium	Np	83	(237)	(7.05)	(1.79)
Nickel	Ni	28	58.71	8.90	9.13
Niobium (Columbium)	Nb	41	92.91	8.4	5.44
Nitrogen	N	7	14.008	1.1649×10^{-3l}	0.00501
Osmium	Os	76	190.2	22.5	7.12
Oxygen	O	8	16.000	1.3318×10^{-3m}	0.00501

Table 8.67—Atomic Numbers, Atomic Weights, Densities, and Atomic Densities
of the Elements [81*] (continued)

Element	Symbol	Atomic number, Z	Atomic weight, A	Density at 20°C, g/cm^3	Atomic density, N, 10^{22} atoms/cm^3 [a]
Palladium	Pd	46	106.7	12.16	6.86
Phosphorus	P	15	30.975	2.34[n]	4.55
Platinum	Pt	78	195.09	21.37	6.60
Plutonium	Pu	94	(242)	19.7[o]	4.90
Polonium	Po	84	210	9.51	2.73
Potassium	K	19	39.100	0.87	1.34
Praseodymium	Pr	59	140.92	6.63	2.83
Promethium	Pm	61	(145)		
Protactinium	Pa	91	231		
Radium	Ra	88	226.05	5.0	1.33
Radon	Rn	86	222	9.73×10^{-3}[p]	0.00264
Rhenium	Re	75	186.22	20.53	6.47
Rhodium	Rh	45	102.91	12.44	7.28
Rubidium	Rb	37	85.48	1.532	1.08
Ruthenium	Ru	44	101.1	12.06	7.18
Samarium	Sm	62	150.35	7.7	3.08
Scandium	Sc	21	44.96	2.5	3.35
Selenium	Se	34	78.96	4.81	3.67
Silicon	Si	14	28.09	2.42	5.19
Silver	Ag	47	107.880	10.492	5.86
Sodium	Na	11	22.991	0.9712	2.54
Strontium	Sr	38	87.63	2.6	1.79
Sulfur	S	16	32.066	2.07	3.89
Tantalum	Ta	73	180.95	16.6	5.53
Technetium	Tc	43	(99)		
Tellurium	Te	52	127.61	6.25[q]	2.95
Terbium	Tb	65	158.93	8.33	3.16
Thallium	Tl	81	204.39	11.86	3.49
Thorium	Th	90	232.05	11.5	2.98
Thulium	Tm	69	168.94	9.35	3.33
Tin	Sn	50	118.70	7.298[f]	3.70
Titanium	Ti	22	47.90	4.54	5.71
Tungsten (Wolfram)	W	74	183.86	19.3	6.32
Uranium	U	92	238.07	18.7	4.73
Vanadium	V	23	50.95	5.96	7.05
Xenon	Xe	54	131.30	5.495×10^{-3}[s]	0.00252
Ytterbium	Yb	70	173.04	7.01	2.44
Yttrium	Y	39	88.92	5.51	3.73
Zinc	Zn	30	65.38	7.133[o]	6.57
Zirconium	Zr	40	91.22	6.44	4.25

* Compiled from data of Refs. 5, 86, 88, 89, 128, 137, and 138.

[a] Calculated from densities and atomic weights listed.

[b] Density of liquid at −183°C is 1.3845 g/cm^3.

[c] Density of crystalline boron is 3.33 g/cm^3; density of amorphous form is 2.34 g/cm^3; corresponding values for N are 18.37 and 12.97×10^{22} atoms/cm^3.

[d] Value is quoted for graphite; density of diamond is 3.51, and corresponding N is 17.6×10^{22} atoms/cm^3.

[e] Density of liquid at −33.6°C is 1.507 g/cm^3.

[f] Latest data quote this value; an older value is 9.16 g/cm^3 and the corresponding N is 3.30×10^{22} atoms/cm^3.

[g] Value at 15°C; density of liquid at −200°C is 1.14 g/cm^3.

[h] Value at 0°C; density of liquid at −269°C is 0.15 g/cm^3.

[i] Value at STP; density of liquid at −252°C is 0.07 g/cm^3.

[j] Density of liquid at −146°C is 2.16 g/cm^3.

[k] Density of liquid at −245.9°C is 1.204 g/cm^3.

[l] Density of liquid at −195°C is 0.81 g/cm^3.

[m] Density of liquid at −184°C is 1.14 g/cm^3.

[n] Density of white phosphorus is 1.83 g/cm^3; of red phosphorus is 2.20 g/cm^3[38]

[o] Value at 25°C.

[p] Density of liquid at −62°C is 4.40 g/cm^3.

[q] Density of amorphous form is 6.02 g/cm^3.

[r] Density of gray tin is 5.8 g/cm^3.

[s] Density of liquid at −109°C is 3.52 g/cm^3.

Table 8.68—Molecular Densities of Compounds Found in Shielding Materials and Atomic Densities of Hydrogen in the Compounds [52]

Compound	Chemical formula	Molecular weight	Density, g/cm^3	Molecular density (N), 10^{22} molecules/cm^3	Atomic density of hydrogen in compound (N_H), hydrogen 10^{22} atoms/cm^3
Acetic acid	$C_2H_4O_2$	60.05	1.05	1.05	4.21
Aluminum oxide	Al_2O_3	101.94	4.00	2.36	
Ammonia*	NH_3	17.03	0.771	2.73	8.18
Arsenous oxide	As_2O_3	197.82	3.85	1.17	
Barium sulfate	$BaSO_4$	233.42	4.50	1.16	
Beryllium carbide	Be_2C	30.05	1.9	3.81	
Beryllium oxide	BeO	25.02	3.02	7.27	
Boron carbide	B_4C	55.29	2.54	2.77	
Boron oxide	B_2O_3	69.64	1.85	1.60	
Calcium carbonate	$CaCO_3$	100.09	2.71	1.62	
Calcium oxide	CaO	56.08	3.32	3.57	
Cellulose	$(C_6H_{10}O_5)_n$	162.14	1.35	0.502	5.02
Chromic oxide	Cr_2O_3	152.02	5.21	2.06	
Dodecane	$C_{12}H_{26}$	170.33	0.75	0.302	6.76
Ferric oxide	Fe_2O_3	159.70	5.12	1.93	
Ferrous oxide	FeO	71.85	5.7	4.78	
Glycerin	$C_3H_6O_3$	92.09	1.26	0.824	6.59
Heavy water	D_2O	20.028	1.1076	3.32	6.64[†]
Lead oxide	PbO	223.21	9.2	2.48	
Limonite	$2Fe_2O_3 \cdot 3H_2O$	373.44	3.8 (av.)	0.61	
Lithium borohydride	$LiBH_4$	21.79	0.686	1.90	7.58
Lithium hydride	LiH	7.95	0.820	6.21	6.21
Lucite	$(C_5H_8O_2)_n$	100.11	1.2	0.722	5.78
Magnesium chloride	$MgCl_2$	95.23	2.32	1.14	
Magnesium oxide	MgO	40.32	3.65	5.45	
Neoprene	$(C_4H_5Cl)_n$	88.54	1.23	0.84	4.20
Octane (n)	C_8H_{18}	114.22	0.703	0.371	6.68
Pentane (n)	C_5H_{12}	72.15	0.626	0.523	6.28
Polyisoprene	$(C_5H_8)_n$	68.11	0.92	0.81	6.51
Polymethyl methacrylate	$(C_5H_6O_2)_n$	100.11	1.2	0.722	5.78
Potassium hydroxide	KOH	56.10	2.044	2.62	2.62
Potassium oxide	K_2O	94.19	2.32	1.48	
Silicon carbide	SiC	40.07	3.17	4.76	
Silicon oxide	SiO_2	60.06	2.32	2.33	
Sodium hydroxide	$NaOH$	40.00	2.13	3.20	3.20
Sodium oxide	Na_2O	61.99	2.27	2.21	
Tetramethyl ammonium borohydride	$(CH_3)_4NBH_4$	89.00	0.813	0.550	8.80
Thorium borohydride	$Th(BH_4)_4$	291.53	2.59	0.535	8.56
Titanium hydride	TiH_2	49.92	3.78	4.56	9.12
Titanium hydride (commercial)	TiH_2	49.92	3.25	3.92	7.84
Titanium oxide	TiO_2	79.90	4.26	3.21	
Uranium hydride	UH_3	241.09	10.86	2.71	8.14
Water	H_2O	18.016	1.00	3.35	6.69

*Values given for the liquid state.

[†] Deuterium atoms/cm^3.

purpose in accordance with predetermined criteria (Table 8.85). In areas where unrestricted access is allowed, the radiation-exposure criterion for the biological shielding is a total dose of 30 mrem during a 40-hr work week. On this basis the allowable exposure rate in these areas is 0.75 mrem/hr, this total to be taken by any combination of gamma rays, fast neutrons, and thermal neutrons.

Certain limited-access areas are designed to allow radiation levels of 7.5 mr/hr. Entry into these areas by any one person is limited to 4 hr per week or less; thus the total weekly allowable level is not exceeded. Administrative control of limited-access areas is the responsibility of the plant health physics supervisors.

8.18.1.2 Protection Against Radiation Damage

A second important function of the shield system is the protection of the reactor vessel and its components as well as shield materials and other materials against radiation damage. Plant-lifetime total radiation exposures (*nvt*) on all materials used

Table 8.69—Neutron 25-Group Cross Sections for Selected Materials (APDA Projects Data) [3]

Group	Energy range, Mev	Lethargy range	Lethargy interval	Sodium Σ_s, cm^{-1}	Σ_c, cm^{-1}	K,* cm^{-1}	Stainless steel Σ_s, cm^{-1}	Σ_c, cm^{-1}	K,* cm^{-1}	Borated graphite† Σ_s, cm^{-1}	Σ_c, cm^{-1}	K,* cm^{-1}	Carbon‡ Σ_s, cm^{-1}	Σ_c, cm^{-1}	K,* cm^{-1}
1	10 – 8.2	0 – 0.2	0.20	0.0556	4.5×10^{-6}	8.66×10^{-4}	0.26	0.117	0.302	0.0876	1.78×10^{-4}	6.84×10^{-3}	0.0876	8×10^{-6}	14.5×10^{-4}
2	8.2 – 7.1	0.2 – 0.33	0.13	0.0556	4.5×10^{-6}	8.66×10^{-4}	0.27	0.1067	0.294	0.1292	1.87×10^{-4}	8.51×10^{-3}	0.1292	8×10^{-6}	17.6×10^{-4}
3	7.1 – 6.4	0.33 – 0.44	0.11	0.0556	4.5×10^{-6}	8.66×10^{-4}	0.29	0.0987	0.293	0.0763	1.99×10^{-4}	6.75×10^{-3}	0.0763	8×10^{-6}	13.5×10^{-4}
4	6.4 – 6.2	0.44 – 0.47	0.03	0.0556	4.5×10^{-6}	8.66×10^{-4}	0.29	0.0967	0.290	0.1519	2.03×10^{-4}	9.62×10^{-3}	0.1519	8×10^{-6}	19.1×10^{-4}
5	6.2 – 4.6	0.47 – 0.76	0.29	0.0556	4.5×10^{-6}	8.66×10^{-4}	0.292	0.0936	0.286	0.0989	2.20×10^{-4}	8.08×10^{-3}	0.0989	8×10^{-6}	15.4×10^{-4}
6	4.6 – 2.1	0.76 – 1.56	0.80	0.0623	4.6×10^{-6}	9.27×10^{-4}	0.287	0.0606	0.228	0.1445	2.88×10^{-4}	11.2×10^{-3}	0.1445	8×10^{-6}	18.6×10^{-4}
7	2.1 – 2.0	1.56 – 1.6	0.04	0.0735	4.6×10^{-6}	1.01×10^{-4}	0.27	0.0385	0.177	0.2655	3.60×10^{-4}	16.9×10^{-3}	0.2655	8×10^{-6}	25.2×10^{-4}
8	2.0 – 1.4	1.6 – 1.96	0.36	0.0623	5.0×10^{-6}	9.66×10^{-4}	0.25	0.0305	0.151	0.1484	3.98×10^{-4}	13.3×10^{-3}	0.1484	8×10^{-6}	18.9×10^{-4}
9	1.4 – 1.0	1.96 – 2.3	0.34	0.0668	5.5×10^{-6}	1.05×10^{-3}	0.24	0.0225	0.127	0.1826	4.79×10^{-4}	16.2×10^{-3}	0.1826	8×10^{-6}	20.9×10^{-4}
10	1.0 – 0.5	2.3 – 3.0	0.70	0.103	5.4×10^{-6}	1.29×10^{-3}	0.25	0.0104	0.088	0.224	6.15×10^{-4}	20.3×10^{-3}	0.224	8×10^{-6}	23.2×10^{-4}
11	0.5 – 0.4	3.0 – 3.22	0.22	0.087	5.3×10^{-6}	1.17×10^{-3}	0.34	0.0086	0.094	0.266	7.32×10^{-3}	24.2×10^{-3}	0.226	8×10^{-6}	25.3×10^{-4}
12	0.4 – 0.035	3.22 – 5.66	2.44	0.100	1.0×10^{-5}	1.73×10^{-3}	0.39	0.0005	0.024	0.327	1.48×10^{-3}	3.81×10^{-2}	0.327	8×10^{-6}	28.0×10^{-4}
13	0.035 – 0.001	5.66 – 9.2	3.54	0.300	1.0×10^{-4}	9.49×10^{-3}	0.80	0.0004	0.031	0.349	6.36×10^{-3}	8.16×10^{-2}	0.349	8×10^{-6}	28.9×10^{-4}
	Ev														
14	1000 – 200	9.2 – 10.8	1.6	0.074	9.5×10^{-5}	4.60×10^{-3}	0.95	0.002	0.024	0.349	2.33×10^{-2}	0.156	0.349	8×10^{-6}	28.9×10^{-4}
15	200 – 60	10.8 – 12	1.2	0.074	1.4×10^{-4}	5.58×10^{-3}	0.89	0.003	0.028	0.349	4.66×10^{-2}	0.221	0.349	8×10^{-6}	28.9×10^{-4}
16	60 – 15	12 – 13.4	1.4	0.069	3.1×10^{-4}	8.01×10^{-3}	0.86	0.0066	0.13	0.349	9.24×10^{-2}	0.311	0.349	9.3×10^{-6}	31.2×10^{-4}
17	15 – 7	13.4 – 14.18	0.78	0.069	5.5×10^{-4}	1.07×10^{-2}	0.88	0.012	0.178	0.349	0.161	0.411	0.349	1.3×10^{-5}	3.69×10^{-3}
18	7 – 4	14.18 – 14.72	0.54	0.069	7.7×10^{-4}	1.26×10^{-2}	0.88	0.016	0.206	0.349	0.220	0.4796	0.349	1.8×10^{-5}	4.34×10^{-3}
19	4 – 2	14.72 – 15.4	0.68	0.069	1.0×10^{-3}	1.44×10^{-2}	0.88	0.022	0.241	0.357	0.280	0.529	0.357	2.5×10^{-5}	5.18×10^{-3}
20	2 – 1	15.4 – 16.1	0.7	0.0713	1.45×10^{-3}	1.76×10^{-2}	0.87	0.03	0.28	0.357	0.424	0.674	0.357	3.5×10^{-5}	6.12×10^{-3}
21	1 – 0.3	16.1 – 17.3	1.2	0.0735	2.3×10^{-3}	2.25×10^{-2}	0.85	0.048	0.35	0.365	0.678	0.861	0.365	5.8×10^{-5}	7.97×10^{-3}
22	0.3 – 0.1	17.3 – 18.41	1.11	0.0756	4.2×10^{-3}	3.09×10^{-2}	1.0	0.09	0.52	0.365	1.27	1.18	0.365	1.1×10^{-4}	1.1×10^{-2}
23	0.1 – 0.05	18.41 – 19.1	0.69	0.078	6.6×10^{-3}	3.93×10^{-2}	0.96	0.14	0.635	0.365	1.99	1.48	0.365	1.6×10^{-4}	1.32×10^{-2}
24	0.05 – 0.0387	19.1 – 19.36	0.26	0.080	8.2×10^{-3}	4.44×10^{-2}	1.0	0.17	0.714	0.357	2.46	1.62	0.357	2.0×10^{-4}	1.46×10^{-2}
25	0.0387	19.36		0.0835	8.6×10^{-3}	4.64×10^{-2}	1.0	0.18	0.735	0.342	2.67	1.66	0.342	2.5×10^{-4}	1.60×10^{-2}

* $K = (3\Sigma_s \Sigma_c)^{1/2}$.
† Borated graphite has density of 1.6 g/cm³ and 5 wt.% natural boron content.
‡ Carbon has a density of 1.6 g/cm³.

Table 8.70—ANL 20-group Mascroscopic Cross Sections [19]

1. U^{235} (values in cm^{-1})

Group	Lethargy range	Σ_a*	$3\Sigma_{tr}$	$\nu\Sigma_f$	$\Sigma_{el,tr+in}^{j\to j+1}$	$\Sigma_{j\to j+2}$	$\Sigma_{j\to j+3}$	$\Sigma_{j\to j+4}$	$\Sigma_{j\to j+5}$	$\Sigma_{j\to j+6}$
1	0–2	0.14354	0.69000	0.16224	0.05530	0.01060	0.00584	0.00304	0.00152	0.00110
2	2–3	0.12156	0.79200	0.14400	0.02880	0.01520	0.00793	0.00397	0.00288	
3	3–3.5	0.10227	0.93600	0.15600	0.01820	0.00761	0.00381	0.00276		
4	3.5–4	0.09898	1.08000	0.17400	0.01220	0.00387	0.00281			
5	4–4.5	0.09791	1.29600	0.19200	0.00571					
6	4.5–5	0.11465	1.51200	0.21600	0.00665					
7	5–6	0.14099	1.72800	0.26400	0.00369					
8	6–7	0.19801	1.87200	0.36000	0.00361					
9	7–8	0.30631	2.30400	0.54000	0.00391					
10	8–10.4	0.76984	3.88800	1.20000	0.00184					
11	10.4–11.6	1.61593	6.19200	2.52000	0.00313					
12	11.6–12.4	2.94152	9.64800	4.56000	0.00552					
13	12.4–12.6	3.97126	13.24800	6.60000	0.01126					
14	12.6–12.8	3.03585	10.51200	5.40000	0.01185					
15	13.0–13.2	5.53096	18.00000	9.84000	0.02056					
16	13.2–13.9	3.83636	12.96000	6.84000	0.00596					
17	13.9–14.3	3.38121	11.80800	6.24000	0.01161					
18	14.3–16.5	1.44187	5.76000	2.88000	0.00187					
19	16.5–18.6	11.23392	35.13600	23.40000	0.00192					
20	18.6– ∞	28.32000	72.00000	60.00000						

2. U^{238} (values in cm^{-1})

Group	Lethargy range	Σ_a	$3\Sigma_{tr}$	$\nu\Sigma_f$	$\Sigma_{j\to j+1}$	$\Sigma_{j\to j+2}$	$\Sigma_{j\to j+3}$	$\Sigma_{j\to j+4}$	$\Sigma_{j\to j+5}$	$\Sigma_{j\to j+6}$
1	See U^{235}	0.12420	0.66300	0.06682	0.06900	0.01320	0.00730	0.00390	0.00190	0.00138
2		0.05538	0.72000		0.02450	0.01270	0.00661	0.00331	0.00240	
3		0.04076	0.86400		0.01890	0.00761	0.00381	0.00276		
4		0.02880	1.00800		0.01300	0.00387	0.00281			
5		0.01767	1.22400		0.00667					
6		0.02124	1.44000		0.00784					
7		0.02150	1.72800		0.00470					
8		0.02904	1.87200		0.00504					
9		0.03896	2.01600		0.00536					
10		0.05018	2.01600		0.00218					
11		0.10033	2.16000		0.00433					
12		0.10318	2.16000		0.00718					
13		13.93185	43.20000		0.01185					
14		0.02009	1.87200		0.01529					
15		13.94016	43.20000		0.02016					
16		0.01030	1.36800		0.00550					
17		16.32984	50.40000		0.00984					
18		0.01706	1.35360		0.00170					
19		0.04726	1.38240		0.00166					
20		0.11520	1.51200							

3. Iron (values in cm^{-1})

Group	Lethargy range	Σ_a	$3\Sigma_{tr}$	$\Sigma_{j\to j+1}$	$\Sigma_{j\to j+2}$	$\Sigma_{j\to j+3}$	$\Sigma_{j\to j+4}$	$\Sigma_{j\to j+5}$	$\Sigma_{j\to j+6}$	Σ_c
1	See U^{235}	0.06264	0.50820	0.04510	0.00815	0.00451	0.00235	0.00117	0.00085	0.00051
2		0.03135	0.53370	0.01760	0.00672	0.00350	0.00175	0.00127		0.00051
3		0.01981	0.81300	0.01930						0.00051
4		0.01981	0.81300	0.01930						0.00051
5		0.01981	0.81300	0.01930						0.00051
6		0.02161	0.88950	0.02110						0.00051
7		0.00956	0.76230	0.00905						0.00051
8		0.00956	0.76230	0.00905						0.00051
9		0.02171	1.77870	0.02120						0.00051
10		0.01121	2.08362	0.01028						0.00093
11		0.03077	2.84592	0.02789						0.00288
12		0.05148	2.87133	0.04657						0.00491
13		0.10629	2.87133	0.09977						0.00652
14		0.10728	2.87133	0.09966						0.00762
15		0.17815	2.87133	0.16926						0.00889
16		0.05983	2.87133	0.04898						0.01085
17		0.09698	2.87133	0.08207						0.01491
18		0.03779	2.87133	0.01552						0.02227
19		0.08233	2.92215	0.01542						0.06691
20		0.19142	3.37957							0.176

$$*\Sigma_a = \Sigma_f + \Sigma_c + \sum_{j=1}^{20} \int (\Sigma_{el,tr} + \Sigma_{in})$$

Table 8.70—ANL 20-group Macroscopic Cross Sections [19] (continued)

4. Sodium (values in cm^{-1})

Group	Lethargy range	Σ_a	$3\Sigma_{tr}$	$\Sigma_{j\rightarrow j+1}$	$\Sigma_{j\rightarrow j+2}$	$\Sigma_{j\rightarrow j+3}$	$\Sigma_{j\rightarrow j+4}$	$\Sigma_{j\rightarrow j+5}$	$\Sigma_{j\rightarrow j+6}$
1	See U^{235}	0.008947	0.13200	0.00704	0.000907	0.000502	0.000261	0.000131	0.0000949
2		0.008029	0.21120	0.00686	0.000582	0.000303	0.000152	0.00011	
3		0.011222	0.19800	0.01120					
4		0.013122	0.23100	0.01310					
5		0.011222	0.19800	0.01120					
6		0.012422	0.21780	0.01240					
7		0.007522	0.26400	0.00750					
8		0.008452	0.29700	0.00843					
9		0.028122	0.99000	0.02810					
10		0.006262	0.52800	0.00622					
11		0.004788	0.19800	0.00463					
12		0.007918	0.19800	0.00768					
13		0.016780	0.19800	0.01645					
14		0.016829	0.19800	0.016433					
15		0.028318	0.19800	0.027919					
16		0.008636	0.19800	0.008086					
17		0.014331	0.19800	0.013561					
18		0.003713	0.19800	0.002569					
19		0.005948	0.19800	0.002539					
20		0.009746	0.19800						

5. B^{10} (values in cm^{-1})

Group	Lethargy range	Σ_a	$3\Sigma_{tr}$	$\Sigma_{j\rightarrow j+1}$
1	See U^{235}	0.00854	0.09600	0.003739
2		0.01289	0.14400	0.008091
3		0.03498	0.21600	0.02218
4		0.04178	0.23040	0.02098
5		0.04578	0.23040	0.01858
6		0.04858	0.22080	0.01498
7		0.05679	0.26400	0.00719
8		0.09399	0.42240	0.01079
9		0.14679	0.58080	0.01079
10		0.26048	0.94080	0.00448
11		0.80990	2.59200	0.00990
12		1.37642	4.27200	0.01642
13		1.84324	5.61600	0.03524
14		2.14724	6.52800	0.03524
15		2.53994	7.63200	0.05994
16		3.04138	9.26400	0.01738
17		4.17325	12.62400	0.02925
18		6.21357	18.81600	0.00557
19		18.56571	55.87200	0.00571
20		53.18400	72.00000	

6. Carbon (values in cm^{-1})

Group	Lethargy range	Σ_a	$3\Sigma_{tr}$	$\Sigma_{j\rightarrow j+1}$	Σ_c
1	See U^{235}	0.01470	0.37710	0.01470	
2		0.02660	0.50280	0.02660	
3		0.07990	0.75420	0.07990	
4		0.09320	0.87990	0.09320	
5		0.10700	1.00560	0.10700	
6		0.11200	1.05600	0.11200	
7		0.05860	1.10610	0.05860	
8		0.05860	1.10610	0.05860	
9		0.05860	1.10610	0.05860	
10		0.02431	1.10616	0.02431	
11		0.04883	1.11622	0.04883	
12		0.08100	1.11622	0.08100	
13		0.17382	1.11622	0.17382	
14		0.17382	1.11622	0.17382	
15		0.29651	1.11622	0.29561	
16		0.08573	1.11622	0.08573	
17		0.14426	1.11622	0.14426	
18		0.02749	1.11622	0.02749	
19		0.02822	1.11622	0.02814	0.00008
20		0.00034	1.13130	0.02814	0.00034

Table 8.70—ANL 20-group Macroscopic Cross Sections [19] (continued)

7. Potassium (values in cm^{-1})

Group	Lethargy range	Σ_a	$3\Sigma_{tr}$	$\Sigma_{j\to j+1}$	$\Sigma_{j\to j+2}$	$\Sigma_{j\to j+3}$	$\Sigma_{j\to j+4}$	$\Sigma_{j\to j+5}$	$\Sigma_{j\to j+6}$
1	See U^{235}	0.00642	0.08040	0.00461	0.000737	0.000408	0.000212	0.000106	0.000077
2		0.003817	0.06030	0.00215	0.000709	0.000369	0.000185	0.000134	
3		0.00296	0.08040	0.00269					
4		0.00187	0.04824	0.00160					
5		0.00228	0.06030	0.00201					
6		0.00296	0.08040	0.00269					
7		0.00128	0.06030	0.00101					
8		0.00114	0.05226	0.00087					
9		0.00128	0.06030	0.00101					
10		0.00069	0.06110	0.00042					
11		0.00124	0.06151	0.00084					
12		0.00193	0.06191	0.00140					
13		0.00380	0.06271	0.00300					
14		0.00393	0.06311	0.00300					
15		0.00617	0.06352	0.00510					
16		0.00282	0.06432	0.00148					
17		0.00436	0.06593	0.00249					
18		0.00315	0.06834	0.000474					
19		0.00866	0.08482	0.000485					
20		0.02345	0.13065						

are limited according to the criteria listed in Table 8.85. Radiation effects in any given region are minimized by proper selection of radiation-resistant materials.

8.18.1.3 Nuclear-heating Limits

A third purpose of the shield system is to prevent injurious effects to concrete from the combined action of radiation and heat. The maximum permissible energy flux incident upon concrete is set at 4×10^{10} Mev/cm^2/sec, which corresponds to a neutron flux (if taken alone) of 5×10^9 neutrons/cm^2/sec or a gamma photon flux from Na^{24} of 1×10^{10} gammas/cm^2/sec. These radiation fluxes correspond to a heat flux of 20 Btu/hr/sq ft. The temperature rise within the shield has a design limit of 10°F.

8.18.1.4 Temperature Limits

The retention of the water of hydration in concrete to be used as a neutron shield is essential if the desired shield performance is to be realized. A maximum design surface temperature of 180°F was established at the Fermi plant for all concrete to be used primarily as a neutron shield, as given in Table 8.85. A maximum concrete design temperature of 350°F was established where gamma-ray shielding was primarily needed. Undue thermal stress in concrete used as shielding is prevented by limiting the temperature gradient at any point.

8.18.1.5 Coolant-activation Limits

The shield system also prevents activation of the secondary coolant system and the primary coolant equipment within the containment vessel. The total neutron flux within the equipment compartment has been limited to a design value of 1×10^4 neutrons/cm^2/sec. This produces a negligible neutron-induced activation of the steel in the equipment compartment and the secondary sodium coolant. With these limits the calculated activation level

of the secondary coolant is less than 2×10^{-4} µc/cm^3; that of the steel equipment is slightly higher. The total dose rate to which a maintenance worker is exposed when working adjacent to the secondary coolant system is less than 0.75 mr/hr.

8.18.2 REACTOR SHIELD SYSTEM

The shield system in the reactor containment building consists of three main parts, as illustrated in Fig. 8.101 (see also Chap. 11). The inner primary shield surrounds the reactor vessel and is designed principally as a neutron shield to reduce neutron leakage from the reactor to levels low enough that the materials used outside this shield will not be damaged. Beyond the primary shield is a secondary shield designed also as a neutron shield. The main purpose of this shield is to prevent activation of the primary coolant system equipment and the secondary sodium coolant. The third major component of the shield system is an outer biological shield, consisting of the operating floor, the upper part of the primary shielding including and surrounding the rotating plug, and the concrete shield outside the containment building. In addition, there are special-purpose shields, such as the sodium exit loop pipe shields.

The neutron-induced activity of the various systems and equipment which helped to determine the proper shielding requirements in various areas of the plant is shown in Table 8.86.

8.18.3 PRIMARY SHIELD

The primary shield system (Fig. 8.102) is divided into four parts: (1) the depleted-uranium blanket, (2) the stainless-steel thermal shield, (3) the rotating plug, which fits into the neck of the upper reactor vessel and acts as a biological shield, and (4) the graphite shield, which is outside the reactor vessel but inside the primary shield tank.

Table 8.71—Los Alamos 18-group Microscopic Cross Sections [139]

1. U^{235} (values in barns)

Group	Lethargy range*	σ_a	$\nu\sigma_f$	σ_{tr}	$\sigma_{j\to j+1}$	$\sigma_{j\to j+2}$	$\sigma_{j\to j+3}$	$\sigma_{j\to j+4}$	$\sigma_{j\to j+5}$
1	0 – 1	1.26	3.557	4.25	0.27	0.37	0.65	0.44	0.06
2	1 – 2	1.3	3.196	4.5	0.24	0.67	0.45	0.07	
3	2 – 3	1.33	3.087	4.65	0.55	0.4	0.07		
4	3 – 4	1.35	2.998	5.2	0.35	0.08			
5	4 – 5	1.66	3.518	7.9	0.08				
6	5 – 6	3.15	6.125	12.4	0.05				
7	6 – 7	5.5	10.29	15.1	0.05				
8	7 – 8	11.1	19.36	21.1	0.05				
9	8 – 9	25.5	42.87	35.5	0.05				
10	9 – 10	93.57	146.3	103.57	0.05				
11	10 – 11	111.5	118.0	121.5	0.05				
12	11 – 12	47.04	59.2	57.04	0.05				
13	12 – 13	32.55	60.4	42.55	0.05				
14	13 – 14	73.1	150.9	83.1	0.05				
15	14 – 15	165.0	336.5	175.0	0.05				
16	15 – 16	253.8	531.1	263.8	0.05				
17	16 – 17	546.2	1161.0	556.2	0.05				
18	17 – ∞	597.5	1230.0	607.5					

2. U^{238} (values in barns)

Group	σ_a	$\nu\sigma_f$	σ_{tr}	$\sigma_{j\to j+1}$	$\sigma_{j\to j+2}$	$\sigma_{j\to j+3}$	$\sigma_{j\to j+4}$	$\sigma_{j\to j+5}$
1	0.566	1.725	4.0	0.33	0.46	0.79	0.53	0.07
2	0.535	1.213	4.4	0.35	0.96	0.64	0.09	
3	0.144	0.108	4.5	0.8	0.55	0.1		
4	0.14		5.25	0.5	0.08			
5	0.16		8.2	0.08				
6	0.45		12.0	0.1				
7	0.70		14.0	0.05				
8	2.01		15.0	0.04				
9	11.0		22.0	0.04				
10	50.0		59.0	0.04				
11	56.0		65.0	0.07				
12	110.0		119.0	0.07				
13	0.33		9.4	0.07				
14	0.52		9.5	0.07				
15	0.87		10.0	0.07				
16	1.43		10.0	0.07				
17	2.3		11.37	0.07				
18	2.44		11.44					

3. Th^{232} (values in barns)

Group	σ_a	$\nu\sigma_f$	σ_{tr}	$\sigma_{j\to j+1}$	$\sigma_{j\to j+2}$	$\sigma_{j\to j+3}$	$\sigma_{j\to j+4}$	$\sigma_{j\to j+5}$
1	0.54	0.368	12.64	1.22	0.53	0.76	0.45	0.14
2	0.42	0.23	10.5499	0.71	1.02	0.6	0.18	0.12
3	0.08	0.0207	7.93	0.54	0.37	0.23	0.11	
4	0.13		7.56	0.43	0.000001	0.000001		
5	0.21		9.11	0.4	0.00001			
5	0.46		12.01	0.4	0.05			
7	1.0		13.43	0.43				
8	1.28		13.6	0.32				
9	1.6968		13.8	0.1032				
10	0.9968		13.1	0.1032				
11	0.9468		13.05	0.1032				
12	0.4278		12.531	0.1032				
13	0.7698		12.873	0.1032				
14	1.3468		13.45	0.1032				
15	2.2808		14.384	0.1032				
16	3.2968		15.4	0.1032				
17	4.8068		16.91	0.1032				
18	7.43		19.43					

*Zero lethargy = 10 Mev.

Table 8.71—Los Alamos 18-group Microscopic Cross Sections [139] (continued)

4. U^{233} (values in barns)

Group	σ_a	$\sigma\nu_f$	σ_{tr}	$\sigma_{j \to j+1}$	$\sigma_{j \to j+2}$	$\sigma_{j \to j+3}$	$\sigma_{j \to j+4}$	$\sigma_{j \to j+5}$
1	1.8	5.285	4.25	0.2	0.27	0.45	0.31	0.04
2	1.91	4.941	4.5	0.18	0.5	0.35	0.05	
3	2.0	4.933	4.8	0.45	0.3	0.06		
4	2.09	4.986	5.7	0.29	0.05			
5	2.47	5.667	8.4	0.05				
6	3.55	8.107	11.77	0.05				
7	6.574	15.0	16.624	0.05				
8	9.861	22.5	19.911	0.05				
9	44.95	60.0	55.0	0.05				
10	56.95	133.0	67.0	0.05				
11	118.95	255.0	129.0	0.05				
12	109.95	225.0	120.0	0.05				
13	343.95	725.0	354.0	0.05				
14	160.95	330.0	171.0	0.05				
15	200.35	456.0	210.4	0.05				
16	309.95	706.0	320.0	0.05				
17	484.95	1104.0	495.0	0.05				
18	520.0	1187.0	530.0					

5. Pu^{239} (values in barns)

Group	σ_a	$\sigma\nu_f$	σ_{tr}	$\sigma_{j \to j+1}$	$\sigma_{j \to j+2}$	$\sigma_{j \to j+3}$	$\sigma_{j \to j+4}$	$\sigma_{j \to j+5}$
1	2.07	6.612	4.25	0.2	0.27	0.31	0.31	0.04
2	2.15	6.026	4.5	0.18	0.35	0.35	0.05	
3	2.05	5.472	4.8	0.3	0.3	0.06		
4	1.81	4.981	5.7	0.29	0.05			
5	1.84	4.81	8.4	0.05				
6	2.67	5.291	12.17	0.05				
7	3.65	6.778	13.15	0.05				
8	8.71	14.671	18.21	0.05				
9	37.6	60.26	47.1	0.05				
10	81.1	128.7	90.6	0.05				
11	109.84	171.6	119.34	0.05				
12	39.476	65.78	48.976	0.05				
13	39.11	65.2	48.61	0.05				
14	163.3	343.2	172.8	0.05				
15	1901.89	3231.8	1911.39	0.05				
16	722.6	1430.0	732.1	0.05				
17	834.1	1716.0	843.6	0.05				
18	1042.6	2145.0	1052.1					

6. Hydrogen (values in barns)

Group	σ_a	σ_{tr}	$\sigma_{j \to j+1}$	$\sigma_{j \to j+2}$	$\sigma_{j \to j+3}$	$\sigma_{j \to j+4}$	$\sigma_{j \to j+5}$
1		1.37	0.53	0.17	0.17	0.1	0.03
2		2.0	0.53	0.53	0.32	0.09	0.01
3		2.77	1.2	0.72	0.2	0.03	0.01
4		3.52	1.89	0.52	0.09	0.02	
5		4.41	2.69	0.45	0.09	0.01	
6		6.92	3.91	0.83	0.11	0.01	
7		10.47	5.39	0.73	0.07	0.03	
8	0.002	10.472	4.99	0.49	0.18	0.07	
9	0.004	10.474	3.65	1.34	0.49	0.18	0.07
10	0.009	12.239	5.33	1.96	0.72	0.27	0.1
11	0.014	12.234	5.32	1.96	0.72	0.27	0.1
12	0.022	12.242	5.32	1.96	0.72	0.27	0.1
13	0.04	12.26	5.32	1.96	0.72	0.27	0.1
14	0.064	12.284	5.32	1.96	0.72	0.37	
15	0.108	12.328	5.32	1.96	1.09		
16	0.174	20.014	10.87	3.96			
17	0.26	22.5	15.3				
18	0.28	34.28					

Table 8.71—Los Alamos 18-group Microscopic Cross
Sections [139] (continued)

7. Beryllium (values in barns)

Group	σ_a	σ_{tr}	$\sigma_{j \to j+1}$	$\sigma_{j \to j+2}$
1	− 0.308*	0.842	0.818	0.35
2	− 0.088*	1.275	0.509	0.12
3		2.38	1.207	
4		3.31	0.913	
5		3.94	0.634	
6		5.18	0.655	
7		5.28	0.68	
8		5.37	0.83	
9		5.42	0.83	
10	0.001	5.46	1.22	
11	0.0003	5.46	1.22	
12	0.0004	5.46	1.22	
13	0.0007	5.46	1.22	
14	0.0012	5.46	1.22	
15	0.0019	5.46	1.22	
16	0.0052	5.46	1.22	
17	0.0084	5.46	1.22	
18	0.009	5.569		

8. Natural boron (values in barns)

Group	σ_a	σ_{tr}	$\sigma_{j \to j+1}$
1	0.04	1.52	0.67
2	0.06	1.79	0.42
3	0.04	2.14	0.88
4	0.08	2.27	0.5
5	0.27	3.16	0.38
6	0.61	4.08	0.36
7	1.5	4.97	0.37
8	3.5	7.0	0.3
9	9.5	13.0	0.3
10	20.5	23.5	0.6
11	33.0	36.5	0.6
12	51.0	54.5	0.6
13	90.0	93.5	0.6
14	146.0	149.5	0.6
15	239.0	242.5	0.6
16	395.0	398.5	0.6
17	634.2	637.7	0.6
18	638.0	641.5	

9. Carbon (values in barns)

Group	σ_a	σ_{tr}	$\sigma_{j \to j+1}$
1		1.23	0.515
2	0.000001	1.42	0.314
3		2.26	0.856
4		2.93	0.604
5		3.59	0.433
6		4.25	0.401
7		4.44	0.43
8		4.34	0.37
9		4.34	0.37
10		4.34	0.73
11		4.34	0.73
12		4.34	0.73
13		4.34	0.73
14		4.34	0.73
15		4.44	0.75
16		4.44	0.75
17	0.001	4.441	0.75
18	0.0027	4.5327	

*The $(n, 2n)$ reaction.

Table 8.71—Los Alamos 18-group Microscopic Cross
Sections [139] (continued)

10. Oxygen (values in barns)

Group	σ_a	σ_{tr}	$\sigma_{j \to j+1}$
1	0.04	1.33	0.424
2		1.18	0.191
3		3.23	0.902
4		3.63	0.556
5		3.71	0.337
6		3.26	0.231
7		3.55	0.255
8		3.64	0.23
9		3.64	0.23
10		3.64	0.46
11		3.64	0.46
12		3.64	0.46
13		3.64	0.46
14		3.64	0.46
15		3.64	0.46
16		3.64	0.46
17		3.64	0.46
18	0.0002	3.6412	

11. Sodium (values in barns)

Group	σ_a	σ_{tr}	$\sigma_{j \to j+1}$	$\sigma_{j \to j+3}$	$\sigma_{j \to j+4}$
1	0.03	1.607	0.44		
2		2.26	0.556		
3	0.0002	2.9902	1.191		
4	0.0005	4.0905	0.7081	0.036	0.008
5	0.0009	3.6898	0.2317		
6	0.001	4.272	0.207		
7	0.001	6.089	0.301		
8	0.001	4.545	0.234		
9	0.011	3.01	0.216		
10	0.018	3.03	0.236		
11	0.032	3.069	0.219		
12	0.076	3.099	0.219		
13	0.057	3.099	0.238		
14	0.1	3.21	0.294		
15	0.094	3.35	0.294		
16	0.094	3.35	0.294		
17	0.19	3.35	0.198		
18	0.447	3.747			

12. Aluminum (values in barns)

Group	σ_a	σ_{tr}	$\sigma_{j \to j+1}$	$\sigma_{j \to j+2}$	$\sigma_{j \to j+3}$	$\sigma_{j \to j+4}$
1	0.0159	1.9289	0.64192	0.12042	0.02955	
2	0.00035	2.32235	0.37962	0.22003	0.03419	0.00176
3	0.00038	2.34438	0.3953	0.17024	0.0119	
4	0.0007	2.8967	0.264			
5	0.002	3.521	0.188			
6	0.005	2.926	0.123			
7	0.005	1.463	0.06			
8		1.41	0.05			
9		1.41	0.05			
10		1.46	0.1			
11	0.01	1.47	0.1			
12	0.02	1.49	0.1			
13	0.03	1.51	0.1			
14	0.04	1.55	0.1			
15	0.07	1.55	0.1			
16	0.11	1.57	0.1			
17	0.18	1.64	0.1			
18	0.18	1.54				

Table 8.71—Los Alamos 18-group Microscopic Cross
Sections [139] (continued)

13. Iron (values in barns)

Group	σ_a	σ_{tr}	$\sigma_{j \to j+1}$	$\sigma_{j \to j+2}$	$\sigma_{j \to j+3}$
1	0.005	1.713	1.21		
2	0.005	2.322	0.477	0.322	0.023
3	0.005	2.61	0.335	0.346	0.03
4	0.005	2.764	0.123		
5	0.00708	2.816	0.071		
6	0.018	4.377	0.089		
7	0.012	5.939	0.151		
8	0.019	7.11	0.3		
9	0.03	11.23	0.2		
10	0.07	11.47	0.2		
11	0.11	11.51	0.4		
12	0.17	11.57	0.4		
13	0.3	11.7	0.4		
14	0.49	11.89	0.4		
15	0.8	12.2	0.4		
16	1.34	12.74	0.4		
17	2.13	13.53	0.4		
18	2.14	12.94			

14. Molybdenum (values in barns)

Group	σ_a	σ_{tr}	$\sigma_{j \to j+1}$	$\sigma_{j \to j+2}$	$\sigma_{j \to j+3}$
1	0.0112	1.81	0.817	0.033	0.013
2	0.0386	2.56	0.351	0.2	0.007
3	0.0575	3.7	0.286	0.176	0.018
4	0.0731	5.49	0.23		
5	0.0963	6.53	0.14		
6	0.12	7.6	0.107		
7	0.114	7.28	0.096		
8	0.3	7.1	0.07		
9	2.71	7.825	0.07		
10	3.9	8.04	0.14		
11	1.465	5.48	0.14		
12	0.2866	5.92	0.14		
13	0.371	6.14	0.14		
14	0.569	6.51	0.14		
15	0.948	6.93	0.14		
16	1.476	7.15	0.14		
17	2.28	7.22	0.14		
18	2.7	7.3			

15. Zirconium (values in barns)

Group	σ_a	σ_{tr}	$\sigma_{j \to j+1}$	$\sigma_{j \to j+2}$	$\sigma_{j \to j+3}$
1		3.33	0.817	0.033	0.013
2		5.11	0.351	0.2	0.007
3		5.79	0.286	0.176	0.018
4		8.54	0.23		
5		8.84	0.14		
6		8.74	0.107		
7		7.64	0.096		
8		6.55	0.07		
9		6.35	0.07		
10		6.15	0.14		
11		6.15	0.14		
12	0.01	6.16	0.14		
13	0.02	6.17	0.14		
14	0.03	6.18	0.14		
15	0.06	6.21	0.14		
16	0.09	6.24	0.14		
17	0.15	6.3	0.14		
18	0.15	6.16			

Table 8.71—Los Alamos 18-group Microscopic Cross
Sections [139] (continued)

16. Nickel (values in barns)

Group	σ_a	σ_{tr}	$\sigma_{j \to j+1}$	$\sigma_{j \to j+2}$	$\sigma_{j \to j+3}$	$\sigma_{j \to j+4}$
1	0.00167	2.16	0.851	0.31	0.354	0.15
2	0.00372	2.56	0.302	0.28	0.158	
3	0.00718	2.95	0.3			
4	0.00691	3.35	0.216			
5	0.00951	5.32	0.118			
6	0.0170	11.5	0.598			
7	0.0195	24.0	0.236			
8	0.032	17.6	0.162			
9	0.051	16.7	0.144			
10	0.11	17.0	0.338			
11	0.18	17.1	0.414			
12	0.31	17.1	0.379			
13	0.52	17.1	0.307			
14	0.875	17.3	0.255			
15	1.42	17.3	0.097			
16	2.4	17.1	0.081			
17	4.0	16.5	0.1			
18	4.26	16.0				

8.18.3.1 Depleted-uranium Blanket

Besides breeding plutonium the depleted-uranium blanket around the core serves to shield out most of the very intense core gamma rays and to reduce the neutron flux leaking to the thermal shield. At a reactor power of 300 Mw, at least 6 Mw of heat is generated within the blanket from the absorption of core gammas. [Total heat generated in the blanket is 30 Mw(t).] The absorbed heat is picked up by the sodium coolant, and the amount of heat released in the external shield is thus reduced.

8.18.3.2 Thermal Shield

The thermal shield is a stainless-steel layer 12 in. thick in the lower reactor vessel and 6 in. thick in the upper reactor vessel. Part of this layer is composed of stainless-steel dummy subassemblies that rest upon the subassembly grid network.

The remainder of the shield consists of layers of steel plate arranged in concentric rings about the reactor vessel and constructed with spaces between them so that sodium can flow between the layers.

The primary purpose of the stainless steel is to prevent radiation damage to the reactor-vessel wall. This is accomplished by making use of the large inelastic-scattering cross section of stainless steel. The 1-ft layer of stainless steel attenuates the high-energy components of the neutron flux by at least a factor of 100. However, steel is not a particularly good neutron absorber at the neutron-energy levels that exist in the Fermi reactor, and a large number of intermediate- and low-energy neutrons are built up within the steel. The resulting attenuation of the total flux through the steel is over a factor of 10. Approximately half of the total flux is above 0.1 Mev. The total neutron flux incident on the vessel walls at the core midplane elevation is about 6×10^{12} neutrons/cm²/sec. This value is low enough to ensure that the integrated flux to the

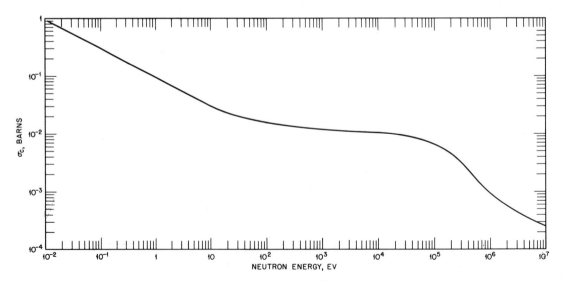

FIG. 8.80—Microscopic capture cross section for Ar[41] as a function of neutron energy.

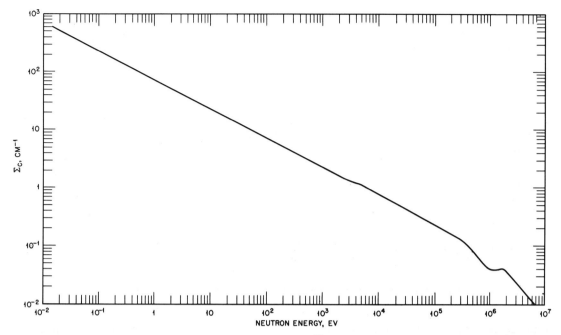

FIG. 8.81—Macroscopic capture cross section for B^{10} as a function of neutron energy.

reactor vessel over the plant life will be less than the design limit. The thermal shield also reduces the intensity of the primary and secondary gamma rays generated in the core and blanket; it absorbs about 1.6 Mw of heat, which is picked up by the sodium coolant.

8.18.3.3 Rotating Plug

The rotating plug (Fig. 8.102) is a stepped 12-ft-thick shield, 9 ft in diameter at the base and 10 ft in diameter at the top, which fits in the top of the reactor vessel. The shell is made of stainless steel, and the shielding within the plug consists of 18 in. of stainless steel, six 11-in. layers of plain graphite, and one 11-in. layer of 1-1/2% borated graphite. Above this there is a 12-in.-thick carbon-steel gamma-ray shield, followed by 1 ft of stainless steel insulating material topped by an 11-in.-thick cover plate of solid carbon steel. The graphite within the rotating plug is in the form of 3 by 3 by 11-in. blocks canned in carbon steel. Each

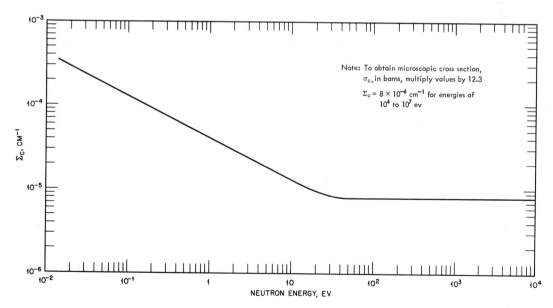

FIG. 8.82—Macroscopic capture cross section for carbon as a function of neutron energy. Density of carbon is 1.6 g/cm^3.

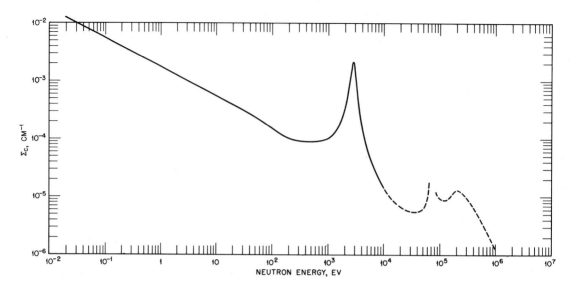

FIG. 8.83—Macroscopic capture cross section for sodium as a function of neutron energy.

of the graphite layers rests on 2-in.-thick steel plates, which serve to support the layer and reduce the penetrating gamma radiation formed by neutron capture in the steel and carbon. A view of the interior of the rotating-plug shield during construction is shown in Fig. 8.103.

Radiation streaming through access holes in the plug is prevented (1) by stepping the annuli, (2) by placing special shield material* within voids and around equipment in the holes, (3) by keeping the void volume to a minimum, and (4) by other design practices, such as the use of patch shields and special materials that reduce or prevent streaming.

---

*Mainly boron steel.

The overall performance of the rotating plug is the reduction of the neutron flux by a factor of about 10^{13}.

8.18.3.4 Graphite Shield

The graphite shield (Fig. 8.102), which lies outside the reactor vessel and within the primary shield tank, has the following basic configuration: (1) an inner 6-in. layer of 5% borated graphite next to the reactor vessel wall, (2) a layer of insulation, (3) a region of plain (unborated) graphite, and (4) a 6-in. layer of 5% borated graphite, which lines the inside of the primary shield tank. Through the section of the shield at the reactor center line, the plain graphite has a thickness of about 34 in., the

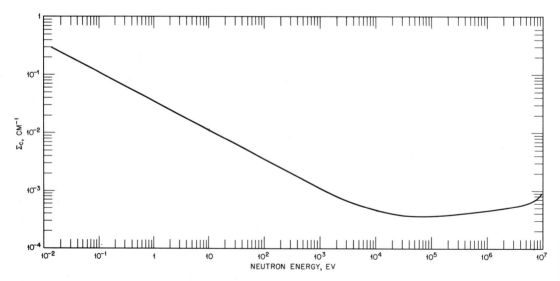

FIG. 8.84—Macroscopic capture cross section of stainless steel as a function of neutron energy (10-group cross sections plus NDA data).

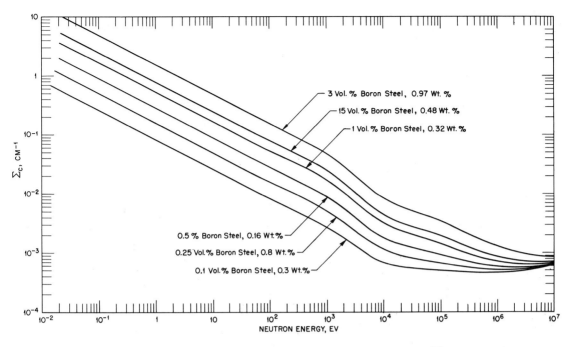

FIG. 8.85—Calculated macroscopic capture cross sections for boron steel [3].

total shield thickness being about 50 in. Room for expansion and movement has been provided. Starting at the 571-ft elevation in the upper reactor vessel section, the inner 6-in. layer of borated graphite and the insulation layer are reversed. The insulation is directly on the vessel, and the borated graphite is outside the insulation. At this elevation nuclear heat-generation rates are low enough that this can be done.

The actual structure of the shield within the primary shield tank is complex. The tank contains the reactor vessel, the inlet and outlet sodium coolant pipes, the exit port shaft, the transfer-rotor drive, the neutron-detector tubes, heater cables, thermocouple leads, gas lines, pipe hangers, cable trays, and other miscellaneous equipment and structural parts. The shielding has been

designed and constructed around these items. Space is required for movement due to thermal expansion of the vessel and the components connected to the vessel. The 30-in.-diameter outlet pipes, the 14-in.-diameter and the 6-in.-diameter sodium inlet lines, together with the space required for instrumentation and insulation, cable leads, and other lines within the vessel, create major gaps and

Table 8.72—Removal Cross Sections for Various Materials [140]

Material	σ_r, barns	N_0 at 20°C, atoms/cm^3	Σ_r, cm^{-1}
Hydrogen	1.00 ± 0.55		
Lithium	1.01 ± 0.04	0.0460×10^{24}	0.046
Beryllium	1.07 ± 0.06	0.120	0.128
Boron	0.97 ± 0.10	0.139	0.135
Graphite	0.72 ± 0.05	0.113	0.092
Oxygen	0.92 ± 0.05		
Fluorine	1.29 ± 0.06		
Aluminum	1.31 ± 0.05	0.0603	0.079
Chlorine	1.2 ± 0.8		
Iron	1.98 ± 0.08	0.0848	0.168
Nickel	1.89 ± 0.10	0.0913	0.173
Copper	2.04 ± 0.11	0.0846	0.173
Tungsten	2.51 ± 0.55	0.0631	0.198
Lead	3.53 ± 0.30	0.0330	0.116
Bismuth	3.49 ± 0.35	0.0282	0.098
Uranium	3.6 ± 0.4	0.0473	0.17
Boric Oxide (B_2O_3)	4.30 ± 0.41	0.016*	~ 0.075
Boron Carbide (B_4C)	5.1 ± 0.4	0.0277*	~ 0.127
Fluorothene (C_2F_3Cl)	6.66 ± 0.8		
Heavy Water (D_2O)	2.76 ± 0.11	0.0332*	~ 0.092
Lithium Fluoride (LiF)	2.43 ± 0.34	0.0605*	~ 0.147
Oil (CH_2)	2.84 ± 0.11		
Paraffin ($C_{30}H_{62}$)	80.5 ± 5.2		
Perfluoroheptane (C_7F_{16})	26.3 ± 0.8		

* Molecules/cm^3.

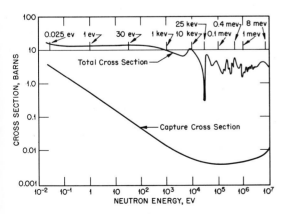

FIG. 8.86—Total and capture cross sections for iron as a function of neutron energy.

Table 8.73—Some Estimated Removal Cross Sections for Selected Elements [81]

Element	Atomic weight	Estimated removal cross section (σ_r), barns
Nitrogen	14.008	1.07
Sodium	22.997	1.21
Magnesium	24.32	1.22
Silicon	28.06	1.26
Sulfur	32.06	1.30
Potassium	39.096	1.54
Calcium	40.08	1.58
Titanium	47.90	1.77
Chromium	52.01	1.87
Manganese	54.93	1.93
Cobalt	58.94	2.02
Zinc	65.38	2.12
Barium	137.36	2.96

voids and streaming paths within the shield. In each instance where the bulk shield was affected by the creation of either a large effective void area or a neutron-streaming path, the neutron-attenuation characteristic of the region was studied separately, and detailed calculations were made to

Table 8.74—Calculated Values of Macroscopic Removal Cross Sections for Selected Shield Materials and for Compounds Found in Shield Materials*[81]

Material	Formula	Density, g/cm^3	Macroscopic removal cross section, cm^{-1}
Aluminum oxide	Al$_2$O$_3$	4.00	0.132
Ammonia, liquid	NH$_3$	0.771[†]	0.111
Barium sulfate	BaSO$_4$	4.50	0.095
Calcium carbonate	CaCO$_2$	2.71	0.087
Calcium oxide	CaO	3.32	0.092
Concrete:			
Barytes		3.5	0.096
Iron-portland		6.0	0.140
Limonite		2.96	0.114
Portland[‡]		2.2	0.091
Ferric oxide	Fe$_2$O$_3$	5.12	0.134
Ferro boron	FeB	6.00	0.160
Gasoline	C$_8$H$_{18}$	0.739	0.095
Gravel			0.092
Lithium amide	LiNH$_2$	1.18	0.126
Lithium hydride	LiH	0.92	0.140
Lucite	(C$_5$H$_8$O$_2$)n	1.18	0.100
Magnesium oxide	MgO	3.65	0.120
Oil	(C$_7{}_3$H$_{12}$)n	0.89	0.096
Polyethylene	(CH$_2$)n	0.92	0.111
Potassium oxide	K$_2$O	2.32	0.060
Rubber:			
Natural	(C$_5$H$_8$)n	0.92	0.098
Neoprene	(C$_4$H$_5$Cl)n	1.23	0.079
Sand		2.2	0.082
Silicon dioxide	SiO$_2$	2.32	0.076
Sodium oxide	Na$_2$O	2.27	0.075
Steel:			
1% carbon		7.83	0.163
2% boron			
stainless		7.83[§]	0.164
Teflon	(CH$_2$)n	2.20	0.090
Water	H$_2$O	1.00	0.100

* Values calculated from known or estimated values of the components of each material.

[†] Density at $-79°$C.

[‡] Latest experimental value of the removal cross section reported in Ref 140 is 0.086 ± 0.005 cm^{-1}.

[§] Type 303 stainless steel has a density of 7.93.

determine the proper shielding. In three locations, where the shield is thin, patch shields on the outside of the primary shield tank are provided. The detailed pattern of the graphite at the reactor midplane elevation is shown in Fig. 8.104.

Neutron streaming in the annular gaps around the sodium inlet lines has been prevented by the addition of shielding rings, or donuts, attached directly to the pipes, as shown in Fig. 8.105. Insulation, leak-detector sheathing, and expansion space have been provided on the outside of these donuts.

The upper portion of the primary shield tank serves as a biological shield. The arrangement of the shielding for this portion of the primary shield tank is shown in Fig. 8.106. A ring of 5% borated graphite and steel shielding material is placed directly around the neck of the reactor vessel. This ring reduces radiation streaming by breaking the annular gap along the side of the rotating plug. A 16- to 24-in.-thick gamma-ray shield of (borated) steel shot is located above this ring, extending outward from the vessel neck to the primary shield tank. This shield reduces capture gammas generated in lower portions of this shield.

The webbed portion of the primary shield tank underneath the reactor vessel is filled with plain graphite; it forms a thermal pad that effectively conducts the heat from the bottom of the reactor vessel to the side of the tank and keeps the concrete-pad temperatures within design limits. Studies indicate that the temperature of the concrete pad will be less than 320°F at full operating power.

The primary shield tank is sealed and supplied with an inert-gas atmosphere during nuclear operation. The temperature in the primary shield is monitored by thermocouples located in the reactor vessel, leak-detection sheath, flex legs, graphite, primary shield tank surface, rotating plug, and concrete pad beneath the vessel.

8.18.3.5 Design Neutron Leakage

The allowable neutron-leakage flux from the primary shield tank as a function of elevation is shown in Fig. 8.107. These levels were determined in accordance with the maximum permissible levels allowed in different areas for (1) personnel protection, (2) protection against too much radiation absorption in concrete, and (3) protection against activation of the equipment and the secondary sodium coolant within the equipment compartment.

8.18.3.6 Primary Shield Performance

Graphite is a good conducting material. Placing the 6-in. layer of borated graphite inside the insulation around the reactor vessel allows most of the nuclear heat generated within the graphite to be returned to the vessel, where it is carried away by the sodium coolant. The maximum heat generation rate within the 6-in. layer is about 0.06 watts/cm^3 at the elevation of the core center line. The nuclear-heat generation rate as a function of position within the shield is shown in Fig. 8.108. This shield configuration has an added advantage in that no aux-

Table 8.75—Gamma-ray Mass-absorption Coefficients at Various Energies for
Selected Elements and Compounds [145]

Photon energy, Mev	Mass-absorption coefficient, μ/ρ, cm^2/g							
	H	Be	C	N	O	Na	Al	Si
0.10	0.294	0.133	0.152	0.154	0.155	0.158	0.169	0.182
0.15	0.265	0.119	0.135	0.136	0.137	0.134	0.138	0.144
0.20	0.243	0.109	0.123	0.123	0.124	0.120	0.122	0.127
0.30	0.211	0.0944	0.107	0.107	0.107	0.103	0.104	0.108
0.40	0.189	0.0846	0.0953	0.0953	0.0956	0.0917	0.0927	0.0961
0.50	0.173	0.0772	0.0870	0.0870	0.0871	0.0835	0.0844	0.0873
0.60	0.160	0.0714	0.0805	0.0805	0.0805	0.0770	0.0779	0.0805
0.80	0.140	0.0628	0.0707	0.0707	0.0708	0.0677	0.0683	0.0708
1.0	0.126	0.0564	0.0635	0.0636	0.0636	0.0608	0.0614	0.0635
1.5	0.103	0.0459	0.0516	0.0516	0.0519	0.0495	0.0500	0.0517
2.0	0.0878	0.0394	0.0443	0.0443	0.0444	0.0427	0.0431	0.0448
3.0	0.0693	0.0313	0.0356	0.0357	0.0359	0.0348	0.0353	0.0367
4.0	0.0580	0.0266	0.0304	0.0306	0.0309	0.0304	0.0310	0.0324
5.0	0.0503	0.0234	0.0270	0.0274	0.0277	0.0272	0.0284	0.0296
6.0	0.0449	0.0212	0.0246	0.0251	0.0255	0.0255	0.0266	0.0279
8.0	0.0373	0.0181	0.0215	0.0220	0.0225	0.0231	0.0243	0.0258
10.0	0.0324	0.0162	0.0195	0.0202	0.0208	0.0218	0.0232	0.0245
15.0	0.0253	0.0136	0.0169	0.0177	0.0186	0.0202	0.0219	0.0234
20.0	0.0214	0.0122	0.0156	0.0166	0.0176	0.0197	0.0217	0.0232
50.0	0.0141	0.0101	0.0142	0.0156	0.0170	0.0203	0.0230	0.0253
80.0	0.0123	0.0099	0.0143	0.0160	0.0176	0.0213	0.0246	0.0270
100.0	0.0118	0.0100	0.0146	0.0163	0.0180	0.0222	0.0254	0.0279

Photon energy, Mev	A	Ca	Fe	Cu	Mo	Su	I	W
0.10	0.202	0.256	0.370	0.458	1.09	1.65	1.92	4.36
0.15	0.142	0.167	0.196	0.222	0.418	0.599	0.688	1.51
0.20	0.120	0.137	0.146	0.156	0.242	0.324	0.363	0.747
0.30	0.0995	0.112	0.110	0.112	0.137	0.163	0.176	0.310
0.40	0.0876	0.0978	0.0939	0.0939	0.104	0.115	0.120	0.184
0.50	0.0795	0.0885	0.0840	0.0834	0.0879	0.0923	0.0964	0.131
0.60	0.0733	0.0813	0.0769	0.0760	0.0778	0.0797	0.0821	0.105
0.80	0.0639	0.0711	0.0668	0.0658	0.0653	0.0660	0.0669	0.0789
1.0	0.0574	0.0637	0.0598	0.0588	0.0581	0.0573	0.0579	0.0655
1.5	0.0467	0.0518	0.0484	0.0475	0.0470	0.0463	0.0464	0.0501
2.0	0.0406	0.0451	0.0422	0.0416	0.0412	0.0407	0.0408	0.0432
3.0	0.0336	0.0378	0.0359	0.0356	0.0362	0.0361	0.0364	0.0400
4.0	0.0300	0.0388	0.0330	0.0328	0.0345	0.0350	0.0355	0.0400
5.0	0.0279	0.0316	0.0314	0.0316	0.0341	0.0351	0.0356	0.0409
6.0	0.0267	0.0302	0.0305	0.0309	0.0343	0.0356	0.0364	0.0426
8.0	0.0252	0.0289	0.0298	0.0306	0.0350	0.0370	0.0380	0.0449
10.0	0.0244	0.0283	0.0300	0.0309	0.0361	0.0388	0.0398	0.0475
15.0	0.0243	0.0284	0.0308	0.0324	0.0395	0.0431	0.0445	0.0537
20.0	0.0247	0.0292	0.0321	0.0341	0.0425	0.0467	0.0484	0.0590
50.0	0.0277	0.0332	0.0384	0.0412	0.0535	0.0594	0.0617	0.0770
80.0	0.0299	0.0361	0.0419	0.0452	0.0590	0.0660	0.0678	0.0855
100.0	0.0311	0.0376	0.0436	0.0470	0.0615	0.0690	0.0707	0.0891

Photon energy, Mev	Pt	Pb	U	Air*	Sodium Iodide, No. 1	Water	Concrete
0.10	4.90	5.46	1.26	0.155	1.65	0.171	0.169
0.15	1.72	1.92	2.49	0.136	0.603	0.151	0.139
0.20	0.836	0.942	1.20	0.123	0.326	0.137	0.124
0.30	0.342	0.378	0.476	0.107	0.165	0.119	0.107
0.40	0.202	0.220	0.273	0.0953	0.116	0.106	0.0954
0.50	0.142	0.152	0.185	0.0869	0.0936	0.0967	0.0870
0.60	0.112	0.119	0.142	0.0804	0.0813	0.0894	0.0804
0.80	0.0827	0.0866	0.0987	0.0706	0.0670	0.0786	0.0706
1.0	0.0676	0.0703	0.0779	0.0635	0.0584	0.0706	0.0635
1.5	0.0509	0.0523	0.0562	0.0516	0.0469	0.0576	0.0517
2.0	0.0444	0.0546	0.0483	0.0443	0.0411	0.0493	0.0445
3.0	0.0407	0.0413	0.0435	0.0357	0.0362	0.0396	0.0363
4.0	0.0407	0.0456	0.0438	0.0307	0.0347	0.0330	0.0317
5.0	0.0420	0.0430	0.0455	0.0275	0.0343	0.0302	0.0287
6.0	0.0435	0.0445	0.0471	0.0252	0.0347	0.0277	0.0268
8.0	0.0460	0.0471	0.0501	0.0222	0.0357	0.0242	0.0243
10.0	0.0490	0.0503	0.0531	0.0204	0.0370	0.0221	0.0229
15.0	0.0555	0.0567	0.0600	0.0180	0.0408	0.0194	0.0214
20.0	0.0608	0.0625	0.0600	0.0169	0.0440	0.0180	0.0209
50.0	0.0793	0.0817	0.0865	0.0161	0.0554	0.0167	0.0217
80.0	0.0879	0.0907	0.0961	0.0166	0.0607	0.0170	0.0230
100.0	0.0922	0.0945	0.1000	0.0169	0.0632	0.0173	0.0237

*To obtain linear absorption coefficient μ, cm^{-1} at STP, multiply given values by 0.001293; to obtain μ at 20°C and standard pressure, multiply by 0.001205.

Table 8.76—Gamma-ray Energy-absorption Coefficients at Various Energies for Selected Materials[*]

Material	Energy-absorption coefficient $(\mu - \sigma_s/\rho)$, cm²/g									
	0.1 Mev	0.25 Mev	0.5 Mev	1 Mev	2 Mev	3 Mev	5 Mev	8 Mev	10 Mev	20 Mev
Hydrogen	0.0405	0.0552	0.0594	0.0553	0.0456	0.0393	0.0318	0.0250	0.0221	0.0150
Beryllium		0.0262	0.0245	0.0245	0.0186	0.0153	0.0126	0.0120		
Carbon	0.0215	0.0283	0.0300	0.0282	0.0237	0.0212	0.0176	0.0152	0.0142	0.0123
Nitrogen	0.0224	0.0283	0.0293	0.0273	0.0236	0.0211	0.0180	0.0155	0.0147	0.0132
Oxygen	0.0248	0.0283	0.0305	0.0281	0.0238	0.0211	0.0183	0.0166	0.0159	0.0140
Sodium		0.0288	0.0292	0.0268	0.0229	0.0208	0.0186	0.0172	0.0172	
Aluminum	0.0445	0.0293	0.0287	0.0270	0.0231	0.0212	0.0193	0.0184	0.0183	0.0190
Silicon			0.0308	0.0273	0.0241	0.0221	0.0206	0.0197	0.0194	
Chromium			0.0305	0.0257	0.0227	0.0218	0.0220	0.0238	0.0240	
Iron	0.265	0.0443	0.0285	0.0259	0.0213	0.0212	0.0231	0.0245	0.0258	0.0315
Nickel		0.0390	0.0313	0.0269	0.0232	0.0221	0.0232	0.0262	0.0265	
Copper	0.0345	0.0495	0.0273	0.0239	0.0206	0.0215	0.0238	0.0255	0.0271	0.0330
Zirconium			0.0345	0.0265	0.0214	0.0231	0.0259	0.0290	0.0310	
Barium			0.0500	0.0278	0.0228	0.0243	0.0282	0.0335	0.0361	
Molybdenum			0.0365	0.0258	0.0230	0.0233	0.0257	0.0299	0.0319	
Tantalum		0.395	0.0910	0.0367	0.0245	0.0263	0.0322	0.0388	0.0426	0.0570
Lead	2.16	0.525	0.118	0.0448	0.0285	0.0293	0.0349	0.0418	0.0455	0.0620
Bismuth			0.113	0.0435	0.0293	0.0305	0.0361	0.0432	0.0471	
Uranium		0.700	0.162	0.0555	0.0310	0.0318	0.0380	0.0455	0.0497	0.0683
Air	0.0232		0.0296	0.0279	0.0237	0.0211	0.0182	0.0162	0.0155	0.0145
Water	0.0253	0.0312	0.0330	0.0310	0.0260	0.0227	0.0189	0.0163	0.0154	
SiO$_2$[†]			0.0870	0.0770	0.0653	0.0620	0.0620			

[*] Compiled from data of Refs. 145 to 147.
[†] Linear absorption coefficient, cm^{-1}.

iliary cooling is needed within the graphite outside the insulation. The 3 kw of heat generated in this region is sufficiently small to be conducted away to the outside of the primary shield tank and removed by the below-floor ventilation system.

Many high-energy and intermediate-energy neutrons that have penetrated through the thermal shield are not captured in the 6-in. layer of borated graphite. They leak through to the unborated graphite, where they become moderated, and a thermal-neutron flux is built up in this region. The detector tubes are located here. As the neutrons migrate out toward the edge of the primary shield tank, most of them are captured by the outer 6-in. layer of borated graphite.

Temperature studies made on the primary shield indicate that the maximum temperature developed within the inner 6-in. graphite layer will not exceed 940°F at the reactor center line and that the temperature on the outside of the insulation will be approximately 450°F. The surface temperature of the graphite adjacent to the primary shield tank wall is expected to be about 200°F. In the region between the reactor vessel and the transfer-rotor container, the temperature on the outside of the insulation may exceed 600°F.

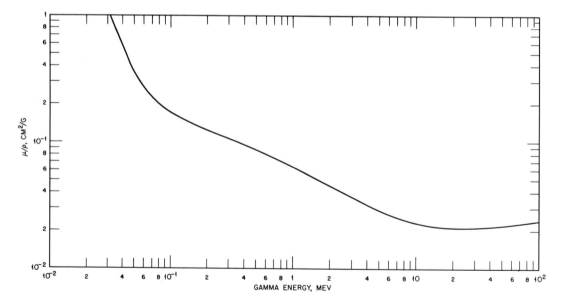

FIG. 8.87—Mass-absorption coefficient (μ/ρ) vs. gamma energy for ordinary concrete.

Table 8.77—Energies of Gamma Rays Emitted in Inelastic Scattering [23,136]

Element	Threshold for inelastic scattering, Mev	Energies, Mev	Reference	Element	Threshold for inelastic scattering, Mev	Energies, Mev	Reference
B^{10}	0.717	0.717	7, 12	Cu	0.90	0.37	2, 4, 8
		2.20				0.66	9, 7
						0.96	
C^{12}	4.42	4.42	7			1.14	
						1.32	
N^{14}	2.30	2.30	7			1.47	
						1.55	
O^{16}	6.09	6.09	7			1.9	
						2.07	
F	0.11	0.11	7, 12			2.42	
		0.20				2.58	
		1.23					
		1.36		Mn	0.126	0.58	9, 4
		1.46				0.67	
		1.56				0.83	
						1.16	
Mg		1.37	7			1.5	
		1.62				1.86	
		1.82				2.2	
Al	0.85	0.17	1, 2, 4,	Zr	0.92 ($Zr^{92,94}$)	0.69	4, 12
		0.85	7, 12		2.17 (Zr^{90})	0.92	
		1.02				1.14	
		1.20				1.5	
		1.70				2.17	
		2.3				3.23	
		3.10		Ta		0.137	7
Ca	1.16 (Ca^{44})	0.51	7			0.164	
	3.35 (Ca^{40})	1.16				0.350	
		3.74				0.485	
		3.90		Pb	0.85 ($Pb^{206,207}$)	0.35	1, 3, 10,
Cr	1.44	1.43	1, 3, 4,			0.53	12, 7
		0.97	5			0.57	
		0.75				0.88	
						1.1	
Fe	0.85	0.12	1, 2, 3,			1.4	
		0.46	4, 5, 7,			1.7	
		0.63	12			2.6	
		0.85				3.0	
		1,25					
		1.44		Bi	0.90	0.49	1, 3, 4,
		1.67				0.90	5, 7
		2.10				1.60	
		2.60				2.6	
		3.52				3.35	
Co	1.10	0.60	4	U^{238}	0.044	0.044	13
		1.15				0.15	
		1.49				0.30	
		1.7				0.98	
		2.5				1.06	
Ni	1.33	1.33	1, 3, 4,			1.26	
		0.85	7				
		1.33					
		1.47					
		2.18					
		2.66					

References

1. R. M. Kiehn, *Phys. Rev.*, **95**:989 (1954).
2. Garrett *et al.*, *Phys. Rev.*, **92**:1507 (1953).
3. Mandeville *et al.*, *Phys. Rev.*, **93**:796 (1954).
4. V. E. Scherrer *et al.*, *Phys. Rev.*, **96**:386 (1954).
5. Halban *et al.*, *Phys. Rev.*, **94**:144 (1954).
6. R. B. Day, *Phys. Rev.*, **89**:908A (1953).
7. R. B. Day, *Phys. Rev.*, **102**:767 (1956).

8. Rayburn *et al.*, *Phys. Rev*, **94**:1641 (1954).
9. Scherrer *et al.*, *NRL Quarterly Nuclear Physics Report*, Oct. 1, 1954.
10. Scherrer *et al.*, Report NRL-4252, Oct. 23, 1953.
11. Lafferty *et al.*, *Phys. Rev.*, **96**:381 (1954).
12. G. L. Griffith, *Phys. Rev.*, **98**:579 (1955).
13. Cranberg *et al.*, *Conference on Neutron Interreactions*, New York, September 1957.

Table 8.78—Neutron-capture Gamma Rays*[a]

Target nucleus	Photons/100 radiative captures							Highest energy γ-ray, Mev	Average no. of photons per capture[b]
	0-1 Mev	1-2 Mev	2-3 Mev	3-5 Mev	5-7 Mev	7-9 Mev	>9 Mev		
H	0	0	100	0	0	0	0	2.230	
D	0	0	0	0	100	0	0	6.244	
He									
Li					∼40	∼60	0	7.26	
Be	0	0	0	54	73	0	0	6.80	
B[10]	0	0	0	>110	>28	≥6	0.8	11.43	
C	0	0	0	100	0	0	0	4.95	1.3
N[14]				>54	≥11	15	12	10.833	
O									
F		>100[c]			≥111	0	0	6.600	
Ne									
Na	>96	127	187	70	31	0	0	6.41	<2
Mg		>28	>72	10	3.3	0.57		11.089	
Al	>236	195[d]	69	62	19	19	0	7.724	∼2
Si	>100	63	30	89	11	4.1	0.1	10.59	
P	>290	97	55	98	27	7.2	0	7.94	
S	>70	32	72	70	44	6.5	0	8.64	
Cl	>49	85	41	47	55	24	0	8.55	3.1
A									
K	>100	81	57	106	37	4.7	0	9.36	
Ca	>14	191	77	85	64	1.8	0	7.83	
Sc	>52	59	38	65	29	12	0	8.85	
Ti	>54	160	16	24	78	1.3	0.2	10.47	
V	>83	132[e]	11.4	21	67	16	0	7.98	2.5
Cr	>85	41	21	12	23	39	6.4	9.716	>2
Mn	>125[f]	91[g]	60[h]	50	34	17	0	7.261	2.6
Fe	>75	60	27	23	25	38	2.1	10.16	1.7
Co	>61	26	17	42	52	8.5	0	7.486	
Ni	>84	40	23	23	34	62	0.8	8.997	
Cu	>68	47	26	30	27	43	0	7.914	2.6
Zn	>156	93	67	48	29	16	1	9.51	
Ga				57	34	0.2	0	7.73	
Ge									
As				47	22	1	0	7.30	2.7
Se				65	27	9	1.7	10.483	
Br				79	41	6.4	0	7.879	
Kr									
Rb									
Sr				69	51	14	0.1	9.22	
Y	>71	23	6	50	59	0	0	6.850	
Zr				113	35	4	0	8.66	
Nb				54	14	0.4	0	7.19	
Mo[a]	>137	>18		84	26	3	0.03	9.15	2.6
Tc									
Ru									
Rh	>91	99	61	38	10	0	0	6.792	
Pd									
Ag	>92	87	64	70	17	0.5	0	7.27	2.9
Cd	>135	92	96	73	17	1	0.1	9.046	4.1
In	>102[i]	197[j]	78[k]	36	4	0	0	5.86	3.3
Sn[a]	>216	153	67	139	33	4	0.4	9.35	
Sb[a]	150	99	58	36	12	0	0	6.80	
Te	>58								
I[a]	>30			97	22	0	0	6.71	
Xe									
Cs[a]	>46			61	25	0	0	6.702	
Ba				75	14	1.4	0.1	9.23	
La	>21.7	8.2		>35	>12.5	0	0	5.045	
Ce									
Pr				34	8	0	0	5.83	
Nd	>105								
Pm									
Sm	>167	150	109	45	5	1	0	7.89	5.6
Eu	106	153	109	56	6.5	0	0	6.05	
Ga	194	117	100	23	34	0.3	0	7.33	3.9
Tb	>7								
Dy	90	102	106	43	10	0	0	5.87	
Ho		98	77	49	8	0	0	6.1	
Er	225	145	133	103	14	0	0	6.680	
Tm[a]									
Yb									

Table 8.78—Neutron-capture Gamma Rays*[a] (continued)

Target nucleus	Photons/100 radiative captures							Highest energy γ-ray, Mev	Average no. of photons per capture[b]
	0-1 Mev	1-2 Mev	2-3 Mev	3-5 Mev	5-7 Mev	7-9 Mev	>9 Mev		
Lu									
Hf	>137	137	85	52	12	0.5	0	7.62	
Ta	>137	99	66	55	5	0	0	6.04	
W	>68	82	59	53	15	0.5	0	7.42	
Re	124	88	62	51	10.5	0	0	6.14	
Os									
Ir	98	85	58	51	19.6	0	0	6.088	
Pt	>109	92	64	45	15	1	0	7.920	
Au	>100	69	33	68	38	0.1	0	6.494	3.5
Hg	>94	122	55	86	41	0	0	6.446	3.3
Tl				76	62	0	0	6.54	
Pb	0	0	0	0	7	93	0	7.38	
Bi	0	0	0	100	0	0	0	4.17	
Po									
At									
Em									
Fr									
Ra									
Ac									
Th	>118	140	64	17	0	0	0	4.92	
Pa									
U^{238}	254	178	91	34	0	0	0	4.062	
Np									
Pu									

* From *Nucleonics*, **18**(11): 172 (1960).

[a] Almost all data, with the exceptions shown below, are from the following USSR and Canadian reports:

G. A. Bartholomew and L. A. Miggs, *Compilation of Thermal Neutron Capture γ-rays*, Canadian Report AECL-669, 1958.

L. V. Groshev, A. M. Demidov, V. N. Lutsenko, and V. I. Pelikov, *Atlas of γ-ray Spectra from Radiative Capture of Thermal Neutrons* (Atomizdat, Moscow, 1958; translation by Pergamon Press, New York).

Data were obtained from the following references for the elements indicated:

Sn, Sb: L. V. Groshev, B. I. Gavrilov, and A. M. Demidov, *Atomnaya Energiya*, **6**:281 (1959).

Mo, Tm: L. V. Groshev, A. M. Demidov, and V. I. Pelekhov, unpublished, 1959.

I, Cs: H. Knoepfel, P. Scherrer, and P. Stoll, *Z. Physik*, **156**:293 (1959).

[b] All values in this column are taken from C. O. Muehlhause, *Phys. Rev.*, **79**:277 (1950). They may therefore differ from the multiplicities deduced from the spectra directly.

[c] Includes a 100% 1.63-Mev gamma ray in Ne^{20} following 11s decay of F^{20}.

[d] Includes a 100% 1.78-Mev gamma ray in Si^{28} following 2.3m decay of Al^{28}.

[e] Includes a 99.75% 1.43-Mev gamma ray in Cr^{52} following 3.8m decay of V^{52}.

[f] Includes a 99% 0.85-Mev gamma ray in Fe^{56} following 2.6h decay of Mn^{56}.

[g] Includes a 23% 1.80-Mev gamma ray in Fe^{56} following 2.6h decay of Mn^{56}.

[h] Includes a 15% 2.13-Mev gamma ray in Fe^{56} following 2.6h decay of Mn^{56}.

[i] Includes a 5% 0.41-Mev and an 8% 0.82-Mev gamma ray in Sn^{116} following 54m decay of In^{116}.

[j] Includes a 36% 1.09-Mev and a 63% 1.29-Mev gamma ray in Sn^{116} following 54m decay of In^{116}.

[k] Includes an 11% 2.12-Mev gamma ray in Sn^{116} following 54m decay of In^{116}.

The effects of radiation damage and operating conditions on the materials used inside the primary shield tank have been studied. The maximum integrated fast-neutron dose to which the graphite in the primary shield tank will be exposed is less than 2×10^{21} neutrons/cm^2 for the 20 year plant life. The irradiation of graphite at this level of exposure and under the temperature conditions within the primary shield tank indicates that the physical properties of the graphite will change somewhat but no harmful effects will take place. The design of the inner 6-in. borated-graphite layer will accommodate changes in the layer due to shrinkage under irradiation.

A study was made of the possibility of obtaining a Wigner energy release within the graphite shield. It is improbable that there will be any significant storage at all within the graphite for the expected conditions of temperature and radiation exposure.

8.18.4 SECONDARY SHIELD WALL

8.18.4.1 Description

The 30-in.-thick secondary shield wall shown in Fig. 8.101 is a concrete shield whose main function is to reduce the neutron-flux leakage from the primary shield entering the equipment compartment to a value below 1×10^4 neutrons/cm^2/sec. The secondary sodium coolant, the primary coolant pump, the heat exchangers, and other equipment outside the wall will not become significantly radioactive at this level (Sec. 8.18.1.2). Neutron leakage from that portion of the primary shield near the transfer-rotor container is higher than neutron leakage from other areas. The thickness of the secondary shield wall in this area has been increased to 39 in. The shield wall has been erected by a prepacked method to ensure a minimum dry density of 144 lb/cu ft. In locations adjacent to the upper elbows of the 30-in.-diameter exit sodium pipes, the density of

Table 8.79—Gamma-ray Dose Buildup Factors for Various Materials from a Point Isotropic Source[*†]

Material	Gamma-ray energy, Mev	Number of mean free paths in material						
		1	2	4	7	10	15	20
H₂O	0.255	3.09	7.14	23.0	72.9	166.	456.	982.
	0.5	2.52	5.14	14.3	38.8	77.6	178.	334.
	1.0	2.13	3.71	7.68	16.2	27.1	50.4	82.2
	2.0	1.83	2.77	4.88	8.46	12.4	19.5	27.7
	3.0	1.69	2.42	3.91	6.23	8.63	12.8	17.0
	4.0	1.58	2.17	3.34	5.13	6.94	9.97	12.9
	6.0	1.46	1.91	2.76	3.99	5.18	7.09	8.85
	8.0	1.38	1.74	2.40	3.34	4.25	5.66	6.95
	10.0	1.33	1.63	2.19	2.97	3.72	4.90	5.98
Al	0.5	2.37	4.24	9.47	21.5	38.9	80.8	141.
	1.0	2.02	3.31	6.57	13.1	21.2	37.9	58.5
	2.0	1.75	2.61	4.62	8.05	11.9	18.7	26.3
	3.0	1.64	2.32	3.78	6.14	8.65	13.0	17.7
	4.0	1.53	2.08	3.22	5.01	6.88	10.1	13.4
	6.0	1.42	1.85	2.70	4.06	5.49	7.97	10.4
	8.0	1.34	1.68	2.37	3.45	4.58	6.56	8.52
	10.0	1.28	1.55	2.12	3.01	3.96	5.63	7.32
Fe	0.5	1.98	3.09	5.98	11.7	19.2	35.4	55.6
	1.0	1.87	2.89	5.39	10.2	16.2	28.3	42.7
	2.0	1.76	2.43	4.13	7.25	10.9	17.6	25.1
	3.0	1.55	2.15	3.51	5.85	8.51	13.5	19.1
	4.0	1.45	1.94	3.03	4.91	7.11	11.2	16.0
	6.0	1.34	1.72	2.58	4.14	6.02	9.89	14.7
	8.0	1.27	1.56	2.23	3.49	5.07	8.50	13.0
	10.0	1.20	1.42	1.95	2.99	4.35	7.54	12.4
Sn	0.5	1.56	2.08	3.09	4.57	6.04	8.64	
	1.0	1.64	2.30	3.74	6.17	8.85	13.7	18.8
	2.0	1.57	2.17	3.53	5.87	8.53	13.6	19.3
	3.0	1.46	1.96	3.13	5.28	7.91	13.3	20.1
	4.0	1.38	1.51	2.82	4.82	7.41	13.2	21.2
	6.0	1.26	1.57	2.37	4.17	6.94	14.8	29.1
	8.0	1.19	1.42	2.05	3.57	6.19	15.1	34.0
	10.0	1.14	1.31	1.79	2.99	5.21	12.5	33.4
W	0.5	1.28	1.50	1.84	2.24	2.61	3.12	
	1.0	1.44	1.83	2.57	3.62	4.64	6.25	(7.35)
	2.0	1.42	1.85	2.72	4.09	5.27	8.07	(10.6)
	3.0	1.36	1.74	2.59	4.00	5.92	9.66	14.1
	4.0	1.29	1.62	2.41	4.03	6.27	12.0	20.9
	6.0	1.20	1.43	2.07	3.60	6.29	15.7	36.3
	8.0	1.14	1.32	1.81	3.05	5.40	15.2	41.9
	10.0	1.11	1.25	1.64	2.62	4.65	14.0	39.3
Pb	0.5	1.24	1.42	1.69	2.00	2.27	2.65	(2.73)
	1.0	1.37	1.69	2.26	3.02	3.74	4.81	5.86
	2.0	1.39	1.76	2.51	3.66	4.84	6.87	9.00
	3.0	1.34	1.68	2.43	3.75	5.30	8.44	12.3
	4.0	1.27	1.56	2.25	3.61	5.44	9.80	16.3
	5.11	1.21	1.46	2.08	3.44	5.55	11.7	23.6
	6.0	1.18	1.40	1.97	3.34	5.69	13.8	32.7
	8.0	1.14	1.30	1.74	2.89	5.07	14.1	44.6
	10.0	1.11	1.23	1.58	2.52	4.34	12.5	39.2
U	0.5	1.17	1.30	1.48	1.67	1.85	2.08	
	1.0	1.31	1.56	1.98	2.50	2.97	3.67	
	2.0	1.33	1.64	2.23	3.09	3.95	5.36	(6.48)
	3.0	1.29	1.58	2.21	3.27	4.51	6.97	9.88
	4.0	1.24	1.50	2.09	3.21	4.66	8.01	12.7
	6.0	1.16	1.36	1.85	2.96	4.80	10.8	23.0
	8.0	1.12	1.27	1.66	2.61	4.36	11.2	28.0
	10.0	1.09	1.20	1.51	2.26	3.78	10.5	28.5

* Compiled from data of Ref. 44.
† Infinite medium assumed.

the prepacked concrete is 160 lb/cu ft.* The 1/2-in.-thick steel plates that served as the forms for the concrete wall during pouring protect the wall from excessive heating due to gamma-ray absorption during operation.

*Magnetite aggregate added.

8.18.4.2 Thermal Shields for Protection of the Concrete Secondary Shield Wall

At full operating power the gamma-radiation level resulting from the Na²⁴ activity in the primary coolant is greater than 10^5 r/hr near the primary coolant system. Extra radiation-absorbing steel is necessary to protect the concrete in areas where the secondary shield wall is close to the sodium system. In these areas 2-in. steel plates are placed

Table 8.80—Gamma-ray Dose Buildup Factors for Various Materials from a
Plane Monodirectional Source*†

Material	Gamma-ray energy, Mev	Number of mean free paths in material					
		1	2	4	7	10	15
H_2O	0.5	2.63	4.29	9.05	20.0	35.9	74.9
	1.0	2.26	3.39	6.27	11.5	18.0	30.8
	2.0	1.84	2.63	4.28	6.96	9.87	14.4
	3.0	1.69	2.31	3.57	5.51	7.48	10.8
	4.0	1.58	2.10	3.12	4.63	6.19	8.54
	6.0	1.45	1.86	2.63	3.76	4.86	6.78
	8.0	1.36	1.69	2.30	3.16	4.00	5.47
Fe	0.5	2.07	2.94	4.87	8.31	12.4	20.6
	1.0	1.92	2.74	4.57	7.81	11.6	18.9
	2.0	1.69	2.35	3.76	6.11	8.78	13.7
	3.0	1.58	2.13	3.32	5.26	7.41	11.4
	4.0	1.48	1.90	2.95	4.61	6.46	9.92
	6.0	1.35	1.71	2.48	3.81	5.35	8.39
	8.0	1.27	1.55	2.17	3.27	4.58	7.33
	10.0	1.22	1.44	1.95	2.89	4.07	6.70
Sn	1.0	1.65	2.24	3.40	5.18	7.19	10.5
	2.0	1.58	2.13	3.27	5.12	7.13	11.0
	4.0	1.39	1.80	2.69	4.31	6.30	
	6.0	1.27	1.57	2.27	3.72	5.77	11.0
	10.0	1.16	1.33	1.77	2.81	4.53	9.68
Pb	0.5	1.24	1.39	1.63	1.87	2.08	
	1.0	1.38	1.68	2.18	2.80	3.40	4.20
	2.0	1.40	1.76	2.41	3.36	4.35	5.94
	3.0	1.36	1.71	2.42	3.55	4.82	7.18
	4.0	1.28	1.56	2.18	3.29	4.69	7.70
	6.0	1.19	1.40	1.87	2.97	4.69	9.53
	8.0	1.14	1.30	1.69	2.61	4.18	9.08
	10.0	1.11	1.24	1.54	2.27	3.54	7.70
U	0.5	1.17	1.28	1.45	1.60	1.73	
	1.0	1.30	1.53	1.90	2.32	2.70	3.60
	2.0	1.33	1.62	2.15	2.87	3.56	4.89
	3.0	1.29	1.57	2.13	3.02	3.99	5.94
	4.0	1.25	1.49	2.02	2.94	4.06	6.47
	6.0	1.18	1.37	1.82	2.74	4.12	7.79
	8.0	1.13	1.27	1.61	2.39	3.65	7.36
	10.0	1.10	1.21	1.48	2.12	3.21	6.58

* Compiled from data of Ref. 44.
† Infinite medium assumed.

5 in. from the concrete wall to form cooling gaps. The lower compartment ventilation system removes the heat generated in these shields.

In other areas the 1/2-in. steel forms are considered satisfactory protection. Temperature studies indicate that the walls could be cooled by natural circulation, but it was found desirable to install duct work from the below-floor ventilation system to distribute the oxygen-depleted air uniformly over the whole wall, both within the gaps and over the surface of the remaining portions of the shield.

8.18.5 BIOLOGICAL SHIELDS

8.18.5.1 Operating-floor Shield

The operating-floor shield is a steel-and-concrete shield 5 ft thick in most areas. It is designed to reduce radiation from the lower compartment areas to the established biological design levels at the shield surface. The determining factor for the shield thickness of the floor above the inner reactor compartment is the neutron-flux leakage from the primary shield tank. Above the equipment compartment the determining factor is the gamma radiation from the radioactive sodium within the primary coolant loops. Varying amounts of steel plate are used beneath the concrete, depending upon the intensity and proximity of the gamma-radiation sources. The operating-floor concrete contains some magnetite aggregate to ensure a minimum dry density of 150 lb/cu ft. A plan view of the operating floor showing the steel thicknesses is given in Fig. 8.109.

8.18.5.2 Use of High-temperature Material

The physical design of the primary and secondary sodium systems is such that the temperature may rise as high as 800°F near the heat exchangers and the primary sodium pumps, which is above the design limits for the ordinary concrete. It was necessary to find a suitable substitute for ordinary concrete. Serpentine rock (an ore of asbestos) was found to fit the need (Sec. 8.11.8). This rock serves as the aggregate in concrete. In areas of the operating-floor shield immediately adjacent to the primary pump and heat-exchanger plugs, serpentine concrete with a density of 130 lb/cu ft is employed. Within the plugs serpentine is used in a dry-packed form, tamped to a density of 130 lb/cu ft.

8.18.5.3 Biological Shield Outside Containment Vessel

A 7-ft-thick concrete shield wall is located outside the reactor containment vessel. It extends

Table 8.81—Gamma-ray Energy Buildup Factors for Various Materials from a Point Isotropic Source[*][†]

Material	Gamma-ray energy, Mev	Number of mean free paths in material						
		1	2	4	7	10	15	20
H₂0	0.255	3.16	6.94	20.6	61.1	134.	358.	750.
	0.5	2.56	5.10	13.5	35.0	68.1	153.	283.
	1.0	2.10	3.58	7.42	15.2	25.1	45.7	73.2
	2.0	1.73	2.55	4.40	7.51	10.9	17.1	24.2
	3.0	1.58	2.18	3.42	5.35	7.35	10.7	14.3
	4.0	1.47	1.95	2.91	4.37	5.85	8.34	10.7
	6.0	1.36	1.72	2.40	3.39	4.36	6.28	7.35
	8.0	1.30	1.59	2.05	2.91	3.67	4.85	5.94
	10.0	1.26	1.51	1.97	2.63	3.26	4.26	5.19
Al	0.5	2.45	4.43	10.0	22.94	41.7	87.0	152.
	1.0	2.01	3.29	6.52	12.95	21.0	37.6	58.1
	2.0	1.67	2.43	4.21	7.21	10.6	16.6	23.2
	3.0	1.53	2.11	3.33	5.31	7.41	11.1	14.9
	4.0	1.44	1.88	2.82	4.28	5.81	8.42	11.2
	6.0	1.33	1.68	2.37	3.47	4.61	6.61	8.60
	8.0	1.27	1.54	2.09	2.95	3.86	5.45	7.04
	10.0	1.22	1.45	1.91	2.64	3.42	4.78	6.18
Fe	0.5	2.02	3.20	6.16	12.1	19.9	36.8	57.7
	1.0	1.84	2.84	5.27	9.95	15.8	27.5	41.5
	2.0	1.60	2.28	3.82	6.54	9.73	15.6	22.2
	3.0	1.48	1.98	3.18	5.17	7.44	11.7	16.5
	4.0	1.38	1.80	2.71	4.30	6.14	9.59	13.6
	6.0	1.28	1.58	2.27	3.51	4.99	8.03	11.8
	8.0	1.21	1.45	1.99	2.99	4.23	6.89	10.3
	10.0	1.17	1.36	1.81	2.66	3.78	6.36	9.14
Sn	0.5	1.56	2.08	3.04	4.54	5.99	8.56	
	1.0	1.61	2.25	3.63	5.96	8.53	13.2	18.1
	2.0	1.50	2.04	3.25	5.31	7.66	12.1	17.2
	3.0	1.39	1.82	2.74	4.63	6.83	11.4	17.0
	4.0	1.31	1.67	2.50	4.12	6.21	10.9	17.3
	6.0	1.21	1.46	2.09	3.48	5.59	11.5	22.1
	8.0	1.15	1.34	1.83	2.97	4.91	11.3	24.7
	10.0	1.11	1.26	1.63	2.54	4.16	10.1	23.9
W	0.5	1.27	1.49	1.83	2.23	2.58	3.09	
	1.0	1.42	1.80	2.51	3.51	4.49	6.05	(7.10)
	2.0	1.39	1.76	2.55	3.79	5.10	7.39	(9.66)
	3.0	1.31	1.64	2.38	3.69	5.26	8.47	12.4
	4.0	1.24	1.52	2.19	3.53	5.40	10.1	17.4
	6.0	1.16	1.35	1.87	3.07	5.15	12.3	27.8
	8.0	1.11	1.26	1.65	2.58	4.34	11.3	29.8
	10.0	1.09	1.20	1.51	2.25	3.71	10.2	27.3
Pb	0.5	1.24	1.41	1.68	1.99	2.26	2.27	(2.71)
	1.0	1.35	1.66	2.21	2.95	3.65	4.34	5.25
	2.0	1.35	1.68	2.37	3.41	4.49	6.33	8.27
	3.0	1.29	1.59	2.25	3.39	4.74	7.46	10.7
	4.0	1.23	1.49	2.06	3.20	4.72	8.33	13.7
	5.11	1.18	1.38	1.89	3.01	4.71	9.64	19.0
	6.0	1.15	1.33	1.79	2.87	4.70	10.91	25.2
	8.0	1.11	1.24	1.59	2.48	4.11	10.68	29.5
	10.0	1.09	1.19	1.46	2.16	3.49	9.25	27.6
U	0.5	1.17	1.29	1.48	1.67	1.84	2.05	
	1.0	1.30	1.54	1.94	2.45	2.91	3.59	
	2.0	1.30	1.59	2.13	2.92	3.71	5.01	(6.08)
	3.0	1.25	1.51	2.07	3.01	4.10	6.26	8.77
	4.0	1.21	1.43	1.93	2.88	4.11	6.92	10.9
	6.0	1.14	1.30	1.70	2.61	4.08	8.75	18.3
	8.0	1.10	1.22	1.53	2.27	3.61	8.69	20.9
	10.0	1.08	1.17	1.42	2.02	3.16	8.04	20.8

[*] Compiled from data of Ref. 44.

[†] Infinite medium assumed.

from the top of the operating-floor (grade) elevation downward to 7 ft below grade. The concrete shield plus earth fill serve to reduce the radiation outside the containment vessel to levels less than the plant design dose rate of 0.75 mr/hr at full reactor operating power. Radiation streaming through the ventilation ducts serving the lower building area is prevented by snaking these ducts underground at depths of from 10 to 15 ft below grade.

8.18.6 SPECIAL-PURPOSE SHIELDS

8.18.6.1 Primary Coolant Piping Shields

A special problem that required attention within the reactor building was the neutron leakage from the 30-in.-diameter primary sodium pipes where they pass through the primary shield tank. The problem of shielding these lines is complicated

Table 8.82—Gamma-ray Energy Buildup Factors for Various Materials
from a Plane Monodirectional Source*†

Material	Gamma-ray energy, Mev	Number of mean free paths					
		1	2	4	7	10	15
H₂O	0.5	2.75	4.49	9.11	20.2	34.5	70.6
	1.0	2.21	3.28	5.89	10.7	16.6	28.3
	2.0	1.73	2.42	3.87	6.08	8.74	12.8
	3.0	1.58	2.09	3.16	4.79	6.44	9.23
	4.0	1.47	1.91	2.74	4.00	5.28	7.24
	6.0	1.36	1.69	2.33	3.26	4.17	5.74
	8.0	1.29	1.56	2.07	2.78	3.49	4.71
Fe	0.5	2.09	2.96	4.91	8.39	12.5	20.9
	1.0	1.89	2.68	4.45	7.57	11.2	18.2
	2.0	1.61	2.20	3.44	5.51	7.85	12.2
	3.0	1.49	1.93	2.95	4.59	6.38	9.67
	4.0	1.39	1.78	2.60	3.96	5.47	8.27
	6.0	1.28	1.57	2.19	3.25	4.47	6.87
	8.0	1.22	1.45	1.93	2.80	3.82	5.94
	10.0	1.17	1.36	1.77	2.51	3.44	5.48
Sn	0.5	(1.70)	(2.02)	(2.75)	(3.71)	(4.68)	(6.43)
	1.0	1.63	2.19	3.30	5.01	6.80	10.1
	2.0	1.52	2.01	3.03	4.66	6.45	9.73
	4.0	1.33	1.66	2.40	3.73	5.35	8.83
	6.0	1.22	1.46	2.02	3.16	4.76	8.74
	10.0	1.13	1.27	1.61	2.40	3.68	7.39
Pb	0.5	1.24	1.39	1.61	1.84	2.04	
	1.0	1.37	1.65	2.12	2.71	3.28	4.17
	2.0	1.36	1.68	2.28	3.14	4.03	5.48
	3.0	1.31	1.61	2.23	3.21	4.31	6.33
	4.0	1.24	1.45	1.99	2.95	4.09	6.70
	6.0	1.15	1.32	1.73	2.60	3.98	7.78
	8.0	1.12	1.22	1.53	2.23	3.39	6.88
	10.0	1.09	1.17	1.40	1.93	2.81	5.60
U	0.5	1.17	1.28	1.44	1.60	1.73	
	1.0	1.29	1.51	1.87	2.28	2.65	3.52
	2.0	1.30	1.57	2.06	2.73	3.38	4.60
	3.0	1.26	1.50	2.01	2.80	3.67	5.38
	4.0	1.21	1.43	1.87	2.67	3.62	5.66
	6.0	1.14	1.30	1.67	2.41	3.51	6.41
	8.0	1.11	1.22	1.50	2.12	3.10	5.92
	10.0	1.08	1.18	1.40	1.90	2.74	5.26

*Compiled from data of Ref. 44.
†Infinite medium assumed.

because they have to be contained within an outer containment, heated, and insulated. The shielding material has to withstand temperatures upwards of 1000°F in a radiation environment. A shield of calcium borate (Fig. 8.110) manufactured by Johns Manville under the trade name Sigma-K (Sec. 8.11.9), having a thickness of 9 to 11 in. is located around the 30-in. pipe loops within the reactor compartment. Figure 8.111 shows the calcium borate shield being erected around the 30-in.-diameter pipes. Ring or donut shields of the same material are installed directly on the pipe and its secondary containment to prevent the neutron streaming in annuli around the pipes. A series of these shields can be seen in Fig. 8.110.

8.18.6.2 Shields in the Secondary Coolant System Pipe Galleries

The extent to which the secondary coolant becomes radioactive is controlled by the primary and secondary shields within the reactor containment building. With the shield system described, the induced radioactivity of the secondary sodium system is less than $2 \times 10^{-4} \mu c/cm^3$. This activity is so low that no shield is required for the secondary coolant system. However, the secondary coolant

pipes leading from the containment building to the steam-generator building pass through secondary piping galleries. There is a high level of gamma radiation in the galleries from the radioactive primary coolant system because of streaming through the pipe penetrations from the containment building. The galleries are shielded by 1-ft-thick concrete walls and earth on the sides and by 1-1/2 ft of concrete and approximately 4 ft of earth overhead. This shielding prevents the radiation from reaching the steam-generator building or the ground level above the galleries. The galleries are designed in the form of a maze to prevent gamma-ray shine from passing into the steam-generator building. Steel donuts or collars around the pipes at their penetrations in the steam-generator building wall reduce residual streaming to a negligible amount.

8.18.6.3 Exit-port Shield

The fuel-removal exit-port shielding provides shielding required during normal reactor operation, shielding required as a result of fission-neutron leakage from spent subassemblies stored in the transfer-rotor container, and shielding required for adequate personnel protection during a fuel-unloading operation. The exit-port shielding shown in Fig. 8.112 consists partially of a series

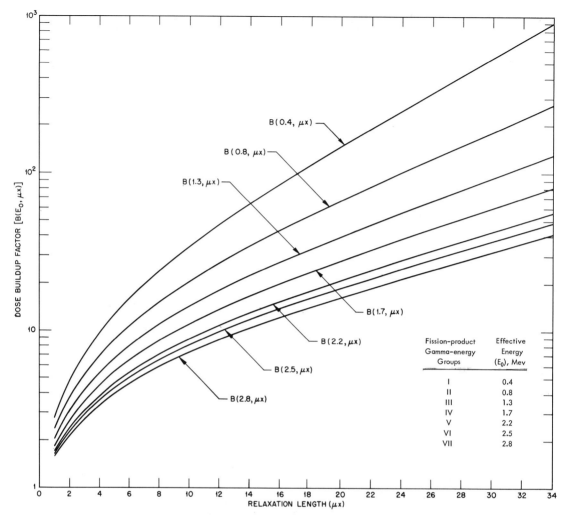

FIG. 8.88—Fission-product gamma-ray-dose buildup factors for ordinary concrete (point isotropic source). Density of concrete is 2.3 g/cm^3.

of ten 6-in.-thick 5% borated-graphite rings or donuts located between the exit tube and the outer liner tube, respectively, to minimize radiation streaming. The rings are sectioned to allow movement of the exit tube with respect to the outer liner tube. Above this are located steel and lead shields. During reactor operation a 2-ft-thick top hat of borated graphite and steel is located over the exit port to complete the shield. Extra lead is required within the floor for protection during spent-fuel removal. A small area of dry-packed serpentine aggregate protects the concrete immediately adjacent to the exit port from excessive temperatures.

8.19 Shield System for Rapsodie [97]

8.19.1 GENERAL DESCRIPTION OF PLANT

Rapsodie is the French fast breeder plant at Cadarache, France. The reactor is sodium cooled

by two coolant loops and is designed to produce a maximum thermal power of 20 Mw. An elevation view of the containment building, housing the reactor and its shielding, is shown in Chap. 11. Many of its basic shield configurations are similar to those at Fermi.

8.19.2 REACTOR SHIELDING

The 238-cm-diameter reactor vessel and its shield are located as a unit within the containment building. Like Fermi, this shield system is composed of three parts: (1) a primary neutron-absorbing shield directly around the reactor outside of which the radiation levels are in the range 10^4 to 10^5 rem/hr, (2) a gamma-ray shield surrounding the radioactive primary coolant near which the gamma-radiation levels are close to 10^5 rem/hr, and (3) biological shielding. The shielding is designed to reduce the radiation intensities on the operating floor above the reactor to the biologically acceptable level of 2.5 mrem/hr.

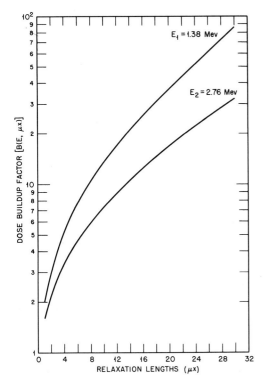

FIG. 8.89—Sodium-24 decay gamma-ray-dose buildup factors for ordinary concrete (point isotropic source).

8.19.3 BLANKET REFLECTOR AND THERMAL SHIELD

A 44-cm-thick depleted-uranium blanket (Chap. 11) surrounding the 38-cm-diameter core, in addition to its prime function as the breeder layer, serves to shield out most of the core gammas. The thermal shield is in three parts. First, as in Fermi, the last two rows of the subassembly support grid contain hexagonally shaped removable stainless-steel reflector subassemblies. Second, there is a series of 10 concentric stainless-steel cylinders each 2.4 cm thick separated by 8-mm coolant gaps. Third, there are four thinner stainless-steel cylindrical liners close to the vessel wall. The liners form a shield against temperature shock to the vessel wall. The total stainless-steel thermal-shield thickness, including the removable subassemblies and the vessel liner plates, is about 37 cm, with about 18 cm of total coolant annuli thickness.

8.19.4 PRIMARY RADIAL NEUTRON-ABSORBING SHIELD

The primary shield for the reactor vessel (Chap. 11) forms a cylindrical compartment about 16 m high and 4.0 m in diameter. It is located in the lower portion of the containment building below the operating floor. There is an 81-cm space between the reactor vessel and the shield, which allows passage of the primary coolant lines alongside the vessel. The shield itself is about 2 m thick and consists of (1) an inner layer 60 cm thick of 3% borated-graphite blocks, (2) a 40-cm-thick cellular concrete blast shield, and (3) a heavily reinforced concrete wall 105 cm thick.

The inner graphite shield is protected by a steel liner, which forms a containment tank for the reactor and serves as the inside wall of the compartment. About 200 kw of heat is generated in this shield at full reactor power. A layer of insulation 7 cm thick and a cooling gap separate the graphite shield from the remainder of the shield. Heat generated in the graphite is removed by a flow of inert gas through this gap and through the graphite. A graphite temperature of 200°C is maintained to limit the amount of Wigner energy storage to a minimum. The cooling gas maintains the cellular concrete shield at a maximum temperature of 80°C. The reinforced concrete is maintained at or below a temperature of 60°C. The shield is designed to reduce the neutron flux within the equipment compartment to levels low enough that the secondary sodium is not activated.

8.19.5 UPPER PRIMARY BIOLOGICAL SHIELD*

The radial neutron shield extends upward above the reactor compartment to the operating floor and is thick enough to reduce the neutron intensities to biologically safe levels. This part of the shield consists of graphite and concrete, with the blast shield extending upward and around the bottom of the fixed access plug over the reactor. Above the blast shield an annular ring of concrete 112 cm thick and 130 cm deep protects against radiation leakage into the above floor areas. An annular ring of reinforced concrete, 100 cm thick, stands 120 cm above the floor level and supports a steel plate covering the reactor plugs. This shield reduces the streaming radiation from the annular gaps around the plugs.

8.19.6 FIXED AND ROTATING PLUGS

8.19.6.1 Purpose and Materials

The fixed and rotating plugs comprise, with the upper primary shield, the biological shield above the reactor. The total shielding thickness within the plugs is 250 cm. The stainless-steel plug shells, like the Fermi rotating plug, are filled mainly with borated graphite (3% boron content) and steel.

8.19.6.2 Fixed Plug

The fixed plug fits into the reactor containment tank and contains the following layers of shielding: (1) a 20-cm layer of borated graphite at the bottom, (2) a 10-cm layer of stainless steel, (3) another layer of borated graphite 65 cm thick, (4) a second 10-cm layer of steel, (5) a third layer of borated graphite about 100 cm thick, and (6) a top layer 45 cm thick consisting of carbon-steel plates. A cooling system is provided within this plug. It keeps

---

*The design of this was undergoing revision at the time of writing; therefore this may not be a completely accurate description.

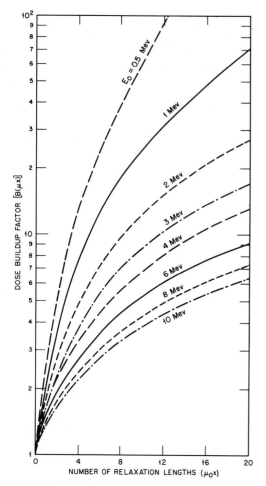

FIG. 8.90—Dose buildup factor for a point isotropic source in ordinary concrete [101].

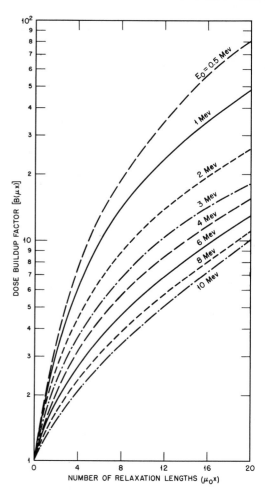

FIG. 8.91—Dose buildup factors for a point isotropic source in ferrophosphorus concrete [101].

the bottom 30-cm thickness of borated graphite below 500°C and the top of the plug to around 30°C. About 40 kw of heat is expected to be generated within the plug, most of which is generated in the borated graphite.

8.19.6.3 Rotating Plugs

Within the fixed plug are two stepped, rotating shield plugs that fit inside the reactor vessel. The shielding for these plugs is essentially the same as for the fixed plug. The outer rotating plug is concentric and supports the inner, stepped eccentric rotating plug. The inner rotating plug, in turn, contains four other smaller fixed plugs. The shielding in all plugs is roughly equivalent to the shielding in the outer fixed plug already described.

8.19.7 BOTTOM REACTOR SHIELD

The primary neutron shield around the reactor extends underneath the reactor with the same materials, thicknesses, and cooling gaps as the radial shield.

8.19.8 OPERATING-FLOOR BIOLOGICAL SHIELD

The operating floor is a 160-cm-thick shield of steel and heavily reinforced concrete. It is designed to reduce radiation leaking from below floor to 2.5 mrem/hr. Near the building walls this shield is increased to 280 cm above compartments containing radioactive sodium. Work galleries provided in the building just under the grade level have floor shields 220 cm thick and cooling-system shields 60 cm thick.

8.19.9 SODIUM-PIPE SHIELDS

The 30-cm-diameter primary coolant lines, together with their secondary containment, penetrate the primary shield near the top of the reactor compartment. At the pipe penetration the graphite shield is enlarged from a thickness of 60 cm to about 100 cm. Beyond this point in the penetration through the concrete shield, the pipe is covered with high-temperature concrete. An annular cooling gap outboard of the special concrete shield is connected with the main cooling gap in the radial shield.

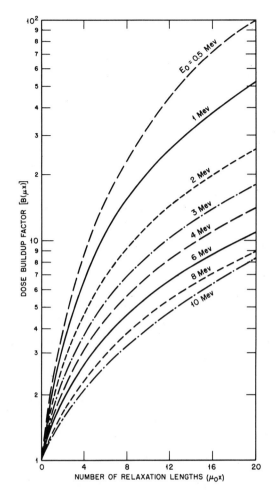

FIG. 8.92—Dose buildup factors for a point isotropic source in magnetite concrete [101].

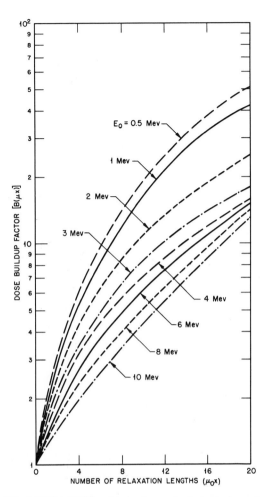

FIG. 8.93—Dose buildup factors for a point isotropic source in barytes concrete [101].

8.19.10 MISCELLANEOUS SHIELD PLUGS

Miscellaneous shield plugs within the operating floor, in the primary heat exchangers, pumps, and other tanks are filled with steel shot.

8.20 Shield System for a Plutonium-fueled Fast Breeder Reactor (Design Studies)

8.20.1 PLANT DESCRIPTION AND PURPOSE

Two design studies of second-generation fast power breeder reactors and their associated power plants have been undertaken [98, 165]. These studies are known as the Plutonium-fueled Fast Breeder Reactor (PFFBR) design studies. Except for reactor power, equipment size, a few mechanical differences, and differences in the arrangement of the fuel, both reactors are essentially the same. Several designs with different thermal capacities have been examined. One reactor has a thermal

power of 775 Mw and a gross electric output of 300 Mw. The second design incorporates a reactor system with a thermal output of 430 Mw and a gross electric output of 150 Mw. In each of these studies, the intent has been to establish a sound conceptual design to form the basis for a plant that can be built and operated economically, using as a basis the design and experience of Dounreay, EBR-II, and Fermi. Being a second-generation plant, the PFFBR requires only a modest design effort and a component development program; the major cost will be its construction. The shield system for each of the designs differs only in detail. Major features are approximately the same. In the larger design the reactor-building outlay is symmetrical, and there are three coolant loops. In the smaller study the reactor is offset to one side, much like the EBR-II facility, and only two coolant loops are employed.

8.20.2 REACTOR-PLANT SHIELDING

8.20.2.1 General Considerations

The basic design of the shielding is similar to that of the Fermi reactor. The major departure is

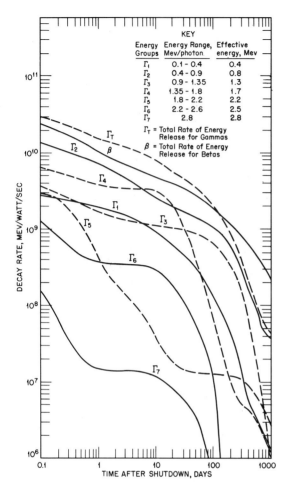

FIG. 8.94—Decay of fission products after infinite operation [151].
Approximation to obtain $E\gamma$ for finite operation: $E\gamma(T_0, T_s) = E\gamma(\infty, T_s) - E\gamma(\infty, T_0 + T_s)$ where T_0 is the operating time and T_s is shutdown time.

the method used for shielding against neutron leakage from the reactor vessel and streaming associated with the primary coolant lines. The streaming problem is compounded by the requirement of pipe flexibility and high-temperature operation. The method used in PFFBR studies is the result of a careful evaluation of a number of possible solutions. The following features of the PFFBR shield are examples of the changes that could occur in second-generation plants as a result of first-generation plant evaluation.

Primary shield wall: The graphite primary shield of the Fermi plant (Sec. 8.18.3) is eliminated, and its function is combined with that of the Fermi secondary shield wall (Sec. 8.18.4). The new shield is called the primary shield wall. This wall separates the lower containment building into an inner reactor compartment and an outer equipment compartment. The design of the primary shield wall is an example of savings that can be achieved by the separation of functions. The first layer is made of crushed iron oxide to absorb gamma rays. This portion of the shielding should be capable of withstanding high heat absorption and relatively high temperatures. The next layer is made of serpentine (an asbestos ore), an inexpensive high-temperature neutron-shielding material. The last layer of the wall, which does most of the neutron attenuation but which is not required to withstand high temperatures or high heat generation, is ordinary concrete.

Arrangement of the coolant lines: In this plant the coolant piping is arranged in a manner such that neutron attenuation effected by geometry is equal to that attained by the primary shield wall. All piping penetrations of the primary shield are located in the lower reactor floor. Elbows are used to scatter the streaming neutrons, and the length of pipe is arranged so that the neutrons are fully attenuated before the pipes enter the equipment compartment.

Use of materials: Because the primary shield wall is located several feet from the reactor, the

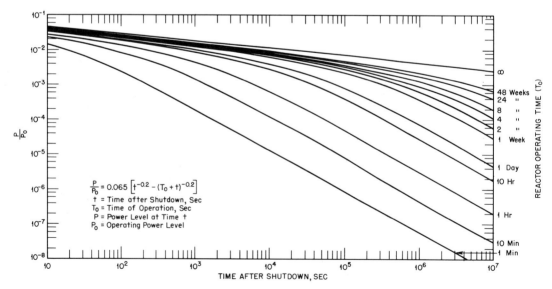

FIG. 8.95—Fission-product shutdown power generation rates [153, 154].

Table 8.83—Characteristics of Fast Reactors [22]

Characteristics	EBR-I (NRTS Arco, Idaho)	BR-5 (Russia)	Dounreay (Thurso, Scotland)	EBR-II (NRTS Arco, Idaho)	Fermi (Lagoona Beach near Monroe, Mich.)
Thermal power, Mw	1.4	5	72	62.5	300
Net electric power, Mw	0.2		20	20	100
Core size, in. Diameter	7.5	11	21	19·	30.5
Height	8.5	11	21	14	30.5
Critical mass, kg	48.2 (U^{235})	49.6 (PuO_2)	~208	200 (U^{235})	466 (U^{235})
Average core flux, neutrons/cm^2/sec	2×10^{14}	1×10^{15} *	2.5×10^{15}	5×10^{15}	5×10^{15}
Average core neutron energy, Mev	0.5	0.2 †		0.5	0.2
Purpose	Feasibility of breeding and power production		Feasibility of large breeder power plant	Breeding, feasibility of nuclear power integral with fuel processing and fabrication	Production of electric power, breeding, demonstration of uranium potential.
Shield type	Unitized	Unitized	Compartmentalized	Unitized	Compartmentalized
Main shield materials (see Table 7.4)	Plain graphite, iron, concrete	Water, iron, heavy concrete	Borated graphite, concrete blocks, Jabroc, poured concrete, Resilon-steel laminate.	Borated graphite, concrete, steel imbedded in graphite, steel	Plain graphite, borated graphite, stainless steel, carbon steel, ordinary concrete, serpentine.
Coolant activity, $\mu c/cm^3$	2.5 (NaK)		3,500 (sodium)	1,300 (sodium)	30,000 (sodium)
Coolant shields	Concrete		Concrete	Same as main shield	Steel, concrete, serpentine, calcium borate
Shield design-criteria biological level, mrem/hr	7.5			0.75 (?)	0.75
Maximum concrete temperature, °F			120		<190
Maximum concrete heat generation, watts/cm^3			0.001		0.001

* Maximum fast flux.
† Estimated value only.

specific nuclear heat generation in the shield is low. The inner layer of iron oxide in this wall in effect performs the same function as a thermal shield within the reactor vessel. Iron oxide in the form of limonite ore contained within steel barriers minimizes internal stresses due to heat generation, which otherwise would need to be considered. Some graphite is used beneath the concrete operating-floor shield over the reactor compartment. Serpentine and calcium borate, two high-temperature shielding materials, are used in special areas of this plant. Borated graphite is used as a shielding material where high conductivity as well as high temperature resistance is important.

8.20.2.2 Design Criteria

The shield system has been designed to ensure safe operation of the reactor plant. Radiation protection for personnel and equipment has been provided. All biological shields have been designed so that plant personnel will receive less than the radiation doses allowed by AEC regulations. Specifically, the shield design surface-exposure rate is 0.75 mrem/hr, including both neutron and gamma radiation. Design criteria for the protection of personnel and systems are the same as given in Table 8.85.

8.20.2.3 Shield Layouts

A plan view of the 150 Mw(e) plant is shown in Fig. 8.113, and an elevation is shown in Fig. 8.114.

8.20.3 PRIMARY SHIELD

8.20.3.1 Side Shield

The side shield (Figs. 8.113 and 8.114), composed of iron oxide, serpentine, and concrete, is designed to function principally as a neutron shield. Its purpose is to attenuate the neutron flux to a biologically safe level in the equipment compartment so that there is no significant activation of the components or the secondary coolant. The only radiation in the equipment compartment is gamma radiation from activated primary coolant. This arrangement simplifies the shielding of penetrations through the biological-shield floor and the walls of the equipment compartment.

The first portion of the side shield is an 18-in.-thick wall of crushed iron oxide ore (Fe_2O_3), which is loosely packed to a density of 306 lb/cu ft. This wall acts as a thermal shield to prevent overheating in the remainder of the shield. It absorbs about 95%

Table 8.84—Comparison of Fast Reactor Shields [22]

Shield Component	EBR-I	BR-5	Dounreay FBR	EBR-II	Fermi	PFFBR
Breeder blanket (U^{238}) thickness	Radial: ~10 in. Axial: 7.5 in. upper 3.6 in. lower	Radial: 4.0 in.	Radial: 26.8 in. Axial: None	Radial: 21.2 in. Axial: 18.0 in.	Radial: 23.6 in. Axial: 18.0 in.	Radial: 18.0 in. Axial: 10.0 in.
Thermal shield	Inside vessel	1. Two nickel reflectors, 6.0 in. 2. Outer uranium reflector, 1.4 in. 3. Copper container, 6 in.	None	Inside vessel, 2.3 in. ss	Inside vessel: Lower reactor vessel, 12 in. ss Upper reactor vessel, 6 in. ss	None
Primary side shield	1. 18 in. plain graphite 2. 4 in. iron 3. 6 ft concrete 4. 30 in. concrete, added water	1. H_2O, 19.7 in. 2. Iron, 15.8 in. 3. Heavy concrete, 43.5 in.	50 in. 0.3 % borated graphite	1. 13.3 in. 0.6% and 3% borated graphite 2. 6 ft concrete	1. 6 in. inner 5% borated graphite 2. 30 in. plain graphite 3. 6 in. outer layer 15% borated graphite	1. Fe_2O_3, 18.0 in. (300 lb/cu ft) 2. Serp. dry pack, 24.0 in. (130 lb/cu ft) 3. 150 lb-density concrete, 7.3 ft
Top shield except plug	Steel: 26 in. See Figs. 11.11 and 11.12	Side of rotating plug: 15.8 in. iron 44.0 in. heavy concrete 7.3 in. (part of top plug)	Side of plug 1. 6 ft removable concrete blocks 2. Steel & Jabroc, 10 in. Above plug: Steel and Jabroc, 10 in.	27.2 in. 0.6 % and 3 % borated graphite Concrete, 7.6 ft.	24 in. 5 % borated graphite 16 in. steel shot, density 300 lb/cu ft	1. 1 in. steel 2. 24 in. plain graphite 3. 6 in. 1 % borated graphite 4. 3 in. steel 5. 2 ft serpentine concrete 6. 6 ft plain concrete
Rotating-plug shield	31.5 in. steel		2.9-ft shield: 1. 18 in. steel plate (hot) 2. 14 in. Resilon and steel layer shield	Biological shield (not part of primary neutron shield) steel balls embedded in graphite and normal steel	12 ft, part of primary shield Biological shield 1. 1.5 ft ss, bottom layer 2. 6 ft plain graphite 3. 1 ft 1.5% borated graphite 4. 2 ft steel	Fixed 10-ft deck plug: 18 in. ss 5 ft plain graphite 2 ft 1% borated graphite 2.2 ft carbon steel
Accessibility to region above (or near) reactor	Restricted	None underneath top plug	Restricted	Probably none	Unlimited	Complete
Other materials in primary shield		1. Graphite thermal col. 2. Top plug: alternate layers of steel and paraffin 55.5 in. thick over rotating plug			Insulation	

Table 8.84—Comparison of Fast Reactor Shields [22] (continued)

Shield Component	EBR-I	BR-5	Dounreay FBR	EBR-II	Fermi	PFFBR
Secondary shield	None	None	None	Boron-steel liner around primary heat exchanger prevents activation of secondary coolant	Protects secondary coolant from activation, 30 in. concrete	None
Biological shield	Top shield See Figs. 11.11 and 11.12 Side shield: 71.5 in. ordinary concrete	Removable top plug: 1. Over rotating plug, 55 in. laminated steel and paraffin shield. 2. Side of rotating plug, see top shield under primary shield	See primary shield	Top shield: 1.9 in. steel bottom layer. 36.0 in. steel shot 2.0 in. steel top Side shield: 71.5 in. ordinary concrete	Operating floor: $6\frac{3}{4}$ in. steel (typ) $53\frac{1}{2}$ in. 150-lb-density concrete with some magnetite Outside building: 7 ft. 144 lb density ordinary concrete Earth below this	Operating floor: 1. Steel 2 in. 2. Concrete 7 ft. 10 in. Outside lower building at center: 1. 2 in. steel 2. 9 ft. concrete, 7 ft. below grade 3. $\frac{1}{2}$ in. steel 4. Earth
Blast shield	None	None	None	Inside biological shield: 1. 8.75 in. vermiculite concrete 2. 8.75 in. aerated concrete 3. 8.0 in. celotex in concentric steel plates	Secondary shield wall is specially reinforced as blast shield	In all designs: 1. 8 in. vermiculite concrete 2. 8 in. aerated concrete 3. 8 in. celotex halves and steel plates

FIG. 8.96—View of EBR-I concrete shield.

of the radiation from the core and is subjected to the brunt of the temperature effects. Iron oxide was chosen as the shielding material because it is able to withstand high temperatures, a necessity in this very high flux area. It has a high melting temperature (~2500°F); and, because it is used in the loose aggregate form, no stress problems arise as a result of the high temperature rise due to internal nuclear heat generation. The calculated temperature rise in the iron oxide shield due to nuclear heating is of the order of 1100°F. Since most of the heating occurs near the inner face of the shield, this wall is cooled by the gas-atmosphere flow in the inner reactor compartment. The next portion of the shield is a 2-ft-thick wall of serpentine rock,

which is dry-packed to a density of 130 lb/cu ft. This wall attenuates the neutrons and gamma rays leaking through the iron oxide enough to prevent damage by nuclear heating to the 7-ft-thick ordinary-concrete shield wall that constitutes the final portion of the shield.

Since the serpentine-rock wall is protected by the iron oxide wall, its internal temperature rise is only of the order of 100°F. Although this is considerably less than the rise of the Fe_2O_3 shield, serpentine rock in the dry-pack form is required because serpentine-aggregate concrete cannot withstand such high temperature differentials. Cooling of the serpentine wall is provided by locating a 6-in.-wide gas space between it and the

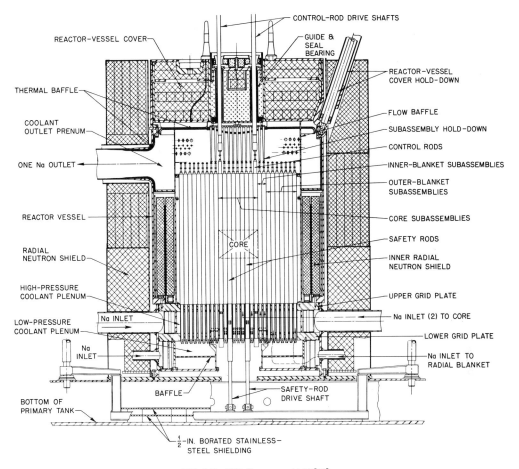

FIG. 8.97—EBR-II neutron shield [19].

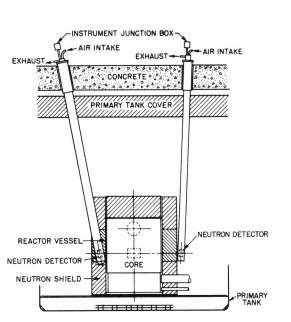

FIG. 8.98—Location of nuclear-instrument thimbles at EBR-II [19].

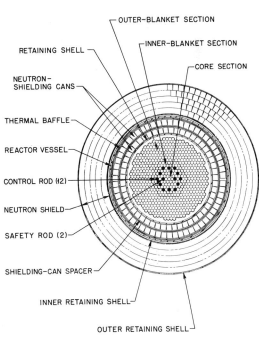

FIG. 8.99—EBR-II primary neutron shield [19].

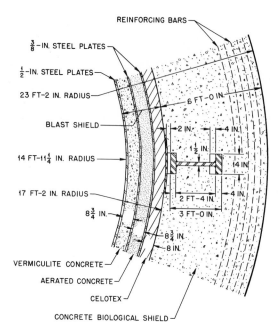

REINFORCING BARS

$\frac{3}{8}$-IN. STEEL PLATES

$\frac{1}{2}$-IN. STEEL PLATES

23 FT-2 IN. RADIUS

6 FT-0 IN.

BLAST SHIELD

2 IN.   4 IN.

$1\frac{1}{2}$ IN.

14 FT-$11\frac{1}{4}$ IN. RADIUS

14 IN.

17 FT-2 IN. RADIUS

4 IN.

$8\frac{3}{4}$ IN.

2 FT-4 IN.

3 FT-0 IN.

$8\frac{3}{4}$ IN.

8 IN.

VERMICULITE CONCRETE

AERATED CONCRETE

CELOTEX

CONCRETE BIOLOGICAL SHIELD

FIG. 8.100—EBR-II blast shield and biological shield [19].

iron oxide wall. The maximum temperature of the serpentine shield wall is kept below 800°F to maintain water retention and thus its neutron shielding ability.

The ordinary concrete in the 7-ft-thick portion of the shield has a density of 150 lb/cu ft. Its purpose is to attenuate the remaining neutron flux to permissible levels in the equipment compartment. The walls of iron oxide and serpentine attenuate the core neutron-leakage radiation to about 1×10^8 neutrons/cm²/sec. The gamma energy flux on the concrete wall from the primary sodium coolant in the equipment compartment is in the order of 4×10^6 Mev/cm²/sec. The temperature rise in the concrete due to internal nuclear heating is only 1 to 2°F, which is well below the 10°F maximum allowable in concrete. A 6-in.-wide gas cooling space is provided between the concrete and serpentine walls so that the maximum temperature of the concrete can be kept below 200°F to prevent water loss.

8.20.3.2 Vessel Biological Shield Plug

The fixed shield plug that rests in the upper portion of the reactor vessel serves as a biological shield. The neutron flux at the bottom of the plug is calculated to be 6×10^{11} neutrons/cm²/sec, and the gamma energy flux is 7.5×10^{11} Mev/cm²/sec. The 12-ft-thick plug, which attenuates both the neutron and gamma radiation to permissible levels at the operating floor, is stepped to prevent streaming in the gap formed between the vessel and plug walls.

The arrangement of the shield materials in the plug, from the bottom to the top, includes 18 in. of stainless steel followed by 5 ft of plain graphite and 2 ft of 1% borated graphite for neutron attenuation.

Table 8.85—Enrico Fermi Atomic Power Plant Shield Design Criteria [3]

Biological dose-rate limitations	
Basis:	30 mrem in 40-hr week
Rates:	Total = 0.75 mrem/hr
	Gamma-rays = 0.75 mr/hr
	Fast neutrons = 3 neutrons/cm²/sec
	Thermal neutrons = 200 neutrons/cm²/sec
Radiation damage: life of plant limits	
Stainless steel[100]	$nvt < 1 \times 10^{22}$
Graphite*	$nvt < 1 \times 10^{21}$
Other materials	$nvt < 1 \times 10^{20}$
Heating in concrete: limitations	
Nuclear heat-flux limitations	
Exposure rate:	$< 4 \times 10^{10}$ Mev/cm²/sec
	< 6 mw/sec/cm²
	< 20 Btu/hr/sq ft
Temperature limitations	
Temperature rise (nuclear heating)	< 10°F
Maximum temperature in ordinary concrete	
Neutron shield	< 200°F interior; 180°F surface
Gamma-ray shield	< 350°F
Maximum temperature in serpentine concrete	800°F
Maximum temperature in calcium borate pipe shield	< 1000°F
Maximum dt/dx in concrete	50°F

* See Sec. 8-3.

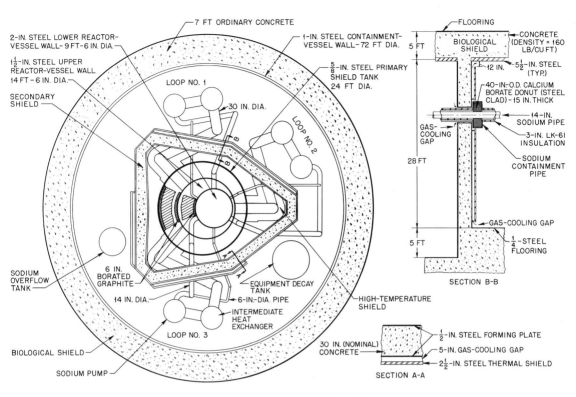

FIG. 8.101—Shield system for Fermi [1].

The carbon and graphite layers are supported by 1/2-in. steel plates. A 1-ft layer of insulation is included in the plug to produce the desired temperature profile. The plug design eliminates the need for machining and canning of graphite blocks.

Two penetrations through the plug accommodate the control- and safety-rod drives during normal operation, the subassembly handling machine during refueling, and the subassembly transfer cask during refueling. Each of these holes is fitted with individual stepped shield plugs whose shielding layers closely match the adjacent bulk shield.

8.20.3.3 Upper- and Lower-floor Shields

The design of these two shields is essentially the same, but their purposes vary. The upper floor shield in the inner reactor compartment is a biological radiation shield, whereas the lower floor shield protects structural concrete, not personnel. The shield consists of 2-ft thickness of plain graphite and a 6-in. thickness of 1% borated graphite followed, in the upper floor, by an 8-ft-thick floor slab, part of which is ordinary concrete and the rest is serpentine concrete. The serpentine-concrete area in the floor around the stationary plug is necessary because ordinary concrete cannot withstand the high temperature of this region. Three inches of steel is also included in the design, 1 in. of which serves as support for the graphite layers. The other 2 in. serve as a thermal-shield liner for the concrete. Gas cooling space is provided between the graphite and concrete so that the

maximum temperature of the concrete can be kept below 200°F to prevent water loss.

The purpose of the steel and graphite layers of the inner floor shields is to absorb gamma and neutron radiation sufficiently to prevent overheating in the concrete. The design is such that the nuclear-induced internal temperature rise above the ambient in the upper floor biological concrete will be limited to a maximum of 10°F and the rise in the lower floor structural concrete will be limited to 50°F. The neutron flux on the concrete is the dominant factor in determining this rise. The graphite layers were chosen so that the neutron flux on the upper biological concrete is kept below 4×10^9 neutrons/cm²/sec and the flux on the lower structural concrete is kept below 2×10^{10} neutrons/cm²/sec.

In the upper floor the 8-ft thickness of ordinary concrete and serpentine concrete attenuates the remaining gamma and neutron radiation to biologically safe values at the operating-floor level.

8.20.4 BIOLOGICAL AND EQUIPMENT–COMPARTMENT BUILDING SHIELD

The biological shield includes the fixed reactor plug, the concrete building operating floor, and the concrete shielding outside the building. The equipment compartment has a gamma-radiation level of about 10^5 r/hr owing to the radioactivity of the primary coolant. The floor above this area is a biological gamma shield. The necessary gamma-flux

Table 8.86—Activity Values Around Fermi Plant at
Full Operating Power* [3]

Primary sodium coolant	
Na^{24}	0.05 curies/cm^3
Na^{22}	1.7 μc/cm^3
Impurities	53 μc/cm^3
Expected normal fission-product contamination	20 μc/cm^3†
Secondary sodium coolant	
Na^{24}	1 × 10^{-4} μc/cm^3
Other	1 × 10^{-8} μc/cm^3
Argon primary cover gas	
Ar^{41}	146 μc/cm^3 at STP
Nitrogen in lower reactor building area	
N^{15}.	3 × 10^{-7} μc/cm^3
O^{17}	0 (< 5% O$_2$ in N$_2$)
Stainless steel	
Within reactor vessel	1 - 20 curies/cm^3
Within equipment compartment	~1 × 10^{-6} μc/cm^3
Subassemblies	
Hottest core subassembly at shutdown	8.8 × 10^6 curies
Hottest core subassembly 7 days after shutdown	1.3 × 10^6 curies
Hottest blanket subassembly at shutdown	9.5 × 10^5 curies
Hottest blanket subassembly 7 days after shutdown	1.4 × 10^5 curies
Wastes	
Waste liquids from subassembly cleaning	~12 μc/cm^3
Waste gases in waste-gas system	~ 5 μc/cm^3

*Full operating power for these calculations taken as 500 Mw.
†Based on results of tests on Fermi Core A pin fission-product leakage under irradiation. This is essentially what would leak out of a 54-mil opening at both ends of the pin. This corresponds to a leakage rate of 6×10^{-7} of the total production rate.

attenuation is achieved by using 7 ft 10 in. of concrete; a 2-in. thickness of steel thermal shielding is also used to limit the nuclear-induced temperature rise in the concrete to 10°F. All concrete located close to the pumps, intermediate heat exchangers, and primary piping requires a 2- to 3-in. thickness of steel because of the high level of sodium activity in the compartment. For the lower structural concrete floor in the equipment compartment, a 1/2-in.-thick steel thermal shield is adequate to prevent overheating because here a temperature rise in the concrete of 50°F can be tolerated. Since the equipment compartment is below grade, earth forms the outer biological shield wall.

8.20.5 PRIMARY PIPE SHIELDING

A unique aspect of the shield design is that the primary-loop inlet and exit sodium lines have been designed so that they do not penetrate the side-shield walls. This minimizes streaming problems and eliminates the use of costly shielding around the pipes. The primary piping runs in S-shaped steel-lined trenches underneath the shield walls. Each pipe makes four bends within the lower floor.

The trenches are lined with a 1/2-in. thickness of steel to prevent overheating in the concrete lower floor from the radioactivity of the primary coolant. The trenches of the vertical runs from the inner reactor compartment are lined with borated graphite to minimize the concrete heating caused by streaming neutrons. The piping in the trenches under the primary shield walls is insulated to prevent the high-temperature sodium from overheating the concrete.

With this design the estimated streaming flux is 1 × 10^4 neutrons/cm^2/sec at the mouth of the primary-pipe penetrations in the equipment compartment. Because the area of the penetrations is small, the overall neutron-flux level is below the significant activation value for sodium and steel. All gas and electrical lines to the inner reactor compartment run underneath the shield wall in trenches similar to those described above.

8.20.6 HEATING IN THE SHIELDS AND THEIR COOLING REQUIREMENTS

Considerable nuclear heat is dissipated in the various shields surrounding the 300-Mw(e) reactor. The total nuclear-heat load in these shields is estimated to be 2 Mw. In addition, about 1 Mw of heat is formed in the reactor vessel and secondary containment-vessel walls; but these compartments are heavily insulated from the rest of the shield system, and most of this heat is returned to the reactor proper. The shields are cooled by nitrogen gas flowing through the duct arrangement shown in Fig. 8.114; the gas temperatures and flows are adjusted to keep temperatures within specified limitations. The nitrogen-gas atmosphere that circulates below the floor has a nitrogen activity estimated at 3 × 10^{-3} μc/cm^3. This value is above the inhalation limit for the gas; and consequently special care is taken in the design to ensure that no harmful leakage of the gas to the atmosphere takes place. Shielding, estimated to be a 9-in. thickness of concrete, is required around the heat exchanger in the ventilation system because of this activity.

8.21 Mathematical Aids

8.21.1 EXPONENTIAL FUNCTIONS
[exp(±x)]

Values of the exponential functions can be found accurately for $x = 0$ to $x = \pm 100$ by the use of Tables 8.87 to 8.89.

Example: Find the value of

$$\exp(-15.87) = \exp[(15 + 0.80 + 0.07)]$$

$$= \exp(-15)\ \exp(-0.8)\ \exp(-0.07)$$

$$= (3.0592 × 10^{-7})(0.44933)(0.9324)$$

Table 8.89   Table 8.88   Table 8.87

$$= 1.2817 × 10^{-7}$$

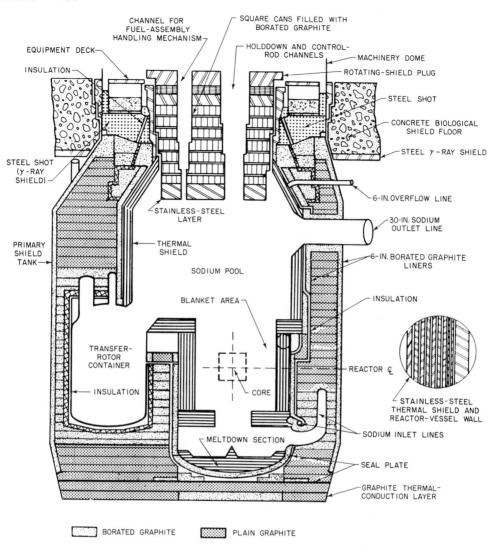

PRIMARY SHIELD SYSTEM

FIG. 8.102—Fermi primary shield system [46].

Table 8.87—Values of the Exponential
Function, exp(±x), from
x = 0 to x = 0.10

$$\exp(-x) = A' \times 10^n$$

x	e^{+x}		e^{-x}	
	A'	n	A'	n
0.00	1.0000	0	1.0000	0
0.01	1.0101	0	0.9901	0
0.02	1.0202	0	0.9802	0
0.03	1.0305	0	0.9705	0
0.04	1.0408	0	0.9608	0
0.05	1.0513	0	0.9512	0
0.06	1.0618	0	0.9418	0
0.07	1.0725	0	0.9324	0
0.08	1.0833	0	0.9231	0
0.09	1.0942	0	0.9139	0
0.10	1.1052	0	0.9048	0

Table 8.88—Values of the Exponential
Function, exp(±x), from
x = 0.10 to x = 1.00

$$\exp(\pm x) = A' \times 10^n$$

x	e^{+x}		e^{-x}	
	A'	n	A'	n
0.10	1.1052	0	9.0484	− 1
0.20	1.2214	0	8.1873	− 1
0.30	1.3499	0	7.4082	− 1
0.40	1.4918	0	6.7032	− 1
0.50	1.6487	0	6.0653	− 1
0.60	1.8221	0	5.4881	− 1
0.70	2.0138	0	4.9659	− 1
0.80	2.2255	0	4.4933	− 1
0.90	2.4596	0	4.0657	− 1
1.00	2.7183	0	3.6788	− 1

FIG. 8.103—Interior of rotating plug showing installation of canned–graphite shielding at Fermi [46].

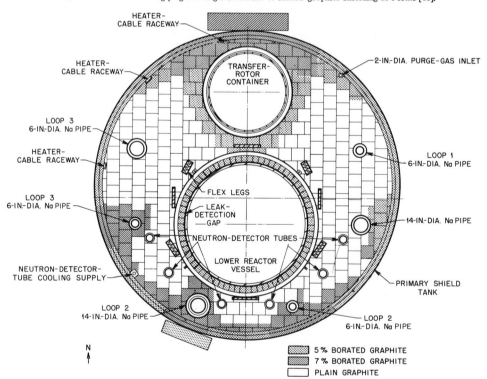

FIG. 8.104—Typical plan view of Fermi primary shield layout at elevation 563 ft [46].

FIG. 8.105—Graphite donut shield erected around Fermi 6-in.-diameter sodium pipe within primary shield tank [46].

8.21.2 EXPONENTIAL INTEGRALS

8.21.2.1 Definitions

$$E_n(x) = \int_1^\infty \exp(-sx) \frac{ds}{s^n}$$

$$= \int_0^1 v^{n-2} \exp\left(\frac{-x}{v}\right) dv$$

$$= x^{n-1} \int_x^\infty \exp(-u) \frac{du}{u^n} \qquad (8.145)$$

$$E_0(x) = \frac{\exp(-x)}{x} \qquad (8.146)$$

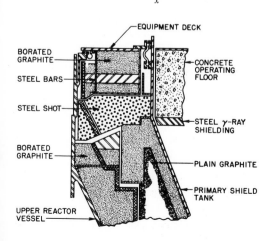

FIG. 8.106—Shielding for Fermi upper primary shield tank [47].

$$E_1(x) = \int_x^\infty \exp(-u) \frac{du}{u} \qquad (8.147)$$

$$E_2(x) = x \int_x^\infty \exp(-u) \frac{du}{u^2} \qquad (8.148)$$

$$E_3(x) = x^2 \int_x^\infty \exp(-u) \frac{du}{u^3} \qquad (8.149)$$

$$E_4(x) = x^3 \int_x^\infty \exp(-u) \frac{du}{u^4} \qquad (8.150)$$

8.21.2.2 General Expansion

The following expansion is equivalent to the definition, Eq. 8.145:

$$E_n(x) = \sum_{\substack{m=0 \\ m \neq n-1}}^{\infty} \frac{(-x)^m}{m!\,(n-1-m)} + \frac{(-1)^n x^{n-1}}{(n-1)!} \left\{ \ln(x) \right.$$

$$\left. - A_n + \gamma \right\} \qquad (8.151)$$

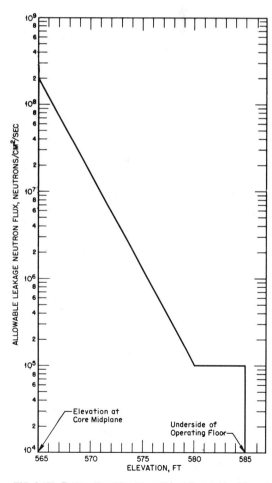

FIG. 8.107—Design allowable neutron flux at the outside of the primary shield tank vs. elevation [47].

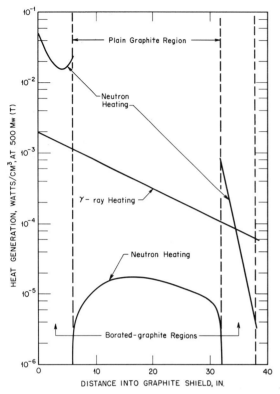

FIG. 8.108—Heat production in graphite shield at core midplane [45].

where $A_1 = 0$

$$A_n = \sum_{m=1}^{n-1} \frac{1}{m} \quad (n > 1)$$

$$\gamma = 0.577216$$

8.21.2.3 Small-value Expansions

For $x < 0.01$, accurate to five significant figures [3]:

$$E_0(x) = \frac{1-x}{x} + \frac{x}{2} \tag{8.152}$$

$$E_1(x) = x\left(\frac{2-x}{2}\right) + \ln\left(\frac{1}{x}\right) - 0.577216 \tag{8.153}$$

$$E_2(x) = 1 - x\left[\frac{x}{2} - \ln\left(\frac{1}{x}\right) + 0.422784\right] \tag{8.154}$$

$$E_3(x) = \frac{1}{2} - x\left\{\frac{2+x}{2}\left[\ln\left(\frac{1}{x}\right) + 0.922784\right]\right\} \tag{8.155}$$

$$E_4(x) = \frac{1}{3} - \frac{x}{2}\left\{1 + x\left[1 - \frac{1}{3}\ln\left(\frac{1}{x}\right) - 0.318708\right]\right\} \tag{8.156}$$

These formulas can be used for values of $x = 0.01$ to $x = 0.2$ with an error of $< 1\%$.

8.21.2.4 Asymptotic Expansion ($x \gg 1$)

For $5 > n > 0$,

$$E_n(x) = \frac{\exp(-x)}{x}\left[1 - \frac{n}{x} + \frac{n(n+1)}{x^2} - \frac{n(n+1)(n+2)}{x^3} + \cdots\right] \tag{8.157}$$

Considerably more useful is the following expansion due to Blanch [166]:

$$E_n(x) = \frac{\exp(-x)}{x+n}\left[1 + \frac{n}{(x+n)^2} + \frac{n(n-2x)}{(x+n)^4} + \frac{n(6x^2 - 8nx + n^2)}{(x+n)^6}\right] + R(n,x) \tag{8.158}$$

where

$$R(x,n) = n\int_1^\infty \frac{\exp(-xu)(-24x^3 u^3 + 58nx^2 u^2 - 22n^2 xu + n^3)}{u^n(xu+n)^8}\,du$$

8.21.2.5 Table of Values of E_0 Through E_4

Table 8.90 presents values of $E_0(x)$, $E_1(x)$, $E_2(x)$, $E_3(x)$, and $E_4(x)$ for $x = 0.00$ to $x = 10.0$.

8.21.2.6 References

For further properties and discussions of these functions see Ref. 25. For a more detailed table of the functions $E_1(x)$, $E_2(x)$, and $E_3(x)$ for $x = 0$ to $x = 20$ in very small increments of x, the reader is referred to Ref. 167.

8.21.3 SECANT INTEGRALS OF THE FIRST AND SECOND KINDS

8.21.3.1 General Considerations

A class of integral functions frequently used in evaluating shielding problems involving the attenuation of radiation through shields is the class known as the secant integrals.

This class of functions can be mathematically defined as

$$I_{n+1}(\theta, b) = b^n \int_0^\theta (\sec\theta')^n \exp(-b\sec\theta')\,d\theta' \quad (n = 0, 1, 2, 3, \ldots) \tag{8.159}$$

where $b = \mu x$, single material

$\quad = \sum_i \mu_i x_i \quad (i = 1, 2, \ldots)$ for a number of layers

μ_i = mass-absorption coefficient for the ith material

x_i = material thickness of the ith material

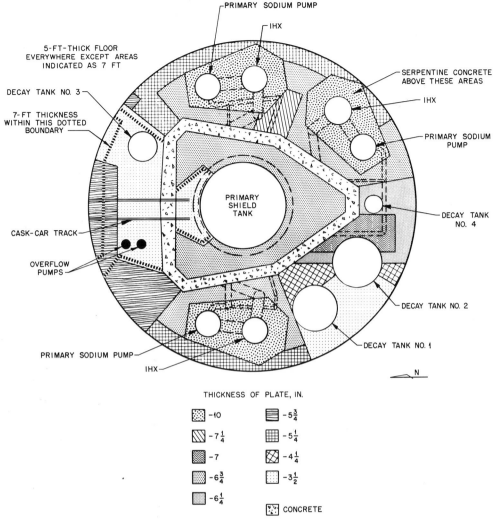

THICKNESS OF PLATE, IN.

▨	-10	▤	$-5\frac{3}{4}$
◩	$-7\frac{1}{4}$	▦	$-5\frac{1}{4}$
▨	-7	⬡	$-4\frac{1}{4}$
▨	$-6\frac{3}{4}$	▢	$-3\frac{1}{2}$
▨	$-6\frac{1}{4}$		

▨ CONCRETE

FIG. 8.109—Plan view of Fermi operating floor showing steel thicknesses [46].

8.21.3.2 Secant Integrals of the First Kind
$$[F(\theta, b)]$$

$$I_1(\theta, b) = F(\theta, b) = \int_0^\theta \exp(-b \sec \theta') \, d\theta' \quad (8.160)$$

Curves of these integrals have been published in Ref. 18.

8.21.3.3 Secant Integrals of the Second Kind
$$\left[G(\theta, \, b)\right]$$

$$I_2(\theta, b) = G(\theta, b) = b \int_0^\theta \sec \theta' \exp(-b \sec \theta') \, d\theta' \quad (8.161)$$

This class of integrals arises wherever a buildup function $B(b, \theta)$, which appears beneath the integral sign, is approximated by a polynominal expression. For example, if we have a function $\Gamma(\theta, b)$ such that

$$\Gamma(\theta, b) = \Gamma_0 \int_0^\theta B(b, \theta) \exp(-b \sec \theta') \, d\theta' \quad (8.162)$$

where $B(b, \theta)$ is approximated as

$$B(b, \theta) = 1 + \beta' b \sec \theta \quad (8.163)$$

and β' is a constant, from the definition of the $F(\theta, b)$ and $G(\theta, b)$ functions, Eqs. 8.160, 8.161, and 8.162 can be rewritten

$$\Gamma(\theta, b) = \Gamma_0[F(\theta, b) + \beta' G(\theta, b)] \quad (8.164)$$

8.21.3.4 Tables of Secant Integrals

The approximation given in Eq. 8.151 is sufficient for most shielding calculations that are used for practical application. The following two tables, the secant integrals of the first kind, Table 8.91, and secant integrals of the second kind, Table 8.92,

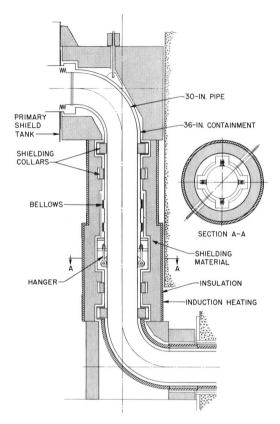

FIG. 8.110—Shielding on Fermi 30-in. primary coolant pipe [45].

$$\exp(\pm x) = A' \times 10^n$$

x	e^{+x}		e^{-x}	
	A'	n	A'	n
1	2.7183	0	3.6788	-1
2	7.3891	0	1.3534	-1
3	2.0086	1	4.9786	-2
4	5.4598	1	1.8316	-2
5	1.4841	2	6.7381	-3
6	4.0343	2	2.4787	-3
7	1.0966	3	9.1191	-4
8	2.9810	3	3.3546	-4
9	8.1031	3	1.2341	-4
10	2.2026	4	4.5401	-5
11	5.9873	4	1.6702	-5
12	1.6275	5	6.1443	-6
13	4.4241	5	2.2603	-6
14	1.2026	6	8.3155	-7
15	3.2689	6	3.0592	-7
16	8.8859	6	1.1254	-7
17	2.4154	7	4.1402	-8
18	6.5660	7	1.5230	-8
19	1.7848	8	5.6029	-9
20	4.8514	8	2.0612	-9
21	1.3188	9	7.5829	-10
22	3.5847	9	2.7896	-10
23	9.7445	9	1.0262	-10
24	2.6488	10	3.7753	-11
25	7.2000	10	1.3889	-11
26	1.9572	11	5.1093	-12
27	5.3200	11	1.8797	-12
28	1.4462	12	6.9147	-13
29	3.9311	12	2.5438	-13
30	1.0686	13	9.3584	-14
31	2.9047	13	3.4427	-14
32	7.8957	13	1.2665	-14
33	2.1463	14	4.6592	-15
34	5.8343	14	1.7140	-15
35	1.5859	15	6.3057	-16
36	4.3109	15	2.3197	-16
37	1.1718	16	8.5338	-17
38	3.1854	16	3.1393	-17
39	8.6588	16	1.1549	-17
40	2.3536	17	4.2488	-18
41	6.3978	17	1.5630	-18
42	1.7391	18	5.7501	-19
43	4.7275	18	2.1153	-19
44	1.2850	19	7.7820	-20
45	3.4930	19	2.8629	-20
46	9.4952	19	1.0532	-20
47	2.5810	20	3.8745	-21
48	7.0161	20	1.4253	-21
49	1.9072	21	5.2434	-22
50	5.1841	21	1.9290	-22
55	7.694	23	1.300	-24
60	1.142	26	8.758	-27
65	1.695	28	5.901	-29
70	2.515	30	3.976	-31
75	3.733	32	2.679	-33
80	5.54	34	1.81	-35
85	8.22	36	1.22	-37
90	1.22	39	8.20	-40
95	1.81	41	5.52	-42
100	2.69	43	3.72	-44

were computed by numerical integration of the Eqs. 8.160 and 8.161 on an IBM-7090 computer.*

8.21.4 SELF-ABSORPTION FACTORS

Figure 8.115 gives the values of gamma-ray self-absorption factors for slabs, cylinders, and spheres as a function of the mean free path, $\mu \chi$.

8.21.5 BESSEL FUNCTIONS

In the investigation of physical problems, one often encounters many differential equations, and the functions that satisfy these differential equations are sought. The solution of a differential equation is generally found in terms of an infinite power series, and, if the solution occurs frequently in problems, the power series is then given a name and tabulated for many values of the argument.

*These tables were originally calculated in 1958, while the author was at APDA, using a Simpson's rule integration technique on an IBM-650 computer. Since then, the author has had occasion to recalculate these values using a 10-point Gaussian quadrature technique of integration on an IBM-7090 computer. The values appearing in Tables 8.91 and 8.92 are the results of the recalculation. Professor Owen Gailar of Purdue University, Department of Nuclear Engineering, programmed the integrations for the computer. For a discussion of the Gaussian quadrature integration, see L. Fox, Numerical Solution of Ordinary and Partial Differential Equations, Pergamon Press, Inc., New York, 1962.

Consider, for example, the differential equation

$$\frac{d^2y}{dx^2} + y = 0 \qquad (8.165)$$

which has as one solution the infinite power series
(Text continued on p. 570.)

Table 8.90—The Functions* $E_n(x)$

x	E_0	E_1	E_2	E_3	E_4
0.00	∞	∞	1.0000000	0.5000000	0.3333333
0.01	99.0049834	4.0379296	0.9496705	0.4902766	0.3283824
0.02	49.0099337	3.3547078	0.9131045	0.4809683	0.3235264
0.03	32.3481844	2.9591187	0.8816720	0.4719977	0.3187619
0.04	24.0197360	2.6812637	0.8535389	0.4633239	0.3140855
0.05	19.0245885	2.4678985	0.8278345	0.4549188	0.3094945
0.06	15.6960756	2.2953069	0.8040461	0.4467609	0.3049863
0.07	13.3199117	2.1508382	0.7818352	0.4388327	0.3005585
0.08	11.5389543	2.0269410	0.7609611	0.4311197	0.2962089
0.09	10.1547909	1.9187448	0.7412442	0.4236096	0.2919354
0.10	9.0483742	1.8229240	0.7225450	0.4162915	0.2877361
0.11	8.1439467	1.7371067	0.7047524	0.4091557	0.2836090
0.12	7.3910036	1.6595418	0.6877754	0.4021937	0.2795524
0.13	6.7545802	1.5888993	0.6715385	0.3953977	0.2755646
0.14	6.2097017	1.5241457	0.6559778	0.3887607	0.2716439
0.15	5.7380532	1.4644617	0.6410387	0.3822761	0.2677889
0.16	5.3258987	1.4091867	0.6266739	0.3759380	0.2639979
0.17	4.9627342	1.3577806	0.6128421	0.3697408	0.2602696
0.18	4.6403901	1.3097961	0.5995069	0.3636795	0.2566026
0.19	4.3524165	1.2648584	0.5866360	0.3577491	0.2529956
0.20	4.0936538	1.2226505	0.5742006	0.3519453	0.2494472
0.21	3.8599250	1.1829020	0.5621748	0.3462638	0.2459563
0.22	3.6478127	1.1453801	0.5505352	0.3407005	0.2425216
0.23	3.4544939	1.1098831	0.5392605	0.3352518	0.2391419
0.24	3.2776161	1.0762354	0.5283314	0.3299142	0.2358162
0.25	3.1152031	1.0442826	0.5177301	0.3246841	0.2325432
0.26	2.9655830	1.0138887	0.5074405	0.3195585	0.2293221
0.27	2.8273315	0.9849331	0.4974476	0.3145343	0.2261517
0.28	2.6992276	0.9573083	0.4877374	0.3096086	0.2230311
0.29	2.5802192	0.9309182	0.4782973	0.3047787	0.2199593
0.30	2.4693941	0.9056767	0.4691152	0.3000418	0.2169352
0.31	2.3659579	0.8815057	0.4601802	0.2953956	0.2139581
0.32	2.2692157	0.8583352	0.4514818	0.2908374	0.2110270
0.33	2.1785568	0.8361012	0.4430104	0.2863652	0.2081411
0.34	2.0934421	0.8147456	0.4347568	0.2819765	0.2052994
0.35	2.0133945	0.7942154	0.4267127	0.2776693	0.2025013
0.36	1.9379898	0.7744622	0.4188699	0.2734416	0.1997458
0.37	1.8668495	0.7554414	0.4112210	0.2692913	0.1970322
0.38	1.7996353	0.7371121	0.4037588	0.2652165	0.1943597
0.39	1.7360433	0.7194367	0.3964766	0.2612155	0.1917276
0.40	1.6758001	0.7023801	0.3893680	0.2572864	0.1891352
0.41	1.6186591	0.6859103	0.3824270	0.2534276	0.1865816
0.42	1.5643972	0.6699973	0.3756479	0.2496373	0.1840664
0.43	1.5128118	0.6546134	0.3690253	0.2459141	0.1815887
0.44	1.4637191	0.6397328	0.3625540	0.2422563	0.1791479
0.45	1.4169514	0.6253313	0.3562291	0.2386625	0.1767433
0.46	1.3723558	0.6113865	0.3500458	0.2351313	0.1743744
0.47	1.3297921	0.5978774	0.3439999	0.2316612	0.1720405
0.48	1.2891321	0.5847843	0.3380869	0.2282508	0.1697410
0.49	1.2502579	0.5720888	0.3323029	0.2248990	0.1674753
0.50	1.2130613	0.5597736	0.3266439	0.2216044	0.1652428
0.51	1.1774423	0.5478224	0.3211062	0.2183657	0.1630430
0.52	1.1433087	0.5362198	0.3156863	0.2151818	0.1608753
0.53	1.1105754	0.5249515	0.3103807	0.2120516	0.1587392
0.54	1.0791634	0.5140039	0.3051862	0.2089739	0.1566341
0.55	1.0489997	0.5033641	0.3000996	0.2059475	0.1545596
0.56	1.0200162	0.4930200	0.2951179	0.2029715	0.1525150
0.57	0.9921499	0.4829600	0.2902382	0.2000448	0.1505000
0.58	0.9653420	0.4731734	0.2854578	0.1971664	0.1485139
0.59	0.9395378	0.4636498	0.2807739	0.1943353	0.1465565
0.60	0.9146861	0.4543795	0.2761839	0.1915506	0.1446271
0.61	0.8907391	0.4453531	0.2716855	0.1888114	0.1427253
0.62	0.8676523	0.4365619	0.2672761	0.1861166	0.1408507
0.63	0.8453838	0.4279973	0.2629535	0.1834656	0.1390028
0.64	0.8238944	0.4196516	0.2587154	0.1808573	0.1371813
0.65	0.8031473	0.4115170	0.2545597	0.1782910	0.1353855
0.66	0.7831081	0.4035863	0.2504844	0.1757658	0.1336153
0.67	0.7637441	0.3958526	0.2464874	0.1732810	0.1318701
0.68	0.7450250	0.3883092	0.2425667	0.1708358	0.1301495
0.69	0.7269218	0.3809500	0.2387206	0.1684294	0.1285433

Table 8.90—The Functions* $E_n(x)$ (continued)

x	E_0	E_1	E_2	E_3	E_4
0.70	0.7094076	0.3737688	0.2349471	0.1660612	0.1267808
0.71	0.6924566	0.3667600	0.2312446	0.1637303	0.1251319
0.72	0.6760448	0.3599179	0.2276114	0.1614360	0.1235061
0.73	0.6601493	0.3532374	0.2240457	0.1591778	0.1219031
0.74	0.6447485	0.3467133	0.2205461	0.1569549	0.1203224
0.75	0.6298221	0.3403408	0.2171109	0.1547667	0.1187638
0.76	0.6153506	0.3341153	0.2137388	0.1526125	0.1172270
0.77	0.6013157	0.3280323	0.2104282	0.1504917	0.1157115
0.78	0.5877000	0.3220876	0.2071777	0.1484037	0.1142170
0.79	0.5744871	0.3162770	0.2039860	0.1463479	0.1127433
0.80	0.5616612	0.3105966	0.2008517	0.1443238	0.1112900
0.81	0.5492075	0.3050425	0.1977736	0.1423307	0.1098567
0.82	0.5371118	0.2996112	0.1947504	0.1403681	0.1084433
0.83	0.5253606	0.2942992	0.1917810	0.1384355	0.1070493
0.84	0.5139411	0.2891029	0.1888641	0.1365324	0.1056744
0.85	0.5028411	0.2840193	0.1859986	0.1346581	0.1043185
0.86	0.4920489	0.2790451	0.1831833	0.1328122	0.1029812
0.87	0.4815535	0.2741773	0.1804173	0.1309943	0.1016622
0.88	0.4713442	0.2694130	0.1776994	0.1292037	0.1003612
0.89	0.4614110	0.2647495	0.1750287	0.1274401	0.0990780
0.90	0.4517441	0.2601839	0.1724041	0.1257030	0.0978123
0.91	0.4423343	0.2557138	0.1698247	0.1239919	0.0965639
0.92	0.4331729	0.2513364	0.1672895	0.1233063	0.0953324
0.93	0.4242513	0.2470495	0.1647977	0.1206459	0.0941177
0.94	0.4155615	0.2428506	0.1623482	0.1190102	0.0929194
0.95	0.4070958	0.2387375	0.1599404	0.1173988	0.0917374
0.96	0.3988468	0.2347080	0.1575732	0.1158113	0.0905713
0.97	0.3908073	0.2307599	0.1552459	0.1142472	0.0894211
0.98	0.3829705	0.2268912	0.1529578	0.1127063	0.0882863
0.99	0.3753300	0.2230998	0.1507079	0.1111880	0.0871669
1.00	0.3678794	0.2193839	0.1484955	0.1096920	0.0860625
1.01	0.3606129	0.2157416	0.1463199	0.1082179	0.0849730
1.02	0.3535245	0.2121711	0.1441804	0.1067654	0.0838981
1.03	0.3466087	0.2086706	0.1420763	0.1053342	0.0828376
1.04	0.3398603	0.2052384	0.1400068	0.1039238	0.0817913
1.05	0.3332740	0.2018728	0.1379713	0.1025339	0.0807590
1.06	0.3268451	0.1985723	0.1359691	0.1011643	0.0797406
1.07	0.3205687	0.1953354	0.1339996	0.0998145	0.0787357
1.08	0.3144403	0.1921605	0.1320622	0.0984842	0.0777442
1.09	0.3084555	0.1890461	0.1301562	0.0971731	0.0767659
1.10	0.3026101	0.1859909	0.1282811	0.0958809	0.0758007
1.11	0.2969000	0.1829935	0.1264362	0.0946074	0.0748483
1.12	0.2913212	0.1800525	0.1246210	0.0933521	0.0739085
1.13	0.2858701	0.1771666	0.1228350	0.0921149	0.0729812
1.14	0.2805430	0.1743347	0.1210775	0.0908953	0.0720661
1.15	0.2753363	0.1715554	0.1193481	0.0896932	0.0711632
1.16	0.2702467	0.1688275	0.1176462	0.0885083	0.0702722
1.17	0.2652709	0.1661500	0.1159714	0.0873402	0.0693930
1.18	0.2604057	0.1635217	0.1143231	0.0861888	0.0685253
1.19	0.2556481	0.1609416	0.1127008	0.0850537	0.0676691
1.20	0.2509952	0.1584084	0.1111041	0.0839347	0.0668242
1.21	0.2464440	0.1559213	0.1095325	0.0828315	0.0659904
1.22	0.2419919	0.1534792	0.1079855	0.0817439	0.0651675
1.23	0.2376362	0.1510812	0.1064627	0.0806717	0.0643555
1.24	0.2333744	0.1487262	0.1049637	0.0796146	0.0635540
1.25	0.2292038	0.1464134	0.1034881	0.0785723	0.0627631
1.26	0.2251222	0.1441418	0.1020353	0.0775447	0.0619825
1.27	0.2211273	0.1419106	0.1006051	0.0765316	0.0612122
1.28	0.2172166	0.1397190	0.0991970	0.0755326	0.0604519
1.29	0.2133882	0.1375660	0.0978106	0.0745476	0.0597015
1.30	0.2096398	0.1354510	0.0964455	0.0735763	0.0589609
1.31	0.2059695	0.1333730	0.0951015	0.0726186	0.0582299
1.32	0.2023752	0.1313313	0.0937780	0.0716742	0.0575085
1.33	0.1988551	0.1293252	0.0924747	0.0707429	0.0567964
1.34	0.1954072	0.1273540	0.0911913	0.0698246	0.0560936
1.35	0.1920298	0.1254168	0.0899275	0.0689191	0.0553998
1.36	0.1887212	0.1235131	0.0886829	0.0680260	0.0547151
1.37	0.1854795	0.1216422	0.0874571	0.0671453	0.0540393
1.38	0.1823033	0.1198033	0.0862499	0.0662768	0.0533722
1.39	0.1791909	0.1179959	0.0850610	0.0654203	0.0527137

Table 8.90—The Functions* $E_n(x)$ (continued)

x	E_0	E_1	E_2	E_3	E_4
1.40	0.1761407	0.1162193	0.0838899	0.0645755	0.0520637
1.41	0.1731513	0.1144729	0.0827365	0.0637424	0.0514222
1.42	0.1702211	0.1127561	0.0816004	0.0629207	0.0507889
1.43	0.1673489	0.1110683	0.0804813	0.0621104	0.0501637
1.44	0.1645332	0.1094089	0.0793789	0.0613111	0.0495466
1.45	0.1617726	0.1077774	0.0782930	0.0605227	0.0489374
1.46	0.1590659	0.1061733	0.0772233	0.0597452	0.0483361
1.47	0.1564119	0.1045959	0.0761694	0.0589782	0.0477425
1.48	0.1538092	0.1030449	0.0751313	0.0582217	0.0471565
1.49	0.1512568	0.1015196	0.0741085	0.0574755	0.0465780
1.50	0.1487534	0.1000196	0.0731008	0.0567395	0.0460070
1.51	0.1462980	0.0985444	0.0721080	0.0560135	0.0454432
1.52	0.1438894	0.0970935	0.0711298	0.0552973	0.0448867
1.53	0.1415266	0.0956664	0.0701660	0.0545908	0.0443372
1.54	0.1392085	0.0942628	0.0692164	0.0538939	0.0437948
1.55	0.1369342	0.0928821	0.0682807	0.0532064	0.0432593
1.56	0.1347026	0.0915240	0.0673587	0.0525283	0.0427307
1.57	0.1325129	0.0901879	0.0664502	0.0518592	0.0422087
1.58	0.1303640	0.0888736	0.0655549	0.0511992	0.0416935
1.59	0.1282551	0.0875805	0.0646726	0.0505481	0.0411847
1.60	0.1261853	0.0863083	0.0638032	0.0499057	0.0406825
1.61	0.1241538	0.0850567	0.0629464	0.0492720	0.0401866
1.62	0.1221597	0.0838251	0.0621020	0.0486467	0.0396970
1.63	0.1202022	0.0826134	0.0612698	0.0480299	0.0392136
1.64	0.1182805	0.0814210	0.0604497	0.0474213	0.0387364
1.65	0.1163939	0.0802476	0.0596413	0.0468209	0.0382652
1.66	0.1145416	0.0790930	0.0588446	0.0462284	0.0377999
1.67	0.1127228	0.0779567	0.0580594	0.0456439	0.0373406
1.68	0.1109369	0.0768384	0.0572854	0.0450672	0.0368870
1.69	0.1091832	0.0757378	0.0565226	0.0444982	0.0364392
1.70	0.1074609	0.0746546	0.0557706	0.0439367	0.0359970
1.71	0.1057695	0.0735885	0.0550294	0.0433827	0.0355604
1.72	0.1041082	0.0725392	0.0542988	0.0428361	0.0351293
1.73	0.1024765	0.0715063	0.0535786	0.0422967	0.0347037
1.74	0.1008738	0.0704895	0.0528686	0.0417645	0.0342834
1.75	0.0992994	0.0694887	0.0521687	0.0412393	0.0338684
1.76	0.0977528	0.0685034	0.0514788	0.0407211	0.0334586
1.77	0.0962333	0.0675335	0.0507986	0.0402097	0.0330539
1.78	0.0947405	0.0665787	0.0501281	0.0397051	0.0326544
1.79	0.0932738	0.0656386	0.0494670	0.0392071	0.0322598
1.80	0.0918327	0.0647131	0.0488153	0.0387157	0.0318702
1.81	0.0904167	0.0638019	0.0481727	0.0382308	0.0314855
1.82	0.0890251	0.0629047	0.0475392	0.0377522	0.0311056
1.83	0.0876577	0.0620213	0.0469146	0.0372800	0.0307304
1.84	0.0863138	0.0611515	0.0462987	0.0368139	0.0303599
1.85	0.0849931	0.0602950	0.0456915	0.0363540	0.0299941
1.86	0.0836950	0.0594515	0.0450928	0.0359001	0.0296328
1.87	0.0824191	0.0586210	0.0445024	0.0354521	0.0292761
1.88	0.0811649	0.0578031	0.0439203	0.0350100	0.0289238
1.89	0.0799322	0.0569976	0.0433463	0.0345737	0.0285759
1.90	0.0787203	0.0562044	0.0427803	0.0341430	0.0282323
1.91	0.0775290	0.0554231	0.0422222	0.0337180	0.0278930
1.92	0.0763578	0.0546537	0.0416718	0.0332986	0.0275579
1.93	0.0752063	0.0538959	0.0411291	0.0328846	0.0272270
1.94	0.0740742	0.0531495	0.0405938	0.0324759	0.0269002
1.95	0.0729611	0.0524144	0.0400660	0.0320727	0.0265775
1.96	0.0718665	0.0516900	0.0395454	0.0316746	0.0262587
1.97	0.0707903	0.0509770	0.0390322	0.0312817	0.0259440
1.98	0.0697319	0.0502744	0.0385259	0.0308939	0.0256331
1.99	0.0686912	0.0495823	0.0380267	0.0305112	0.0253261
2.0	6.76676 (−2)	4.89005 (−2)	3.75343 (−2)	3.01334 (−2)	2.50228 (−2)
2.1	5.83126	4.26143	3.29663	2.66136	2.21893
2.2	5.03651	3.71911	2.89827	2.35207	1.96859
2.3	4.35908	3.25023	2.55036	2.08002	1.74728
2.4	3.77991	2.84403	2.24613	1.84054	1.55150
2.5	3.28340	2.49149	1.97977	1.62954	1.37822
2.6	2.85668	2.18502	1.74630	1.44349	1.22476
2.7	2.48909	1.91819	1.54145	1.27932	1.08879
2.8	2.17179	1.68553	1.36152	1.13437	0.96826
2.9	1.89735	1.48240	1.20336	1.00629	0.86136

Table 8.90—The Functions* $E_n(x)$ (continued)

x	E_0	E_1	E_2	E_3	E_4
3.0	1.65957	1.30484	1.06419	0.89306	0.76650
3.1	1.45320	1.14944	0.94165	0.79290	0.68231
3.2	1.27382	1.01330	0.83366	0.70425	0.60754
3.3	11.17672 (−3)	8.93904 (−3)	7.38433 (−3)	6.25744 (−3)	5.41120 (−3)
3.4	9.81567	7.89097	6.54396	5.56190	4.82093
3.5	8.62782	6.97014	5.80189	4.94538	4.29619
3.6	7.58992	6.16041	5.14623	4.39865	3.82953
3.7	6.68203	5.44782	4.56658	3.91360	3.41440
3.8	5.88705	4.82025	4.05383	3.48310	3.04500
3.9	5.19023	4.26715	3.60004	3.10087	2.71618
4.0	4.57891	3.77935	3.19823	2.76136	2.42340
4.1	4.04212	3.34888	2.84226	2.45969	2.16264
4.2	3.57038	2.96876	2.52678	2.19156	1.93034
4.3	3.15548	2.63191	2.24704	1.95315	1.72334
4.4	2.79030	2.33601	1.99890	1.74110	1.53883
4.5	2.46867 (−3)	2.07340 (−3)	1.77869 (−3)	1.55244 (−3)	1.37434 (−3)
4.6	2.18518	1.84101	1.58321	1.38454	1.22765
4.7	1.93517	1.63525	1.40960	1.23507	1.09682
4.8	1.71453	1.45299	1.25538	1.10197	0.98010
4.9	1.51971	1.29148	1.11831	0.98342	0.87594
5.0	1.34759	1.14830	0.99647	0.87780	0.78298
5.1	1.19544	1.02130	0.88812	0.78368	0.70000
5.2	10.6088 (−4)	9.0862 (−4)	7.9173 (−4)	6.9978 (−4)	6.2590 (−4)
5.3	9.4181	8.0861	7.0597	6.2498	5.5974
5.4	8.3640	7.1980	6.2964	5.5827	5.0064
5.5	7.4305	6.4093	5.6168	4.9877	4.4784
5.6	6.6033	5.7084	5.0116	4.4569	4.0067
5.7	5.8701	5.0855	4.4725	3.9832	3.5852
5.8	5.2199	4.5316	3.9922	3.5604	3.2084
5.9	4.6431	4.0390	3.5641	3.1830	2.8716
6.0	4.1313	3.6008	3.1826	2.8460	2.5704
6.1	3.6768	3.2109	2.8424	2.5451	2.3012
6.2	3.2733	2.8638	2.5390	2.2763	2.0603
6.3	2.9148	2.5547	2.2683	2.0362	1.8449
6.4	2.5962	2.2795	2.0269	1.8217	1.6522
6.5	2.3130	2.0343	1.8115	1.6300	1.4798
6.6	2.0612	1.8158	1.6192	1.4586	1.3256
6.7	1.8372	1.6211	1.4475	1.3055	1.1875
6.8	1.6379	1.4476	1.2942	1.1685	1.0639
6.9	1.4606	1.2928	1.1573	1.0461	0.9533
7.0	1.3027	1.1548	1.0351	0.9366	0.8543
7.1	1.1621	1.0371	0.9259	0.8386	0.7656
7.2	10.3692 (−5)	9.2188 (−5)	8.2831 (−5)	7.5100 (−5)	6.8622 (−5)
7.3	9.2540	8.2387	7.4112	6.7261	6.1511
7.4	8.2602	7.3640	6.6319	6.0247	5.5142
7.5	7.3745	6.5831	5.9353	5.3970	4.9437
7.6	6.5849	5.8859	5.3125	4.8352	4.4326
7,7	5.8809	5.2633	4.7556	4.3323	3.9747
7.8	5.2530	4.7072	4.2576	3.8821	3.5644
7.9	4.6930	4.2104	3.8122	3.4790	3.1967
8.0	4.1933	3.7666	3.4138	3.1181	2.8672
8.1	3.7474	3.3700	3.0573	2.7949	2.5719
8.2	3.3494	3.0155	2.7384	2.5054	2.3071
8.3	2.9942	2.6986	2.4530	2.2461	2.0698
8.4	2.6770	2.4154	2.1975	2.0138	1.8570
8.5	2.3937	2.1621	1.9689	1.8057	1.6662
8.6	2.1408	1.9356	1.7642	1.6192	1.4952
8.7	1.9148	1.7331	1.5810	1.4521	1.3418
8.8	1.7129	1.5519	1.4169	1.3024	1.2042
8.9	1.5325	1.3898	1.2700	1.1682	1.0808
9.0	1.3712 (−5)	1.2447 (−5)	1.1384 (−5)	1.0479 (−5)	0.9701 (−5)
9.1	1.2271	1.1150	1.0205	0.9400	0.8708
9.2	10.9825 (−6)	9.9881 (−6)	9.1492)	8.4335 (−6)	7.8169 (−6)
9.3	9.8306	8.9485	8.2033	7.5668	7.0177
9.4	8.8004	8.0179	7.3558	6.7896	6.3006
9.5	7.8791	7.1848	6.5965	6.0927	5.6571
9.6	7.0551	6.4388	5.9160	5.4677	5.0797
9.7	6.3179	5.7709	5.3061	4.9071	4.5614
9.8	5.6583	5.1727	4.7595	4.4044	4.0963
9.9	5.0681	4.6369	4.2695	3.9533	3.6788
10.0	4.5400	4.1570	3.8302	3.5488	3.3041

*The figures in parentheses in this table indicate the power of ten by which the numbers to the left, and those below in the same column, are to be multiplied.

Table 8.91—TABLE OF SECANT INTEGRALS OF THE FIRST KIND*

$$F(\theta,b) = \int_0^\theta e^{-b\sec\theta'}d\theta'$$

b	θ = 1°	θ = 2°	θ = 3°	θ = 4°	θ = 5°	θ = 6°	θ = 8°	θ = 10°
0.5	1.058569 -2	2.116976 -2	3.175061 -2	4.232661 -2	5.289615 -2	6.345758 -2	8.454959 -2	1.055894 -1
1.0	6.420381 -3	1.283881 -2	1.925332 -2	2.566196 -2	3.206276 -2	3.845375 -2	5.119843 -2	6.388010 -2
1.5	3.894059 -3	7.786339 -3	1.167506 -2	1.555844 -2	1.943470 -2	2.330206 -2	3.100293 -2	3.864677 -2
2.0	2.361806 -3	4.722174 -3	7.079664 -3	9.432839 -3	1.178026 -2	1.412050 -2	1.877369 -2	2.338099 -2
2.5	1.432472 -3	2.863852 -3	4.293052 -3	5.718983 -3	7.140559 -3	8.556697 -3	1.136835 -2	1.414540 -2
3.0	8.688159 -4	1.736838 -3	2.603273 -3	3.467331 -3	4.328223 -3	5.185165 -3	6.884089 -3	8.557944 -3
3.5	5.269501 -4	1.053339 -3	1.578605 -3	2.102189 -3	2.623537 -3	3.142095 -3	4.168657 -3	5.177571 -3
4.0	3.196033 -4	6.388172 -4	9.572535 -4	1.274525 -3	1.590248 -3	1.904041 -3	2.524334 -3	3.132456 -3
4.5	1.938443 -4	3.874229 -4	5.804711 -4	7.727251 -4	9.639237 -4	1.153808 -3	1.528616 -3	1.895161 -3
5.0	1.175695 -4	2.349600 -4	3.519932 -4	4.684915 -4	5.842794 -4	6.991833 -4	9.256590 -4	1.146594 -3
5.5	7.130770 -5	1.424960 -4	2.134459 -4	2.840393 -4	3.541593 -4	4.236907 -4	5.605373 -4	6.937057 -4
6.0	4.324921 -5	8.641943 -5	1.294320 -4	1.722088 -4	2.146728 -4	2.567480 -4	3.394367 -4	4.197041 -4
6.5	2.623131 -5	5.241071 -5	7.848656 -5	1.044076 -4	1.301234 -4	1.555842 -4	2.055484 -4	2.539296 -4
7.0	1.590969 -5	3.178548 -5	4.759365 -5	6.330079 -5	7.887399 -5	9.428100 -5	1.244716 -4	1.536335 -4
7.5	9.649469 -6	1.927691 -5	2.886043 -5	3.837833 -5	4.780931 -5	5.713250 -5	7.537503 -5	9.295237 -5
8.0	5.852550 -6	1.169085 -5	1.750074 -5	2.326822 -5	2.897953 -5	3.462123 -5	4.564419 -5	5.623897 -5
8.5	3.549661 -6	7.090141 -6	1.061232 -5	1.410718 -5	1.756589 -5	2.097984 -5	2.764041 -5	3.402644 -5
9.0	2.152924 -6	4.299952 -6	6.435230 -6	8.552979 -6	1.064754 -5	1.271341 -5	1.673803 -5	2.058723 -5
9.5	1.305781 -6	2.607788 -6	3.902275 -6	5.185548 -6	6.453993 -6	7.704105 -6	1.013597 -5	1.245608 -5
10.0	7.919761 -7	1.581543 -6	2.366310 -6	3.143923 -6	3.912081 -6	4.668557 -6	6.138000 -6	7.536458 -6
10.5	4.803456 -7	9.591571 -7	1.434913 -6	1.906116 -6	2.371305 -6	2.829068 -6	3.716974 -6	4.559900 -6
11.0	2.913370 -7	5.816992 -7	8.701205 -7	1.155651 -6	1.437365 -6	1.714369 -6	2.250883 -6	2.758961 -6
11.5	1.767003 -7	3.527826 -7	5.276346 -7	7.006547 -7	8.712580 -7	1.038881 -6	1.363068 -6	1.669314 -6
12.0	1.071714 -7	2.139518 -7	3.199537 -7	4.247971 -7	5.281128 -7	6.295458 -7	8.254348 -7	1.010026 -6
12.5	6.500111 -8	1.297552 -7	1.940176 -7	2.575486 -7	3.201155 -7	3.814954 -7	4.998607 -7	6.111242 -7
13.0	3.942417 -8	7.869251 -8	1.176508 -7	1.561481 -7	1.940381 -7	2.311806 -7	3.027026 -7	3.697673 -7
13.5	2.391136 -8	4.772459 -8	7.134261 -8	9.467044 -8	1.176162 -7	1.400922 -7	1.833092 -7	2.237329 -7
14.0	1.450260 -8	2.894349 -8	4.326163 -8	5.739739 -8	7.129314 -8	8.489395 -8	1.110077 -7	1.353734 -7
14.5	8.796051 -9	1.755334 -8	2.623354 -8	3.479925 -8	4.321439 -8	5.144460 -8	6.722380 -8	8.191038 -8
15.0	5.334939 -9	1.064556 -8	1.590783 -8	2.109831 -8	2.619444 -8	3.117476 -8	4.070932 -8	4.956176 -8
15.5	3.235722 -9	6.456203 -9	9.646393 -9	1.279162 -8	1.587779 -8	1.889151 -8	2.465276 -8	2.998864 -8
16.0	1.962515 -9	3.915488 -9	5.849503 -9	7.755389 -9	9.624341 -9	1.144803 -8	1.492925 -8	1.814550 -8
16.5	1.190295 -9	2.374623 -9	3.547097 -9	4.701989 -9	5.833809 -9	6.937371 -9	9.040900 -9	1.097952 -8
17.0	7.219323 -10	1.440136 -9	2.150934 -9	2.850754 -9	3.536173 -9	4.203968 -9	5.475024 -9	6.643545 -9
17.5	4.378630 -10	8.733981 -10	1.304311 -9	1.728375 -9	2.143458 -9	2.547559 -9	3.315594 -9	4.019931 -9
18.0	2.655706 -10	5.296891 -10	7.909251 -10	1.047891 -9	1.299261 -9	1.543794 -9	2.007879 -9	2.432425 -9
18.5	1.610726 -10	3.212401 -10	4.796114 -10	6.353226 -10	7.875502 -10	9.355233 -10	1.215947 -9	1.471846 -9
19.0	9.769300 -11	1.948223 -10	2.908330 -10	3.851819 -10	4.773755 -10	5.669180 -10	7.363640 -10	8.906102 -10
19.5	5.925230 -11	1.181537 -10	1.763591 -10	2.335344 -10	2.893624 -10	3.435470 -10	4.459349 -10	5.389084 -10
20.0	3.593742 -11	7.165659 -11	1.069429 -10	1.415889 -10	1.753978 -10	2.081864 -10	2.700544 -10	3.260952 -10

b	θ = 15°	θ = 20°	θ = 25°	θ = 30°	θ = 35°	θ = 40°	θ = 45°	θ = 50°
0.5	1.578714 -1	2.095224 -1	2.603051 -1	3.099565 -1	3.581790 -1	4.046287 -1	4.489001 -1	4.905078 -1
1.0	9.520289 -2	1.257745 -1	1.553273 -1	1.835786 -1	2.102283 -1	2.349559 -1	2.574209 -1	2.772673 -1
1.5	5.741279 -2	7.550809 -2	9.270671 -2	1.087825 -1	1.235114 -1	1.366772 -1	1.480797 -1	1.575500 -1
2.0	3.462414 -2	4.533490 -2	5.534420 -2	6.449220 -2	7.263350 -2	7.964441 -2	8.543329 -2	8.995427 -2
2.5	2.088147 -2	2.722137 -2	3.304679 -2	3.825281 -2	4.275324 -2	4.648718 -2	4.942684 -2	5.158596 -2
3.0	1.259374 -2	1.634651 -2	1.973702 -2	2.269987 -2	2.518788 -2	2.717683 -2	2.866999 -2	2.970156 -2
3.5	7.595567 -3	9.816980 -3	1.179039 -2	1.347669 -2	1.485228 -2	1.591189 -2	1.667051 -2	1.716357 -2
4.0	4.581179 -3	5.896143 -3	7.044777 -3	8.004588 -3	8.765210 -3	9.329797 -3	9.715310 -3	9.951073 -3
4.5	2.763159 -3	3.541565 -3	4.210156 -3	4.756492 -3	5.177108 -3	5.477979 -3	5.673937 -3	5.786716 -3
5.0	1.666656 -3	2.127449 -3	2.516632 -3	2.827630 -3	3.060247 -3	3.220605 -3	3.320236 -3	3.374206 -3
5.5	1.005305 -3	1.278085 -3	1.504633 -3	1.681676 -3	1.810334 -3	1.895815 -3	1.946481 -3	1.972319 -3
6.0	6.064021 -4	7.678856 -4	8.997662 -4	1.000557 -3	1.071723 -3	1.117296 -3	1.143069 -3	1.155443 -3
6.5	3.657928 -4	4.613912 -4	5.381653 -4	5.955494 -4	6.349172 -4	6.592175 -4	6.723304 -4	6.782591 -4
7.0	2.206587 -4	2.772540 -4	3.219494 -4	3.546219 -4	3.764016 -4	3.893608 -4	3.960341 -4	3.988758 -4
7.5	1.331123 -4	1.666179 -4	1.926389 -4	2.112426 -4	2.232930 -4	2.302050 -4	2.336019 -4	2.349645 -4
8.0	8.030203 -5	1.001384 -4	1.152880 -4	1.258814 -4	1.325493 -4	1.362365 -4	1.379660 -4	1.386196 -4
8.5	4.844469 -5	6.018865 -5	6.900908 -5	7.504160 -5	7.873151 -5	8.069871 -5	8.157950 -5	8.189312 -5
9.0	2.922651 -5	3.617955 -5	4.131516 -5	4.475061 -5	4.679273 -5	4.784243 -5	4.829109 -5	4.844164 -5
9.5	1.763270 -5	2.174933 -5	2.473959 -5	2.669615 -5	2.782642 -5	2.838662 -5	2.861521 -5	2.868751 -5
10.0	1.063829 -5	1.307563 -5	1.481680 -5	1.593115 -5	1.655679 -5	1.685580 -5	1.697229 -5	1.700702 -5
10.5	6.418537 -6	7.861643 -6	8.875515 -6	9.510231 -6	9.856572 -6	1.001619 -5	1.007557 -5	1.009226 -5
11.0	3.872676 -6	4.727128 -6	5.317520 -6	5.679061 -6	5.870805 -6	5.956024 -6	5.986300 -6	5.994323 -6
11.5	2.336669 -6	2.842592 -6	3.186397 -6	3.392346 -6	3.498509 -6	3.544014 -6	3.559453 -6	3.563312 -6
12.0	1.409919 -6	1.709483 -6	1.909697 -6	2.027020 -6	2.085806 -6	2.110108 -6	2.117983 -6	2.119839 -6
12.5	8.507498 -7	1.028128 -6	1.144727 -6	1.211566 -6	1.244120 -6	1.257100 -6	1.261118 -6	1.262011 -6
13.0	5.133581 -7	6.183899 -7	6.862956 -7	7.243760 -7	7.424047 -7	7.493387 -7	7.513890 -7	7.518190 -7
13.5	3.097775 -7	3.719713 -7	4.115200 -7	4.332167 -7	4.432022 -7	4.469068 -7	4.479533 -7	4.481604 -7
14.0	1.869347 -7	2.237630 -7	2.467971 -7	2.591597 -7	2.646908 -7	2.666703 -7	2.672045 -7	2.673043 -7
14.5	1.128082 -7	1.346166 -7	1.480326 -7	1.550771 -7	1.581411 -7	1.591990 -7	1.594718 -7	1.595198 -7
15.0	6.807727 -8	8.099160 -8	8.880588 -8	9.282019 -8	9.451767 -8	9.508310 -8	9.522242 -8	9.524560 -8
15.5	4.108413 -8	4.873179 -8	5.328343 -8	5.557111 -8	5.651160 -8	5.681386 -8	5.688503 -8	5.689621 -8
16.0	2.479457 -8	2.932346 -8	3.197478 -8	3.327855 -8	3.379968 -8	3.396127 -8	3.399764 -8	3.400303 -8
16.5	1.496407 -8	1.764610 -8	1.919052 -8	1.993359 -8	2.022238 -8	2.030878 -8	2.032736 -8	2.032997 -8
17.0	9.031360 -9	1.061969 -8	1.151937 -8	1.194290 -8	1.210294 -8	1.214915 -8	1.215865 -8	1.215990 -8
17.5	5.450885 -9	6.391533 -9	6.915639 -9	7.157050 -9	7.245752 -9	7.270465 -9	7.275321 -9	7.275928 -9
18.0	3.289965 -9	3.847048 -9	4.152375 -9	4.289987 -9	4.339152 -9	4.352372 -9	4.354855 -9	4.355148 -9
18.5	1.985755 -9	2.315685 -9	2.493564 -9	2.572010 -9	2.599264 -9	2.606336 -9	2.607606 -9	2.607748 -9
19.0	1.198590 -9	1.393992 -9	1.497624 -9	1.542346 -9	1.557455 -9	1.561239 -9	1.561888 -9	1.561957 -9
19.5	7.234783 -10	8.392077 -10	8.995863 -10	9.250827 -10	9.334595 -10	9.354843 -10	9.358167 -10	9.358498 -10
20.0	4.367075 -10	5.052510 -10	5.404299 -10	5.549665 -10	5.596112 -10	5.606948 -10	5.608649 -10	5.608809 -10

*Note: The number with the minus sign appearing to the right of each value in the table indicates the power of 10 by which that value is to be multiplied.

Table 8.91—Continued

b	$\theta = 55°$		$\theta = 60°$		$\theta = 65°$		$\theta = 70°$		$\theta = 75°$		$\theta = 85°$		$\theta = 80°$		$\theta = 90°$	
0.5	5.288612	-1	5.632356	-1	5.927424	-1	6.163205	-1	6.328299	-1	6.415269	-1	6.436563	-1	6.436937	-1
1.0	2.941358	-1	3.076944	-1	3.176988	-1	3.241097	-1	3.272881	-1	3.282129	-1	3.282864	-1	3.282864	-1
1.5	1.649745	-1	1.703297	-1	1.737311	-1	1.754850	-1	1.761071	-1	1.762109	-1	1.762139	-1	1.762139	-1
2.0	9.322444	-2	9.534244	-2	9.650193	-2	9.698465	-2	9.710829	-2	9.712045	-2	9.712058	-2	9.712058	-2
2.5	5.302736	-2	5.386615	-2	5.426245	-2	5.439608	-2	5.442100	-2	5.442247	-2	5.442247	-2	5.442247	-2
3.0	3.033735	-2	3.066997	-2	3.080577	-2	3.084297	-2	3.084805	-2	3.084823	-2	3.084823	-2	3.084823	-2
3.5	1.744420	-2	1.757627	-2	1.762293	-2	1.763333	-2	1.763438	-2	1.763441	-2	1.763441	-2	1.763441	-2
4.0	1.007503	-2	1.012754	-2	1.014361	-2	1.014653	-2	1.014673	-2	1.014676	-2	1.014676	-2	1.014676	-2
4.5	5.841509	-3	5.862410	-3	5.867956	-3	5.868783	-3	5.868829	-3	5.868829	-3	5.868829	-3	5.868829	-3
5.0	3.398442	-3	3.406772	-3	3.408692	-3	3.408926	-3	3.408936	-3	3.408936	-3	3.408936	-3	3.408936	-3
5.5	1.983047	-3	1.986371	-3	1.987036	-3	1.987103	-3	1.987105	-3	1.987105	-3	1.987105	-3	1.987105	-3
6.0	1.160195	-3	1.161523	-3	1.161774	-3	1.161773	-3	1.161773	-3	1.161773	-3	1.161773	-3	1.161773	-3
6.5	6.803652	-4	6.808963	-4	6.809769	-4	6.809824	-4	6.809824	-4	6.809824	-4	6.809824	-4	6.809824	-4
7.0	3.998098	-4	4.000225	-4	4.000506	-4	4.000522	-4	4.000522	-4	4.000522	-4	4.000522	-4	4.000522	-4
7.5	2.353790	-4	2.354643	-4	2.354741	-4	2.354746	-4	2.354746	-4	2.354746	-4	2.354746	-4	2.354746	-4
8.0	1.388037	-4	1.388379	-4	1.388414	-4	1.388415	-4	1.388415	-4	1.388415	-4	1.388415	-4	1.388415	-4
8.5	8.197493	-5	8.198867	-5	8.198988	-5	8.198992	-5	8.198992	-5	8.198992	-5	8.198992	-5	8.198992	-5
9.0	4.847801	-5	4.848354	-5	4.848396	-5	4.848397	-5	4.848397	-5	4.848397	-5	4.848397	-5	4.848397	-5
9.5	2.870369	-5	2.870592	-5	2.870607	-5	2.870607	-5	2.870607	-5	2.870607	-5	2.870607	-5	2.870607	-5
10.0	1.701423	-5	1.701513	-5	1.701518	-5	1.701518	-5	1.701518	-5	1.701518	-5	1.701518	-5	1.701518	-5
10.5	1.009547	-5	1.009583	-5	1.009585	-5	1.009585	-5	1.009585	-5	1.009585	-5	1.009585	-5	1.009585	-5
11.0	5.995754	-6	5.995900	-6	5.995906	-6	5.995906	-6	5.995906	-6	5.995906	-6	5.995906	-6	5.995906	-6
11.5	3.563950	-6	3.564009	-6	3.564011	-6	3.564011	-6	3.564011	-6	3.564011	-6	3.564011	-6	3.564011	-6
12.0	2.120124	-6	2.120147	-6	2.120148	-6	2.120148	-6	2.120148	-6	2.120148	-6	2.120148	-6	2.120148	-6
12.5	1.262138	-6	1.262148	-6	1.262148	-6	1.262148	-6	1.262148	-6	1.262148	-6	1.262148	-6	1.262148	-6
13.0	7.518758	-7	7.518797	-7	7.518798	-7	7.518798	-7	7.518798	-7	7.518798	-7	7.518798	-7	7.518798	-7
13.5	4.481858	-7	4.481873	-7	4.481874	-7	4.481874	-7	4.481874	-7	4.481874	-7	4.481874	-7	4.481874	-7
14.0	2.673156	-7	2.673163	-7	2.673163	-7	2.673163	-7	2.673163	-7	2.673163	-7	2.673163	-7	2.673163	-7
14.5	1.595249	-7	1.595252	-7	1.595252	-7	1.595252	-7	1.595252	-7	1.595252	-7	1.595252	-7	1.595252	-7
15.0	9.524787	-8	9.524794	-8	9.524798	-8	9.524798	-8	9.524798	-8	9.524798	-8	9.524798	-8	9.524798	-8
15.5	5.689723	-8	5.689727	-8	5.689727	-8	5.689727	-8	5.689727	-8	5.689727	-8	5.689727	-8	5.689727	-8
16.0	3.400348	-8	3.400350	-8	3.400350	-8	3.400350	-8	3.400350	-8	3.400350	-8	3.400350	-8	3.400350	-8
16.5	2.033017	-8	2.033018	-8	2.033018	-8	2.033018	-8	2.033018	-8	2.033018	-8	2.033018	-8	2.033018	-8
17.0	1.215999	-8	1.216000	-8	1.216000	-8	1.216000	-8	1.216000	-8	1.216000	-8	1.216000	-8	1.216000	-8
17.5	7.275969	-9	7.275970	-9	7.275970	-9	7.275970	-9	7.275970	-9	7.275970	-9	7.275970	-9	7.275970	-9
18.0	4.355166	-9	4.355167	-9	4.355167	-9	4.355167	-9	4.355167	-9	4.355167	-9	4.355167	-9	4.355167	-9
18.5	2.607756	-9	2.607756	-9	2.607756	-9	2.607756	-9	2.607756	-9	2.607756	-9	2.607756	-9	2.607756	-9
19.0	1.561960	-9	1.561960	-9	1.561960	-9	1.561960	-9	1.561960	-9	1.561960	-9	1.561960	-9	1.561960	-9
19.5	9.358514	-10	9.358515	-10	9.358515	-10	9.358515	-10	9.358515	-10	9.358515	-10	9.358515	-10	9.358515	-10
20.0	5.608817	-10	5.608817	-10	5.608817	-10	5.608817	-10	5.608817	-10	5.608817	-10	5.608817	-10	5.608817	-10

Table 8.92—TABLE OF SECANT INTEGRALS OF THE SECOND KIND*

$$G(\theta,b) = b \int_0^\theta \sec \theta'\, e^{-b\sec\theta'}\, d\theta'$$

b	$\theta = 1°$		$\theta = 2°$		$\theta = 3°$		$\theta = 4°$		$\theta = 5°$		$\theta = 6°$		$\theta = 8°$		$\theta = 10°$	
0.5	5.293112	-3	1.058703	-2	1.588256	-2	2.118051	-2	2.648169	-2	3.178690	-2	4.241265	-2	5.306424	-2
1.0	6.420707	-3	1.284141	-2	1.926212	-2	2.568281	-2	3.210349	-2	3.852413	-2	5.136516	-2	6.420556	-2
1.5	5.841385	-3	1.168188	-2	1.752059	-2	2.335662	-2	2.918906	-2	3.501700	-2	4.665564	-2	5.826489	-2
2.0	4.723852	-3	9.446265	-3	1.416580	-2	1.888100	-2	2.359042	-2	2.829261	-2	3.766934	-2	4.699925	-2
2.5	3.581361	-3	7.161085	-3	1.073713	-2	1.430907	-2	1.787404	-2	2.143080	-2	2.851308	-2	3.554255	-2
3.0	2.606580	-3	5.211572	-3	7.813387	-3	1.041044	-2	1.300113	-2	1.558388	-2	2.071917	-2	2.580356	-2
3.5	1.844419	-3	3.687433	-3	5.527639	-3	7.363633	-3	9.194014	-3	1.101738	-2	1.463750	-2	1.821288	-2
4.0	1.278478	-3	2.555788	-3	3.830762	-3	5.102236	-3	6.369047	-3	7.630039	-3	1.012996	-2	1.259288	-2
4.5	8.723435	-4	1.743757	-3	2.613312	-3	3.480083	-3	4.343147	-3	5.201588	-3	6.900979	-3	8.571053	-3
5.0	5.878774	-4	1.175039	-3	1.760769	-3	2.344357	-3	2.925093	-3	3.502277	-3	4.643210	-3	5.761699	-3
5.5	3.922123	-4	7.838871	-4	1.174488	-3	1.563482	-3	1.950340	-3	2.334535	-3	3.092877	-3	3.834462	-3
6.0	2.595084	-4	5.186218	-4	7.769461	-4	1.034090	-3	1.289664	-3	1.543286	-3	2.043166	-3	2.530792	-3
6.5	1.705121	-4	3.407388	-4	5.103953	-4	6.791971	-4	8.468704	-4	1.013133	-3	1.340353	-3	1.658763	-3
7.0	1.113735	-4	2.225435	-4	3.333075	-4	4.434642	-4	5.528150	-4	6.611642	-4	8.740944	-4	1.080779	-3
7.5	7.237468	-5	1.446062	-4	2.165519	-4	2.880704	-4	3.590223	-4	4.292704	-4	5.671225	-4	7.006004	-4
8.0	4.682277	-5	9.354579	-5	1.400698	-4	1.862963	-4	2.321286	-4	2.774715	-4	3.663210	-4	4.521385	-4
8.5	3.017365	-5	6.027843	-5	9.024582	-5	1.200080	-4	1.494983	-4	1.786514	-4	2.356937	-4	2.906533	-4
9.0	1.937730	-5	3.870742	-5	5.794346	-5	7.703905	-5	9.594861	-5	1.146276	-4	1.511226	-4	1.861983	-4
9.5	1.240555	-5	2.477901	-5	3.708850	-5	4.930252	-5	6.139015	-5	7.332126	-5	9.659832	-5	1.189148	-4
10.0	7.920163	-6	1.581864	-5	2.367388	-5	3.146463	-5	3.917005	-5	4.676988	-5	6.157520	-5	7.573449	-5
10.5	5.043885	-6	1.007319	-5	1.507345	-5	2.003038	-5	2.493003	-5	2.975882	-5	3.915218	-5	4.811347	-5
11.0	3.204869	-6	6.399989	-6	9.575684	-6	1.272242	-5	1.583089	-5	1.889207	-5	2.483825	-5	3.049691	-5
11.5	2.032157	-6	4.057823	-6	6.070561	-6	8.064034	-6	1.003206	-5	1.196866	-5	1.572493	-5	1.929075	-5
12.0	1.286122	-6	2.567942	-6	3.841192	-6	5.101679	-6	6.345314	-6	7.568153	-6	9.936553	-6	1.217931	-5
12.5	8.125551	-7	1.622268	-6	2.426323	-6	3.221954	-6	4.006468	-6	4.777272	-6	6.268000	-6	7.676159	-6
13.0	5.125402	-7	1.023210	-6	1.530157	-6	2.031562	-6	2.525660	-6	3.010752	-6	3.947550	-6	4.830277	-6
13.5	3.228197	-7	6.444125	-7	9.635633	-7	1.279081	-6	1.589811	-6	1.894643	-6	2.482472	-6	3.035004	-6
14.0	2.030468	-7	4.052910	-7	6.059384	-7	8.042110	-7	9.993552	-7	1.190649	-6	1.558999	-6	1.904376	-6
14.5	1.275492	-7	2.545749	-7	3.805594	-7	5.049957	-7	6.273397	-7	7.472849	-7	9.778085	-7	1.193422	-6
15.0	8.002815	-8	1.597157	-7	2.387259	-7	3.167296	-7	3.934086	-7	4.684597	-7	6.125563	-7	7.470001	-7
15.5	5.015624	-8	1.000914	-7	1.495871	-7	1.984298	-7	2.464138	-7	2.933430	-7	3.833155	-7	4.670537	-7
16.0	3.140183	-8	6.266050	-8	9.363459	-8	1.241861	-7	1.541821	-7	1.834963	-7	2.396158	-7	2.917178	-7
16.5	1.964087	-8	3.918922	-8	5.855370	-8	7.764525	-8	9.637821	-8	1.146714	-7	1.496412	-7	1.820275	-7
17.0	1.227347	-8	2.448727	-8	3.658250	-8	4.850179	-8	6.019007	-8	7.159519	-8	9.336598	-8	1.134786	-7
17.5	7.662991	-9	1.528756	-8	2.283582	-8	3.027087	-8	3.755737	-8	4.466190	-8	5.820379	-8	7.068344	-8
18.0	4.780513	-9	9.536334	-9	1.424312	-8	1.887720	-8	2.341590	-8	2.783788	-8	3.625435	-8	4.399149	-8
18.5	2.979994	-9	5.944146	-9	8.876840	-9	1.176291	-8	1.458786	-8	1.733805	-8	2.256496	-8	2.735814	-8
19.0	1.856261	-9	3.702373	-9	5.528336	-9	7.324448	-9	9.081447	-9	1.079064	-8	1.403436	-8	1.700158	-8
19.5	1.155478	-9	2.304464	-9	3.440563	-9	4.557578	-9	5.649601	-9	6.711097	-9	8.722698	-9	1.055829	-8
20.0	7.187849	-10	1.433422	-9	2.139829	-9	2.834052	-9	3.512328	-9	4.171137	-9	5.417815	-9	6.552606	-9

*Note: The number with the minus sign appearing to the right of each value in the table indicates the power of 10 by which that value is to be multiplied.

Table 8.92—Continued

b	θ = 15°	θ = 20°	θ = 25°	θ = 30°	θ = 35°	θ = 40°	θ = 45°	θ = 50°
0.5	7.984883 -2	1.069371 -1	1.344305 -1	1.624296 -1	1.910301 -1	2.203177 -1	2.503560 -1	2.811653 -1
1.0	9.629901 -2	1.283643 -1	1.603619 -1	1.922213 -1	2.238280 -1	2.550033 -1	2.854775 -1	3.148524 -1
1.5	8.710604 -2	1.155742 -1	1.435047 -1	1.706953 -1	1.968943 -1	2.217866 -1	2.449795 -1	2.659936 -1
2.0	7.003805 -2	9.250471 -2	1.141768 -1	1.348055 -1	1.541109 -1	1.717805 -1	1.874746 -1	2.008428 -1
2.5	5.279624 -2	6.941873 -2	8.518427 -2	9.985727 -2	1.131950 -1	1.249556 -1	1.349140 -1	1.428901 -1
3.0	3.820805 -2	5.001486 -2	6.102524 -2	7.104508 -2	7.989209 -2	8.740773 -2	9.347544 -2	9.804580 -2
3.5	2.688339 -2	3.503686 -2	4.251296 -2	4.916557 -2	5.487136 -2	5.954152 -2	6.313678 -2	6.568395 -2
4.0	1.852977 -2	2.404552 -2	2.901839 -2	3.334544 -2	3.695056 -2	3.979376 -2	4.188107 -2	4.327226 -2
4.5	1.257270 -2	1.624582 -2	1.950203 -2	2.227265 -2	2.451510 -2	2.621925 -2	2.741243 -2	2.816070 -2
5.0	8.425647 -3	1.084154 -2	1.294744 -2	1.469967 -2	1.607741 -2	1.708638 -2	1.776020 -2	1.815785 -2
5.5	5.590168 -3	7.163295 -3	8.511672 -3	9.608813 -3	1.044690 -2	1.103839 -2	1.141519 -2	1.162449 -2
6.0	3.678357 -3	4.694261 -3	5.550500 -3	6.231825 -3	6.737472 -3	7.081404 -3	7.290422 -3	7.399714 -3
6.5	2.403632 -3	3.055145 -3	3.595110 -3	4.015297 -3	4.318278 -3	4.516905 -3	4.632073 -3	4.688770 -3
7.0	1.561407 -3	1.976765 -3	2.315277 -3	2.572895 -3	2.753382 -3	2.867431 -3	2.930527 -3	2.959777 -3
7.5	1.009146 -3	1.272603 -3	1.483744 -3	1.640894 -3	1.747872 -3	1.813032 -3	1.847432 -3	1.862451 -3
8.0	6.493352 -4	8.157027 -4	9.468175 -4	1.042260 -3	1.105391 -3	1.142459 -3	1.161135 -3	1.168816 -3
8.5	4.161936 -4	5.208427 -4	6.019471 -4	6.596887 -4	6.968026 -4	7.178106 -4	7.279127 -4	7.318265 -4
9.0	2.658445 -4	3.314446 -4	3.814418 -4	4.162560 -4	4.380010 -4	4.498676 -4	4.553143 -4	4.573026 -4
9.5	1.692890 -4	2.102847 -4	2.410116 -4	2.619385 -4	2.746407 -4	2.813239 -4	2.842522 -4	2.852595 -4
10.0	1.075069 -4	1.330560 -4	1.518881 -4	1.644331 -4	1.718331 -4	1.755872 -4	1.771575 -4	1.776666 -4
10.5	6.810325 -5	8.398625 -5	9.549975 -5	1.030017 -4	1.073024 -4	1.094061 -4	1.102463 -4	1.105031 -4
11.0	4.304519 -5	5.289689 -5	5.992022 -5	6.439648 -5	6.689046 -5	6.806687 -5	6.851548 -5	6.864474 -5
11.5	2.715152 -5	3.324969 -5	3.752526 -5	4.019077 -5	4.163418 -5	4.229076 -5	4.252985 -5	4.259481 -5
12.0	1.709436 -5	2.086203 -5	2.346002 -5	2.504436 -5	2.587823 -5	2.624405 -5	2.637126 -5	2.640385 -5
12.5	1.074405 -5	1.306785 -5	1.464379 -5	1.558391 -5	1.606486 -5	1.626834 -5	1.633593 -5	1.635226 -5
13.0	6.742153 -6	8.173148 -6	9.127611 -6	9.684599 -6	9.961569 -6	1.007459 -5	1.011045 -5	1.011862 -5
13.5	4.224712 -6	5.104628 -6	5.681859 -6	6.011384 -6	6.170666 -6	6.233360 -6	6.252360 -6	6.256445 -6
14.0	2.643689 -6	3.184014 -6	3.532639 -6	3.727335 -6	3.818818 -6	3.853551 -6	3.863607 -6	3.865647 -6
14.5	1.652266 -6	1.983643 -6	2.193936 -6	2.308830 -6	2.361311 -6	2.380531 -6	2.385848 -6	2.386865 -6
15.0	1.031439 -6	1.234432 -6	1.361136 -6	1.428860 -6	1.458932 -6	1.469558 -6	1.472366 -6	1.472873 -6
15.5	6.431839 -7	7.673958 -7	8.436537 -7	8.835310 -7	9.007458 -7	9.066137 -7	9.080955 -7	9.083481 -7
16.0	4.006684 -7	4.765963 -7	5.224464 -7	5.459039 -7	5.557489 -7	5.589866 -7	5.597679 -7	5.598936 -7
16.5	2.493569 -7	2.957253 -7	3.232667 -7	3.370526 -7	3.426779 -7	3.444628 -7	3.448744 -7	3.449370 -7
17.0	1.550491 -7	1.833403 -7	1.998693 -7	2.079642 -7	2.111757 -7	2.121589 -7	2.123756 -7	2.124067 -7
17.5	9.632780 -8	1.135748 -7	1.234863 -7	1.282357 -7	1.300677 -7	1.306090 -7	1.307230 -7	1.307384 -7
18.0	5.979844 -8	7.030417 -8	7.624297 -8	7.902733 -8	8.007168 -8	8.036939 -8	8.042935 -8	8.043702 -8
18.5	3.709396 -8	4.348854 -8	4.704430 -8	4.867549 -8	4.927040 -8	4.943407 -8	4.946557 -8	4.946938 -8
19.0	2.299374 -8	2.688318 -8	2.901065 -8	2.996562 -8	3.030429 -8	3.039420 -8	3.041075 -8	3.041264 -8
19.5	1.424379 -8	1.660791 -8	1.787996 -8	1.843868 -8	1.863136 -8	1.868073 -8	1.868942 -8	1.869035 -8
20.0	8.817915 -9	1.025398 -8	1.101409 -8	1.134077 -8	1.145033 -8	1.147743 -8	1.148199 -8	1.148245 -8

b	θ = 55°	θ = 60°	θ = 65°	θ = 70°	θ = 75°	θ = 80°	θ = 85°	θ = 90°
0.5	3.126825 -1	3.446842 -1	3.766389 -1	4.074193 -1	4.347613 -1	4.545201 -1	4.619651 -1	4.622095 -1
1.0	3.425515 -1	3.677600 -1	3.893741 -1	4.060322 -1	4.164517 -1	4.205435 -1	4.210236 -1	4.210244 -1
1.5	2.842646 -1	2.991780 -1	3.101729 -1	3.169770 -1	3.200063 -1	3.206801 -1	3.207083 -1	3.207083 -1
2.0	2.115635 -1	2.194165 -1	2.244017 -1	2.268872 -1	2.276827 -1	2.277861 -1	2.277877 -1	2.277877 -1
2.5	1.487917 -1	1.526736 -1	1.547983 -1	1.556546 -1	1.558533 -1	1.558688 -1	1.558689 -1	1.558689 -1
3.0	1.011668 -1	1.030115 -1	1.038831 -1	1.041679 -1	1.042162 -1	1.042185 -1	1.042185 -1	1.042185 -1
3.5	6.728980 -2	6.814311 -2	6.849164 -2	6.858424 -2	6.859580 -2	6.859613 -2	6.859613 -2	6.859613 -2
4.0	4.408222 -2	4.446940 -2	4.460627 -2	4.463592 -2	4.463865 -2	4.463870 -2	4.463870 -2	4.463870 -2
4.5	2.856313 -2	2.873628 -2	2.878932 -2	2.879870 -2	2.879935 -2	2.879936 -2	2.879936 -2	2.879936 -2
5.0	1.835546 -2	1.843204 -2	1.845239 -2	1.845534 -2	1.845549 -2	1.845549 -2	1.845549 -2	1.845549 -2
5.5	1.172063 -2	1.175419 -2	1.176194 -2	1.176286 -2	1.176290 -2	1.176290 -2	1.176290 -2	1.176290 -2
6.0	7.446128 -3	7.460740 -3	7.463670 -3	7.463957 -3	7.463965 -3	7.463965 -3	7.463965 -3	7.463965 -3
6.5	4.711038 -3	4.717362 -3	4.718465 -3	4.718554 -3	4.718556 -3	4.718556 -3	4.718556 -3	4.718556 -3
7.0	2.970405 -3	2.973128 -3	2.973542 -3	2.973570 -3	2.973570 -3	2.973570 -3	2.973570 -3	2.973570 -3
7.5	1.867500 -3	1.868669 -3	1.868823 -3	1.868832 -3	1.868832 -3	1.868832 -3	1.868832 -3	1.868832 -3
8.0	1.171206 -3	1.171705 -3	1.171763 -3	1.171766 -3	1.171766 -3	1.171766 -3	1.171766 -3	1.171766 -3
8.5	7.329540 -4	7.331670 -4	7.331885 -4	7.331893 -4	7.331893 -4	7.331893 -4	7.331893 -4	7.331893 -4
9.0	4.578330 -4	4.579236 -4	4.579316 -4	4.579318 -4	4.579318 -4	4.579318 -4	4.579318 -4	4.579318 -4
9.5	2.855084 -4	2.855469 -4	2.855498 -4	2.855499 -4	2.855499 -4	2.855499 -4	2.855499 -4	2.855499 -4
10.0	1.777832 -4	1.777995 -4	1.778006 -4	1.778006 -4	1.778006 -4	1.778006 -4	1.778006 -4	1.778006 -4
10.5	1.105576 -4	1.105645 -4	1.105649 -4	1.105649 -4	1.105649 -4	1.105649 -4	1.105649 -4	1.105649 -4
11.0	6.867016 -5	6.867307 -5	6.867322 -5	6.867323 -5	6.867323 -5	6.867323 -5	6.867323 -5	6.867323 -5
11.5	4.260665 -5	4.260788 -5	4.260794 -5	4.260794 -5	4.260794 -5	4.260794 -5	4.260794 -5	4.260794 -5
12.0	2.640936 -5	2.640988 -5	2.640990 -5	2.640990 -5	2.640990 -5	2.640990 -5	2.640990 -5	2.640990 -5
12.5	1.635482 -5	1.635504 -5	1.635505 -5	1.635505 -5	1.635505 -5	1.635505 -5	1.635505 -5	1.635505 -5
13.0	1.011981 -5	1.011990 -5	1.011991 -5	1.011991 -5	1.011991 -5	1.011991 -5	1.011991 -5	1.011991 -5
13.5	6.256997 -6	6.257035 -6	6.257036 -6	6.257036 -6	6.257036 -6	6.257036 -6	6.257036 -6	6.257036 -6
14.0	3.865902 -6	3.865919 -6	3.865919 -6	3.865919 -6	3.865919 -6	3.865919 -6	3.865919 -6	3.865919 -6
14.5	2.386984 -6	2.386991 -6	2.386991 -6	2.386991 -6	2.386991 -6	2.386991 -6	2.386991 -6	2.386991 -6
15.0	1.472928 -6	1.472930 -6	1.472930 -6	1.472930 -6	1.472930 -6	1.472930 -6	1.472930 -6	1.472930 -6
15.5	9.083735 -7	9.083747 -7	9.083747 -7	9.083747 -7	9.083747 -7	9.083747 -7	9.083747 -7	9.083747 -7
16.0	5.599053 -7	5.599058 -7	5.599058 -7	5.599058 -7	5.599058 -7	5.599058 -7	5.599058 -7	5.599058 -7
16.5	3.449426 -7	3.449426 -7	3.449426 -7	3.449426 -7	3.449426 -7	3.449426 -7	3.449426 -7	3.449426 -7
17.0	2.124092 -7	2.124093 -7	2.124093 -7	2.124093 -7	2.124093 -7	2.124093 -7	2.124093 -7	2.124093 -7
17.5	1.307396 -7	1.307396 -7	1.307396 -7	1.307396 -7	1.307396 -7	1.307396 -7	1.307396 -7	1.307396 -7
18.0	8.043755 -8	8.043756 -8	8.043756 -8	8.043756 -8	8.043756 -8	8.043756 -8	8.043756 -8	8.043756 -8
18.5	4.946963 -8	4.946963 -8	4.946963 -8	4.946963 -8	4.946963 -8	4.946963 -8	4.946963 -8	4.946963 -8
19.0	3.041275 -8	3.041275 -8	3.041275 -8	3.041275 -8	3.041275 -8	3.041275 -8	3.041275 -8	3.041275 -8
19.5	1.869041 -8	1.869041 -8	1.869041 -8	1.869041 -8	1.869041 -8	1.869041 -8	1.869041 -8	1.869041 -8
20.0	1.148248 -8	1.148248 -8	1.148248 -8	1.148248 -8	1.148248 -8	1.148248 -8	1.148248 -8	1.148248 -8

FIG. 8.111—Partially erected calcium borate shield for Fermi 30-in. sodium pipe.

$$y(x) = x - \frac{x^3}{3!} + \frac{x^5}{5!} - \frac{x^7}{7!} + \frac{x^9}{9!} - \cdots \quad (8.166)$$

Because of the frequent occurrence of this solution in physical and mathematical problems and its relation to trigonometry, the function $y(x)$ has been called the familiar sine function, i.e., $y = \sin x$ (x in radian measure). Because of the widespread use of the **sine** function, extensive tables have been prepared giving the values of $\sin x$ for many values of x. These tables are prepared by actually evaluating the above series to the required significant figures.

Similarly, the function $u(x)$, which satisfies the differential equation

$$\frac{d^2u}{dx^2} + \frac{1}{x}\frac{du}{dx} + \left(1 - \frac{n^2}{x^2}\right)u = 0 \quad (8.167)$$

where n is some fixed number, occurs often in physical problems. Because of the frequent occurrence of this function, $u(x)$, satisfying the above differential equation, the solutions for each value of n have been given the name Bessel functions of

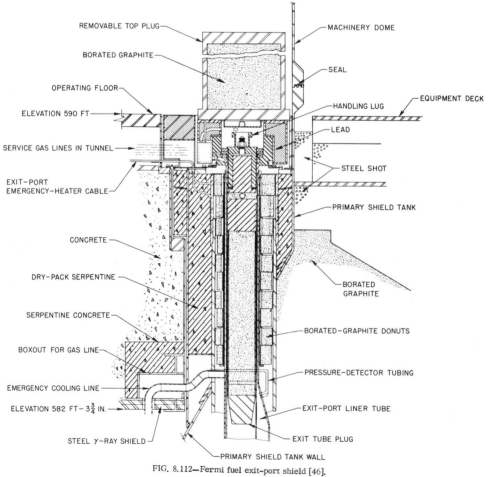

FIG. 8.112—Fermi fuel exit-port shield [46].

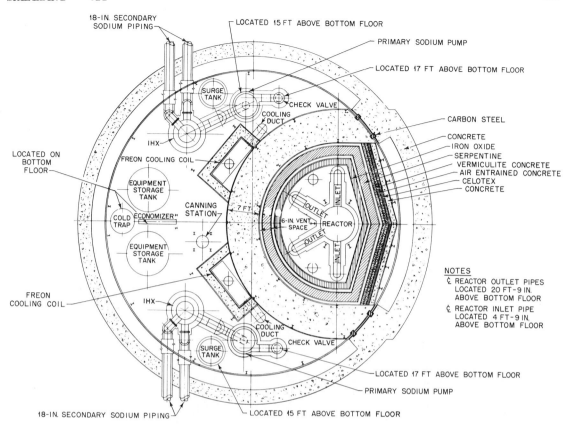

FIG. 8.113--Plan view of PFFBR 150-Mw(e) electric plant [98].

order n. The value of n in the differential equation will always depend on the physical problem of concern and may have integer, noninteger, or imaginary values. Furthermore, for any one value of n, there are several different series that satisfy Eq. 8.165. For n having integer values, the infinite series

$$J_n(x) = \frac{x^n}{2^n n!}\left[1 - \frac{x^2}{2(2n+2)} + \frac{x^4}{8(2n+2)(2n+4)} - \cdots\right]$$

$$(8.168)$$

is called the Bessel function of the first kind of order n. For $n=0$, the series becomes*

$$J_0(x) = 1 - \frac{x^2}{4} + \frac{x^4}{64} - \frac{x^6}{2304} + \frac{x^8}{147456} - \cdots$$

$$(8.169)$$

The Bessel functions of the first kind of orders 0 and 1 [$J_0(x)$ and $J_1(x)$] are plotted in Fig. 8.116 for values of x from 0 to 10. Values of $J_0(x)$ and $J_1(x)$ are given in Table 8.93.

As can be seen from Fig. 8.116, the Bessel functions of the first kind are oscillatory functions

which decrease in amplitude. It is often useful to know for what values of x the functions become equal to zero. Table 8.94 gives the first ten values of x for Bessel functions up to order $n=5$. Another property of the Bessel functions of integer order is

$$J_n(-x) = (-1)^n J_n(x) \qquad (8.170)$$

A similar infinite series for n having integer values, which is a solution to the differential equation

$$\frac{d^2 u}{dx^2} + \frac{1}{x}\left(\frac{du}{dx}\right) - \left(1 + \frac{n^2}{x^2}\right) = 0$$

has been given the symbol $K_n(x)$ and is called the Bessel function of the second kind of order n. Values of $K_0(x)$, $K_1(x)$, $K_2(x)$, and $K_3(x)$ are given in Table 8.95.

Consider the problem of evaluating

$$K_0\left\{\mu\left[d^2 + \left(\frac{2y-L}{2}\right)^2\right]^{1/2}\right\} \qquad (8.171)$$

where $\mu = 0.1$ cm^{-1}
$d = 3$ cm
$y = 6$ cm
$L = 20$ cm

---

*0! = 1.

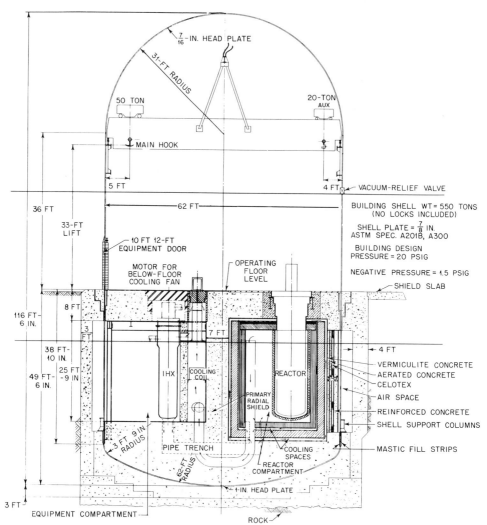

FIG. 8.114—Reactor containment building (elevation) for the 150-Mw(e) plant showing shielding [98].

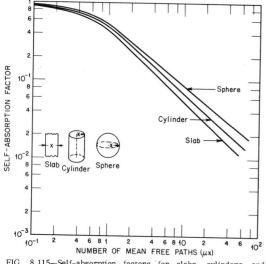

FIG. 8.115—Self-absorption factors for slabs, cylinders, and spheres as a function of the number of mean free paths [3].

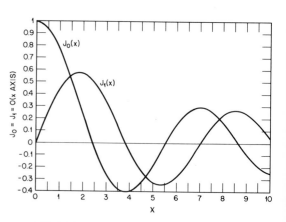

FIG. 8.116—Graph of Bessel function $J_0(x)$ and $J_1(x)$.

Table 8.93—Bessel Functions $J_0(x)$ and $J_1(x)$

x	$J_0(x)$	$J_1(x)$	x	$J_0(x)$	$J_1(x)$	x	$J_0(x)$	$J_1(x)$
0.0	1.0000	.0000	5.0	−.1776	−.3276	10.0	−.2459	.0435
0.1	.9975	.0499	5.1	−.1443	−.3371	10.1	−.2490	.0184
0.2	.9900	.0995	5.2	−.1103	−.3432	10.2	−.2496	−.0066
0.3	.9776	.1483	5.3	−.0758	−.3460	10.3	−.2477	−.0313
0.4	.9604	.1960	5.4	−.0412	−.3453	10.4	−.2434	−.0555
0.5	.9395	.2423	5.5	−.0068	−.3414	10.5	−.2366	−.0789
0.6	.9120	.2867	5.6	.0270	−.3343	10.6	−.2276	−.1012
0.7	.8812	.3290	5.7	.0599	−.3241	10.7	−.2164	−.1224
0.8	.8463	.3688	5.8	.0917	−.3110	10.8	−.2032	−.1422
0.9	.8075	.4059	5.9	.1220	−.2951	10.9	−.1881	−.1603
1.0	.7652	.4401	6.0	.1506	−.2767	11.0	−.1712	−.1768
1.1	.7196	.4709	6.1	.1773	−.2559	11.1	−.1528	−.1913
1.2	.6711	.4983	6.2	.2017	−.2329	11.2	−.1330	−.2039
1.3	.6201	.5220	6.3	.2238	−.2081	11.3	−.1121	−.2143
1.4	.5669	.5419	6.4	.2433	−.1816	11.4	−.0902	−.2225
1.5	.5118	.5579	6.5	.2601	−.1538	11.5	−.0677	−.2284
1.6	.4554	.5699	6.6	.2740	−.1250	11.6	−.0446	−.2320
1.7	.3980	.5778	6.7	.2851	−.0953	11.7	−.0213	−.2333
1.8	.3400	.5815	6.8	.2931	−.0652	11.8	.0020	−.2323
1.9	.2818	.5812	6.9	.2981	−.0349	11.9	.0250	−.2290
2.0	.2239	.5767	7.0	.3001	−.0047	12.0	.0477	−.2234
2.1	.1666	.5683	7.1	.2991	.0252	12.1	.0697	−.2157
2.2	.1104	.5560	7.2	.2951	.0543	12.2	.0908	−.2060
2.3	.0555	.5399	7.3	.2882	.0826	12.3	.1108	−.1943
2.4	.0025	.5202	7.4	.2786	.1096	12.4	.1296	−.1807
2.5	−.0484	.4971	7.5	.2663	.1352	12.5	.1469	−.1655
2.6	−.0968	.4708	7.6	.2516	.1592	12.6	.1626	−.1487
2.7	−.1424	.4416	7.7	.2346	.1813	12.7	.1766	−.1307
2.8	−.1850	.4097	7.8	.2154	.2014	12.8	.1887	−.1114
2.9	−.2243	.3754	7.9	.1944	.2192	12.9	.1988	−.0912
3.0	−.2601	.3391	8.0	.1717	.2346	13.0	.2069	−.0703
3.1	−.2921	.3009	8.1	.1475	.2476	13.1	.2129	−.0489
3.2	−.3202	.2613	8.2	.1222	.2580	13.2	.2167	−.0271
3.3	−.3443	.2207	8.3	.0960	.2657	13.3	.2183	−.0052
3.4	−.3643	.1792	8.4	.0692	.2708	13.4	.2177	.0166
3.5	−.3801	.1374	8.5	.0419	.2731	13.5	.2150	.0380
3.6	−.3918	.0955	8.6	.0146	.2728	13.6	.2101	.0590
3.7	−.3992	.0538	8.7	−.0125	.2697	13.7	.2032	.0791
3.8	−.4026	.0128	8.8	−.0392	.2641	13.8	.1943	.0984
3.9	−.4018	−.0272	8.9	−.0653	.2559	13.9	.1836	.1165
4.0	−.3971	−.0660	9.0	−.0903	.2453	14.0	.1711	.1334
4.1	−.3887	−.1033	9.1	−.1142	.2324	14.1	.1570	.1488
4.2	−.3766	−.1386	9.2	−.1367	.2174	14.2	.1414	.1626
4.3	−.3610	−.1719	9.3	−.1577	.2004	14.3	.1245	.1747
4.4	−.3423	−.2028	9.4	−.1768	.1816	14.4	.1065	.1850
4.5	−.3205	−.2311	9.5	−.1939	.1613	14.5	.0875	.1934
4.6	−.2961	−.2566	9.6	−.2090	.1395	14.6	.0679	.1999
4.7	−.2693	−.2791	9.7	−.2218	.1166	14.7	.0476	.2043
4.8	−.2404	−.2985	9.8	−.2323	.0928	14.8	.0271	.2066
4.9	−.2097	−.3147	9.9	−.2403	.0684	14.9	.0064	.2069

The argument of the Bessel function is

$$x = \mu \left[d^2 + \left(\frac{2y - L}{2} \right)^2 \right]^{1/2}$$

$$= (0.1 \,\mathrm{cm}^{-1}) \sqrt{9 \,\mathrm{cm}^2 + \left[\frac{12 - 20}{2} \right]^2 \,\mathrm{cm}^2}$$

$$= 0.5$$

From Table 8.95 we see that, for $x = 0.5$, $K_0(x) = 0.9244191$, which is the result sought.

For other Bessel functions and their applications and additional tables of values of Bessel functions, see A Treatise on the Theory of Bessel Functions, G. N. Watson, Cambridge University Press, 1958.

Table 8.94—Roots of $J_n(x_s) = 0$

s	$n = 0$	$n = 1$	$n = 2$	$n = 3$	$n = 4$
1	2.405	3.832	5.135	6.379	7.586
2	5.520	7.016	8.419	9.760	11.064
3	8.654	10.173	11.620	13.017	14.373
4	11.792	13.323	14.796	16.224	17.616
5	14.931	16.470	17.960	19.410	20.827
6	18.071	19.616	21.117	22.583	24.018
7	21.212	22.760	24.270	25.749	27.200
8	24.353	25.903	27.421	28.909	30.371
9	27.494	29.047	30.571	32.050	33.512
10	30.635	32.190	33.717	35.219	36.699

Table 8.95—Table of Bessel Functions

Values of $K_n(x)$

x	$K_0(x)$	$K_1(x)$	$K_2(x)$	$K_3(x)$	x
0.1	2.4270690	9.8538448	199.5039646	7990.0124305	0.1
0.2	1.7527039	4.7759725	49.5124293	995.0245583	0.2
0.3	1.3724601	3.0559920	21.7457403	292.9991958	0.3
0.4	1.1145291	2.1843544	12.0363013	122.5473670	0.4
0.5	0.9244191	1.6564411	7.5501836	62.0579095	0.5
0.6	0.7775221	1.3028349	5.1203052	35.4382031	0.6
0.7	0.6605199	1.0502835	3.6613300	21.9721690	0.7
0.8	0.5653471	0.8617816	2.7198012	14.4607876	0.8
0.9	0.4867303	0.7165336	2.0790271	9.9566542	0.9
1.0	0.4210244	0.6019072	1.6248389	7.1012628	1.0
1.1	0.3656024	0.5097600	1.2924388	5.2095375	1.1
1.2	0.3185082	0.4345924	1.0428289	3.9106886	1.2
1.3	0.2782476	0.3725475	0.8513976	2.9922325	1.3
1.4	0.2436551	0.3208359	0.7019921	2.3265275	1.4
1.5	0.2138056	0.2773878	0.5836560	1.8338037	1.5
1.6	0.1879548	0.2406339	0.4887471	1.4625018	1.6
1.7	0.1654963	0.2093625	0.4118051	1.1783157	1.7
1.8	0.1459314	0.1826231	0.3488460	0.9578363	1.8
1.9	0.1288460	0.1596602	0.2969093	0.7847324	1.9
2.0	0.1138939	0.1398659	0.2537598	0.6473854	2.0
2.1	0.1007837	0.1227464	0.2176851	0.5373847	2.1
2.2	0.0892690	0.1078968	0.1873570	0.4485459	2.2
2.3	0.0791399	0.0949824	0.1617334	0.3762579	2.3
2.4	0.0702173	0.0837248	0.1399880	0.3170382	2.4
2.5	0.0623476	0.0738908	0.1214602	0.2682271	2.5
2.6	0.0553983	0.0652840	0.1056168	0.2277714	2.6
2.7	0.0492554	0.0577384	0.0920246	0.1940711	2.7
2.8	0.0438200	0.0511127	0.0803290	0.1658685	2.8
2.9	0.0390062	0.0452864	0.0702383	0.1421668	2.9
3.0	0.0347395	0.0401564	0.0615105	0.1221704	3.0
3.1	0.0309547	0.0356341	0.0539444	0.1052398	3.1
3.2	0.0275950	0.0316429	0.0473718	0.0908577	3.2
3.3	0.0246106	0.0281169	0.0416512	0.0786032	3.3
3.4	0.0219580	0.0249990	0.0366633	0.0681323	3.4
3.5	0.0195989	0.0222394	0.0323071	0.0591618	3.5
3.6	0.0174996	0.0197950	0.0284968	0.0514581	3.6
3.7	0.0156307	0.0176280	0.0251593	0.0448273	3.7
3.8	0.0139659	0.0157057	0.0222321	0.0391079	3.8
3.9	0.0124823	0.0139993	0.0196614	0.0341649	3.9
4.0	0.0111597	0.0124835	0.0174014	0.0298849	4.0
4.1	0.0099800	0.0111363	0.0154123	0.0261727	4.1
4.2	0.0089275	0.0099382	0.0136599	0.0229477	4.2
4.3	0.0079880	0.0088722	0.0121146	0.0201416	4.3
4.4	0.0071491	0.0079233	0.0107506	0.0176965	4.4
4.5	0.0063999	0.0070781	0.0095475	0.0155631	4.5
4.6	0.0057304	0.0063250	0.0084804	0.0136993	4.6
4.7	0.0051321	0.0056538	0.0075380	0.0120691	4.7
4.8	0.0045972	0.0050552	0.0067036	0.0106415	4.8
4.9	0.0041189	0.0045212	0.0059643	0.0093900	4.9
5.0	0.0036911	0.0040446	0.0053089	0.0082918	5.0

Glossary

A	atomic weight, grams/mole, area
A_n	atomic weight, of nth nuclear species
a	area, cm^2, sq in., sq ft
$a(\gamma)$	fractional gamma-ray yields
B	arbitrary constant
$B(\mu x)$	gamma buildup function
b	arbitrary constant
c_p	heat capacity, cal/g/°C
C	conversion factor, gammas/cm^2/sec to r/hr
c	arbitrary constant
D	dose rate, r/hr
d	distance, cm, in., or ft
E	modulus of elasticity, psi
E'	modulus of elasticity, psi
E	energy, ev, Mev, cal, or Btu
E'	energy/gram
$E_n(x)$	exponential integral
e	electrostatic unit of charge on a electron, esu
F	arbitrary constant
$F(t)$	relaxation release rate, sec^{-1}
f	arbitrary constant
f_n	fractional yield
G	arbitrary constant
g	weight, grams
H	heat-generation rate, Mev/cm^3/sec, watts/cm^3, Btu/cu ft/hr
H_1	heat transfer coefficient, Btu/hr/sq ft/°F
h	Planck's constant, 6.625×10^{-27} erg/sec
I	arbitrary constant
$I_n(x)$	neutron current, neutrons/cm^2/sec
i	an integer

J	current, neutrons/cm²/sec		ρ	density, g/cm³
$J_n(x)$	Bessel function, first kind, order n		Σ	macroscopic cross section, cm⁻¹
j	an integer		σ	microscopic cross section, cm²/atom, barns
$K_n(x)$	Bessel function, second kind, order n		τ	average time, sec
k	thermal conductivity, cal/sec/cm/°C, Btu/hr/ft/°F		ϕ	neutron flux, neutrons/cm²/sec
L	distance, ft, in., or cm		$\phi(E)$	neutron energy flux, Mev/cm²/sec
M	isotropic mass of scattering medium		Φ	vector flux, neutrons/cm²/sec/steradian
M_1	arbitrary constant		Ψ	scattering angle
m	mass, grams		Ω	solid-angle unit vector
$m(\gamma)$	m th gamma ray		Ω	solid angle
N_0	Avogadro's number, atoms/mole		ω	arbitrary constant
N	atoms or nuclei/cm³		ϵ	half width of a hole for neutrons

N_1	total number of incident neutrons
n	an integer
P	load, lb/ft
P_m	moderating ratio
p	arbitrary constant, offset function
Q	heat flux, Btu/hr/sq ft
q	arbitrary constant, angular neutron source density
R_E	energy reflection coefficient
R_n	number reflection coefficient
R	radius
R_ϕ	increase in neutron flux
r	radius
$r(\gamma)$	r th gamma ray
S_0	point source strength, particles/sec
S_V	volume source strength, dis/cm³/sec
S_{VC}	volume source strength, curies/cm
s_n	distance along pipe axis
T	temperature, °C or °F
u	variable
t	time, sec
V	volume, cm³
v	velocity, cm/sec
W	arbitrary constant
w	probability of scattering
x	distance, ft, cm
Y	arbitrary constant
y	arbitrary constant
Z	atomic number, length or width, cm
z	length, cm
α'	energy, ergs
α''	energy, ergs
α	albedo
α_1	arbitrary constant
β	arbitrary constant
β'	arbitrary constant
β_0	arbitrary constant
β_1	arbitrary constant
γ	Poisson's ratio for concrete
$\Gamma(E)$	gamma flux, gammas/cm²/sec
ΓE	gamma energy flux, Mev/cm²/sec
Δ	an arbitrary constant
$\delta(x)$	Dirac delta function
ζ	linear coefficient of thermal expansion for concrete, in./in./°F
η	particles/cm³
θ	angle
λ	mean free path, relaxation length, cm
λ'	decay constant, sec⁻¹
κ	neutron-attenuation coefficient, cm⁻¹
μ	linear absorption coefficient, cm⁻¹; also used to abbreviate micro-
ν	frequency, sec⁻¹
ξ	average logarithmic energy decrement per collision, $\ln E_0/E$, E_0 is initial energy, and E is energy considered

Conversion Factors

cm × 0.3937	= in.
cm × 0.03281	= ft
cm² × 1.08 × 10⁻³	= sq ft
cm³ × 3.5314 × 10⁻⁵	= cu ft
1.8°C + 32	= °F
g × 2.2046 × 10⁻³	= lb
(g/cm³) × 62.428	= lb/cu ft
watts × 3.4137	= Btu/hr
(watts/g) × 1548	= Btu/hr/lb
(watts/cm³) × 9.67 × 10⁴	= Btu/hr/cu ft
cal × 3.9685 × 10⁻³	= Btu
(cal/g) × 1.8000	= Btu/lb
(cal/sec/g) × 6480	= Btu/hr/lb
(cal/g/°C) × 1.000	= Btu/lb/°F
(cal/sec/cm/°C) × 241.90	= Btu/hr/ft/°F
(μohm-cm) × 0.3937	= μohm-in.

References

1. H. E. Hungerford and R. F. Mantey, Shielding the Enrico Fermi Fast Breeder Reactor, Nucleonics, 16:11 (November 1958).
2. H. V. Lichtenberger et al., Operating Experience and Experimental Results Obtained from a NaK-Cooled Fast Reactor, in Proceedings of the First United Nations International Conference on the Peaceful Uses of Atomic Energy, Geneva, 1955, Vol. 3, p. 345, United Nations, New York, 1956.
3. H. E. Hungerford, Activity of Sodium and Its Impurities, private communication to R. S. Grettum, May 28, 1956.
4. EBR Progress Report for April 1, 1951 through January 31, 1953, USAEC Report ANL-5023, Argonne National Laboratory, 1953.
5. T. Lyman (Ed.), Metals Handbook, 1948 edition, American Society for Metals, Cleveland, Ohio, 1948.
6. R. F. Miller and J. J. Hegger, Report on the Strength of Wrought Steels at Elevated Temperatures, Am. Soc. Testing Mater. Spec. Tech. Publ., No. 100 (1950).
7. What Heat Will Concrete Withstand Without Deterioration?, J. Am. Concrete Inst., 36:216-218 (November 1939).
8. A. E. Pavlish and J. C. Wynd, Concretes for Pile Shielding, USAEC Report AECD-3007, Battelle Memorial Institute, 1948.
9. R. P. Lambert, Determination of the Loss in Weight at Various Soaking Heat Temperatures of a Sample of Concrete Taken from the Secondary Shield Wall of the Enrico Fermi Power Plant, Report 61H75, Detroit Edison Company, Aug. 30, 1962.
10. J. H. Kittel, M. Novick, and R. F. Buchanan, The EBR-I Meltdown Physical and Metallurgical Changes in the Core, USAEC Report ANL-5731, Argonne National Laboratory, November 1957.
11. W. K. Woods, L. P. Bupp, and J. F. Fletcher, Irradiation Damage to Artificial Graphite, in Proceedings of the First United Nations International Conference on the Peaceful Uses of Atomic Energy, Geneva, 1955, Vol. 7, p. 455, United Nations, New York, 1956.
12. R. E. Nightingale, Irradiation Annealing in Graphite. I. An Experimental Study, USAEC Report HW-55274, Hanford Atomic Products Operation.
13. J. L. Dickson, G. H. Kinchin, R. F. Jackson, W. M. Lorner, and J. H. W. Simmonds, BEPO Wigner Energy Release, in Proceedings of the Second United Nations International Conference on the Peaceful Uses of Atomic Energy, Geneva, 1958, Vol. 7, p. 250, United Nations, New York, 1958.

14. US-UK Graphite Conference, St. Giles Court, London, England, December 16-18, 1957, USAEC Report TID-7565, Part 1, Mar. 16, 1959.

15. J. M. Davidson, Stored Energy in Irradiated Graphite, USAEC Report HW-55736, Hanford Atomic Products Operation.

16. H. Bridge, B. T. Kelly, and B. S. Gray, Stored Energy in Graphite and Reactor Degisn, Nucl. Eng., 7(70):91-96 (March 1962).

17. Title 10, Atomic Energy Rules and Regulations, Chapter 1, Atomic Energy Commission, Part 20, Standards for Protection Against Radiation, Federal Register, U. S. Government Printing Office, Nov. 17, 1960.

18. T. Rockwell III (Ed.), Reactor Shielding Design Manual, USAEC Report TID-7004, March 1956, U. S. Government Printing Office; also published by D. Van Nostrand Company, Inc., Princeton, N. J., 1956.

19. M. Grotenhuis, A. E. McArthy, and A. D. Rossin, Experimental Breeder Reactor-II (EBR-II) Shield Design, USAEC Report ANL-6614, Argonne National Laboratory, September 1962.

20. J. Adamson, AERE, private communication to H. E. Hungerford, APDA, 1961.

21. M. Grotenhuis, ANL, private communication to H. E. Hungerford, APDA.

22. Compiled by H. E. Hungerford from various sources.

23. H. Goldstein, The Attenuation of Gamma Rays and Neutrons in Reactor Shields, U. S. Government Printing Office, May 1, 1957; also published with corrections and revisions as Fundamental Aspects of Reactor Shielding, Addison-Wesley Publishing Company, Inc., Reading, Mass., 1959.

24. A. M. Weinberg and E. P. Wigner, The Physical Theory of Neutron Chain Reactors, University of Chicago Press, Chicago, Ill., 1958.

25. K. M. Case, F. de Hoffmann, and G. Placzek, Introduction to the Theory of Neutron Diffusion, Vol. I, U. S. Government Printing Office, June 1953.

26. B. Davison and J. B. Sykes, Neutron Transport Theory, Clarendon Press, Oxford, England, 1957.

27. S. Glasstone and M. C. Edlund, Elements of Nuclear Reactor Theory, D. Van Nostrand Company, Inc., New York, 1952.

28. H. A. Bethe, L. Tonks, and H. Hurwitz, Jr., Neutron Penetration and Slowing Down at Intermediate Distances Through Medium and Heavy Nuclei, Phys. Rev., 80:11 (1950).

29. B. T. Price, C. C. Horton, and K. T. Spinney, Radiation Shielding, Pergamon Press, London, England, 1957.

30. S. Glasstone, Principles of Nuclear Engineering, D. Van Nostrand Company, Inc., New York, 1955.

31. B. Carlson, Solution of the Transport Equation by S_n Approximation, USAEC Report LA-1891, Los Alamos Scientific Laboratory, 1955.

32. S. Preiser, G. Robinowitz, and E. de Dufour, A Program for the Numerical Integration of the Boltzmann Transport Equation—NIOBE, Report ARL-TR-60-314, Nuclear Development Associates, Inc., September 1960.

33. D. Yetman, B. Eisenman, and G. Robinowitz, Description of Input Preparation and Operating Procedures for 9-NIOBE, an IBM-7090 Code, Report NDA-2143-18, Nuclear Development Associates, Inc., and General Motors Corp., Aug. 31, 1961.

34. J. Certaine, A Solution of the Neutron Transport Problem, Part I, USAEC Report NYO-3081, July 25, 1954; Part II, USAEC Report NYO-6268, May 31, 1955; Part III; USAEC Report NYO-6270, July 31, 1956.

35. H. Yamauchi, Slowing Down of Neutrons in Non-Hydrogenous Multilayer Shield, Report NDA-14-71, Nuclear Development Associates, July 15, 1955.

36. R. F. Christy, The Slowing Down of Neutrons, Lecture Series in Nuclear Physics, Lecture 39, Report MDDC-1175, U. S. Government Printing Office, December 1947.

37. H. E. Hungerford, A Modified Straight Ahead Approximation to Diffusion Theory for Neutron Transmission Calculations, paper delivered before The American Nuclear Society, Second Winter Meeting, October 28-31, 1957.

38. H. Kahn, Random Sampling (Monte Carlo) Techniques in Neutron Attenuation Problem (Rev. I), Nucleonics, 6(5):27 (1950).

39. H. Kahn, Random Sampling (Monte Carlo) Techniques in Neutron Attenuation Problems (II), Nucleonics, 6(6):50 (1950).

40. A. S. Householder, Principles of Numerical Analysis, pp. 242-246, McGraw-Hill Book Company, Inc., New York, 1953.

41. Monte Carlo Method, U. S. National Bureau of Standards, Applied Mathematics Series, No. 12, June 11, 1951.

42. H. Kahn, Application of Monte Carlo, USAEC Report AECU-3259, RAND Corporation, Apr. 19, 1954.

43. C. N. Klahr, Calculations of Neutron Distributions by Methods of Stochastic Processes, Nucl. Sci. Eng., 3:269 (March 1958).

44. H. Goldstein and J. E. Wilkins, Jr., Calculations of The Penetration of Gamma-Rays, USAEC Report NYO-3075, Nuclear Development Associates, Inc., June 30, 1954.

45. Enrico Fermi Atomic Power Plant, Report APDA-124, Atomic Power Development Associates, Inc., January 1959.

46. Enrico Fermi Atomic Power Plant, Technical Information and Hazards Summary Report, 3, Power Reactor Development Company, June 1961.

47. H. E. Hungerford, R. I. Beaudry, and W. F. Chaltron, Detailed Conceptual Design of The Graphite Primary Shield for The Enrico Fermi Fast Breeder Reactor, APDA Technical Memorandum No. 23, Atomic Power Development Associates, Inc., Dec. 15, 1959.

48. H. Yamauchi, Preliminary Calculations for the APDA Shield Design, USAEC Report NDA-14-72, Nuclear Development Associates, Inc., May 9, 1955.

49. H. E. Hungerford, A Study of the Primary Shield for the Enrico Fermi Atomic Power Reactor, unnumbered APDA report, Apr. 2, 1957.

50. E. P. Blizard (Ed.), Reactor Handbook, 2nd ed., Vol. III, Part B, Shielding, Interscience Publishers, New York, 1962.

51. H. E. Hungerford, Introduction to Shielding, lecture notes on shielding given in an APDA nuclear engineering course, 1958.

52. J. F. Hogerton and R. F. Grass (Eds.), The Reactor Handbook, 1st ed., Vol. 1, Physics, USAEC Report AECD-3645, March 1955.

53. R. F. Mantey, Temperature Distribution and Thermal Stresses in a Concrete Shield due to Gamma Radiation, paper delivered before The American Nuclear Society, Fourth Annual Meeting, Los Angeles, California, June 2-5, 1958.

54. F. P. Storrer, APDA, private communication to R. F. Mantey, APDA.

55. Edward Fisher, Streaming of Neutrons in Shields, Nucl. Sci. Eng., 1:222-238 (1956).

56. R. D. Schamberger, F. J. Shore, and H. P. Sleeper, The Transmission of Neutrons and Gamma Rays Through Air Slots, Parts I-X, USAEC Reports BNL-2019 to BNL-2028, Brookhaven National Laboratory, 1954.

57. A. Simon and C. E. Clifford, The Attenuation of Neutrons by Air Ducts in Shields, USAEC Report ORNL-1217, Oak Ridge National Laboratory, Mar. 8, 1954.

58. J. W. Crawford, Jr., E. E. Kintner, and Clark Goodman, The Effect of Ducts on the Attenuation of Neutrons and Gamma-Rays in the MIT Cyclotron Shield, Nuclear Shielding Studies, Part VII, Laboratory for Nuclear Science and Engineering, Massachusetts Institute of Technology, Technical Report 38, September 1950.

59. G. M. Roe, The Penetration of Neutrons Through a Shield, USAEC Report KAPL-712, Knolls Atomic Power Laboratory, Mar. 29, 1952.

60. C. C. Horton and D. B. Halliday, The Attenuation of Thermal Neutrons in Cylindrical Ducts Through A Water Shield, British Report SWP/P-28, 1956.

61. D. C. Piercey and D. E. Bendall, The Transmission of Fast Neutrons Along Air-Filled Ducts in Water, British Report AEEW-R-69, June 1962.

62. D. C. Piercey, The Transmission of Thermal Neutrons Along Air-Filled Ducts in Water, British Report AEEW-R-70, June 1962.

63. K. Spinney, AERE, private communication to H. E. Hungerford, APDA, 1962.

64. Duct Streaming, Transactions of the American Nuclear Society, November 1962. Two sessions held by the Shielding Division of the American Nuclear Society Meeting, November 1962. Summaries of 10 papers given in the transactions.

65. E. B. Roth, E. P. Cooper, J. R. Gallagher, and J. C. Greene (Eds.), NRDL-OCDM Shielding Symposium Proceedings, October 31-November 1, 1960, Reviews and U. S. Naval Radiological Defense Laboratory and Office of Civil and Defense Mobilization.

66. H. E. Hungerford, Transmission of Monoenergetic Neutrons Around a Bend in a Pipe Carrying a Scattering and Weakly Absorbing Medium, paper delivered before the 1959 (Fifth) annual meeting of the American Nuclear Society, Gatlinburg, Tenn., June 15-17, 1959. Nucl. Sci. Eng. 2 (No. 1 Supplement) 33-34 (June 1959).

67. C. O. Zerby, A Monte Carlo Calculation of Air-Scattered Neutrons, USAEC Report ORNL-2277, Oak Ridge National Laboratory.

68. Applied Nuclear Physics Division Annual Progress Report For Period Ending September 1, 1957, USAEC Report ORNL-2389, Oak Ridge National Laboratory.

69. M. S. Plesset, Scattering of Gamma-Rays and Neutrons, Report RAD-196, Project RAND, Douglas Aircraft Corp., Aug. 29, 1947.

70. M. B. Wells, Monte Carlo Calculations of Fast Neutron Scattering in Air, USAEC Report NARF-60-8T, Vol. I, Convair, May 1960.

71. H. E. Hungerford, Air Scattering Experiments at the BSF, USAEC Report CF-52-7-37, Oak Ridge National Laboratory, July 1952. (Classified)

72. S. S. Holland and P. I. Richards, Scattered Neutron Flux Spectra in Air, J. Appl. Phys., 27:1042 (1956).

73. C. R. Mehl, A Monte Carlo Calculation of the Neutron Flux from a Monoenergetic Point Source in Air, USAEC Report SC-4174(TR), Sandia Corporation, April 1958.

74. B. L. Jones, J. W. Harris, and W. P. Kunkel, Air and Ground Scattering of Cobalt 60 Gamma Radiation, Report CVAC-170T, Consolidated Vultee Aircraft Corp., Mar. 30, 1955.

75. H. A. Bethe, Nuclear Physics, Part II, Nuclear Dynamics, Theoretical, Rev. Mod. Phys. 9:153 (April 1937).
76. E. Fermi, On The Motion of Neutrons in Hydrogenous Substances (English translation), Report NP-2385, 1951.
77. H. E. Hungerford, Some Ground Scattering Experiments Performed at the BSF, USAEC Report CF-52-4-99, Oak Ridge National Laboratory, April 1952.
78. R. B. Theus and L. A. Beach, Gamma-Ray Albedo from Iron, Report NRL-4701, Naval Research Laboratory, Feb. 8, 1956.
79. A. M. Judd, Radiation Survey Over The Fast Reactor, Dounreay Experimental Reactor Establishment, December 1960, unpublished.
80. H. E. Hungerford, Enrico Fermi Atomic Power Plant Shield Test Program, APDA Memos SHP-60-162-702, June 28, 1960, and SHP-60-180-0702, Atomic Power Development Associates, Inc., July 25, 1960.
81. C. R. Tipton, Jr. (Ed.), Reactor Handbook, 2nd ed., Vol. I, Materials, Interscience Publishers, New York, 1960.
82. H. A. Ohlgren, Cost Analysis for Materials Testing Reactor, National Reactor Testing Station, Idaho Operations Office, Aug. 24, 1954.
83. Handy-Whitman Index, Bulletin No. 65, Public Utility Construction Costs-Trends, Whitman, Requardt Associates, Baltimore, Md., Jan. 1, 1957.
84. Second Semiannual Financial Report of Power Reactor Development Company, as of June 30, 1959, Power Reactor Development Company, Sept. 10, 1959.
85. N. Scott, Commonwealth Associates, Inc., private communication to H. E. Hungerford, APDA, 1961.
86. J. F. Hogerton and R. F. Grass (Eds.), The Reactor Handbook, 1st ed., Vol. 3, Materials, USAEC Report AECD-3645, March 1955.
87. L. M. Currie, V. C. Hamister, and H. G. MacPherson, The Production and Properties of Graphite for Reactors, National Carbon Company, 1955.
88. N. A. Lange (Ed.), Handbook of Chemistry, 9th ed., Handbook Publishers, Inc., Sandusky, Ohio, 1956.
89. J. H. Perry (Ed.), Chemical Engineers Handbook, 3rd ed., McGraw-Hill Book Company, Inc., New York, 1950.
90. D. F. Minor and J. B. Seastone, Handbook of Engineering Materials, John Wiley & Sons, Inc., New York, 1955.
91. National Carbon Company, Catalogue S-5005, August 1951.
92. National Carbon Company, Catalogue S-4905, Apr. 6, 1956.
93. H. M. Epstein, D. A. Dingee, and J. W. Chastain, A Study of the Primary Shield for the PRDC Reactor, USAEC Report BMI-APDA-622, Battelle Memorial Institute, Apr. 15, 1957.
94. D. O. Leeser, Atomic Power Development Associates, Inc., Sept. 15, 1961, unpublished data.
95. W. G. Driscoll and J. G. Bell, Graphite, Its Properties and Behavior, Nucl. Eng. 3:479-485 (November 1958).
96. National Carbon Company, The Industrial Graphite Engineering Handbook, p. 5D02.02, Union Carbide Corporation, New York, 1962.
97. C. P. Zaleski and L. Vautrey, Le Reacteur Rapide Surregenerateur, Commissariat a l'Energie Atomique, Paris, France. Volumes I and II, Oct. 23, 1961.
98. 150-Mw Plutonium-Fueled Fast Breeder Atomic Power Plant, Report APDA-136, Atomic Power Development Associates, Inc., March 1960.
99. S. L. Hoyt (Ed.), Metal Properties, McGraw-Hill Book Company, Inc., New York, 1954.
100. R. E. Bailey and M. A. Silliman, Effects of Irradiation on the Type 347 Stainless Steel Flow Separator in the EBR-I Core, in Symposium on Radiation Effects on Materials, Vol. 3, p. 84, American Society for Testing Materials Special Publication 233, 1958.
101. R. Walker and M. Grotenhuis, A Summary of Shielding Constants for Concrete, USAEC Report ANL-6443, Argonne National Laboratory, November 1961.
102. Stainless Steel Handbook, Allegheny Ludlum Steel Corporation, Pittsburg, Penn., 1956.
103. E. J. Callon, Concretes for Radiation Shielding, J. Am. Concrete Inst., 25:1 (September 1953).
104. H. S. Davis, F. L. Browne, and H. C. Witter, Properties of High-Density Concrete Made with Iron Aggregate, J. Am. Concrete Inst., 27:705-726 (March 1956).
105. R. B. Gallaher and A. S. Kitzes, Summary Report on Portland Cement Concretes for Shielding, USAEC Report ORNL-1414, Oak Ridge National Laboratory, Feb. 7, 1953.
106. E. G. Peterson, Shielding Properties of Ferrophosphorous Concrete as A Function of Temperature, USAEC Report HW-64774, Hanford Atomic Products Operation, July 15, 1960.
107. E. G. Peterson, Shielding Properties of Ordinary Concrete as a Function of Temperature, USAEC Report HW-65572, Hanford Atomic Products Operation, Aug. 2, 1960.
108. T. V. Blosser et al., A Study of the Nuclear and Physical Properties of the ORNL Graphite Reactor Shield, USAEC Report ORNL-2195, Oak Ridge National Laboratory, Sept. 8, 1958.
109. R. E. Bell, C. H. Millar, and J. M. Robson, Canadian Report PD-246, 1951.

110. J. R. Harrison, A. M. Mills and D. Bendall, Distribution of Gamma-Rays and Neutrons in the Control Face Shield of BEPO, British Report AERE-RE-R-1604, 1955.
111. Applied Physics Division Annual Report for Period Ending September 10, 1956, USAEC Report ORNL-2081, Oak Ridge National Laboratory, Nov. 20, 1952.
112. C. E. Branyan, ANL, private communication to H. E. Hungerford, APDA, 1958.
113. R. F. Mantey and J. G. Feldes, Shielding and Waste Disposal Aspects of The Fuel Cleaning and Storage System at the Enrico Fermi Plant, paper delivered at the 1960 Winter Meeting of the American Nuclear Society, San Francisco, Calif. Dec. 11-15, 1960.
114. D. M. Wheeler and L. H. Bostick, Military Field Expedient Shielding Experiment, Report FZK-122, Convair Division, General Dynamics, Oct. 18, 1960.
115. H. E. Hungerford, R. F. Mantey, and L. P. Van Maele, New Shielding Materials for High-Temperature Applications, Nucl. Sci. Eng., 6:396-408 (November 1959).
116. W. H. Jens, trip report to HAPO, Richland, Washington, APDA Memo A-210, Atomic Power Development Associates, Inc., Apr. 4, 1963.
117. S. A. Tompkins, Johns-Manville Sales Corporation, private communication to R. C. Williams, APDA, Nov. 5, 1957.
118. S. A. Tompkins, Johns-Manville Sales Corporation, private communication to L. P. Van Maele, APDA, Nov. 27, 1957.
119. Toledo Testing Laboratory, Inc., Reports 308907 and 308987, Nov. 11, 1958, and 309587, Feb. 5, 1959.
120. R. R. Balsbaugh, APDA, private communication to H. E. Hungerford, APDA, September 1958.
121. H. E. Hungerford, R. F. Mantey, and L. Van Maele, New Shielding Materials for High Temperature Application, paper delivered before the American Nuclear Society Meeting, Detroit, Michigan, December 1958.
122. Detroit Edison Company Engineering Laboratory Report 58D11, Aug. 22, 1958.
123. R. R. Balsbaugh, report on conference between Johns-Manville Company and Atomic Power Development Associates, Inc., Feb. 11, 1957.
124. M. Daniels, Commonwealth Associates, Inc., trip report to Johns-Manville Corporation during temperature tests, Apr. 6, 1956, APDA project data.
125. F. Rough, Battelle Memorial Institute, monthly report on contract work to APDA, to A. P. Donnell, APDA, Columbus, Ohio, June 25, 1958.
126. Detroit Edison Company Engineering Laboratory Report 57E02.
127. R. N. Lyon (Ed.), Liquid-Metals Handbook, U. S. Government Printing Office, 1952.
128. S. Hoyt, Metals Data, 2nd ed., Reinhold Publishing Company, New York, 1952.
129. C. K. Taylor, Lor-Mac Associates, private communication to R. F. Mantey, APDA, Oct. 3, 1956.
130. Lor-Mac Associates, Technical Bulletin No. EP-56-62, Los Angeles, Calif., 1956.
131. A. S. Moseley, Permali, Inc., private communication to H. E. Hungerford, APDA, Feb. 9, 1961.
132. Permali, Inc., Brochure of Design Data and Information Sheets, Mount Pleasant, Penn., 1961.
133. D. E. Gray (Ed.), American Institute of Physics Handbook, McGraw-Hill Book Company, Inc., New York, 1957.
134. J. O. Blomeke and M. F. Todd, Uranium-235 Fission-Product Production as a Function of Thermal Neutron Flux, Irradiation Time, and Decay Time, Vols. I and II, USAEC Report ORNL-2127, Oak Ridge National Laboratory.
135. K. Way et al., Nuclear Level Schemes, USAEC Report TID-5300, June 1955.
136. Reactor Physics Constants, USAEC Report ANL-5800, Argonne National Laboratory, July 1, 1958.
137. C. D. Hodgmann (Ed.), Handbook of Chemistry and Physics, 35th ed., Chemical Rubber Publishing Co., Cleveland, 1955-1956.
138. C. A. Hampel, Rare Metals Handbook, Reinhold Publishing Company, New York, 1954.
139. C. B. Mills, Neutron Cross Sections for Fast and Intermediate Nuclear Reactors, USAEC Report LAMS-2255, Los Alamos Scientific Laboratory, October 1958.
140. G. T. Chapman and C. L. Storrs, Effective Neutron Removal Cross Sections for Shielding, USAEC Report ORNL-1843, Oak Ridge National Laboratory, Sept. 19, 1955.
141. J. M. Miller, Effective Removal Cross Section of Tungsten, USAEC Report ORNL-2389, p. 187, Oak Ridge National Laboratory, 1957.
142. D. J. Hughes and R. S. Schwartz, Neutron Cross Sections, 2nd ed., USAEC Report BNL-325, Brookhaven National Laboratory, July 1, 1958.
143. R. J. Howerton, Tabulated Neutron Cross Sections, USAEC Report UCRL-5226 (Part 1, Rev.), October 1959.
144. H. P. Flatt and D. C. Baller, The Aime-6 Code, Atomics International, January 1961.
145. G. W. Grodstein, X-Ray Attenuation Coefficients from 10 Kev to 100 Mev, Nat. Bur. Standards Circ. 583, Apr. 30, 1957.

146. J. Moteff, Miscellaneous Data for Shield Calculations, USAEC Report APEX-General Electric Company, December 1954.

147. W. S. Snyder and J. L. Powell, Absorption of Gamma-Rays, Supplement to USAEC Report ORNL-421, Oak Ridge National Laboratory, Mar. 4, 1958.

148. P. S. Mittelman, Gamma-Rays Resulting From Thermal Neutron Capture, Nucleonics, 13(5):50-51 (May 1955).

149. F. E. Deloume, Gamma-Ray Energy Spectra from Neutron Capture, USAEC Report DC-58-1-30, General Electric Company, Jan. 2, 1958.

150. E. Troubetzkay and H. Goldstein, Gamma-Rays from Thermal Neutron Capture, Nucleonics, 18(11):171-173 (November 1960).

151. J. F. Perkins and R. W. King, Energy Released from the Decay of Fission Products, Nucl. Sci. Eng., 3(6):726 (June 1958).

152. D. Strominger, J. M. Hollander, and G. T. Seaborg, Table of Isotopes, Rev. Mod. Phys., 30(2):585-904 (April 1958).

153. K. Way and E. P. Wigner, The Rate of Decay of Fission Products, Phys. Rev., 73:1318 (1948).

154. E. Garelis, APDA memorandum, Fuel Element Decay Heating, Mar. 26, 1958.

155. Permali, Inc., Mount Pleasant, Penn.

156. Nuclear Reactor Data-2, 2nd ed., Raytheon Manufacturing Company, Waltham, Mass., December 1956.

157. A. I. Leipunsky et al., Experimental Fast Reactor, in Proceedings of the Second United Nations International Conference on the Peaceful Uses of Atomic Energy, Geneva, 1958, Vol. 9, p. 348, United Nations, New York, 1958.

158. R. R. Matthews, Soviet Fast Reactor-BR-5, Nucl. Eng., 4(41):359 (October 1959).

159. A. H. Barnes et al., The Engineering Design of EBR-II, A Prototype Fast Neutron Reactor Power Plant, in Proceedings of the First United Nations International Conference on the Peaceful Uses of Atomic Energy, Geneva, 1955, Vol. 3, p. 330, United Nations, New York, 1956.

160. H. Cartwright et al., Dounreay Fast Reactor—Basic Problems in Design, in Proceedings of the Second United Nations International Conference on the Peaceful Uses of Atomic Energy, Geneva, 1958, Vol. 9, p. 316, United Nations, New York, 1958.

161. J. L. Koch et al., Construction Design of EBR-II, in Proceedings of the Second United Nations International Conference on the Peaceful Uses of Atomic Energy, Geneva, 1958, Vol. 9, p. 323, United Nations, New York, 1958.

162. J. L. Koch, Hazards Summary Report on EBR-II, USAEC Reports ANL-5719, May 1957, and ANL-5719 (Add.), Argonne National Laboratory.

163. J. R. Dietrich and W. H. Zinn (Eds.), Solid Fuel Reactors, Chap. 3, Addison-Wesley Publishing Company, Inc., Reading, Mass., 1958.

164. H. O. Monson and M. M. Sluyter, Containment of EBR-II, in Proceedings of the Second United Nations International Conference on the Peaceful Uses of Atomic Energy, Geneva, 1958, Vol. 11, p. 125, United Nations, New York, 1958.

165. A Plutonium-Fueled Fast Breeder Atomic Power Plant, Report APDA-129, Atomic Power Development Associates, Inc., Apr. 2, 1959.

166. G. Blanch and G. Placzek, The Functions $E_n(x)$, Canadian Report MT-1.

167. D. K. Trubey, A Table of Three Exponential Integrals, USAEC Report ORNL-2750, Oak Ridge National Laboratory, July 1959.

168. C. D. Zerby, Transmission of Obliquely Incident Gamma-Radiation Through Stratified Slab Barriers, USAEC Report ORNL-2224, Vol. I, Appendix B, Oak Ridge National Laboratory, 1956.

CHAPTER 9

Plant Instrumentation and Control

CLYDE C. SCOTT
Atomic Power Development Associates, Inc.
Detroit, Michigan

Contents

9.1 Control-system Design

9.1.1 REACTOR CONTROL

Nuclear reactor control can be defined as a process of changing the neutron-flux density to regulate the reactor power output to a desired value. Regulation of the neutron-flux density can be accomplished by manual or automatic means. A reactor-control system is a combination of instrumentation and auxiliary equipment operating as an integrated system to regulate the reactor power output. The control system is usually designed to be independent of the safety system.

The important parameters affecting the variation of reactor neutron density as a function of time are k, δk, λ_i, C_i, and l^*. Table 9.1 lists symbols, definitions, and units employed in reactor control.

These parameters are related to neutron density, n, by the following simplified equations:

$$\frac{dn}{dt} = \left(\frac{\delta k - \beta}{l^*} \right) n + \sum_{(i=1)}^{6} \lambda_i C_i \qquad (9.1)$$

$$\frac{dC_i}{dt} = \frac{\beta_i}{l^*} n - \lambda_i C_i \qquad (9.2)$$

9.1.2 REACTOR TRANSFER FUNCTION

The transfer-function concept of reactor neutron-density response to δk variations can be expressed by the following equation:

$$\frac{n'(s)}{\delta k (s)} = \frac{n_0}{l^* s \left\{ 1 + \sum_{i=1}^{6} \beta_i / [l^* (s + \lambda_i)] \right\}} \qquad (9.3)$$

where s is the Laplace transform operation and $n'(s)$ is the Laplace transform of n'.

The limitations for the above equation are stated in Refs. 2 and 3. The important parameters are l^* and β. Reference 4 shows the frequency-response curve of a reactor with $l^* = 10^{-4}$ sec as

Table 9.1—Instrumentation Control Nomenclature [1]

Symbol	Definition	Units
n	Neutron density	neutrons/cm^3
n'	Variations in neutron density from a specified density	neutrons/cm^3
n_0	Minimum reactor neutron density in the regulated range	neutrons/cm^3
n_d	Demand neutron density for regulation	neutrons/cm^3
$n\upsilon$	Neutron flux	neutrons/cm^2/sec
k	Ratio of the number of neutrons present at a given time to the number present one finite lifetime earlier	
δk	$k - 1$	
l^*	Mean effective neutron lifetime or the mean time that elapses from the time a neutron is produced until it returns to fission or is lost to the reaction	sec
β	Total fraction of delayed neutrons	
β_i	Fraction of delayed neutrons of group i	
	Decay constant for delayed-neutron emitter	sec^{-1}
i	Decay constant for delayed-neutron emitter of group i	sec^{-1}
C	Concentration of delayed-neutron emitter	neutrons/cm^3
C_i	Concentration of delayed-neutron emitter of group i	neutrons/cm^3
P	Power at time t	
P_0	Power at time $t = 0$	

well as a family of curves indicating the amplitude and phase shift of the reactor transfer function for different values for $l*$.

Typical values of $l*$ for different reactor types are shown in Table 9.2.

Table 9.2—Mean Neutron Lifetimes ($l*$)

Reactor type	$l*$, sec
Large graphite moderated	10^{-3}
Heavy-water moderated and cooled	2.3×10^{-3}
Natural-water moderated and cooled	5×10^{-4}
Sodium cooled, graphite moderated	3×10^{-4}
Sodium cooled, unmoderated	10^{-7}

The total delayed-neutron fractions for fast fission are shown in Table 9.3.

Table 9.3—Total Delayed-neutron Fractions for Fast Fission [6]

Nuclide	β
Th^{232}	0.022
U^{233}	0.0027 ± 0.0002
U^{235}	0.0065 ± 0.0003
U^{238}	0.0157 ± 0.0012
Pu^{239}	0.0021 ± 0.0002
Pu^{240}	0.0026 ± 0.0003
Pu^{241}	0.0053*
Pu^{242}	0.0080*

* Estimate by Argonne National Laboratory.

The delayed-neutron fraction, β, for U^{235} is about 8% smaller for fast fission than for thermal fission. However, the amount of U^{238} fission is larger in fast reactors, and, since β for U^{238} is higher than for U^{235}, the overall fraction of delayed neutrons in fast reactors is almost the same as in thermal reactors. The delayed-neutron periods and yields from fission by high-energy neutrons for Th^{232}, U^{233}, U^{235}, U^{238}, Pu^{239}, and Pu^{240} are shown in Table 9.4.

9.1.3 POWER COEFFICIENTS OF REACTIVITY

A change in reactor power may change the overall reactor temperature as well as the temperature distribution. If the reactivity changes as a result of changing power, the reactor is said to have a power coefficient of reactivity that is due to the change in temperature. In fast reactors all known power coefficients of reactivity are related to either temperatures or temperature gradients. Thermal reactors, on the other hand, may have power coefficients of reactivity that are due to other factors, e.g., changes in xenon concentration.

A reactor having a power coefficient of reactivity can be considered as part of a feedback loop, and the power coefficient of reactivity will influence control. If an increase in reactor power causes reactivity to increase, the power coefficient of reactivity is positive, and the loop has positive feedback. Conversely, if reactivity decreases with an increase in power, the reactor has a negative coefficient of reactivity, and the loop has a negative feedback. The power coefficient of reactivity

Table 9.4—Delayed-neutron Periods and Yields from Fission by High-energy Neutrons [5, 6]

Fissile isotope	Group	Half-life, sec	$\beta i/\beta$, % of delayed neutrons	Absolute yield, neutrons/fission
Th^{232}	1	56.03 ± 0.95	3.4 ± 0.2	0.00169
	2	20.75 ± 0.66	15.0 ± 0.5	0.00744
	3	5.74 ± 0.24	15.5 ± 2.1	0.00769
	4	2.16 ± 0.08	44.6 ± 1.5	0.02212
	5	0.571 ± 0.042	17.2 ± 1.3	0.00853
	6	0.211 ± 0.019	4.3 ± 0.6	0.00213
Total			100	0.0496 ± 0.0020
U^{233}	1	55.11 ± 1.86	8.6 ± 0.3	0.00060
	2	20.74 ± 0.86	27.4 ± 0.5	0.00192
	3	5.30 ± 0.19	22.7 ± 3.5	0.00159
	4	2.29 ± 0.18	31.7 ± 1.1	0.00222
	5	0.546 ± 0.108	7.3 ± 1.4	0.00051
	6	0.221 ± 0.042	2.3 ± 0.7	0.00016
Total			100	0.0070 ± 0.0004
U^{235}	1	54.51 ± 0.94	3.8 ± 0.3	0.00063
	2	21.84 ± 0.54	21.3 ± 0.5	0.00351
	3	6.00 ± 0.17	18.8 ± 1.6	0.00310
	4	2.23 ± 0.06	40.7 ± 0.7	0.00672
	5	0.496 ± 0.029	12.8 ± 0.8	0.00211
	6	0.179 ± 0.017	2.6 ± 0.3	0.00043
Total			100	0.0165 ± 0.0005
U^{238}	1	52.38 ± 1.29	1.3 ± 0.1	0.00054
	2	21.58 ± 0.39	13.7 ± 0.2	0.00564
	3	5.00 ± 0.19	16.2 ± 2.0	0.00667
	4	1.93 ± 0.07	38.8 ± 1.2	0.01599
	5	0.490 ± 0.023	22.5 ± 1.3	0.00927
	6	0.172 ± 0.009	7.5 ± 0.5	0.00309
Total			100	0.0412 ± 0.0017
Pu^{239}	1	53.75 ± 0.95	3.8 ± 0.3	0.00024
	2	22.29 ± 0.36	28.0 ± 0.4	0.00176
	3	5.19 ± 0.12	21.6 ± 1.8	0.00136
	4	2.09 ± 0.08	32.8 ± 1.0	0.00207
	5	0.549 ± 0.049	10.3 ± 0.9	0.00065
	6	0.216 ± 0.017	3.5 ± 0.5	0.00022
Total			100	0.0063 ± 0.0003
Pu^{240}	1	53.56 ± 1.21	2.8 ± 0.3	0.00022
	2	22.14 ± 0.38	27.3 ± 0.4	0.00238
	3	5.14 ± 0.42	19.2 ± 5.3	0.00162
	4	2.08 ± 0.19	35.0 ± 2.0	0.00315
	5	0.511 ± 0.077	12.8 ± 1.8	0.00119
	6	0.172 ± 0.033	2.9 ± 0.6	0.00024
Total			100	0.0088 ± 0.0006

is expressed as the ratio of reactivity change to the related power change [7]:

$$\text{Power coefficient of reactivity} = \frac{\delta k/k}{\delta P/P_0}$$

The power coefficients for fast reactors can be made small, negative, and rapid in response by proper design. These factors tend to produce coefficients that lead to stability. Table 9.5 lists the temperature and power coefficients for the Fermi and EBR-II reactors.

When present-day fast reactors are operating at powers high enough to produce sensible heat, programmed changes in the operating conditions should be made very slowly. The reactor and the entire heat-transport system should be operating in a quasi-steady state. For each set position of the controls, there is a corresponding equilibrium set of values of reactor power and of temperature throughout the system. In such an equilibrium condition, the reactivity is always zero; the inserted reactivity is exactly compensated by the thermal reactivity feedback.

Table 9.5—Temperature and Power Coefficients for Fermi and EBR-II

	Fermi [8]	EBR-II [9]
Isothermal temperature coefficients of reactivity	-1.99×10^{-5} $\Delta k/k/^{\circ}$C	-3.6×10^{-5} $\Delta k/k/^{\circ}$C
Power coefficients of reactivity	-1.64×10^{-5} $\Delta k/k/$Mw(t)	-3.2×10^{-5} $\Delta k/k/$Mw(t)* -6.0×10^{-5} $\Delta k/k/$Mw(t)†

* 0-22.5 Mw(t).
† 22.5-62.5 Mw(t).

A servo block diagram of a nuclear power plant with constant coolant flows is shown in Fig. 9.1. Feedback can be considered as the sum to two components: (1) the internal feedback, caused directly by a power change, assuming a constant reactor inlet temperature, and (2) the external feedback, caused by a change in the reactor inlet coolant temperature fed back around the coolant loop from a change of the reactor outlet coolant temperatures.

The reactor transfer function, G_P, at power P is

$$G_P = \frac{\delta P/P}{\delta R_i} = \frac{G_0}{1 - PG_0[X + (E_1 E_2 E_3/1 - E_2 E_4)]} \quad (9.4)$$

where G_0 = zero power reactor transfer function
  X = the internal power coefficient
  δR_i = inserted reactivity
  $\dfrac{E_1 E_2 E_3}{1 - E_2 E_4}$ = the external power coefficient

The power coefficient of reactivity, X, can be determined by the method developed in Ref. 10, and the transfer function E_1, E_3, and E_4 can be determined by one of the methods developed in Ref. 11

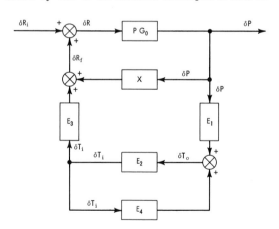

R_i = Inserted Reactivity
R_f = Feedback Reactivity
R = Total Reactivity = $R_i + R_f$
P = Reactor Power
T_o = Reactor Outlet Coolant Temperature
T_i = Reactor Inlet Coolant Temperature
G_0 = ($\delta P/P)/\delta R$ = Zero-power Reactor Transfer Function
X = Power Coefficient of Reactivity, Assuming Constant T_i
E_1 = $\delta R_f/\delta P$, Assuming Constant T_i
E_2 = $\delta T_i/\delta T_o$ = Transfer Function for the Transmission of a
          Temperature Signal Around the Coolant Loops
E_3 = $\delta R_f/\delta T_i$, Assuming Constant Power
E_4 = $\delta T_o/\delta T_i$, Assuming Constant Power

FIG. 9.1—Servo block diagram of a nuclear power plant.

selected for the desired accuracy. If a secondary heat-transport system is used between the primary coolant system and the feedwater and steam systems, the transfer function E_2 concerns the transmission of the reactor outlet temperature around both heat-transport systems, partly around the primary heat-transport system only and partly around the primary and secondary heat-transport systems in series.

9.1.4 REACTOR STABILITY

A reactor is said to be stable if, for any small disturbance, such as a change in coolant flow or movement of the control rods, and at powers up to and slightly above its design power level, the reactor response will tend to hold the power at a constant value that differs from the initial power by only a small amount. This implies also a definition of an unstable reactor. In the latter, a slight change in coolant flow or control-rod setting could cause a power excursion or an oscillation of increasing amplitude. Either type of behavior could result in core damage if it were not terminated quickly by the control system.

Every reactor should be designed to be stable. Two kinds of instability, namely, autocatalytic and oscillating instability, should be considered by the designer. The techniques for detecting these instabilities are well known because analogous effects occur in electronic and control circuits; in fact, the term autocatalytic effect is borrowed from chemical-reaction kinetics.

9.1.4.1 Autocatalytic Effects

A mechanism for autocatalytic instability exists if the net temperature coefficient in a reactor is positive. Thus an increase in reactor power leads to an increase in reactivity, which causes further a rise in power and thereby results in a power excursion.

When the power in a reactor is increased slowly, with respect to the time constants of the system, only the total temperature coefficient is important. Thus, a reactor with a temperature coefficient that is net negative even though it has positive components will be safe under these conditions. However, if the power in a reactor is increased rapidly, owing to a sudden increase in reactivity, the fuel will be heated more quickly than will be the coolant and the structure. Consequently, if the fuel has a positive temperature coefficient, the reactor could be autocatalytic even if the coolant and structure temperature coefficients were large and negative. The long time constants of the coolant and structure would prohibit their negative temperature coefficients from responding quickly enough to counteract the prompt positive temperature coefficient of the fuel.

Two possible autocatalytic mechanisms are the Doppler effect and bowing of the fuel elements. The probability of a neutron's causing fission in, or being captured by, a nucleus is dependent on their relative velocities. At certain relative velocities the interaction probabilities are much higher than average. These probability maxima are called resonances. If the fuel nuclei were at rest, then on a graph of capture or fission-interaction probability vs. neutron speed the resonances would show up as very tall but narrow peaks.

The nuclei are not at rest, however, but vibrate owing to thermal agitation. The nuclei have a statistical distribution of speeds; the average speed increases with increasing fuel temperature. The result of this distribution is that neutrons having velocities slightly different from one of the peak interaction velocities, v_0, can interact with nuclei having a motion such that their relative velocity is v_0. The overall effect of the thermal agitation is to decrease the heights and increase the widths of the resonances. This is called Doppler broadening of resonances.

When the fuel temperature increases, Doppler broadening of capture and fission resonances promptly changes the reactivity. The Doppler temperature coefficient is defined as the fractional change in k, due to Doppler broadening, caused by a 1°C rise in fuel temperature. Doppler broadening of fission resonances in U^{235}, Pu^{239}, or U^{233} increases k, whereas broadening of capture resonances in both fissile and fertile material decreases k. The overall Doppler coefficient is the sum of these effects; thus, in a fast reactor highly enriched in U^{235} isotope, the coefficient would be positive, but, in a moderately enriched reactor, it would be negative. The Doppler effect, however, decreases rapidly with increasing neutron speed. A small highly enriched fast reactor will normally have very few low-speed neutrons; so, although the Doppler coefficient is positive, it is small in magnitude. As the enrichment, i.e., U^{235} to U^{238} ratio, is decreased and the size of the core is increased, the proportion of low-speed neutrons increases, and the Doppler coefficient goes from small positive through zero to small negative and, in the case of very large fast reactors, to significantly large negative values.

Bowing is the term applied to certain behavior of the fuel pins. Consider a fuel pin that is held fixed at its lower and upper ends. When a reactor operates, the side of the fuel pin which is closer to the center of the reactor will become hotter than the side away from the center. This will make the inner side expand, relative to the outer, and the fuel pin will bow. Since its top and bottom are fixed with the top vertically above the bottom, the middle of the fuel pin will move closer to the center of the reactor, which makes the core more compact and increases reactivity. The designer must take the necessary precautions to prevent bowing from causing a net positive temperature coefficient of reactivity that will produce reactor instability.

9.1.4.2 Oscillating Instability

The second type of reactor instability to be considered is oscillating instability. Even if the prompt and delayed temperature coefficients are both negative, an instability of the oscillating type can occur in principle although the possibility is quite remote. In this type of instability, small power oscillations at a particular frequency increase in amplitude, and the peak power can increase by several orders of magnitude above the initial power. The mechanism can be explained as follows: If the reactivity is made to oscillate, the power and the temperature will oscillate with the same frequency. The temperature acts back on the reactivity via the temperature coefficient. This is called feedback. The temperature changes in the various reactor components will take place later than the power and reactivity changes because it takes time for the heat to be transported throughout the system. Thus the feedback reactivity is not in phase with the driving reactivity oscillation. If the temperature coefficient is negative and the feedback reactivity is just out of phase with the driving function, then a resonant condition will exist, and the amplitude of the oscillation will become larger and larger. If the oscillations are permitted to continue, excessive heat may be generated, and the core may be damaged.

9.1.5 GENERAL CONSIDERATIONS FOR PLANT CONTROL

In a nuclear power plant, the purpose of the automatic control system is to control the reactor power level in accordance with demand [12-14]. This demand may be either a preset value or the load. In the former case, the load is following the reactor, and in the latter case the reactor is following the load. In addition, the control system must maintain the required coolant temperatures and coolant flows according to a predetermined temperature–flow vs. power program. This program can be either a constant coolant flow with a temperature increase through the reactor proportional to the power or a variable coolant flow with an almost constant temperature variation through the reactor. A control scheme combining these programs can be used with constant coolant flow at low power (below 10% or 15% of full power) and variable coolant flow above this limit. The neutron density can then be controlled by a power demand, a temperature demand, a flow demand, or any combination of these variables.

The variable-coolant-flow program has the advantage of minimizing thermal shocks on reactor scram from full-power operation. It provides increased efficiency for the plant at low power because of a reduction in required pumping power. It also minimizes lags due to loop delay time, thus providing faster system response. However, the variable-coolant-flow program has some definite disadvantages. Nuclear stability is more difficult to analyze since the time delays associated with flow vary with it, and the sodium flows are additional variables in the analysis. Owing to an essentially constant differential temperature through the reactor, regardless of power level, thermal shocks can be greater when a scram occurs from low power than from a corresponding power level in a reactor having constant coolant flow.

The average temperature increase of the liquid-metal coolant as it flows through the reactor core may be 250 to 350°F at 100% power and flow. This can be compared with an approximately 50°F rise in water-cooled reactors. Because the low heat capacity of the fast reactor core results in a fast coolant-temperature response, and because a relatively large temperature rise of the coolant provides a sensitive measuring sink, the coolant outlet temperature can be used to regulate the neutron power level.

A fast reactor can be controlled with neutron level as the basic variable instead of temperature. The EBR-II is controlled by neutron level. Combinations of temperature and neutron level may conceivably be used for reactor control. In any of the above cases, the remainder of the operating control system must hold flows and temperatures of the remainder of the heat system to scheduled values.

9.1.5.1 Coolant-flow Control

If the coolant flow rates are held constant through the entire power range, the temperature rise will be directly proportional to the reactor power. This assumes constant specific heat of the coolant, which is essentially correct. Since coolant-temperature rates of change for reactor plant systems and components have prescribed limits, there are corresponding prescribed limits to rates of change in reactor power level when constant coolant flow rates are used. When the coolant flow rate is varied to correspond with the reactor power level, the coolant temperature rise is the same for all power levels. When the average reactor temperature is the same at all loads, coolant temperatures in the primary heat-transport system remain constant. Through combinations of schedules for primary coolant flow rates, secondary coolant flow rates, and average reactor temperatures (or reactor outlet temperatures), a great deal of flexibility is available to the designer for obtaining desirable temperatures and rates of change of temperatures during power operations.

In EBR-II, for each primary coolant flow rate, there is a scheduled secondary coolant flow rate. If a different secondary flow rate is used from the one scheduled, the temperatures of the secondary coolant are changed, and thus the temperature differences across the various parts of the intermediate heat exchanger are used. The steam temperature is changed because the sodium entering the superheater is changed from the scheduled value.

The problem of controlling the variable coolant flow rates is further complicated in a multiple-circuit plant, such as Fermi or the Hallam sodium-graphite plant. Hallam and Fermi have three primary heat-transport systems feeding the reactor. In Fermi the major portion of the primary system pressure drop is in the reactor. Consequently, unless the head-capacity curves at the various speeds of the primary pumps have sufficient slope, there is a tendency for a change in the speed of one

pump to affect significantly the flow from the pumps in the other two systems as well. If one pump is increased in speed, its flow will increase, but the flow from the other two primary pumps will decrease.

The Fermi plant is equipped with variable-speed drives for each of the three primary and three secondary pumps, but sodium flows (during the early years of operation) will be kept constant for all power levels. There are some advantages to a constant-coolant-flow system. The operating control system is less complex because automatic control or manual manipulation of six pump speeds is eliminated during power operation. Scrams from any power level other than full power produce less severe thermal shocks with constant flow. In a developmental fast reactor plant, such as the Fermi reactor plant, there are other reasons for installing variable-speed coolant pumps. The initial reactor-core power rating is substantially less than the plant heat-system power rating. At the lower power outputs, the pumps will be operated at reduced constant speeds to provide desired coolant-temperature rises and steam temperatures. Increased pump speeds will be used for future cores of higher power ratings. Plans for reactivity oscillator tests for stability analyses of the initial core at Fermi require reduced coolant flow rates to permit the study of temperature effects on nuclear properties at low power levels. Successive steps to higher powers and higher flow rates were planned as part of the stability tests.

An additional use for variable-speed drives in plants using constant flow rates is to permit plant operation with one primary and one secondary heat-transport system out of service, if necessary. The two primary pumps that are operating may need to be run at speeds other than that which they are run when all primary pumps are operating. Flexibility is available to permit maximum permissible power to be obtained from the two heat-transport systems. It should also be possible with variable-speed pumps to delay a plant shutdown until a more convenient time by continuing operation with the remaining circuits at reduced power when one of the systems is shut down because of equipment troubles.

9.1.5.2 Control of Plant Having Steam Generators with Steam Drums

The type of steam-generation equipment is important in determining the type of plant control system and also in setting a limit on the load-regulating ability of the plant. Turbines can take larger transient load changes from conventional fossil-fueled plants or nuclear plants with steam drums than they can from plants with once-through steam generators.

A fast reactor plant with steam drums can be designed to operate in any of the following modes: (1) operate the turbine governor to meet system demand and have the reactor follow the turbine loading, (2) operate the turbine with a blocked governor but manually initiate power changes with the turbine throttle valve and cause the reactor to follow turbine load, or (3) initiate power changes, either from system demand or manual operation, at the reactor and cause the turbine to follow.

The Hallam sodium–graphite reactor plant (three steam generators with drums) is designed to operate in either mode 1 or mode 2. When the plant is operating to accommodate system demand, an increase in power demand causes the turbine governor to open the throttle valve sufficiently to increase the steam flow to generate the needed power. The steam flow is used as the signal to schedule the new sodium flow to each of the six coolant-pump controllers. In turn, the increased primary coolant flow rate provides an anticipatory signal to the neutron-flux controller to cause the reactor to begin to increase power. Reactor outlet temperature is scheduled to be constant at all loads above 15% of full load. The error in the reactor outlet temperature is used as a reset signal to obtain the final desired neutron flux. The same control sequence occurs, of course, for decreased system power demand. Coolant flow rates are scheduled to provide constant steady-state steam pressure. The magnitude of load increase accepted by the turbine is limited by its initial pressure regulator. When the steam pressure has dropped to a given value, the throttle valve will open no further. During a sudden decrease in power demand, the turbine valves close the required amount and cause a rise in the steam pressure. If the rise in pressure is beyond the pressure setting of the steam-dump valve, some of the steam will be bypassed to the condenser. Conventional water-level, water-flow, and steam-flow control can be used with these steam generators. The control for the bypass steam valve is the principal change in the turbine-generator plant control system from fossil-fueled plants. The control system for Hallam would probably be satisfactory for a fast reactor plant using steam generators with steam drums. The control-system settings would need to take into account the magnitudes of heat-transport lags and delays in reservoirs between the reactor and steam generators for the particular plant and also the scheduled flow rates for each load.

The EBR-II is designed to have the turbine (together with the bypass steam flow) follow the reactor loading. Changes in reactor power are initiated by manual control of the control-rod position. The plant is independent of system demand. The primary coolant flow rate is varied manually to maintain a scheduled reactor outlet temperature that will provide a constant steam temperature. The secondary heat-transport-system coolant flow rate is manually adjusted to provide a constant temperature to the large sodium tank, which is the source of coolant supply to the reactor. A certain amount of steam flow is continually bypassed as required to maintain constant steam pressure while all heat generated by the reactor is being removed.

9.1.5.3 Control of Plants Having Once-through Steam Generators

Water is preheated, evaporated, and superheated in a single pass in a once-through generator operating at its design conditions. When there is a demand for a sudden increase in the steam flow rate, the once-through steam generator does not have the large storage of saturated water to provide the additional steam that steam generators with steam drums do. However, response time is rapid because of the heat storage effect in liquid metals. Load response is better with variable flows, since the time lag on a load change is minimized; therefore the requirement for water storage is minimized. This type of plant should be operated in mode 1 (Sec. 9.1.5.2), within its limitations, with variable coolant flow and a control system. It can also operate in mode 2 with a blocked turbine governor so that turbine load would be changed manually. The entire control-system instrumentation should be analyzed for any reactor plant to ensure that instrument or control-system malfunctions will not produce plant instability and will not increase temperatures or otherwise cause the plant variables to move toward conditions of decreased safety.

9.1.6 ENRICO FERMI ATOMIC POWER PLANT CONTROL SYSTEM

9.1.6.1 Control Concept

The design of the Enrico Fermi control system[8, 12, 15, 16] is predicated upon three basic conditions: (1) power changes will be initiated at the reactor, (2) sodium flows in the primary and secondary loops will be constant from start-up to 100% of specified power levels, and (3) the normal rate of change of power will be preset in the control system. The system programs the reactor outlet temperature from a temperature set point and maintains a programmed reactor outlet temperature regardless of the action of other variables, such as actual reactor power or sodium flows. With constant sodium flows and a scheduled reactor inlet temperature, reactor power is a function of the reactor outlet temperature. The reactor outlet temperature signal is used to position the regulating rod.

9.1.6.2 Reactor Control

The major components of the reactor control system are shown in Fig. 9.2. The system consists of three channels: a temperature-error rate of change of power demand channel, a neutron-flux or actual rate of change channel, and a regulating-rod-velocity demand channel. A given power-level setting is represented by the temperature demand signal, which is compared with the actual reactor outlet temperature signal. The difference between the temperature demand signal and the actual temperature signal is converted to a rate of change of power demand. A limiter provides positive protection against excessive loading rates. The lag unit prevents a sudden change in the rod-velocity demand channel if a step change is made in the rate of change of power demand channel.

The neutron-flux or actual rate of change channel is driven by the larger of two auctioneered signals from uncompensated ionization chambers.

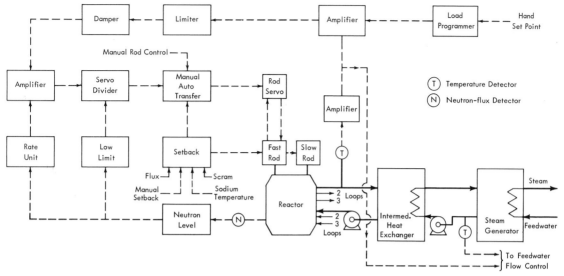

FIG. 9.2—Fermi reactor control system.

After amplification to a level compatible with the control system, the signal is differentiated in the rate unit. The output of the rate unit is the actual rate of change signal.

The regulating-rod-velocity demand channel compares the neutron rate of change signal with the temperature demand signal, and its output is the error signal. Because of reactor nonlinearity with power level, the error signal is divided by the neutron-flux signal in the servo divider to provide a constant control-loop gain at all power levels. The output of the servo divider is the regulating-rod-velocity demand signal, which is one input to the control servo. The second input is actual rod velocity. The two inputs are combined, and the resulting error signal is used to supply a variable voltage to the regulating-rod drive motor.

A manual–automatic transfer station is provided so that the operator can remove the regulating rod from automatic control. This enables the operator to drive the regulating rod in or out of the reactor core at a fixed rate.

9.1.6.3 Shim-rod Control

The regulating-rod drive is equipped with limit switches that will energize the shim-rod drive motor. The switches are so arranged that, when the regulating rod is withdrawn from the region of its maximum effectiveness, the shim rod will withdraw until the fast rod has returned to its most effective region. Conversely, the shim rod will be inserted if the regulating rod inserts below its region of maximum effectiveness. The limit switches are set 2 in. on either side of the point of maximum effectiveness.

9.1.6.4 Regulating-rod Control

Regulating-rod rate is based on the criteria that the rate of reactivity insertion be limited to no more than 2/3 cent/sec of the rod-drive-motor

runaway speed when the rod is in its most effective position and the drive-motor runaway speed is 150% of maximum design speed. The shim-rod rate is based on a reactivity insertion of approximately 1 cent/min.

Setback circuitry is used to return the reactor to desirable operating conditions if the reactor outlet temperature exceeds a preset value or the neutron flux exceeds a preset value. Setback action is accomplished by inserting the regulating rod at a fixed rate for a given time and removing both the regulating and shim rods from automatic control.

An automatic programmer, shown in Fig. 9.3, is used to bring the plant up to the desired power level at a rate controlled so that none of the criteria of temperature changes is violated. The control signal is obtained from the hand set point made by the operator. The signal, T_U, is the demand set point and is compared with the actual set point, T_I, which is the timer output signal. The error signal, whose polarity determines the direction of rotation of the timer motor, is used to drive equipment that generates the timer output signal.

The timer output signal is called the actual set point, T_I. The actual set point is supplied to an amplifier, where it is compared with the signal proportional to reactor outlet temperature, T_A. The resulting error signal is used in the control system as the rate of change of power demand signal. The error signal is also used as an input to a timer-reversing amplifier. If the actual set point is more than 5°F greater than reactor outlet temperature, the timer will reverse until the actual set point is within 5°F of reactor outlet temperature.

The steam temperatures at the outlet of the three steam generators are measured, and the signals are auctioneered for the highest and lowest temperature. These signals are used to change the rate of change of temperature set point when the superheated-steam region is reached. The rate of change of temperature set point is changed from 100°F/hr to 30°F/hr when the highest steam

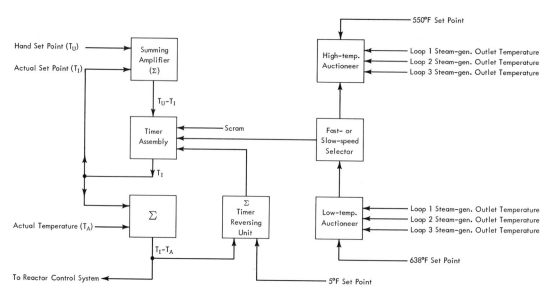

FIG. 9.3—Fermi plant programmer.

temperature reaches 550°F. When the lowest steam temperature reaches 638°F, the rate of change of temperature is again changed to 100°F.

9.1.6.5 Feedwater-flow Control

Feedwater flow is scheduled to maintain the steam-generator outlet temperatures at a constant value and in accordance with the established temperature vs. power schedule shown in Fig. 9.4. Signals to schedule feedwater flow are from the reactor outlet temperature and steam-generator sodium outlet temperature (Fig. 9.5). Reactor outlet temperature is a load index since, with constant sodium flow and constant temperature of the sodium leaving the steam generator, it is a measure of the

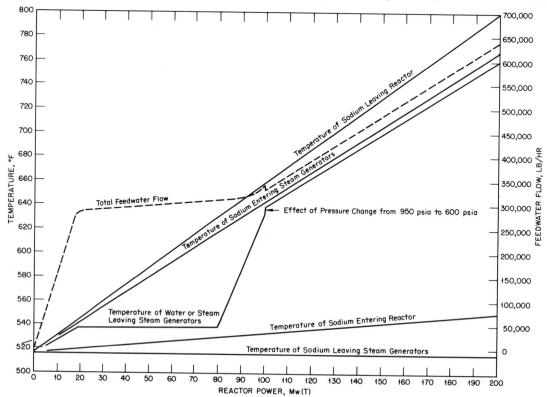

FIG. 9.4—Fermi temperatures vs. power schedule [8].

Btu input to the steam generators. Therefore a function of this temperature is used to schedule feedwater flow in the amount necessary to remove the heat input to the steam generators. In addition, a signal proportional to steam-generator sodium outlet temperature is compared with a temperature demand set point to establish a feedwater-flow correction signal if the flow scheduled from reactor outlet temperature does not provide the correct steam-generator sodium outlet temperature. The correction signal is fed to the scheduled feedwater-flow relay, where it is compared with the reactor outlet temperature signal. The modified signal is the final feedwater-flow demand.

Feedwater flow to each steam generator is measured by pressure drop across an orifice. A signal proportional to actual flow is compared with the feedwater-flow demand signal. If a difference between the two signals exists, the feedwater regulating valve is opened or closed until the measured flow equals demand.

9.1.6.6 Feedwater-pump Speed Control

The feedwater pumps are driven through hydraulic couplings. Pump speeds are regulated so that a constant pressure differential is maintained between the feedwater header and the highest outlet header pressure from the steam generators. An increase or decrease in feedwater-flow demand will cause the flow-control valves to open or close. This will result in an increase or decrease in the differential pressure across the steam generators. The change in pressure generates an error signal between the pressure set point and the actual pressure difference. The signal is used to decrease or increase pump speed to maintain the desired pressure differential. In the event the differential pressure decreases to a value indicating a feedwater deficiency to the steam generators with respect to reactor power level, a signal is generated to decrease reactor power through the plant programmer.

9.1.6.7 Emergency Feedwater Control

The emergency flow-control valves are operated from the steam-generator sodium outlet temperatures (Fig. 9.5). The valves are partially open at all times; back flow through the emergency feedwater lines is blocked by check valves.

If emergency cooling is required, valves on the steam side of the steam generators are opened, venting the steam generators to the atmosphere. Water from the No. 4 heater and from a storage tank flows through the steam generators to remove decay heat from the reactor.

9.1.6.8 Steam-generator Pressure Control

Figure 9.6 is a schematic diagram of the steam-generator pressure control. One of the operating

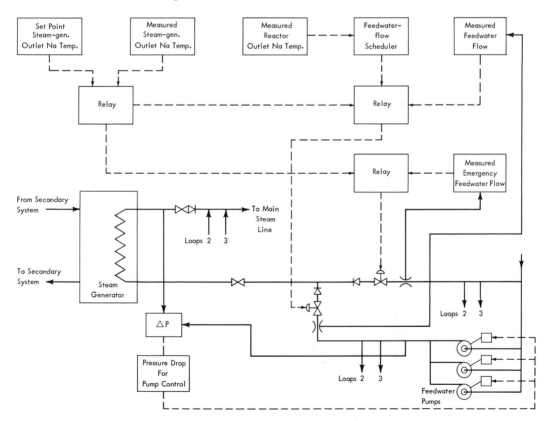

FIG. 9.5—Fermi feedwater-flow control [8].

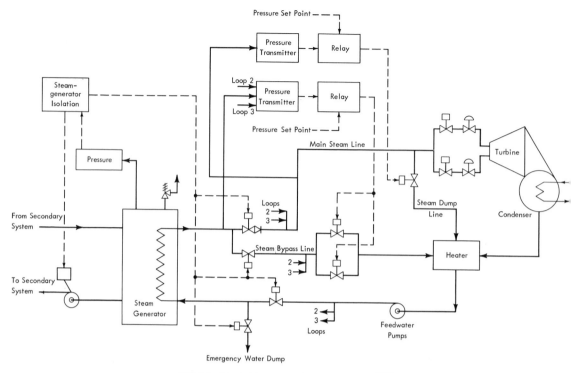

FIG. 9.6—Fermi steam-generator pressure control [8].

limitations on the steam generator is that no appreciable steaming be allowed to occur below a loop flow of 100,000 lb/hr so that an adequate flow distribution to the 1200 tubes in each steam generator is assured. During start-up the steam-generator pressure is elevated to 950 psia to prevent low-flow steaming. After steaming occurs in the steam generator, pressure is reduced to the turbine operating pressure of 600 psia.

At start-up the main-steam-line pressure set point is maintained at 960 psia. The pressure in the steam bypass line is controlled to 950 psia. When superheated steam becomes available, the main-steam-line pressure set point is reduced on a timed ramp below the pressure of the steam bypass line. The result is the transfer of steam flow from the bypass line to the main steam line, from which it is discharged to the deaerating heater. When the main-steam-line pressure is reduced to 915 psia, a reduction of the pressure set point in the main steam bypass line is started. The 35-psia differential between the two steam lines is maintained until the main-steam-line pressure reaches 600 psia. At this pressure the steam is transferred to the turbine.

9.1.6.9 Steam-generator Isolation

If, as a result of leaks in the tubes, a sodium–water reaction occurs in a steam generator, the generator is isolated (see Fig. 9.6). Pressure transducers sense the cover-gas pressure, and, when the pressure reaches a preset value, the isolation system will operate. In addition, a rupture disk is mounted at the top of each steam generator.

The disk is selected to rupture at some pressure above the settings of the pressure transducers. A disk rupture also isolates the steam generator.

Isolation consists in closing a valve in the feed-water piping to stop feedwater flow and opening another valve that allows the water and steam in the steam generator to drain to atmosphere. Valves on the steam lines close to prevent further communication with the steam system. The sodium pump in the affected secondary heat-transport loop is shut down, and its pony motor is not permitted to start. See Chap. 4 for further discussions on steam generators.

9.1.6.10 Sodium Flows

The heat-transport systems in the Fermi plant operate with discrete but constant sodium flows during refueling and when the reactor is loaded with cores designed for thermal outputs of 200, 300, and 400 Mw. Sodium flows in the primary heat-transport loops are changed by variable resistors (liquid rheostats) in series with the pump–motor windings. Electrical resistance is increased or decreased by positioning electrodes in an electrolyte solution. The electrodes are motor driven; the drive motors are manually actuated by the operator.

The motors and pumps in the secondary heat-transport loops are coupled via magnetic couplings. With essentially constant motor speeds, the pump speeds and, hence, sodium flows are set by manual adjustments of current to the couplings.

9.1.6.11 Pony Motors

Each primary and secondary heat-transport loop sodium pump is equipped with a pony motor.

The pony motors for two primary and two secondary heat-transport loops are energized from the noninterruptible power supplies provided for the plant (Sec. 9.5). These motors assure adequate decay-heat-removal capabilities in the event all pumping power to the main sodium and feedwater pump motors is lost. The circuitry is arranged so that the pony motors start automatically in the event the main pump-motor breakers open, with one exception. The pony motors are not permitted to start in a primary and secondary heat-transport loop if a sodium–water reaction has occurred in that loop.

Pony-motor operation for the sodium pumps in the secondary heat-transport loops automatically initiates maximum coupling between the motors and pumps.

9.1.6.12 Two-circuit Operation

The Fermi plant is designed to operate with two of three primary and secondary heat-transport circuits and two of three feedwater and steam circuits. This feature allows the plant to operate at 67% of normal power without shutdown in the event that malfunctions cause a shutdown of one circuit. A single-circuit shutdown stops the main pump motors in the affected primary and secondary heat-transport loop and closes the feedwater flow valves to the steam generator. The following conditions will automatically initiate a single-circuit shutdown: (1) low sodium flow in primary heat-transport loop, (2) low sodium flow in secondary heat-transport loop, (3) feedwater flow greater than feedwater demand by preset amount, (4) feedwater flow less than feedwater demand by present amount, (5) high outlet sodium temperature from steam generator, (6) low outlet sodium temperature from steam generator, and (7) sodium–water reaction in steam generator.

If one heat-transport circuit is shut down as the result of a single-circuit signal, a similar signal in one or both of the circuits that are operating will cause a shutdown of both circuits. This is referred to as a multicircuit shutdown. A multicircuit shutdown deenergizes the main sodium pump motors on all primary and secondary heat-transport systems. Reactor scram results from low sodium flows or negative rate of change of reactor power. The sodium pumps are driven at reduced speeds by pony motors to remove decay heat from the reactor. Feedwater flow to the steam generators is automatically reduced to low values.

9.1.7 EBR-II CONTROL SYSTEM

9.1.7.1 Control Concept

The basic control philosophy for the EBR-II power system [7, 9, 17] consists in providing control of the reactor power level, balance between the rates of heat removal effected by each of the major thermal systems, from the cooling tower to the reactor, and essentially complete isolation of the reactor from the effects of turbine-generator load variation. Only the simplest control functions, or those which might adversely affect facility safety

if handled manually, are automatic. Control of primary and secondary heat-transport-system coolant flow rates is manual. Control of reactor power level is manual during raising or lowering of power but can be automatic at steady state. Control of feedwater flow rate and steam pressure is automatic.

9.1.7.2 Reactor Control

A schematic diagram of the control system is given in Fig. 9.7. The EBR-II is controlled by moving 12 fuel-bearing control rods in the reactor. During steady-state reactor operation, 11 rods are used for shimming and 1 rod for regulating. The regulating rod is defined as the rod being controlled by the automatic control system. Any of the 12 rods can be used as the regulating rod. During manual operation (reactor power level change or steady-state operation), all 12 rods are defined as shim rods. The power supply is arranged to supply power to only 1 shim-rod drive unit at a time, thereby restricting rod movement to 1 rod at a time. At steady-state reactor operation, with the regulating rod on automatic control, 1 shim rod can be moved to permit adjustment of the position of the regulating rod in the reactor. Operating control is achieved by a 14-in. vertical motion of the control rod, whose motion is mechanically limited to a speed of 5 in./min. Since the total worth of each rod is calculated to be not more than $0.004 \, \Delta k/k$ for a full stroke of 14 in., the drive speed of 5 in./min will limit the reactivity addition rates from this source to less than $0.00008 \, \Delta k/k$ per second. Automatic control of regulating-rod motion is based on the sensing of neutron-flux level. Either one of two linear amplifier channels, measuring current from ion chambers, is selected for input to the regulating-rod amplifier. These two channels indicate power level and also provide flux-level trip below 50% of full power.

9.1.7.3 Balance of Major Thermal Systems

Balance between the thermal systems consists principally of balancing the heat-removal rate of the secondary heat-transport system with the heat generation rate in the reactor. Any unbalance in these two rates produces a continuous change in the primary tank bulk-sodium temperature. The EBR-II temperature and flow program is shown in Fig. 9.8.

Proper balance is maintained by regulating the primary-system flow rate to provide a predetermined reactor coolant outlet temperature varying from 900°F at full power [62.5 Mw(t)] to 850°F at very low power. This 50°F variation is employed to maintain a constant steam pressure of 850°F at all power levels. The secondary heat-transport-system flow rate is regulated so that the primary-tank bulk-sodium temperature remains constant at 700°F. Irrespective of reactor power level, the temperature of the cold leg of the secondary heat-transport system remains between 580 and 610°F, and the temperature of the hot leg remains relatively constant, varying from about 880°F at full power to

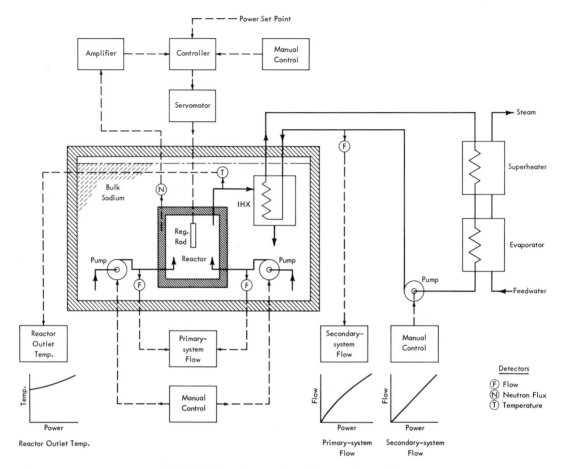

FIG. 9.7—EBR-II primary and secondary control system[9].

about 850°F at very low power (reflecting control of the reactor outlet coolant temperature). Thus, the rates of heat removal from both the primary system and the secondary heat-transport system are approximately proportional to the secondary heat-transport-system flow rate. Feedwater flow rate and feedwater temperature to the steam generator are automatically controlled. System-throttle pressure is held by a power pressure valve, which dumps excess steam directly to the condenser.

9.1.7.4 Operating Control System

As stated previously, only the simplest control functions are automatically operated. Figures 9.7 and 9.9 are block diagrams of the primary, secondary, and steam and feedwater operating control systems, showing the operations that are controlled either automatically or manually. Primary- and secondary-systems sodium flow, as well as reactor power level, are manually programmed to provide a constant steam temperature. (Reactor power can be automatically controlled at steady-state conditions.) Feedwater flow rate is maintained by operating a valve that is automatically controlled by a conventional three-element control system,

operating on steam-drum level, steam flow, and feedwater flow. Feedwater pressure is automatically maintained by controlling the speed of the feedwater pump. Steam-throttle pressure is automatically controlled by dumping excess steam into the condenser. A steam-throttle temperature of 850°F and a pressure of 1250 psia are thus maintained by the operating control system for all power levels.

9.1.7.5 Reactor Isolation from Load-variation Effects

An important feature of the EBR-II in regard to reactor stability is the virtual isolation of the reactor from the effects of changes in power-system conditions external to the reactor. There is no automatic-control adjustment link between reactor-power and the electrical-load demand or any other power-system operating condition (other than scram). The steam system incorporates a full-flow steam bypass around the turbine to the condenser, a turbine-generator load-limiting device, and a regenerative feedwater system, which delivers constant-temperature feedwater to the steam generator under all load conditions. This arrangement eliminates any effect of change in turbine-generator

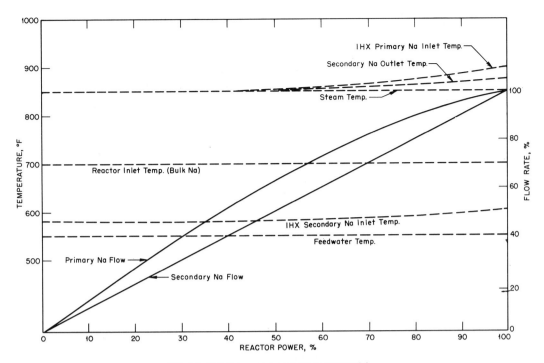

FIG. 9.8—EBR-II temperature and flow program [9].

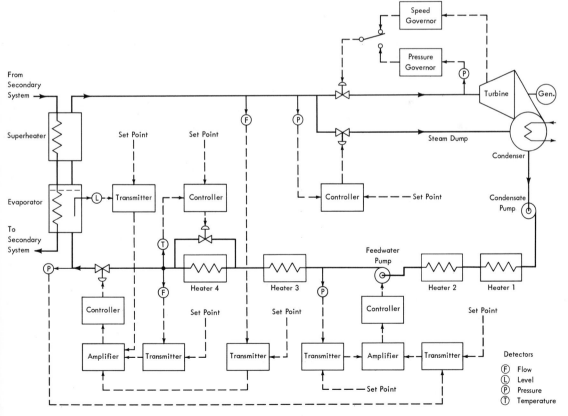

FIG. 9.9—EBR-II steam and feedwater control system [9].

load upon reactor inlet coolant temperature. The primary system employed has a very large thermal capacity; thus the reactor inlet temperature can change only very slowly. With the reactor operating at full power [62.5 Mw(t)] and no heat being removed from the primary tank, the rate of the bulk-sodium temperature rise would be about 14°F/min.

9.1.8 SODIUM GRAPHITE REACTOR (SGR) CONTROL SYSTEM

9.1.8.1 Control Concept

Although the SGR plant at Hallam, Neb., is not a fast reactor, it uses sodium as a coolant, and therefore its control system is of interest to designers of fast reactors using sodium as a coolant[18, 19]. The plant control system is designed to automatically supply demanded steam flow at rated pressure and temperature over the range of from 15 to 100% of rated load. Primary sodium inlet and outlet temperatures are held fairly constant to minimize transient stresses in the reactor. Maximum design rate of change of load is 5 Mw(e)/min. So that this load-following objective can be achieved, reactor power level and sodium flow rates in both primary and secondary heat-transport systems are varied as a function of steam demand. This control concept provides operation comparable to that of a conventional coal-fired steam power plant. The plant temperature program is shown in Fig. 9.10.

9.1.8.2 Control System

The control system is divided into the following subsystems: (1) plant-power control, (2) sodium-flow control, (3) neutron-flux control, (4) convection-flow control, and (5) feedwater and steam control. These subsystems are shown in Figs. 9.11 and 9.12.

When all subsystems are on automatic, a variation in load causes the turbine governor to open or close the steam throttle valve, causing steam flow and pressure to change. The power-plant control system detects the change in steam flow and commands a corresponding change in sodium flow from the division-of-load computer. Steam pressure acts as a trim signal on the steam-flow signal to maintain correct turbine pressure. Sodium-flow demand signals for the three primary and the three secondary heat-transport loops are generated in the division-of-load computer to match the demanded total steam flow from the plant-power control system. Circuit flow ratios are manually set by the operator.

Sodium flow in each of the three secondary heat-transport systems is varied by an eddy-current coupling to the pump. The secondary sodium-flow control system detects the error between measured and demanded flow rate and varies pump speed to provide the correct flow. Similarly, the primary sodium-flow control system regulates the primary flow rate in response to demanded flow from the division-of-load computer. In addition, the reactor inlet temperature is maintained (at a value dependent upon load) by trimming

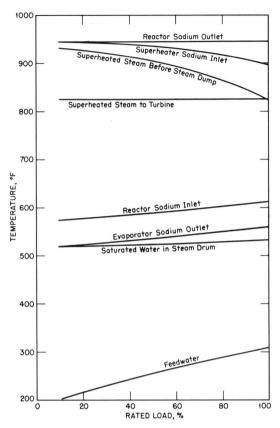

FIG. 9.10—Hallam (SGR) plant temperature program[18, 19].

primary flow with a temperature-error signal. Sodium flow rates in the three primary loops are summed and multiplied by the temperature rise across the reactor (as set by the operator) to provide the power demand signal to the neutron-flux control system. A power trim signal is also generated in the nuclear power computer as a function of outlet temperature errors. Both the reactor outlet plenum temperature and fuel-channel outlet temperature are used to provide temperature compensation to the power demand signal.

The neutron-flux control system operates on power demand from the nuclear power computer and the actual measured neutron flux. The difference between these two signals operates the rod-drive relays, which drive the shim-regulating rods at constant speeds in the proper direction to reduce the error to zero. The signal to the relays is gain compensated by the demanded neutron flux and the number of rods on automatic control. (Any combination of 1 to 19 rods may be used simultaneously, with the usual number being 6. The remaining rods will be positioned either full up or full down.) An inner loop with velocity feedback is used for improved stability and for generation of proportional and reset actions. Travel limits on the inner loop automatically limit reactivity insertion.

The convection-flow control system operates only when the reactor is scrammed. On a scram the pump speeds are automatically reduced to zero.

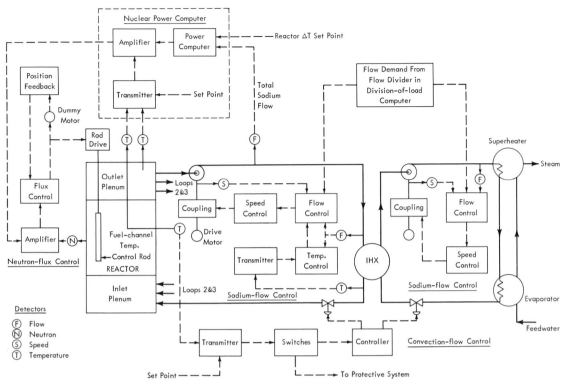

FIG. 9.11—Hallam (SGR) primary and secondary control system [18, 19].

Free convection primary sodium flow is then greater than necessary to remove reactor decay heat. The convection-flow control system throttles this flow to maintain the fuel-channel outlet temperature at a constant value. Evaporator feedwater level is maintained constant by the conventional three-element feedwater control system principle operating on feedwater level, feedwater flow rate, and steam flow rate. Constant pressure is maintained at the input of the feedwater control valve by the feedwater-pressure control system. Superheater outlet temperature varies with load, but the turbine steam temperature is maintained by a set value by the attemperator control system. This is accomplished through bypassing saturated steam around the superheater and mixing it with superheated steam to obtain the desired temperature. Protection against high steam pressure is provided during normal operation by the power-relief system, with backup from the steam-dump control system. Safety valves are also provided.

The steam-dump control system provides a means for conserving feedwater while dissipating reactor power when a turbine-generator outage occurs during periods of low-power testing. It also functions during hot transfer to the coal-fired boiler or for dissipating reactor decay heat following a shutdown. The steam-dump system is capable of handling 110,000 lb of steam per hour at 800 psig and 850°F (equivalent to about 15% reactor power).

All controllers have deviation alarms, which are actuated upon excessive error between set point and the measured variable being controlled. In addition,

the six pump controllers, the flux controller, and the moderator–coolant and convection-flow control automatically transfer to manual upon deviation alarm. These same units have rate limiters installed which automatically limit the rate of change of controller set point to safe values. Temperature changes are limited to 50°F/hr; sodium flow rates, to 20% of rated flow per minute; and neutron flux, to 40% of rated flux per minute.

9.1.9 RAPSODIE CONTROL SYSTEM

9.1.9.1 Control Concept

Rapsodie is an experimental fast reactor whose first phase will be to dissipate heat produced in the primary circuit through a secondary system employing sodium-to-air heat exchangers. In the second phase these heat exchangers will be replaced by steam generators for the basic purpose of obtaining the necessary technology for the overall nuclear power plant, including the turbine-generator steam cycle and control system. The secondary heat exchangers (sodium to sodium) are rated at 10 Mw(t).

9.1.9.2 Control System

Normal procedure for operating the reactor will be by manual control of two regulating rods [20]. Rapid insertion of the control rods (setback)

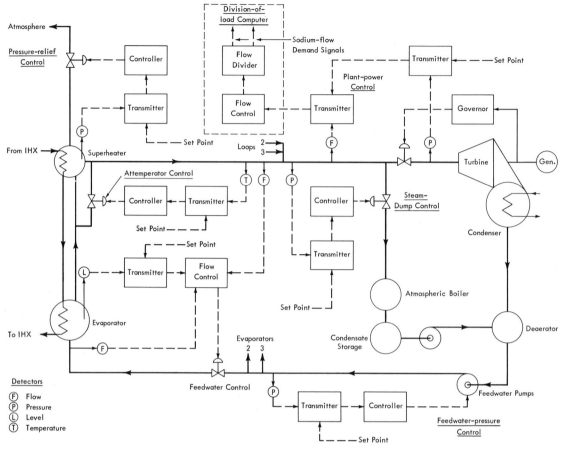

FIG. 9.12—Hallam (SGR) steam and feedwater control system [18, 19].

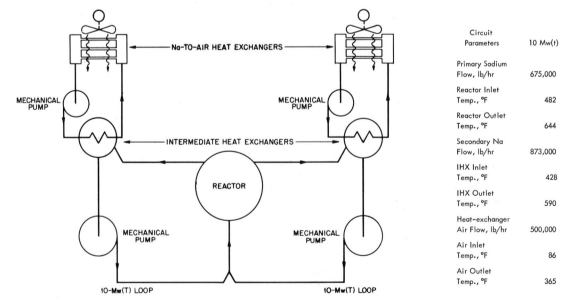

FIG. 9.13—Rapsodie flow diagram [20].

is automatically initiated under certain defective functions of the reactor to prevent a scram; if the setback action does not prevent a scram, it will at least reduce any thermal shock that may result from a scram.

The 10 Mw(t) loops will use variable-frequency motors driving mechanical pumps whose maximum speed will be seven times greater than minimum speed. Flow control for the sodium-to-air heat exchangers will be accomplished by variable pitch of the fan blades. Initially all flow control will be manual. The flow diagram for Rapsodie and some of the circuit parameters are shown in Fig. 9.13.

9.1.10 DOUNREAY FAST REACTOR CONTROL SYSTEM

9.1.10.1 Control Concept

The prime objective at Dounreay was to reduce the risk of cooling-system breakdown rather than to design an economic heat-rejection system. This objective meant that some design problems that needed to be solved to build a fast reactor at low capital cost, e.g., economic liquid-metal-to-water heat exchangers, have been bypassed in the interests of soundness and reliability of the project. In general, control of the reactor and liquid-metal systems is manual; the steam system is automatically controlled. Figure 9.14 is the flow diagram for the Dounreay plant.

9.1.10.2 Reactor Control

Control of the reactor is maintained manually by the operator, who varies the position of the control-rod groups and the rate of coolant flow [21, 22]. Control is achieved by moving 12 groups of 10 fuel elements each situated around the core. These groups are split into 2 safety rods, 6 control rods, and 4 shutoff rods. (In addition, there are three B^{10} shutoff rods, which can be dropped by gravity into the innermost layer of breeder elements). The start-up and control of the reactor requires the insertion of safety, shutoff, and control groups, in that order. Interlocks are provided to ensure that this sequence is maintained. The movements of the groups is controlled at a constant speed corresponding to the safe rate of addition of positive reactivity. The safe maximum addition of positive reactivity is specified as $2 \times 10^{-5} \Delta k/\text{sec}$, and the rate of control-rod insertion is limited to a speed giving half this amount. Should the interlocks fail, allowing all 12 groups to be raised together, the limit of positive reactivity insertion would not be raised. The rate of control-rod insertion is limited to 0.003 in./sec to maintain the reactivity increase within specified limits. There are two out speeds: one of 0.003 in./sec and a fast speed of 0.15 in./sec to prevent power overshoots during divergence.

9.1.10.3 Liquid-metal Systems

The primary heat exchangers consist of 24 concentric tubes, each forming a separate heat-

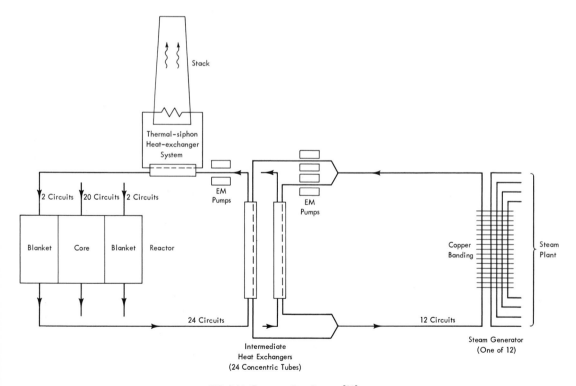

FIG. 9.14—Dounreay flow diagram [22].

transport circuit having its own electromagnetic pump and flowmeter. This piping is so arranged that 20 of the circuits carry NaK or sodium to the core section of the reactor and 4 circuits feed the blanket section. The circuits are manually controlled, in pairs, with the flow regulated so that a constant inlet temperature of 392°F is maintained. At full-power operation of 60 Mw(t), the primary outlet temperature is 662°F. Primary coolant flow can be trimmed (the core circuits having a different flow rate than the breeder circuits, if required) to balance the heat outputs to the secondary liquid-metal-to-water heat exchangers. Control of the EM pumps is achieved by the manually regulating induction-voltage regulators feeding the d-c rectifiers for the pumps.

In the event of total coolant-pump failure, the reactor would be scrammed. Decay heat would then be removed by the thermal-siphon heat-exchanger system. This system consists of 24 heat exchangers, of similar construction to the primary heat exchangers, situated between the EM pumps and the reactor vessel. Owing to natural convection, coolant flow will reverse, and decay heat will be transferred to the NaK on the secondary side of the siphon heat exchanger located at the base of a chimney. The thermal-siphon system will remove 2.24 Mw(t) of heat on a complete pump failure.

Adjacent pairs of secondary piping on the 24 primary heat exchangers are connected in parallel to form 12 NaK- or sodium-coolant circuits, 10 of which extract heat from the primary core circuits and 2 extract heat from the blanket circuits. There are 24 EM pumps operating in pairs with control similar to the primary pumps. The 12 secondary liquid-metal-to-water heat exchangers transfer heat from the sodium to the steam plant through copper banding of the stainless-steel tubing, carrying the liquid-metal and water.

9.1.10.4 Steam Plant

The secondary side of each of the 12 liquid-metal-to-water heat exchangers consists of economizer, evaporator, and superheater sections, a boiler drum, a circulating pump, a feedwater pump, and a steam-dump condenser (Fig. 9.15). Each heat exchanger is capable of producing 8000 lb/hr at 185 psig and 525°F. The plant is designed so that the steam dump automatically accepts all the steam produced in excess of turbine requirements, up to 100% of steam production. If all the steam-dump system should fail, the full reactor heat output can be extracted by exhausting steam to the atmosphere through the superheater safety valves as long as the supply of feedwater is maintained. Boiler-drum safety valves act as a backup for the superheater safety valves. Condensate from the turbine feeds into two surge tanks. All 12 heat exchangers are tied to common headers, which are connected to the turbine and the surge tanks.

The steam-dump condenser can also be used for water dumping by dumping the evaporator water directly into the steam-dump condenser. Greater flexibility is obtained in this manner for controlling temperature conditions in the core as well as increasing the total heat-exchanger capacity to 50 Mw(t).

9.1.10.5 Temperature and Flow Control

The temperature at which the steam-dump condenser outlet is controlled will determine the mean temperature at which the reactor core and breeder elements will operate. Control of the outlet of the steam-dump condenser is within the range of 32 to 392°F. Control is fully automatic, and adjustment of the desired level of control is effected by the operator through the automanual control panel. Manual control is possible if the automatic system fails.

Temperature at the outlet of each steam-dump condenser is measured by means of a temperature transmitter whose output signal feeds into a pneumatic controller. The output of the controller is 3 to 15 psig, corresponding to a temperature range of 32 to 392°F. The controller receives its set-point pressure through the automanual control panel. During normal operation of the reactor, all 10 circuits extracting heat from the core will operate at the same temperature, and the local automatic panel will be arranged for remote automatic control. The two circuits extracting heat from the blanket will also be operated at the same temperature, which may differ from the setting for the 10 circuits. The automatic system maintains the temperature to within ±3.6°F.

A further requirement of the steam plant is that the feedwater flow in each of the 12 circuits remain constant under all conditions of operation. Since the temperature-control valve, which is installed in series with the respective steam-dump condenser, will throttle the flow to the condenser and hence determine the amount of heat rejected, it is necessary to provide a further control system to meet the requirement that the feedwater flow be kept constant under all conditions of operation. A pneumatic control valve is installed in parallel with the temperature-control valve and the steam-dump condenser. This flow-control valve is operated by a pneumatic flow recorder controller. If the temperature at the outlet of the heat exchangers should increase, the temperature controller opens the temperature control valve in series with the heat exchanger to increase the flow and, hence, to increase the heat rejected by the steam-dump condenser. The flow controller will thus momentarily see an increase in flow and will adjust (throttle) the flow-control valve to produce the required flow. Flow is kept constant to within limits of +3%. Because of the thermal lag in the system, the series valve operates slowly; the shunt valve, however, will respond very rapidly to a change in flow. Both series and shunt valves are arranged to lock into position should the air-supply system fail during operation.

Delivery from the boiler feed pump is controlled by a regulator that maintains the water level in the boiler drum, which is fed from the evaporator section. Discharge from the boiler drum to the evaporator section is held constant for all loads by the circulating pump.

9.1.10.6 Steam-dump System

A spill valve in the steam inlet to the steam-dump condenser controls the pressure in the system.

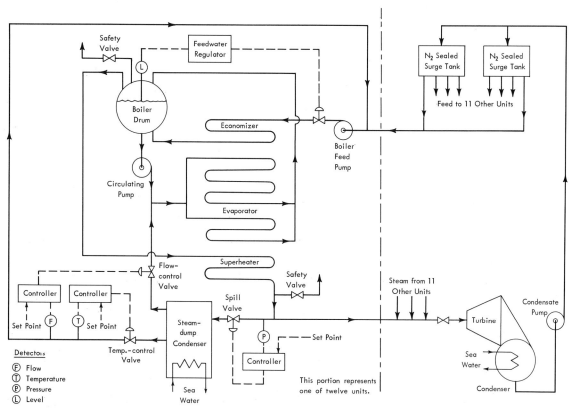

FIG. 9.15—Simplified control diagram of Dounreay steam plant [22].

Steam generated in excess of turbine requirements causes a buildup of pressure until the valve opens and passes the surplus steam to the dump condenser. The condensate is continuously returned to the suction of the feed pump by the pressure head in the steam-dump condenser. Since the feed-pump suction is connected directly to the surge tanks and the dump condenser, the system can be looked upon as forming the two legs of a U-tube, the pressure in the steam-dump condenser balancing the head of water in the surge tanks situated 25 ft above it. An increase in the rate at which steam enters the condenser causes a pressure rise that depresses the water level in the condenser and exposes more cooling surface until the steam is being condensed at the rate at which it is entering. A spill valve can be set to lift at pressures ranging from 135 to 235 psig. A bypass is fitted which allows pressures below 135 psig to be obtained by hand control. The spill valve is a pneumatically controlled diaphragm valve of the pressure-to-close type. It receives air at pressure varying from 3 to 15 psig from a force-balance type pneumatic controller that is actuated by steam pressure in the superheater outlet.

Distribution of reactor heat among the individual units can be varied by these valves since raising the pressure set point in one unit will reduce the temperature difference between steam and liquid metal and cause the heat transferred in the liquid-metal-to-water heat exchanger to fall.

9.1.10.7 Water-dump System

When the evaporator water circuit carries heat from the liquid metal to the seawater without raising and condensing steam, greater flexibility in the temperature conditions in the reactor core are obtained. This process is known as water dumping. Only the top part of the evaporator is used; the bottom part is closed off, drained, and vented. The economizer and superheater are also shut off, drained, and vented. The steam to, and condensate from, the dump condenser are closed off, and the condenser is used to cool the water in the evaporator circuit. This valving is not shown on the control diagram.

The temperature of the water in the evaporator circuit is controlled for any given reactor power level by shunt across the dump condenser. A pneumatically operated diaphragm valve, called a series valve, controls the flow through the dump condenser. The force-balance pneumatic controller for this valve is situated in the unit control cubicle and is actuated by the temperature at the water inlet to the evaporator. Selection of the temperature can be carried out locally or remotely from the reactor control room. A shunt valve of similar type is actuated by the flow in the main circuit, opening as the series valve closes, and vice versa, to keep the total flow constant.

The pressure in the boiler drum is the vapor pressure associated with the temperature at the evaporator outlet and can vary from subatmosphere (for temperatures below 212°F) to full boiler pressure. If subatmosphere pressures are used, plant steam is admitted to the boiler drum to prevent ingress of air. During water dumping the dump condenser is subject to the full boiler pressure plus the circulating pump head. The boiler-drum safety valve is set to lift at 210 psig during water dumping.

9.2 Safety-system Design

9.2.1 OBJECTIVES

The safety system (Refs. 8, 9, 20, 22-24) should rapidly recognize reactor deviations from normal which may be beyond the control capabilities of the operating control system and which, if not corrected, could cause reactor or plant damage. The safety system should be entirely automatic and should not require backup from operating personnel. In the design of a safety system, the two most important objectives are (1) the safety of the reactor and operating personnel and (2) minimum plant shutdown. The first is achieved by ensuring that the plant will always scram (rapid and complete shutdown) when necessary. The second is satisfied by ensuring that the plant scrams only when absolutely necessary; i.e., false scrams are avoided to prevent possible material fatigue due to unnecessary thermal stresses and to prevent loss of plant operating time.

Since these two objectives are conflicting, the system designer should make his decision based on judgment. The first objective is best satisfied by channel redundancy; i.e., more than one channel performs a single safety function, and each channel is capable of scramming the plant. However, redundancy of this type would increase false scrams, owing to instrument failures or spurious signals, and thereby violate the second objective. Coincidence techniques, requiring that more than one channel in a single safety function call for a scram before a scram is actuated, achieve the second objective by minimizing the number of false scrams. An optimum coincidence system commonly used is a coincidence of two out of three channels to initiate a scram from a single safety function. However, since circuits used to date are not 100% fail-safe, the use of coincident circuits may reduce reactor safety. If one channel in a two out of three coincident circuit should not fail safe, then two out of two would be required for reactor shutdown. The ability to test a large part of the safety-system electronic equipment during operation (e.g., a continuous self-testing system) would increase the safety system's reliability since two channels must be operating to give protection.

In practice, both channel redundancy and coincidence techniques are used. Table 9.6 shows the methods used for various safety functions at EBR-II, Dounreay, Rapsodie, and Fermi.

Other modes of safety action, less drastic than a scram, are often employed to avoid a scram when a scram is not absolutely necessary. Insertion of

Table 9.6—Reactor Safety System: Examples of Channel Redundancy and Coincidence Techniques

	EBR-II	Dounreay	Rapsodie	Fermi
Nuclear:				
Period				
Source range	2 of 3	2 of 3	1 of 3	1 of 2
Intermediate range	2 of 3	1 of 2	2 of 3	2 of 3
Power range		2 of 3		
Power level	2 of 3	2 of 3	2 of 3	2 of 3
Negative rate of change of power				2 of 3
Thermal:				
Flow				
Core inlet	1 of 2	1 of 1		
Blanket inlet	1 of 2	1 of 1		
Reactor outlet	1 of 1			2 of 3
Core outlet		2 of 3	2 of 3	2 of 4
Temperature				
Upper plenum	2 of 4			
Core outlet	1 of 1	2 of 3	2 of 3	2 of 4
Bulk sodium	2 of 4			
Power-to-flow ratio			2 of 3	
Upper plenum coolant pressure	1 of 1			
Bulk-sodium level	1 of 1			
Other:				
Loss of power to pump	1 of 1			
Gas-blanket pressure	1 of 1	2 of 3		
Seismograph	1 of 1			

control rods at a fixed rate, called setback, is often used as a safety action prior to a scram. Either nuclear or thermal channels, or both, can initiate setback action from the safety system. Setback will stop automatically when the reactor is back in a safe operating condition. Alarms are also actuated at levels below those initiated by setback, where action by the operator may be used to avoid scrams. Conversely, the operator normally has the option of manually scramming the reactor if, in his opinion, plant conditions warrant such action.

9.2.2 SPEED OF RESPONSE

As a general rule, scrams once initiated should occur as rapidly as possible for any type of reactor. The time required to complete a scram depends upon the response time of the nuclear, thermal, or mechanical process variables up to the necessary relay action, the response time of the scram relays and magnets, and the time required for the safety rods to fall and insert enough negative reactivity to shut down the reactor. Of the above variables for the time required for completing a scram, the electronics for the nuclear process variable leading to a period scram in the source or intermediate range is the most complex to design.

Period information is derived by means of electrically differentiating the logarithmic neutron-flux-level signal. Basically, the process of differentiating a signal is a poor one because of noise problems. If a small noise pulse occurs on the level signal, the differential of that pulse is a much larger pulse; hence, a response such as is shown in Fig. 9.16 becomes necessary. This curve is read as follows: If a 1-sec period lasts for more than 0.4 sec, the plant must scram; if it lasts for less than 0.3 sec, the plant need not scram. The intermediate area represents the accuracy limits

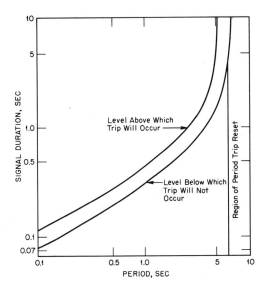

FIG. 9.16—Signal duration vs. period response [24].

of the response. This type of response is desirable whenever the process of differentiation is used.

A time-constant problem usually exists in the count-rate amplifier used in source-range period protection. Present count-rate channels cover from about 1 to 10^6 counts/sec. If the pulse-integrating (smoothing) section is made sufficiently slow to achieve stability, then the period protection is too slow to be useful. If the integration is not sufficient at the low count rates, statistical variations in the count rate can result in false scrams. A method used to solve the problem is to divide the response into two or three time-constant networks. This method results in the response curve shown in Fig. 9.17. As the count rate increases, the time constant decreases. Fast-period protection is maintained at all times because the outputs are added. For example, if the count rate were at 10 counts/sec, the long time-constant section would not be completely

charged. If a 10^4 counts/sec step function were inserted, the fast section would immediately charge independent of the slow section. A period scram would then be actuated.

A similar problem exists in the $\log_n$ amplifier of the intermediate range. If the response is too fast, statistical variations and flux perturbations in the very slow region could cause a false scram. This is particularly a problem down below 10^{-10} amp where the gamma compensation is questionable. A method of avoiding this problem is to completely bias off the period signal at a point where the gamma compensation is questionable and then have a response time that is inversely proportioned to the current level, as shown in Fig. 9.18. Fast-period protection is again maintained, providing the inverse time constant is determined by a feedback loop and not by a combination of excess cable capacity and amplifier input impedance.

9.2.3 RELIABILITY REQUIREMENTS

For reliability the following major points should be considered:

1. Good circuit design is essential.

2. The equipment should be designed for long life, with minimum replacement. This feature dictates the use of transistors and high-quality components, such as silicon transistors, tantalum and silver-coated mica capacitors, wire-wound resistors (where precision is necessary), and wire-wound potentiometers, derated at least 50% (in many cases more derating is desirable). Component packing density should be low (i.e., the equipment should not be overly miniaturized since conserving space is usually not important).

3. Redundancy should be used so that failures of components will not result in loss of scram protection. This allows any one channel to fail without causing either a false scram or the failure to scram when necessary. Each channel should be completely independent; i.e., it should have its own power supplies, oscillators, and other necessary equipment. True independence is difficult to obtain

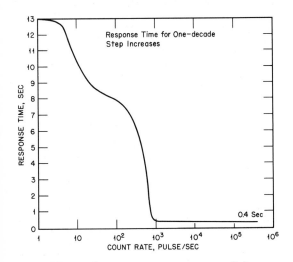

FIG. 9.17—Response of log count-rate circuits [24].

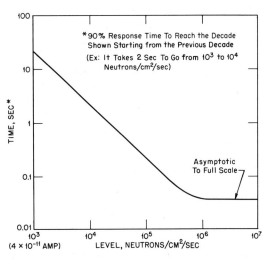

FIG. 9.18—Response time of log circuits [24].

since common mixing of elements of coincidence circuits is hard to eliminate.

4. If an instrument failure does occur, it should be immediately apparent to the operator; hence continuous (high-frequency) self-testing becomes a requirement. If a failure occurs in the self-testing system, it should be annunciated, but it should not affect the normal operation of the equipment it is testing. The simplest method of testing analog circuitry where redundancy is used is to compare it with its redundant neighbor. An analog test is performed on an analog channel. Equipment, including transducers and cables, is continuously tested by this technique.

5. The circuit testing should be such that detection of an instrument failure will tend to cause a scram rather than prevent one.

6. The circuit designer should consider outputs and intercoupling of circuits so that failures are not cascaded. For example, all test jacks should be isolated so that, if the technician short-circuits the output, no failure will occur. Power supplies also should be protected against short circuits. Meter and recorder outputs should be isolated so that, if they are either short-circuited or opened, other outputs will not be affected.

7. The equipment should be easy to operate. Adjustments should be kept to a minimum. Manual operations, such as scale switching, should be avoided.

8. The equipment should be designed so that calibration can be accomplished easily. The calibration required should be infrequent.

9. Scram relays and safety-rod holding mechanisms (magnets) should depend upon loss of power for their operation in order to be fail-safe. Redundancy in this circuitry is most important.

9.3 Control- and Safety-rod Drive Mechanism

9.3.1 GENERAL DESIGN CONSIDERATIONS

9.3.1.1 Selection of Control Method

Three basic methods of control have been used in fast reactors: movement of reflector, movement of fuel, and the introduction of a poison (absorber).

Reflector control is used in EBR-I. Reflector control elements, relatively large and usually located around the core, can in gas-cooled reactors limit reactor power as a result of temperature rise in the reflector, as in EBR-I. In a liquid-metal-cooled reactor, there may be a substantial increase in reactor-vessel size and coolant volume to accommodate the control elements. The choice of reflector materials, the method of drive, the problem of bearings, and space considerations have precluded the use of reflector control for large plants. Reflector control for propulsion plants may be worth exploring. The disadvantages of reflector control have resulted in the choice of either fuel or poison as the control elements in the Fermi, EBR-II, Dounreay, and Rapsodie reactors. Fermi uses poison control; EBR-II and Dounreay use fuel. Dounreay also has an independent backup shutdown capability furnished by three boron poison

rods peripherally located. Because of their location, however, they are of relatively low worth and are not too effective.

Burnup and cooling considerations increase the difficulty of achieving satisfactory fuel control. Fuel as control improves neutron economy and the breeding ratio. The control element is in its most effective location during reactor operation; thus the maximum change in reactivity takes place at the beginning of the shutdown stroke, and potentially faster shutdown during scram occurs. Contributing to faster scram time is the fact that fuel can be located close to the core region whereas poison is generally well removed from the core.

One of the chief drawbacks of the use of poison is its adverse effect on neutron economy and the breeding ratio. A safety rod using poison is kept in its least reactive location during reactor operation so that the effect on neutron absorption is minimized. The location may introduce a significant delay in scram time. Poison control elements can be made reasonably compact. The mechanical design is not too complicated. The effects of burnup are less severe than they are on fuel rods; thus long residence time before rod replacement is necessary can be realized.

9.3.1.2 Drive-mechanism Design

Locating control elements near the center of the reactor may place limitations on physical space for drive mechanisms; locating the control elements peripherally may provide more space but may also require a larger number of drives. Fast reactor control-system drives to date have generally been electromechanical. Other types to consider include hydraulic, pneumatic, straight mechanical, or combinations of these. In a fast reactor use of conventional hydrogenous hydraulic fluids poses problems of reactor safety. A drive using the liquid-metal coolant as the hydraulic fluid introduces technological difficulties. An initial step in this direction could be the use of sodium in dash pots for stopping a scrammed rod. Pneumatic systems could, perhaps, be adapted to use the reactor primary-system gas. Straight mechanical systems requiring mechanical scramming mechanisms have not been adequately designed to date. The scram mechanisms on all three control drives to be described utilize electromagnetic latches. All subsequent discussion is based on an electromechanical system although much can be applied to other types.

The basic elements in any control-rod drive system are (1) a power unit, (2) a drive shaft to connect the power unit to the latch mechanism, (3) a latch mechanism to connect the shaft to the rod, (4) a scram mechanism, (5) inert-gas seals, both static and reciprocating, (6) shielding, and (7) a control or safety rod (element).

The power unit is generally an electric-motor-gear reducer of suitable design, driving a rotary reciprocating-motion device, such as a rack and pinion, or ball nut and screw. In principle, an air or hydraulic motor might also be used or an air or hydraulic reciprocating cylinder.

Fast power reactors are vertically operating systems with the core located a substantial distance below the operating floor. Control and safety drives are located above the reactor plug, a considerable distance from the control element. The drive shafts penetrate the biological-shield plug. To date the shafts have been tubular in form, either round or hexagonal, with the interior sealed from the reactor environment. The shafts are long and slender, imposing fabrication problems from the standpoint of tolerances and straightness.

The latch mechanisms provide a means of connecting the control element to the drive and may vary in design from no direct connection at all, as in Dounreay, to a relatively tight positive connection as in EBR-II. The latch operates in liquid metals at relatively high temperatures and high radiation fields. It should be a simple positively actuated rapid-response device, designed for no hang-up or holdup. Chapter 7 presents details on grippers.

All scram mechanisms now in use are electromagnetic and consist of a fast-acting electromagnet that holds the release member against gravity and a spring load or a pneumatic load. The advantages of this type of scram mechanism are that it is relatively simple and compact, fast acting, and fail-safe in that loss of power causes scram. Scram time should be as short as possible. This time is influenced by such factors as stroke, mechanism delay time, type of scram assist if any (gravity, spring, pneumatic), magnitude of scramming mass, velocity-reduction method, and control method. The amount of scram assist and the type of velocity reduction required are strongly influenced by the magnitude of the scrammed mass. In Fermi, for instance, the scrammed mass for the safety rod is small (about 27 lb), and a substantial spring assist is used; at Dounreay the scrammed mass is several hundred pounds, and no assist is used. With fuel the highest rate of shutdown occurs at the beginning of the stroke; with poison it occurs near the end of the stroke. Velocity-reducing systems may take several forms, such as spring cushioning, pneumatic or hydraulic snubbing, with a dash pot and piston external to the system, or hydraulic snubbing, with the system coolant in a dash pot. The last method is used at Dounreay and Fermi. The EBR-II uses a hydraulic dash pot external to the reactor.

Satisfactory seals for long reciprocating strokes are difficult to achieve with standard packing seals because available materials cannot meet the temperature and radiation requirements and because of the erratic and rather substantial friction loads imposed on reciprocating shafts. Use of a welded self-nesting type reciprocating bellows has improved the situation in this respect and has proved to be a reliable method of sealing long strokes with relatively short small-diameter bellows. These bellows are generally not required to move at high speeds, i.e., they are not required to scram. The bellows seal on the EBR-II control rod does scram; but it is of relatively short stroke (about 14 in.), and the length-to-diameter ratio is small. At Dounreay, where no bellows are used, the entire reciprocating portion of the machine is sealed inside the reactor compartment by means of static O-rings and welded joints. This avoids the reciprocating seal problem. An electromagnetic drive operates through a stainless-steel diaphragm without direct connection.

Control- and safety-rod drive shafts are located in a relatively high flux area. The penetrations should be shielded to maintain the integrity of the biological shield. Small clearances, steps, and special shielding materials, such as borated graphite, boron steel, and depleted uranium, can be used to maintain the integrity.

Rate of change of reactivity is limited by rod requirements. Safety-rod withdrawals are set by consideration of start-up incidents. Control-rod speeds are set by normal shim and burnup requirements.

For normal operation force requirements for the drives are low since the drive is required to move only a few hundred pounds at most at slow speeds. The use of a-c motors running at, or near, their maximum rpm and geared down to achieve the proper rod speed results in a large available force. The purpose here is twofold: (1) to prevent inadvertent overspeeding of the drive through loss of control signals and (2) to have reserve power available to overcome a stuck rod or crud buildup in the system.

If poison is used for control, safety rods must be moved a greater distance from the core than if fuel were used. The stroke is kept as short as possible consistent with nuclear requirements to minimize scram time, to reduce the problems of sealing long strokes, and to reduce headroom requirements.

The portion of the control drive shaft and element inside the reactor primary system is generally subject to sodium at high temperatures and high radiation levels and to sodium contaminants. The power unit is generally operated in areas of relatively high temperature (for electrical equipment). These conditions limit the number and kinds of materials that can be used. Bearings and gears are often required to run with dry lubricants or no lubricant at all. Use of antifriction bearings is generally not possible. Close clearances between mating surfaces may subject the mechanism to clogging and sticking, particularly in areas near the top of the sodium pool or in the vapor space above the sodium.

A detailed description of the control- and safety-rod drive systems for the three major fast reactors now operating or nearing completion (Fermi, EBR-II, and Dounreay) is given in the following sections. The machines used in these reactors are representative of fast reactor control-rod drive systems and are examples of varied approaches to the design principles enumerated above.

9.3.2 FERMI CONTROL AND SAFETY RODS AND DRIVE SYSTEMS

9.3.2.1 General

Control of the Fermi reactor is accomplished by means of 10 poison control rods (8 safety rods and 2 operating control rods). The poison material is B^{10} contained in boron carbide. As shown in Chapter 11, the eight safety rods are spaced nearly uniformly about, and approximately 7 in. from the

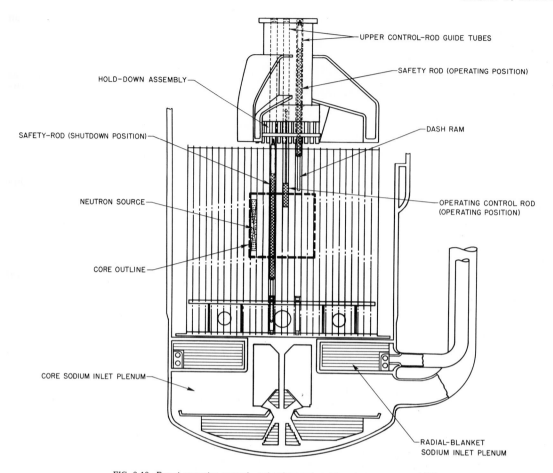

FIG. 9.19—Fermi operating control- and safety-rod positions in reactor vessel [8].

vertical center line of the core. The two operating control rods are on opposite sides approximately 2 5/8 in. from the vertical center line of the core. The operating and shutdown positions of the rods are shown schematically in Fig. 9.19.

9.3.2.2 Control-rod Characteristics

Operational control of the reactor is accomplished by vertical movement of the two operating control rods. One rod is used for shimming and operates at a fixed slow speed of 0.4 in./min, which is equivalent to a reactivity change of approximately 1 cent/min. The other rod is a regulating rod and operates at a variable speed of 1 to 10 in./min, corresponding to a reactivity change of less than 2/3 cents/sec maximum. The two rods have a combined reactivity worth limited to 92 cents total. Design parameters for the operating control rods are given in Table 9.7.

9.3.2.3 Safety-rod Characteristics

The eight safety rods, identical to each other in characteristics and function, are used for normal reactor shutdown or scram. Each rod is worth a minimum of 1 dollar of negative reactivity, and during scram the negative-reactivity insertion rate

is about 17 dollars/sec for eight rods dropping simultaneously. Figure 9.20 shows a curve of reactivity vs. time after scram for this condition. The total time from receipt of scram signal to full insertion is approximately 0.9 sec. Design parameters for the safety rods are given in Table 9.7.

In reactor start-up, all eight safety rods are withdrawn simultaneously at a fixed speed of 1.6 in./min, corresponding to a maximum rate of reactivity increase of less than 1 cent/sec. The reactor is designed to be slightly subcritical with the safety rods fully withdrawn. An electrical interlock prevents withdrawal of the operating control rods unless the safety rods are fully withdrawn.

The safety rods are normally operated together and are either fully withdrawn or fully inserted. During refueling all 10 safety rods and operating rods are in the reactor core and uncoupled from their drive mechanisms. Under this condition, the reactor is approximately 9 dollars subcritical.

9.3.2.4 Mechanical Design of Safety and Operating Control Rods

Each safety rod and control rod is housed in a cylindrical guide tube (Fig. 9.21) which, in turn, is mounted inside a square tube. The guide tubes for

Table 9.7—Fermi Control-rod Design Parameters

	Safety rods	Operating control rods
General:		
Reactor power, Mw(t)	200	200
Total coolant flow through each guide tube, gal/min	27	39
Coolant flow through each rod, gal/min	11	29
Coolant-temperature rise, °F	90	110
Rod life, years	8.9*	0.6*
Poison material:		
B^{10} contained, g/rod	535	88
B_4C volume, cm^3/rod	554	158
B^{10} enrichment, at.%	57	32
B^{10} burnup, %	7†	10
Gas release, liters/rod	3.5(STP)*	6.6(STP)*
Maximum B_4C temperature, °F	1000	1100
Poison containment tube:		
Design temperature, °F	1200	1200
Maximum wall temperature, °F	700	750
Thermal stress in tube wall, psi	400	8000
Internal pressure at end of life, psi	660‡	430‡
Pressure stress at end of life, psi	6800‡	2400‡

* Based on 10% B^{10} burnup.
† Limited by stress.
‡ Based on ASME Unfired Pressure Vessel Code where allowable fiber stress at 1200°F is 6,800 psi.

all rods are made in two sections. The upper section is mounted permanently in the hold-down mechanism and moves with it. The lower guide tubes are seated in the reactor support plates and can be removed and replaced through access holes in the rotating plug.

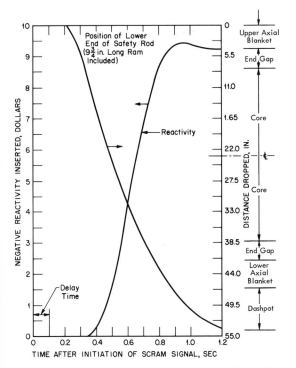

FIG. 9.20—Reactivity inserted vs. time after scram for an eight-rod scram at Fermi[8].

Provision is made in the safety-rod guide tube for scramming the rod. The inner cylindrical tubes in the safety-rod lower guide tubes are perforated by 270 scram holes. These holes are 3/8 in. in diameter and are distributed over most of the length of the tubes. A dashpot at the lower end of the guide tube accepts the dash ram on the lower end of the safety rod as shown in Fig. 9.22. On scram part of the sodium flowing up through the cylindrical guide tube is diverted through the scram relief holes into the annulus between the square and the cylindrical tubes. This reduces pressure drop and drag forces in the rod.

The inner cylindrical tubes of the control rod lower guide tubes are not perforated, and no dashpot is provided. All guide tubes are spring loaded at their lower ends to allow for differential expansion. Pressure breakdown orifices are provided to control sodium flow through the control and safety rods for purposes of removing heat generated in the poison section.

Mechanically the eight safety rods are identical in construction and operation. Each safety rod is made up of four sections (Fig. 9.22). These sections are the dash ram, the poison section, the extension rod, and the handling head. The dash ram is a composite-tapered piston. The lower end has a relatively short, high-angle taper which changes to a long, very slightly tapered section over the remainder of its 6-in. effective length. This piston fits closely in the guide-tube dashpot and during scram acts as a hydraulic shock absorber to dissipate the kinetic energy of the free-falling safety rod. Nearly constant deceleration is obtained with this dash-ram design, and the velocity of the rod is nearly zero as it reaches the bottom of the dashpot. The poison section is approximately 36 in. long and consists of a 2 1/4-in.-OD stainless-steel tube that contains six hermetically sealed stainless-steel tubes 5/8 in. in diameter. These tubes are filled with hollow cylinders of boron carbide. Heat generated in the B_4C is removed by sodium flow directed around the tubes. At the lower end of the rod, just above the dash ram, sixteen 3/8-in.-diameter holes admit sodium to the poison-section tube from the guide tube. Sodium then circulates up around the poison containment tubes and leaves the rod immediately below the handling head. The extension rod is a transition piece that connects the poison section to the handling head. This section is enclosed by the upper shell and contains an Inconel-X spring, which is compressed by the lower end of the drive mechanism when the drive is latched to the drive. This spring exerts a force of about 110 to 115 lb at reactor operating temperature, and upon scram it imparts an average acceleration of about 2 g to the safety rod. The safety-rod stroke is about 54 in., and the rod achieves a maximum velocity of 6.5 ft/sec during scram. The handling head is located at the top of the rod and is designed with two diameters. The smaller diameter is gripped by the drive-mechanism latch, and the larger diameter is gripped by the fuel-handling machine when the rod is being removed from the reactor. When the rod is fully inserted in the reactor, the rod handling head is 2 in. lower than the surrounding core subassemblies. Because of this, four adjacent subassemblies must be removed before the fuel-handling

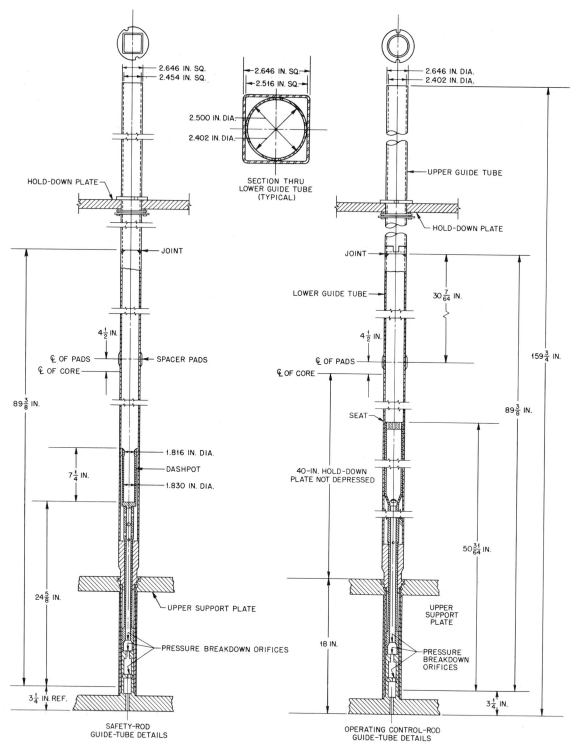

FIG. 9.21—Fermi safety- and control-rod guide tubes [8].

machine can remove the rod. This ensures against accidental pickup of a rod by the fuel-handling machine.

The two operating control rods are identical. Each rod is composed of three sections, as shown in Fig. 9.23. These sections are the poison section, the extension rod, and the pickup head.

The poison section is made up of 19 hermetically sealed stainless-steel tubes, approximately 30 in. long, arranged on a triangular pitch inside

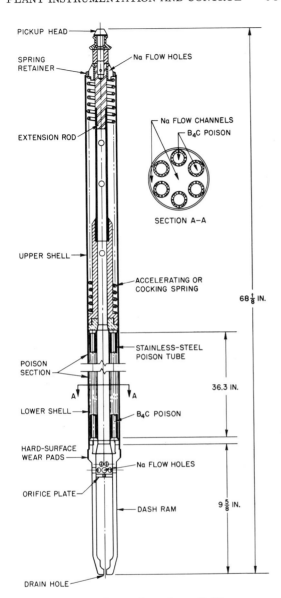

PICKUP HEAD

Na FLOW HOLES

SPRING RETAINER

EXTENSION ROD

Na FLOW CHANNELS

B₄C POISON

SECTION A–A

UPPER SHELL

ACCELERATING OR COCKING SPRING

68⅛ IN.

STAINLESS-STEEL POISON TUBE

POISON SECTION

36.3 IN.

LOWER SHELL

B₄C POISON

HARD-SURFACE WEAR PADS

Na FLOW HOLES

ORIFICE PLATE

DASH RAM

9⅝ IN.

DRAIN HOLE

FIG. 9.22—Fermi safety-rod assembly[8].

control rods is approximately 20 in. Rod worth is shown in Fig. 9.24.

9.3.2.5 Design of Safety-rod Drive Mechanism

The safety-rod drive mechanisms are electro-mechanical devices and consist of two major parts: the power unit (Fig. 9.25) and the drive extension (Fig. 9.26). The drives are mounted above the rotating-shield plug of the reactor on the top plate of the hold-down mechanism vertical drive assembly, as shown in Figs. 9.27 and 9.28.

The safety rods are grasped by a mechanical latch at the lower end of the drive extension (Fig. 9.26, Sec. D) and are raised or lowered by the power unit through the ball screw and nut (Fig. 9.25). The drive extension penetrates the rotating-shield plug through a seal thimble that is bolted into the shield-plug cover with a metal O-ring seal. The reciprocating stroke is sealed by a stainless-steel welded self-nesting type bellows that connects from the seal thimble to the drive extension and isolates the radioactive primary-system gas from the atmosphere outside the reactor. The bellows is backed by a packing seal operating on the reciprocating shaft. The seal thimble and bellows are located in Sec. B of Fig. 9.26. The pickup fingers of the latch are cammed shut by differential motion between the fingers and cam during the latching operation. They grasp the pickup head as shown in Sec. D of Fig. 9.26. The fingers are held in the latched position by the armature of the latch magnet located at the upper end of the extension shown in Sec. A of Fig. 9.26.

A cam extension shaft passing upward through the drive-extension housing connects the camming parts of the latch to the armature of the latch magnet. The combined weight of the armature, cam-extension shaft, and cam, together with the stored energy of the delatch-assist spring (Sec. A, Fig. 9.26) positively cam the fingers open to release the rod when delatching. Loss of current to the latch magnet scrams the reactor. The time from initiation of a scram signal to complete release of the safety rod is specified to be 0.2 sec or better. Figure 9.29 shows the various positions of the rod. The total time to insert the more than 8 dollars of negative reactivity in the eight safety rods is approximately 0.9 sec from the time of scram-signal initiation. The rods can be scrammed from any point in their strokes.

9.3.2.5.1 POWER UNIT. Details of the power unit are shown in Fig. 9.25. These are motor-gear reducer units designed for two-speed operation. Speed change is accomplished by two drive motors operating through separate gear trains to drive a ball nut and screw. Both gear trains are contained in one housing, and they terminate in a common output shaft. An electrically operated brake on this output shaft positively stops the shaft when power is removed from the drive motor. The brake is energized to release; so loss of power to the brake also stops the drive. The gear trains are connected to their respective drive motors through adjustable torque-limiting clutch couplings and are

a 2 1/4-in.-OD tube, which serves both as a support tube and as mechanical protection for the poison containment tubes. The hot-pressed boron carbide poison material is located in the lower 10 in. of the containment tubes in the form of solid cylinders approximately 1/4 in. in diameter. The upper 19 in. of the tubes contains the helium gas evolved from the boron carbide during reactor operation. The extension rod is a transition piece that connects the poison section to the pickup head. A spring, similar to that in the safety rod, is used to assure positive delatching from the drive mechanism when the rod is placed in the core during normal reactor shutdown. The pickup head is located at the top of the extension rod. Coolant holes are provided to permit circulation of sodium around the poison containment tubes as in the safety rod. Total stroke of the

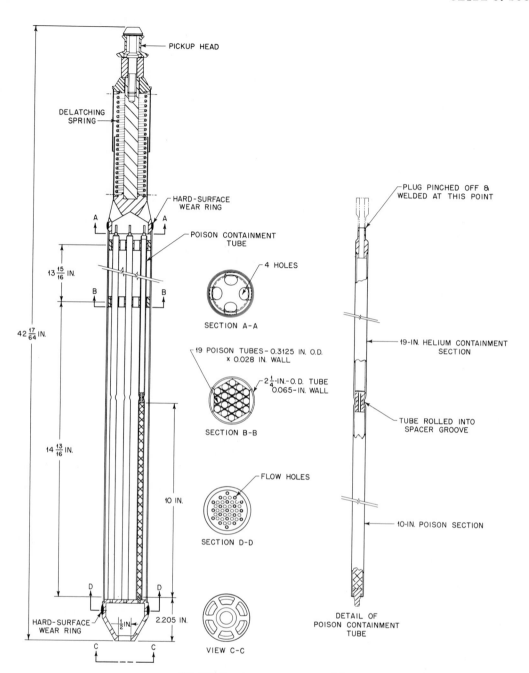

FIG. 9.23—Fermi operating control rod [8].

interlocked so that only one motor can be energized at a time. Both motors are operated at fixed speeds.

With rods latched, the fast drive operates the safety rod at a speed of 10 ft/min and can be used to drive in the down direction only. This is equivalent to a negative-reactivity insertion rate of approximately 60 cents/sec for eight rods simultaneously. With the rod delatched, a limit switch stops the fast drive at about 8 in. above the full down position and switches to the slow drive for the last 8 in. of travel to reduce impact loads as

the drive contacts the safety rod and goes through its latch stroke. The fast drive can be energized either for running the safety rods down at a fast rate under power or for a fast follow-down by the extension after a scram. Any scram signal, either manual or automatic, energizes the fast-drive motors for all extensions. The run-down time is approximately 23 sec for 46 in. of travel, at which time the slow drive is energized.

If, upon initiation of a scram, one or more safety rods do not fall all the way into the core, the drive

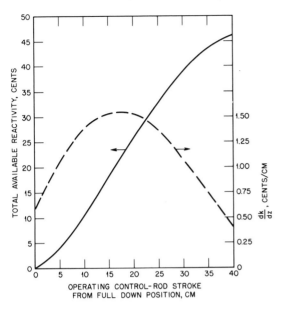

9.24—Fermi operating control-rod reactivity curve and its derivative[8]. (Z is displacement in centimeters).

extension in fast-drive mode would make contact with the rod at some intermediate position and the normal latching sequence would occur. This sequence involves the application of a downward force to the rod of approximately 300 lb. If the safety rod is not freed and driven into the core by this force, the latching sequence will be completed, and the operator will observe that the indicator lights are on but that the rod is at some intermediate position as shown by the indicator for that particular drive. Normal clutch settings will permit driving with an additional force of up to approximately 1200 lb in the down direction or about 900 lb in the up direction for purposes of freeing a stuck rod. Maximum capability of the drive in the down direction is in excess of 2500 lb but is limited by the clutches to prevent mechanical damage to the rod.

In addition, if a scram signal fails to deenergize the latch magnet or if the fingers fail to open for some reason, the fast drive is energized after a delay of approximately 50 msec, and the rods are run in at the 10 ft/min rate. The slow drive is used to drive the safety rods out of the core and to drive them in for the last 8 in. at the fixed speed of 1.6 in./min. The same load capabilities and limitations apply to the slow drive as apply to the fast drives.

Position indication is taken as a voltage from the position helipot shown in Fig. 9.25. The helipot is geared to the drive so that output voltage is proportional to vertical position of the rod. Readout is from a digital counter in the control room. A quick-disconnect coupling, not shown in Fig. 9.25, has been incorporated between the ball screw and the drive extension to facilitate removal of the drives. A strain-gauge transducer has also been added between the ball screw and the extension on all the drives to permit monitoring loads applied to the extension. All electrical equipment operates at a 150°F ambient but has a 225°F maximum design temperature.

9.3.2.5.2 LATCH AND SCRAM MECHANISM. The safety-rod latch and scram mechanisms are shown in Fig. 9.26. The middle portion of the drive extension, which is approximately 21 ft long, has been removed so that the relation between these components can be shown more clearly. The latch-magnet assembly, or scram mechanism, is located in the machinery compartment above the rotating-shield plug, approximately 24 ft above the tops of the fuel subassemblies in the reactor. The latch mechanisms are in sodium at approximately 800°F. The latch-magnet assembly, shown in Sec. A of Fig. 9.26, consists of magnet, armature, magnet guide, overtravel spring, delatch-assist spring, and limit switches. The magnet and guide form an assembly that mounts in, and is supported by, the latch-magnet housing. The limit switches are also mounted on the housing and are actuated by ramps, which are part of the cam extension shaft.

The latch assembly, shown in Sec. D of Fig. 9.26, consists of cam, cam extension shaft, latch fingers, extension housing, and cocking tube. The fingers are supported in a groove in a bearing collar, which is fixed to the extension housing and effectively connects the fingers to the drive-extension housing. The cocking tube is also part of the extension housing and has an internal step that serves to stop the downward motion of the cam and to set its lower travel limit. The cam is piloted in the inside diameter of the cocking tube and is connected to the armature at the upper end of the extension by the cam extension shaft. A flexible connection between the cam and cam extension shaft is provided to avoid transmitting bending loads to the shaft in the event the cam does not seat squarely on the step in the cocking tube.

The lower end of the cam extension shaft is provided with an acme screw thread on its outside diameter. The guide in which it travels has axial grooves in its inside diameter. The purpose of this combination is threefold. First, it reduces the contact area between the parts and thus reduces friction loads; second, it provides a relatively unrestricted flow passage for sodium during the rapid travel during scram; and third, it acts as a scraper to clear possible accumulation of crud.

A latch bellows between the cam extension shaft and the housing prevents sodium from entering the interior of the drive-extension housing above the latch area and thus simplifies cleanup if the extension has to be removed for maintenance. A similar bellows at the upper end of the extension isolates the interior of the extension from the machinery compartment and thus prevents release of radioactive cover gas in this area in the event of a failure of the latch bellows.

A description of the latching, delatching, and scramming sequences is given below to illustrate the operation of the latch and scram mechanism.

The open position of the latch mechanism shown in Sec. D of Fig. 9.26 illustrates the relation of mechanism components immediately prior to the beginning of the latch stroke. The cam rests on the internal stop in the cocking tube and holds the fingers open. The armature is separated from the coil by 7/16 in. The cam is shown just in contact with the handling lug and cannot move further downward. As the drive unit continues to move

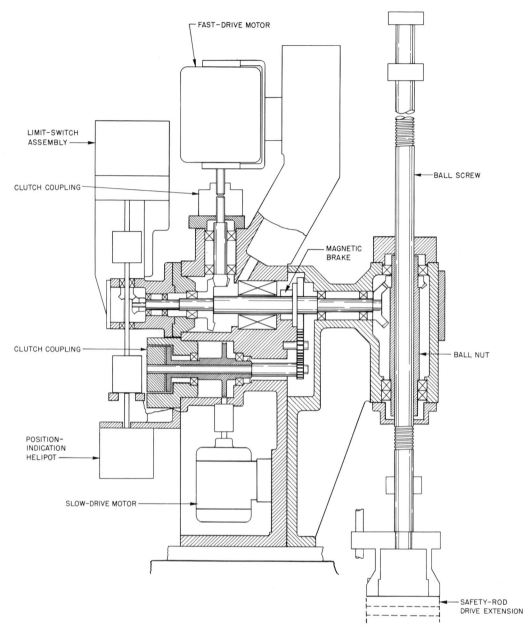

FIG. 9.25—Fermi safety-rod-drive power unit section or elevation view [8].

the extension downward, the latch fingers are carried down with respect to the cam and are closed under the handling head as they are cammed inward. The stroke required to cam the fingers fully closed, 7/16 in., brings the magnet down in contact with the armature (Sec. A of Fig. 9.26). After an additional 1/8 in. overtravel to ensure contact between magnet and armature, the down limit switch is actuated by differential movement of the cam extension shaft and the housing and stops the down travel of the drive extension and energizes the magnet, which holds the armature and maintains the fingers in the latch-closed position. In

this process the delatch-assist spring is compressed; this compression tends to separate the armature from the magnet. The total load supported by the magnet is equal to the weight of the latch rod plus the spring load, a total of approximately 185 lb. In addition, during the latching stroke the cocking tube at the lower end of the extension compresses the cocking spring in the safety-rod drive. This spring exerts a force of approximately 110 lb, which tends to separate the safety rod from the fingers. The drive extension, however, sees only the weight of the safety rod, approximately 27 lb. The fingers see the weight of

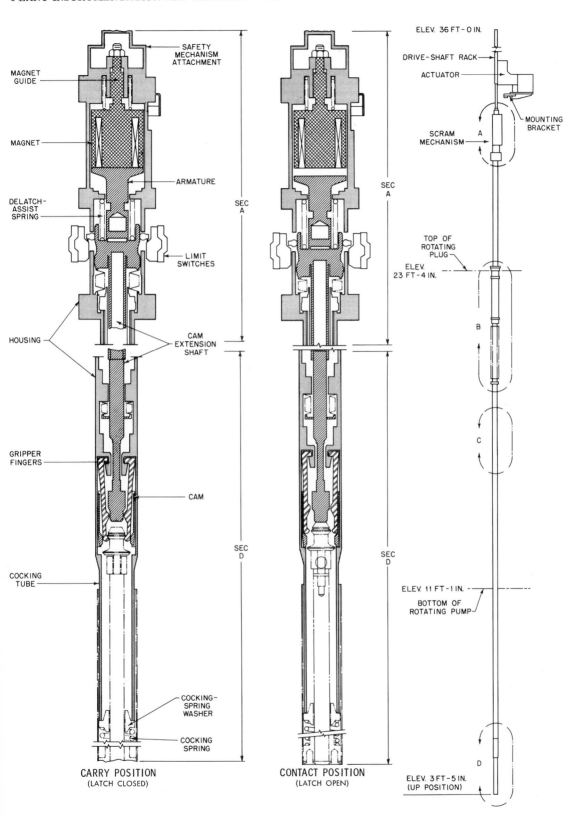

FIG. 9.26—Fermi safety-rod drive extension[8].

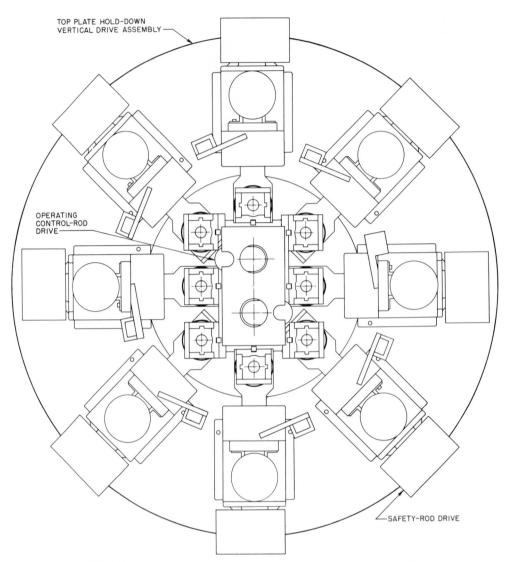

FIG. 9.27—Plan view of Fermi safety- and operating control-rod drive mounting [8].

the rod plus the cocking spring force, about 137 lb. The weight of the safety rod is not reflected to the latch magnet, however, but is transferred through the fingers directly to the drive-extension housing.

The normal delatching sequence requires that the drive mechanism be driven full into the normal down limit. The magnet is then deenergized, and, as the machine moves upward, the magnet moves away from the armature. This permits the drive extension carrying the fingers to move upward with respect to the cam and thus open the fingers and release the safety rod.

With the rod latched and being carried by the drive mechanism, scram is accomplished by interrupting current to the latch magnet, which releases the armature. The weight of the armature, cam extension shaft, and cam (approximately 35 lb), aided by the delatch-assist-spring force of approximately 150 lb, causes the cam to move downward with respect to the fingers. At the same time

the force of the cocking spring, plus the weight of the safety rod, tends to pull the safety-rod handling head out of the latch. As the cam moves down, the fingers are cammed open from the inside as soon as the outside cam surface releases them. Opening of the fingers then permits the handling head to move downward; this action releases the rod. Release of the safety rods by the latch fingers is indicated to the operator in the control room by the "latched" lights' on the control console going off and the "delatched" lights' switching on. These lights, as well as the down-limit switches, are actuated by relative motion between the cam extension shaft and the latch-magnet housing.

9.3.2.6 Design of Operating Control-rod Drive Mechanisms

With two significant exceptions, the operating control-rod mechanisms are similar in design and operation to the safety-rod drive mechanisms. These exceptions are the use of a variable-speed drive for the regulating rod and the use of a special safety-latch arrangement to ensure nonrelease of the control rods at any time except by conscious effort of the operator, and then only when the rods are seated in their guide tubes or are within approximately 1 in. of being seated. Only those

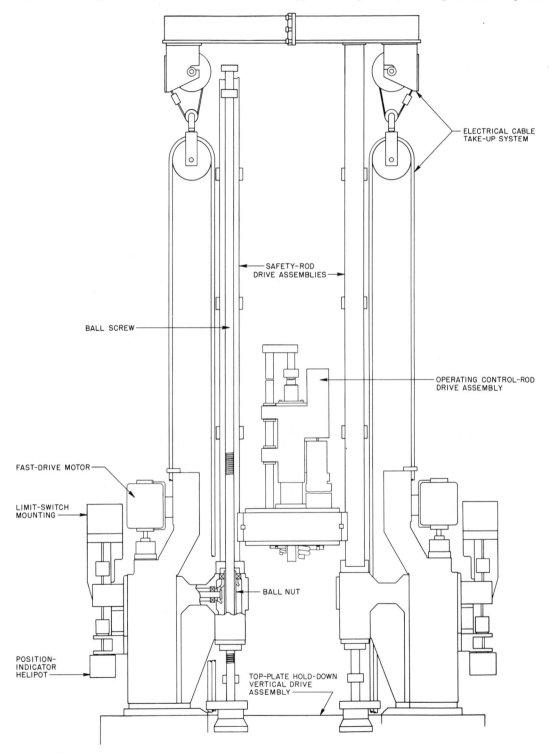

FIG. 9.28—Fermi safety- and operating control-rod drives, elevation view [8].

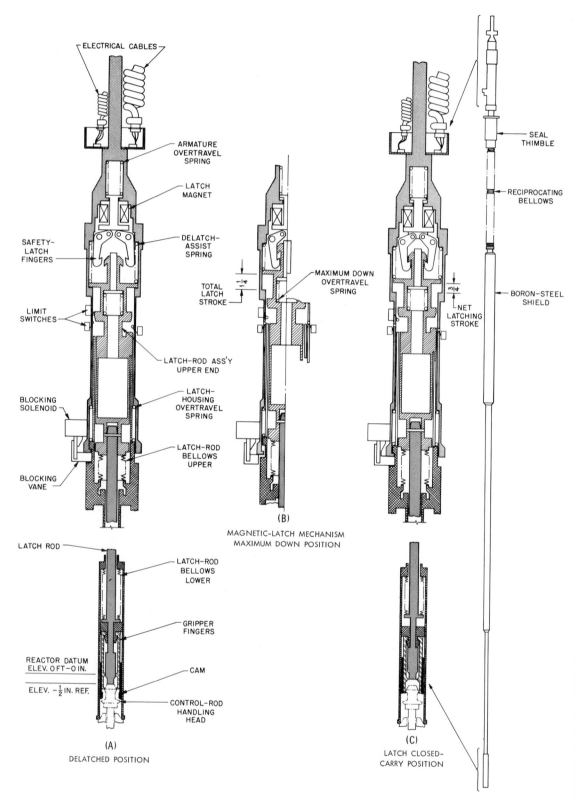

FIG. 9.29—Fermi operating control-rod latch mechanism [8].

features which differ significantly from the safety-rod drive mechanisms will be described in any detail.

9.3.2.6.1 POWER UNIT. The control-rod-drive power units are outlined in Fig. 9.28. They are mounted in the center of the drive nest and are supported from the safety-rod-drive power unit superstructure. The shim-rod drive is operated at a fixed speed of 0.4 in./min in both directions, whereas the drive for the regulating rod can be operated over a continuously variable range of 1 to 10 in./min as required by the control system.

The shim-rod drive extension is driven by a fixed-speed electric motor through a gear train and ball screw and nut assembly similar in principle to that used for the safety-rod drives. No special speed regulation is used since the fixed speed of 0.4 in./min is sufficiently slow to prevent significant speed variations resulting from changing load or line-voltage fluctuations. This is particularly true since the mode of operation of the shim rod is to position the regulating rod so that it normally operates within ±2 in. of its reference position. The shim rod is adjusted as necessary to keep the regulating rod in that range.

The regulating-rod-drive unit utilizes a velocity-control servo system. The demand signal to the servo system is a voltage proportional to the desired rate of change of reactor power. The drive mechanism is then driven by a servomotor through a gear train and ball screw and nut assembly of the same design as that used for the shim-rod drive.

A rate-generator feedback loop maintains the speed, which is determined by the magnitude of the control-system temperature set point and dn/dt error signals. In the event of loss of the rate-generator feedback signal, maximum speed of the drive is limited by the synchronous speed of the servomotor to 15 in./min, or a maximum of 1 cent/sec reactivity change.

The operating stroke of both rods is approximately 20 in., but a maximum capability of 34 in. of stroke is built into the machine. Normal stroke and latching limits are automatically controlled by limit switches with positive, adjustable mechanical stops provided for backup at each end of the stroke. Both drives are supplied with digital readout from position-indicating systems capable of showing relative evaluation of the drive extension to within ±0.030 in. for testing and calibration purposes.

The connection between the ball screw and the drive extension has been revised from that shown in Fig. 9.29 to provide a quick-disconnect capability for ease of removal of the power units. In addition, calibrated strain-gauge transducers have been added between the ball screw and the extension to provide for monitoring the loads on the extension. These connectors and strain-gauge units are similar to those used on the safety-rod drive mechanisms for the same purposes.

9.3.2.6.2 LATCH MECHANISM. The operating control-rod-drive latch mechanism is shown in Fig. 9.29. The design of the safety-rod-drive magnetic scramming mechanism has been modified from the safety drive latch (Fig. 9.26) by the addition of a set of linkage-actuated fingers internal to the latch housing and a rotary solenoid-operated blocking vane external to the housing. A description of the latching sequence will illustrate the difference in design and function.

Latching of the fingers to the control-rod head is accomplished in the same manner as for the safety-rod mechanism. The fingers are cammed closed in the same manner, and completion of the normal latch stroke of approximately 3/4 in. actuates a limit switch that energizes the blocking solenoid. This rotates the blocking vane clear, as shown in B of Fig. 9.29. Removal of the blocking vane permits an additional 1/2 in. of travel of the upper portion of the extension housing against the latch-housing overtravel spring. This overtravel actuates the safety-latch finger linkage, which closes the fingers under the mushroom shaped head at the upper end of the latch rod and brings the armature into contact with the latch magnet. Energizing the latch magnet then maintains the gripper-latch fingers closed on the control-rod handling head and also maintains the safety-latch fingers closed under the latch-rod safety head. Reversing the drive permits the upper portion of the latch housing to move back up 1/2 in. to the position shown in A of Fig. 9.29. This permits the blocking vane to be closed and prevents inadvertent actuation of the safety-latch fingers. The fingers maintain the latch rod in the latch-closed position as shown in C of Fig. 9.29.

Normally the latch magnet keeps the safety-latch fingers closed and maintains the relation just described. However, the configuration of the upper end of the latch rod and of the safety fingers is such that even if power to the magnet is lost the fingers will not open. It is necessary to go through the required latch-stroke overtravel and positively actuate the linkage to open the fingers and release the control rod. This overtravel can only be accomplished when the solenoid-actuated blocking vane is clear, permitting relative motion between the two sections of the latch housing against the overtravel spring. An interlock switch prevents energizing of the blocking vane solenoid unless the drive extension, and hence the control rod, is within 1 in. of the full down position.

9.3.2.7 Materials and Design Stresses

Materials used for the major portion of the structure of both drives are type 304 stainless steel below the rotating plug and type 304 stainless steel or plain carbon steel above the plug. The service required of the latch mechanisms, particularly for the safety-rod latch, which must scram, is severe enough to require special materials. The environment of liquid sodium at design temperatures of 1000°F and the high radiation levels led to the selection of Inconel-X for the safety-rod-drive cocking tube, the lower end of the cam extension shaft, the latch-finger bearing collar, and the safety-rod cocking spring. Because of the shock loads on the cam and fingers resulting from scramming and the possibility of embrittlement of Inconel-X under irradiation, these pieces are made from wrought Stellite 6-B. Comparable parts in the control-rod-drive latch mechanism are all Inconel-X, except the fingers, which are type 310 stainless steel. The cam is also Inconel-X since it does not scram and so sees no shock loads.

The design approach used was to keep all working clearances as large as possible, usually greater than 0.010 in., and to keep bearing loads light. With one or two exceptions, normal operating stresses in all load-bearing members are kept below 4000 psi.

9.3.3 EBR-II CONTROL AND SAFETY SUBASSEMBLIES AND DRIVE SYSTEMS

9.3.3.1 General

A plan view of the reactor arrangement through the core is shown in Fig. 9.30. Control of this reactor is by movement of peripherally located fuel. Two centrally located safety subassemblies, also fuel, provide additional available negative reactivity only during loading or unloading operations.

9.3.3.2 Control-rod Characteristics

Operational control of EBR-II is accomplished through vertical movement of the 12 control rods, located as shown in Fig. 9.30. Movement of each rod is independently controlled from the control room, and the position of each rod is continuously indicated in the control room. Although the 12 control rods and drives are physically identical, they are defined, for descriptive purposes, as regulating and shim rods. The regulating rod is defined as the rod being controlled by the automatic control system. Design of the system is such that any of the 12 rods can be used as the regulating rod. During steady-state reactor operation on automatic control, 11 rods are used for shimming and 1 is used for regulating. During manual control, either steady state or during a change in reactor power level, all 12 rods are defined as shim rods. The power supply is so arranged that power can only be applied to one shim-rod drive unit at a time; thus

movement is restricted to one rod at a time. During steady-state operation on automatic control, one shim rod can be moved to permit the position of the regulating rod with respect to the core to be adjusted.

During scram all 12 rods are ejected downward out of the core by air pressure plus gravity as described in Sec. 9.3.3.6.2. The time between receipt of a scram signal at the rod drive and start of rod movement has been determined experimentally, after the final installation, to be less than 0.020 sec.

Measurements obtained during dry critical experiments indicate the expected worth is 0.004 $\Delta k/k$ for each rod and 0.048 $\Delta k/k$ for all 12 rods. With rod drive speed mechanically limited to 5 in./min, the maximum possible rate of reactivity addition by two rods moving simultaneously is less than 0.00008 $(\Delta k/k)/$sec. However, an automatic flux-control system is designed to preclude the simultaneous movement of two rods in the direction of increased reactivity. Maximum control-rod acceleration during scram is approximately 1.5 g, determined by adjusting scram-assist pressure as described in Sec. 9.3.3.6.2 below. A curve showing rod displacement vs. time after start of rod movement during scram is shown in Fig. 9.31.

The fraction of total rod worth effective vs. time after start of rod movement is shown in Fig. 9.32.

9.3.3.3 Safety-rod Characteristics

The safety rods, shown in Fig. 9.30, are not part of the normal operational control system and are in their most effective position during operation and shutdown. Their primary purpose is to provide backup safety during reactor loading and unloading operations. The relation between rod insertion and fraction of total rod worth effective is similar to that of the control rods (Fig. 9.33). Rod displacement vs. time after start of rod movement is shown in Fig. 9.34. The fraction of total rod worth effective vs. time after start of rod movement is indicated in Fig. 9.35. Measurements obtained during dry critical experiments permitted an estimate of the total worth of the two rods of approximately 0.013 $\Delta k/k$.

9.3.3.4 Mechanical Design of Control Subassembly

The control subassembly consists of a control rod and a guide thimble, shown in Fig. 9.36. The

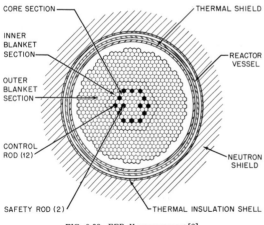

FIG. 9.30—EBR-II arrangement [9].

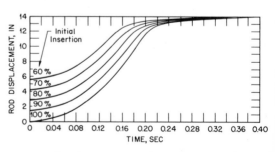

FIG. 9.31—EBR-II control-rod displacement vs. time after start of rod movement (maximum acceleration of 1.5 g)[9].

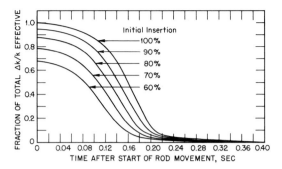

FIG. 9.32—EBR-II fraction of total control-rod worth effective vs. time after start of rod movement (maximum rod acceleration of 1.5 g)[9].

guide thimble is hexagonal in cross section and of the same dimensions as the subassembly tubes. The control rod consists of a modified core subassembly with a core section comprised of 61 cylindrical fuel-element pins identical with those employed in the core subassembly. The control rod is housed in a hexagonal tube 1.908 in. across the flats. This tube is smaller than the hexagonal thimble by the equivalent of one row of fuel elements. The control rod, in lieu of an upper axial blanket, is provided with a void section equivalent in height to the reactor core. Figure 9.36 shows the full down and full up positions. Reactor control is effected by adjusting the proportion of fuel to void (sodium) in the core region of the reactor. Steel reflectors are located above the void and below the fuel. The handling lug is adapted for both control-rod drive and fuel handling.

The control rod is removed from the reactor by the fuel-handling system. Control-rod life is dictated by fuel burnup. The guide thimble is removable. It is locked in the lower reactor grid by a latch that is engaged by rotating the thimble. Rotation of the thimble is normally prevented by the six surrounding subassemblies. Before a thimble can be removed or inserted, the six adjacent subassemblies must be removed.

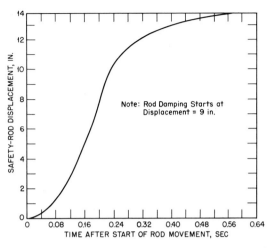

FIG. 9.34—EBR-II safety-rod displacement vs. time after start of rod movement[9].

Sodium enters the control rod through slots in the lower end of the thimble and through a set of holes in the lower end of the control rod. The thimble slots are above the holes in the control rod throughout its stroke. The lower end of the thimble is open, and the lower control-rod bearing acts as a flow restrictor to prevent appreciable sodium leakage from the bottom of the thimble. Since the vertical position of the control rods in the reactor is variable, heat generation within the control rod is also variable. Arrangement of the control-rod coolant holes and the guide-tube coolant slots is such as to permit variable orificing proportional to the position of the control rod in the reactor. Relative size and location of these holes and slots were established experimentally to approach a constant outlet sodium temperature from the control rod in all operating positions. Results of experiments indicate a flow reduction of approximately 35% with the control rod full down. A flow twister incorporated in the void section immediately above the core section of each control subassembly (Fig. 9.36) reduces temperature differentials across the control-rod hexagonal tube and, thereby, minimizes bowing of the control rod in its guide thimble.

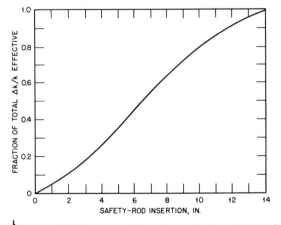

FIG. 9.33—EBR-II safety-rod insertion vs. fraction of total rod worth effective[9].

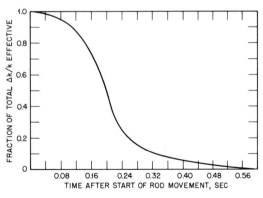

FIG. 9.35—EBR-II fraction of total safety-rod worth effective vs. time after start of rod movement[9].

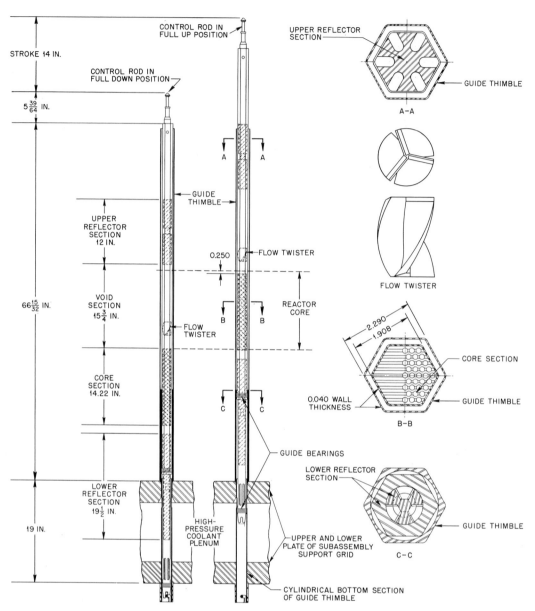

FIG. 9.36—EBR-II control subassembly [9].

9.3.3.5 Mechanical Design of Safety Subassembly

The safety subassembly consists of a safety rod and a guide thimble, as shown in Fig. 9.37. The guide thimble is locked to the lower reactor grid structure in a manner similar to the control-rod guide thimble. The safety rods are attached to a common drive unit extending below the reactor structure, as shown in Fig. 9.38. The unit is driven by two shaft extensions outside the fuel-transfer system and is unaffected by fuel-transfer operations. This drive system is described in Sec. 9.3.3.7. The safety rod is engaged to the drive mechanism by a bayonet type locking device.

Inadvertent disengagement of the rod is prevented by a hexagonal collar on the upper end of the safety rod which normally engages the inside of the upper end of the thimble, preventing rotation of the safety rod. Before the safety rod can be connected or disconnected for change-out purposes, the rod must be raised 1 in. above its normal up position by the drive mechanism. The safety-rod upper adapter is identical to that on the control-rod and fuel subassembles and is handled in the normal manner by the fuel-transfer system. The guide thimble is removed in the same manner as the control-rod guide thimble. Cooling of the safety rod is accomplished in the same manner as in the control rod, except that no provision is made for

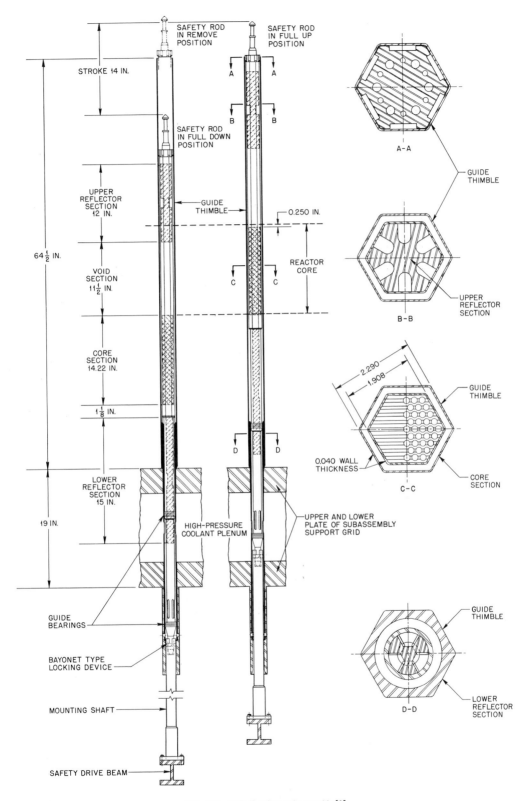

FIG. 9.37—EBR-II safety subassembly [9].

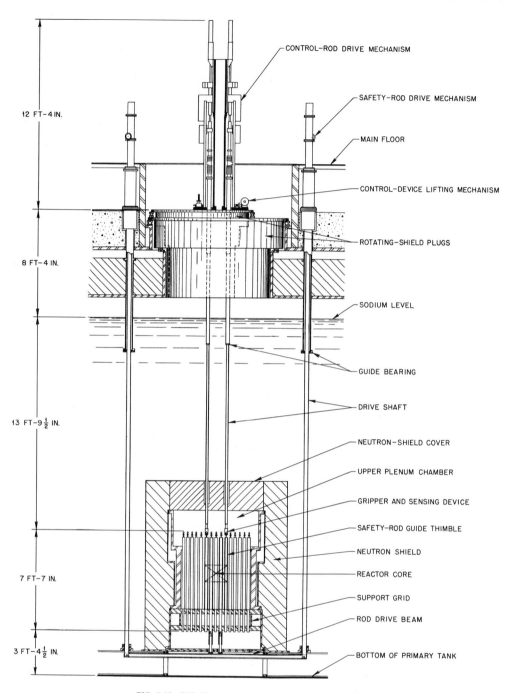

12 FT-4 IN.

8 FT-4 IN.

13 FT-9½ IN.

7 FT-7 IN.

3 FT-4½ IN.

CONTROL-ROD DRIVE MECHANISM

SAFETY-ROD DRIVE MECHANISM

MAIN FLOOR

CONTROL-DEVICE LIFTING MECHANISM

ROTATING-SHIELD PLUGS

SODIUM LEVEL

GUIDE BEARING

DRIVE SHAFT

NEUTRON-SHIELD COVER

UPPER PLENUM CHAMBER

GRIPPER AND SENSING DEVICE

SAFETY-ROD GUIDE THIMBLE

NEUTRON SHIELD

REACTOR CORE

SUPPORT GRID

ROD DRIVE BEAM

BOTTOM OF PRIMARY TANK

FIG. 9.38—EBR-II control- and safety-rod drive system [9].

variable flow since the safety rod is a one-position device.

9.3.3.6 Mechanical Design of Control-rod Drive Mechanism

The control rods are actuated by 12 identical drive mechanisms, which are mounted on a support platform and surround a central support structure on the top of the inner shield rotating plug. The drive mechanism (Fig. 9.39) consists of the main shaft which extends upward through the biological shield into the operating area above the primary system, and the gripper, which is attached to the lower end of the shaft. The drive shaft penetrates the biological shield through a seal thimble, which is connected to the drive extension by a reciprocating bellows. The bellows accommodates the control-rod reciprocating stroke and isolates the

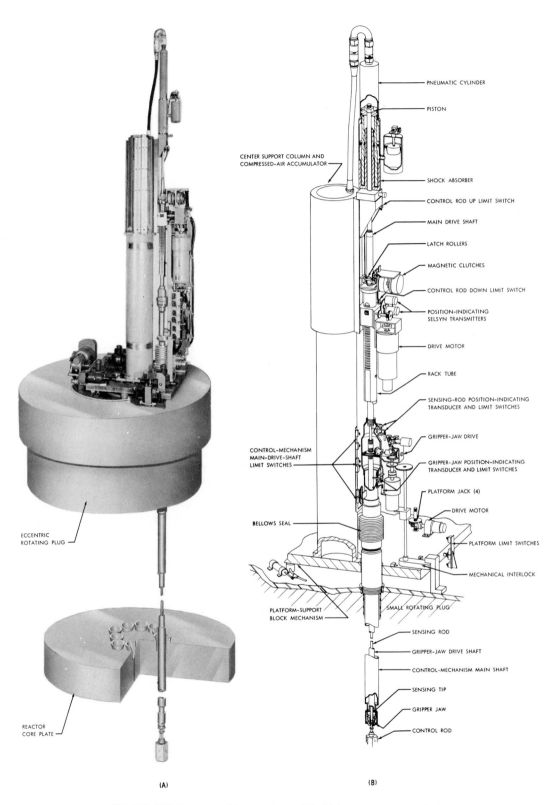

FIG. 9.39—EBR-II control-rod drive mechanism [9]. (A) Location in reactor. (B) Details.

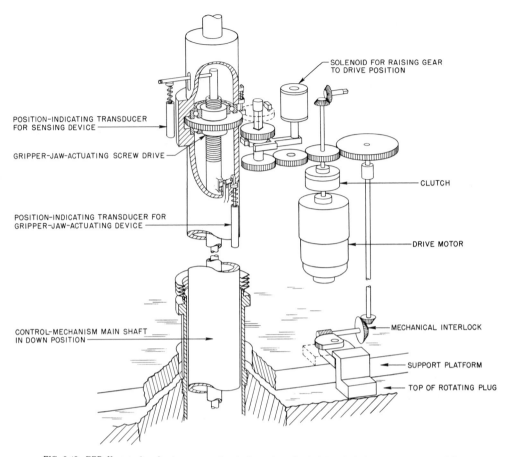

FIG. 9.40—EBR-II control-rod gripper-actuating device and mechanical interlock for support platform [9].

primary-system atmosphere from the above-floor atmosphere. Above the seal the main shaft houses the gripper-actuating device (Fig. 9.40); above this device the shaft reduces in diameter, extends through the rack tube to the latch mechanism (Fig. 9.41), and terminates in the piston of the pneumatic scram cylinder. The main shaft, and hence the control rod, is driven by the drive motor and pinion through the rack tube. The drive motor is fixed to the center support column, which also houses the accumulator for the pneumatic scram assist. The rack tube has the rack gear teeth cut on the outside diameter of the tube and is attached to the main shaft through the fast-acting magnetic latch. This latch consists of two rollers that engage notches in the shaft and are actuated by a magnetic clutch, as shown in Figs. 9.39 and 9.41. The magnetic clutch is energized to engage the latch. The drive motor is a fixed-speed instantly reversible polyphase motor, and it drives the shaft at 5 in./min in both the up and down directions. The control-rod drive mechanisms perform three major functions: (1) connect the control rod inside the reactor with the drive power unit outside the reactor, (2) provide for slow-speed motor drive into and out of the core for normal reactor control, and (3) provide a high-speed drive into the core for reactor scram. Appropriate interlocking and readout for all functions is provided to ensure proper sequence of operation.

9.3.3.6.1 GRIPPER OPERATION. The control-rod drive main shaft is attached to the control rod by means of the gripper at the lower end of the shaft. Attachment is made to the conical adaptor at the upper end of the control rod. This adaptor is

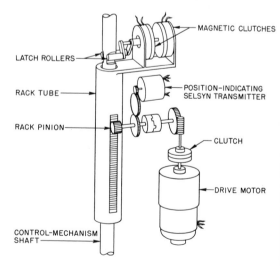

FIG. 9.41—EBR-II control-rod drive and latch mechanism [9].

also used for transfer of the control rod by the fuel-handling machine. Details of the gripper are discussed in Chap. 7.

The gripper incorporates a probe shaft, connected through the center of the main shaft to the sensing position indicator (Fig. 9.40). The sensing probe rod can be used to forcibly eject the control-rod adaptor from the gripper after delatching. This is a manual operation and requires partial disassembly of the machine. Both the gripper-actuating and sensing mechanisms are easily accessible for inspection and maintenance. Motions of the sensing probe and gripper-jaw actuating shaft are transmitted to the control room by position-indicating transducers. This is a manual operation and requires partial disassembly of the machine.

The relation between the control-rod adaptor, the sensing probe rod, and the gripper jaws is such that, after the control rod is released and the probe rod has returned to the down position, the jaws cannot be closed if the adaptor is still in contact with the probe rod. Closing the jaws after the control rod has been released provides a final check that release has actually been accomplished.

The gripper-actuating and probe-rod sensing mechanisms (Fig. 9.40) are so constructed that the control cannot be disengaged except when it is in the down position, i.e., reactor is shut down. This is accomplished as follows: The gripper-actuating drive motor and gear train are fixed with respect to the plug. For all vertical positions of the main shaft, except the full down position, the drive gear is disengaged from the gripper-jaw actuating screw (Fig. 9.40). In addition, the position of the jaw-actuating mechanism and the position of the sensing device are indicated by the position transducers and are interlocked into the system in such a manner that the actuating device must be in its proper position and the sensing probe must affirm that it is before the subsequent operations can be performed.

9.3.3.6.2 SCRAM. Since the control rod cannot be released except in the full down position, scram is accomplished by dropping the entire main drive shaft-control rod complex with a pneumatic assist. This is done as follows: As stated earlier, the upper end of the main shaft terminates in a piston operating in a pneumatic cylinder, as shown in Fig. 9.39. The upper end of the cylinder is under air pressure at 25 to 35 psig. The bottom of the piston is open to atmosphere. Attached to the bottom of the piston is a sleeve operating an annular hydraulic dashpot. Dashpot action takes place only during the lower 5 in. of stroke. Overflow from the dashpot is received in the chamber shown attached to the pneumatic cylinder. Air pressure is maintained on the piston at all times and tends to drive the shaft, and hence the control rod, down. Movement is prevented by the magnetic latch-rack tube-drive motor complex.

A scram signal deenergizes the clutch, which releases the main shaft from the rack tube. The weight of the machine, assisted by pressure in the pneumatic cylinder, drives the control rod down and out of the reactor core, shutting the reactor down. Scram can occur at any position in the operating stroke of the machine and is fail-safe in that loss of power deenergizes the magnetic clutch and scrams the drive. As assurance that the scram-assist cylinders will always be supplied with air, they are fed from accumulators, which are, in turn supplied from an air compressor. The accumulators are located in the central support column. Check valves are provided in the connecting lines between the air compressor. The accumulators, and scram cylinders to prevent loss of air pressure in the event of line failure. In addition, pressure-actuated switches scram the reactor in the event of failure of the air supply. The compressed air available in the accumulators and/or the cylinder is sufficient to ensure pressure assist during a scram resulting from an air supply failure.

Deceleration of the scram stroke is accomplished by the hydraulic dashpot action in the lower end of the scram cylinder. This dashpot action takes place only in the lower 5 in. of stroke. The air-cylinder pressure has been determined experimentally on tests of the drive mechanism. Figure 9.42 shows time-displacement data from these tests. Curves are shown for 50 psig and 0 psig air pressures only. Fifty pounds per square inch gives approximately 2 g acceleration and a total scram time of approximately 0.300 sec. In operation the pressure will be about 25 to 35 psig, which will give an acceleration of approximately 1.5 g and a total scram time slightly greater than 0.3 sec. Test data taken from all drive units fell within the shaded areas of the curve and were taken with 100% initial displacement of the control rods. Tests have shown that the magnetic-latch release time is 0.003 to 0.007 sec.

9.3.3.6.3 DRIVE MOUNTING. It will be seen from Fig. 9.39 that the drives are all mounted on a support platform that is mounted on four motor-driven jacks on the top of the inner rotating plug. This platform can be raised 3 in. and lowered 3/4 in. from its normal operating position. The upward movement is required to raise the lower end of the drive mechanisms clear of the subassembly adaptors during fuel-handling operations after the drives have been disconnected from the control rods. The normal down position of the control rod when attached to the drive is 3/4 in. above the bottom seat in the guide sleeve. This clearance is built in to provide for differential expansion and to assure that

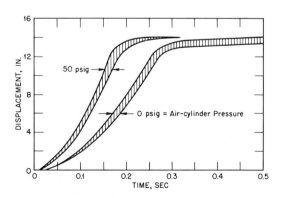

FIG. 9.42—Displacement vs. time for EBR-II control rods during scram.

during scram the drive bottoms in the dashpot rather than in the guide sleeve. When the control rods are delatched, they drop down to seat in the guide sleeve, and the support platform must then be lowered this 3/4 in. to permit relatching to the drives.

The motion of the support platform is electrically interlocked with the gripper-actuating mechanism and the sensing mechanism to prevent the platform from being raised before the control rods have been disconnected from the drive mechanisms. Two mechanical interlocks are provided as an additional safety feature (Figs. 9.39 and 9.40). Two of the twelve individual gripper-actuating devices are geared to operate two rotating stops for the support platform when the gripper jaws are opened. The platform cannot be raised until these two gripper mechanisms have been opened. The platform can only be raised if all 12 electrical circuits have been properly sequenced and the mechanical stops are also properly positioned.

9.3.3.7 Mechanical Design of Safety-rod Drive Mechanism

The two safety rods (Fig. 9.38) are connected at their lower ends to a horizontal member that passes underneath the reactor. The connection is by means of a bayonet type lock (Fig. 9.37). The horizontal beam is connected at each end to vertical shafts that extend upward through the biological shield. Each shaft is coupled to a rack tube by a magnetic-latch arrangement similar in design to that described for the control-rod designs. The rods are similar in design to that described for the control-rod drives. The rods are driven by synchronous motor drives, which simply raise the system to the cocked position, i.e., the safety rods are fully inserted into the core. When the latch is released, the entire drive and the safety rods drop out of the core under the force of gravity. A pneumatic shock absorber decelerates the mechanism during the last 5 in. of travel.

A curve of safety-rod displacement vs. time during scram is shown in Fig. 9.43. The total time required for complete scram travel is about 0.320 sec; the first 9 in. of travel occur occur in approximately 0.2 sec.

9.3.3.8 Seals

Four seals isolate the primary system from the above-floor atmosphere in the control-rod drive mechanisms. The first seal is a flat aluminum gasket, and it forms the seal between the bellows tube and the rotating plug. The bellows tube is threaded into the plug against the gasket to make this seal (Figs. 9.39 and 9.40). The primary reciprocating seal is the bellows located above the reactor; it accommodates a 14-in. stroke. Two more bellows seals within the main shaft near the lower end of the shaft seal the gripper-actuating rod to the inside diameter of the main shaft and seal the sensing probe to the inside diameter of the gripper-actuating shaft.

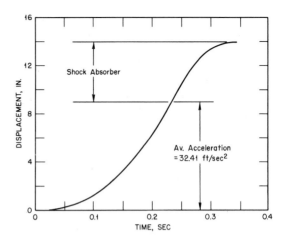

FIG. 9.43—Displacement vs. time for EBR-II safety rods during scram [9].

9.3.3.9 Materials

The following materials are used in the gripper and control-rod adapter head: (1) gripper jaws, type 420 stainless steel hardened to Rockwell C 40 to 45 and chrome plated 0.0002 to 0.0004 in. thick after final machining; (2) guide sleeve, same as gripper jaws; (3) pin, 18-4 tool steel, hardened to Rockwell C 55 and chrome plated 0.0002 to 0.0004 in. thick after machining; (4) sensing device, same as gripper jaws; (5) cam, Stellite 6; (6) main shaft, type 304 stainless steel; and (7) control-rod adapter, type 304 stainless steel.

9.3.3.10 Bearings

Guide "bearings" are used on each control-rod drive shaft at two places, as shown in Fig. 9.37. One guide bearing is used at about the midpoint of the main shaft, and a second is used where the main shaft penetrates the reactor-vessel shield cover. The "bearings" in the reactor cover are in the form of a labyrinth seal and act also as flow restrictors. The upper guide bearings are in the form of a Stellite ring insert in the outer sleeve. The inside diameter of the Stellite ring is semicircular in cross section, resulting in a line contact with the shaft, which is type 304 stainless steel. Diametral clearance is 0.049 to 0.040 in. on a 2 17/32-in. nominal diameter. The guide and seal bearing combination through the reactor cover consists of an Ampco bronze sleeve fitted over the main shaft, running in a wrought Stellite 6-B bushing. The Ampco bronze sleeve, which is about 18 in. long, has labyrinth type rings machined in the outside diameter. Diametral clearance is 0.036 to 0.024 in. on a nominal 2 17/32-in. diameter. Similar bearing arrangements are used in the safety-rod drive shafts. Over 1100 successful test cycles in 750°F sodium, including 18 gripper operations and 80 scram cycles, were run on one test unit. Operation of this unit was satisfactory, and no difficulty was experienced with these materials.

9.3.4 DOUNREAY FAST REACTOR CONTROL- AND SAFETY-ROD DRIVE SYSTEM

9.3.4.1 General Design Considerations

A perspective view of the control-rod drive and position-indicator system is shown in Fig. 9.44. The overall relation of this equipment to the reactor complex is shown in Fig. 9.45. Operating control of this reactor, like EBR-II, is by movement of peripherally located fuel. Of the three basic control methods available, fuel movement was selected since the quantity of B^{10} available was inadequate and the total reactivity that could be controlled by a reflector was limited. The adoption of a double-rotating-plug system for refueling and a requirement that at least 0.01 $\Delta k/k$ negative reactivity be available at all times, including during shutdown, prohibited use of a simple directly coupled control-rod drive unit on the top face of the plug. The space limitations imposed by the double-plug arrangement led to the location of the control-rod drive mechanisms outside the rotating shields. This arrangement permits permanent mounting of the drive mechanisms; i.e., they do not have to be removed

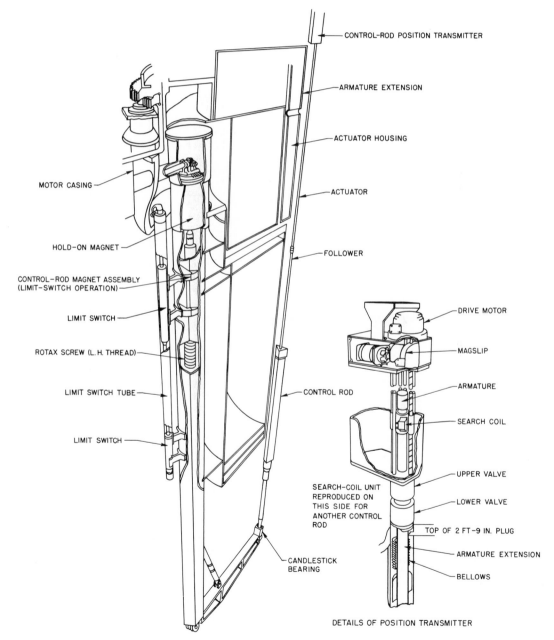

CONTROL-ROD POSITION TRANSMITTER

ARMATURE EXTENSION

ACTUATOR HOUSING

ACTUATOR

MOTOR CASING

HOLD-ON MAGNET

FOLLOWER

CONTROL-ROD MAGNET ASSEMBLY (LIMIT-SWITCH OPERATION)

LIMIT SWITCH

DRIVE MOTOR

MAGSLIP

ROTAX SCREW (L.H. THREAD)

LIMIT SWITCH TUBE

CONTROL ROD

ARMATURE

SEARCH COIL

LIMIT SWITCH

UPPER VALVE

SEARCH-COIL UNIT REPRODUCED ON THIS SIDE FOR ANOTHER CONTROL ROD

LOWER VALVE

TOP OF 2 FT-9 IN. PLUG

ARMATURE EXTENSION

CANDLESTICK BEARING

BELLOWS

DETAILS OF POSITION TRANSMITTER

FIG. 9.44—Arrangement of Dounreay control-rod drive and position indicator [22].

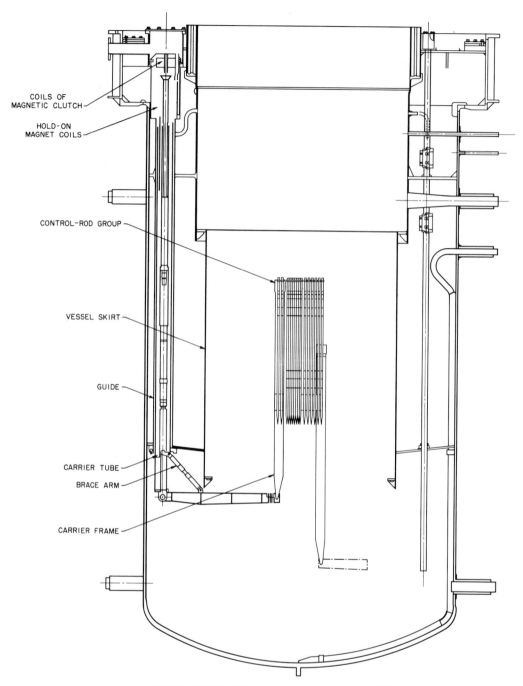

FIG. 9.45—Elevation of Dounreay control-rod mechanism [22].

for fuel change-out as would be required if they were mounted in the inner rotating plug. However, it introduces a design complication in that an offset arm must be used to transfer vertical motion back to the control rod. It further requires that dashpot action to stop the rod when scrammed must be applied to the drive since the control rod has no seat except the offset arm. This, in turn, introduces a requirement that the entire drive be scrammed, rather than just the control rod.

The main control system consists of 12 groups of control elements arranged symmetrically at the corners of the core hexagon, as shown in Fig. 9.46. Each of the 12 groups contains 10 fuel elements held in a carrier frame that can be moved vertically into or out of the core from the bottom of the reactor by the drive-mechanism offset arm. In all respects these rods are identical, but for operational control their functions are subdivided into (1) two safety rods, (2) four shutoff rods, and (3) six control

rods. The reactivity controlled by each group for
the first core loading was (1) safety rods, 0.014
$\Delta k/k$; (2) shutoff rods, 0.028 $\Delta k/k$; and (3) control
rods, 0.043 $\Delta k/k$. This has been increased by 40 to
50% in subsequent core loadings as a result of
increased fuel loading.

In addition, there are three boron shutoff rods
located at the centers of the hexagonal faces
(Fig. 9.46). These rods provide an independent
shutdown system. They can also be used for negative reactivity necessary during reactor shutdown
or refueling periods as referred to above. Separate
drives, mounted on the inner rotating plug, are
provided for these rods.

The most important factors influencing design
of the control rods and drives were (1) guaranteed
availability of the rods at all times; (2) high heat
generation in the core region; (3) necessity for
minimum clearances to reduce coolant flow bypass
and reactivity effects resulting from fuel movement;
(4) positive sealing against leakage of radioactive
cover gas; and (5) little or no experience with
bearings operating in liquid metal.

9.3.4.2 Mechanical Design of Control Element

The control rod proper is composed of a triangular carrier containing 10 fuel elements. This
carrier is raised and lowered by the drive mechanism in a triangular guide tube. The top of the
carrier has a set of high-speed roller bearings
operating against hardened S.80 stainless-steel
strips set in the guide tube. The carrier is artic-
ulated to reduce the effects of thermal expansion,
and a second set of roller bearings is incorporated
in the top of the carrier extension.

9.3.4.3 Mechanical Design of Control-rod Drive Mechanism

The problem of achieving a satisfactory seal
against radioactive cover gas was approached
differently at Dounreay than at EBR-II or Fermi.
Use of bellows was avoided as a method of sealing
the 25-in. reciprocating stroke of the drive. An
electromagnetic–mechanical drive is used with all
the reciprocating portions of the machine sealed
inside the primary system and operating under
sodium. This includes the Rotax screw-and-nut
(ball screw and nut) actuating mechanism. Some
difficulty was experienced with the initial operation
of the Rotax screw and nut. This was attributed to
the pick up of oxide from the liquid-metal surface.
Accordingly modifications were made to the equipment, and the sodium level was raised approximately 6 in. These changes assure that the nut and
screw are always submerged, even with the control
rod in the full up (most reactive) position. The
figures referred to in this description do not
reflect this change.

The complete drive mechanism consists of
(1) the primary drive with shaft and bevel-gear
assembly, (2) an electromagnetic coupling, (3) a
hold-on magnet and thrust flange, (4) a Rotax
screw-and-nut actuator, (5) the support tube, and

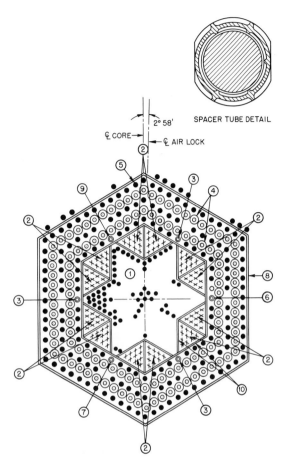

SPACER TUBE DETAIL

FIG. 9.46—Plan of Dounreay reactor core and inner breeder section[22]. 1, reactor core; 2, control-rod groups; 3, B[10] shutoff rods;
4, spacer tubes; 5, breeder elements; 6, neutron-source position;
7, reactor-oscillator position, 8, gagging skirt; 9, spare position;
and 10, inner and outer core skirts.

(6) the carrier arm. These parts are shown in
Fig. 9.47.

9.3.4.3.1 PRIMARY DRIVE. Analog-computer
studies showed that a maximum reactivity insertion
rate of 0.00001 $\Delta k/k/\sec$ should be used in the
control-rod design. This is equivalent to all rods
driving in at 0.003 in./sec, and, although interlocks
prevent insertion of all rods simultaneously, this
limit on the insertion rate was retained.

The primary drive train consists of a three-
phase induction motor (1500 rpm at 110 volts a-c)
driving the horizontal shaft (B, Fig. 9.47) and bevel
gear (C, Fig. 9.47) through a double-train epicyclic
reduction gearbox. Three speeds are available for
the drive: "slow in" and "slow out" at 0.003 in./sec
and "fast out" at 0.15 in./sec. The speed change is
effected by a solenoid-operated clutch between the
two gear trains. A counterweight is attached to the
clutch linkage so that, in the event of solenoid failure, the clutch will be automatically moved to its
slow-speed position. A mechanical interlock prevents operation at high speed when the control rods
are being driven into the core. The horizontal
drive shaft (B, Fig. 9.47) is of telescopic construc-

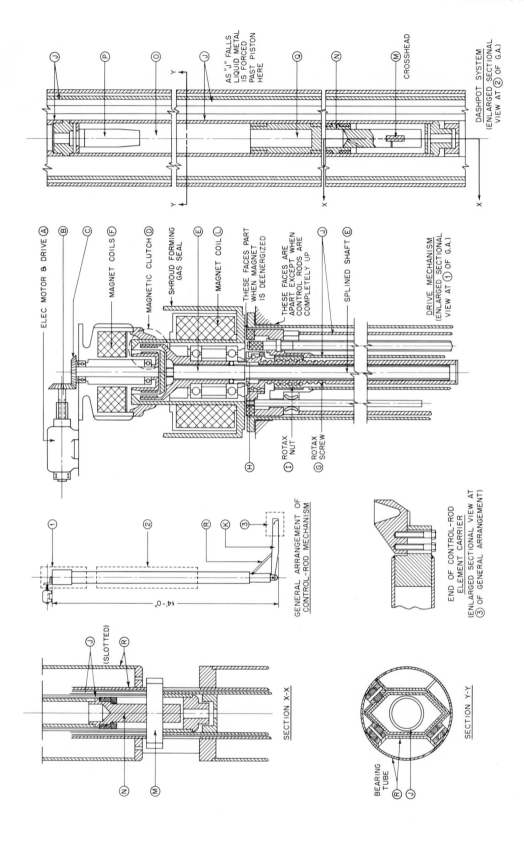

FIG. 9.47—Detail of Dounreay control-rod mechanism [22].

tion to permit the bevel gear to be retracted when it is necessary to remove the drive mechanism from the reactor. Bearings are lubricated with molybdenum disulfide.

9.3.4.3.2 ELECTROMAGNETIC COUPLING. The electromagnetic coupling is composed of the magnet coils (F, Fig. 9.47), the magnetic clutch (D, Fig. 9.47), and a stainless-steel diaphragm. Thus, there is no direct mechanical connection between the primary drive and the reciprocating mechanism. The stainless-steel diaphragm is the gas seal isolating the radioactive primary system from the above-floor atmosphere. Space in this area is limited, and no cooling is possible. Ambient temperature is approximately 180°C (356°F), and the hot-spot temperature at rated output torque (15 ft/lb) of the coupling is approximately 240°C (464°F). Class H insulation is used on the couplings. The driven side of the electromagnetic coupling is part of a splined shaft (E, Fig. 9.47), which is supported on two deep-grooved ball bearings with steel cages. These bearings are also treated with molybdenum disulfide and operate in an ambient temperature of approximately 180°C (356°F). The spline shaft is made from hardened S.80 stainless steel and drives the Rotax screw (G, Fig. 9.47) through a spline collar (H, Fig. 9.47).

9.3.4.3.3 HOLD-ON MAGNET AND THRUST FLANGE. The Rotax screw and, in turn, the rest of the drive mechanism are supported from the thrust flange by a thrust bearing. The thrust flange is made from mild steel and in normal operation forms part of the magnetic circuit of the hold-on magnet, from which it is supported by the energized magnet coil (L, Fig. 9.47). The Rotax screw rotates freely on the thrust bearing.

9.3.4.3.4 ROTAX SCREW AND NUT. The Rotax screw is a high-efficiency recirculating ball unit type. The nut is captive in the upper end of the support tube and carries the weight of the moving parts of the system plus hydraulic forces, which act downward on the system since the coolant flow is downward rather than up as in EBR-II and Fermi. Rotation of the screw raises and lowers the nut and, in turn, the control rod by means of the support tube and carrier arm.

9.3.4.3.5 SUPPORT TUBE. The support tube (J, Fig. 9.47) is of complex construction; it has an outer irregular hexagonally shaped member fixed rigidly at its upper end to an inner cylindrical portion. The Rotax nut is secured in this cylindrical part. Rotation of the support tube is prevented by needle roller bearings in the hexagonal bearing tube (R, Fig. 9.47) within which it moves. The bearing tube is supported in the control rod tube which is a part of the fixed reactor-vessel structure. The carrier arm is supported from the lower end of the support tube.

9.3.4.3.6 CARRIER ARM. The carrier arm (K, Fig. 9.47) is connected to the lower end of the support tube and is normally held in a horizontal position by a pin-jointed diagonal link. As originally designed the end of the carrier arm is terminated by a candlestick bearing in which the control rod carrier frame sits. The control-rod carrier frame was designed with a mating tapered end. It was found during initial operation that misalignment between these parts could take place and that jamming between the mating parts took place. It was not possible to increase the size of the cone support because of restrictions on overall dimensions imposed by the permanent vessel installation. Therefore relative positions of the cone and socket were reversed; the male part is now on the carrier arm, and the female part is on the lower end of the control-rod carrier frame. This arrangement permitted an increase in cone size, and no further misalignment problems occurred.

9.3.4.3.7. SCRAM. Scram is accomplished by deenergizing the hold-on magnet, disengaging the thrust flange, and permitting the Rotax screw–support tube–carrier arm assembly to fall under the force of gravity. A dashpot is incorporated in the support tube, to reduce impact on the mechanism from this gravity drop. When the thrust flange is released by deenergizing the hold-on magnet, the Rotax screw (G, Fig. 9.47) and support tube (J, Fig. 9.47) fall freely for 3 in. until the crosshead (M, Fig. 9.47) strikes stops attached to the bearing tube. The piston (N, Fig. 9.47) then remains stationary while the support tube, which is slotted over the appropriate part of its length, continues to fall. The speed of the fall is reduced initially by the liquid metal in space (O, Fig. 9.47) being forced past the piston and, finally, by plunger (P, Fig. 9.47) entering socket (Q, Fig. 9.47) in the top of piston. During this operation the spline shaft (E, Fig. 9.47) remains engaged with the drive collar (H, Fig. 9.47). Before the control rods can be raised following a scram, it is necessary to raise the screw–thrust flange assembly to its normal position. This is done by driving the screw in the up direction until the thrust flange is in contact with the magnet, which can be energized to hold the screw in its normal operating position.

9.3.4.4 Control-rod Position Indicator

The design of the control-rod drive mechanism is such that there is no positive connection between the carrier arm and the control rod at the candlestick bearing. It is possible to lower the carrier arm either through the normal drive system or by scramming and leave the control rod in the core. Since movement of the drive mechanism in the downward direction does not necessarily result in movement of the control rod, position indication is taken from the rod and not the drive.

Ten position transmitters are provided, one for each control and shutoff rod in the core. No position transmitters are used for the two safety rods. The position transmitters are mounted on the inner rotating plug and consist of the following components: (1) the follower (57 in. long), (2) the actuator (82 in. long), (3) the armature extension (34 1/2 in. long), (4) the armature (1 1/2 in. long), and (5) the search coils and servomechanism. Details of the position-indication system are shown in Fig. 9.44.

The follower is a stainless-steel extension piece that fits into the top of the center element in the control- and shutoff-rod group. With the rods in the fully lowered position, the top of the follower is about 2 1/2 in. below the underside of the 2-ft 9-in. plug.

The actuator is a second stainless-steel extension piece. It rests on top of the follower and is normally captive within the 2-ft 9-in. plug in a collar and bellows arrangement known as the actuator housing.

The armature extension is a third extension piece; it rests on top of the actuator. It extends upward above the top of the 2-ft 9-in. plug, passing through two valves and into a sealed stainless-steel containment called the armature housing. The armature is fixed to its upper end.

The position indicator consists of a balanced induction bridge, the basic elements of which are two search coils mounted coaxially around the armature housing and embracing the armature as shown in Fig. 9.44. A servomotor and selsyn transmitter are mounted on top of the armature housing. The servomotor is geared to drive the search coils up or down the length of the housing by means of a lead screw as shown. At balance the armature is shared equally by the two coils. Any movement of the control rod causes an axial movement of the armature with respect to the coils, and disturbs the balance of the bridge. The servomotor then drives the coils to rebalance the bridge. The position of the search coils during operation is coincident with the position of the iron armature. The selsyn transmitter is geared to the servomotor and transmits the coil, and hence the control-rod position, to a receiver indicator in the control room. So that the accuracy and incremental sensitivity requirements will be met, the transmitter and receiver selsyns are balanced by an additional electrical servo amplifier and motor.

9.3.4.5 Refueling and Maintenance

When the reactor is shut down and the rotating shields are to be moved, the position-indication mechanism must be disconnected and removed. Before this can be done, the search-coil element of the indicator must be removed, and a special magnet must be used to raise the armature and extension to their top position. This places the armature extension above the top valve. The upper and lower valves are then closed and the valve interspace is purged. The upper valve, armature extension, and housing are then removed to permit the fuel-charge machine to be located on the plug.

9.3.4.6 Boron Shutoff Rods

Three boron shutoff rods are provided as an independent method of shutting down the reactor if all the 12 uranium control rods fail to fall out of the reactor. The boron rods are expected to have a reactivity control of $1.0 \pm 0.1\%$. In plan, the rods are situated in the center of the alternate hexagonal faces of the core in the innermost row of breeder elements. The neutron source, the oscillator, and a spare position are in the other three positions. Each boron rod and its operating mechanism consists of the following parts: (1) dashpot tube, (2) boron shutoff rod, (3) makeup piece, (4) machine lower valve, (5) machine upper valve, (6) hold-on magnet, (7) chain mechanism, (8) actuator assembly, (9) drive unit, and (10) snout position indicator. A general arrangement of the assembly is shown in Fig. 9.48.

9.3.4.6.1 DASHPOT TUBE. The dashpot tube is similar to a breeder element in outward appearance. It is made of 18/8/1 stainless steel. Inside the tube is a dashpot made of S.80 stainless steel. The boron rod will fall freely for 27 in. (i.e., for 0.4 sec); in the last 5 in., however, the rod will be retarded and will take 0.6 sec to come to rest. The top of the tube is recessed so that it can be picked up with the charge machine. There are three drain holes to drain the tube of sodium when it is removed from the reactor. The overall length of the tube is 99.3 in. It is supported in its position in exactly the same way as a breeder element.

9.3.4.6.2 BORON ROD. The boron rod consists of a tapered high-speed steel dash tip and a 18/8/1 stainless-steel tube. The tube is 1.032 in. in outside diameter and 0.030 in. thick and contains the boron. The boron, in the form of $80\% B^{10}$ sintered compacts, occupies a cylindrical space 27.8 in. long and 0.9 in. in diameter and has a density of 1.91 g/cm^3. At the top of the rod is an 18/8/1 stainless-steel fitting similar to the top of a fuel element which allows the rod to be removed by the charge machine.

9.3.4.6.3 MAKEUP PIECE. This piece is a tubular extension piece to the boron rod and, under normal conditions, is attached to the top of the rod by claws which grip the top end fitting in the same manner as does the charge-machine snout. The claws are operated by a spring-loaded rod that runs down the inside of the tubular makeup piece. The makeup piece itself moves within the 2-ft 9-in.-diameter plug; it has a collar that rests on a shoulder in the plug when the rod assembly is in the fully down position. A special removal machine is used to operate the claws holding the makeup piece to the boron rod and to remove the makeup piece from the reactor when necessary. The snout of the removal machine engages in the top of the makeup piece, and the same action compresses the spring to release the claws. In the fully raised position, the rod and the makeup piece are supported only by the hold-on magnets; because of this the makeup piece top end fitting is made of Remco iron, which has better magnetic properties than stainless steel.

9.3.4.6.4 MACHINE UPPER AND LOWER VALVES. The lower valve is permanently attached to the 2-ft 9-in.-diameter plug. In the shutdown condition it forms the seal on the boron-rod position. It is a cam-operated full-way valve. There is a nitrogen purge connection on this valve for purging the space between the valves and between the valve and removal machine. The upper valve is similar to the lower valve except that it has no purge connection.

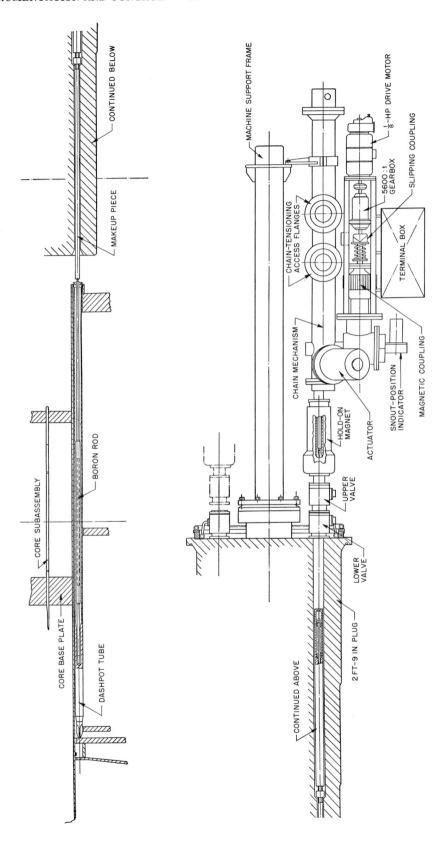

FIG. 9.48—Arrangement of Dounreay boron-rod machine [22].

9.3.4.6.5 HOLD-ON MAGNET. This is the electromagnet that holds the makeup-piece boron rod out of the reactor core. It consists of a center tube of 18/13/1 stainless steel. To the underside is bolted the machine upper valve, and to the top end is fastened the chain mechanism. An inner Remco iron pole is fastened inside the tube to form a stop and hold-on face to receive the makeup piece. The coil is wound around the outside of the tube. In the same assembly there are two search coils that initiate signals to indicate when the makeup piece is in its top position and held by the magnet and when the makeup piece has left the magnet and dropped into the reactor. The coils form a part of a bridge circuit, which is balanced only when the Remco iron top of the makeup piece is close to the coils.

9.3.4.6.6 CHAIN MECHANISM. This mechanism drives the snout up and down through the center of the magnet and valves. The snout has claws that engage the top of the makeup piece to withdraw it and the boron rod from the reactor to a position where they can be held by the magnet. The snout carriage moves in the block of the chain mechanism on two sets of three rollers which run on tracks in the block. Running in the block are two 8-mm continuous chains, one a duplex type carrying the snout and the other a simple type that is used to operate the snout claws. Both chains are driven by the splined shaft from the drive unit, the duplex chain direct and the simple chain via a splined sliding bushing. The bushing has a grooved collar at one end to receive the push—pull fork from the actuator. At the other end there are two diametrically opposite pins. These pins fit into helical slots in the simple chain-drive sprocket, and, with the sliding bushing held in one position on the shaft, both sprockets revolve together. When it is necessary to open and close the snout claws, the duplex chain sprocket remains stationary in one position on the shaft, and the sliding bushing is moved a distance of 15/16 in. along the shaft; the subsequent movement of the pins in the helical slots causes angular rotation of the simple chain-drive sprocket, which produces a movement of 0.6 in. of the claw-actuating rod. The mechanism is open to the active-gas blanket; so none of the bearings are lubricated. There is a possibility that NaK will find its way into the mechanism. This is prevented by two O-rings that are mounted in the chain-mechanism block walls to fit over the snout shaft as it comes up through the bottom of the machine and to rub off any NaK that may be sticking to it.

9.3.4.6.7 ACTUATOR ASSEMBLY. This is the mechanism that initiates the opening and closing of the snout carried by the chain mechanisms. It consists of a small electric motor geared to operate the sliding bushing (see chain-mechanism description) which opens and closes the snout. The motor is operated by limit switches incorporated in the drive unit (see sequence of operations). There is a bellows seal inside the actuator which forms the seal on the gas blanket at this point. The whole assembly is in a gastight mild-steel casing that backs up the bellows seal. A glove-box technique

will be used if and when the actuator has to be removed.

9.3.4.6.8 DRIVE UNIT. The drive unit consists of a 1/8-hp reversible motor complete with brake, a heliocentric gearbox with a reduction ratio of 5600:1, a spring-loaded slip clutch, an electromagnetic coupling, and a pair of bevel gears taking the drive to the main spindle in the chain mechanisms. The slip clutch is of the saw tooth type with only two teeth. One half of the coupling moves away from the other as the torque transmitted exceeds 10 ft-lb. The total relative movement of the two halves is 1 3/4 in., and this movement is used to operate three limit switches (see operational sequence). The magnetic coupling, which is situated after the slip clutch, will transmit a torque of 12 ft-lb. It is this coupling which forms the seal between the drive motor and the gas blanket.

9.3.4.6.9 SNOUT-POSITION INDICATOR. The indicator is bolted into the side of the chain mechanism and is driven from the chain-mechanism drive shaft. The drive is taken via a bevel-gear reduction to a small disk magnet, which drives a similar magnet through the thin-wall seal, which, in turn, drives a magslip transmitter to give position indication of the snout on a dial in the control room. To back up this system, the signals from a magnetic pulse counter are also transmitted back to the control room. This counter consists of a disk carrying four permanent magnets, mounted on the drive spindle on the high-speed side of the bevel gears, which magnetically operate an external counter through the thin wall of the housing. This indication is shown on a four-figure counter below the dial position indicator on the desk in the control room.

9.3.5 COMPARISON OF CONTROL- AND SAFETY-ROD DRIVE SYSTEMS OF THE FERMI, EBR-II, AND DOUNREAY FAST REACTORS

Examples of systems using both fuel and poison control have been discussed in considerable detail. These systems include mechanical arrangements that range from relatively simple to quite complex. At this writing each system has seen rather extensive test operation at high temperatures in sodium or NaK. In addition, Dounreay has had several years of reactor operating experience. Operation has, in general, been successful with all three systems although all systems have required many field changes. For comparison, tabulation of the salient features of each system is given in Table 9.8.

9.4 Auxiliary Control Systems

9.4.1 INERT-GAS CONTROL

A description of inert-gas systems is given in Chap. 4. The inert-gas control systems maintain the pressure, regulate the flow of the inert gas in the coolant systems within specified limits for steady-state and transient conditions, and provide

Table 9.8—Comparison of Fermi, EBR-II, and Dounreay Fast Reactor
Control- and Safety-rod Drive Systems

Feature	Fermi	EBR-II	Dounreay
Method of control	Centrally located poison	Peripheral fuel with central fuel backup	Peripheral fuel with peripheral poison backup
Number and type of control rods	10 rods (8 safety rods, 2 control rods); control rod functions separated into 1 shim and 1 regulating	14 rods (12 peripheral control rods and 2 central safety rods)	12 rods (2 safety rods, 4 shutoff rods, 6 control rods); backed up by 3 boron poison rods
Total negative reactivity available	$> 0.063\ \Delta k/k$	0.063 to $0.068\ \Delta k/k$	$> 0.09\ \Delta k/k$
Shield-plug system	Single rotating plug	Double rotating plug	Double rotating plug
Location of drives	On the plug, in line with rods	On the plug, in line with rods	Outside the plug; rod is actuated by an offset arm
Method of connection of drive to control rod	Direct, relatively flexible connection to rod by gripper	Direct, relatively tight connection to rod by gripper	Rod sits on the end of the offset carrier arm, located by a mating cone and pin
Stroke	Safety rods 54 in., control rods 20 in.	14 in.	25 in.
Scramming method	Only safety rods scram; only the rod is dropped; drive follows down at fast speed to assure that all rods go full in; scrammed mass is small with spring assist; uses sodium dashpot to stop rod; electromagnetic-latch actuation	All 12 control rods scram; entire machine is dropped; scrammed mass large with pneumatic pressure assist; uses hydraulic dashpot located external to reactor for snubbing; center safety rods are not scrammed except during refueling and start-up operation; similar system with entire machine dropped; rods remain latched to drives; electromagnetic-latch actuation	Control rods; all rods scram; entire machine is dropped under gravity; scrammed mass highest of three systems; drive is stopped by sodium dashpot; boron shutoff rods; rod and makeup piece scrammed; mass comparatively small; snubbing by means of sodium dashpot; electromagnetic-latch actuation
Scram time (total)	~ 0.9 sec	~ 0.320 sec	~ 0.5 sec (including 0.14 sec release, excluding final dashpot slowdown)
Type of drive unit	Electric motor — gear reducer driving ball nut and screw external to reactor	Electric motor — gear reducer driving rack and pinion external to reactor	Electric motor — gear reducer external to reactor driving ball nut and screw internal to reactor through an electromagnetic coupling
Position indication	Digital readout in control-room gear driven from the drive gear train	Selsyn system driven from rack-drive pinion shaft; readout in control room	Special system separate from drive; uses direct pickup from control rod actuating a servo operated electromagnetic armature and search coil with readout in control room
Sealing	Metal O-rings and reciprocating metal bellows; bellows with backup packing seals; bellows located inside reactor primary system; bellows does not scram	Aluminum gasket and reciprocating metal bellows; main bellows located outside reactor; bellows scrams	O-rings or other metal gaskets; no bellows; entire reciprocating portion of drive is sealed inside reactor primary system so all seals are static
Speeds	Safety rods 1.6 in./min out and 120 in./min in; shim rod 0.4 in./min in and out (fixed); regulating rod 1 to 10 in./min in and out (variable)	Fixed at 5 in./min in and out for all rods	Fixed at 0.18 in./min out and either 0.18 or 9 in./min in for all rods except for boron shutoff rods; boron shutoff rods run at fixed speed of 0.36 in./min
Coolant flow direction	Up	Up	Down

means for relief in the event of overpressure. The inert gas is used as a blanket over the liquid-metal coolant, is used to purge radioactive gases, and is used for cooling and ventilating purposes. Inert-gas systems may also be used for heating systems and components. Maintenance of gas pressure may be necessary for several reasons: (1) to provide a flow of gas, (2) to provide pressures required to maintain seals operable by inflation or compression, (3) to prevent inleakage of the external atmosphere, (4) to prevent outleakage of radioactive gases to the external atmosphere, (5) to maintain coolant levels within prescribed limits, and (6) to transfer coolant

from one location to another in conjunction with or without a vacuum.

The maintenance of gas flows are required to (1) purge radioactive cover gas, (2) purge other gaseous contaminants, (4) cool and ventilate equipment, and (5) maintain an inert atmosphere within prescribed levels of contaminants by continuous or intermittent bleed and feed.

The inert-gas system control concept should be based on (1) the gas to be used and its physical and chemical properties; (2) pressure limits; (3) whether the inert-gas system is stagnant or is to be recirculated; (4) gas volumes; (5) choice of coolant, volume of coolant, and physical and chemical properties of the coolant; (6) system temperatures, pressures, flows, gas radioactivity, and fission-product release, for both normal and emergency conditions; and (7) capacity, volume, pressures, and allowable flows of the supply and exhaust systems.

The secondary coolant system is designed for nonradioactive operations. This system, in general, requires no recirculation of inert gas. The seals can be designed to withstand the range of operating-pressure fluctuations. Flow control may be needed for the secondary pump-shaft seals if the pump is of the centrifugal gas-seal type; the secondary-system storage tanks; and the cold traps if gas cooling is used. Pressure control may be needed for the steam-generator gas space, the sodium storage tanks, the pump casing, and the surge tanks.

The primary coolant system may require extensive inert-gas system controls. Primary inert-gas system flow control may be required for the (1) primary sodium pump-shaft seals, (2) intermediate heat-exchanger shell side purging, (3) reactor cover-gas purging, (4) reactor biological-shield cooling if open to primary coolant, (5) primary pump casing, and (6) purging of surge tanks, expansion tanks, overflow tanks, and storage tanks. Pressure control may be required for primary-system pressure equalization to maintain coolant levels; pressurization of seals in the reactor plug, control rods, permanent machinery in reactor, intermediate heat-exchanger and pump plug seals, and seals in other equipment connected to the primary coolant system; and pressurization of storage tanks and expansion tanks in the service system.

The inert-gas supply system may require liquid-level alarms in the purification system, pressure alarms, and relief valves to prevent overpressurization of the supply systems. Flow and pressure control may be required for the waste-disposal system, fuel- and equipment-handling machinery external to the reactor, fuel- and handling-equipment cleaning machinery, and fuel and machinery external storage compartments. Flow and pressure control may be required for machinery domes located over the reactor, containment tanks located around the reactor, and reactor-building under-floor atmosphere.

Differential pressures in inches of water may exist between the inert-gas system pressure and some reference pressure, such as the upper containment building ambient pressure, or across seals. It is impractical to control the absolute system pressure at each location to the close tolerance required. Differential pressure control may be necessary.

Pressure and flow controllers are usually conventional. The detectors and control valves are not. Control valves should be tight on shutoff, should be designed to meet the required pressure and flow characteristics and the standards established for containment, and should require little or no maintenance for the life of the plant. In the primary inert-gas system, valves are in a radioactive atmosphere containing liquid-metal coolant vapors. Conventional control valves requiring lubrication or other periodic maintenance are not acceptable.

Condensation of the coolant vapors inside the valves, which could cause subsequent failure of the valves, should be avoided. Detectors in the primary system are not accessible during normal operation and should be designed to meet the plant containment standards and to withstand overpressures, system temperatures, coolant and coolant vapor condensation (or be provided with means to prevent condensation), and nuclear radiation for the life of the plant without losing accuracy or sensitivity within prescribed limits. Transmission of signals from the detectors to the receivers may be electrical or pneumatic. Some systems may have the detectors, receivers (gauges, recorders, controllers), and control valves at different ambient pressures; electric transmission is preferred. If pneumatic signals are used, they would be referred to the ambient pressure at the point of transmission, and the received signals would be referred to ambient pressure at the receiver. The resulting readout may be in error. For some devices the error is directly proportional to the difference in reference to atmospheric pressures; for other devices it is not. Test connections to check detector calibration should be installed wherever practical.

9.4.2 WASTE-GAS DISPOSAL

Waste-gas disposal systems collect gases from buildings, work areas, plant systems, and equipment where radioactivity may exist. The gases are treated and then discharged to the atmosphere in a prescribed manner. Control is necessary to provide proper dilution with air and to discharge the diluted gases to atmosphere when the radiation level falls below prescribed limits. Radiation-level measurements are made after storage of gases, after removal of particulate matter, and prior to discharge. The waste-gas compressor controls the collection-header vacuum within prescribed limits to assure the correct flow of waste gases. Systems supplying gases to the collection header may have long time responses; and wide fluctuations of vacuum in the collection header, without control, may cause recirculation problems.

Radiation monitors in the collection header signal the control system to divert waste gases to the decay storage tanks from the waste-gas compressor. Radiation monitors in the exhaust stack shut off the radioactive-gas discharge to the stack when radioactivity or particulate matter is in excess of prescribed limits. Discharge is a function of radiation level and mass flow through the stack. Flow through the stack should be controlled. Alarms to the operator or interlocks can be installed to prevent operation of the waste-gas system during periods of low wind velocity.

Conventional types of instrumentation are normally acceptable in the waste-gas control system if valves and detectors can meet the leakage requirements.

Before the waste-gas disposal control systems and instrumentation can be designed, the following information must be gathered: (1) gas flow rates, temperatures, and pressures, (2) radiation levels for the alarms and control action, (3) waste-gas composition, (4) gas temperatures, (5) accuracy requirements, (6) system layout showing piping runs and sizes, (7) filter and compressor characteristics, and (8) leakage requirements.

9.4.3 SODIUM SERVICE

Chapter 4 provides a detailed description of the sodium service systems. Sodium service systems provide for the storage, filling, draining, and purification of sodium. The sodium as received is circulated through a contaminant indicator. If contamination is negligible, the sodium can be used without further treatment. If not, the sodium is circulated through cold traps or hot traps to remove the impurities, usually oxide. The sodium in the primary coolant system is checked for contamination periodically and is purified as necessary.

The sodium in the secondary sodium system is continuously tested for impurities to determine water leakage from the steam generators into the secondary coolant. A rise in plugging-indicator temperature can be detected in a relatively short time owing to the relative insolubility of the reaction products (sodium oxide and sodium hydride for sodium systems). A hydrogen detector may be required as a fast-response indicator of water leakage from the steam system into the secondary system.

Instrumentation functions (level, pressure, temperature, and flows) can normally be supplied by conventional instruments if these instruments meet the leakage standards for the detectors and valves, are compatible with the liquid metal and its vapors, and can withstand the operating temperatures and, for the primary coolant system, the effects of radiation. Some or all the following instruments may be required in the sodium service system: (1) flow controllers and flowmeters to monitor liquid-metal flow through the containment indicator, liquid-metal flow through cold traps and hot traps, and liquid-metal flow to and from storage tanks; (2) temperature indicators and alarms to be used in contaminant indicators, storage tanks, cold and hot traps, economizers, electromagnetic pumps, and pipe lines; (3) liquid-level instruments and possible alarms for storage tanks, expansion tanks; and (4) hydrogen detectors in the secondary system.

9.4.4 RESERVE SODIUM SUPPLY

Sodium systems may require a reserve supply of sodium for the primary system in the event of sodium leakage from the system. Demand can be set from the level detectors in the reactor vessel. The demand may actuate pumps and/or open control valves automatically.

9.5 Plant Electrical Systems

In common with electrical systems in conventional generating stations, the electrical systems for nuclear power plants (Refs. 8, 9, 22, and 25) act as both a source and a load. However, safety considerations for nuclear power plants dictate that primary consideration be given to the plant acting as a load so as to provide a reliable source of auxiliary power for the components that must remove heat from the reactor core. Electrical systems for fast and thermal reactors are similar except for the facilities required for the liquid-metal coolant, such as electrical heating of the coolant piping and components.

A nuclear power plant electrical system is generally divided into two parts: the normal auxiliary power system, consisting of the turbogenerator and its associated switching station, which is tied into the step-down transformers feeding the bulk of the plant auxiliary equipment, and the emergency auxiliary power system, which feeds the essential loads of the plant. Figures 9.49 to 9.51 are one-line diagrams of the electrical systems for Fermi, EBR-II, and Dounreay, respectively.

9.5.1 NORMAL AUXILIARY POWER SYSTEM

For reliability, usually two well-separated high-voltage transmission lines are brought into the switching station from the transmission network. These two lines feed separate buses. The turbogenerator is connected into one of the buses through a step-up transformer. High-speed relaying is utilized to isolate either line in case of trouble. Two step-down transformers, each rated to carry the entire station load for a limited period if one of the transformers is out of service, are connected to the main auxiliary bus.

The main auxiliary bus is usually designed to achieve reliability through simplicity and through redundancy in its supply. The bus is normally fabricated with isolated phases and is enclosed in metal-clad switch gear. The entire plant electrical system is usually operated ungrounded with ground-detection facilities for immediate annunciation of a single-phase ground fault, which allows for orderly shutdown and maintenance of the faulted section. Large auxiliaries, such as liquid-metal pumps and boiler feed pumps, are fed directly from the main auxiliary bus; smaller auxiliaries are fed from lower voltage buses supplied from the main auxiliary bus through step-down transformers. Typical loads fed at lower voltages are electric heating for liquid-metal piping and equipment, smaller auxiliaries for the process systems, and the bulk of the building services.

9.5.2 EMERGENCY AUXILIARY POWER SYSTEM

Certain loads essential to the safety of equipment and personnel are classified as essential loads and are divided into two categories, noninterruptible loads and interruptible loads. Noninterruptible loads are those which should be capable of operating continuously upon loss of normal station power. These loads are supplied with emergency power derived from a station battery that is sized to provide sufficient power to remove decay heat from the reactor as well as to supply the load for essential controls and monitors. The following are normally classified as noninterruptible loads: (1)

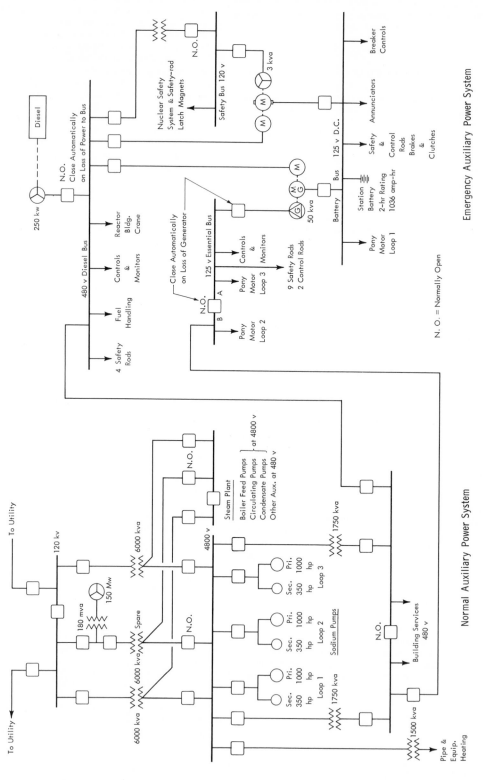

FIG. 9.49—Fermi electric power distribution [8].

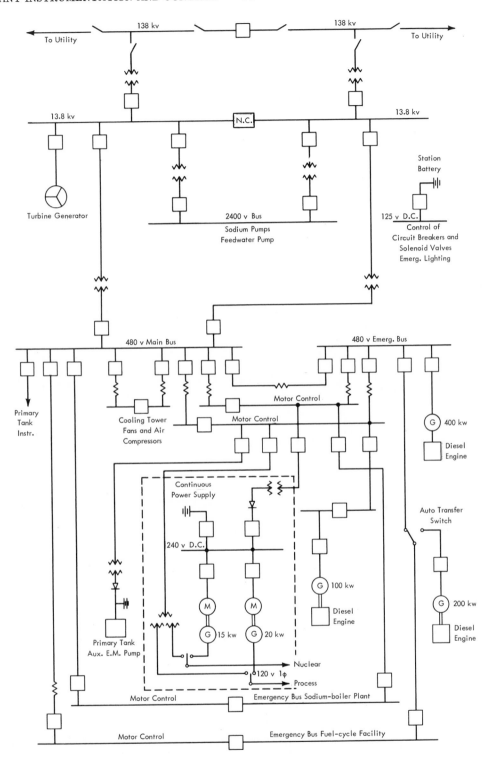

138 kv

To Utility

138 kv

To Utility

13.8 kv

N.C.

13.8 kv

Turbine Generator

2400 v Bus
Sodium Pumps
Feedwater Pump

Station
Battery

125 v D.C.

Control of
Circuit Breakers and
Solenoid Valves
Emerg. Lighting

480 v Main Bus

480 v Emerg. Bus

Primary
Tank
Instr.

Cooling Tower
Fans and Air
Compressors

Motor Control

Motor Control

G   400 kw

Diesel
Engine

Continuous
Power Supply

Auto Transfer
Switch

240 v D.C.

G   100 kw

Diesel
Engine

G   200 kw

Diesel
Engine

Primary Tank
Aux. E.M. Pump

M

M

G   15 kw

G   20 kw

Nuclear

120 v 1φ

Process

Motor Control

Emergency Bus Sodium-boiler Plant

Motor Control

Emergency Bus Fuel-cycle Facility

FIG. 9.50—EBR-II electric power distribution[9].

nuclear safety system, (2) all pumping facilities and controls required to remove decay heat, (3) safety- and control-rod drives, (4) essential functions and interlocks following a scram, and (5) any continuous monitoring or control required for the safety of equipment and/or personnel. Interruptible loads are those essential services which can tolerate a temporary loss of power. These loads are supplied

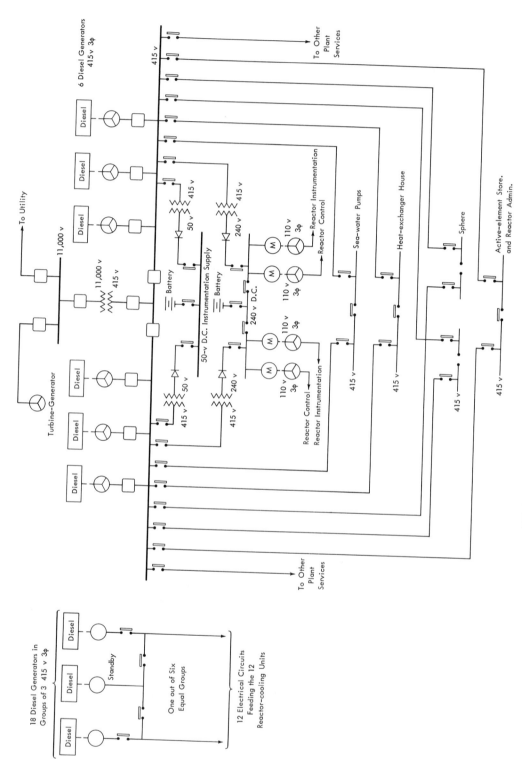

FIG. 9.51—Dounreay electric power distribution [22].

with emergency power derived from a diesel-driven generator that is automatically started upon interruption of the main power supply. The diesel-fuel supply should be large enough to carry the load of fuel-handling facilities, the reactor-building crane, and other essential services until the main auxiliary power system can be restored. The diesel could be operated during fuel handling and remote maintenance, and the diesel-driven generator could be added to the noninterruptible capability of the emergency power system during that time.

A typical method of connecting the emergency power system into the normal auxiliary power system is to feed the emergency interruptible loads from a bus supplied by both the main auxiliary bus and the diesel-driven generator. Prime objectives are to provide dependable cooling for decay heat produced by spent fuel when it is being transported from the reactor; to provide dependable power to the crane handling radioactive components during maintenance; and to provide power to important cooling systems, such as those needed for neutron detectors and shielding.

In most nuclear power plants, the noninterruptible loads derive their power from diesel-driven generators and/or station batteries. At the Enrico Fermi plant, the method of connecting these power supplies is somewhat unique. The system is outlined below and is shown in Fig. 9.49. The emergency noninterruptible loads are fed from the diesel bus and also from the station battery through a three-unit motor–generator set. This bus is referred to as the essential bus. The three-unit motor–generator sets consists of a generator feeding the essential bus, a d-c generator normally providing a trickle charge to the station battery, and an a-c motor fed from the diesel bus that normally drives the three-unit motor–generator set. Upon loss of power to the a-c motor, the starter of the a-c motor opens, and the d-c generator shifts to a monitoring condition; it is fed from the station battery and provides the drive for the generator. This transfer from a-c drive to d-c drive and back to a-c drive upon restoration of power is completely automatic with no change in essential bus voltage and frequency.

It is important that, if the liquid-metal pumps are interrupted, some pumping power be made available to remove decay heat from the reactor. Pony motors are used at Fermi to operate the pumps at reduced speeds. These motors are fed from the essential and battery buses. The battery bus is the most reliable source of uninterruptible power, and, besides applying the essential bus upon loss of normal a-c power, it also provides power for operating the circuit breakers in that plant.

Since the nuclear safety system is a vital part of any nuclear power plant, it is treated as a noninterruptible load. The nuclear safety system is treated as a special load and is fed from a generator driven by both an a-c motor fed from the diesel bus and a d-c motor fed from the station battery, both motors sharing the load. Upon loss of either motor, the remaining motor assumes the full load.

Other types of power supplies, such as diesel-driven generators and batteries, may be employed to feed the nuclear safety system. However, the designer must be cognizant that it is extremely important that voltage and frequency remain constant since this power supply normally feeds the nuclear instrumentation, the rod-latch magnets, and the reactor safety and control systems. This type of load is extremely sensitive to voltage and frequency changes since such changes may appear as reactor power output changes and could cause a reactor scram.

9.6 Fuel-subassembly Accountability

Fuel subassemblies are received, checked, and placed in storage preparatory to loading them into the reactor (Fig. 9.52). During this phase of handling, accountability can be visual. However, once the subassembly starts its journey through the reactor and until it is loaded in its shipping container for shipment to a reprocessing facility, visual observation is no longer possible. The designer should include equipment to assure adequate accounting of each subassembly during its cycle through the reactor. The accounting can be achieved with programmers to receive input signals from the equipment handling the subassembly and a logger to record the information; in this way the location of the subassembly can be noted during its entire cycle. The accounting systems can provide for the preparation of program tapes indicating a sequence of operations. The tapes control the compilation of a typewritten set of operator instructions and supply a reference for comparison with the operations actually performed. An alarm indication is given when the operations performed deviate from those indicated by the program tape. Chapter 7 has details on accountability systems.

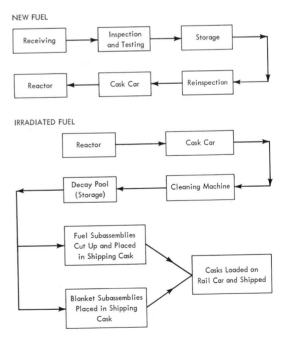

FIG. 9.52—Fuel-cycle flow diagrams.

9.7 Interlock Systems

Interlock systems are used to assure a proper sequence of operations during such processes as loading and unloading reactor fuel. The interlocks make it mandatory for the operator to perform required steps in the proper sequence. A key interlock system is commonly used for this type operation. The system designed for the Fermi plant fuel loading and unloading procedure is shown in Fig. 9.53.

All switches used for power supply circuits involved in the fuel-handling process are non-automatic circuit breakers. The operating handle of each switch is enslaved to one of five slide bars. Movement of a slide bar is manual and causes all the switches associated with it to operate in unison to the "off" or "on" position. The five slide bars group the power supply switches as follows: (1) three switches for the three liquid rheostat electrode drive motors, (2) three switches for the safety and operating control-rod latch magnets, (3) three switches for the safety and operating control-rod drive motors, (4) one switch for the hold-down mechanism drive, and (5) one switch for the rotating-shield-plug drive.

Each of the five slide bars can be locked by one or two key-operated interlock assemblies in which the key is held in the unlocked bar position and from which it can be removed in the locked bar position. The same key is used in two or three interlock assemblies in series. Some key interlock units have a solenoid-operated latch bar-release unit. A push button is used to energize the solenoid, which permits the lock bolt to be moved by the key from its latched position. Various conditions are required before the solenoid can be energized. An indicating lamp is illuminated when the conditions are satisfied. A special two-key unit is also used; conditions for removing and holding the key are opposite for both keys. A mimic bus shows the correct operating sequence. The correct sequence for the refueling operation is as follows: (1) reduce reactor power and scram safety rods at low power level, (2) reduce primary sodium flow to its minimum value corresponding to the maximum liquid rheostat resistance, (3) lock the power supply switches for the liquid rheostat electrode drive motors in the "off" position, (4) detach the safety- and operating-rod drives from the rods and lock the power supply switches for rod-gripper magnets in the "off" position, (5) lower the safety- and operating-rod drives and lock the drive power supply switches in the "off" position, (6) raise the hold-down plate (HDP) and lock its power supply switch in the "off" position, (7) raise the safety- and operating-rod drives and lock the drive power supply switches in the "off" position, (8) close the equipment-door permissive switch and lock it (the equipment door can then be opened to allow the cask car to pass and the plug can be turned for refueling; when fuel handling is complete, the opposite sequence of operation should be followed), (9) place the plug in the 185° position and lock its power supply switch in the "off" position,

(10) seal the equipment door after closing, (11) open the equipment door permissive switch and lock it, (12) lower and load the hold-down plate and lock its power supply in the "off" position, (13) lock the power supply switches for the safety- and operating-rod drives in the "on" position, (14) lock the power supply switches for rod-gripper magnets in the "on" position, and (15) lock the power supply switches for the liquid rheostat electrode drive motors in the "on" position.

9.8 Detectors

Detectors, transducers, transmitters, and sensors are terms that have been used interchangeably in the control field to refer to those devices which sense some parameter, such as pressure or temperature, and give an indication of the parameter level directly on a scale or indirectly to a receiver through electrical, pneumatic, or hydraulic transmission lines. Common usage has extended these terms to include the complete instrument, e.g., "hydrogen detector," which may be a package that includes instruments for the detection, transmission, and recording of hydrogen concentration. This section is intended to present facts pertinent to the use of these devices in nuclear power plants (Refs. 4, 8, 9, 19, 22, 23, 26, and 27). Devices developed for nuclear power plants will be discussed in greater detail than those having common usage in other industries.

9.8.1 NEUTRON DETECTORS

Liquid-metal coolants used in fast reactors are chosen for their good thermal characteristics and their low absorption cross section for neutrons. To date, the most commonly used coolant in fast reactors has been sodium or sodium—potassium alloy (NaK). The sodium or NaK in the primary coolant piping and equipment is highly radioactive. The high radiation level of the reactor and its coolant makes the location of neutron detectors unique for fast reactors. The detector guide tubes are normally positioned vertically rather than horizontally because of the inaccessibility of portions of the reactor building. Because of the location of the guide tubes and also because graphite rather than water is used as a neutron shield, the high temperatures encountered force the designer to use cooling for the detectors and the associated coaxial cables. In addition to the temperature problem, shielding of the detector guide tubes to prevent neutron and gamma streaming to accessible areas should be taken into account. Radiation damage to cables should also be considered. Extensive shielding, plus the use of metal-sheathed cable to circumvent radiation damage, decreases accessibility to the detectors. It is therefore important that the designer make his cooling system as reliable as possible. A loss of cooling, with an associated temperature increase, would cause a change in detector response. Manual shutdown, or

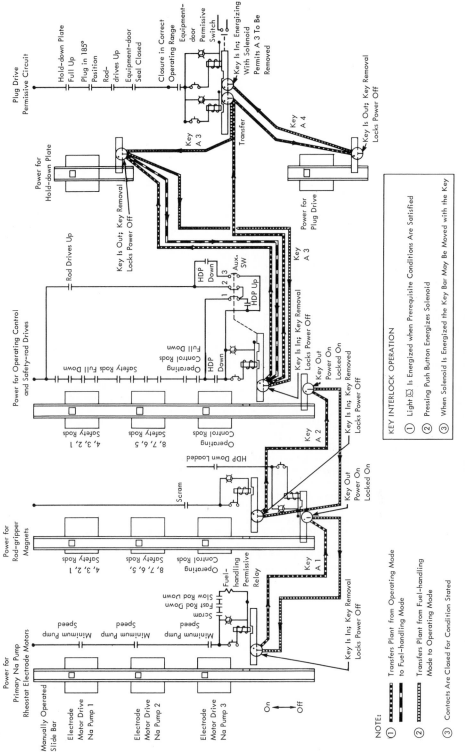

FIG. 9.53—Fermi key interlock operation sequence [8].

possibly a scram, would therefore be necessary if the cooling system were disrupted. If damage to the operating detectors resulted from the temperature excursion, then a plant shutdown would be required (because of the inaccessibility of the detectors) to make replacements. It would be prudent to install spare detectors and cables initially.

Neutron detectors employed in the control and safety channels of fast reactors are similar to those used in thermal reactors. Information regarding the neutron population in the reactor is obtained by measuring the thermalized neutron flux in detector guide tubes located in the reactor-vessel shield. Fission counters, compensated ion chambers, and uncompensated ion chambers, operating on established principles, are used to cover a range of about 12 decades from initial source level to above full power. Typical neutron-detector design data are shown in Table 9.9. Figure 9.54 presents typical counters and some of their design features. The overlapping of the safety channels is shown in Fig. 9.55.

Additional monitoring channels employing more-sensitive detectors may be required for initial core loading and nuclear tests. Since this work is performed at essentially zero or low power levels, shielding is not a problem. The designer therefore would normally use a completely different set of nuclear detectors for initial start-up and would provide one or more guide tubes for this purpose. Standard polyethylene coaxial cable would be used for ease of handling. The transfer to permanent detectors could be made one channel at a time. Cooling of the start-up detectors may or may not be required, depending on the temperature in the start-up guide tube. High-sensitivity BF_3 proportional counters [approximately 100 counts/(neutrons /cm^2/sec)] are available for monitoring and for source-range safety channels. Uncompensated ion chambers may be used for the intermediate- and power-range safety channels since gamma would not be a factor at low power levels. During fuel loading and low-power operation, an additional monitoring channel may be provided through use of an instrument thimble containing a high-temperature (500°F) fission counter that penetrates into the core region.

The use of metal-sheathed radiation-resistant cable, plus the shielding required in the detector guide tubes, makes the positioning of detectors inflexible. Optimum detector positions with relation to the neutron spectrum at the detector guide tubes are determined usually from flux maps of the guide tubes made with high-sensitivity BF_3 counters. This is normally one of the nuclear rests performed at low power operation.

During the past five years, the state of the art in the fabrication of neutron detectors has advanced to the level where detectors are not available for operation up to 550°F. The designer now has the option of not cooling the detectors if he so desires. Detectors are cooled at EBR-II and Dounreay; high-temperature detectors are utilized without cooling at Fermi.

Mineral-insulated or hermetically sealed vacuum insulated cables are available for high-temperature application. Ceramic-insulated high-voltage coaxial connectors are also available for connection to the detectors, or the cable may be made an integral part of the detector. However, this method of connection increases the time required for changing out detectors since the cable would also have to be replaced. One spare detector and its associated cables are normally placed in the guide tubes for each safety and operating channel to reduce maintenance. The spare detector can be connected to the appropriate channel at the operating floor with a minimum of reactor shutdown time if an operating detector fails.

Coaxial cables and connectors associated with the use of high-temperature detectors should be capable of withstanding temperatures on the order of 550°F and should have the following characteristics: (1) radiation resistance, i.e., long life with exposure to neutron fluxes of 10^{12} neutrons/cm^2/sec and gamma fluxes of 10^5 r/hr, (2) flexibility, i.e., can be formed in a helix for shielding requirements of the detector guide tubes, and (3) at operating conditions: (a) operating voltage, 1500 volts rms; (b) resistance to ground, 10^9 to 10^{15} ohms; (c) nominal capacitance, 10 to 30 mmf/ft; (d) nominal impedance, 50 to 75 ohms, and (e) attenuation, maximum 0.1 db/ft at 10 Mc.

9.8.2 FISSION-PRODUCT DETECTION

Gross melting in the core of a reactor may be indicated by transient behavior of the neutron flux

Table 9.9—Neutron-detector Design Data

Type	Neutron sensitivity	Gamma sensitivity	Range	Operating voltage	Channel and electronics range
Fission counter	0.4 (counts/sec)/(neutrons/cm^2/sec)		1.4 to 1.4×10^5 neutrons/cm^2/sec	300 volts	Source-range safety channels starting about one decade below initial source level; range of about five decades
Compensated ion chamber	4×10^{-14} amps/(neutrons/cm^2/sec)	3×10^{-13} amps/(r/hr)	2.5×10^2 to 2.5×10^{10} neutrons/cm^2/sec	300 volts	Intermediate-range safety channels extending about seven decades; overlaps source range by one or two decades and extends to 100% of full power
Uncompensated ion chamber	4×10^{-14} amps/(neutrons/cm^2/sec)	5×10^{-11} amps/(r/hr)	2.5×10^4 to 2.5×10^{10} neutrons/cm^2/sec	300 volts	Power-range safety and operating channels having a range of two or three decades and extending to about 150% of full power

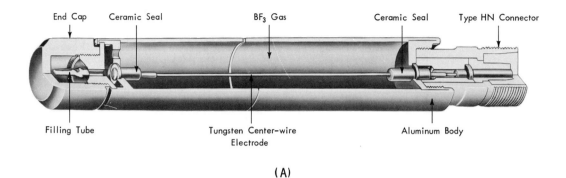

(A)

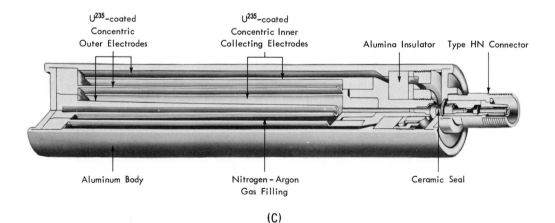

FIG. 9.54—Neutron counters and their design features [28]. (A) BF$_3$ proportional counter. (B) Compensated ion chamber. (C) Fission counter. (Courtesy of Westinghouse Electric Corporation.)

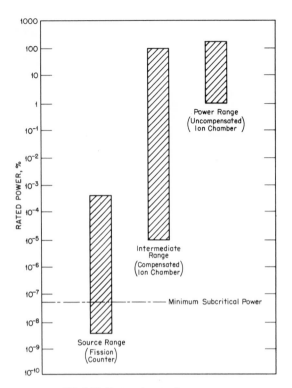

FIG. 9.55—Neutron-detector flux coverage.

or core temperature. However, slow melting in one or two fuel elements is likely to go unnoticed unless provision is made to monitor released fission products. Some method for early detection of ruptured fuel before gross meltdown occurs is desirable. Melting is generally preceded by cladding rupture and the release of fission products. In gas-cooled reactors the gas coolant would be monitored for fission products. In water- or sodium-cooled reactors, either the coolant or the cover gas above the coolant can be monitored.

In sodium-cooled reactors monitoring of the coolant can be accomplished by periodically performing a radiochemical analysis of coolant samples. This method has the disadvantage of not being continuous. Other possibilities of coolant monitoring, which, however, require some more development work, are the detection of coincident gamma-neutron emissions from selected fission products or the detection of fission-product gamma in the coolant. The detectors required for either method could be installed in the vicinity of the coolant piping and would provide continuous monitoring. One disadvantage would be the inaccessibility to the equipment due to the high level of radioactivity in this region.

The coincident technique would entail the detection of gamma emission followed by the detection of the delayed neutron from the same fission product a known fraction of time afterward. The two detectors would have their signals applied to an electronic coincidence circuit, which would allow a signal to pass only if the time interval of the signal from the two detectors were correct for

the selected fission product under investigation. Spurious background neutrons and gammas striking the detectors would not be counted.

Detection of fission-product gamma in the coolant would depend on nuclides' emitting a sufficient yield of gamma with energy levels different from the coolant gamma emission. The electronics would then discriminate against all energy levels other than the fission-product gamma.

A method that is being used for detecting fission products in the coolant is the counting of delayed neutrons of long-lived precursors with neutron detectors. The longest half-life of fission products emitting delayed neutrons with sufficient yields capable of detection is less than 60 sec. The neutron detectors should therefore be located along the coolant piping as close to the reactor as possible. High-sensitivity [approximately 100 counts per neutron] BF_3 proportional counters are commercially available for detecting these delayed neutrons. The pulse counting electronic circuitry is also commercially available. Adequate shielding of the detectors against gamma- and neutron-flux background must be provided. This technique is being used at both EBR-II and Dounreay.

Sampling of the coolant cover gas may be somewhat more convenient because of the lower level of radioactivity in comparison to the coolant. This would be especially true if helium or nitrogen, rather than argon, were used as a cover gas. The relatively unknown diffusion rates of the xenon and krypton fission-product gases from the coolant to the cover gas may present a problem to the designer and may require some experimental work on his part.

One method used to monitor the cover gas is gas chromatography. Molecular sieves could be used to collect the cover gas as well as the xenon and krypton fission-product gases. Detectors would then be used to determine the quantitative and qualitative radioactivity of the gases collected. This type system would not be continuous since the chromatograph requires periodic flushing with a clean gas.

Another method used to sample the cover gas for fission products is a technique employing an electrostatic precipitator. This system has been used in gas-cooled and water-cooled reactors and also at the Fermi plant. A simplified block diagram of the system is shown in Fig. 9.56. The gas passes through an electrostatic field in the precipitation chamber of the monitor. The direction of the electric field is such that solid positive ions entering or produced in the chamber are deposited on a steel collecting wire, which is grounded and extends along the axis of the chamber. After a preset period of soak time, the collecting wire is advanced so that the collecting wire upon which the solid positive ions were deposited is positioned under a scintillation detector located outside the precipitation chamber. The detector output provides means for measuring the activity of the wire, which, in turn, is a measure of the fission-product activity in the cover gas. The detector is purged with clean gas in preparation for counting the next sample. The collecting wire moves onto a storage reel for further radioactive decay before moving into the precipitation chamber again. The gas sample entering the precipitation

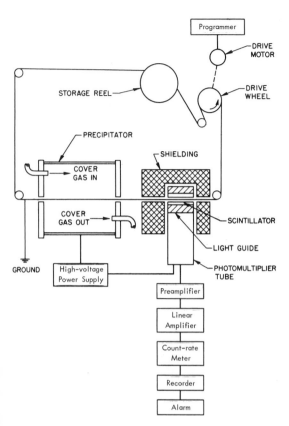

FIG. 9.56—Block-diagram precipitator type fission-product detector.

chamber contains the reactor cover gas and several isotopes of the fission-product gases xenon and krypton. If the cover gas is argon, the isotope Ar^{41} is also present. The positively charged solid daughters cesium and rubidium produced by beta decay of the xenon and krypton are deposited on the wire located in the center of the chamber. Also deposited on the wire is K^{41}, produced by the beta decay of Ar^{41}. When the wire is indexed into the detector, further beta decay by the cesium and rubidium is counted, giving an indication of the fission-product activity. The K^{41}, being stable, has no further beta decay and therefore is not counted.

Of the two methods used in existing fast reactors (delayed-neutron detection and electrostatic precipitation), the precipitator method will detect a smaller fuel rupture, but the response time will be faster with the delayed-neutron technique.

9.8.3 TEMPERATURE

Temperatures are usually detected in nuclear plants by resistance thermometers or thermocouples. Filled-system detectors, bimetallic thermometers, thermistors, and radiation thermometers are not, in general, adaptable to nuclear plants because of the temperature spans involved, the accuracy of measurements required, the transmission distances, the radiation levels, the fast speeds of

response required, or all five factors in combination. Resistance thermometers and thermocouples have a minimum number of limitations. Resistance thermometers are normally used over relatively narrow temperature ranges where high accuracy is required. Thermocouples are normally used where limited accuracy is required over wide ranges of temperature or where a number of temperature points are to be scanned on the same instrument.

9.8.3.1 Thermocouples

Thermocouples are used extensively in nuclear plants to sense temperature; a power plant may have as many as 300 to 500 thermocouples in the primary system alone. An experimental or test reactor may have 1000 thermocouples or more. Nuclear plants pose problems in thermocouple selection, i.e., the atmosphere (reducing or oxidizing), the correct type of couple for the temperature range, wire size for a particular application, and corrosion requirements. The thermocouples should be as small as possible and should be insensitive to nuclear radiation. Thermocouples may exhibit unusual characteristics under radiation influences; for example, it has been reported[36] that thermocouples may develop as much as 40 volts from the couple to sheath in an insulated-sheath couple during irradiation. By proper selection, application, and installation, system errors can be held within reasonable tolerance. Thermocouples are used inside the reactor to detect fuel, coolant, shielding, and vessel temperatures. Several (up to 24) thermocouples can be read on one instrument chart. Deviations from normal temperatures can disclose hot spots or cold spots in the system due to channelling or plugging of coolant through the reactor. Thermocouple measurements in the primary coolant system indicate any deterioration of insulation, cooling-system failure, cooling-system plugging, and other malfunctions. Thermocouples are used to monitor such items as the temperature of pump bearings, motor bearings, lubricating systems, and motor windings.

Thermocouples used to detect critical temperatures, especially those used for safety shut-down systems, should have fast time responses. The thermocouple should be hermetically sealed in a metallic sheath to prevent oxidation of the thermocouple wire or junction in the atmosphere to which it is exposed and/or to prevent shorting of the thermocouple by the liquid-metal coolant system. Thermocouple speed of response is a function of the mass of the couple and sheath and of whether the thermocouple is bonded to the sheath or thermally insulated from the sheath (Fig. 9.57). The fastest speed of response is attained from minimum-diameter sheath thermocouples with the couple junction welded to the tip of the thermocouple assembly. Sheath thermocouples 1/16-in. in outside diameter are available with time constants of the order of 0.5 sec for a 250°F step change in sodium; 1/8-in.-OD sheath thermocouples have time constants of about 2 sec for the same step change. Although smaller sheath thermocouples are available, they are more difficult to fabricate and install and the average operating life is generally reduced.

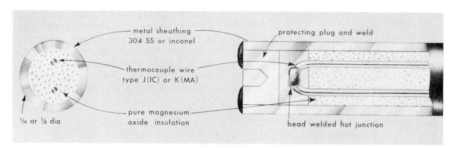

Magnified cross section shows construction of thermocouple. The pure magnesium oxide insulation provides high electrical resistance and long life.

TYPES OF MEASURING JUNCTIONS

Designation	Type of Junction		Description
P	Insulation / Wire / Sheath	Plug Weld	Junction is welded. A plug is inserted in the end and welded to the sheath. Junction may or may not be grounded.
G	Insulation / Wire / Sheath	Integral (Grounded)	Junction is welded to tip of sheath.
E	Insulation / Wire / Sheath / Seal	Exposed	Sheath end is left open. Wires are welded and exposed for a length of one sheath diameter. Sheath end is sealed with cement. Seal effective to 1000°F.
R	Insulation / Wire / Sheath	Remote (Insulated)	Junction is embedded in the insulation. Junction is insulated from sheath both at room temperature and elevated temperature.

SPEED OF RESPONSE

Type of Junction	Sheath Diameter (in.)	Speed of Response (Seconds)		
		From Room Temp. to Boiling Water	From Room Temp. to Salt Bath at 800°F	From Still Air at 200°F to Still Air at 1500°F
Plug Weld	1/16	0.4	0.5	9.1
	1/8	1.2	2.3	18.0
	3/16	2.6	4.9	26.0
	1/4	5.0	8.2	34.0
	3/8	12.0	14.5	50.4
Integral (Grounded)	1/16	0.2	0.3	9.0
	1/8	0.7	1.1	16.0
	3/16	1.5	3.0	23.0
	1/4	1.7	3.8	32.3
	3/8	2.8	7.3	44.5
Exposed	1/16	0.1	0.1	8.3
	1/8	0.1	0.1	13.0
	3/16	0.1	0.2	21.0
	1/4	0.1	0.2	27.0
	3/8	0.1	0.2	27.5
Remote (Insulated)	1/16	0.8	0.8	9.7
	1/8	2.2	2.8	22.0
	3/16	4.8	7.8	31.5
	1/4	7.8	9.5	42.0
	3/8	13.5	17.6	76.0

FIG. 9.57—Types of thermocouple junctions [29]. (Courtesy Minneapolis–Honeywell Regulator Company.)

The 1/16- and 1/8-in.-OD sheath thermocouples normally satisfy thermocouple requirements in a nuclear plant.

The measuring circuits using the fast-speed thermocouples with the couple welded internally to the sheath should be capable of performing properly with the thermocouple grounded or ungrounded. It is possible that the thermocouple-to-sheath junction can be broken (possible by thermal shocks); this would not affect the use of the thermocouple as a temperature-measuring device. The receiving-instrument design should take into account the difference in the ground potential at the thermocouple and the ground potential at the instrument. The difference may result in ground loops through the thermocouple wiring.

Thermocouples may not repeat the original calibration closer than about 25°F at 1000°F after temperature cycling. This repeatibility can be improved (to within 5°F at 1000°F) if the thermocouple is calibrated after aging at temperatures 150 to 200°F above the maximum plant operating temperatures for a period of 150 to 200 hr. Nonrepeatibility may be caused by moisture in the thermocouple insulation rather than by any thermal effect on the couple.

Induction heating used on liquid-metal systems to keep the metal in a molten state during nonpower operation may induce errors in the thermocouple system. The measuring circuits should be designed to filter out the induction-heating frequency (usually 60 cycles/sec). Heat may also be induced into the system. The thermocouple sheath should be installed to have minimum contact with the field created by the induction-heating wiring. The sheath and wire should be installed, if possible, perpendicular to the face of the helicord formed by the induction wiring. Errors of 1 to 8°F have been reported as a result of induction-heating systems near the thermocouples and thermocouple leads.

The sheath material should be compatible for corrosion strength and weldability with that of the vessel of which it is a part. The thermocouple wiring should be free of terminal-contact resistances. Thermocouples should be calibrated just prior to installation and should be tested for grounds and insulation resistance between leads to detect any damage from handling. They should be retested after installation for continuity and insulation resistance between leads.

Magnesium oxide–insulated chromel–alumel, and iron–constantan thermocouples with type 304 stainless-steel sheaths have been used successfully in nuclear reactors up to liquid-metal temperatures of 1000°F. The use of type 316 stainless steel and Inconel can extend this range to 1200°F or more.

9.8.3.2 Resistance Thermometers

There are resistance thermometers that can accurately detect temperatures within 0.1°F or less in nuclear reactors up to 1000°F. Platinum elements are particularly well suited to these applications because of their long life with negligible drift, their predictable resistance vs. temperature curves, their resistance to radiation damage, and availability. Units are available with time constants (63.2% of a step change) as low as 1 sec.

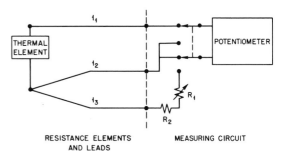

FIG. 9.58—Resistance-thermometer circuitry, scheme A.

There are two major factors that influence the accuracy of measuring temperature with resistance thermometers. These are thermometer self-heating and the effect of lead resistance between the thermal element and the measuring circuit. Self-heating is the error due to I^2R losses in the thermal element. This error is negligible if the current through the thermometer is small (5 ma). The effect of lead resistors can be eliminated (assuming matched leads are exposed to the same ambient temperature variations) by the modification to the normal circuit shown in Fig. 9.58.

In this circuit R_1 is a resistor having zero temperature coefficient of resistivity located in the thermometer terminal block to replace R_2 in the conventional measuring circuit. The current through the thermal elements must be kept constant. If R_1 is manufactured to be equal in resistance of the thermal elements at some specific temperature, $E_1 = E_2$ at that temperature. As the temperature increases, the resistance of the thermal element increases in accordance with the temperature vs. resistance curve of the element. The difference in voltages E_1 and E_2 is proportional to the differences in resistances between the thermal element and R_1. Leads 1_1 and 1_2 should be matched in resistance.

An alternate scheme commonly used for compensating for lead resistance is shown in Fig. 9.59. In this circuit changes in lead resistance are periodically checked by manually switching to a high-precision variable potentiometer. Thermometer-lead resistance is included in the circuit. This circuit can be used for initial instrument calibrations as well as periodic instrument-calibration checks. All leads (1_1, 1_2, and 1_3) should be matched in resistance values.

Maximum accuracy in the test circuit is achieved if R_1 is selected to have a resistance about

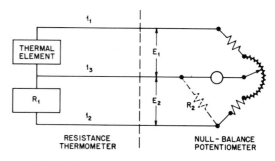

FIG. 9.59—Resistance-thermometer circuitry, scheme B.

5% below the resistance of the thermal element at the minimum temperature desired, and R_2, a precision potentiometer (3 to 10 turns), has a range about 10% greater than instrument span, high resolution, and a minimum temperature coefficient of resistivity. A calibrated dial on the potentiometer permits use of the potentiometer for the calibration of the instrument.

Resistance-thermometer installations in radioactive systems usually require thermometers to be manufactured to a special configuration to satisfy the shielding requirements of the system. Fabrication should be followed very closely. Some units may be quite long, perhaps 10 to 15 feet. This frequently requires the entire unit to be X-rayed to determine element and conductor locations in the assemblies to assure that no shifts in thermal elements or conductor positions or damage occur during fabrication. Dye-penetrant examination may be employed to detect any cracks or flaws in the sheath. Prior to assembly, all weld joints in the wiring, including the wiring on each side of the joint, should be radiographed or X-rayed to assure adequate weldments. Insulations should be carefully selected to be compatible with the nuclear and temperature environments of the plant. These thermometers are normally not accessible after installation and should be designed for maximum reliability.

If the unit has been properly fabricated, tested, and installed, there should be no problems associated with the thermometer. The thermometer should be checked for original calibration just prior to final installation to determine if stresses were introduced during handling that would affect calibration. The unit should meet all dielectric strength and insulation resistance (between wires and ground) requirements of the instrument system. All terminal connections should be mechanically and electrically (soldering, brazing, or welding) secured to eliminate contact resistance.

9.8.4 SODIUM-LEVEL DETECTORS

It may be necessary to know sodium levels in various parts of reactor systems. The required accuracy of level detectors depends on the application. The difference between the level during low sodium circulation rates through the reactor and the level at which the sodium reserve supply system must be actuated may be small. Level detectors should meet the following criteria: (1) detect coolant level within 1/4 to 1/2 in. of actual value, (2) be insensitive to temperature changes in the detector over the full range of temperatures during normal and abnormal conditions (full power, low power, shut down, transients, changes in atmospheric temperature), (3) be insensitive to system and atmospheric pressure changes, nuclear radiation, coolant-density changes, coolant wetting characteristics, and buildup of films (oxides, corrosion products, crud) on the surfaces of the detector exposed to the coolant and coolant vapors, (4) meet the materials and leakage requirements of the systems of which it is a part, and (5) be maintenance free.

Many types of devices to measure level have been described in the literature [15, 36–40]. These include bubbler type devices, differential-pressure systems, induction probes, resistance probes, buoyant

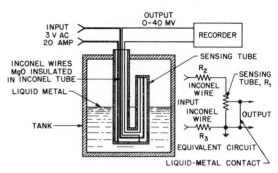

FIG. 9.60—Operating principle of resistance type level transducer [40].

type devices, and spark-plug devices. Of these, the most promising at this time are the induction probes and the differential-pressure systems with coolant-temperature and detector-temperature compensation. The operating principle of a resistance type level transducer is shown in Fig. 9.60. A resistance type level probe designed for Rapsodie is shown in Fig. 9.61. Spark-plug on–off level detectors are shown in Fig. 9.62. A differential-pressure transmitter is shown in Fig. 9.63. A differential-pressure pickup designed for Rapsodie is shown in Fig. 9.64.

9.8.5 FLOW

Flow of liquid metals with low electrical resistivity is most commonly measured with permanent-magnet flowmeters similar to the one in Fig. 9.65. This instrument operates in a manner similar to

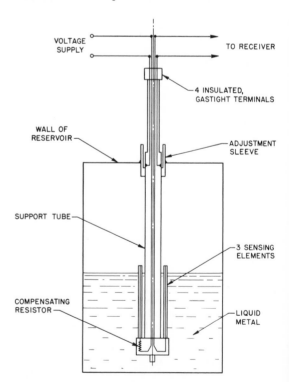

FIG. 9.61—Rapsodie resistance type liquid-level probe [20].

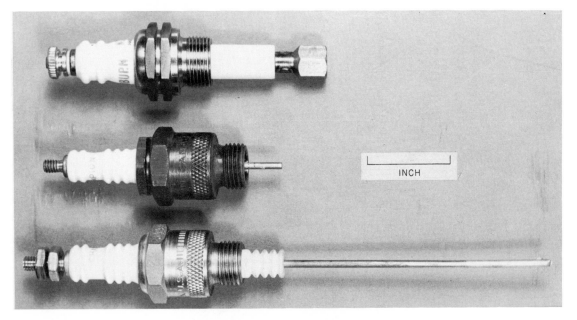

FIG. 9.62—Spark-plug level probes [40].

the operation of an electric generator. When a conductor in a magnet field is moving in a direction perpendicular to that of the flux, a voltage is generated at right angles to both the direction of the flux and the movement of the conductor. Applying this principle to the flowmeter, the pole faces of a permanent magnet are located diametrically opposite on a nonmagnetic tube, such as austenitic stainless steel. The liquid metal is the moving conductor. Electrodes on small-diameter flowmeters (smaller than 6 in. in diameter) are mounted at right angles to a line between pole-face centers.

The liquid metal moving in the tube through the magnetic field causes a voltage to be generated, which, in turn, is transmitted by the electrodes to the measuring instrument. The voltage generated is a function of the liquid velocity and thereby of its flow rate.

Nonlinearity of large-diameter flowmeters (6 in. and larger) is an inherent characteristic for center-mounted output electrodes (Fig. 9.66). The nonlinearity is caused by a distorting magnetic force due to eddy currents tending to buck the main field upstream and reinforce it downstream. This

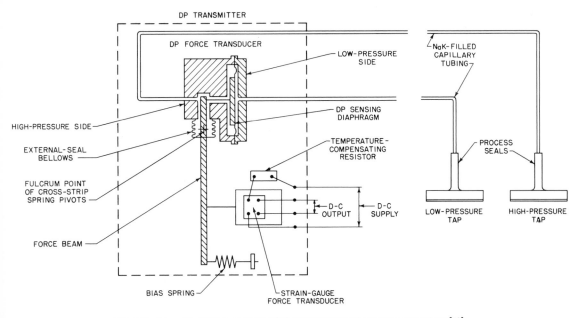

FIG. 9.63—Schematic diagram of Taylor NaK-filled differential-pressure transmitter [41].

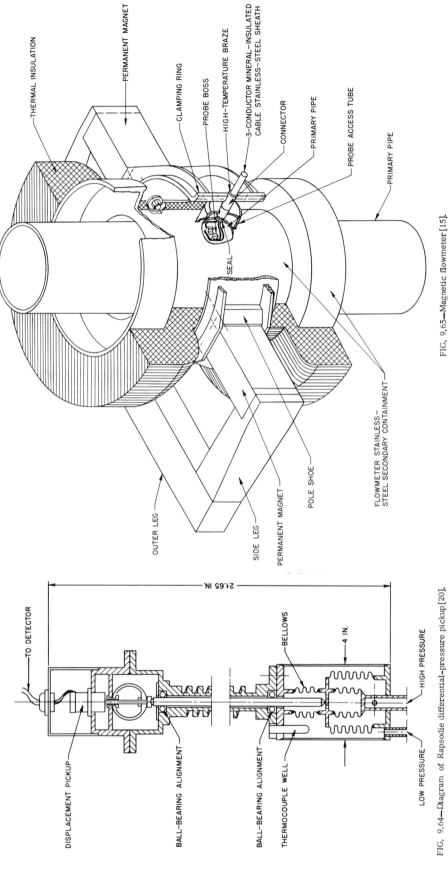

PERMANENT MAGNET

THERMAL INSULATION

CLAMPING RING

PROBE BOSS

HIGH-TEMPERATURE BRAZE

3-CONDUCTOR MINERAL—INSULATED
CABLE STAINLESS-STEEL SHEATH

CONNECTOR

PRIMARY PIPE

PROBE ACCESS TUBE

PRIMARY PIPE

SEAL

OUTER LEG

SIDE LEG

PERMANENT MAGNET

POLE SHOE

FLOWMETER STAINLESS—
STEEL SECONDARY CONTAINMENT

FIG. 9.65.—Magnetic flowmeter[15].

21.65 IN.

TO DETECTOR

DISPLACEMENT PICKUP

BALL—BEARING ALIGNMENT

BALL—BEARING ALIGNMENT

THERMOCOUPLE WELL

BELLOWS

4 IN.

HIGH PRESSURE

LOW PRESSURE

FIG. 9.64.—Diagram of Rapsodie differential—pressure pickup[20].

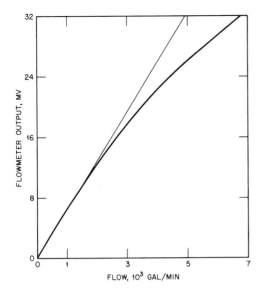

FIG. 9.66—Flowmeter calibration (center electrode, 350°F)[42].

distortion would move the point of maximum flux density downstream and decrease the magnitude as the flow increases. Figure 9.67 indicates the improvement in linearity by moving the electrode positions downstream, as represented in curves d and e. Curve e, which represents an electrode position 7 1/2 in. downstream, more nearly approaches a linear output than curve d. Curves a and b, which represent electrode positions upstream, are not as linear as the center electrode position.

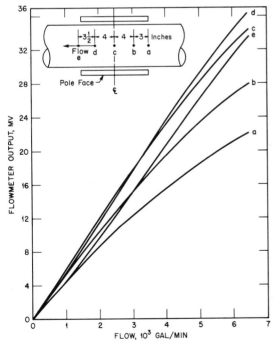

FIG. 9.67—A comparison of flowmeter outputs from five electrode locations[42].

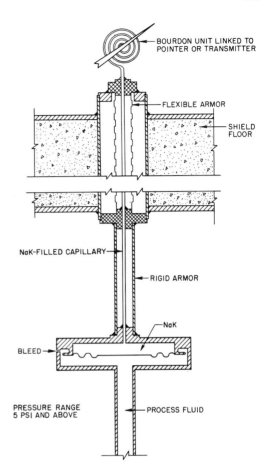

FIG. 9.68—High-temperature NaK-filled pressure detector[15].

The magnetic flowmeter can be operated with liquid metals to temperatures of 1500°F. No appreciable change will occur in flux density at high liquid-metal temperatures if the permanent-magnet pole shoes are limited to a temperature below the magnet stabilization temperature. The main advantage of the magnetic flowmeter is that there are no moving parts and thus practically no maintenance. The meter tube can be the same size as the piping to which it is connected, which minimizes pressure losses. Cables should be carefully selected and secured to the detector leads to avoid any thermoelectric potentials at the wire junctions which add to, or subtract from, the detector signal and create readout errors. The detectors should be calibrated for internal surfaces wetted by the liquid metal; errors can be induced if the surfaces are not wetted.

Another type of flowmeter that can be used for liquid-metal service is an orifice meter. Differential pressure from the pressure taps is measured by an NaK-filled differential-pressure transmitter (Fig. 9.63), which, in turn, transmits an output signal to a square-root recorder. One advantage of the orifice flowmeter is it can be calibrated in water prior to installation. There are some disadvantages to the orifice flowmeter when applied to sodium service; they are (1) pressure taps require penetration of primary piping, (2) the orifice plate is

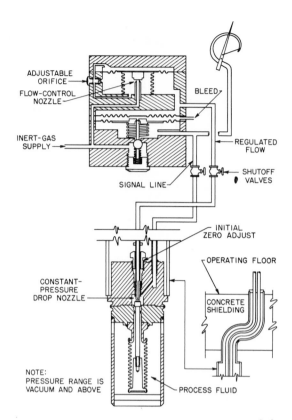

FIG. 9.69—High-temperature force-balance pressure detector [15].

not readily accessible for maintenance, and (3) blockage of pressure-tap holes cause the meter to be inoperative. The EBR-II uses an orifice in series with a magnetic flowmeter for calibration purposes, and as a backup for the magnetic flowmeters.

9.8.6 PRESSURE

For liquid-metal applications, a NaK-filled pressure detector (Fig. 9.68) has been used satisfactorily for ranges of 0 to 150 psig and greater. The force-balance pressure detector (Fig. 9.69) may be used for lower ranges of pressure. Each of these units is subject to a slight zero shift due to temperature changes. In the case of the force-balance unit, this shift may be 5 to 10 in. H_2O for a temperature change from 500 to 1000 F. Where this shift is significant to the plant operation, the units should be tested for zero shift, and the units exhibiting least shift should be used in the more critical areas.

For accurate pressure measurements below and above barometric pressure to be obtained, a "live zero" must be used. This is achieved by adjusting the output signal to approximately 2 psig for a 0 psig process pressure. For vacuum service, this live zero (zero bias) output signal must be set to obtain a positive output pressure equivalent to the maximum vacuum to be measured plus approximately 2 psig.

Because of the restriction in the nozzle and the high temperatures involved, the instrument air (or inert-gas supply) must be dry and 100% free of oil and dirt. The detector must be kept free of oxide and crud buildup, and freezing of the coolant should be avoided. If the detector bellows become frozen, application of heat to 700 or 750°F followed by internal pressuring of the bellows to a differential pressure of 10 to 15 psi will usually free the bellows.

Differential-pressure pickups are shown in Figs. 9.63 and 9.64.

9.8.7 LEAK DETECTORS

Leak detectors are used to detect leakage of liquid metal from a coolant system. Figure 9.70 shows a sketch of a typical detector installed in a low spot in the secondary containment piping of a reactor coolant system. Leak detectors may be installed below the reactor vessel, in the chamber surrounding the bellows in a bellows-seal valve, and at other locations where leakage of the coolant might occur. If the probe wire is made of thermocouple wire, the thermocouples may be used for spot-checking temperatures in these areas. Additional contacts can be added on the test push button for detecting an open circuit in each probe.

Another method of leak detection for pipes is the use of a two-conductor electrical tape. Covered sections can be wound with the tape prior to covering them with thermal insulation. One brand of tape manufactured by The Russel Manufacturing Co. consists of stranded No. 18 Chromel wires held in place by weaving in a Fiberfrax tape. Part of the tape disintegrates at 1600°F, but the wires are held in place by thermal lagging. Electrical circuits can be arranged for any necessary degree of leak localization.

Smoke detectors are also used as sodium leak detectors in structures that contain an air atmosphere. Figure 9.71 is a schematic diagram of a Pyrotronics smoke-alarm system. This detector utilizes the principle wherein the air is made conductive by means of alpha particles emitted from a minute source of radium. The alpha particles ionize the air molecules into positive ions and negative electrons. When a voltage is applied across an ionization chamber, a minute electrical current is caused to flow. Products of

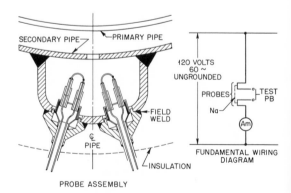

FIG. 9.70—Typical leak detector [15].

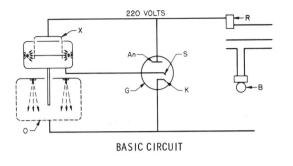

BASIC CIRCUIT

A	Alpha Source	O	Outer Chamber
An	Anode	P	Control Pin
B	Bell	R	Alarm Relay
G	Gas-discharge Tube	S	Starter Electrode
J	Locking Shell	W	Inner-chamber Electrode
K	Cathode	X	Inner Chamber
N	Neon Lamp		

DETECTOR HEAD

FIG. 9.71— Smoke detector. (Courtesy Pyrotronics, a Division of Baker Industries, Inc.)

combustion, which are usually generated in advance of any visible fire, also become ionized when they enter the chamber, but they move more slowly owing to their relative larger size and thereby reduce current flow.

The current that exists is extremely small, and, for an alarm circuit to be completed, the current must be amplified. This is achieved by using two ionization chambers and a cold-cathode tube of special design connected in parallel with the chambers. The cold-cathode tube contains no filament, and an anode current passes only during alarm.

With the outer chamber open to the air and the inner chamber virtually sealed, any reduction of current in the outer chamber increases the voltage at the trigger electrode of the tube, causing it to operate and to actuate relays for alarms, etc.

9.8.8 HYDROGEN DETECTOR

In the event of a steam—water side to liquid-metal side leak in the steam generator, a water-liquid metal reaction will occur if the metal is reactive. Early detection of such leakage is needed. The reaction products of a water-sodium reaction are sodium oxide, sodium hydride, and hydrogen.

Gas chromatographs can detect 1 ppm of hydrogen (0 to 25 ppm full range) in argon gas cover. A channel can be provided on the chromatograph to detect nitrogen (from air inleakage) and to differentiate hydrogen from nitrogen.

Other techniques for detecting hydrogen might be necessary if the cover gas were other than argon. Atomics International has performed feasibility tests on a device using the diffusion properties of hydrogen through nickel membranes as a means of detecting hydrogen in liquid-metal systems.

A Greenbrier Instruments Inc. gas chromatograph is shown in Figs. 9.72 and 9.73.

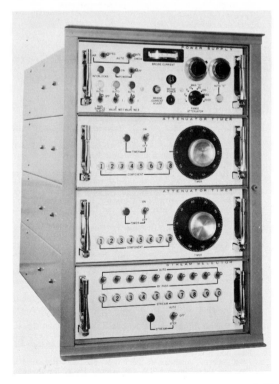

FIG. 9.72—Hydrogen-detector instrument-control section [43]. (Courtesy Greenbrier Instruments, Inc.)

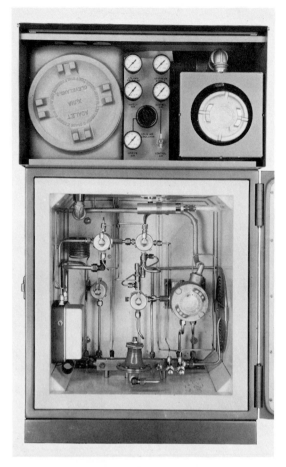

FIG. 9.73—Hydrogen detector 008 analyzer section [43]. (Courtesy Greenbrier Instruments, Inc.)

References

1. The Reactor Handbook, Vol. 2, Engineering, 1st ed., USAEC Report AECD-3646, May 1955.
2. R. G. Durnal, Reactor Kinetics, USAEC Report WAPD-32 (Vol. 1) Sec. 2, Westinghouse Atomic Power Division, August 1951. (Classified)
3. J. M. Harrer, R. E. Boyer, and D. Krucoff, Transfer Function of Argonne CP-2 Reactor, Nucleonics 10(8):32-36(1952).
4. M. A. Schultz, Control of Nuclear Reactors and Power Plants, pp. 44-45, McGraw-Hill Book Company, Inc., New York, 1955.
5. G. Robert Keepin, Neutron Data for Reactor Kinetics, Nucleonics, 20(8):150(1962).
6. L. J. Templin et al., Reactor Physics Constants, 2nd ed., USAEC Report ANL-5800, Argonne National Laboratory, 1963.
7. J. R. Dietrich and W. H. Zinn, Solid Fuel Reactors, Addison-Wesley Publishing Company, Inc., Reading, Massachusetts, 1958.
8. Power Reactor Development Company, Technical Information and Hazards Summary Report, Enrico Fermi Atomic Power Plant, October 1962.
9. L. J. Koch et al., Hazards Summary Report on EBR-II, USAEC Report ANL-5719, Argonne National Laboratory, May 1957, and Addendum, 1961.
10. Fred Storrer, Temperature Response to Power, Inlet Coolant Temperatures and Flow Transients in Solid Fuel Reactors, Report APDA-132, Atomic Power Development Associates, Inc., June 5, 1959.
11. Fred Storrer, Analysis of the Power Feedback Relations in Fast Reactors, Report APDA-138, Atomic Power Development Associates, Inc., May 1960.
12. Analysis and Simulation Study of the Operating Control System for the Enrico Fermi Atomic Power Plant, Holley Carburetor Company, November 1959.
13. Transient and Oscillator Analysis for Hazards Evaluation, and Oscillating Analysis for Reactor Startup Tests, for the Enrico Fermi Atomic Power Plant, Report No. 1653, The Bendix Company, December 1960.
14. A. Amorosi and J. G. Yevick, An Appraisal of the Enrico Fermi Power Plant, Proceedings of the Second United Nations International Conference on the Peaceful Uses of Atomic Energy, Geneva, 1958, Vol. 9, p. 358, United Nations, New York, 1958.
15. Enrico Fermi Atomic Power Plant, Report APDA-124, Atomic Power Development Associates, Inc., January 1959.
16. Specification for the Main Instrumentation and Controls of the Enrico Fermi Atomic Power Plant, Revision No. 1, Atomic Power Development Associates, Inc., December 1958.
17. L. J. Koch et al., Construction Design of EBR-II: An Integrated Unmoderated Nuclear Power Plant, Proceedings of the Second United Nations International Conference on the Peaceful Uses of Atomic Energy, Geneva, 1958, Vol. 9, p. 323, United Nations, New York, 1958.
18. R. L. Olson et al., The Sodium Graphite Reactor Power Plant for CPPD, Proceedings of the Second United Nations International Conference on the Peaceful Uses of Atomic Energy, Geneva, 1958, Vol. 9, p. 161, United Nations, New York, 1958.
19. Final Summary Safeguards Report for the Hallam Nuclear Power Facility, Atomics International, USAEC Report NAA-SR-5700, Atomics International, Apr. 16, 1961.
20. C. P. Zaleski and L. Vautrey, Le Reacteur Rapide Surregenerateur Rapsodie, French Report CEA-2193, Vols. 1 and 2, Oct. 23, 1961.
21. H. Cartwright, J. Tatlock, and R. R. Mathews, The Dounreay Fast Reactor — Basic Problems in Design, Proceedings of the Second United Nations International Conference on the Peaceful Uses of Atomic Energy, Geneva, 1958, Vol. 9, p. 316, United Nations, New York, 1958.
22. Fast Reactor Descriptive Manual Dounreay, The Control System and Electrical Supplies and Reactor Instrumentation, Secs. A.2.4, A.5 and A.7, British Report IG-170(D).
23. J. M. Harrer, Nuclear Reactor Control Engineering, D. Van Nostrand Co., Inc., Princeton, N. J., 1963.
24. C. H. Claridge, Safety System, original draft for Fast Reactor Technology — Plant Design, Stromberg-Carlson, Dec. 29, 1960.
25. A. E. Knowlton, Standard Handbook for Electrical Engineers, 8th ed., McGraw-Hill Book Company, Inc., New York, 1949.
26. H. Etherington, Nuclear Engineering Handbook, 1st ed., McGraw-Hill Book Company, Inc., New York, 1958.
27. W. J. Price, Nuclear Radiation Detection, McGraw-Hill Book Company, Inc., New York, 1958.
28. Westinghouse Electric Corporation, Descriptive Bulletin 57-450.
29. Minneapolis–Honeywell Buyers Guides G-100-4 and G-100-7.
30. W. Macrae, Sec. 5.0, Detection of Faults in Fuel Containers, Brit. J. Appl. Phys., Supplement 5, p. S-79, 1956.
31. A. C. Lapsley, Precipitation Monitor Detects Fuel Failures, Nucleonics, 19(5):74(1961).
32. W. R. Kritz, An Automatic Gas Chromatograph for Monitoring of Reactor Fuel Failures, Part I, Design, USAEC Report DP-356, Savannah River Laboratory, April 1959.
33. J. O. Blomeke and Mary F. Todd, Uranium-235 Fission Product Production as a Function of Thermal Neutron Flux, Irradiation Time, and Decay Time, Part 1, Atomic Concentrations and Gross Totals, USAEC Report ORNL-2127 (Part I, Vols. 1 and 2), Oak Ridge National Laboratory, August 1957.
34. J. O. Blomeke, Nuclear Properties of Uranium-235 Fission Products, USAEC Report ORNL-1783, Oak Ridge National Laboratory, November 1955.
35. Catching Burst Slugs, Engineering, 191:599 (Apr. 28, 1961).
36. Nuclear Process Instrumentation and Controls Conference, USAEC Report ORNL-2695, Oak Ridge National Laboratory, Apr. 22, 1960.
37. C. B. Jackson, Liquid-Metals Handbook, Sodium-NaK Supplement, USAEC Report TID-5277, July 1, 1955.
38. G. E. Turner, A Coil Type Level Gauge for High Temperature Liquid Metals, USAEC Report NAA-SR-4195, Atomics International, Nov. 15, 1959.
39. W. R. Miller, High Temperature Pressure Transmitter Evaluation, USAEC Report ORNL-2483, Oak Ridge National Laboratory, July 21, 1958.
40. R. G. Affel, G. H. Burger, and R. E. Pidgeon, Level Transducers for Liquid Metals, USAEC Report ORNL-2792, Oak Ridge National Laboratory, April 1960.
41. Taylor NaK Filled High Temperature Differential Pressure Transmitter for Power Reactor Development Company, instructions, Taylor Instrument Companies, Rochester, N. Y., April 1961.
42. G. E. Turner, The Non-Linear Behavior of Large Permanent Magnet Flowmeters, USAEC Report NAA-SR-4544, Atomics International, Apr. 1, 1960.
43. Greenbrier Instruments, Inc., Bulletin 100-61, Ronceverte, W. Va., September 1961.

CHAPTER 10

Economics

JOHN G. YEVICK*
Atomic Power Development Associates, Inc.
Detroit, Michigan

Contents

The capital costs given in this chapter include the direct costs for the Enrico Fermi Atomic Power Plant, a fast breeder, but exclude the repair costs incurred during construction and shakedown of the first plant of its kind. The plant includes many innovations necessary for the operation of a sodium-cooled fast reactor and a scale of components hitherto untried. The resulting costs are higher than those that will be achieved in future plants.

The presentation is in a logical sequence; it starts with an outline of indirect costs followed by a breakdown of annual charges. Examples are given in all cases. In conformance with other nuclear-plant estimates, the indirect costs are based on the Atomic Energy Commission Guide to Nuclear Power Cost Evaluation [1]. This is also true, wherever possible, for other items of expense. The fuel-cycle costs are estimates for what may be the prototype fuel, achievable in the late 1960's.

10.1 Categories of Expense

The three categories of annual expense are (1) carrying charges on the capital investment, (2) operation and maintenance, and (3) fuel cycle.

Annual carrying charges on the capital investment are based on an estimate of plant cost and the estimate of required working capital and on the estimate of plant life and required return on capital. These charges include a return on money invested,

depreciation, interim replacements, taxes, and insurance.

Operation- and maintenance-expense estimates are a function of plant manpower and maintenance-equipment and materials requirement.

The annual fuel-cycle expense is a function of burnup, fabrication cost, adequate fuel-inspection charges, value of fuel, fuel losses and scrap recovery, shipping, reprocessing and waste-disposal cost, and the inventory charge for fuel in and out of the reactor.

10.2 Fixed-capital Investment in Plant

The general level of capital costs for a plant is dependent primarily on the size of plant, type of reactor, degree of development, and exclusion area required.

10.2.1 150-Mw(e) FAST REACTOR POWER PLANT

The costs, charges, and expenses analyzed in this chapter for the 150-Mw(e) Enrico Fermi Atomic Power Plant (hereinafter referred to as Fermi) are used throughout the chapter as an illustration for a reference plant. Figure 11.54 (Chap. 11) shows the Fermi plot plan. Reactor containment, the coolant systems, system components, steam conditions, and the turbine-electric plant, which are described in Chaps. 4, 5, and 6, form the basis for the plant capital-cost estimate.

10.2.2 ESTIMATE OF CAPITAL COSTS

The estimate of capital costs is divided into:
1. Direct construction costs (Include AEC system of accounts Nos. 21 through 25, Ref. 2.)
2. Indirect construction costs
   (a) General contractor's field supervision and general construction costs including general overheads incurred by the owner

---

*Now with the U. S. Atomic Energy Commission.

(b) Architect—engineer and nuclear engineering services
(c) Contingency on construction
(d) Local taxes during construction
(e) Escalation, either as a separate item or with contingency
3. Other capitalized costs
(a) Preoperational testing and training
(b) Plant start-up
(c) Interest during construction
(d) Cost of land

10.2.3 DIRECT CONSTRUCTION COSTS

For estimating purposes the direct construction costs include the purchase cost of construction materials and equipment components together with freight and transportation costs incident to their delivery on site. Nuclear engineering costs incurred by the equipment manufacturers are included in the direct cost of the equipment. Direct construction costs should include all direct labor used on the job site and is generally based on a normal 40-hr work week with no allowance for premium pay. No labor benefits are included in the direct labor costs.

Reference 1 includes payroll burden (taxes and insurance, workmen's transportation and subsistence allowance, contributions to welfare plans, holidays, sign-up and termination pay) in the direct costs. The Fermi example direct costs do include the burden. For purposes of estimates, the payroll burden is generally placed in the General and Administrative account as described below. The direct costs for Fermi, detailed in Appendix A to this chapter, include all overtime since there is no contingency in the final Fermi estimate.

10.2.4 INDIRECT COSTS

For estimating purposes indirect construction costs and other indirect costs are computed using accumulative application of fixed percentages based on the total of direct construction costs. The cost of land and land rights is included in the indirect costs. Table 10.1 is a summary of indirect construction-cost percentages and of other charges that were used in the preparation of Table 10.2. The Fermi indirect costs listed in Table 10.2 are based on Ref. 1 percentages.

10.2.4.1 General and Administrative and Miscellaneous Construction Costs

These costs include supervision and job office expense, field engineering, temporary construction facilities, watchmen, utility bills, construction equipment and tools including rentals, insurance, travel expense, payroll taxes, union welfare funds, and workmen's unemployment compensation. The general contractor's fee is included in this category as well. These costs are estimated in accordance with Fig. 110-2 of Ref. 1. The indirect costs for Fermi consist of the General and Administrative percentage applied to the Direct, and the Miscel-

Table 10.1—Summary of Indirect-cost Percentages and Other Capital-cost Charges

	Expressed as a per cent of accumulated capital cost
Indirect construction cost:	
General and Administrative	7.7
Miscellaneous	1.0
Architect-Engineer services	12.0
Nuclear Engineering services	6.7
Contingency	10.0
Other capitalized costs	
Plant start-up	35% of one year's operation and maintenance
Interest during construction	8.2%
Cost of land	$360,000

laneous Construction percentage applied to the subsequent total.

10.2.4.2 Architect—Engineer and Nuclear Engineering Services

The total is divided into two groups, Architectural and Engineering Services (A-E) and Nuclear Engineering. The A-E services include A-E design; preliminary investigations; expediting, inspection, and procurement of materials and equipment; inspection of construction work to secure compliance with plans and specifications; engineering consultant services; and engineering supervision in connection with construction work. Nuclear Engineering services include nuclear engineering and design for the reactor plant and auxiliary systems, including core physics analyses, reactor-systems design, reactor-hazards evaluation, operator training, license application, and procurement; initial radiological site-surveys; and related items.

The A-E and Nuclear Engineering services should include applicable costs whether incurred by the owner, by the architect—engineer, or by a nuclear design group. The percentages should be determined separately from Fig. 110-2 of Ref. 1. The A-E percentage should be applied to the sum of the Direct, General and Administrative (G & A), and Miscellaneous costs. The Nuclear Engineering percentage should be applied to the sum of the Direct, G & A, Miscellaneous, and A-E costs.

10.2.4.3 Plant Start-up

Plant start-up costs include the costs of loading the reactor with fuel to criticality and the costs that accrue during the operating and maintenance period from criticality through the nuclear test period until the plant is available for commercial service. The tests include low-power tests, such as absolute power calibration, operating control-rod calibration, safety-rod calibration, determination of isothermal temperature coefficient, and dynamic oscillator tests. Successively higher power levels up to a rated power of the reactor result in some power generation. The amount of expense to be capitalized during the start-up period should show a credit for electric energy produced. For estimating purposes, start-up costs are assumed to be

Table 10.2—Fermi Plant Capital-cost-estimate Summary as of March 31, 1963

Account No.	Description		Total cost
21	Structures and improvements		$ 7,985,545
22	Reactor-plant equipment		28,304,135
23	Turbine-generator units		6,829,570
24	Accessory electric equipment		1,962,320
25	Miscellaneous power-plant equipment		744,230
		Total	$45,825,800
98	Indirect construction costs		
982	General and Administrative @ 7.7%		$ 3,528,600
		Subtotal	$49,354,400
	Miscellaneous costs @ 1%		493,500
		Subtotal	$49,847,900
981	Architectural–Engineering services @ 12%		5,981,700
		Subtotal	$55,829,600
981	Nuclear Engineering @ 6.7%		3,740,600
		Subtotal	$59,570,200
984	Start-up costs = 0.35 × $1,220,000		427,000
		Subtotal	$59,997,200
985	Interest during construction @ 8.2%		4,919,800
		Subtotal	$64,917,000
20	Cost of land		360,000
		Total plant capital cost	$65,277,000
		Cost per kw (e) gross	$435

35% of the annual operation and maintenance costs, including supplies but excluding fuel-cycle costs. Start-up costs are capitalized. The plant during this period produces little or no return on the investment.

10.2.4.4 Contingency on Construction

Contingency on construction should be included in estimates to cover unforeseen costs. The contingency should be applied to all direct and indirect costs accumulated to this point in the estimate. A contingency allowance of 10%, adjusted for the degree of uncertainty, is generally used. The Fermi costs of Table 10.2 do not list a contingency since the direct costs are final estimates.

10.2.4.5 Interest During Construction

Interest during construction covers the net cost of funds used for construction purposes. The period of time for capitalizing the interest is limited to the period of construction. Interest during construction takes into account the fact that capital is nonproductive during the construction period. In regulated industries, such as public utilities, regulatory bodies provide for a reasonable rate of interest on funds used during construction. The appropriate rate of interest to be used is the current cost of borrowing based on the existing capital structure. The interest computation is based on anticipated yearly disbursements which follow a curve such as shown in Fig. 110-3 of Ref. 1. The Fermi costs of Table 10.2 include an annual rate of 6%. A 36-month construction period for a 150-Mw(e) plant results in a total cumulative interest rate of 8.2% if Fig. 110-3 of Ref. 1 is used.

10.2.4.6 Cost of Land

Cost of land is based on 1200 acres at approximately $300 per acre as shown in Sec. 110 of Ref. 1. The land area corresponds closely to the exclusion area determined by applying the AEC site criteria covered in Chap. 6. Consideration should be given to apportioning the costs where more than one unit is contemplated.

10.2.4.7 Other Costs To Be Considered

Though not included in Ref. 1 and not listed in Table 10.2 of Fermi costs, the preoperational testing and training costs and local taxes during construction should be considered as part of the costs incurred during construction and start-up.

10.2.5 TOTAL PLANT INVESTMENT

Total plant investment is determined by the cumulative application of the aforementioned indirect and other capitalized costs to the direct cost as shown for Fermi in Table 10.2. All these costs are entered in the fixed-capital account for the plant.

10.3 Working-capital Investment in Plant

Working capital represents the excess of current assets over current liabilities. It includes cash plus prepaid accounts and materials and supplies on hand minus accrued Federal income taxes. For purposes of working-capital estimates, the requirements of cash plus average prepaid accounts minus accrued Federal income are 2.7%

of the annual operating expenses, based on Federal Power Commission statistics in the years 1953 through 1958.

Working capital is required for operating and maintenance expense, materials and spare-parts inventory expense, and fuel-cycle expense. It is computed in a similar way for both nuclear and conventional plants, except for fuel management, which is a requirement in a nuclear plant not found in conventional plant accounting. A nuclear plant requires a complete initial fuel loading to be operative. This initial loading may exceed the equilibrium load and may represent several years of fuel consumption, depending on the burnup characteristics of the fuel.

Working capital for a fast reactor plant should include the following items:

1. Plant Operation and Maintenance. The estimate of working capital for plant operation and maintenance should include the following items: (1) 2.7% of the annual operating expense, which includes annual fuel cost and total annual operating and maintence costs, and (2) the average value of materials and supplies in inventory, other than nuclear fuel (where factual data are not available, this value is assumed to equal 25% of the annual cost of maintenance materials and operating supplies).

2. Fuel Cycle. Although the entire fuel loading may have a life of several years, it may be necessary, because of uneven burnup through the core, to refuel in batches. Fuel cycles have an average life of one to three years. Uneven burnup and shuffling generally calls for batch refueling every six months to one year. As a result of batch refueling, there should be a periodic replenishment, reprocessing, accounting of fuel, and a periodic sale of plutonium. Once equilibrium is established, the periods are the same although not in phase. The reprocessing, plutonium sales, and fuel-depletion charges will lag behind the batch-fabrication costs. The time elapsed between refueling and completion of reprocessing is dependent on the time taken for decay storage.

3. Fuel-cycle Operations. The estimate of working capital for nuclear fuel-cycle operations should be based on the average value of nuclear fuel in inventory. For study and evaluation purposes, it can be assumed that equilibrium fuel-cycle conditions prevail and spare fuel on hand at all times is equal to 10% of the annual nuclear fuel throughput. The term "nuclear fuel in inventory" includes the following items: (1) new fuel in process of manufacture, in transit, and in storage at the reactor site, (2) all fuel in the reactor, (3) spare fuel on hand, and (4) spent fuel in storage, in transit, and during reprocessing.

For the study and evaluation of nuclear power plants, separate estimates to determine the average value of nuclear fuel in inventory should be made covering the core-fabrication cost component and the nuclear materials cost component, as follows:

Core Fabrication. This cost component should be computed on the basis of all costs incurred in the chemical conversion and fabrication of nuclear material into usable form for the reactor. It should not include the cost of nuclear materials, such as thorium, plutonium, and enriched, natural, or depleted uranium, whether such material is purchased or leased. The cost of such nuclear material that is lost during the conversion and fabrication processes, however, should be included. The estimate should provide for the fabrication of a complete core for the reactor and include allowances for spare fuel on hand and for new fuel in process of manufacture. If factual data are not available, the average value of the core-fabrication cost component of nuclear fuel in inventory, as described above, is assumed to be 60% of the core-fabrication cost.

Nuclear Materials. Where nuclear material is not leased, this cost component should be computed on the basis of all nuclear material purchased for chemical conversion and fabrication into forms usable in the reactor, including recycled scrap. The estimate should include the average value of the nuclear material in the reactor, allowances for spare fuel on hand and new fuel in the process of manufacture, and the value of purchased nuclear material remaining in spent fuel until completion of reprocessing. When nuclear material, such as plutonium and enriched uranium, is leased, the use charges are treated as an operating-expense item and are included in the annual fuel cost.

Working-capital percentages can be approximated [1] by the following: (1) operation and maintenance working capital to consist of (a) 2.7% of the annual operating expense, which expense is defined as the annual fuel cost plus the total annual operation and maintenance costs, and (b) the average value of materials and supplies in inventory equal to 25% of the total annual cost of maintenance materials and operating supplies and (2) fuel-cycle working capital equal to 60% of an entire core-fabrication cost. Table 10.3 illustrates, for the reference plant, the amount of working capital in each of these categories as derived from the above relations.

10.4 Annual Carrying Charges on Capital

Expenditures for generating-plant construction are not paid directly out of revenues, because revenues are insufficient to meet large annual construction expenditures and because both present and future customers should pay for the facilities that will serve them. Since these construction expenditures do not come directly from revenue, they must come from borrowed money to be invested in the plant. These monies are obtained from retained earnings, money set aside for depreciation of existing plant, deferred Federal income tax, and the sale of securities. Carrying charges, consisting of return, depreciation, Federal income taxes, property taxes, and insurance, are the annual costs incurred by money obtained from the above sources. A more detailed understanding of these costs may be obtained from Ref. 3.

10.4.1 RETURN

The return is the annual amount (carrying charge) due the investor for the use of his money. The return is made up of earnings on equity capital and interest on bonds (debt). The return is based

Table 10.3—Working-capital Requirement for a 150-Mw (e) Fast Reactor Plant

1. Operation and maintenance working capital			
Annual fuel-cycle cost		$1,483,200	
Annual operation and maintenance cost		1,220,000	
	0.027 × $2,703,200	= $	73,000
Annual cost of maintenance materials and supplies		477,000	
	0.25 ×	477,000 =	119,300
2. Fuel-cycle working capital			
Fabrication cost of 1 year supply to core		$ 684,200	
Number of subassemblies per year	55.4		
Total number of subassemblies in core	140		
Total fabrication cost of one core	140/55.4 × 684,200		
	=	1,729,000	
	0.60 ×	1,729,000 =	$1,037,400
3. Total working capital	=	1 + 2 =	$1,229,700

on monies currently in use, i.e., against unrecovered investment, the depreciated plant. The recovered funds (depreciation funds) are generally reinvested in new plant. The total obligation to both equity and debt holders is the company's capitalization, and the percentage distribution to each is called the "capitalization structure." Debt ratios, the ratio of bond investment to total investment, for investor-owned utilities vary from 50 to 60% depending on management policy and investor acceptance. For the Fermi estimate the composite return is assumed to be 6.75%. Assuming a 52% debt to 48% equity, 4.5% debt financing, and a cost of equity financing of 9.2%, then the return to be paid is $0.52 \times 4.5 + 0.48 \times 9.2 = 6.75\%$ of capital investment.

10.4.1.1 Stocks

Stocks are generally of two types, common and preferred. The common-stock holder owns a part of the company in common with other stockholders. His voting rights gives him a voice in management. The market value of his stock is variable; it is generally a function of the return, which is dependent on company net earnings. The company's obligation to pay a return on common stock is last among its other obligations. The return on liquidation is last below bonds and preferred stock. Preferred-stock holders are also part owners of the company and generally have voting rights. The rate of return on preferred stock is usually fixed, and liquidation rights and the obligation of the company to pay a return take priority over common stock.

10.4.1.2 Bonds

Bonds are generally of two types, first-mortgage bonds and debenture bonds. Mortgage bonds are secured by a mortgage on the physical assets, are usually stable, with a fixed life of around 30 years, have first priority on returns, usually have the lowest return, do not represent voting rights, and are first to receive liquidation assets. Debentures are unsecured obligations; they rank below mortgage bonds but pay a higher rate of return.

10.4.2 DEPRECIATION

The depreciation is a carrying charge providing for the repayment of the initial investment. Various depreciation methods may be used to distribute the annual depreciation charges over the plant life. Sinking-fund and straight-line depreciation are two of the methods. Straight-line depreciation is prescribed by most United States regulatory bodies. Sinking-fund depreciation of 1.11% based on a 30-year plant life is used in the Fermi estimate. Values for depreciation at different return rates and plant lives can be obtained from standard interest tables found in engineering and accounting handbooks similar to Ref. 4.

10.4.3 INTERIM REPLACEMENT

Interim replacement is a carrying charge that provides for replacement of those units of equipment which have a service life shorter than the assumed average plant life. Interim replacements include such items as control rods and pump internals, which may need replacement at intervals shorter than the life of the plant. The carrying charge for the reference plant is assumed equal to 0.35% and is additive to the depreciation charge. Interim replacement could also be handled by "retirement dispersion" [5].

10.4.4 UNITED STATES FEDERAL INCOME TAXES

These taxes are a carrying charge incurred as the result of a levy on earnings in excess of allowable expenses. The 1963 tax rate on net taxable income as levied by the United States Bureau of Internal Revenue was 52%. Net taxable income is defined as income remaining after subtraction of the allowable tax deductions. The allowable tax deductions for 1963 were tax depreciation and debt return. To get one dollar of equity return, $N - XN = \$1.00$, where N = net taxable income required to get the dollar return and X = Federal tax rate. If the rate X is 52%, then $N = \$2.0833$, which would make the Federal tax equal to $1.0833. The following method to determine the Federal tax in terms of equity return using book depreciation is a simplification to be used only as a guide:

$$\text{Net taxable income} = C - B - T.D. \qquad (10.1)$$

where B = bond return
$T.D.$ = tax depreciation

C $= B.D. + (B + E) + F$

$B.D.$ = book depreciation

E = equity return

F = Federal taxes

The Federal tax

$$F = f \times (\text{net taxable income}) = f(C - B - T.D.) \quad (10.2)$$

where f is the tax rate. Substituting for C in Eq. 10.2

$$F = f[B.D. + (B + E) + F - B - T.D.] \quad (10.3)$$

If $B.D. = T.D.$, then

$$F = f[E + F]$$

or

$$F = \left(\frac{f}{1-f}\right)E \quad (10.4)$$

For income-tax purposes, a depreciation schedule may be followed which does not correspond to the actual book depreciation for capital recovery. Federal income-tax laws permit the use of sum-of-the-years digits (SYD) as a depreciation for tax computation, as shown in Ref. 6. The reference plant uses Ref. 1 for the schedule.

10.4.5 STATE AND LOCAL TAXES

State and local governments may also collect income taxes.

These taxes are a carrying charge incurred as the result of a levy by local governments. The tax for the Fermi plant estimate is assumed to be 2.45%.

10.4.6 INSURANCE

Insurance, other than nuclear liability insurance, is a carrying charge consisting of an annual premium paid to cover the loss of the plant through fire, wind, vandalism, and machinery damage. The annual insurance expense for a conventional plant is approximately 0.20% of the total plant investment. Property damage insurance for nuclear plants in the formative stage of the industry is higher because of the insurance statistics on such plants. The carrying charge for the Fermi plant is assumed to be 0.40%. This level of charge is based on 1960 premium levels (see Sec. 110 of Ref. 1).

10.4.7 ANNUAL CARRYING-CHARGES SUMMARY

Nonleveled annual carrying charges on fixed capital for the depreciable part of the Fermi plant are

Table 10.4—Leveled Annual Fixed-charge Rate on Original Cost of Depreciable Plant

	Leveled at the discount rate of		
	6.50%	6.1%	$r - Tib = 4.93\%$*
Interest	1.50	1.48[†]	1.42[†]
Return on equity	2.83	2.53[‡]	2.44[‡]
Depreciation (no salvage credit)	3.33	3.33	3.33
Local taxes	2.00	2.00	2.00
Federal income tax (straight line)	3.07	2.74[§]	2.64[§]
Insurance	0.50	0.50	0.50
Interim replacement (including allowance for Federal income tax)	1.00	1.00	1.00
Total	14.23%	13.58%	13.33%
Income-tax credit due to SYD depreciation	1.04	1.00[¶]	0.81[¶]
Net total	13.19%	12.58%	12.52%
Net total rounded to	13.20%	12.60%	12.50%

*$r' = r - Tib$

where r' = discount rate for present-worth and sinking-fund techniques

r = annual return rate on total capital (6.1%)

T = Federal income-tax rate (52%)

i = interest rate on debt capital (4.5%)

b = ratio of debt capital to total capital (0.50).

[†] $i_0 = \dfrac{ib}{r}\left[r + \dfrac{r}{r'}\left(d_{r'} - \dfrac{100}{L}\right)\right]$

where i_0 = leveled interest rate

L = life expectancy of depreciable plant (30 years)

$d_{r'}$ = constant annual sinking-fund rate on the original cost, based on the discount rate of r', to equal the original cost in L years.

[‡] Return on equity $= \dfrac{r - ib}{ib} i_0$

[§] Federal income tax $= \dfrac{0.52}{0.48} \times$ return on equity (see Eq. 10.4).

[¶] Income-tax credit due to SYD depreciation (taxes not normalized) $= \dfrac{T}{1-T}\left(\overline{D}_{tr'} - \dfrac{100}{L}\right)$

where $\overline{D}_{tr'} = \dfrac{2\left(r' + d_{r'} - \dfrac{100}{L}\right)}{r'(L+1)}$

Return	6.75%
Depreciation	1.11%
Interim replacement	0.35%
Federal income tax	3.40%
State and local taxes	2.45%
Property-damage insurance	0.40%
Total	14.46%

It should be noted that the annual carrying charges as shown have not been leveled to show a decline in the return as the plant equity decreases. Three different leveled annual fixed-charge rates on original cost of depreciable plant are shown in Table 10.4. The main difference in the three methods is the rate of return. The third column has the largest change. Its discount rate is based on a discount rate that factors in the Federal income tax.

10.4.8 CARRYING CHARGES ON NONDEPRECIABLE PLANT

Carrying charges on nondepreciable plant, such as land, do not require a depreciation charge and therefore incur the maximum income tax charge. Interim replacements and damage insurance do not apply. The total carrying charge on a nondepreciable plant includes return, income tax, and property

tax. A value of 12.60% shall be used for example purposes. Property insurance is added if necessary.

10.5 Nuclear Liability Insurance

Nuclear liability insurance is determined in accordance with the provisions of "Title 10-Atomic Energy, Chapter 1 — Atomic Energy Commission, Part 140 — Financial Protection Requirements and Indemnity Agreements, Sub-part B Amended," published in the Federal Register on Feb. 17, 1961, as amended by any subsequent revisions. Nuclear plant licensees are required to maintain a total amount of nuclear liability insurance equal to $150 times the maximum power level, expressed in thermal kilowatts, multiplied by a location factor which varies from 1.0 to 2.0. In arriving at the location factor, account is taken of the total population of the area surrounding the reactor and the proximity of that population to the reactor site. The annual premium required by private syndicates for liability insurance on a plant such as Fermi will be approximately as follows for a location factor of 1.0:

Mw (t)	Amount, 10^6	Annual Premium, 10^3
110	16.5	186
200	30.0	220
300	45.0	245
430	60.0	260

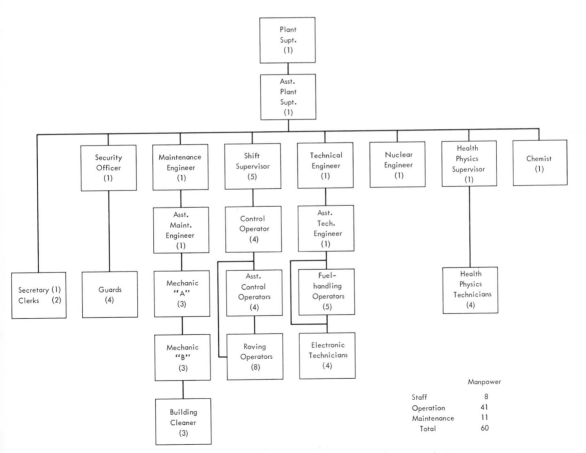

Manpower	
Staff	8
Operation	41
Maintenance	11
Total	60

FIG. 10.1—Organization chart for a 150-Mw(e) fast reactor nuclear power plant.

The fee for federal government indemnification is charged at the rate of $30/year/Mw(t)$.

10.6 Operation and Maintenance Costs

The nuclear plant organization and the operating and maintenance procedures represent, wherever possible, standard practices of conventional generating plants. The following assumptions form the basis for fast breeder plant staffing:

1. The essential functions are organized in a manner consistent with the best operating practices.
2. The plant is operated with no other nuclear or conventional stations at the site.
3. The staff provides only for normal power-plant operations. It does not include supplemental personnel required for initial start-up or major overhaul.
4. Day-shift maintenance coverage is provided, and supplemental personnel for major maintenance are provided from overall system resources.
5. Technical personnel are provided for support of routine operations, tests, and maintenance. If additonal technical personnel are needed for special test programs or special operating requirements, they are provided from the overall system resources.
6. The standard work week is 40 hr, and the staff size is to be large enough to provide coverage for vacations and absenteeism. It

is assumed that the plant has reached an equilibrium condition, the start-up phase has been completed, and the chief technical and mechanical difficulties have been eliminated.

10.6.1 PLANT ORGANIZATION DIAGRAM

The organization chart shown in Fig. 10.1 represents the complement for the Fermi plant. Estimated variations in plant manpower with plant size are shown in Table 10.5. Section 530 of the AEC Guide [1] was written for water reactors, but the differences are not substantial.

10.6.2 ANNUAL OPERATION AND MAINTENANCE EXPENSES

Annual operation and maintenance expenses are shown in Table 10.6 for the Fermi plant. Maintenance labor and materials are more expensive for a nuclear plant than for a conventional plant mainly because of the need for remote operations. Also it may be necessary in some cases to discard contaminated parts rather than repair them. The differences between the costs shown in Table 10.6 and those from the AEC Guide [1], Sec. 530, are ascribed to contract maintenance required for sodium components.

10.7 Fuel-cycle Expense

The most complex item of annual expense is the fuel cycle. The various components of fuel-

Table 10.5—Fast Reactor Plant Personnel Requirements for Various Size Plants

		Net plant rating, Mw (e)				
		50	150	300	500	1000
Administrative:						
Station superintendent		1	1	1	1	1
Assistant superintendent			1	1	1	1
Clerk-steno-storekeeper		1	1	1	1	1
Clerk-storekeeper			1	1	1	1
Secretary-typist		1	1	1	1	1
	Subtotal	3	5	5	5	5
Technical:						
Nuclear engineer		1	1	1	1	1
Technical engineer		1	2	2	3	3
Health physics supervisor		1	1	1	1	1
Health physics technician		2	4	4	4	4
Chemist		1	1	1	1	1
	Subtotal	6	9	9	10	10
Operation:						
Shift supervisor		5	5	5	5	5
Control operator		4	4	5	5	5
Assistant control operator		4	4	5	5	5
Fuel-handling operators		4	5	5	5	5
Electronic technicians		3	4	5	5	5
Roving operators		5	8	8	9	9
Janitor		2	3	3	3	4
Security guard		5	5	5	5	5
	Subtotal	32	38	41	42	43
Maintenance:						
Maintenance engineer		1	2	2	2	2
Mechanic A		3	3	4	4	5
Mechanic B		3	3	4	4	5
	Subtotal	7	8	10	10	12
Total station personnel		48	60	65	67	70

Table 10.6—Annual Operation and Maintenance Expenses,
150-Mw (e) Fast Reactor Plant

	Labor	Material
Administrative and technical on site:		
Plant superintendent, assistant superintendent, and office staff	$ 50,000	
Technical engineer and assistant technical engineer	20,000	
Reactor engineer	11,500	
Health physics supervisor	11,500	
Chemist	11,500	
Miscellaneous expense	5,000	2,000
Subtotal	$109,500	$ 2,000
Total administrative and technical expense		$ 111,500
Operation:		
Shift supervisors	$ 58,000	
Security	34,000	
Plant operators	100,000	
Health physics technicians	32,000	40,000
Fuel-handling operators	40,000	
Electronic technicians	32,000	
Liquid metal		55,000
Waste disposal		25,000
Water and services		50,000
Miscellaneous operating expense	10,000	90,000
Subtotal	$306,000	$ 260,000
Total operation expense		$ 566,000
Maintenance:		
Maintenance engineer and assistant maintenance engineer	$ 20,000	
Mechanics	43,000	
Janitors	15,000	
Instruments and controls		35,000
Fuel handling		70,000
Liquid-metal system		40,000
Inert-gas system		5,000
Steam-generator equipment		20,000
Turbine-electric plant		35,000
Miscellaneous maintenance expense	5,000	10,000
Subtotal	$ 83,000	$ 215,000
Total on-site maintenance expense		298,000
Contract maintenance (outside maintenance firm)		130,000
Total maintenance expense		$ 428,000
Total administrative, technical, operation, and maintenance expense		$1,105,500
Allocated production overhead expense		114,500
Total annual operation and maintenance expense		$1,220,000

cycle expense are discussed in this section. Factors influencing the fuel-cycle expense will be analyzed, and a procedure for computing the expense will be established. There is no intention in the example used to show an economically competitive fuel cycle. Rather, it is an example of what could possibly be an interim step for a prototype fuel cycle in the 150-Mw(e) class. Ground rules described by the AEC in Ref. 1 are used wherever possible.

10.7.1 ITEMS OF FUEL-CYCLE EXPENSE

The items included in the fuel-cycle expense are:

1. The purchase price of new fuel assemblies, including:
   (a) Conversion of the fuel material and fertile blanket material to the desired form.
   (b) Fabrication of fuel and fertile material into subassemblies, including design and inspection.
   (c) Handling, packaging, shipping, and insuring of fuel and fertile raw materials, fabricated materials, and finished assemblies.
   (d) Payment for material loss and scrap recovery.
   (e) Use charges for plutonium and other enriched fuels during conversion, fabrication, shipping, and storage.

2. Cost of fissionable (fuel) materials, including:
   (a) Fuel burnup or depletion charge, which is the value stated in the AEC Schedule of Charges, Ref. 1, for the difference in enrichment of uranium fuels. The value of plutonium is based on current estimates.
   (b) Credit for plutonium delivered to AEC as metal.

3. Use charge for all plutonium and enriched uranium contained in core and blanket on the basis of both government-owned and privately owned fuel. The use charge under government ownership should be based on the

existing rate (4.75% in 1963-64). The use charge under private ownership is yet to be determined.

4. Use charge on fuel in decay storage.
5. Shipping charges, including insurance coverage on irradiated fuel sent to chemical processing plants and on processed material sent to an AEC receiving point.
6. Chemical-processing costs, including separation and conversion of irradiated fuels.
7. Charge for material lost during processing.
8. Use charges during shipping, storage, and processing of irradiated fuel and during storage of processed material.

10.7.2 ASSUMPTIONS

In the computation of fuel-cycle expenses, it is assumed (1) that the fuel cycle has reached equilibrium and (2) that any carrying charges on fuel-cycle working capital is part of the annual fixed charge and is excluded from the fuel-cycle cost.

10.7.3 PROCEDURE

The procedure for calculating annual fuel-cycle expenses is illustrated by considering the annual

core and blanket costs for the reference plant. The fuel-cycle flow diagram (Fig. 10.2) illustrates the movement of material through the fuel cycle. The throughput quantities at each location in the core and blanket cycle are shown in kilograms of depleted uranium and plutonium isotopes in the fuel-cycle material-balance diagram (Fig. 10.3). Data for the material balance are prepared from the reactor characteristics, allowable burnup, and the plant operating factor. Detailed fuel-cycle material-balance computations are given in Appendix B to this chapter. The design, operating, and economic parameters for the fuel-cycle computation are given in Table 10.7. The design parameters are those for the reference plant. Operating parameters, such as shipping time, decay time, reprocessing rates, and fabrication rate losses, were taken from Refs. 1 and 7. Unit prices for reprocessing and fuel destruction are based on AEC prices. Wherever possible, fabrication and shipping unit prices correspond to an average of current prices proposed by several firms.

10.7.4 CALCULATIONS

The sample calculations shown in Table 10.8 are to be used in conjunction with Fig. 10.3. Unit

$$\text{Net } PuCr = \frac{0.045\,(0.16)\,(10)}{0.305} \qquad G = 0.305$$

$$BR = 1.16 \qquad Pu\,Val = 10$$

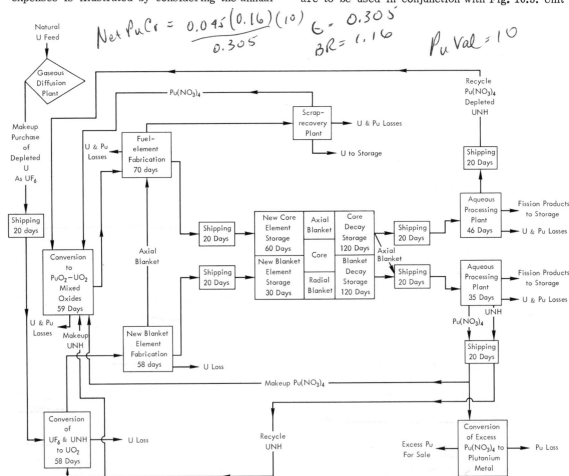

FIG. 10.2—Fuel-cycle flow diagram for 150-Mw(e) fast reactor using PuO_2–UO_2 fuel (based on aqueous reprocessing off-site).

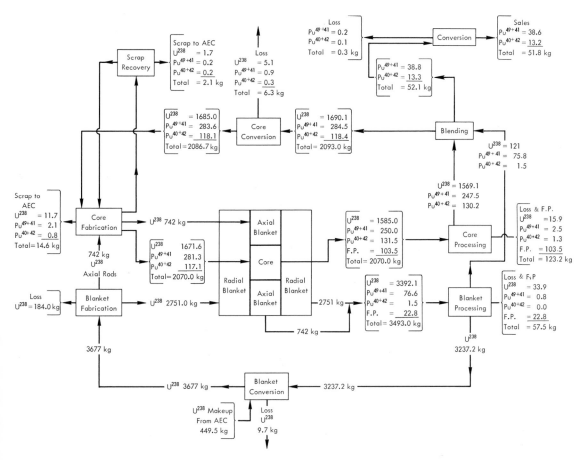

FIG. 10.3—Fuel-cycle annual material balance for 150-Mw(e) fast reactor using PuO_2–UO_2 fuel. Notes: 1. Burn up, core—50,000 MWD/1000 Kg, axial blanket—5900 MWD/1000 Kg, radial blanket—6350 MWD/1000 Kg; 2. Reactor power—430 MW thermal; 3. plant operating factor—80%.

costs, processing rates, and other costs that have been assumed are shown in Table 10.7. The expenses are developed in the following sequence: (1) charges incurred prior to delivery to the reactor site, (2) charges incurred at the reactor site, (3) charges incurred after removal from the reactor site.

The computation has been set up on an actual annual throughput basis of either total weight, plutonium weight, or subassembly movement, depending on which throughput is most logical at the point of computation. A column is devoted to showing the charges in dollars per kilogram of plutonium plus uranium in the core at equilibrium.

10.7.5 UNIT ENERGY EXPENSE FOR FUEL CYCLE

The total fuel-cycle expense is $1,483,200 per year. Based on a gross plant capacity rating of 150,000 kw, 7% plant auxiliary power, and an annual operating factor of 80%, the fuel cycle expense in mills per kilowatt-hour is

$$\frac{\$1,483,200/\text{year} \times 10^3 (\text{mills}/\$)}{0.98 \times 10^9} = 1.51 \text{ mills/kw-hr, net}$$

10.8 Power-generating Expenses

The total annual generation expense for the reference 150-Mw(e) fast reactor power plant using the fuel-cycle example is as follows:

1. Carrying charges on capital. The annual carrying charges are 14.46% on fixed capital and 12.60% on nondepreciable and on working capital. The total annual carrying-charge expense consists of the following categories:

a. Depreciable plant:
$65,277,000 depreciable plant
at 14.46% $9,439,100
b. Nondepreciable plant:
$360,000 land at 12.60%   45,400
c. Working capital:
$1,229,700 at 12.60%   154,900
                                          ――――――――――
                                            $9,639,400

2. Nuclear liability insurance. [430 Mw(t) operation] $ 273,000

3. Operation and maintenance expenses. Operation and maintenance expenses are detailed in Table 10.6 and are summarized as follows:

	Labor	Material
Administrative and technical	$109,500	$ 2,000
Operation	306,000	260,000
Maintenance	213,000	215,000
Subtotal	$628,500	477,000
Direct plant, total		1,105,500
Allocated production overheads		114,500
Total annual operation and maintenance expense		$1,220,000

4. Fuel expense. The annual fuel expense is computed to be $1,483,200. A breakdown of the expense is shown in Table 10.9.

5. Unit power-production expense. The unit production expense is developed from the net plant capacity, plant operating factor, and total annual production expenses. The unit power-production expense is shown in Table 10.10.

10.9 Foreseeable Reductions in Plant Capital Costs and Annual Operating Expenses

10.9.1 REDUCTION IN PLANT CAPITAL COST

As with a conventional plant, the investment per kilowatt (electrical) of installed capacity can be

(Text continues on p. 669.)

Table 10.7—Fuel-cycle Data for 150-Mw (e) Fast Reactor Plant

I. Design Data	Clean	Equilibrium	Final
General:			
Reactor thermal output, Mw (t)		434 (a)	
Electric output			
Gross, Mw (e)		150	
Net, Mw (e)		142	
Plant operating factor, %		80	
Reactor core:			
Output, Mw (t)		355	
Volume, cu ft		50	
Power density, kw (t)/cu ft		7100	
Average burnup, Mwd/tonne		50,000	
Number of subassemblies		140	
Number of fuel pins per subassembly		127	
Fuel (89% theoretical density)		PuO_2-UO_2	
Fuel composition:	Clean	Equilibrium	Final
Pu^{239} plus Pu^{241} (fissile material), wt. %	12.01	10.94	10.65
Pu^{240} (fertile material), wt. %	4.94	5.47	5.60
U^{238} (fertile material), wt. %	71.22	68.24	67.52
Fission products, wt. %	0.00	3.52	4.40
Oxygen, wt. %	11.83	11.83	11.83
Total, wt. %	100.00	100.00	100.00
Critical mass:			
Pu^{239} and Pu^{241} at equilibrium, kg		650	
U^{238} at equilibrium, kg		3985	
Pu^{240} and Pu^{242} at equilibrium, kg		325	
Total Pu + U in core at equilibrium, kg		4960	
Fraction of core fissions in Pu^{239} and Pu^{241}		0.810	
Fraction of core fissions in Pu^{240}		0.066	
Fraction of core fissions in U^{238}		0.124	
Total		1.000	
Content of each tonne of heavy metal in core:			
Pu^{239} and Pu^{241}, kg	135.9		120.8
Pu^{240}, kg	56.6		63.5
U^{238}, kg	807.5		765.7
Fission products, kg	0.0		50.0
Total, kg	1000.0		1000.0
Reactor blanket:	Axial		Radial
Output, Mw (t)	15		60
Volume, cu ft	20.8		111.7
Number of subassemblies	(b)		227
Number of rods per subassembly	36 (c)		37
Total number of rods	5040		8399

Table 10.7—Fuel-cycle Data for 150-Mw (e) Fast Reactor Plant (continued)

	Axial	Radial
Reactor blanket: (continued)		
Composition	UO_2	UO_2
Average burnup, Mwd/tonne	4550	6350
U^{238} at equilibrium, kg	1875	17,200
Pu (49 + 41) at equilibrium, kg	43	257

	Core	Blanket
II. Operating Data		
Shipping time, AEC to fabricator, days	20	20
Shipping time, fabricator to reactor, days	20	20
Shipping time, reactor to processing plant, days	20	20
Shipping time, processing plant to fabricator, days	20	20
Decay period for irradiated fuel, days	120	120
Storage period at processing plant, days	30	30
New-fuel conversion throughput, kg/day	10	1000
Fabrication throughput, kg Pu/day	7	3
New-fuel storage period prior to refueling, days	60	30
Spare-fuel inventory at reactor (10% of throughput), No. of S.A. (d)	5.54	22.7
Annual fuel input Pu (e)(f), kg	281.3	0
Annual fuel discharge of fissile Pu (f), kg	250	76.6
Annual processing throughput Pu + U (g), kg	2070	3493
Processing rate:		
Pu, kg/day	31	31
U, kg/day	1000	1000
Losses during conversion, %	0.3	0.3
Losses during fabrication, %	0.7	5.0
Losses, scrap recovery, core %	0.1	
Losses during processing, %	1.0	1.0
Losses, Pu nitrate to metal, %	0.5	0.5
III. Unit Costs		
Conversion cost:		
Pu (NO₃)₄ to PuO₂, $/g Pu	0.10	
UNH to UO_2, $/kg U		5
UF_6 to UO_2, $/kg U		2.10
Fabrication cost:		
Pins, $/pin	50	
Axial rods, $/rod	20	
Assembly, $/S.A.	3000	1000
Chemical-processing-plant daily charge, $/day	22,000	22,000
Shipping charge, AEC to fabricator, $/kg	5	1.5
Shipping charge, fabricator to reactor, $/S.A.	120	60
Shipping charge, reactor to processing plant (including cask-car rental):		
Core, $/S.A.	750	
Axial blanket, $/section		215
Radial blanket, $/S.A.		315
Shipping charge, processing plant to fabricator, $/kg Pu	5	1.5
Shipping charge, processing plant to AEC receiving plant, $/kg Pu		5
Pu value, charge and credit, $/g	10	10
Depleted uranium charge, $/kg	2.5	2.5
Use charge rate, assuming government ownership, %	4.75	4.75

(a) Includes 4 Mw (t) frictional heating of coolant.
(b) Included in core subassemblies.
(c) Total number above and below core region.
(d) S.A. = subassemblies.
(e) See Fig. 10.3.
(f) Pu^{239} and Pu^{241}.
(g) Pu + U + fission products.

Table 10.8—Fuel-cycle Computation (annual basis)

	Pu$^{239+241}$, 10^3g	Time, days	Annual charge $/g	Annual charge %	Annual charge Total	Pu + U at equilibrium, $/kg
I. Core-cycle Computation						
A. Fabrication cycle						
1. Use charges						
In transit to conversion and fabrication	284.5	20	10	4.75 (a)	7,400	
In conversion and fabrication	284.5	129 (b)	10	4.75	47,800	
In transit to reactor	281.3	20	10	4.75	7,400	
Total use charge					62,600	12.62
2. Losses (c)						
Conversion losses	0.9		10		9,000	
Fabrication losses	2.1		10.91 (d)		22,900	
Scrap-recovery losses	0.2		10		2,000	
Total loss charge					33,900	6.83
3. Shipping (including insurance)						
To converter and fabricator (Pu + U)	2093		0.005		10,500	
Scrap to AEC (Pu + U)	16.7		0.005		Negl.	
Fabricator to reactor (Pu + U)	2070		0.005		10,400	
Total shipping charge					20,900	4.21
4. Conversion						
Pu(NO$_3$)$_4$ to PuO$_2$	402.9 (e)		0.10 (f)		40,300	
UNH TO UO$_2$	1690.1 (g)		0.005		8,500	
Total conversion					48,800	9.84
5. Fabrication						
Fabrication of 7035.8 core pins @ $50	283.6		1.2405		$351,800	
Fabrication of 55.4 S.A. @ $3000	283.6		0.58603		166,200	
Total fabrication					518,000	104.44
6. Total conversion and fabrication					566,800	114.27
7. Total fabrication cycle					684,200	137.94
B. Charges at reactor						
1. Use charge						
New fuel prior to refueling	281.3	60	10	4.75	22,000	
During irradiation	650 (h)	365	10	4.75	308,800	
During decay storage	250 (i)	120	10	4.75	39,000	
Spare fuel	28.1 (j)	365	10	4.75	13,300	
Total use charge					383,100	77.24
2. Deficiency of fuel						
Plutonium	31.3				(k)	
Uranium	86.6				(l)	
C. Chemical processing						
1. Use charges						
Transit to process plant	250	20	10	4.75	6,500	
During separations	250	46 (m)	10	4.75	15,000	
Total use charge					21,500	4.33
2. Losses						
Plutonium	2.5		10		25,000	5.04
Uranium					Negl.	
3. Shipping to processing plant (including insurance)						
Core section 55.4 S.A. @ $750	2070 (i)		0.016		33,100	
Total shipping					33,100	6.67

Table 10.8—Fuel-cycle Computation (annual basis) (continued)

	$Pu^{239} + {}^{241}$, 10^3 g	Time, days	Annual charge $/g	Annual charge %	Annual charge Total	Pu + U at equilibrium, $/kg
4. Processing	250	16 (n)	22,000 (o)		352,000	70.97
5. Total chemical processing					431,600	87.02
D. Total core cost (p)					1,498,900	302.20

	Uranium, 10^3 g		Annual charge $/g	Annual charge %	Annual charge Total	U + Pu at equilibrium, $/kg
II. Blanket Fuel-cycle Computation						
A. Fabrication cycle						
1. Use charge						
Transit to conversion and fabrication	3237.2	20			None	
Conversion and fabrication	3677	116 (q)			None	
Transit to reactor	3493	20			None	
2. Losses						
Conversion	9.7				Negl.	
Fabrication	184			0.0341 (r)	6,100	0.31
3. Shipping						
Transit to fabrication	3677		0.0003		1,100	
Transit to AEC scrap	184		0.0003		100	
Transit to reactor	2751		0.0003		800	
Total shipping					2,000	0.10
4. Conversion						
UNH to UO_2	3237.2 (UNH)		0.005		16,200	
UF_6 to UO_2	449.5 (UF_6)		0.0021 (s)		1,000	
Total conversion					17,200	0.88
5. Fabrication						
1994.4 axial rods @ $20	742		0.0537		39,900	
1343.1 radial rods @ $100	2751		0.0488		134,300	
36.3 radial S.A. @ $1000	2751		0.0132		36,300	
Total fabrication					210,500	10.78
6. Total conversion and fabrication					227,700	11.66
7. Total fabrication cycle					235,800	12.08
B. Charges incurred at the reactor site						
1. Use charges (none)						
Spare subassemblies (6 S.A.)		60			None	
In-reactor inventory	243 (t)	365			None	
Decay storage	77.7 (u)	120			None	
2. U^{238} Consumed	101		0.0025		Negl.	
3. Plutonium Credit ($Pu^{239} + Pu^{241}$)	38.6		10		(386,000) (v)	(19.77)
C. Chemical processing						
1. Use charge						
Transit to process plant	76.6	20	10	4.75	2,000	
Separation process	76.6	35 (w)	10	4.75	3,500	
Total use charge					5,500	0.28
2. Losses						
Plutonium processing	0.76 (x)		10		7,600	
Uranium processing					Negl.	
Total losses					7,600	0.39
3. Shipping						
Transit to processing 36.3 S.A. @ $315 (U + Pu + F.P.)	3493		0.00326		11,400	0.58
Transit of Pu to AEC	52.1				Negl.	

Table 10.8—Fuel-cycle Computation (annual basis) (continued)

| | Uranium, 10^3 g | Time, days | Annual charge | | | U + Pu at equilibrium, $/kg |
			$/g	%	Total	
4. Processing Separation	76.6	5.0(y)	22,000(z)		110,000	5.63
5. Total chemical processing					(251,500)	(12.88)
D. Total blanket					(15,700)	(0.80)
III. Total Blanket and Core Cost All U and Pu in core and blanket at equilibrium					1,483,200	60.58

Note: assumed no use charge for $Pu^{240+242}$

(a) Based on government ownership.

(b) A 10 kg/day conversion rate and a 7 kg/day fabrication rate + 60 days process lag time.

(c) Depleted uranium loss is negligible in value.

(d) Includes 50% fabrication cost.

(e) Includes all plutonium.

(f) Plant based on 5000 kg of plutonium annual throughput per year, $250,000 equipment and handling, annual write-off 30%, $65,000 for personnel, $140,000 for materials, and about a 50% contingency factor.

(g) Based on 10^3 g of depleted uranium.

(h) Based on 140 subassemblies, equilibrium content.

(i) Based on 55.4 subassemblies (Pu + U + F.P.).

(j) 10% of throughput.

(k) Core depletion made up from blanket plutonium.

(l) U^{238} depletion neglibible.

(m) Based on 31 kg per day plus 8 days turnaround time plus 30 days process lag; separation rate of 31 kg/day based on 2/3 of AEC separation rate.

(n) Based on 31 kg/day plus 8 days turnaround time.

(o) Escalated to 1965.

(p) Does not include charge against depletion, which in turn would be a credit to the blanket.

(q) 15 days per tonne plus 60 days process lag.

(r) Includes 50% fabrication costs.

(s) See Ref. 8.

(t) Based on 227 S.A. @ $1.07 × 10^3 g of Pu average per S.A.

(u) Based on 36.3 S.A. @ $2.14 × 10^3 g of Pu per S.A.

(v) Plutonium sold as nitrate to AEC.

(w) Includes 30 days storage, turnaround time, and 31 kg per day processing.

(x) A 1% loss.

(y) Based on 31 kg of Pu per day and turnaround time equal to processing time of 2.5 days.

(z) Escalated to 1965.

Table 10.9—Fuel-cycle Expense Summary for 150-Mw(e) Fast Reactor Plant

	Processing	Shipping	Use charge	Pu loss and credit	Totals	
Core						
Fabrication						
Transit to fabricator		10,500	7,400		17,900	
Conversion and fabrication	566,800		47,800	33,900	648,600	
Transit to reactor		10,400	7,400		17,800	
Subtotal	566,800	20,900	62,600	33,900	684,200	684,200
At reactor						
Preirradiation inventory			35,300		35,300	
Irradiation			308,800		308,800	
Decay inventory			39,000		39,000	
Subtotal			383,100		383,100	383,100
Chemical processing						
Transit to process plant		33,100	6,500		39,600	
Separation	352,000		15,000	25,000	392,000	
Subtotal	352,000	33,100	21,500	25,000	431,600	431,600
Blanket						
Fabrication						
Transit to fabricator		1,100	None		1,100	
Conversion and fabrication	227,700		None	6,100(U)	233,800	
Transit to reactor and AEC		900	None		900	
Subtotal	227,700	2,000		6,100	235,800	235,800
Chemical processing						
Transit to process plant		11,400	2,000		13,400	
Separations	110,000		3,500	7,600	121,100	
Plutonium credit				(386,000)	(386,000)	
Subtotal	110,000	11,400	5,500	(378,400)	(251,500)	(251,500)
Total	1,256,500	67,400	472,700	(313,400)		1,483,200

$$\frac{386,000}{0.8\,(8760)\,150}$$

Table 10.10—Unit Power Production Expense for 150-Mw (e) Fast Reactor
Plant (80% Operating Factor = 0.98 × 10⁹ kw-hr Net Per Year)

	Annual expenses, $1000	Units costs, mills/kw-hr net
Carrying charges on capital:		
Depreciable plant	9,439.1	9.63
Nondepreciable plant	45.4	0.05
Working capital	154.9	0.16
Subtotal	9,639.4	9.84
Nuclear liability insurance	273.0	0.28
Operation and maintenance expense	1,220.0	1.25
Fuel cycle expense	1,483.2	1.51
Total expense	$12,615.6	12.88

reduced considerably with increased plant size. Cost variation, based on today's technology and price levels, range from $245/kw(e) for a second-generation 150-Mw(e) plant to $105/kw(e) for a 1000-Mw(e) plant. The variation of capital cost per kilowatt (electrical) from 150 to 1000 Mw(e) is illustrated in Fig. 10.4. Figure 10.5 shows the variation in the cost of various sections of a fast reactor plant as the size varies from a 150-Mw(e) second-generation plant to a 1000-Mw(e) plant.

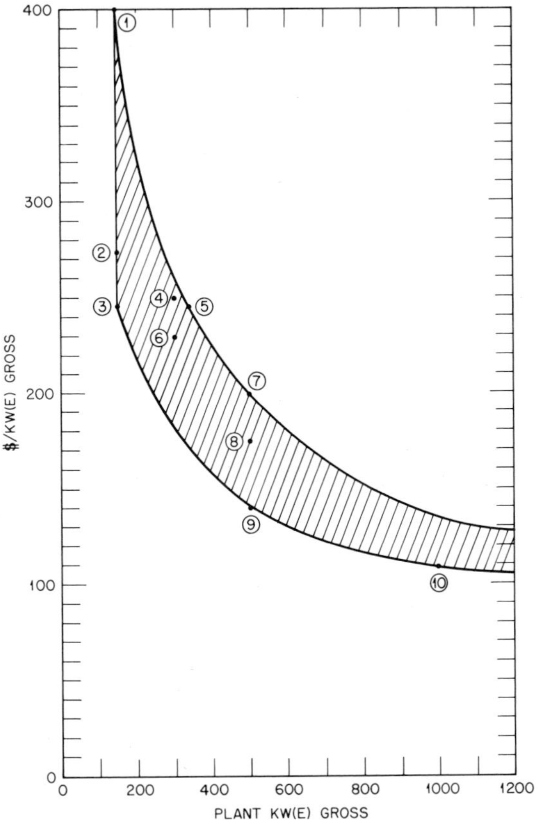

Higher steam pressures and temperatures result in higher efficiencies. Cost optimization of the entire plant is necessary to determine savings, if any, resulting from efficiencies. Reduced containment requirements and improved shielding design should result in reductions in direct construction cost. Total indirect construction costs also decrease as nuclear engineering and the overall contingency allowance are reduced following the establishment of technology based on several generations of power-production reactors. Preoperation training and testing are reduced since previously qualified personnel can be used on start-up of a new plant and the new staff can qualify during commercial operation. Further reductions are possible with advanced designs discussed elsewhere in the book.

10.9.2 REDUCTION IN OPERATION AND MAINTENANCE EXPENSE

The operation and maintenance expenses given in Table 10.6 are for a single-unit plant. Reduction

FIG. 10.4—Fast reactor cost estimates showing variation in cost vs. plant size. (1) Fermi; (2) 1960 AEC study; (3) 150-Mw plant (Report APDA-136); (4) 1960 AEC study; (5) 1959 AEC study; (6) Report APDA-129; (7) General Electric report to AEC, 1962; (8) Walker Cisler's report to AEC, 1962; (9) 1963 General Electric cost estimate; (10) Allis-Chalmers proposal to Southwest Atomic Energy Associates (SAEA).

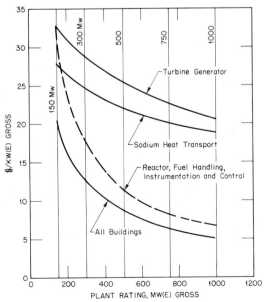

FIG. 10.5—Installed building and equipment direct costs per kilowatt (electrical) gross.

in single-unit expenses may be made by having the control operator operate both reactor and turbine. This would eliminate assistant control operators, one fuel-handling operator, and one health physics technician. This reduction in staff, together with minor reductions in materials, would possibly reduce the operation and maintenance expense by $100,000, or approximately 10%. Major reductions in operation and maintenance expense are possible only when multiunit nuclear power stations are built. A second 150-Mw(e) unit added to an existing plant would possibly require the addition of only 20 men, which would reduce the number of men per megawatt from 0.4 to 0.266. This would represent a 33% reduction in manpower and would result in a decrease in the operation and maintenance expense for a 150-Mw(e) plant from 1.25 mills/kw-hr to 0.75 mills/kw-hr.

10.9.3 REDUCTION IN FUEL-CYCLE EXPENSE

An appreciable part of the fuel-cycle expense is inversely proportional to burnup. If burnup could be increased from 6 to 10%, the fuel-cycle component of generating expense would approach 1.0 mills/kw-hr. On-site reprocessing would reduce shipping charges, and, with the processing plant integrated with the reactor plant, the investment in processing plant, manpower to operate the processing plant, and fuel inventory would be effectively reduced. Fabrication technology should also improve, and this would lead to reduced core and blanket subassembly prices. On-site reprocessing and improved fabrication should reflect another 10% saving in these areas of cost.

A foreseeable near-future (1973) unit power-production expense for a solid-plutonium-fuel reactor plant of a 300 Mw(e) gross rating at an 80% plant factor with only a stepwise improvement is:

	Mills/kw-hr (net)
Carrying charges on capital	4 to 5
Operation and maintenance expense	0.75 to 1
Fuel-cycle expense	1 to 1.2
Total	5.75 to 7.2

For a 1000-Mw(e) plant operating at 80% plant factor with $105 per gross kw(e) and 6% auxiliaries, the following costs are estimated:

	Mills/kw-hr (net)
Carrying charges on capital	2.3
Operation and maintenance expense	0.2 to 0.3
Fuel-cycle expense	0.8 to 1.0
Total	3.3 to 3.6

Appendix A
Fermi Detailed Direct Cost Estimate as of Mar. 31, 1963
(Aec Account Classification)

		Amounts	Totals
21	Structures and Improvements		
211	Ground improvements		
.1	Access roads for permanent use	93,090	
.2	General yard improvements	493,680	
.3	Railroads	125,850	
.4	Water-front improvements	740,005	
	Total ground improvements (item 211)		1,452,625
212	Buildings		
A.	Subassembly receiving, storage, decay, and disassembly building		
.1	Substructure	858,700	
.2	Superstructure	261,725	
.3	Building services	325,400	
	Total subassembly etc. building (item 212A)		1,445,825

Fuel and repair building (Figs. 6.65, 6.66, and 7.12)

The building is 105 ft by 91 ft, with a superstructure 52 ft above grade except the east side, which has a 25 ft 10 in. wide bay 32 ft high. The wall in the bay area is of 10-in. thick concrete. All other superstructure walls are of steel and corrugated-asbestos siding. The excavation was 14,000 cu yd. Required were 7000 cu yd of concrete and 200 tons of structural-steel framing. The 25-ton bridge crane has a 58-ft span.

B.	Steam-generator building		
.1	Substructure	246,070	
.2	Superstructure	150,515	
.3	Building services	71,210	
	Total steam-generator building (item 212B)		467,795

Steam-generator building (Figs. 6.59 to 6.61)

This building is 90 ft by 55 ft by 58 ft above grade and 25 ft below grade. The substructure has two walls with 33-in.-thick concrete. One 90-ft wall is made of 48-in.-thick concrete. The side common with the turbine building is 12 in. thick. The superstructure has one wall partly of 30-in.-thick concrete (45 ft by 39 ft) with the remainder faced with corrugated asbestos. A second exterior wall (58 ft) has a corrugated-asbestos siding. The other two walls common to the turbine and control buildings have 12-in. concrete blocks. Floor at grade is of 12-in.-thick concrete.

C.	Reactor ventilation building		
.1	Substructure	8,670	
.2	Superstructure	7,330	
.3	Building services	3,500	
	Total reactor ventilation building (item 212C)		19,500

Ventilation building

This building is a one-story 48 ft by 20 ft by 11 ft high concrete-block building resting on a concrete pad.

D.	Reactor control and instrument-service building		
.1	Substructure	20,835	
.2	Superstructure	140,540	
.3	Building services	72,725	
	Total reactor control etc. building (item 212D)		234,100

Control building (Figs. 6.62 to 6.64)

This building has three stories 60 ft by 60 ft by 47 ft above grade and rests on a 12-in.-thick concrete slab. One wall toward the reactor is a 40-in.-thick concrete wall. One wall is common to the office building except for a third story with a corrugated-asbestos side. One wall is common to the steam-generator building and is made of 12-in.-thick concrete. The other wall is common to the turbine building and is of 8-in. concrete blocks.

E.   Sodium-storage building

.1	Substructure	36,920
.2	Superstructure	172,265
.3	Building services	35,815
	Total sodium-storage building (item 212E)	245,000

Sodium service building (Figs. 6.67 to 6.70)

This building at grade level is 102 ft 6 in. long by 40 ft wide with a 21-ft-high first story. The first floor is divided into a sodium storage room and a cold-trap cell having a common wall of 4-ft-thick concrete. The other walls of the sodium storage room are of 30-in. concrete, and the cold-trap cell walls are 6-ft-thick concrete. The control room (see Fig. 6.70) located above the cold-trap cell and extending over most of the inert-gas building has 12-in. concrete-block walls.

F.   Health physics building

.1	Substructure	20,900
.2	Superstructure	32,500
.3	Building services	80,000
	Total health physics building (item 212F)	133,400

Health physics building (Fig. 6.72)

Single-story concrete-block structure built on a 6-in.-thick concrete slab; 96 ft by 28 ft by 10 ft high.

G.   Office building

.1	Substructure	36,660
.2	Superstructure	91,410
.3	Building services	83,050
	Total office building (item 212G)	211,120

Office building

This building has two stories, 35 ft by 85 ft by 29 ft high above grade with a 35 ft by 42 ft by 12 ft deep basement. Basement has 15-in.-thick concrete walls and a 12-in.-thick floor. First and second floors are 9-in.-thick concrete. A 22 ft by 56 ft by 15 ft high cafeteria of similar construction is adjacent to, and part of, the office building.

H.   Inert-gas building

.1	Substructure	23,570
.2	Superstructure	76,950
.3	Building services	21,135
	Total inert-gas building (item 212H)	121,655

Inert gas building (Figs. 6.68 to 6.70)

This is a two-story concrete and steel reinforced building erected on an 18-in. concrete slab on grade beams. The lower story is 41 ft by 64 ft by 21 ft high. It contains a tank room enclosed by 4-ft-thick concrete walls 21 ft high, a compressor room, which is subdivided by two 15-in. concrete walls into three cubicles, a valve room, and a NaK equipment room. The north wall of the building is formed by the cold-trap cell wall, the south wall is formed by the tank-room wall, the east wall is a 12-in. concrete wall, and the concrete west wall varies from 4 ft thick to 12 in. thick. The second story is part of a control room extending from the sodium building and over about 40 ft of the inert-gas building.

I.   Waste-gas building

.1	Substructure	39,285
.2	Superstructure	40,215
.3	Building services	14,120
	Total waste-gas building (item 212I)	93,620

Waste-gas building (Figs. 6.68 to 6.70)

This building has a rectangular super structure (Figs. 6.68 and 6.70) 37 ft by 34 ft by 18 ft high with 2-ft-thick concrete walls. Adjacent to the super structure is a valve room 13 ft by 29 ft by 11 ft high made of 8-in. concrete blocks. The L shaped substructure (Fig. 6.69) is 11 ft deep by 27 ft by 34 ft with 12-in. concrete walls.

J.   Turbine-house building

.1	Substructure	383,250
.2	Superstructure	703,385
.3	Building services	241,755
	Total turbine-house building (item 212J)	1,328,390

Turbine-house building

Main section is 183 ft by 67 ft high with the auxiliary bay 183 ft by 36 ft by varying heights. The building has corrugated-asbestos siding, metal sash, metal roof deck, builtup roofing and structural-steel frame with concrete foundation on concrete bearing piles. Superstructure above floor grade has 1,500,000 cu ft. The overhead traveling crane has a 62 ft 6 in. span and a capacity of 110/25 tons.

K.   Plant-service building

.1	Substructure	72,930
.2	Superstructure including service	91,335
.3	Heating-plant equipment	73,915
	Total plant services building (item 212K)	238,180

L.   Miscellaneous minor buildings

.1	Gate house including services	14,565
.2	Screen house including services	36,705
.3	Retained temporary field office, shop, and warehouse, depreciated cost	51,035
	Total minor buildings (item 212L)	102,305

Total buildings (item 212)	4,640,890

219   Reactor containment structure

.1	Excavation and backfill	157,135
.2	Substructure concrete	241,315
.3	Superstructure	988,280
.4	Building services	505,300
	Total reactor containment structure (item 219)	1,892,030

TOTAL STRUCTURES AND IMPROVEMENTS (ACCOUNT 21)	7,985,545

Reactor containment building

The building (Fig. 11.61) is designed in accordance with Sec. VIII, ASME Code, has ASTM A-201 firebox qualtiy grade-B steel, has ASTM A-300 requirements, walls 1.03 in. thick, double-butt welded joints 100% radiographed, an inside diameter of 72 ft, an overall height 120 ft, 51 ft below grade, a hemispherical top head with 5/8-in.-thick walls, ellipsoidal bottom head with 1 1/4-in.-thick walls, and a design pressure of 32 psig.

22   Reactor-plant Equipment

221   Reactor equipment

.1	Reactor vessel		
.11	Vessel supports	includes internal shielding	1,967,370
.12	Vessel	and fixed internals	
.13	Vessel internals (hold-down actuator, etc.)		240,457
.2	Reactor controls		
	Control-rod actuators	408,240	
	Prototype shim-rod actuators	66,400	
	Mechanical rod oscillators	94,310	
	Control rods	292,220	
	Neutron source	95,910	
			957,080
.3	Reactor shielding		
	Reactor containment building		
	Exterior shield wall	83,000	

Miscellaneous iron including sleeves	37,980	
Operating-floor concrete	87,300	
Structural steel and miscellaneous iron	258,390	
Steel shielding plates (floors and walls)	570,200	
Concrete fill, in and under building shell	20,220	
Primary shield tank graphite	2,309,025	
Primary shield tank steel shielding	100,000	
Primary shield tank accessories	267,170	
Rotating-plug shielding (graphite and steel)	810,578	
Primary piping system neutron shielding	255,400	
		4,799,263

.5 Reactor-plant containers (within building) — 381,930

Total reactor equipment (items 221.1-221.3 and item 221.5) — 8,346,100

.7 Reactor-plant cranes and hoists — 252,900   252,900

Total reactor equipment (item 221) — 8,599,000

Reactor vessel

The reactor vessel (see Fig. 4.34) is principally made of 304 stainless steel. Component weights are as follows:

Vessel alone	170,366 lb
Plug and cover (without shield)	76,275 lb
Carbon steel, stainless steel, and graphite shielding in plug	130,640 lb
Vessel shielding	257,503 lb
Vessel supports and other external material	21,508 lb
Internal structures	8,171 lb
Piping plus shield on piping	18,912 lb
Primary shield tank graphite	6,659 cu ft (approx. 700,000 lb)
Primary shield tank cast iron shot	60,901 lb

222   Heat-transfer systems

.1 Reactor coolant system
.11 Pumps and drives — 982,020

Three primary pumps, vertical-shaft centrifugal-sump type (see Fig. 4.56), are each rated at 11,800 gal/min, 1000°F, 310-ft dynamic head, 77% efficient and are each driven by a 1060-brake hp 900-rmp wound rotor motor with a liquid-metal rheostat control. Sealing from sodium is by means of an oil-lubricated mechanical shaft seal. Parts in contact with sodium are made of 304 stainless steel. Each pump weighs 17,600 lb without the motor and the shield plug. The shield plug weighs 30,600 lb, and the motor weighs approximately 15,000 lb.

.12 Coolant piping and valves — 1,722,180

Total reactor coolant system (item 222.1) — 2,704,200

.2 Intermediate cooling system
.21 Pumps and drives — 348,940

Three secondary pumps, vertical-shaft centrifugal-sump type (see Fig. 4.59), are each rated at 12,000 gal/min, 675°F, 93-ft dynamic head and 80% efficient, and are each driven by 350-hp 900-rpm induction motor using an eddy-current coupling speed control. All parts in contact with sodium are made of 2.25 wt. % chrominum – 1 wt. % molybdenum alloy. Each pump weighs 15,800 lb without the motor. The motor weighs approximately 6,000 lb.

.22 Piping and valves — 808,345
.23 Intermediate heat exchangers — 1,903,675

Total intermediate cooling system (item 222.2) — 3,060,960

Three intermediate heat exchangers, vertical with single-wall tubes (see Fig. 4.83), are each rated at 489×10^6 Btu/hr, 5840 sq ft heat-transfer surface, 5.3×10^6 lb/hr of sodium, with primary sodium at 900°F/600°F, and secondary sodium at 820°F/520°F. Material in contact with sodium is type 304 stainless steel. There are 1860 tubes, each with a 7/8-in. OD and a 0.049-in. wall. Each intermediate heat exchanger weighs 130,600 lb. This includes the shield plug.

Three loops of piping (see Figs. 4.16 and 11.60) with ³/₈-in.-thick wall total:

Primary loop of 304 stainless steel	
216 ft. 30 in. dia. pipe	25,704 lb
188.3 ft. 14 in. dia. pipe	10,265 lb
176.7 ft. 6 in. dia. pipe	3,363 lb
36.9 ft. 16 in. dia. pipe	2,316 lb
Subtotal	41,648 lb

Secondary loop of 304 stainless steel and 2.25 wt.% Cr–1 wt.% Mo	
601 ft. 12 in. dia. pipe	29,810 lb
454 ft. 18 in. dia. pipe	32,052 lb
Subtotal	61,862 lb
Grand total	103,510

.3 Steam generators
.31 Steam generators — 2,103,905

Total steam generators (item 222.3) — 2,103,905

Three steam generators, vertical with single-wall tubes (Fig. 4.39), are each rated at 10,800 sq ft heat transfer, 5.3×10^6 lb/hr of sodium, sodium inlet 820°F, sodium outlet 520°F, 476,000 lb steam/hr, feedwater 380°F, steam 780°F, steam pressure 900 psia. They are made of 2.25 wt. % Cr–1 wt. % Mo. Each generator weighs 114,000 lb.

.4 Reactor coolant receiving, supply, and treatment

Sodium service system	
System piping	652,090
Pipe tunnel	92,785
Heating equipment	47,940
Insulation and lagging	118,490
Sodium unloading facilities	62,040
Sodium storage tanks	40,350
NaK cooling equipment	46,760
Sodium forwarding pump	12,640
Plugging indicator and cold-trap equipment	278,145
Sodium overflow tank and pumps	134,860
Sodium drain tanks and pump	41,030
Temporary hot trap	148,580
Reactor vessel Na-sampling system	41,625
Inert-gas system Compressors including drives and coolers	53,710
Inert-gas system piping	667,235
Pipe tunnel	42,590

	Heating equipment	15,400	
	Insulation and lagging	40,600	
	Gas-receiving and -storage tanks	21,950	
	Gas-purification equipment	41,950	
	Gas bottle storage	13,390	
	Initial inert-gas supply	19,500	
	Painting	23,000	
	Total reactor coolant receiving, supply and treatment (item 222.4)	2,656,660	2,656,660
.6	Coolant, initial charge (except D₂O)	143,655	
	Total coolant etc. (item 222.6)		143,655

Total heat-transfer system (item 222)   10,669,380

223   Nuclear fuel handling and storage equipment

.1	Cranes and hoisting equipment	82,090	
.2	Special tools and service equipment		
	Transfer rotor and drive	172,140	
	Offset handling mechanism	313,047	
	Rotating plug and drive (excluding shielding)	69,000	
	Subassembly transfer cask car	643,058	
	Subassembly transfer pots and storage racks	237,650	
	Underwater subassembly equipment	349,000	
	Industrial track for cask car	66,000	
	New subassembly receiving and storage equipment	73,200	1,923,095
.3	Spent-fuel storage, cooling, cleaning, and inspection equipment		
	Subassembly sodium removal and washing equipment	701,900	
	Decay storage pool water circulating and treating equipment	89,100	
	Miscellaneous	242,735	1,033,735
	Total nuclear fuel handling and storage equipment (item 223)		3,038,920

225   Radioactive-waste treatment and disposal

.1	Liquid waste		
.2	Gaseous waste	592,510	
.3	Solid wastes		
	Total radioactive-waste treatment and disposal (item 225)		592,510

226	Instrumentation and control		
	Health physics instruments and equipment	197,600	
	Reactor-plant instrumentation		
	Instruments, controls, and panels	2,161,750	
	Conduit and wiring	104,540	
	Piping and tubing	249,800	
	Television systems	51,800	
	Total instrumentation and control (item 226)	2,765,490	2,765,490

227	Feedwater supply and treatment		
.1	Raw-water supply system	134,095	
.2	Makeup water supply	125,980	
.3	Steam-generator feedwater purification and treatment system	124,795	
.4	Feedwater heaters	246,905	
.5	Feedwater pumps and drives	215,360	
	Total feedwater supply and treatment (item 227)		847,135

No. 1 feedwater heater is rated at 1,168,000 lb/hr of feedwater and 78,900 lb/hr of steam; has 5190 sq ft effective surface, No. 18 BW gauge wall, 3/4-in.-OD tube, 412 Admiralty metal 32-ft two-pass tubes, and a 77,300,000 Btu/hr rating; the shell has an inside diameter of 42 in., is 3/8 in. thick, and is 37 ft long; weight dry is 27,000 lb.

No. 2 feedwater heater is rated at 1,168,000 lb/hr of feedwater and 99,980 lb/hr of steam; has 6700 sq ft effective surface, No. 18 BW gauge wall, 3/4-in.-OD tube, 458 Admiralty metal 37-ft two-pass tubes, and a 116,900,000 Btu/hr rating; the shell has an inside diameter of 44 in., is 3/8 in. thick, and is 43 ft long; weight dry is 36,600 lb.

No. 3 feedwater heater is rated at 1,168,000 lb/hr of feedwater and 62,180 lb/hr of steam; has 3900 sq ft effective surface, No. 18 BW gauge wall, 3/4-in.-OD tube, 347 Admiralty metal 29-ft two-pass tubes, and a 59,400,000 Btu/hr rating; the shell has an inside diameter of 36 in., is 3/8 in. thick, and is 34 ft long; weight dry is 21,000 lb.

No. 4 deaerating feedwater heater is rated at 1,357,871 lb/hr of feedwater leaving heater, shell pressure 181.4 psia, 58,827 lb/hr of bled steam, and 650°F; has a 10-ft-diameter shell with 1 3/4 in. wall, and is 25 ft long. Storage unit is designed for 650°F, is 11 ft in diameter, has a 1 1/4 in. shell, and is 39 ft long. Heater tank weighs 63,900 lb. Storage tank weighs 95,000 lb.

Three horizontal boiler feed pumps are each rated at 921,469 lb/hr, 1632 gal/min, suction pressure 175 psig, net dynamic head 482 psi, suction temperature 377.5°F at 0.882 specific gravity, 2126 ft of head, 3425 rpm at full speed, 85% efficiency, 973 brake hp pump input, and 25 ft NPSH. Each unit weighs 27,150 lb including motor and fluid drive. Motors are squirrel-cage induction, 3600 rpm, 1000 hp, 4600 volt.

228	Steam, condensate, and feedwater piping (item 228)	1,114,580	1,114,580

Includes one steam dump with eight 36-in. lines dumping 750,000 lb/hr of steam at 2.5 psia. The steam is initially at 195 psia in No. 4 heater and is gradually reduced in pressure by means of pressure-control valves, pipe size increase, orifices, an increase in the number of pipe lines with orifices, and the use of perforated plates which act as orifices.

229	Other reactor-plant equipment		
	Reactor maintenance equipment		
	Equipment decay tanks	181,000	

Coffins for component transfer	45,600		
Special tools and equipment for assembly and disassembly of radioactive components	249,220		
Removable and portable shield blocks and barriers	201,300		
Total other reactor-plant equipment (item 229)	677,120	677,120	

TOTAL REACTOR-PLANT EQUIPMENT (ACCOUNT 22)   28,304,135

23	Turbine-generator Units		
231	Turbine generators		
.1	Foundation	120,525	
.2	Turbine generators	4,804,685	
	Total turbine-generators (item 231)		4,925,210

One turbine generator (TCSF), rated at 1800 rpm, 156 Mw(e), 850 psig, and 780°F, has a turbine-cycle heat rate of 9800 Btu/kw-hr gross and a return shell reheater between high- and low-pressure sections reheating from 340°F to 530°F.

232	Circulating-water systems		
.1	Pumping and regulating equipment	208,430	

Two vertical wet pit-mixed flow-enclosed impeller circulating-water pumps are each rated at 66,000 gal/min, 19.0 ft dynamic head, 290 rpm, 85% efficiency, and 373.5 brake hp to shaft. Suction diameter is 72 in., and discharge diameter 54 in. The drive is a squirrel-cage induction 300-rpm 400-hp 4000-volt motor. The weight of each pump is 50,000 lb, and motor weight is 15,000 lb.

.2	Circulating-water lines	55,185	
.3	Intake and discharge structures	252,050	
.4	Fouling, corrosion control, and water treatment systems	30,650	
	Total circulating-water systems (item 232)		546,315

233	Condensers (item 233)	943,310	943,310

One condenser is rated at 973,000 lb steam, heat input of 924 × 10⁶ Btu/hr, 1.0 in. Hg absolute, 132,200 gal/min cooling water at 56°F, 14°F cooling water rise, 6.72 ft/sec cooling water; has 18850 tubes of Admiralty metal, No. 18 BW gauge 3/4-in.-OD tubes, total length of tubes 30 ft, 110,000 sq ft total effective cooling surface, dry weight with tubes 738,300 lb, with no tubes 498,300 lb, 153,000 lb hot well, tube head thickness 1 3/8 in. and shell made of 7/8-in.-thick copper bearing ASTM A-285 grade C flange quality steel.

Three vertical condensate pumps, each rated at 722,100 lb/hr, 1450 gal/min, suction pressure 9.0 psia, 349.3 psig discharge pressure, 50 to 100°F suction temperature, 1.0 specific gravity, 875 ft of head, 1180 rpm, 74% efficiency, 420 brake hp pump input, 10 ft NPSH, and a weight of 14,491 lb per unit including motor. Motor is squirrel cage, 1200 rpm, 450 hp, 4600 volt.

235	Turbine-plant boards, instruments, and controls (item 235)	414,735	414,735

TOTAL TURBINE-GENERATOR UNITS (ACCOUNT 23)   6,829,570

24	Accessory Electric Equipment		
241	Switchgear		
.1	Generator main and neutral circuits	44,755	
.2	Station service	281,260	
	Total switchgear (item 241)		326,015
242	Switchboards		
.1	Main control board		
.2	Auxiliary power, battery, and signal boards	198,785	
.3	Motor control centers		
	Total switchboards (item 242)		198,785
243	Protective Equipment (item 243)	23,470	23,470
245	Conduit (item 245)	323,695	323,695
246	Power and control wiring (item 246)	768,120	768,120
247	Station service equipment (item 247)	322,235	322,235

TOTAL ACCESSORY ELECTRIC EQUIPMENT (ACCOUNT 24)   1,962,320

25	Miscellaneous Power-plant Equipment		
251	Cranes and hoisting equipment (item 251)	159,885	159,885
252	Compressed air and vacuum-cleaning systems (item 252)	66,445	66,445
253	Other power-plant equipment		

Miscellaneous plant equipment		
Cafeteria equipment	24,725	
Office furniture and equipment	10,365	
Signal systems equipment	14,835	
Fire-protection equipment	10,820	
Caterpillar-tractor fork lift	14,340	
General service water	139,255	
General service water (painting)	3,230	
General service water pumps	23,805	
Fire pump	19,310	
Conventional physics and chemical laboratory equipment	9,700	
Furniture and equipment	48,000	
Transportation equipment	12,200	
Machine-shop tools	41,610	
Station maintenance tools and equipment	49,300	
Weather tower and instruments	19,500	
Signal and communication systems	35,505	
Emergency eye-wash showers	21,300	

Diesel yard locomotive	20,100	
Total other power plant equipment (item 253)	517,900	517,900
TOTAL MISCELLANEOUS POWER PLANT EQUIPMENT (ACCOUNT 25)		744,230

Appendix B
Computation of Fuel-cycle Material Balance, 150 Mw (e) Fast Reactor Plant
(See Fig. 10.3.)

Core-cycle material-balance computation

Core throughput

Thermal power output, Mw(t)	355
Plant factor (P.F.), %	80
Megawatt days per year, Mwd/year	$355 \times 365 \times 0.8 \stackrel{\sim}{=} 103,500$
Burnup, Mwd/tonne	50,000
Core throughput of heavy-metal atoms, kg	$\dfrac{103,500}{50,000 \text{ Mwd}/1000 \text{ kg}} = 2070$

Fabrication-plant input

Plant input, heavy metal atoms, kg

$=$ Plant output + fabrication loss + scrap recovery loss

$= 2070 + 0.007$ plant input $+ 0.001$ plant input

$= 2086.7$

Conversion-plant input

Plant input, heavy-metal atoms, kg

$=$ Plant output + conversion loss

$= 2086.7 + 0.003$ plant input

$= 2093.0$

Core-processing-plant material balance

Plant output, heavy-metal atoms, kg

$=$ Plant input – fission products – losses

$= 2070.0 - 103.5 - 0.01 (2070 - 103.5)$

$= 1946.8$

Core-fuel blending at processing plant

Fuel for conversion, heavy-metal atoms, kg

$=$ Processing-plant output $+ U^{238}$ makeup from blanket processing $+ Pu^{249+241}$ makeup $- Pu^{240+242}$ discard

$= 1946.8 + 121 + 37.7 - 12.5$

$= 2093.0$

Blanket-cycle material-balance computation

Blanket throughput
Radial:

Power output, Mw(t)	60
Plant factor (P.F.), %	80
Megawatt days per year, Mwd/year	$60 \times 365 \times .80 = 17,520$
Burnup, Mwd/tonne	6350
Radial blanket throughput, depleted uranium, kg	$\dfrac{17,520}{6350 \text{ Mwd}/1000 \text{ kg}} = 2751$
S.A./year*	$\dfrac{2751}{17,200} \times 227 = 36.3$

Axial

Power output, Mw(t)	15
Plant factor (P.F.), %	80
Megawatt days per year, Mwd/year	$15 \times 365 \times .80 = 4380$
Burnup, Mwd/tonne	5900 Mwd/tonne

*S.A. = subassemblies. Note: total S.A. in radial blanket = 227 with 17,200 kg uranium.

Axial blanket throughput, depleted uranium, kg

$$\frac{4380}{5900 \text{ Mwd}/1000 \text{ kg}} = 742$$

Total blanket throughput, depleted uranium, kg

2751 + 742 (radial and axial)

= 3493

Fabrication-plant input

Plant input, depleted uranium, kg

= Plant output + fabrication loss

= 3493 + 0.05 plant input

= 3677

Processing-plant material balance

Processing plant output, depleted uranium, kg

= Plant input - fission products - losses - Pu to core and sale - U^{238} to core makeup

= 3493 - 22.8 - 0.01 × (3470.2) - 77.3 - 121

= 3237.2

Conversion-plant material balance

Plant output, depleted uranium, kg

= Plant input + AEC makeup - losses

= 3237.2 + AEC makeup - 9.7

= 3677

AEC makeup

449.5

Notes: 1. The isotopic analysis of fuel and blanket and various locations in the fuel cycle were derived from physics computations.

2. All weights are on an annual basis.

References

1. Guide to Nuclear Power Cost Evaluation, USAEC Report TID-7025, Vols. I, II, III, IV, V, and Supplement 1, Kaiser Engineers.
2. Uniform System of Accounts for Public Utilities and Licensees, Federal Power Commission, U. S. Government Printing Office, Washington 25, D. C., January 1961.
3. E. L. Grant and W. G. Iveson, Principles of Engineering Economy, 4th ed., The Ronald Press Company, New York, 1960.
4. F. C. Kent and M. E. Kent, Ten Place Interest and Annuity Tables, McGraw-Hill Book Company, Inc., New York, 1926.
5. R. Winfrey, Depreciation of Group Properties, Bulletin No. 155, Iowa State College of Agriculture and Mechanical Arts, Ames, Iowa, June 3, 1942.
6. Economic Comparison of Alternative Plans, System Planning Subcommittee, Edison Electric Institute, unpublished, 1960.
7. Fast Reactor Core Design Parameter Study, USAEC Report APDA-133, Atomic Power Development Associates, Inc., March 1960.
8. G. D. Collins, Fabrication Cost Estimate for UO_2 and Mixed PuO_2 - UO_2 Fuel, SUAEC Report GEAP-3824, General Electric Co., Jan. 24, 1962.

CHAPTER 11

Description of Fast Reactors

ALEXANDER SESONSKE
Purdue University, and Lafayette, Indiana
JOHN G. YEVICK*
Atomic Power Development Associates, Inc., Detroit, Michigan

Contents

A description of each of the fast reactors actually constructed is provided in this chapter. The length of treatment varies to some extent with the availability of source information and the general applicability of design features.

Some background conceptual thinking is included for each reactor. Although a portion of the description is included in other chapters, particularly descriptions of components, structures, and instrumentation (Chaps. 4, 6, 7, 8, and 9), some duplication is included here as a convenience to the reader and to provide the necessary perspective regarding specific plants.

An important objective of this chapter is to provide in one place a description in some detail of a number of fast reactor systems. In many cases the specific design approach used may be outdated and may not therefore constitute "recommended practice."

The general characteristics of fast reactors are described in Chap. 1 and Ref. 1. Wherever possible, however, mention is made in this chapter of those characteristics for each reactor which add to the picture presented here. References 1 through 6 are to articles covering general aspects, to status reports of fast reactors, or to symposiums dealing with fast reactors.

For each reactor a tabulation of design specifications is given. Although details vary with the information available, the listing given is generally as complete as is possible. The reactors described here are treated in chronological order insofar as is practical.

In the case of three power reactors for which construction has been completed, Dounreay, EBR-

II, and Fermi, the design data are presented on a consistent basis in Table 11.1. Although differences in capacities exist, there is a similarity in parameters, such as specific power and power density, among reactors of different size.

11.1 Clementine

11.1.1 INTRODUCTION

Clementine [7, 8], the first fast reactor and the first to use Pu^{239} as fuel, was developed at the Los Alamos Scientific Laboratory. Although it served primarily as a source of fast neutrons for experimental purposes, it also demonstrated the feasibility of plutonium as a fast reactor fuel. Operation began in November 1946 with a power of 1 watt. In March 1949, the power was increased to 25 kw(t). After several years of very satisfactory operation, failure of at least one fuel element and the resulting contamination of the mercury coolant led to the decision to dismantle the reactor. This was effected in 1953. Although the operating temperatures were too low for power production, the reactor was used for research and it did demonstrate the feasibility of plutonium as a fuel for fast power reactors. Sufficient plutonium for such a reactor existed solely at Los Alamos during this period.

A cross-sectional view of the reactor is shown in Fig. 11.1. The reactor and shielding formed a rectangular block-like structure. A summary of design data for Clementine is given in Table 11.2.

11.1.2 CORE ARRANGEMENT

The 5.9-in. diameter core contained 55 fuel and blanket elements, as shown in Fig. 11.2. The fuel rods, of delta-phase plutonium, were 0.647 in. in diameter and 5.5 in. long, as shown in Fig. 11.3. They were clad with type 1020 steel, 0.02 in. thick, and assembled in a vertical lattice (Fig. 11.2).

11.1.3 CONTROL ELEMENTS

Control of the reactor was effected by several components. A reflector, consisting of a large block

---

*Now with the U. S. Atomic Energy Commission.

Table 11.1—Plant and Reactor Design Data (Dounreay, EBR-II, and Fermi)

	Dounreay	EBR-II	Fermi
Plant Data			
Net electrical output, Mw(e)		17.4	60.9
Gross electrical output, Mw(e)	15	20.0	65.9
Reactor thermal output, Mw(t)	72	62.5	200.0
Reactor thermal output, 10^6 Btu/hr	246	213.0	683.0
Btu/net electrical kw-hr, Btu/kw-hr		12,200	11,200
Net station efficiency, %		27.9	30.5
Steam pressure, psia	165	1265	576
Steam temperature at turbine, °F	520	850	760
Steam flow at turbine throttle, 10^5 lb/hr	1.7	1.98	6.4
Reactor Data			
Core:			
Core power, Mw(t)	60	53	174
Dimensions and volume:			
Length, ft	1.75	1.19	2.73
Diameter, ft	1.75	1.59	2.72
Volume, cu ft	4.2	2.32	13.40
Fuel element (1st loading only):			
Geometry	Annular rod	Pin	Pin
No. of elements	367	4277	14,700
Dimensions (overall incl. clad)			
Length, in.	21	14.22	30.5
OD, in.	0.752	0.174	0.158
ID, in.	0.258		
Cladding thickness, in.	0.020	0.009	0.005
Cladding material	Niobium OD; Vanadium ID	SS	Zr
Fuel	U—0.5 wt.% Cr*	(U—fissium)	(U—10 wt.% Mo)
Fuel enrichment, %	45.5	49.4	25.6
Max. fuel burnup, at. %		2	0.4
Max. fuel burnup, Mwd/tonne		24,000	6000
Coolant characteristics:			
Sodium flow, 10^6 lb/hr	3.1†	3.6‡	7.1
Flow velocity (core), ft/sec	16	26	16
Pressure drop through core, psi	11	23	35
Heat-transfer characteristics:			
Inlet temperature, °F	392	700	550
Average outlet temperature, °F	752	890	800
Average power density, kw(t)/cu ft	14,250	22,800	13,000
Specific power, kw/kg U^{235}	286	314	350
Max. heat flux, 10^6 Btu/hr/sq ft	1.156	1.030	0.640
Max. to average heat flux	1.7	1.7	1.7
Max. fuel temperature, °F	1544	1320	1115
Nuclear characteristics:			
Critical mass, kg U^{235}	210	170	496
Core conversion ratio		0.30	0.29
Average core neutron flux, neutrons/cm²/sec	3.3×10^{15} §	2×10^{15}	3×10^{15}
Blanket:			
Power, Mw(t)	12	9	24.8
Uranium (approx.), tons	62	28	35
Radial blanket rod:			
Outside diameter, in.	1.362	0.493	0.443
Length, in.	84	55	65
Cladding material	SS	SS	SS
Cladding thickness, in.	0.036	0.018	0.004
No. rods	1872	10,944	14,300
Blanket material	Depleted U	Nat. U	(Depleted U—3 wt.% Mo)
Blanket conversion ratio		1.16	0.87
Total conversion ratio		1.26	1.16

* Initial loadings; subsequent loadings were U—10 wt.% Mo.
† NaK flow.
‡ Through entire reactor.
§ At 60 Mw(t).

of uranium immediately below the active region, could be raised into position to increase the reactivity and quickly dropped out to reduce it. Two safety rods, located in positions immediately outside the central region, were composed of a section of uranium and a section of B^{10} poison. For shutdown the uranium section was dropped out, and the B^{10} section was inserted into the region in one motion. In addition, the reactor was provided with two uranium rods which acted as control rods.

11.1.4 HEAT-TRANSPORT SYSTEM

A flow sheet of the mercury coolant system is shown in Fig. 11.4. Since the reactor was primarily

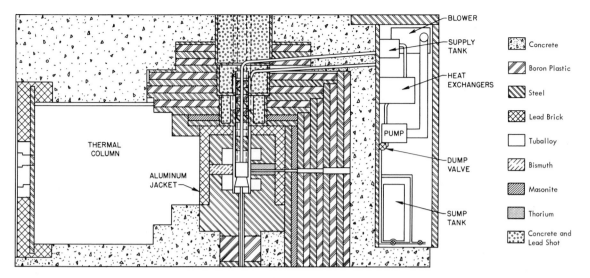

FIG. 11.1—Cross section through the Clementine reactor shield[8].

a research facility, with 25 kw(t) at full power, heat-removal requirements were quite modest. The mercury coolant was pumped by an eddy-current type of electromagnetic pump at a rate of 2.4 gal/min through the core and then through a mercury-to-water heat exchanger. In the two heat exchangers, mercury flowed through a helical coil of 7/8 in.-ID steel tubing inside a solid water-cooled copper cylinder.

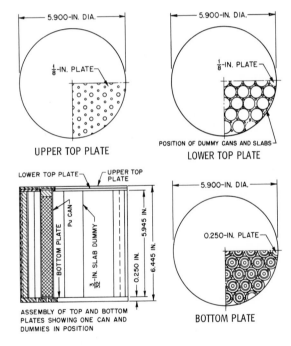

FIG. 11.2—Clementine core cross section and elevation [7].

Table 11.2—Design Data for Clementine

Reactor Data

Thermal power, kw	25
High energy flux, neutrons/cm^2/sec	4.3×10^{12}
Hg flow, gal/min	2.4
Hg velocity in core, ft/sec	0.16
Core dimensions:	
Length, in.	5.5
Diameter, in.	5.9
Inlet temperature, °F	100
Outlet temperature, °F	250
Pu temperature, °F	275

Fuel Data

Fuel	Delta-phase Pu
Fuel clad material	Nickel
Thickness of cladding, in.	0.003
Fuel can material	Mild steel
Fuel diameter, in.	0.647
Fuel length, in.	5.5
Fuel can ID, in.	0.652
Fuel can OD, in.	0.692
Fuel rod swaged to OD, in.	0.686
Fuel-rod triangular spacing, in.	0.718

Control

Regulating control	Uranium reflector
Safety	B^{10} poison

Coolant System

Volume Hg, cu ft	0.64
Volume Hg, lb	540
Cover-gas pressure, psig	50
Pressure drop in cooling system components, psi	6.4
Efficiency of Hg pump @ 7.7 psi head, 2.4 gal/min and 11 amps, %	2

11.1.5 STRUCTURAL COMPONENTS

A 46-in.-long, 6.2-in.-OD, and 6.00-in.-ID mild-steel cylinder served as the core container. The fuel cage, described previously, rested on the bottom of this cylinder. Immediately above the case and filling the space to the top of the pot, or vessel, was a removable reflector and shield plug. This plug contained a number of layers of various materials (Fig. 11.1) all in a steel cylinder having a 1/4-in. wall thickness. A side shield, consisting of a permanent assembly of laminations and con-

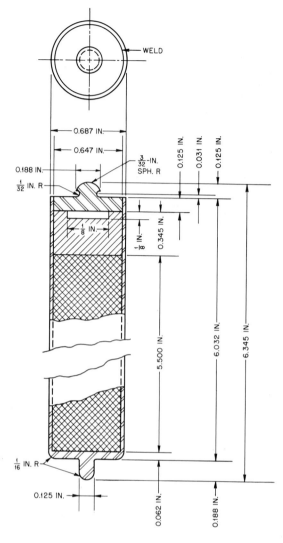

FIG. 11.3—Clementine fuel rod [7].

irradiation work. Four horizontal holes ran completely through the reactor. In addition, three reentrant horizontal holes and ten vertical holes were provided.

11.1.7 OPERATING EXPERIENCE

Following the attainment of criticality in November 1946, the reactor was operated as a critical assembly; considerable information was obtained concerning the physics of fast reactors. During low-power operation of the reactor from February 1947 through January 1949, measurements were made of the critical mass, effectiveness of reactor control, temperature coefficient, neutron spectrum, and general behavior. The information obtained was valuable in establishing the feasibility of fast reactor operation, including the demonstration of control by delayed neutrons.

From March 1949 to December 1952, when the rupture of a plutonium fuel rod was noted, the reactor was used for fast-neutron irradiation research, as well as for a continuing program of reactor physics research. As a result of the fuel-rod rupture, plutonium was released into the mercury coolant circuit. Since the primary objectives of the experiment had by then been achieved, the reactor was dismantled. The Omega West Research Reactor now occupies the Clementine reactor site.

11.2 EBR-I

11.2.1 INTRODUCTION

The Argonne National Laboratory Experimental Breeder Reactor I (EBR-I) (Fig. 4.14 of Chap. 4) is located at the National Reactor Test Station, Idaho [3, 9-22]. It was designed to demonstrate fast reactor breeding and to prove the use of liquid-metal coolants for power production. As a model, a power level on the order of 1 Mw(t) was chosen. The electrical power generated is about 200 kw(e).

EBR-I was based on concepts proposed in 1945. The research and development program was approved early in 1945, and the Manhattan Engineer District approved construction in November 1945. Design and construction occupied the years from 1948 to 1951. Criticality with the Mark-I core was reached in August 1951, and electricity was generated on Dec. 22, 1951. The Mark-II core was installed in 1954. A series of kinetic experiments led to its meltdown on Nov. 20, 1955.

The Mark-I and Mark-II cores were similar with the exception of some changes in spacing ribs and composition, as described in Refs. 6, 13, and 14. The Mark-III core was designed primarily to investigate fast reactor stability. The Mark-IV core, loaded in 1962, utilizes plutonium as a fuel and provides a facility in which the general operating characteristics of solid-plutonium-fueled reactors can be investigated.

11.2.2 REACTOR FEATURES

It should be borne in mind that the design effort of the EBR-I was pioneering in nature; much of the

crete, also served as a supporting and retaining wall for the reactor parts.

In addition to the 35 plutonium fuel rods, the central active core contained 20 reflector rods of natural uranium, having the same dimensions and cladding as the fuel rods. A 6-in.-thick reflector—blanket of natural uranium surrounded the core. A 1/4-in.-thick aluminum jacket, containing water-cooling tubes, removed the heat generated in the uranium blanket. The core and blanket were surrounded by a 6-in. steel reflector and a 4-in. thickness of lead shielding. The top shielding was made of a series of blocks which could be removed to give access to the reactor.

11.1.6 EXPERIMENTAL HOLES

Since an important purpose of this reactor was to provide fast neutrons for experimental purposes, a number of holes were provided for

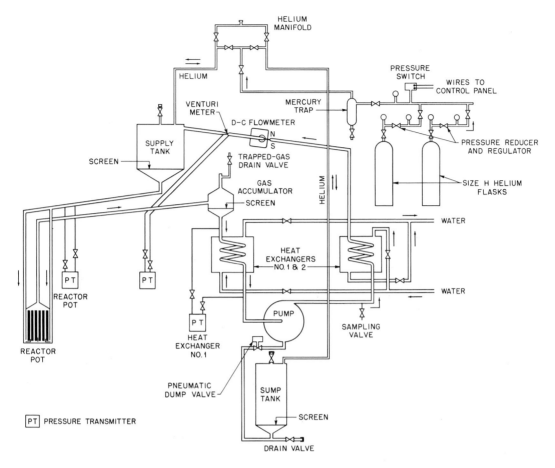

FIG. 11.4—Clementine mercury system [7].

present nuclear reactor technology had not yet developed. A schematic drawing of the reactor installation is shown in Fig. 4.14 of Chap. 4, and a summary of design data is given in Table 11.3. For the Mark-I core, the power density was 170 kw(t)/liter, and the average heat flux was 218,000 Btu/hr/sq ft. Although these values have been exceeded in more recently designed fast reactors, EBR-I may be considered as the first high power density reactor. Initial plans called for a conservative design that would permit operation at power levels greater than 1 Mw. Heat generation in the outer blanket proved greater than anticipated, however, and limited the operating power.

11.2.3 CORE ARRANGEMENT

The Mark-II core arrangement is shown in Figs. 11.5 and 11.6. The inner fuel rods, 0.448 in. in outside diameter, were separated without spacer ribs by 0.046 in. The Mark-I core used spacer ribs. Enriched fuel was used in the middle of each rod, and natural uranium was used at the top and bottom to form an axial blanket. An inner blanket consisted of natural-uranium slugs, 15/16 in. in diameter and 20 1/4 in. long, jacketed in 0.022-in.-thick

stainless steel. The core itself and the inner blanket were cooled by circulating sodium—potassium alloy.

An air-cooled outer blanket is located outside the reactor tank. It consists of 84 keystone-shaped natural-uranium bricks, each weighing 100 lb, clad with stainless steel 0.020 in. thick. This section is movable and contains the control rods. The moving parts are kept outside the liquid metal. The air cooling of the blanket proved to be the limitation on the operating power available for the reactor. Surrounding the external blanket is a graphite reflector 19 in. thick, followed by 9 ft of concrete shielding. Six experimental beam holes pierce the concrete shield and graphite reflector. A thermal column and a "rabbit hole" also provide facilities for experiments, as shown in Fig. 11.7.

11.2.4 FUEL

Most of the rods for the Mark-I core were loaded with four 0.364-in.-diameter slugs, each of which was 1 7/8 in. in length. Some of the rods, however, contained 2.5-in.-long 0.384-in.-diameter slugs. Below the fuel section a 4.5-in.-long natural-uranium slug served as a lower blanket, and above

Table 11.3—EBR-I Design Data

	Mark-I	Mark-II	Mark-III	Mark-IV
Flow and Temperature Conditions, Reactor Core and Inner Blanket				
Temperature of NaK in, $^\circ$C/$^\circ$F	230/446	230/446	230/446	230/446
Temperature of NaK out, $^\circ$C/$^\circ$F	322/612	322/612	322/612	322/612
Flow rate, gal/min	291	291	291	291
Total power produced:				
Kw(t)	1203	1203	1203	1203
10^6 Btu/hr	4.11	4.11	4.11	4.11
Power produced in core, kw(t)	1000	1000	1054	1054
Power produced in internal blanket, kw(t)	203	203	149	149
Dimensional Data - Reactor Core				
Fuel-rod lattice spacing, in.	0.494	0.494	0.450	0.348
Cladding diameter (outer), in.	0.448	0.448	0.404	0.299
Fuel-slug diameter, in.	0.364	0.384	0.364	0.232
NaK-bond thickness, in.	0.020	0.010	0.000	0.0125
Cladding material	347 SS ribbed	347 SS plain	Zircaloy-3 ribbed	Zircaloy-2 ribbed
Cross-sectional area for coolant flow, sq ft	0.1008	0.1008	0.0795	0.0972
Coolant velocity, ft/sec	6.5	6.5	6.85	5.6
NaK flow area per lattice triangle, sq in.	0.0248	0.0248	0.0204	0.0137
Flow area in lattice, %	23.5	23.5	23.2	26.1
NaK flow area per rod in lattice, sq in.	0.0496	0.0496	0.0408	0.0274
NaK flow area of total area, %	28.2	28.2	26.5	29.4
Core volume, liters	5.9	6.1	6.07	5.80
Total area of core section, sq ft	0.338	0.338	0.348	0.348
Total fuel-rod surface area, sq ft	15.68	16.20	15.33	19.5
Heat Transfer Data - Reactor Core				
Average heat flux:				
Cal/sec/cm^2	16.3	15.8	17.6	13.9
Btu/hr/sq ft	218,000	210,000	234,000	184,500
Average power density, kw/liter	170	164	174	182
Average specific power, kw/kg	18.8	19.2	21.9	33.5
Ratio maximum/average power	1.25	1.35	1.35	1.35
Maximum heat flux:				
Cal/sec/cm^2	20.7	21.4	23.8	18.8
Btu/hr/sq ft	274,000	284,000	316,000	249,000
Maximum specific power, kw(t)/kg fissile material	23.5	25.9	29.6	45.3
Temp. difference in slug, $^\circ$C/$^\circ$F	72/130	84/151	83/149	85/153
ΔT across NaK bond, max., $^\circ$C/$^\circ$F	18/32	10/18	0/0	11/20
ΔT across cladding, max., $^\circ$C/$^\circ$F	18/32	21/36	38/63	31/56
ΔT across coolant film, max., $^\circ$C/$^\circ$F	12/22	13/23	20/36	12/22
Total temp. difference, $^\circ$C/$^\circ$F	120/216	128/230	141/254	139/250
NaK coolant temp. at reactor center line, $^\circ$C/$^\circ$F	338/640	338/640	338/640	338/640
Fuel-slug temp. at reactor center line, $^\circ$C/$^\circ$F	458/856	466/871	479/894	477/891
Maximum slug temp., $^\circ$C/$^\circ$F	477/891	485/905	498/928	495/923
Inner Blanket				
Total surface area of rods, sq ft	56.2	56.2	30.4	30.4
Average heat flux:				
Cal/sec/cm^2	0.928	0.928	1.25	1.25
Btu/hr/sq ft	12,300	12,300	16,600	16,600
Total cross-section area of blanket section, sq ft	1.02	1.02	0.599	0.599
Uranium area, sq ft	0.57	0.57	0.312	0.312
Cross-sectional area for coolant flow, sq ft	0.368	0.368	0.155	0.155
Coolant velocity, series flow, ft/sec	1.77	1.77	3.51	3.51
Outer Blanket				
Inlet air temperature, $^\circ$C/$^\circ$F	20/68	20/68	20/68	20/68
Outlet air temperature, $^\circ$C/$^\circ$F	108/226	108/226	108/226	108/226
Air flow rate, cu ft/min	5800	5800	5800	5800
Power produced in outer blanket, kw(t)	222	222	222	222
Components of Core and Blanket				
Critical mass (wet, cold), kg	51.5	48.2	47.5	30.4*/27.1†
Core composition, vol.%:				
U	48.2	48.9	49.5	
SS type 304	15.3	15.3	7.3	
NaK	36.50	32.9	25.6	
Zr		2.9	17.6	
Radial inner blanket composition, vol.%:				
U	70.8	70.8	48.9	
SS type 304	9.3	9.3	7.3	
NaK	19.9	19.9	25.6	
Zr			18.2	

* Calculated clean.

† Actual clean.

Table 11.3—EBR-I Design Data (continued)

	Mark-I	Mark-II	Mark-III	Mark-IV
Upper and lower blanket composition, vol.%:				
U	48.2	48.9	48.9	
SS type 304	15.3	15.3	7.3	
NaK	36.5	32.9	25.6	
Zr		2.9	18.2	
Neutron Fluxes, Center Line of Reactor				
Center of core, neutrons/cm^2/sec	1.1×10^{14}	1.1×10^{14}		
Boundary between core and blanket, neutrons/cm^2/sec	5.7×10^{13}	5.7×10^{13}		
Reactor tank wall, neutrons/cm^2/sec	2.9×10^{12}	2.9×10^{12}		
Outer edge of external blanket, neutrons/cm^2/sec	3.4×10^{11}	3.4×10^{11}		
6 in. from edge of blanket in thermal column, neutrons/cm^2/sec	1.8×10^{12}	1.8×10^{12}		

Data on the EBR-I Heat-removal System

INTERMEDIATE HEAT EXCHANGER

Overall length, ft	14.67
Shell outside diameter, in.	17
Type	Double-pass shell and tube
Tubes	
Number	102
Type	Hairpin
Material	"A" nickel
Outside diameter, in.	0.75
Gauge	16
Outside area of tubes, sq ft	495
Log mean temperature difference, °C/°F	11/20
Overall heat-transfer coefficient, Btu/hr/sq ft/°F	400

HEAT-EXCHANGER TUBE IN SUPERHEATER, BOILER, AND ECONOMIZER:

Effective length, ft	9.563
Outside diameter, in.	2.625
Inside diameter, in.	2

SUPERHEATER

Number of heat exchangers	4
Arrangement	Series with countercurrent flow
Total inside area of tube, sq ft	20
Shell size, in. (IPS)	5
Shell-side cross-sectional flow area, sq in.	14.6
NaK velocity, ft/sec	6.15
Steam velocity, average, ft/sec	58.8

ECONOMIZER

Number of heat exchangers	9
Arrangement	Series with countercurrent flow
Total inside tube area, sq ft	45
Shell size, in. (IPS)	5
Shell-side cross-sectional flow area, sq ft	14.6
NaK velocity, ft/sec	6.15
Water velocity in annulus around 1¾-in.-OD baffle, ft/sec	3.43

BOILER

Number of heat exchangers	18
Arrangement	Parallel with countercurrent flow
Total inside tube area, sq ft	90
Shell-side cross-sectional flow area per tube, sq in.	1.98
Shell size, in. (IPS)	3
NaK velocity, ft/sec	2.51
Water flow rate (× steam rate)	13

Reactivity Insertion (Mark IV)

	No.	Speed, in./sec	Reactivity change (per rod, block, or cup)	
			$\Delta k/k$/sec	Inhour/sec
Control rods (withdrawal)	4	0.64	1.1×10^{-5}	1.05
Safety rods	8	0.64	1.1×10^{-5}	1.05
Safety block	1	5.0	4.9×10^{-4}	45.9
Cup (80 in. to 30 in.)	1*	0.32		
Cup (30 in. to 5.15 in.)	1*	0.095	3.75×10^{-4}	35.6
Cup (5.15 in. to 0 in.)	1*†	0.005	1.54×10^{-5}	1.46

* Movable outer blanket, upward motion of elevator.

† Manual control.

Table 11.3—EBR-I Design Data (continued)

	No.	Time to initiate motion, sec	Total time for indicated travel		Reactivity change*		
			Sec	Travel, in.	%$\Delta k/k$	$	Inhour/sec
Control rods	4		No scram provision				
Safety rods	8	0.085	0.38	16	0.18	0.61	177
Safety block	1	0.15	0.35	6	0.06	0.20	57
Cup	1†	0.10	0.31	5.15	1.28	4.32	1215
			0.56	12	3.50	11.8	3320
			Total travel		5.25	17.5	5000

Control and Safety-rod Data

Diameter of rods, in.	2
Type	Natural uranium
Cladding	SS

* 950 inhours = 1%$\Delta k/k$ for plutonium loading.
  β = 0.00296 for Mark IV.
  β = 0.00685 for Mark III.
† Outer blanket, downward motion of elevator.

the fuel section an 8-in.-long natural-uranium slug was loaded as the top blanket.

During operation of the first core, experiments showed that an alloy fuel composed of U—2 wt.% Zr was more resistant than beta-quenched uranium to irradiation growth and was free of the irradiation-induced surface-roughening characteristic of beta-quenched uranium. Accordingly, in early 1954, a

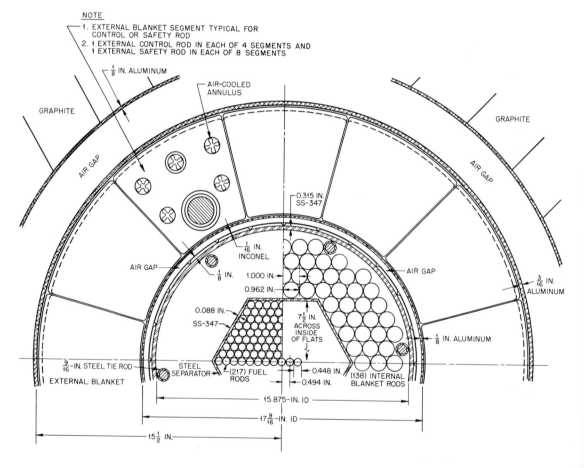

FIG. 11.5—EBR-I horizontal cross section at midplane of Mark-II core [19].

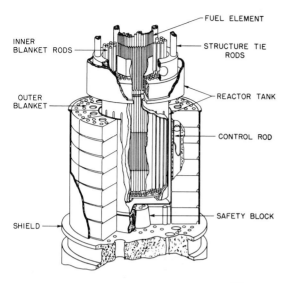

FIG. 11.6—EBR-I Mark-II reactor cutaway view [9].

Mark-II core was installed with U—2 wt.% Zr alloy in both the fuel and blanket slugs. The fuel slugs were 4 1/4 in. long by 0.384 in. in diameter, with a lower blanket slug 4 1/4 in. long and an upper blanket 8 in. long. As in the Mark-I core, the annulus between slug and fuel tube was filled with NaK as a heat-transfer bond.

11.2.5 CONTROL AND INSTRUMENTATION

There are twelve control rods, each 2 in. in diameter, made of natural uranium with a jacket of

stainless steel. These move vertically in the outer blanket bricks. Eight of these control rods normally are used as safety rods. Their time of travel out of the blanket is short: 0.085 sec to initiate motion, 0.29 sec to reach 16 in. The remaining four normally are used as regulating control rods and can be positioned with considerable accuracy. Their maximum speed is 0.64 in./sec. The entire outer blanket is mounted on a hydraulically driven elevator. The main platform of the elevator carries a shield section on which the outer blanket rests. The arrangement permits accurate location of the outer blanket around the reactor. For shutdown the outer blanket, the shield plug on which it rests, and the elevator can be dropped quickly.

For Mark-IV about 45% of the safety circuits provide signals indicating abnormal operation, 5 provide signals indicating danger (and are designed to scram the reactor after 2 min without correction), and 16 scram the reactor immediately. The immediate scrams were designed to act when any one of the following parameters left its specified range: reactor period, fuel and blanket temperature, coolant flow rate, inlet and outlet coolant temperatures, elevator hydraulic pressure, reactor neutron-flux level, or position of any of the four NaK valves. All safety circuits were duplicated to further increase their reliability. In addition, check lists are used periodically by the operators, and frequent detailed inspections of all equipment and safety devices are made.

The operation controls contain a total reactivity worth of about 1.28%. The safety rods and safety plug can remove 0.24% reactivity in 0.38 sec, and the external blanket can remove 5.25% reactivity at an elevator speed of 26 in./sec. The average temperature coefficient for Mark-I was 3.5×10^{-5} Δk/°C from 38°C to 200°C (100°F to 392°F). Filling with the coolant added reactivity approximately equal to that added by 2 kg of U^{235}. Loss of coolant reduced reactivity. Separate instrumentation is

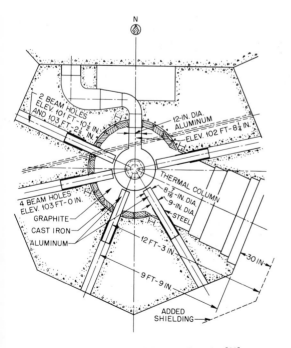

FIG. 11.7—EBR-I shield, horizontal section [22].

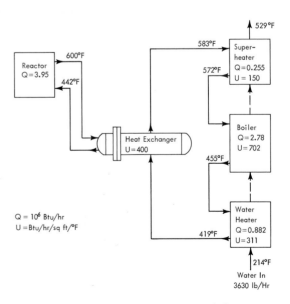

FIG. 11.8—EBR-I heat-transfer diagram [19].

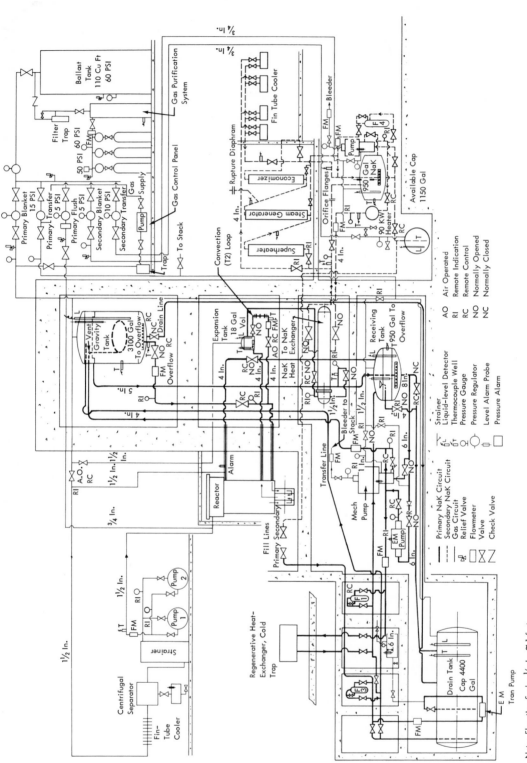

FIG. 11.9.—EBR-I NaK systems [11].

provided for start-up, for safety, and for steady operation, and all safety circuits are duplicated.

11.2.6 HEAT-TRANSPORT SYSTEM

The heat-transport system is shown schematically in Fig. 11.8 and in detail in Fig. 11.9. The primary NaK flow through the reactor, normally 291 gal/min, is from an elevated constant-level tank, shown in Fig. 4.14 of Chap. 4. The flow proceeds down through the inner blanket, up through the core, and out of the reactor. The coolant then flows through the intermediate heat exchanger, returns to a receiving tank, and is then pumped continuously by an electromagnetic pump to the constant-head tank.

Information regarding typical components is given in Chap. 4. In EBR-I the NaK-to-NaK intermediate heat exchangers are of a shell and tube design, with primary flow passing through the tubes. As indicated in Fig. 11.10, the steam generator is divided into an economizer, a boiler, and a superheater. NaK passage through these units is countercurrent to the flow of water and steam. Heat-transfer tubes in each component are similar and consist of a composite assembly of inner nickel, intermediate copper, and outer nickel tubes. The tubes were assembled by a mechanical drawing process, together with a thermal diffusion bonding process, which results in good heat transfer between the tubes. Total wall thickness of the tube is 5/16 in., of which 3/16 in. is nickel. An outer stainless-steel tube makes up the shell of the heat exchanger, and a bellows is used to allow for differential thermal expansion. Thus, each heat exchanger is of a "single tube in a shell" type, where NaK flow is on the shell side and water or steam is in the tube.

A forced-circulation falling-film type boiler is used to limit the quantity of water in the system and to increase the heat-transfer rate. The heat exchangers are in a vertical position. A baffle is used to establish a water film at the upper end of the internal tube on its inner surface. The film runs to the bottom where excess water and generated steam are piped into a drum. Steam is led through a separator in the drum out to the superheater, which consists of horizontal heat exchangers with NaK in the shell side. The economizer is a horizontal unit and serves to heat the feedwater from the deaerating tank to steaming temperature before injection into the boiler drum.

11.2.7 REACTOR VESSEL AND SHIELDING

11.2.7.1 Reactor Vessel

The reactor vessel, or tank, is double walled and extends through the reactor shield. The section of the reactor vessel surrounding the reactor core has an inside diameter of 15.87 in. and a length of 28 in. Above this small section the vessel increases in diameter and is filled with shielding material, mostly steel. The whole reactor vessel rests on the shoulder formed by the change in diameter; thus the reactor core itself projects below the point of support as a smooth cylinder.

The small-diameter part of the reactor tank consists of a stainless-steel vessel of 5/16-in. wall thickness, made by deep drawing. It is surrounded by a second tank made of Inconel, 1/16 in. thick, which fits snugly on ribs formed in the Inconel. The upper portion of the reactor vessel also is double walled. The gas space between the two walls provides some thermal insulation and provides a method for testing vessel integrity. In the event that the inner vessel should develop a leak, the outer vessel would prevent complete loss of sodium.

11.2.7.2 Shielding

An 18-in.-thick 35-in.-high section of graphite surrounds the outer blanket in the radial direction. Its cooling-air gap is shown in Fig. 11.5. This graphite layer, in addition to serving as a moderator for fast neutrons for shielding purposes, acts as a reflector to improve the breeding in the outer blanket. Although ordinary concrete is the basic shielding material, a 4-in. layer of iron is provided between the graphite and the 102-in.-thick concrete cylinder; this serves as a thermal shield by absorbing gamma rays. In the axial direction above the core, layers of steel and NaK (Figs. 11.11 and 11.12) are followed by a 13-in.-thick stainless-steel plate, a 2 1/4-in. plate, a 24-in. thickness of concrete, and finally, an 8-in. thickness of laminated masonite and iron. The reactor structure is shown in Fig. 11.12. The bottom shield consists of a 5-ft-thick layer of ordinary concrete. Since the elevator room is the only area below the reactor and since it is a limited-access area, the bottom-shield design was not considered critical. Additional details of the EBR-I shield system are given in Chap. 8.

At the time the EBR-I was designed, much of shield design theory had not been developed. One of the purposes of the reactor was to improve the concept of fast reactor physics and permit experimental measurements of neutron-source distribution and other parameters. Flexibility was incorporated in the design to permit the addition of more shield thicknesses if necessary.

Since the EBR-I is of modest power and is located in a nonpopulated area, a containment type building is not utilized.

11.2.8 OPERATING EXPERIENCE

When the Mark-I reactor was started up in 1951, it was found that radiation levels around the reactor were higher than had been anticipated. An additional 30 in. of concrete shielding was provided, and operation was resumed. In June 1952 a leak of NaK to NaK was discovered in the primary heat exchanger, and the reactor was shut down for repair. During the shutdown, 16 fuel elements were removed for examination and were replaced by new elements. More than 1500 Mw(t) hours of operation had been accumulated by Apr. 15, 1953.

During the four-year period EBR-I gave essentially trouble-free operation. The operation of EBR-I demonstrated among other things that breeding was a technically achievable objective, with a

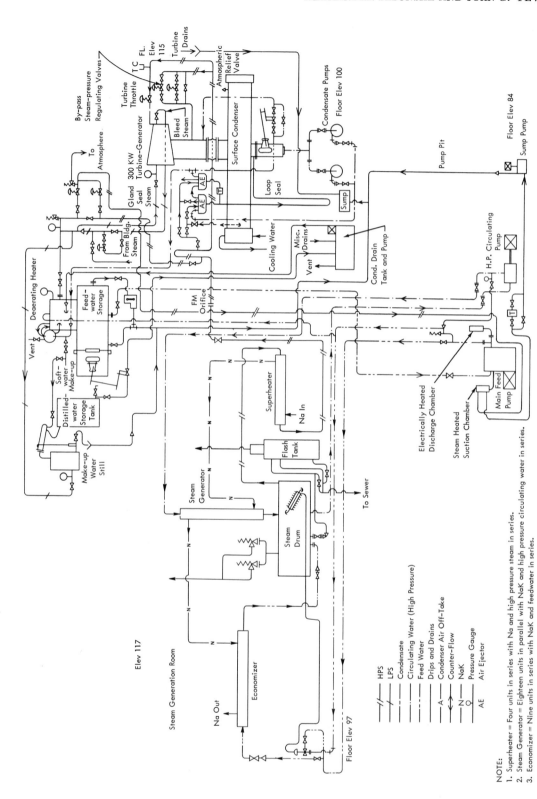

FIG. 11.10—EBR-I steam system [11].

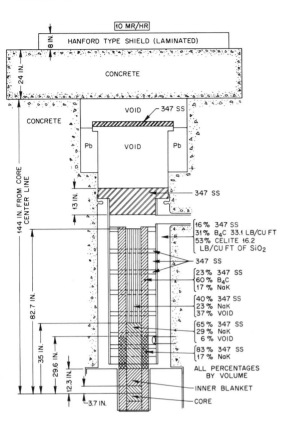

FIG. 11.11—EBR-I upper shield, vertical section [11].

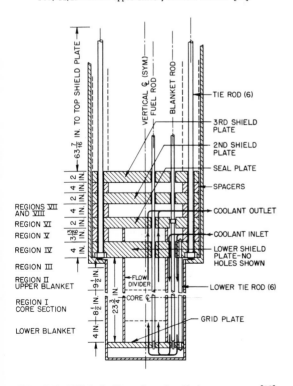

FIG. 11.12—EBR-I shield, seal, and grid-plate structure [10].

measured conversion ratio of 1.01 ± 0.05, and that the use of liquid-metal coolant (sodium—potassium alloy in this case) was compatible with breeding economy as well as metallurgically and mechanically feasible. Since U^{235} fuel was utilized for the Mark-I, Mark-II, and Mark-III cores, breeding in a plutonium recycle [2] will only be demonstrated with operation of the Mark-IV core. Breeding, however, based on U^{235} fuel was demonstrated in the first cores. The EBR-I operation and theoretical determinations show that neutron behavior below prompt critical is the same in both fast and thermal reactors.

Under normal operating conditions the reactor was very stable and did not exhibit either a prompt positive temperature coefficient or a resonance. Under purposely imposed and drastically abnormal operating conditions, anomalies were observed: resonance consisting of oscillations in power level appeared during experiments in which the coolant flow rate was drastically reduced; a prompt positive temperature coefficient appeared during start-ups undertaken with reduced coolant flow. Even under conditions where the net positive coefficient appeared, the reactor could be operated safely. Oscillator tests successfully demonstrated the presence of instability.

In November 1955 the Mark-II core of the EBR-I partially melted during the last of a series of experiments designed to study its behavior when put on positive periods with reduced or zero coolant flow. The accident occurred under extremely abnormal operating conditions purposely imposed on the reactor for the experiment and recognized to involve a risk of fuel melting. Two of the normally operative safety mechanisms, the flow interlock (which automatically shuts down the reactor if substantially full coolant flow is not maintained) and the period scram meter interlock (which automatically shuts down the reactor if the period becomes too short), were purposely disconnected. The coolant flow was stopped completely. A certain fixed amount of reactivity was put into the reactor with the control rods, and the reactor was started up on a short enough period so that temperature differentials would be established in the fuel slugs. The prompt positive temperature coefficient previously observed appeared, and, as the power increased, the reactivity increased, thus further shortening the period. It was planned to scram the reactor when the period reached 0.27 sec and the temperature of the fuel 932°F. When the period reached 1 sec, the operator mistakenly activated the slow-acting motor-driven control rods instead of the faster acting scram rods. By the time the scram was initiated, the period had reached 0.3 sec. The temperature overshot so that the uranium became heated above 1328°F, roughly the temperature at which the uranium—iron eutectic forms. The center of the core melted, forming the eutectic. After the manually operated scram button was pressed (in less than 2 sec), the reactor shut down and the meltdown stopped. The automatic power-limitation circuits also operated.

As a result of the accident, melting occurred in 40 to 50% of the EBR-I core. No explosive force developed. None of the remainder of the reactor, including the inner blanket and the reactor vessel, was damaged. A negligible amount of radioactive material reached the atmosphere through temporary thermocouple wire seals. Neither the operating personnel nor any other persons were injured in any way. Evacuation steps were precautionary. Operating personnel returned to the reactor building after a minor amount of surface decontamination. The core assembly was removed from the reactor by use of a temporary hot cell and shipped to Argonne National Laboratory (ANL) for examination and disassembly. Observations during disassembly and subsequent simulated meltdown experiments indicated that the porous structure formed in the core could have resulted from the vaporization of entrained NaK.

11.2.9 MARK-III PROGRAM

After the Mark-II incident, a new core was designed to further study the previously observed instabilities with the belief that they could be eliminated by changes in mechanical design. Other objectives included an investigation of channel transient characteristics, such as a measurement of transfer function, reactivity feedback effects, and the development of mathematical models to describe the observed results.

11.2.9.1 Core Arrangement

A typical fuel rod used in the Mark-III core is shown in Fig. 11.13. Cladding consists of 0.020 in. of Zircaloy-2 metallurgically bonded to the fuel through a coextrusion process, rather than the

arrangement used for Mark-I and Mark-II, where NaK served as a heat-transfer bond between the loose-fitting slugs and the stainless-steel can. On each rod three 0.046-in. wires were spot welded to the cladding at 1/4-in. intervals; they served to stabilize the rod. At full loading the core contained 252 rods, or 60 kg of enriched uranium. The central core section of each rod consisted of three slugs welded end to end; in the lower and upper blanket section, each rod consisted of a single slug of natural U—2 wt.% Zr alloy, 3 9/16 in. long and 7 3/4 in. long, respectively. A triangular tip at the bottom of each rod was provided to simplify insertion in the lower tube sheet during the loading operation. Blanket rods were of identical design but consisted of a single 19 3/16-in.-long section of natural uranium—zirconium alloy.

Fuel-rod subassemblies (Fig. 11.14) contain 37 individual rods supported in a grid at the bottom of each subassembly. A nozzle admits the NaK coolant. One central position is occupied by an expandable tightening rod that forces the rods outward against the hex wall and limits radial movement of the fuel rods. Seven fuel subassemblies comprise the core assembly (Fig. 11.15). Blanket subassemblies (Fig. 11.14), each containing 37 rods, have a different design for coolant flow. Twelve of the blanket subassemblies (Fig. 11.15) surround the core. Double-wedge clamps are located on each of the six flats at the outer periphery of the assemblies at the core center line. The clamps serve to force the outer assemblies inward against the center assembly. A second set of six shoe type clamps, mounted along the inner edge of the seal plate, limits the bypass leakage rate and serves to lock fuel and blanket assemblies into

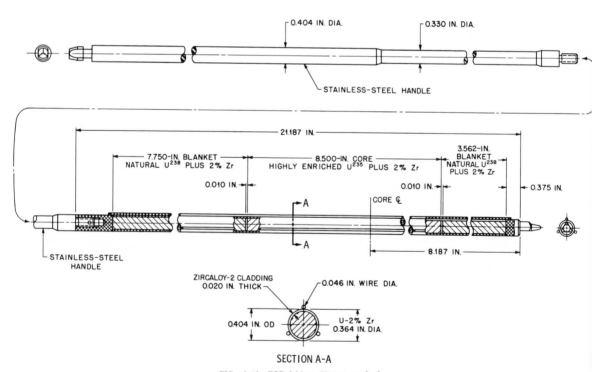

SECTION A-A

FIG. 11.13—EBR-I Mark-III fuel rod [11].

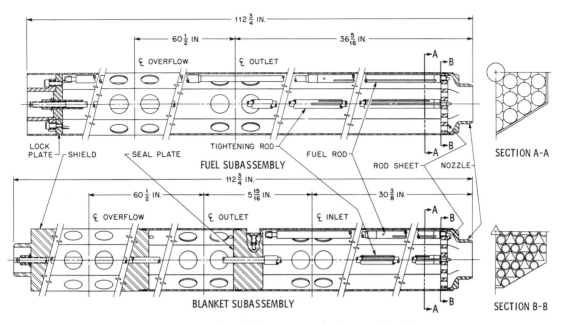

FIG. 11.14—EBR-I Mark-III fuel and blanket assemblies [9].

a rigid array. Also shown in Fig. 11.15 are the twelve downcomers through which the coolant passes in parallel flow, the six tie rods holding the lower structure rigid, the antimony—beryllium source, and the oscillator rod and thimble.

A cutaway view of the inner tank assembly is shown in Fig. 11.16. A tube sheet at the bottom of the structure receives, supports, and locates the nozzles of the rod assemblies. A seal plate above the outlet plenum restricts the bypass leakage occurring between the tank and the outer edge of the

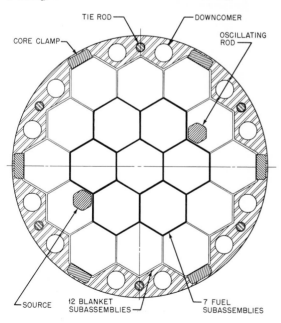

FIG. 11.15—EBR-I Mark-III core cross section [9].

seal plate. Restriction is accomplished by a system of two expandable Inconel seal rings. Seal-plate shoes located between the inner edge of the seal plate and the blanket assemblies restrict bypass leakage.

The coolant, in series flow, enters the annular inlet plenum located immediately below the seal plate and flows into the outer ring of 12 blanket assemblies. At the bottom of the blanket assemblies, the flow is reversed 180°, directed upward through the seven fuel assemblies, through the outlet holes at the top, and then radially outward through the perforated portion of the blanket assemblies into the outlet plenum. The coolant, in parallel flow, flows into a lower annular plenum located immediately above the mounting plate. Here the coolant is distributed to the 12 downcomers through which it flows to the lower plenum. Upward flow through fuel and blanket assemblies is partitioned by a series of throttle valves. The actual flow through the core, both in series and parallel, is less than the flow indicated through the metering of the primary inlet. Of a nominal metered flow of 290 gal/min, approximately 16% (47 gal/min) is bypassed as leakage and for seal-plate cooling in series flow. The remaining 84% passes through the blanket and core. For a metered flow of 278 gal/min in parallel flow, approximately the same fraction, 84%, passes through the core; the remaining 16% passes through the blanket. Coolant from the blanket outlet cools the seal plate.

11.2.9.2 *Experimental Program for Mark-III Core*

The effects of rod bowing were explored by systematically removing part of the stiffening ribs. Although the rods were rigidly fixed at the upper and

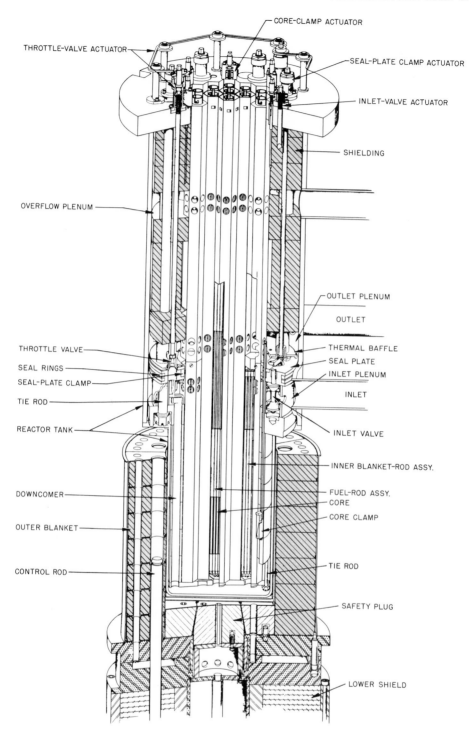

CORE-CLAMP ACTUATOR

THROTTLE-VALVE ACTUATOR

SEAL-PLATE CLAMP ACTUATOR

INLET-VALVE ACTUATOR

SHIELDING

OVERFLOW PLENUM

OUTLET PLENUM

OUTLET

THROTTLE VALVE

THERMAL BAFFLE

SEAL RINGS

SEAL PLATE

SEAL-PLATE CLAMP

INLET PLENUM

TIE ROD

INLET

REACTOR TANK

INLET VALVE

INNER BLANKET-ROD ASSY.

DOWNCOMER

FUEL-ROD ASSY.
CORE

OUTER BLANKET

CORE CLAMP

CONTROL ROD

TIE ROD

SAFETY PLUG

LOWER SHIELD

FIG. 11.16—EBR-I Mark—III inner tank assembly [9].

lower ends, a radial motion in the fuel section accompanied differential expansion during a power increase and resulted in a bow directed at the center high-flux region. In 14 tests involving various types of changes, transfer-function measurements showed a progressively larger positive effect consistent with the removal of ribs. The amplitude of the power feedback decreased, and the phase lag increased as ribs were removed.

It was concluded that the original fully ribbed and rigid Mark-III design was completely stable under normal operating conditions. The ribs provide strong radial coupling between individual fuel rods and between the fuel rods and the hexagonal can, and therefore they provide a large radial contribution to the power coefficient. The positive feedback effect from the inward bowing of the rods during power increases is likewise eliminated. The test did indicate that the core could be brought into a resonant condition at an extrapolated power above 1000 Mw(t), well above the design value of 1.2 Mw(t).

Power-coefficient nonlinearities were observed, which complicated the interpretation of test data in terms of a single model that may be applied over wide ranges of power, flow, and temperature conditions. These nonlinearities apparently result from the power- and temperature-sensitive clearances existing between rods, between rods and hexes, and between hexes, which are complicated by differences in the coefficients of expansion of the materials involved. Furthermore the power coefficient itself was found to be sensitive to the temperature of the inlet coolant.

At one-third flow the reactor would reach resonance instability at a power of about 10 Mw(t). At full coolant flow but with the ribs sheared, feedback measurements indicated a probable resonance instability at a power level of 11 Mw(t).

11.2.9.3 Delayed Power-coefficient Component

It has also been shown that rib shearing results in an unexpected and unexplained increase in the magnitude of the delayed structural power-coefficient component. An empirical fit of feedback data to a model describing the dynamic and static behaviors of the partially sheared core resulted in the following values for the respective prompt-negative, rod-bowing, and delayed structural power-coefficient components: -2.21×10^{-6}, $+0.543 \times 10^{-6}$, and -0.873×10^{-6} $\Delta k/k/\text{kw}$. These values correlate in a curious manner with those empirically deduced for the prompt-negative and delayed structural power-coefficient components for the fully ribbed core, namely, -2.21×10^{-6} and -0.330×10^{-6} $\Delta k/k/\text{kw}$. The magnitude of the positive power-coefficient component is equal to the increase in the magnitude of the structural component. Apparently rib shearing introduces two feedback processes: rod-bowing, which is prompt and positive, and one of an unspecified nature, which is negative and extremely delayed in time.

Because the model predicts the general shape of the experimentally measured feedback and comes within a reasonable margin of explaining the feedback magnitude, it may be concluded that the structural member responsible for the delayed negative power coefficient was the lower shield plate. There seems little doubt that any credible interpretation of the feedback must involve the concept of a delayed feedback which almost certainly must have originated at some structural member located downstream from the core. A careful scrutiny of all downstream structural members

supplemented by attenuation concepts narrows the suspect region to that included between the lower shield plate and the seal plate. The facts that thermally induced ligamental motions have actually been observed in such a plate and that the maximum temperature differential across the shield plate occurs close to the natural resonant frequency of the reactor strongly support this conclusion. The strong increase in the negative structure term does not affect conclusions regarding the resonance stability of the partially or fully sheared cores since the process acts so slowly that the reactor oscillating at frequencies as low as 0.02 cycles/sec cannot sense the feedback.

The Mark-III core, even with ribs partially sheared, was found to be much more stable than the Mark-II core. In addition to the elimination of the inward rod bowing found in Mark-II, the Mark-III design resulted in a negative prompt power coefficient contributed by both axial and radial expansion of the rods. In Mark-II the negative coefficient associated with axial fuel expansion and coolant expulsion was insufficiently large to cancel the prompt component from rod bowing. It was therefore concluded that the instabilities noted in Mark-II were completely the result of design peculiarities and not an inherent feature of the reactor concept itself.

After the conclusion of the stability tests in 1960, the reactor was used on a part-time basis to study various loading arrangements, radiation effects of different types of fuel elements, and fuel isotopic changes.

11.2.10 MARK-IV CORE

The full potential of breeding in a fast spectrum is realized only when plutonium is utilized as the fuel in the core, rather than U^{235}. The EBR-I Mark-IV core, loaded in 1962, represented the first use of plutonium in this country for the full core of a fast breeder power reactor. Operation of this reactor facility with the plutonium loading has as its objective the determination of general operating characteristics, the measurement of breeding gain, and the determination of radiation effects and nuclear parameters.

An alloy of plutonium with 1.25 wt. % aluminum is used in the core. Slugs of this material, 0.232 in. in diameter and 2.121 in. long, are contained in Zircaloy-2 fuel tubes 0.299 in. in outside diameter with a 0.021-in. wall thickness. Three full-length ribs serve to center the slug in the jacket tube. Each fuel rod contains a lower depleted-uranium blanket slug 3.552 in. long, four plutonium-alloy fuel slugs totaling 8 1/2 in., and a single 7.745-in.-long upper-blanket depleted-uranium slug. A 0.0125-in. NaK layer bonds the cladding to the fuel. A number of rods have 0.08-in.-diameter Zircaloy thermocouple tubes attached. Blanket rods are similar to those used in the fuel section; depleted-uranium slugs are substituted for the plutonium alloy.

At shutdown the Mark-III core had operated for 3220 Mw-hr. The Mark-III core was completely unloaded by Nov. 8, 1962, and the Mark-IV loading went critical on Nov. 27, 1962, with 27.1 kg of Pu^{239}

(327 fuel rods). The initial loading consisted of 60
fuel rods in the central subassembly. Ten subsequent loadings, four of 42 rods each, two of 24
each, two of 18 each, one of 8, and a final one of 7
rods were made to reach criticality. Foil-irradia-
tion runs at low power were carried out in early
1963 to determine constants necessary for the
calculation of breeding ratio.   After transfer-
function runs at low and moderate power indicated
that the reactor was quite stable, the system was
gradually brought up to a power of 900 kw(t)
during April 1963. Although operation was very
satisfactory, some loss of reactivity was noted.

The EBR-I was shut down and secured on
December 30, 1963. Total power produced by the
Mark-IV loading was 577 Mwh. Eleven fuel rods
were removed from the reactor for return to the
Metallurgy Division for examination of the ir-
radiated plutonium fuel slugs.

The reactor was secured subcritical by 1.75%
$\Delta k/k$ with the controls in their most reactive position and the reactor temperature at 30°C. Surveillance of the reactor blanket gas is to be maintained
during this indefinite, extended shutdown period.

Fifty irradiated Mark-III fuel rods have been
shipped from the facility for reprocessing, thus
completing the removal of irradiated Mark-II
fuel.

11.3 USSR BR-5

11.3.1 INTRODUCTION

The first USSR fast reactor, BR-I, was built
in 1955 as a zero-energy assembly; it was fueled
with plutonium and was used to investigate fast
reactor physics [23-26]. The work was extended
by BR-2, a plutonium-fueled mercury-cooled reactor built in 1956 and operated to 100 kw(t).
The BR-2 provided facilities for physics experiments and irradiation of materials in fast-neutron
fluxes to 10^{14} neutrons/cm^2/sec and furnished
experience in operating at temperatures to 140°F.

The BR-2 was dismantled, and parts, such as
shielding, were used for construction of the BR-5
reactor (Figs. 11.17 and 11.18), which was completed in 1958. It went cold critical in the summer

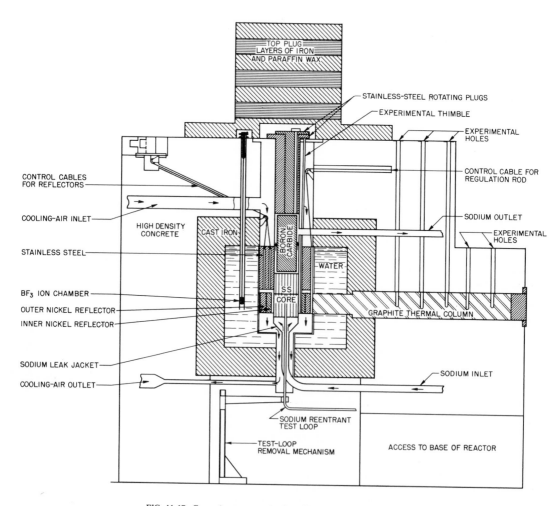

FIG. 11.17—General arrangement of the USSR fast reactor BR-5 [23].

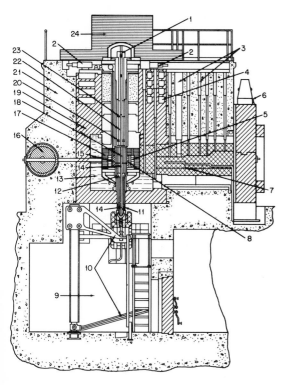

The reactor started up at zero power in July 1958. During the period July 1958 to January 1959, the assembly of the primary loop was completed and start-up modifications were accomplished. In January 1959, the reactor was started up with sodium coolant. From January to July 1959, the reactor operated to 1,000 kw. On July 21, 1959, the full power of 5,000 kw(t) was reached. Later the reactor was operated at various levels to 5,000 kw(t) for a 450°C (842°F) sodium outlet temperature. The temperature of the sodium in the primary loop was raised to 500°C (932°F) in December 1960. During 1960-1961, the reactor was used for experimental purposes. The following operations were carried out: (1) calibration of control rods, (2) determination of the effect on reactivity of circulating sodium, (3) measurement of temperature and power coefficients, 4) determination of the effect on reactivity of circulating sodium, (3) measurement of temperature and power coefficients, 4) determination of spatial neutron-energy distribution and heat generation, (5) measurement of neutron flux in experimental channels and in sections of the reactor, and (6) determination of radioactivity effects and safety aspects.

11.3.2 REACTOR FEATURES

The general arrangement of the reactor is shown in Fig. 11.17. Additional features are shown in Fig. 11.18. An unusual feature is the horizontal graphite column, 120 in. long, which penetrates one

1. Transfer Mechanism	13. Water Shield Tank
2. Control and Safety Drive Mechanism	14. Central Test Loop
3. Experimental Holes	15. Control Rod
4. Shield	16. Gate Valve for Neutron Beam Channel
5. Outer Reflector	17. Stationary Nickel Shield
6. Shielding Door for the Thermal Column	18. Core
7. Thermal Column	19. Cast-iron Shielding
8. Movable Reflector	20. Primary Reactor Pipe
9. Reactor Vault	21. Concrete Shield
10. Remote-handling Gear for Central Test Loop	22. Rotating Plugs for Fuel-element Transfer
11. Coolant Inlet	23. Sodium Level
12. Reactor Jacket	24. Top Shield

FIG. 11.18—Section through the BR-5 reactor [6].

of 1958 and was in operation in the summer of 1959. The BR-5 has a maximum power of 5 Mw(t), is fueled by plutonium oxide, and has sodium inlet and outlet temperatures of 375°C (707°F) and 450°C (842°F). The main purpose of the reactor is to gain burnup data on fuel elements, to obtain experience in the operation of radioactive sodium circuits, and to irradiate various materials. Since it was not considered necessary to obtain further data on breeding gain, the design was simplified by omitting the normal blanket of natural or depleted uranium.

It has been reported that the design effort on a 250-Mw(t) fast reactor (the BN-50 Project) led to a decision not to build a reactor of such size but it presumably led to a study of reactors of considerably higher power, i.e., 800 Mw(t) or higher. The use of a mixture of plutonium and uranium oxides as a fuel is being planned although carbides are being considered.

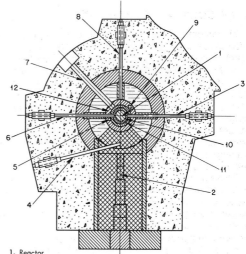

1. Reactor
2. Thermal Column
3. Horizontal Beam Hole
4. Horizontal Beam Hole
5. Vertical Beam Hole
6. Horizontal Beam Hole
7. Horizontal Beam Hole
8. Horizontal Beam Hole
9. Vertical Beam Hole
10. Inner Movable Cylinder Reflector
11. Outer Movable Cylinder Reflector
12. Stationary Nickel Reflector

FIG. 11.19—Plan view of BR-5 reactor [6].

side of the shield and provides a number of horizontal and vertical experimental locations. The plan view of the reactor arrangement in Fig. 11.19 shows additional experimental places in the shield. A summary of design data for BR-5 is given in Table 11.4. A maximum power density of 500 kw(t)/liter corresponds to a maximum heat flux of 440,000 Btu/hr/sq ft.

11.3.3 CORE ASSEMBLY

The core consists of 88 hexagonal fuel subassemblies, 1.023 in. across flats and approximately 33 in. long, surrounded by two rows of blanket subassemblies. Each fuel subassembly (Fig. 11.20) contains 19 stainless-steel-clad pins, which are filled with plutonium oxide pellets and sealed after they have been charged with helium gas. The pins are 0.197 in. in outside diameter, the fuel is about 0.16 in. in diameter, and the cladding is 0.016 in. thick. The pins are separated by spiral wire spacers. The subassemblies are supported at the bottom by a perforated plate. The core subassemblies and a ring of tubes loaded with natural uranium are enclosed in a stainless-steel "vessel" approximately 14 in. in diameter. Clearance between subassemblies is 0.020 in. The core itself is approximately 11 by 11 in. There is no top plate, and no positive lateral restraint is provided either at the center or top. Sodium flows upward through the core from a single inlet at the bottom of the central sodium tube to a single outlet above the core which supplies two cooling circuits.

11.3.4 CONTROL ELEMENTS

Movement of an inner and outer cylindrical reflector is used to control the reactor. The inner nickel cylinder, 2 in. thick, is raised or lowered by cables; the outer 4-in.-thick nickel cylinder has two movable sections that provide fine control. In addition, two control rods operating in the outer cylinder provide shim adjustment. Emergency shutdown may be accomplished by an electromagnetic release of these two cylinders. Heat generated in the reflector is removed by air. Start-up instrumentation is located in the water tank outside the reflector, as shown in Fig. 11.17.

Two temperature coefficients of reactivity have been measured in BR-5, one relative to the inlet temperature and the second relative to the outlet temperature (power coefficient). These agreed with predictions and are both negative. The fuel elements supported in a lower support plate are free to move at the top to take up any tolerances in the lower plate. The pins within the subassemblies are welded together at the bottom. Alternate pins are wound spirally with stainless-steel wires, which act as spacers. Bowing of pins or subassemblies tends to cause the tubes of the outer elements to move outward to reduce reactivity. An increase in coolant flow has a similar effect.

11.3.5 COOLANT SYSTEM

The coolant system is split into two 4-in.-diameter primary loops, as shown in Fig. 11.21.

Each loop includes a sodium—NaK heat exchanger, a vertical mechanical pump with an overhung shaft, and a cold trap.

Table 11.4—USSR BR-5 Design Data [26]

Reactor Data	
Thermal power, Mw	5
Maximum fast flux, neutrons/cm²/sec	1×10^{15}
Fuel	PuO_2
Fuel density, % of theoretical	93
Critical mass PuO_2 at 150°C/302°F, kg	49.6
Burnup achieved, at. %	5
Flow of sodium through the reactor, lb/hr	465,000
Velocity of sodium in subassemblies, ft/sec	15
Pressure drop in subassemblies, psi	12
Na inlet temperature, °C/°F	430/806
Na outlet temperature, °C/°F	500/932
Reactor temperature difference, °C/°F	70/126
Reactor maximum temperature difference, °C/°F	110/198
Core length, in.	11
Core diameter, in.	11
Maximum density of heat generation in the active zone:	
Kw(t)/liter	500
Kw(t)/cu ft	14,000
Maximum to average heat flux:	
Radial	1.21
Axial	1.16
Overall	1.40
Fuel Data	
Number of fuel subassemblies	80
Dimensions:	
Shape of subassembly can	Hexagon
Size of subassembly can over key, in.	1.02
Thickness can wall, in.	0.020
Overall subassembly height, in.	32.7
Number of fuel pins in a subassembly	19
Fuel-pin dimensions:	
Outer diameter, in.	0.20
Cladding thickness (321 SS)* in.	0.016
Diameter of fuel, in.	0.16
Height of fuel, in.	11
Spacing of fuel pins, in.	0.217
Maximum heat flux, Btu/hr/sq ft	440,000
Maximum cladding temperature, °C/°F	600/1110
Blanket	
Number of uranium subassemblies	40
Number of uranium elements in a subassembly	7
Uranium composition	U—9 wt.% Mo
Uranium rod dimensions:	
Diameter, in.	0.354
Clad thickness (321 SS)* in.	0.016
Diameter of uranium, in.	0.30
Length of rod, in.	11
Bond material	NaK
Heat-transport System Design Data	
Primary system:	
Volume of sodium	
Cu ft	70
Gal	570
Flow of sodium, lb/hr	~230,000
Secondary system:	
Pump-developed pressure, psi	60
Volume of NaK:	
Cu ft	120
Gal	90
Flow of NaK, lb/hr	~271,000
IHX outlet temperature, °C/°F	470/880
NaK-air heat-exchanger inlet temperature, °C/°F	370/700
Steam system:	
Steam flow, lb/hr	10,000
Steam pressure, psig	~230
Steam temperature, °C	400
Thermal power generated in nickel reflector, kw	220
Air flow in reflector cooler, cu ft/sec	39

*Some question as to whether cladding may be 304 stainless steel.

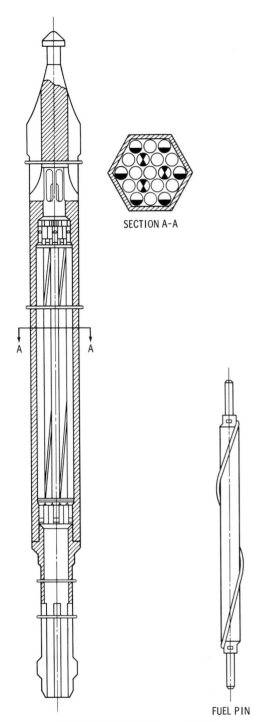

SECTION A-A

A

A

FUEL PIN

FIG. 11.20—BR-5 fuel subassembly [23].

The pump seal and bearings operate in argon cover gas, which is continuously circulated through a silica gel drier and then through copper-coated silica gel heated to 250°C (482°F). The totally enclosed pump motor is likewise maintained under an argon-gas pressure slightly higher than that of

the system so that leakage, if any, is through the gland into the system.

Heat is transferred from the primary loops by two intermediate heat exchangers to two secondary loops. One of these NaK-filled secondary loops is provided with a 230-psig steam generator having duplex tubes. Mercury is used as the heat-transfer medium in the space between the inner and the outer tube. An air-cooled heat exchanger and a blower, delivering 1.4×10^6 cu ft/hr of air, are used to reject the heat in the other loop through an 80-ft stack. Residual heat after shutdown is also removed in this loop by natural convection.

11.3.6 SHIELDING, COMPONENTS, AND STRUCTURES

A water tank surrounds the core and provides a 20-in. shielding annulus. Surrounding this is a 16-in.-thick cast-iron ring followed by a concrete wall with an average thickness of 43 in., as shown in Fig. 11.17. A boron carbide plug, two rotating steel plugs, and finally a removable top plug (consisting of layers of paraffin wax and iron) comprise the upper shield. The lower shield consists of an 8-in.-deep water layer, which enables the cell under the reactor to be entered only during shutdown.

Fuel loading is accomplished through a double eccentric rotating plug arrangement. During refueling the reactor is shut down, and sodium circulation in the primary loop is stopped. Decay heat is removed by natural convection. A transfer cask unit is used for charging of fuel, uranium, and experimental units.

The reactor has no outer containment building. The primary loops are housed in separate concrete cells, and the secondary-circuit equipment is contained within a single compartment.

11.3.7 EXPERIMENTAL FACILITIES

The reactor has been designed not only to permit sample radiation under fast flux conditions but also to allow the insertion of special fuel subassemblies in the core in place of normal elements. A 1-in.-diameter reentrant tube in the center of the core, designed for testing fuel elements, is cooled with a separate NaK cooling system. In this central loop a peak flux of 10^{15} neutrons/cm^2/sec is available. A flux of one-half this value is available in the exposure holes at the edge of the core.

11.3.8 OPERATING EXPERIENCE

Pump life was mainly determined by ball-bearing capability; it averaged 8000 hr. Replacement of primary equipment including cold traps usually started a week after shutdown, i.e., after sodium gamma decay. The cold traps in the primary system were replaced four times during 4 years of operation.

By October 1960, with about 2.5% maximum plutonium burnup, the leakage of fission products into the sodium became pronounced. By September

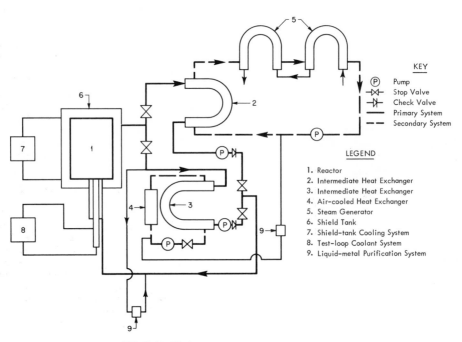

FIG. 11.21—BR-5 primary and secondary systems.

1961, the cesium activity in the sodium was 70% of total cesium plus Na^{22} activity after Na^{24} decay. Fuel burnup had reached 5%. The reactor was unloaded, and the subassemblies were steam blast cleaned. During cleaning some of the subassemblies showed considerable increase in steam condensate activity owing to increased failure of fuel-pin cladding. Steam cleaning was discontinued, and a leak test with an ionization chamber was then used to check each subassembly to measure fission-gas activity. Of the 81 subassemblies tested, 8 had been washed with steam; of the remainder, 63 showed normal sodium impurity activity and 10 had a gas activity higher by a factor of 1000. Examination of the 5% burnup pins showed longitudinal cracks in the cladding due to fuel swelling. The cracks showed up where the clearance between cladding and fuel was minimum.

After fuel removal the primary system was drained, cleaned with steam at several pounds per square inch gauge and about 260°F injected into vent lines, and removed from the low point. The system was kept at about 300°F prior to steam injection. About 10 tons of steam was used, and no violent reactions occurred. Contamination of the primary system was reduced 50%. The system was then filled with pure water twice with no circulation and drained. There was no decrease in activity. Each section of the primary system except a nickel basket in the reactor was then cleaned with a solution of 5% nitric acid at about 160°F for three successive flushes to reduce the activity two to threefold in one of the sections. Two sections of the primary system were further subjected to a 0.5% $KMnO_4$ solution flush for 24 hr at about 160°F, a 5% nitric acid and 1% oxalic acid mixture flush for 3 to 4 hr at 160°F, and to a pure-water flush for 1 hr at about 160°F. These three flushes were

repeated five times. Activity was reduced to a value low enough so that repair work could begin. A total of 21 flushes per section was used, including the steam flush. This indicates the possible consequences of plating out of fission products on system components. Radiochemical analysis showed plutonium, zirconium, and cesium as the residual activity. After the final drain the primary system was dried by vacuum and heat. Following repairs the system was filled with distilled sodium. The reactor was placed back in operation in March 1962 after a 7-month shutdown. Eighty per cent of the original bundles were placed back in the reactor. Subsequent reports indicate some of these began to leak soon after start-up.

11.4 LAMPRE-I

11.4.1 INTRODUCTION

Interest in the development of plutonium fuels for fast breeder reactor applications continued at the Los Alamos Scientific Laboratory after the dismantlement of Clementine (Sec. 11.1). Parallel to this effort has been the development of homogeneous reactors wherein the fissile material was dissolved in an aqueous system. Reactors of this type include the water-boiler series, as well as LAPRE-I and LAPRE-II. The resulting specialization in plutonium-fueled fast breeder reactors, on the one hand, and the homogeneous concept, on the other, logically led to the concept of using plutonium in the molten state as fuel for a fast breeder system.

An early reactor design, for example, called for the plutonium fuel to be contained in a cylindrical vessel through which tubes carrying sodium coolant would flow in a typical calandria arrangement. The need for additional information regarding the behavior of container and fuel materials, however, led to the decision to first build a molten-plutonium-fueled reactor in which the fuel would be contained in cylindrical capsules with the sodium coolant flowing outside. This arrangement, used in LAMPRE-I, could be readily adapted to the testing of a variety of fuel and container material combinations. A cell in an existing building, which had previously been used for the LAPRE-I reactor, was available for LAMPRE-I [27-39]. The limitations of this location fixed the reactor power at 1 Mw(t).

11.4.2 REACTOR FEATURES

A plan view of the reactor installation is shown in Fig. 11.22 and an elevation view in Fig. 11.23. Component design was based on the need for installation in the existing cell facilities. No secondary sodium coolant system is used. The heat generated is exchanged to air and exhausted up a stack. A summary of LAMPRE-I design data is given in Table 11.5. Although thermal performance specifications are high, specific power and power density were not intended as representative of optimum values for a larger power-reactor system.

11.4.3 CORE ARRANGEMENT

The core consists of approximately 140 fuel capsules filled with plutonium—iron alloy and surrounded by approximately 60 stainless-steel reflector pins of similar design. A cross section of the core region is shown in Fig. 11.24, and a vertical

section of the core is shown in Figs. 11.25 and 11.26. An annular movable stainless-steel reflector is contained in an inner vessel outside the core. It is 20 in. in outside diameter by 10 3/4 in. in inside diameter by 16 in. long. Final control can be obtained by moving four control rods, each consisting of a nickel cylinder 3.8 in. in diameter and 16 in. long, which moves vertically in the stainless-steel reflector.

Coolant sodium flows down through a 3/8-in. annulus between the vessel and the flow divider. The coolant stream reverses in a plenum at the bottom of the flow divider. The sodium then flows through a bottom reflector, consisting of an Armco iron cylinder 6 7/8 in. in diameter by 6 in. high. Flow continues through a locater-plate assembly, then finally past the fuel capsules, through a top reflector region, and into the outlet plenum.

The core arrangement contains several safety features. Double-wall construction of the reactor vessel, with no pipes entering the lower part, prevents accidental drainage of coolant. A catchpot and a diluent plug are designed to contain any fuel in a noncritical geometry in the event of a leak from the core. The Armco iron diluent plug will dissolve in molten fuel to form an alloy with a higher melting point. As solution continues, the resulting alloy will solidify.

11.4.4 FUEL ELEMENTS

A single fuel capsule, or "pin," as shown in Fig. 11.27, is used in each complete element (Fig. 11.28). The components of the capsule assembly shown are the thimble, fuel slug, closure

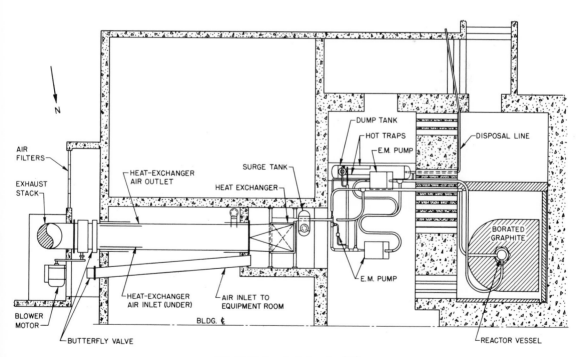

FIG. 11.22—Lampre-I plan view [27].

Table 11.5—LAMPRE-I Design Data

Core Parameters

Capsule material	Ta—9.1 wt.% W
Capsule size:	
Inside diameter, in.	0.376
Wall thickness, in.	0.025
Length, in.	8
Core capacity, No. capsules	199
Number of capsules for criticality (calculated)	143
Capsule spacing, pitch, in.	0.497
Core composition, vol. %:	
Fuel	51.5
Na	33.5
Ta	15.0
Fuel height, in.	6
Fission-gas volume height, in.	2
Thermal power, Mw(t)	1
Average fuel temperature, °C/°F	637/1179
Maximum fuel temperature, °C/°F	870/1598
Na inlet temperature, °C/°F	450/842
Na outlet temperature, °C/°F	563/1045
Na flow rate, gal/min	133
Central-to-edge power ratio	1.8
Axial power ratio	1.8
Cylindrical radius, in.	∼3.1
Cylindrical height, in.	∼6.4
Fuel alloy mass, kg	∼24.99
Core volume, liters/cu ft	∼3.06/0.11
Central median fission energy, Mev	∼1
Prompt-neutron lifetime, sec	∼8.9 × 10⁻⁹

	Average	Maximum	Minimum
Specific power, kw/kg	40	61	19
Heat flux:			
Watts/cm²	145	220	68
Btu/hr/sq ft	460,000	700,000	214,000
Na outlet temperature, °C/°F	563/1045	597/1107	531/988
ΔT in fuel, °C/°F	200/360	307/553	93/167
ΔT in Ta, °C/°F	17/31	24/43	8/14
Ta thermal stress, psi	2800	4300	1300

Materials and Their Thicknesses

	Thickness		Composition
	Cm	In.	
Side reflector			
Reflector pins	1.27	0.5	0.34587 Na, 0.65413 SS 430
Flow divider	0.635	0.25	SS 304
Na (inlet flow region)	0.9525	0.365	Na
Inner containment vessel	0.635	0.25	SS 304
Heaters	0.9525	0.365	0.15 SS 304
Outer containment vessel	0.635	0.25	SS 304
Air gap	0.3175	0.125	Air
Shim	11.7475	4.63	0.98 SS 430
Air gap	0.15875	0.0625	Air
Circular flue wall	0.635	0.25	SS 430
Air gap	1.27	0.5	Air
Hexagonal flue wall	0.635	0.25	Carbon steel
Shield	50.8	20	0.9108 B¹⁰ + C (0.4 wt.% boron)
Top reflector			
Gas space in fuel capsules	5.08	2	0.15403 Na, 0.34587 Na, 0.5001 air
Fuel-capsule plugs	1.27	0.5	Ta
Capsule handles	50.8	20	0.61518 SS 430, 0.38482 Na
Bottom reflector			
Locator-plate facing	0.508	0.2	Ta
Locator plate	4.572	1.8	0.23795 Na, 0.76205 SS 304
Locator-plate plenum	1.905	0.75	Na
Bottom reflector	12.70	5.0	0.1422 Na, 0.8578 Armco Fe
Turn-around plenum	1.905	0.75	Na
Catchpot	15.24	6.0	0.47 Na, 0.53 Armco Fe
Inner containment vessel	1.905	0.75	SS 304
Air gap	6.35	2.5	Air
Bottom-vessel shield	11.43	4.5	SS 304

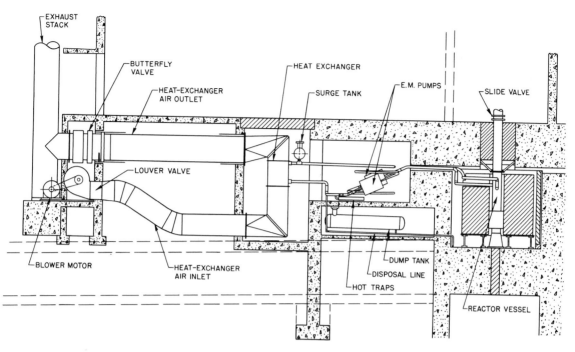

FIG. 11.23—Lampre-I elevation [27].

plug, and adaptor. Capsule fuel thimbles were constructed of various tantalum types, depending upon the desired materials test. A typical thimble, fabricated from tantalum—0.1 wt. % tungsten, is 0.426 in. in outside diameter and 8.312 in. in overall length with an inside diameter tapered from 0.376 in. at the top to 0.362 in. at the cone end. Solid plutonium—iron alloy fuel slugs, 0.358 in. in diameter and of variable length depending on the fuel weight required (but averaging 6.33 in.), were machined immediately before assembly into the thimbles.

The remainder of the assembly, shown in Fig. 11.28, includes a 90-in. shielding section and a so-called capsule handle, constructed of Armco 17-4 ph stainless steel, which is used to insert and withdraw the fuel capsules from the core and also to maintain radial core configuration.

11.4.5 COOLING SYSTEM

The sodium coolant system is shown in schematic form in Fig. 11.29. Two parallel Callery a-c electromagnetic conduction pumps, each rated at 100 gal/min at 20-psi head, are used for circulating sodium to the reactor. Heat is removed directly from this primary circulating system to air in a finned-section heat exchanger which exhausts up a stack. The coolant loop, constructed of 2 in. and 3 in. schedule 40 type 316 stainless-steel pipe, includes a number of accessory components, such as flow meters, a heating transformer for raising the temperature of the flowing sodium to the melting point of the fuel, three getter hot traps, and a fill and dump tank system.

11.4.6 SHIELDING

The shielding requirements for this installation are somewhat unusual since the reactor was installed in existing facilities adjacent to the control room (Fig. 11.30). A borated graphite shield, 3 1/2 ft thick, surrounds the reactor vessel. In addition, an 8-in. lead curtain and a 5 1/2-ft-thick normal concrete wall shield the control room. Control-room radiation levels during initial operation were found to be excessive. The installation of improved shielding in the concrete-wall penetrations and a supplementary lead shield reduced the levels to below tolerance values.

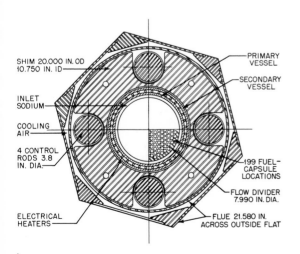

FIG. 11.24—Lampre-I horizontal cross section [28].

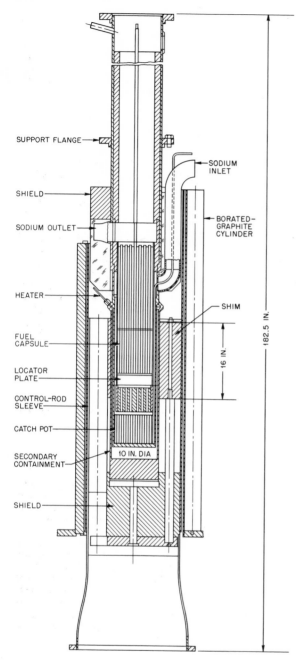

FIG. 11.25—Lampre-I vertical cross section [39].

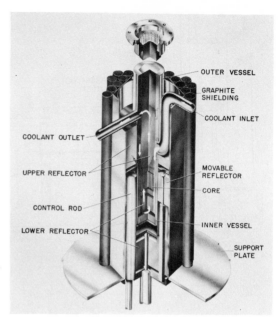

FIG. 11.26—Lampre-I cutaway view [27].

concrete ceiling. During initial low-power operation, it was found necessary to add an additional laminated iron–masonite shield on top of the shield plug and a concrete shield around and on top of the fuel-transfer area.

11.4.7 OPERATION

The LAMPRE-I reactor was designed as a facility for the study of molten-plutonium fuels and containers and the investigation of operating problems that might be unique to the fluid nature of the fuel. The reactor started in 1961 with dry-critical and low-power operation. It was brought up to its designed power of 1 Mw in early 1961. In April 1962, the reactor was re-loaded with a Mark-II core. After capsule failure in September 1962, which permitted 75 g of plutonium–iron fuel to enter the coolant, the power level was temporarily limited to 500 kw.

11.4.8 STABILITY AND CONTROL

Although bubbles of fission-product gases tend to rise to the surface of the fuel, some separation of large portions of the fuel regions apparently results in reactivity changes with time (Fig. 11.32). In the Mark-I loading, solid additives of carbon or plutonium carbide used to inhibit corrosive attack of the tantalum capsule by the fuel at high temperatures were believed to interfere with the release of the accumulated gas and hence to accentuate this reactivity loss. Although approximately ten dollars of reactivity was lost in the Mark-I loading, there was at no time any indication of instability caused by the froth or low-density portion of the fuel. In the Mark-II loading

A vertical cross section of the shielding is shown in Fig. 11.31. The shield below the core, based on a design specification of 2 mr/hr dose rate in the exclusion area in the shadow of the shield, consists of a 16-in.-thick iron bottom reflector and a 7-ft-long floor shield plug filled with lead shot in the bottom 2 ft and magnetite aggregate in the remainder.

The fuel-capsule handles themselves provide approximately 9 ft of iron shielding directly above the core. A ceiling shield plug of heavy concrete and steel shot provides access through the 5 1/2-ft

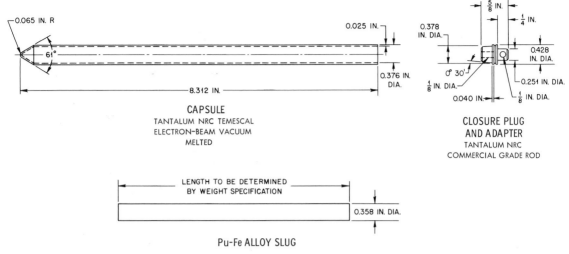

CAPSULE
TANTALUM NRC TEMESCAL
ELECTRON-BEAM VACUUM
MELTED

CLOSURE PLUG
AND ADAPTER
TANTALUM NRC
COMMERCIAL GRADE ROD

Pu-Fe ALLOY SLUG

FIG. 11.27—Lampre-I fuel capsule and slug [27].

the disengagement of evolved gases is cleaner with a smaller reactivity loss resulting as a function of integrated power (Fig. 11.32). During operation the dynamic characteristics of the reactor were evaluated. Temperature coefficients, power coefficients, and reactor transfer functions were measured. Typical results are shown in Figs. 11.33 and 11.34. Substantial negative temperature coefficients provide a high degree of operational stability.

11.4.9 FUEL TEST PROGRAM

LAMPRE-I fuel consists of 24 kg of a plutonium alloy, 90 at. % Pu—10 at. % Fe. The rather unusual density characteristics of this alloy (Fig. 11.35) can lead to a plug during solidification since the lower density solid material will tend to float to the top of the remaining fluid portion. In the initial loading the presence of a few hundred parts per million of carbon in the plutonium-fuel alloy was believed to be effective in reducing the intergranular

attack on tantalum. Subsequent tests, however, indicated that fuel made with pure iron is less corrosive than fuel with added impurities. The pure system likewise has the advantage of reducing the formation of a froth region, with resulting reactivity loss. The fuel alloy used in the Mark-I and Mark-II cores has a high plutonium concentration and is not particularly suitable for high-performance reactors because of heat-removal limitations. Attention has therefore been given to ternary alloys, i.e., plutonium—cobalt—cerium and plutonium—copper—cerium, which permit plutonium concentrations from 2 to 4 g/cm^3 at operating temperatures. Some test capsules containing the former alloy have been irradiated in the LAMPRE core.

11.5 Dounreay Fast Reactor (UKAEA)

11.5.1 INTRODUCTION

The Dounreay reactor plant [5, 40-45], using a sodium—potassium eutectic as coolant, is designed

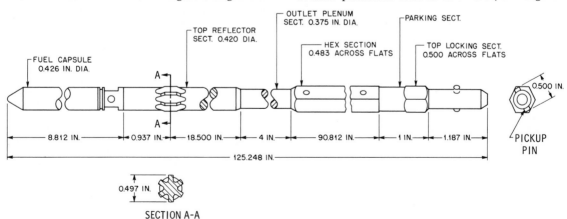

SECTION A-A

FIG. 11.28—Lampre-I fuel subassembly [27].

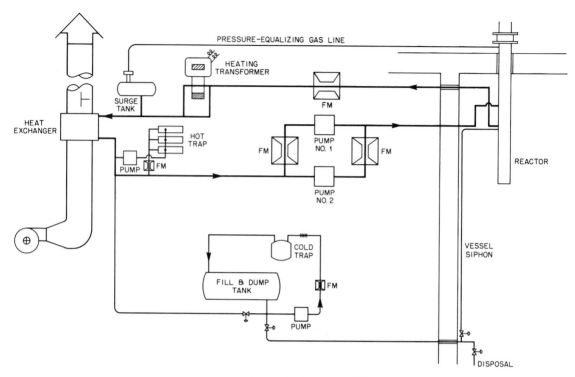

FIG. 11.29—Lampre-I sodium system [27].

for a maximum power of 72 Mw(t) and a core power of 60 Mw(t). The reactor design evolved from low-power experiments carried on at Harwell on the ZEUS experiment. Construction was started in 1955, and the reactor went critical in November 1959. The reactor was operated as a zero-power assembly until April 1960, when it was shut down for the installation of a modified core tube nest, to facilitate the radiation testing of fuel subassemblies for a prototype fast reactor.

An unusual feature of the reactor is the use of 24 coolant loops, each provided with a pump and heat exchanger to circulate the liquid metal through the reactor core and blanket. This feature was the result of a design decision to utilize heat exchangers and pumps of a size with which experience had been accumulated in previous experimental loop work.

11.5.2 REACTOR FEATURES

The general arrangement of the Dounreay plant is shown in Fig. 11.36. A containment sphere contains the reactor vessel and the primary coolant system. Provision is made for shutdown heat removal by a natural-convection loop which vents up the stack. A summary of design data is presented in Table 11.6. The design was not optimized to represent a prototype.

11.5.3 CORE ARRANGEMENT

The cylindrical core, 21 in. in diameter by 21 in. high with a volume of 4.2 cu ft, contains 361 enriched-uranium fuel elements in the form of hollow cylinders, 0.7 in. in outside diameter and 0.3 in. in inside diameter, clad on the outside by niobium and on the inside by vanadium. Sodium—potassium coolant flows in a downward direction, both through the center and around the outside of each fuel element; the ratio is controlled by pressure drops. An upper axial blanket of natural uranium is included as part of each fuel-element assembly. The core is surrounded radially by a natural-uranium blanket consisting of 2000 elements.

After the EBR-I meltdown incident, the initial core design for Dounreay, which provided for bottom support only, was revised to avoid the possibility of thermal bowing of the fuel elements. The present core structure features a "tube nest", shown in Figs. 11.37 and 11.38, which mechanically restrains the fuel elements at the top, center, and bottom. A series of long and short interlocking tubes is used, with the long tubes located in counterbored sockets in the top and bottom plates. Side plates enclose the tube nest, and the whole is positioned within the core skirt as a complete unit.

Details of the core fuel element are shown in Fig. 11.39. Beta-quenched uranium, enriched to 45% and alloyed with 0.5 at. % chromium, was used as the initial fuel. The central element design was based on a maximum uranium temperature of 840°C (1544°F), a maximum coolant—inner vanadium cladding interface temperature of 610°C (1130°F), and a maximum coolant—outer niobium cladding interface temperature of 515°C (960° F). The fuel containers, or cans, were designed to

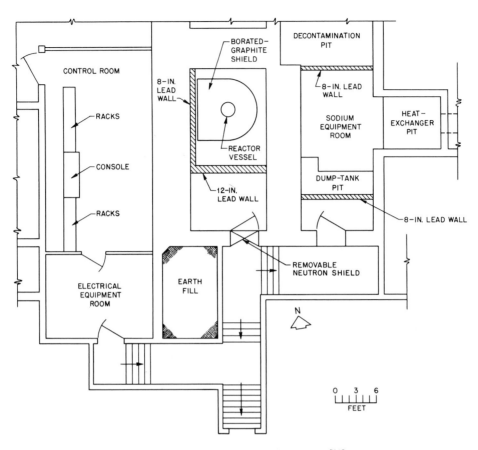

FIG. 11.30—Lampre-I shield, horizontal cross section [39].

restrict radial swelling and are provided with a free space to accommodate axial expansion. Fission gases are permitted to escape into the coolant through a vent in the upper end of the fuel element.

11.5.4 CONTROL AND STABILITY

Control is accomplished by movement of the fuel, a design decision based on the initial unavailability of B^{10}. Twelve groups of control rods, each consisting of 10 fuel elements, are situated around the edge of the core. Six operate as control rods, four are for shutoff, and two are safety rods. The reactivity involved is listed as 0.043 $\Delta k/k$ for control, 0.028 $\Delta k/k$ for shutoff, and 0.014 $\Delta k/k$ for safety. Interference with the top plug arrangement and refueling system is avoided by locating the control-rod actuating unit outside the rotating shields. Electromechanical drives are utilized to avoid gas-leakage problems. Movement of the control-rod mechanism is obtained by the use of a vertical ball-nut and screw actuator driven through an electromagnetic clutch. These features have resulted in a relatively complicated design. A detailed description of the safety and control rods is presented in Chap. 9.

11.5.5 HEAT-TRANSPORT SYSTEM

Since the primary objective of the Dounreay reactor is a demonstration of the feasibility of fast reactor core operation, the heat-transfer system was not designed as a suitable prototype of an economical system but rather as the most reliable combination of available components that would accomplish the purpose. A period of at least two years would have been required for the development and testing of shell-and-tube heat exchangers and pumps of larger size. The coolant loops were constructed of piping varying in diameter from 3/4 to 6 in. without the use of valves. Concentric-tube construction was used for the intermediate heat exchangers. These various restrictions led to the design requirement of 24 primary loops. A detailed discussion of the heat-transport system is given in Chap. 4. An unusual feature of the heat-transport design is the downward flow of coolant through the core. This permits the various components at the top of the reactor to operate in cooler regions and simplifies the structural design of the core since the coolant does not tend to lift the fuel elements.

The 24-loop primary system is designed to remove 60 Mw(t) from the core and 12 Mw(t) from the breeder blanket. As shown in Fig. 11.40, the coolant leaves the bottom of the reactor vessel at

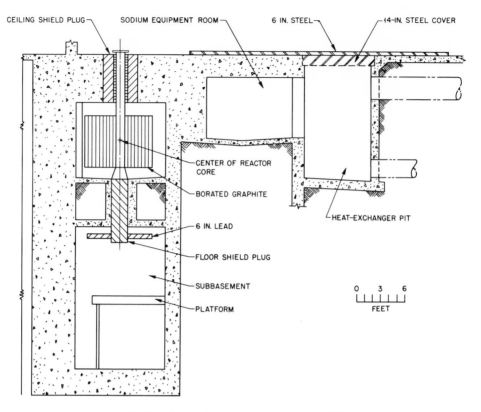

FIG. 11.31—Lampre-I shield, vertical cross section [39].

350°C (662°F), leaves the intermediate exchanger at 200°C (392°F), then passes through the
electromagnetic pump and a thermal-siphon heat
exchanger before reentering the vessel. The pump
was installed in the cooler part of the circuit
since the coolant operating temperature was restricted to 200°C (392°F) to prevent overheating
of the windings. Each secondary loop removes heat
from two primary loops, necessitating 12 independent secondary units, each complete with a steam
generator. The intermediate heat exchangers, each
designed for 3 Mw(t), consist of an inner stainless-
steel pipe, 300 ft long and 4 in. in diameter,

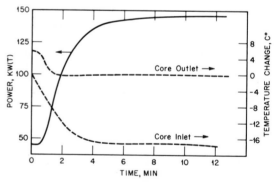

FIG. 11.33—Lampre-I core power and inlet and outlet temperature
changes from 45 kw(t) vs. time [33].

surrounded by an outer stainless-steel pipe of
6-in. diameter which is formed into 7 loops, as
shown in Fig. 4.84 of Chap. 4. Each of the 12 secondary loops contains two electromagnetic pumps
installed in parallel in a cool return leg from the
steam generator. The steam generators, in turn,
each of 6 Mw(t) capacity, consist of 13 rows of
20 heat-transfer elements each. These elements
were constructed by spirally winding copper laminations to stainless-steel tubes. Since the sodium-
containing tubes are connected to the steam-
generating tube by copper laminations, heat transfer
is by conduction from one tube to another via the
copper. The possibility of leakage from the NaK to
the water system is thereby minimized. The heat-

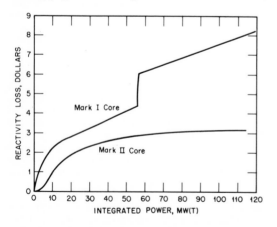

FIG. 11.32—Reactivity loss during Lampre-I operation [38].

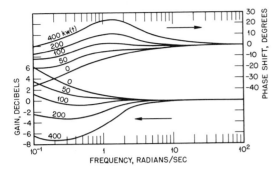

FIG. 11.34—Lampre-I transfer functions for various power levels [33].

transport system includes the usual array of accessory equipment, i.e., cold traps, hot traps, sampling equipment, filling stations, and an inert-gas (nitrogen) system. In the design of the heat-transfer system, considerable attention was devoted to a number of emergency and standby arrangements to assure integrity of the system and the removal of decay heat during reactor shutdown for any reason. For example, a thermal-siphon system is installed to remove the shutdown heat of the core from the primary circuits to a convection air-cooled heat exchanger outside the containment sphere with no requirement for electrical power.

11.5.6 STRUCTURAL AND SHIELDING COMPONENTS

A view of the reactor-vessel assembly and associated components and shielding is shown in Fig. 4.42 of Chap. 4. The core and blanket, weighing approximately 100 tons, are supported by an inner structure within the vessel. This system, built

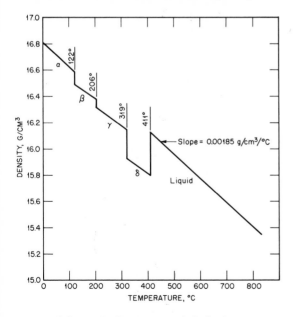

FIG. 11.35—Lampre-I Plutonium—iron fuel density vs. temperature [39].

up from a flange mounted on the inner skirt of the reactor vessel itself, includes the core skirt, various plates, and other members. In addition to providing the necessary support, the system separates the coolant flow to the core, inner blanket, and outer blanket breeder. A system of rotating plugs forms the closure for the top of the vessel and permits access by the refueling machine to any fuel or blanket element. Details are shown in Fig. 4.43 of Chap. 4. The plugs are moved only during shutdown. During normal operation O-rings prevent leakage of the cover gas; during refueling a leak-tight seal around the plugs is accomplished by two concentric metal rings dipping into a trough of sodium—mercury amalgam in the case of the inner seal and a trough of mercury for the outer seal. Such a seal is possible during refueling since the reactor pressure is then reduced to less than 0.5 psig. When the vessel is pressurized, the liquid metal in these seals is discharged to a dump tank located on the plugs.

The reactor vessel and the primary coolant loops, which contain Na^{24} activated by passage through the reactor, are contained in a 135-ft-diameter steel sphere (Fig. 11.36). The primary coolant system and the intermediate heat exchanger are (Fig. 11.40) within the containment sphere. Since the secondary NaK coolant is neither radioactive nor likely to contain fission products in the event of a fuel-element failure, the secondary-loop system, which includes the steam generators, is not within this sphere. The shielding, shown in Figs. 11.40 and 11.41, is described in Chap. 8. The design is based on a reactor output of 100 Mw(t). Fast neutrons leaking from the vessel are thermalized in a 4-ft-thick graphite shield containing 0.3 wt.% of boron. This shield surrounds the reactor vessel. The graphite is cooled by recirculating nitrogen. Zones of pure graphite are provided in the thermal shield to enable neutron-flux measurements by ion and fission chambers. An outer annulus of 5 wt.% boron in graphite surrounds these regions. The top shield, shown in Fig. 11.41, includes layers of borated graphite and steel plates in the rotating plugs and a removable concrete block assembly. A 10-in.-thick jabroc and steel shield covers the reactor top and is removable for shutdown operations. Secondary shielding is provided by a 5-ft-thick layer of concrete on the inside of the containing sphere which encloses the reactor and primary heat-transport system.

11.5.7 OPERATING EXPERIENCE

A number of difficulties were encountered during the initial start-up procedures. Contamination of the NaK with oxide proved much higher than anticipated and required considerable cleanup effort. The cold traps installed in each of the coolant loops failed to operate effectively. The installation of a better trap system and more satisfactory impurity measurement instrumentation were found to be necessary. There was considerable stress corrosion in the 321 stainless-steel superheaters and evaporators, starting in late 1961. The contributory causes were chlorides in the water,

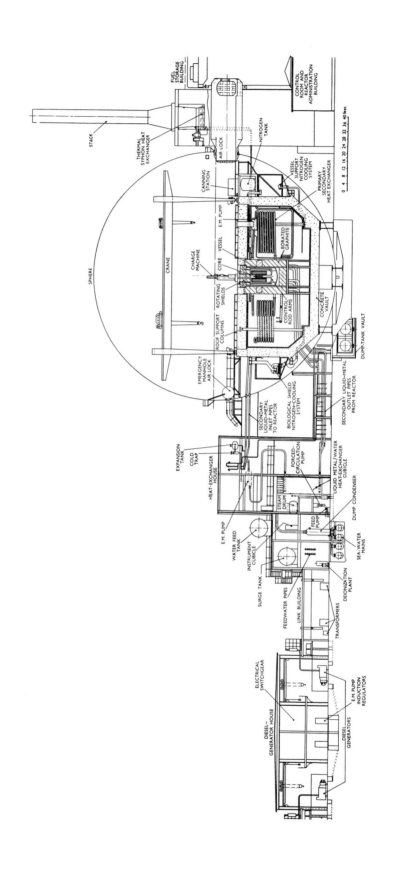

FIG. 11.36—Dounreay plant elevation [41].

Table 11.6—Dounreay Design Data
(First Core Loading)

Core Design and Performance

Core power, Mw(t)	60
Number of fuel elements	367
Heat transfer surface, sq ft	168
Average heat flux, Btu/hr/sq ft	680,000
Maximum to average heat flux	1.7
Power density (per unit volume of core):	
Kw(t)/cu ft	14,250
Kw(t)/liter	500
Specific power, kw(t)/kg U^{235}	286
Coolant inlet temperature, $^{\circ}C/^{\circ}F$	200/392
Coolant outlet average temperature from core, $^{\circ}C/^{\circ}F$	400/784
Diameter of core, in.	21
Length of core, in.	21
Core NaK flow rate, 10^6 lb/hr	2.1
Coolant flow area, sq ft	0.694
NaK velocity, ft/sec	15.8
Pressure drop across the core, psi	11
Core composition, vol. %:	
U^{235}	9.3
U^{238}	22.7
Nb	5.5
Va	1.9
SS	19.1
NaK	41.5
Fuel OD, in.	0.698
Fuel ID, in.	0.316
Outer tube (fuel element) OD, in.	0.752
Outer tube (fuel element) ID, in.	0.712
Inner tube (fuel element) OD, in.	0.298
Inner tube (fuel element) ID, in.	0.258
Maximum outer tube temperature, $^{\circ}C/^{\circ}F$	550/1022
Maximum inner tube temperature, $^{\circ}C/^{\circ}F$	680/1256
Maximum uranium temperature, $^{\circ}C/^{\circ}F$	840/1544

Blanket (Breeder) Design and Performance

Blanket power, Mw(t)	12
Number of blanket elements	1872
Heat transfer surface, sq ft	4420
Average heat flux, Btu/hr/sq ft	5150
Coolant inlet temperature, $^{\circ}C/^{\circ}F$	200/392
Average coolant outlet temperature, $^{\circ}C/^{\circ}F$	350/662
Diameter of breeder, in.	74.6
Length of breeder, in.	84
Breeder NaK flow rate, lb/hr	561,600
Coolant flow area, sq ft	8.1
NaK velocity (inner region average), ft/sec	0.5
Average blanket composition (percentage varies radially), vol. %:	
U^{235}	0.4
U^{238}	60.1
SS	9.5
NaK	30.0
Fuel OD, in.	1.277
Clad ID, in.	1.290
Clad thickness, in.	0.036

Heat-removal System Data [60 Mw(t) core output]

Primary circuits	
Number of core circuits	20
Number of breeder circuits	4
Mw(t) per circuit	3
Number of pumps per circuit	1
Flow rate per circuit, lb/hr	145,800
Pressure drop external to reactor, psi	13
Total volume of NaK (referred to $300^{\circ}C/556^{\circ}F$), cu ft	2160
Total weight of NaK, tonnes	51.3
Primary-secondary heat exchanger	
Inlet temperature, $^{\circ}C/^{\circ}F$	350/662
Outlet temperature, $^{\circ}C/^{\circ}F$	200/392
Heat transfer surface, sq ft	378
Mean temperature difference, $^{\circ}C/^{\circ}F$	20/36
Electromagnetic pumps (flat linear-induction type)	
Flow rate, lb/hr	145,800
Pressure drop (core circuit), psi	24
Line voltage, volts	410
Power:	
Kw	14.7
Kva	16.5
Pump efficiency at 410 volts and 145,800 lb/hr, %	24
Minimum pressure at pump inlet, psig	12
Maximum allowable winding temperature, $^{\circ}C/^{\circ}F$	240/464
Hot traps	
Number of traps	5
Flow rate through trap, lb/hr	7560
Oxide absorption material	Zirconium
Foil thickness, in.	0.005
Surface area in contact with NaK per trap, sq ft	4000
Trap inlet temperature, $^{\circ}C/^{\circ}F$	200/392
Temperature of NaK flowing over zirconium, $^{\circ}C/^{\circ}F$	600/1112
Trap outlet temperature, $^{\circ}C/^{\circ}F$	220/428
Electrical heating input, kw	35
Other components (No.)	
Oxide corrosion meter (hot-trap circuit)	1
Oxide sampling unit (cold-trap circuit)	1
Resistivity meters (cold-trap circuit)	2
Blanket-gas system	
Gas	Nitrogen
Operating pressure, psig	50
Shutdown pressure, psig	0.5
Volume of system including buffer tanks, cu ft	2370
Secondary circuits	
Number of circuits	12
Number of pumps per circuit	2
Flow rate per pump, lb/hr	137,880
Pressure drop, psi	26
Number of cold traps per circuit	2
Steam generator	
Number of units	12
NaK flow rate per unit, lb/hr	275,760
Steam generation rate per unit, lb/hr	16,800
Pre-heater section:	
Water inlet temperature, $^{\circ}C/^{\circ}F$	40/104
Water outlet temperature, $^{\circ}C/^{\circ}F$	90/194
Heat transfer surface area, sq ft	173.5
Evaporator section heat-transfer-surface area, sq ft	400
Superheater section:	
Steam inlet temperature, $^{\circ}C/^{\circ}F$	195/383
Steam outlet temperature, $^{\circ}C/^{\circ}F$	280/536
Pressure at outlet, psig	185
Heat transfer surface area, sq ft	78
Thermal syphon circuits	
Number of circuits	4
Heat-transfer duty per circuit during thermal-syphon conditions, Mw(t)	0.45
Steam plant	
Dump condenser:	
Number of condensers	12
Type	Vertical shell and tube, two pass
Duty	To condense generated steam or to cool pressurized water
Total surface area, sq ft	1980
Maximum sea water flow rate, lb/hr	1,321,200
Feed pump	
Number of pumps	12
Type	6-stage centrifugal
Capacity, lb/hr	25,850
Suction pressure, psig	6.5
Discharge pressure, psig	300
Circulating pump	
Number of pumps	12
Type	Single-stage centrifugal submersible motor

Table 11.6—Dounreay Design Data (continued)

Capacity at 405°F, lb/hr	158,760
Head, ft	59.5
Turbine generator	
Electrical output, Mw	15
Steam pressure at stop valves, psig	150
Steam temperature at stop valve, °C/°F	270/518
Steam supplied, lb/hr	169,000
Sea-water pumps	
Diesel-driven vertical centrifugal:	
Number of pumps	4
Output, lb/hr	5,220,000
Pressure head, ft	75
Power required, hp	241
Electrical supply	
Number of independent diesel-generators supplying power to the 12 heat transfer units:	
Operating	12
Standby	6
Output, kw	120
Voltage, volts	415
Number of diesel-generators supplying auxiliary equipment	6
Output, kw	220
Voltage, volts	415
Capacity of grid-supply transformers connected in parallel, kva	1000

aerated conditions, and carbide precipitation particularly at the surface of the steel. Extensive repairs have been made to the steam generators, and careful control of water purity was instituted. Repairs were not completed until April 1963.

Niobium and vanadium fuel-cladding failures occurred as a result of hydrogen embrittlement induced by hydride in the coolant. This contamination was believed to have been introduced with the first charge of fuel. Carbon in the system may also contribute to the embrittlement of the cladding. Considerable work is being done to determine this effect. Loops are in operation with a hot trap and specimens of zirconium, Zircaloy, Nimonic, and three types of low-carbon stainless steel. Additional efforts are being made in the United States by APDA, AI, and other groups to determine the effects of carbon on structural material. An extensive cold- and hot-trap system was installed to reduce oxygen, hydrogen, nitrogen, and carbon concentrations in the coolant to very low levels. Excessive niobium corrosion was reported as late as March 1963.

Considerable gas entrainment in the coolant circuit required a number of modifications. These included changes in the expansion tanks and a separate gas enclosure for the control-rod mechanism.

Troubles encountered with the control-rod thrust head were traced to the pickup of scum from the contaminated liquid-metal surface. These problems were eliminated by the hermetically sealed drive described above and in Chap. 9. During the start-up period, problems were also encountered with numerous components, such as the control units and the mercury seals on the rotating shield.

Low-power experiments were concerned with the determination of physics parameters. The predicted critical mass, neutron flux and power

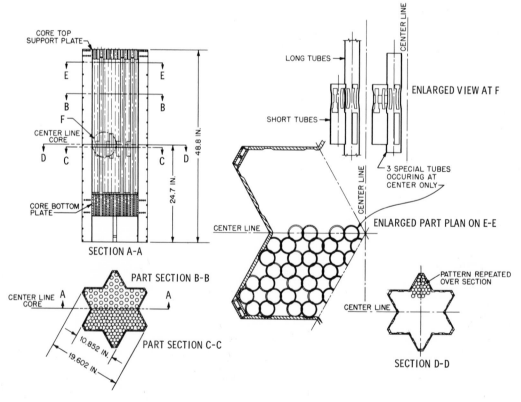

FIG. 11.37—Details of Dounreay core tube nest [41].

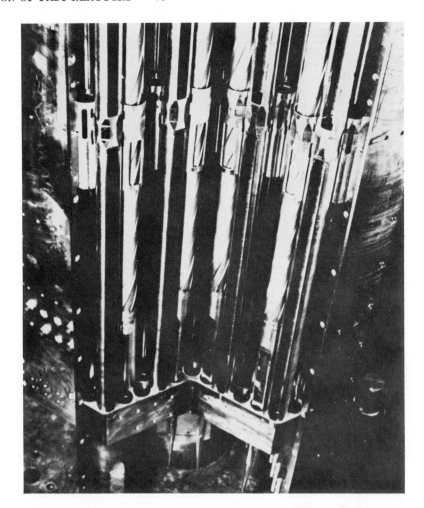

FIG. 11.38—Dounreay core tube nest showing interlocking of long and short tubes [41].

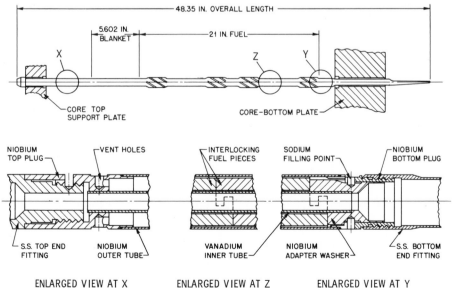

FIG. 11.39—Details of Dounreay fuel subassembly [41].

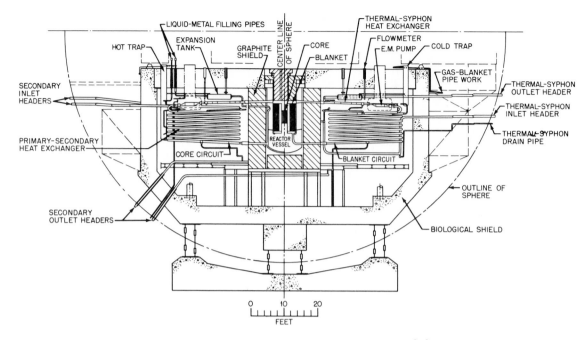

FIG. 11.40—Arrangement of Dounreay primary-circuit pipe work [41].

distribution for the core region, and the neutron-energy spectrum at the core center were reasonably well confirmed.

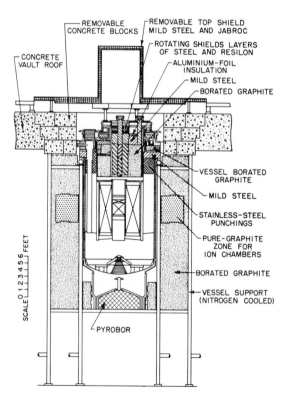

FIG. 11.41—Dounreay shield [41].

The new core tube nest, designated as core B, was installed in April 1960. Many of the start-up problems were subsequently solved, and a power level of 11 Mw was reached in late 1961. The second charge of fuel of 345 elements was discharged in the period Dec. 21, 1961, to Feb. 9, 1962. After the discharge the primary system had 4 complete fills of sodium and 12 dumps. Only after cleanup operations were completed in June of 1962 and the hold-up of oxide in the clocked by-pass circuits eliminated was the plugging temperature reduced from 230°C to about 140°C. The third fuel loading was uranium—10 wt. % molybdenum, and the loading was completed in the period June to July 1962. During this loading the roller bearings on the charge machine were replaced with ball bearings to prevent further bearing seizure, previously experienced. Criticality was reached on July 26, 1962, and operation at 30 Mw(t) was realized on August 7. During this period the NaK rose in the rotating plug, owing to unbalance in the gas lines, contaminating the mercury dip seal and requiring about 1300 lb of mercury to free the seal. New balance lines were added to eliminate this problem. Plugging temperature was further reduced to 110°C by isolating the rotating-plug graphite from the reactor cover gas. Testing of uranium—18 at. % molybdenun, uranium—20 at.% molybdenum, and uranium—25 at. % molybdenum indicated that the uranium—18 at.% molybdenum transformation from gamma to gamma plus alpha started in 40 to 45 min at 890°F with completion of tranformation in 150 to 250 hr; uranium—20 at.% molybdenum at 800°F took 5 to 7 hr to initiate the transformation and over 1000 hr to complete it, whereas at 1020°F it took 1 to 2 hr to initiate and 200 to 300 hr to complete; and the uranium—25 at. % molybdenum at 800°F took 50 to 70 hr to initiate and was only 5% complete in 500 hr. Examination of the uranium–molybdenum alloy fuels indicated that fuel slugs irradiated to burnups of 0.3% had cracks that increased with fuel temperature up to 450°C. Cracking is greatest in slugs that have the large fuel-cladding clearances. Increase of molybdenum content from 20 at. % to 25 at. % showed no improvement in irradiation behavior at burnups of 0.48 to 0.6%. It is hypothesized that steep temperature gradients occur, as high as 2000°C per inch in the fuel. Center swelling, produced by gas pressures in the high-temperature center of the fuel, acts against the restrained cooler outer layers. The combined action results in the cracks.

Modifications were made to the fuel-handling system in early 1963 to include a 10-ton hoist to move a fuel-transfer cask from the canning station to the air lock trolley. A second carrier was added to the canning-station trolley permitting the refueling machine to pick up a new subassembly immediately after releasing a spent fuel subassembly. These changes increased the rate of fuel changing from 14 to 20 per day with the possibility of increasing to 24 fuel subassemblies per day.

After a fourth loading of fuel, completed in June 1963, the operation of the reactor reached 55 Mw(t) on June 18, 1963, with a subsequent increase to 60 Mw(t) in July. The so called Mark-III fuel subassemblies with uranium–molybdenum fuel were designed to achieve this rating.

The 60-Mw(t) run achieved a fuel burnup up to 1.12% of the heavy atoms. Condition of the fuel cans externally was good. The fuel as expected was cracked and swollen. Operations through the fall of 1963 were at a maximum burnup of the uranium–molybdenum of 1.2% of heavy atoms. Electricity was first generated on Oct. 9, 1963, and a tie-in was made to the national grid on October 14. References 42 through 45 cover operating experiments at Dounreay in more detail up to August 1962. The operating conditions for the 60-Mw(t) run were as follows:

Primary coolant flow through the core, lb/hr	3.21×10^6
Primary coolant flow through the blanket, lb/hr	0.64×10^6
Core pressure drop, psi	10.2
Inlet coolant temperature, °C/°F	230/446
Mixed outlet temperature, °C/°F	330/626
Maximum outlet temperature, °C/°F	395/743
Maximum fuel temperature in standard element near core center, °C/°F	617/1142
Maximum fuel temperature in pilot element in control rod, °C/°F	649/1200
Central neutron flux, neutrons/cm²/sec	2.64×10^{15}
Duration of run, days	37
Integrated power for run, Mwd	2015
Total integrated power, Mwd	4390

The use of the uranium-molybdenum fuel is planned through 1965. Irradiation of central subassemblies containing oxide fuels is planned preliminary to the adoption of an oxide core.

11.6 EBR-II

11.6.1 INTRODUCTION

The Experimental Breeder Reactor II (EBR-II) [Refs. 3,5,6, 13–18, 46–50], located at the National Reactor Testing Station in Idaho, is a reactor power plant integrated with a complete fuel-processing and -fabrication facility. Although the plant is rated at 62.5 Mw(t) with an electrical power output of 20 Mw(e), the major objective of the facility is to establish the feasibility of a plutonium-fueled fast power reactor system under operating conditions comparable to those existing in a large-scale power plant.

A major feature of this concept is the demonstration of on-site fuel reprocessing and fabrication, a procedure believed to result in favorable fuel-cycle costs for high-power-density fast reactors. The design of the entire reactor system is affected by this requirement. A comparatively high enrichment necessitates this high power density, which, in turn, results in a high rate of fuel burnup. A finely divided fuel is necessary to achieve this high thermal performance. The fuel achieves a high specific activity after irradiation with the resulting limitations on fission-product separation processes. A high level of fission-product decay heating also results; thus there is a need for substantial cooling in the reactor during fuel handling and in the fuel cycle. The fuel also has a high monetary value, and this provides the incentive to minimize total fuel inventory by reducing "out-of-reactor" processing time requirements.

The fuel cycle utilizes pyrometallurgical processing, which can be accomplished with small equipment and requires a relatively short cooling time. Incomplete decontamination, however, associated with the process necessitates the use of remote-control procedures for the fabrication of new fuel elements from the processed product. The fuel process itself has likewise affected the core design, specifically the composition of the metallic uranium–fissium alloy for the first core, a mixture of noble-metal fission products not easily removed by processing. Fissium contributes desirable characteristics to the fuel. Both the reactor and the associated fuel recycle facility were designed with the philosophy of providing a highly flexible installation that would permit the investigation and evaluation of various core configurations, types of fuel, fuel-element designs, and processing techniques.

11.6.2 REACTOR FEATURES

The facility is shown in Fig. 11.42 and the major reactor components in Fig. 4.39 of Chap. 4. The fuel-cycle facility is seen to be a major portion of the installation.

The reactor and the primary heat-removal system, including the intermediate heat exchanger, are completely submerged in a large bulk volume

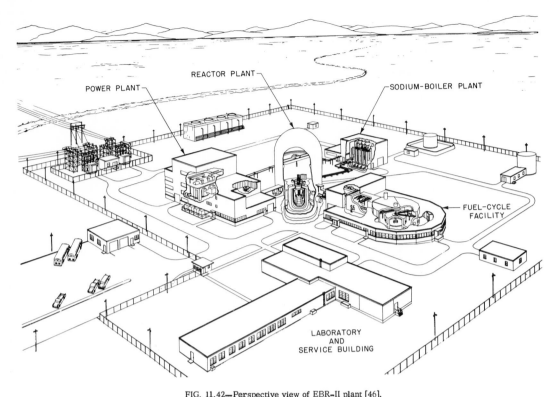

FIG. 11.42—Perspective view of EBR-II plant [46].

(80,000 gal) of sodium within the primary tank (Fig. 4.39 of Chap. 4). Fuel handling is carried out under sodium.

A steel containment vessel is used to house the primary-system components, and power-generation facilities are housed in a separate building. A summary of design data is given in Table 11.7. Approximately 85% of the power is generated in the core with a power density of 890 kw(t)/liter and an average specific power of 314 kw(t)/kg of U^{235}.

Table 11.7—EBR-II Design Data

Plant Data	
Heat output, Mw(t)	62.5
Gross electrical output, Mw(e)	20
Primary sodium temperature, reactor inlet, °F	700
Primary sodium temperature, reactor outlet, °F	900
Primary sodium flow rate, through reactor, gal/min	8200
Primary sodium maximum velocity, in core, ft/sec	26
Primary system sodium capacity, gal	86,000
Secondary sodium temperature, to IHX, °F	610
Secondary sodium temperature, from IHX, °F	880
Secondary sodium flow rate, gal/min	6050
Steam generator:	
Output, lb/hr	248,000
Steam temperature, °F	850
Steam pressure, psig	1300
Feedwater temperature, °F	550
Turbine throttle conditions:	
Steam flow, lb/hr	198,000
Steam temperature, °F	850
Steam pressure, psig	1250
Reactor Data	
Core dimensions:	
Equivalent diameter, in.	19.04
Height, in.	14.22
Total volume, liter/cu ft	66.3/2.32
Upper- and lower-blanket dimensions:	
Equivalent diameter, in.	19.04
Length (each end), in.	18
Inner-blanket dimensions:	
Equivalent outside diameter, in.	27.46
Length, in.	55.0
Radial thickness, in.	4.21
Outer-blanket dimensions:	
Equivalent outside diameter, in.	61.5
Length, in.	55.0
Radial thickness, in.	17.02
Core composition:	
Fuel alloy, vol. %	31.8
Stainless steel (type 304), vol. %	19.5
Sodium, vol. %	48.7
Control- and safety-rod composition (fuel section):	
Fuel alloy, vol. %	21.3
Stainless steel (type 304), vol. %	20.8
Sodium, vol. %	57.9
Upper- and lower-blanket composition:	
Uranium (depleted), vol. %	32
Stainless steel (type 304), vol. %	20.4
Sodium, vol. %	47.6
Inner- and outer-blanket composition:	
Uranium (depleted), vol. %	60
Stainless steel (type 304), vol. %	17.6
Sodium, vol. %	22.4
Subassemblies:	
Number:	
Core	47
Control (rod and thimble)	12
Safety (rod and thimble)	2
Inner blanket	66
Outer blanket	510
Total	637
Configuration	Hexagonal
Dimension across flats, in.	2.290

Hexagonal-tube thickness, in.	0.040
Structural material	304 SS
Lattice spacing (pitch), in.	2.320
Clearance between subassemblies, in.	0.030
Fuel elements (pin type, sodium bonded):	
Fuel-pin diameter, in.	0.144
Fuel-pin length, in.	14.22
Fuel-tube outside diameter, in.	0.174
Fuel-tube wall thickness, in.	0.009
Thickness Na-bond annulus, in.	0.006
Elements per subassembly	91
Upper- and lower-blanket elements (pin type, sodium bonded):	
Blanket-pin diameter, in.	0.3165
Blanket-pin length (total), in.	18
Blanket-tube outside diameter, in.	0.376
Blanket-tube wall thickness, in.	0.022
Thickness Na-bond annulus, in.	0.008
Blanket elements per subassembly (each end)	19
Control and safety rods:	
Configuration	Hexagonal
Dimension across flats, in.	1.908
Fuel elements (same as core subassembly)	
Fuel elements per rod	61
Inner- and outer-blanket elements (pin type, sodium bonded):	
Blanket-pin diameter, in.	0.433
Blanket-pin length (total), in.	55
Blanket-tube outside diameter, in.	0.493
Blanket-tube wall thickness, in.	0.018
Thickness Na-bond annulus, in.	0.012
Blanket elements per subassembly	19
Fuel alloy (enriched U—fissium):	
Total core loading, kg	363
U^{235} enrichment, %	49
Critical mass, U^{235}, kg	170
Fuel-alloy composition (fissium):	
Uranium, wt. %	95.0
Zirconium, wt. %	0.2
Molybdenum, wt. %	2.5
Ruthenium, wt. %	1.5
Rhodium, wt. %	0.3
Palladium, wt. %	0.5
Fertile blanket material (depleted uranium):	
Total blanket loading, kg	28,100

Nuclear Data

Total fissions per cm^3/sec at center of core	4.4×10^{13}
Neutron-energy distribution at center of core:	
Flux above 1.35 Mev, neutrons/cm^2/sec	0.8×10^{15}
Flux below 1.35 Mev, neutrons/cm^2/sec	2.9×10^{15}
Total neutron flux, neutrons/cm^2/sec	3.7×10^{15}
Prompt neutron lifetime, sec	8×10^{-8}

Reactor Control

Power coefficients:	
0–22.5 Mw, $\Delta k/k$/Mw	-3.2×10^{-5}
22.5–62.5 Mw, $\Delta k/k$/Mw	-6.0×10^{-5}
Doppler effect, average, $\Delta k/k$/°C	$+0.04 \times 10^{-5}$
Isothermal temperature coefficient, $\Delta k/k$/°C	-3.6×10^{-5}
Total reactivity (worth):	
12 control rods, $\Delta k/k$	0.06
2 safety rods, $\Delta k/k$	0.015–0.020
Control rod:	
Number	12
Operating drive (each rod)	Rack and pinion
Velocity, in./min	5
Total movement, in.	14
Scram drive	Pneumatic
Safety rod:	
Number	2
Operating drive	Rack and pinion
Velocity, in./min	2
Total movement, in.	14
Scram drive	Gravity
Long-term reactivity effects (from clean to 2% burnup):	
Burnup of U^{235} in core, $\Delta k/k$	-0.02
Buildup of Pu in core, $\Delta k/k$	$+0.002$

Buildup of Pu in blanket, $\Delta k/k$	$+0.0072$
Buildup of fission products, $\Delta k/k$	-0.002
Irradiation growth of fuel (4% growth), $\Delta k/k$	-0.011

Heat Transfer

Heat generation in reactor:	
Core and control and safety subassemblies, Mw	53.3
Upper and lower blanket, Mw	1.2
Inner blanket, Mw	5.2
Outer blanket, Mw	2.6
Neutron shield, Mw	0.2
Heat generation in core:	
Radial maximum-to-average power density at reactor center plane	1.33
Axial maximum-to-average power density at reactor center line	1.17
Power density, average, kw/liter	890
Power density, maximum, kw/liter	1370
Power density, maximum to average	1.53
Specific power (fissionable material), kw/kg	314
Fuel elements, surface area, sq ft	231
Control elements, surface area (in active zone), sq ft	32.4
Safety elements, surface area, sq ft	6.6
Total surface area, sq ft	270
Maximum heat flux, 10^6 Btu/hr/sq ft	1.03
Average heat flux, 10^6 Btu/hr/sq ft	0.68

11.6.3 REACTOR CORE AND VESSEL ARRANGEMENT

The reactor-vessel assembly is shown in Fig. 8.97 of Chap. 8, and the core arrangement is shown in Fig. 8.99 of Chap. 8. In the radial direction the reactor is divided into three main zones, a core, an inner blanket, and an outer blanket. Twelve control rods are located at the outer edge of the core, and two safety rods are located within the core. The core, including the control and safety rods, has an equivalent radius of 9.52 in. (27.17 cm) and a height of 14.22 in. (36.12 cm), with a total core volume of 2.32 cu ft. Located in the core zone are 47 core subassemblies, each containing 91 fuel pins, 2 core subassemblies acting as safety rods, and 12 core subassemblies acting as control rods. In addition to the central core section, each core subassembly contains an upper and lower blanket section (Figs. 11.43 and 11.44). The 12 control rods and the 2 safety rods consist of modified movable core subassemblies. These rods move in stationary thimbles having external dimensions and lattice spacing identical to the core and blanket subassemblies.

In each radial zone of the reactor, the hexagonal subassemblies of identical size measure 2.29 in. across the external flats and have a wall thickness of 0.040 in. Each subassembly contains a number of fuel and/or blanket elements, of size and shape appropriate to the particular type of subassembly.

The subassemblies are spaced on a triangular pitch with a 2.32-in. center-to-center distance, which provides a nominal clearance of 0.030 in. between each subassembly to permit removal of the units from the reactor. Each face of a core or inner blanket subassembly hexagonal tube contains a projection or button, 3/8 in. in diameter by 0.014 in. high, located approximately at the horizontal center line of the reactor and providing a plane of contact at that location. All subassemblies, including those for control and safety purposes, have an identical upper design and are accommodated by the same handling and transfer devices.

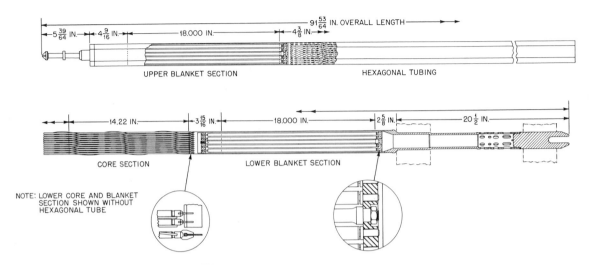

FIG. 11.43—EBR-II fuel subassembly details [46].

The core subassembly consists of three active sections: an upper blanket, a core section, and a lower blanket. The fuel elements in the core central section are pin type and consist of a right–circular cylinder of fuel alloy (0.144 in. in diameter by 14.22 in. long) fitted into a thin-walled stainless-steel tube (Fig. 11.45). A 0.006-in. sodium-filled annulus between the pin and the inside of the tube provides a thermal bond. Above the sodium an inert-gas space is provided to accommodate sodium expansion. The 91 cylindrical fuel elements (pins) contained in the core section are spaced on a triangular lattice by a single helical rib on the outside of each element. The lower ends of the pins are fastened to a parallel strip support grid, with the upper ends unrestrained.

The upper- and lower-blanket sections, identical in construction, consist of 19 pin type elements spaced on a triangular lattice. In this case the pins, of unalloyed depleted uranium, are 0.316 in. in diameter and 18 in. long. They are contained within a stainless-steel tube having a 0.008-in. sodium-filled annulus to provide the necessary thermal bond. Bond ends of the blanket elements are positioned in the subassembly by a parallel strip grid similar to that used in the core section. Axial expansion is permitted, but other movements are restricted. The upper adapter of the assembly is provided with an attachment knob for the various fuel-handling gripper units and a collar for the transfer arm. The lower adapter is a cylindrical inlet nozzle for the coolant, which also serves as a locating and support plug in the reactor grid plate. The bottom end of the nozzle is closed; the coolant enters the nozzle through holes in the cylindrical wall.

The inner and outer radial blanket subassemblies each consist of 19 cylindrical blanket elements spaced on a close-packed triangular pitch and contained in a hexagonal can (Fig. 11.46). The central active blanket section consists of depleted-uranium cylinders, 0.433 in. in diameter and 55 in. long. They are contained in a stainless-steel tube with a 0.012-in. sodium annulus as a thermal bond

and an argon-gas expansion region above the sodium. The end closure unit is sealed with welds. The two types of blanket subassemblies differ from the core subassembly only in the design of the lower adapter (Fig. 11.46). In the case of the outer-blanket subassembly, a small-diameter adapter contains an opening at the bottom through which the coolant enters.

11.6.4 CONTROL RODS

Operational control of the reactor is achieved through 12 control assemblies with a fuel-pin core section identical with that in other core positions. Control is achieved by the removal or insertion of the fuel. Instead of an axial blanket, a void section normally filled with sodium is above the core section, and a steel cylindrical-tube reflector is below the fuel section. The middle section of the rod consists of a modified core subassembly comprised of 61 fuel elements identical to those employed in the other core subassembly units. This assembly is encased in a hexagonal tube 1.908 in. across flats, which is smaller than the normal hexagonal tube by the equivalent of one row of fuel elements.

The drive arrangement for the control and safety rods is shown in Fig. 11.47 and Fig. 9.38 of Chap. 9. The two identical safety rods employed to provide shutdown reactivity during reactor loading operations are driven from below the core. They are essentially identical with the control rods, except for modifications at the lower end which provide the necessary attachment to the drives.

11.6.5 HEAT-TRANSPORT SYSTEM

A schematic flow diagram of the coolant power-cycle system is given in Fig. 11.48. A unique feature of this system is the primary tank, which contains the reactor vessel and primary coolant system submerged in a large volume of bulk sodium, as shown in Fig. 4.39 of Chap. 4.

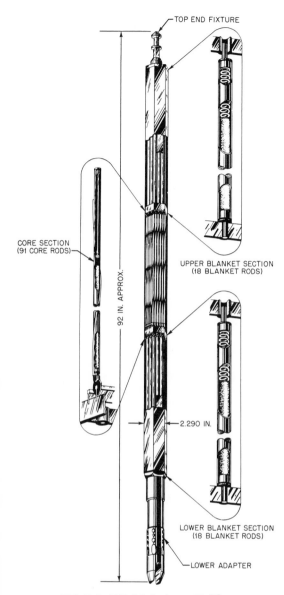

FIG. 11.44—EBR-II fuel subassembly [5].

Two identical vertically mounted single-stage centrifugal pumps, operating in parallel, force coolant from the bulk sodium in the primary tank through the reactor at a rate of about 8500 gal/min. Flow through the reactor itself totals 8200 gal/min, with 7000 gal/min flowing from a high-pressure plenum through the core and inner blanket subassemblies, 700 gal/min flowing from a separate low-pressure plenum through the outer blanket subassemblies, and 500 gal/min flowing through the clearance spaces between subassemblies. The remaining 300 gal/min represents leakage back to the primary tank through the pump ball seat disconnects and the subassembly hold-down devices at the bottom of the vessel. The coolant passes into a common outlet plenum chamber and then out of the reactor through a single outlet nozzle to the intermediate heat exchanger, shown in Fig. 11.48. Finally, after passing through the heat exchanger, the coolant returns to the bulk sodium supply at approximately 700°F, which is slightly above the bulk temperature since it is necessary to compensate for small heat losses from the primary-system tank. For maintenance purposes the pumps may be removed from the primary tank with ball seat type pipe disconnects provided. The heat-exchanger shell is permanently attached to the cover of the primary tank, but the tube bundle and associated structure are removable as a unit. Additional component details are given in Chap. 4.

In the secondary system, an a-c electromagnetic linear induction pump, which provides close control of flow rate, circulates sodium through the tubes of the primary heat exchanger at a flow rate of 6030 gal/min. The sodium then enters the superheated section of the steam generator at 880°F and returns to the pump at 610°F.

The steam generator, shown in Fig. 11.49, is of the natural recirculation type with separate superheater and evaporator sections connected to a single steam drum. Each evaporator unit is connected to the steam drum by a single downcomer and riser. Dry and saturated steam from the steam drum passes downward through the superheater units. Double-walled tube construction is used for both the evaporator and superheater units; no welds are used in the portions in contact with sodium. The steam-cycle system is shown in Fig. 11.48.

At full load [62.5 Mw(t)] when the generator produces 20,700 kw(e) gross, the steam-system flow includes 5000 lb/hr of steam bypassed to the condenser. A full-capacity automatic steam bypass system permits reactor operation without turbine-generator operation, or with turbine load at any fraction of reactor power. This bypass system prevents major load changes from effecting changes in the secondary system. Feedwater heating is accomplished by extraction from the main turbine, the exhaust from the feedwater pump turbine, and high-pressure steam from the main steam line.

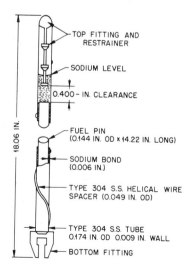

FIG. 11.45—Reference design for EBR—II fuel pin [48].

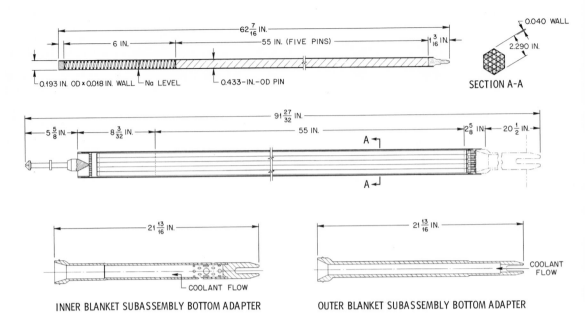

FIG. 11.46—Inner and outer EBR-II blanket subassemblies [46].

11.6.6 COMPONENTS, SHIELDING, AND STRUCTURES

In EBR-II the reactor-vessel assembly is completely submerged within a large volume of bulk sodium contained in the primary tank. The assembly itself is mounted on the bottom structure of the tank in such a manner that the distance from the top of the reactor vessel to the free surface of the bulk sodium is approximately 12 ft. The reactor vessel assembly, as shown in Fig. 8.97 of Chap. 8, includes the lower grid plenum with inlet nozzles

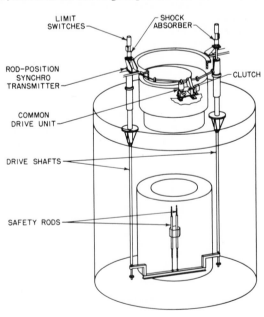

FIG. 11.47—EBR-II safety-rod drive system [46].

and safety-rod drives, an inner radial neutron shield, the subassembly hold-down and flow-baffle structure with outlet plenum and outlet nozzles, the vessel cover and hold-down structure, thermal baffles, the cylindrical-vessel wall, and the outer radial neutron shield.

Located within the primary tank, but outside the reactor vessel, are the fuel-handling components, which are an important feature of the reactor design. This system, shown in Fig. 7.48 of Chap. 7, has the capacity to remove a subassembly from the reactor, transfer it to the storage rack, and remove it from the primary tank after a 15-day cooling period. The system consists of a gripper mechanism, a subassembly hold-down rod, and the transfer-arm assembly. Positioning of the gripper mechanism is accomplished by rotating two eccentric plugs in the shield. Details of the fuel-handling procedures and equipment are given in Chap. 7.

The shield system consists of two sections. A neutron shield between the blanket and the bulk sodium tank reduces neutron leakage into the sodium and thus reduces activation. A biological shield outside the sodium tank reduces radiation levels to acceptable limits at accessible locations around the reactor. This arrangement is shown in Fig. 11.50 and Fig. 8.100 of Chap. 8. Within the reactor vessel part of the neutron shield consists of two rows of stainless-steel cans, each 4 in. square, filled with graphite. Five additional rows are located outside the reactor vessel; the fifth and seventh rows consist of 3% boron carbide. Graphite is substituted for the boron carbide in areas immediately adjacent to the neutron-detecting instruments.

The primary heat exchanger, located within the primary tank, is surrounded by a 1-in.-thick shell of 1.5% borated steel to reduce activation of the secondary sodium system.

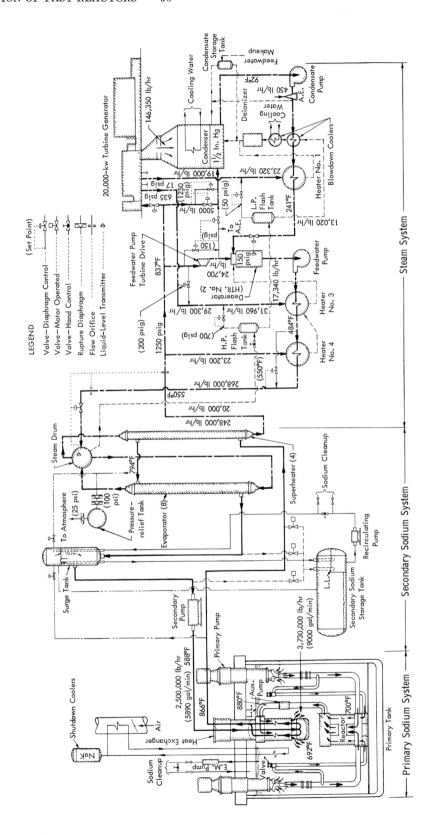

FIG. 11.48–EBR-II flow diagram [46].

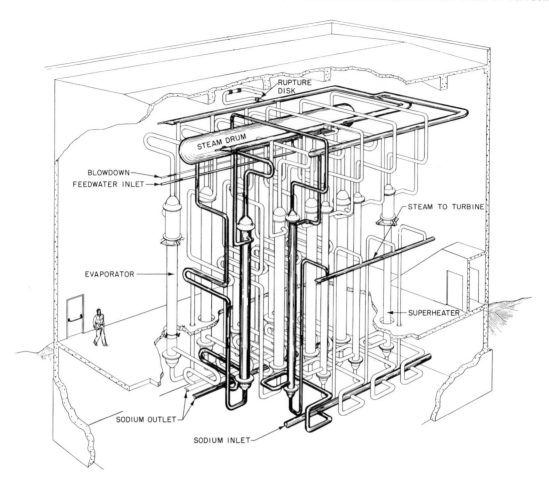

FIG. 11.49--EBR-II steam generator [46].

The biological shield, outside the primary tank, consists of a 6-ft thickness of ordinary concrete in the radial direction wherever space is available and a top shield consisting of a layer of steel balls directly above the primary tank. Heavy concrete is used elsewhere. Rotating plugs in the top shield are stepped to reduce streaming through the large number of voids and penetrations necessary to provide access. Control rods, however, are not stepped, but streaming is reduced by keeping clearances as small as possible and providing more thickness than otherwise required. Additional details of the shield system are given in Chap. 8. A steel containment vessel, 80 ft in diameter and approximately 140 ft high, houses the reactor plant.

11.6.7 FUEL CYCLE

Since a very important objective of this reactor is the demonstration of an integral fuel-processing facility, some of the features are given here [51-65]. Melt refining is planned for the recovery of the first loading although other processes involving liquid-metal solvents and molten salts are being developed for the processing of subsequent cores.

The first fissium core consists of stainless-steel-jacketed pins containing 50% enriched uranium alloyed with 5% noble-metal fission-product elements. Irradiated fuel assemblies are allowed to cool for 15 days in the primary tank and then are removed to the fuel-cycle facility. Prior to processing, the pins are to be declad mechanically and chopped. A batch of about 10 kg of chopped pins is added to a lime-stabilized zirconia crucible, melted, and liquated at 1400°C (2552°F) for about 3 hr. During this period approximately two-thirds of the fission products present in the melt are removed by volatilization and selective oxidation by the crucible. The non-rare gas volatilized fission products are collected by a Fiberfax cover over the crucible, which also collects sodium used as a thermal bond in the fuel. The purified alloy is poured into the mold to provide the ingot for fabrication; the oxidized fission products, principally the rare earths, are left behind in a so-called "skull" retained by the crucible.

An economically significant portion of the fissionable material processed remains behind in the skull and will eventually be recovered. The process contemplated has the skull material converted to an oxide powder suspended in a molten chloride flux; the noble metals are removed by reduction and

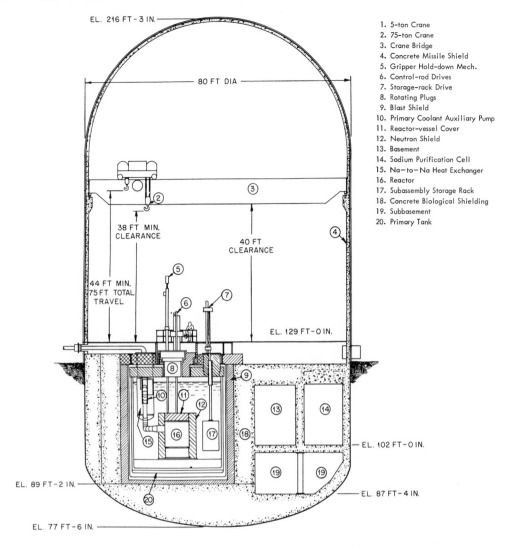

EL. 216 FT - 3 IN.

80 FT DIA

38 FT MIN.
CLEARANCE

40 FT
CLEARANCE

44 FT MIN.
75 FT TOTAL
TRAVEL

EL. 129 FT - 0 IN.

EL. 102 FT - 0 IN.

EL. 89 FT - 2 IN.

EL. 87 FT - 4 IN.

EL. 77 FT - 6 IN.

1. 5-ton Crane
2. 75-ton Crane
3. Crane Bridge
4. Concrete Missile Shield
5. Gripper Hold-down Mech.
6. Control-rod Drives
7. Storage-rack Drive
8. Rotating Plugs
9. Blast Shield
10. Primary Coolant Auxiliary Pump
11. Reactor-vessel Cover
12. Neutron Shield
13. Basement
14. Sodium Purification Cell
15. Na-to-Na Heat Exchanger
16. Reactor
17. Subassembly Storage Rack
18. Concrete Biological Shielding
19. Subbasement
20. Primary Tank

FIG. 11.50—Vertical cross section of EBR-II reactor building [46].

extraction by zinc. A dilute magnesium—zinc alloy then reduces the uranium oxides and other fission-product oxides. A uranium—zinc intermetallic compound is precipitated from this metallic solution by cooling; the desired uranium is then recovered in several additional processing steps. Although the melt-refining separation itself is quite simple, the need for the skull-recovery process may result in a complicated overall operation.

A separate process, which utilizes liquid metals as solvents, is planned for the recovery of plutonium from the uranium blanket material. The blanket material is first dissolved in 12 wt.% magnesium—zinc solution to a uranium concentration of 14%. Additional magnesium precipitates uranium but not plutonium. The plutonium is therefore recovered after phase separation and distillation of the magnesium—zinc.

In the fuel-pin fabrication sequence, the purified ingot is remelted, and pins are cast by pressurizing the melt directly into Vicor tube molds. The tubes are broken away, leaving the pins formed to the

finished diameter. The pins are sheared to length, inspected, and inserted into preassembled tubes. Several finishing steps complete the fabrication operation for the fuel elements and subassemblies shown in Figs. 11.43 to 11.45. A view of the fuel-cycle facility is shown in Fig. 11.51.

11.6.8 CONSTRUCTION AND PREOPERA-
TIONAL EXPERIENCE

In 1962 construction of the EBR-II complex was essentially completed with the exception of the fuel-cycle facility, which was completed in 1963. In both facilities, however, some work was found to be inadequate and required correction. Particularly troublesome was the secondary sodium piping system, which was found to be contaminated. Dry critical experiments were carried out in the late fall of 1961, including the check-out of necessary reactor instrumentation.

After dry criticality in December, operations were started to ready the reactor for wet criticality.

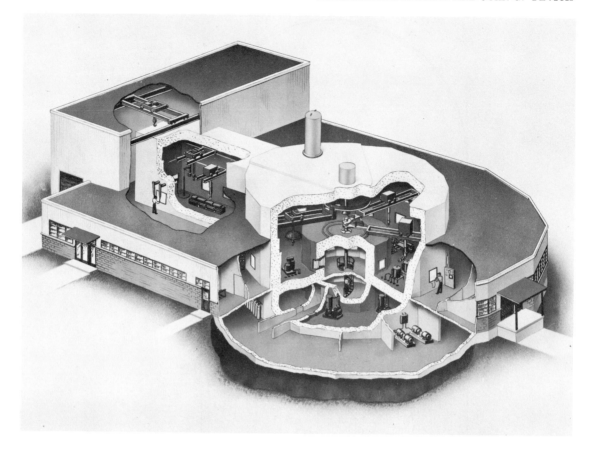

FIG. 11.51—EBR-II fuel pyroprocessing facility [5].

The subassembly gripper and transfer arm were hung up in the early spring of 1962 during test and required extensive repairs to the transfer-arm drive shaft and transfer arm. Dry heat tests were conducted in March and April of 1962 at 350°F in the primary tank to assure that the primary tank cover would operate successfully at design differential temperatures. The rotating-plug dip seals were filled in April 1962. In July of 1962 the seals were sticking; both rotating plugs had to be removed. Extensive modifications were made; they were completed in October 1962. These modifications included installation of new cooling dampers, the reworking of some dampers, replacement of the lower dip-seal rings, and a change in the method of operation of the dip seal to provide for freezing of only part of the dip seal during normal operation. In February 1963, 2100 lb of Cerrotru alloy, 58% bismuth and 42% tin, was placed in the large rotating-plug dip seal and 1300 lb of the alloy was placed in a small rotating-plug dip seal.

Nitrogen purging of the primary tank in February 1963, with 90,000 cu ft of nitrogen, reduced the oxygen concentration to 0.56%. The primary tank was filled with 88,000 gal of sodium at 275°F. The primary tank sodium was raised to 650°F in March 1963. Difficulty was experienced with all three reactor-vessel-cover locking mechanisms. The upper tie-rod shaft bearings were galled; the bearing material was changed from Stellite to aluminum bronze. In April 1963, No. 1 pump became difficult to rotate and had to be removed. Pump-removal equipment utilized a transition section between the ellipsoidal nozzle of the primary tank and a cylindrical shell. The shell was 7 ft in diameter and 30 ft high, with a movable internal-piston type seal attached to the crane. The pump was removed to a storage tank in the reactor building, where it was cleaned and disassembled. Inspection showed that the labyrinth was cocked with respect to the shaft center line owing to the tilt of the bottom flange of the shield plug (Fig. 4.52, Chap. 4). The pump bowed presumably owing to the high temperature caused by its rubbing on the aluminum—bronze labyrinth bushing. The shield-plug bottom flange was remachined, and a new shaft and labyrinth bushing were installed.

11.7 Enrico Fermi Atomic Power Plant

11.7.1 INTRODUCTION

The Enrico Fermi Atomic Power Plant [3, 66–70] located on the Michigan shore of the western end of Lake Erie near Monroe, Mich., is the first full-scale industrial fast reactor power plant in the United States. The design and development work was carried out under the auspices of a group of electrical utility companies and industrial firms, incorporated as the Atomic Power Development Associates (APDA). A separate corporation, consisting of a slightly different group of electrical power companies and industrial firms, known as the Power Reactor Development Company (PRDC), provided funds for the actual construction of the reactor plant and the sodium heat-transport systems. The Detroit Edison Company owns and operates the electricity- and steam-generating facilities of the plant.

Some features of the Fermi reactor are similar to those of EBR-II. However, EBR-II is of lower capacity [20 Mw(e)] while the Fermi reactor, al-though developmental, is designed for an ultimate capacity of 156 Mw(e), comparable to an average size conventionally fueled unit.

In the case of the Fermi reactor, fuel will be reprocessed off-site, in contrast with the EBR-II integrated fuel concept. Considerable flexibility exists in the development of future fuel systems.

11.7.2 REACTOR FEATURES

The arrangement of components within the primary reactor tank is illustrated in Fig. 11.52.

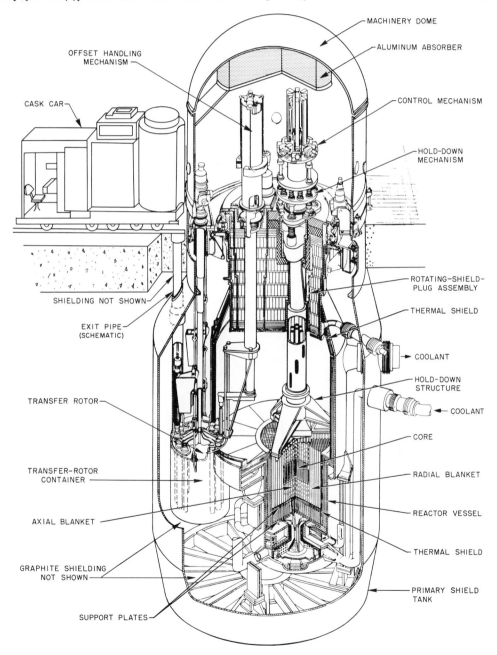

FIG. 11.52—Perspective view of Fermi reactor [66].

The reactor core and blanket, as well as the fuel-transfer system, are contained within an irregularly shaped lower section of the reactor vessel. Attention is drawn to the "open" region between the reactor vessel and the primary tank (Fig. 11.52), which is filled with graphite shielding. The upper section of the reactor vessel contains a large sodium pool above the core and blanket. Access to the core is accomplished by a rotating top shield plug arrangement.

The location of other plant equipment is shown in Fig. 11.53. Several connected buildings adjacent to the reactor building contain steam generators, the turbogenerator, and control equipment. A plot plan for the reactor plant is shown in Fig. 11.54. Lake Erie provides a convenient source of condenser cooling water.

A summary of design specifications is given in Table 11.8. Performance data are generally based on an initial power level of 200 Mw(t) planned for the first core. The heat-removal system has a design capability of 430 Mw(t) for subsequent core designs. Somewhat greater detail is included here since more information was available than was available for other reactors.

11.7.3 CORE ARRANGEMENT

The lower reactor vessel, core, and blanket, shown in Fig. 11.55 and Fig. 4.34 of Chap. 4 are located asymmetrically in the primary tank for fuel-handling purposes and to permit decay-heat removal during shutdown by natural circulation. The coolant flow is upward in this natural-circulation system; the large supply of sodium in the primary system (300,000 lb) provides the heat capacity needed to reduce transients.

A cylindrical section in the lower reactor vessel, 80 in. in diameter and 70 in. high, contains the core and blanket square subassemblies. The central core region, which is surrounded by the breeder blanket, is in the form of a 31-in.-diameter cylinder, 31 in. high. Figure 11.55 shows a reactor cross-section plan view that illustrates the core and blanket subassembly arrangement. For 200-Mw(t) power level operation, 105 central lattice positions contain fuel subassemblies. Within this region 10 positions are provided for control rods. Each of the core subassemblies (Fig. 11.56) contains an upper and lower axial blanket section in addition to the central fuel-bearing core region.

An inner-radial-blanket region, with provision for 34 subassemblies, is provided outside the core.

LEGEND

1. Steam-generator House
2. Gastight Building
3. Transfer-cask car
4. Primary Sodium Overflow Tank
5. Reactor
6. Primary Sodium Pump
7. Intermediate Heat Exchanger
8. Secondary Sodium Pump
9. Steam Generator
10. Secondary Sodium Dump Tank
11. Control Room
12. Turbine Generator

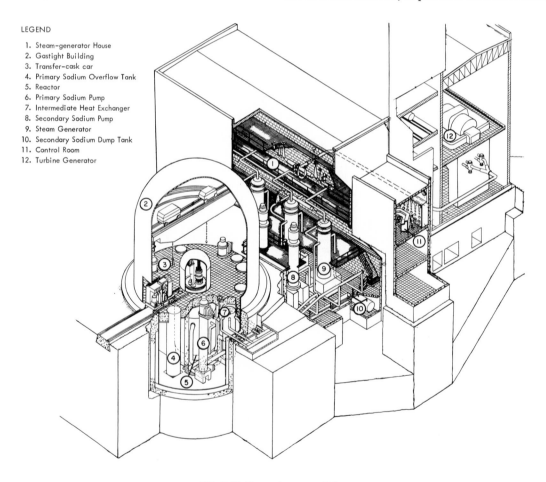

FIG. 11.53—Fermi plant layout [66].

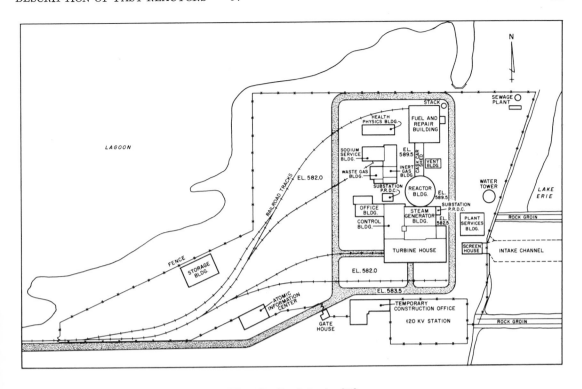

FIG. 11.54—Fermi plot plan [66].

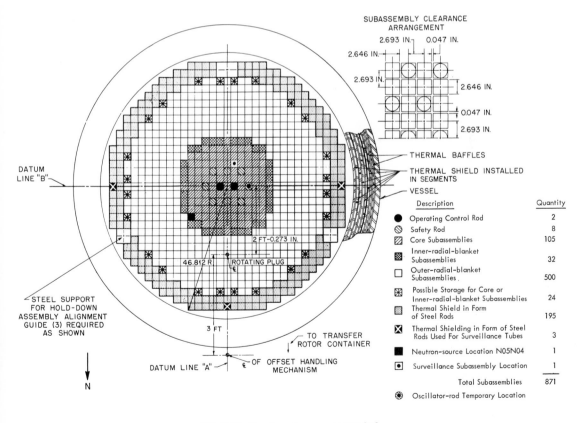

FIG. 11.55—Fermi reactor cross section [66].

Table 11.8—Fermi Design Data

Plant Performance

Reactor thermal power, Mw(t)	200
Gross electric power, Mw(t)	65.9
Net electric power, Mw(t)	60.9
Net thermal efficiency, %	30.5

Design Characteristics of Core and Blanket Regions

	Core region	Axial-blanket region	Radial-blanket region
Number of subassemblies or sections	105	105*	531
Elements per subassembly or section	140	16	25
Element shape	Round pin	Round rod	Round rod
Active volume, cu ft	13.4	7.5*	156
Dimensions:			
Uranium alloy outside diameter, in.	0.148	0.395	0.395
Uranium alloy length, in.	30.5	14.0*	61.75
Cladding inside diameter, in.	0.148	0.423	0.423
Cladding outside diameter, in.	0.158	0.443	0.443
Cladding thickness, in.	0.005	0.010	0.010
Inside diameter of region, in.			32.7
Outside diameter of region, in.	32.7	32.7	79.9
Length of region, in.	32.78	17*	65.0
Composition:			
U alloy	U-10 wt.% Mo	U-3 wt.% Mo	U-3 wt.% Mo
U^{235} enrichment, wt.%	25.6	0.35	0.35
U^{235}, vol.%	7.03	0.09	0.14
U^{238}, vol.%	20.27	25.51	39.86
Zr, vol.%	4.6		
Mo and SS, vol.%	22.9	17.9	20.9
Na, vol.%	45.2	56.5	39.1

Design Performance of Core and Blanket Regions

	Core region	Axial-blanket region	Radial-blanket region
Power, Mw(t)	174	1.2*	23.6
Power density, Mw(t)/cu ft	13	0.16	0.151
Specific power, Mw(t)/kg U^{235}	0.35		
Maximum heat flux, 10^3 Btu/hr/sq ft	640	72.2	217
Maximum to average heat flux	1.69	4.1	21.7
Sodium flow, 10^6 lb/hr	7.10†	7.10	1.47‡
Sodium velocity, ft/sec	15.7	14.1	
Maximum nominal coolant temperature, °F	1014	959	899
Maximum nominal outer clad temperature, °F	1051	960	900
Maximum nominal uranium temperature, °F	1115	991	950
Maximum local removal burnup, at.%	0.4	0.25	0.25

General Nuclear Characteristics (static)

U^{235} enrichment in fuel, wt.%	25.6
Critical mass (105 subassemblies), kg of U^{235}	496
Core conversion ratio	0.29
Blanket conversion ratio	0.87
Total conversion ratio	1.16
Radial/axial blanket Pu production	8.9
Median energy of core flux, Mev	0.32
Mean fission energy, Mev	0.25
Average core flux, neutrons/cm²/sec	3×10^{15}
Maximum to average core power density	1.69
Radial maximum to radial average power ratio	1.38
Axial maximum to axial average power ratio	1.23
Blanket fissions/total fissions	0.076
Average neutron generation time, sec	0.084

Reactor Kinetics

Effective delayed-neutron fraction	0.0066
Prompt neutron lifetime, sec	1.4×10^{-7}

Delayed-neutron groups:

Group	1	2	3	4	5	6
Effective fraction × 10^2	0.021	0.127	0.123	0.261	0.104	0.026
Decay constant, sec⁻¹	0.0127	0.032	0.120	0.323	1.40	3.94

Isothermal temperature reactivity coefficients, $\Delta k/k/°C \times 10^6$:

	Core region	Axial-blanket region	Radial-blanket region
Sodium expansion	−4.4	−5.2	−1.7
Uranium-alloy expansion	−6.2	−0.1	−0.2
Hold-down plate expansion	0.0	−0.4	−0.3
Doppler (at 550°F)	−2.6		
Subassembly-can radial expansion	−11.3		
Lower-support expansion	−1.5		−0.7

* Each axial blanket section (upper or lower).
† Does not include 0.15×10^6 lb/hr flow through control rods, neutron source, and surveillance channels.
‡ Does not include 0.14×10^6 lb/hr flow through vessel shielding.

Table 11.8—Fermi Design Data (continued)

	Core region	Axial-blanket region	Radial-blanket region
Power coefficients, 10^{-2} ¢/Mw(t):			
Sodium expansion	−2.1	−2.7	−0.9
Uranium alloy expansion	−6.8	−0.1	−0.2
Hold-down plate expansion	0.0	−0.2	−0.1
Bowing	+0.2		
Doppler [at 200 Mw(t)]	−1.9		
Subassembly-can radial expansion	−9.4		−0.3

Reactor Control

Reactivity requirements:

Temperature override to 200 Mw(t), ¢	60.0
Total reactivity loss, weekly unloading, ¢	15.4
Control margin, ¢	16.6
Total reactivity in operating control, ¢	92.0
Net reactivity loss, ¢/day of operation	2.2

Operating control rods:

Number of rods	2
B^{10} contained per rod, lb	0.19
Weight per rod, lb	16
Poison-section length, in.	10
Operating stroke of each rod, in.	15.8
Reactivity in each operating control rod, ¢	46
Maximum reactivity per rod-inch, ¢/in.	4
Maximum to average reactivity per rod	1.37
Regulating-rod design speed range, in./min	1 to 10
Regulating-rod runaway (synchronous) speed, in./min	15
Regulating-rod maximum reactivity insertion rate, at runaway speed, ¢/sec	1
Regulating-rod drive type	Velocity servo
Shim-rod speed, in./min	0.4
Shim-rod average reactivity insertion rate, ¢/min	1.17

Safety rods:

B^{10} contained per rod, lb	1.18
Weight per rod, lb	23.5
Poison-section length, in.	36
Total operating stroke, in.	54
Active reactivity stroke, in.	38
Retraction speed, in./min	1.6
Follow-down speed, ft/min	10
Total reactivity in 8-rod bank, $	9.20
Minimum reactivity in individual rods, $	1
Maximum negative reactivity withdrawal rate, ¢/sec	1
Reactivity withdrawal rate at $1 subcritical, ¢/sec	0.6
Delay of reactivity insertion after scram signal, sec	0.25
Total scram duration after scram signal, sec	0.8
Average rate of reactivity insertion on scram, $/sec	16.7

Sodium-system and Steam-system Performance

Sodium-system operating characteristics:

Temperature of sodium leaving reactor, °F	800
Temperature of sodium entering reactor, °F	550
Temperature of sodium entering steam generator, °F	767
Temperature of sodium leaving steam generator, °F	517
Primary or secondary sodium 200 Mw(t) reference flow, lb/hr	8.86×10^{6}

Steam parameters:

Feedwater temperature, °F	340
Steam temperature at steam-generator outlet, °F	764
Steam pressure at steam-generator outlet, psia	600
Steam temperature at turbine, °F	760
Steam pressure at turbine, psia	576
Steam flow, lb/hr	6.4×10^{5}

Sodium-system pressure drops [at 200 Mw(t) reference flow]:

Primary sodium pump-head limit, ft	260
Total primary sodium-system pressure drop, ft	126
Core and axial-blanket pressure drop, ft	106
Secondary sodium pump-head limit, ft	100
Total secondary sodium-system pressure drop, ft	36

Reactor and Containment Vessels

Reactor vessel:

Height, ft	36.3
Maximum diameter, ft	14.5
Maximum wall thickness, in.	2
High-pressure-plenum design pressure, psig	110
High-pressure-plenum design temperature, °F	750
Radial-blanket-plenum design pressure, psig	50
Radial-blanket-plenum design temperature, °F	1000

Table 11.8—Fermi Design Data (continued)

Reactor vessel (continued):
  Upper-reactor-vessel design pressure, psig 50
  Upper-reactor-vessel design temperature, °F 1000

Primary shield tank:
  Overall height to top of dome, ft 62
  Height of primary shield tank, ft 40.2
  Maximum diameter, ft 24
  Wall thickness, in. 0.625
  Design pressure, psig 7.38
  Design temperature, °F 250

Reactor building:
  Overall height, ft 120
  Inside diameter, ft 72
  Average thickness, in. 1.03
  Design pressure, psig 32
  Design temperature, °F 650

Primary-coolant-system Performance Data (200 Mw Operation)
  Coolant Data:
    Primary coolant .... Sodium
    Flow rate per loop, 10^6 lb/hr 2.95
    Flow rate per loop at pump temperature, gal/min 6700
    Total flow rate, 10^6 lb/hr 8.86
    Total flow rate at pump temperature, gal/min 20,000
    Heat-exchanger inlet temperature, °F 800
    Heat-exchanger outlet temperature, °F 550
    Total sodium volume, cu ft 5450
    Total sodium weight, lb 345,200

  Piping layout:
    Piping material .... SS 304
    Design pressure, psig 125
    Design temperature, °F 1000
    Pipe size and velocity
      Reactor to pump .... 30 in., $\frac{3}{8}$ in. wall, 3.3 ft/sec
      Pump discharge .... 16 in., $\frac{3}{8}$ in. wall, 11.7 ft/sec
      90% flow to core .... 14 in., $\frac{3}{8}$ in. wall, 14.0 ft/sec
      10% flow to blanket .... 6 in., Sch. 40, 7.3 ft/sec
    Pipe cold-spring, % 100

  Intermediate heat exchangers:
    Number of units 3
    Tube-side pressure loss, ft of Na 3.9
    Shell-side pressure loss, ft of Na 0.9
    Heat-transfer surface, sq ft 6320
    Overall heat-transfer coefficient, Btu/sq ft/hr/°F 1090
    Heat transferred per unit, 10^6 Btu/hr 227.5

  Pumping equipment:
    Number of pumps 3
    Design data (each pump):
      Capacity, gal/min 11,800
      Temperature, °F 1000
      Total dynamic head, ft 310
      Efficiency, % 77
      Brake horsepower, hp 1060

Primary-sodium-system Pressure Drops

	% of total sodium flow in section	Calculated pressure drops, ft
Pump-head limit		260.0
Check valve and 16-in. piping to tee	100	6.4
30-in. piping	100	0.6
IHX (including nozzles)	100	0.9
		7.9
14-in. piping	87	4.0
High-pressure reactor plenum	87	5.6
Core and axial blanket	80.2	106.1
Hold-down mechanism	87	2.4
		118.1
6-in. piping and throttle valve, adjusted lift	13	109.6
Low-pressure reactor plenum and radial blanket	13	8.5
		118.1
Total system pressure drop for design flow condition of 8.86×10^6 lb/hr		126.0

Intermediate-heat-exchanger Design Data (430-Mw* Operation)

Heat transferred per unit, 10^6 Btu/hr 489
Heat-transfer surface, sq ft 4840
Overall heat-transfer coefficient, Btu/hr/sq ft/°F 1048

*Designed for use to 430 Mw(t) although initial use will be at 200 Mw(t).

Table 11.8—Fermi Design Data (continued)

Shellside fluid:	Na
Flow rate, shell side, 10^6 lb/hr	5.3
Temperature in, °F	900
Temperature out, °F	600
Pressure loss, ft of Na	2.9
Fluid in tubes:	Na
Flow, 10^6 lb/hr	5.3
Temperature in, °F	520
Temperature out, °F	820
Pressure loss, ft of Na	12.8
Material, tubes and shell	SS 304
Number of tubes	1860
Tube size:	
Outside diameter, in.	7/8
Wall thickness, in.	0.049

Secondary-coolant-system Design and Performance Data (200-Mw Operation)

Secondary sodium coolant	
Flow rate per loop, 10^6 lb/hr	2.95
Flow rate per loop at pump temperature, gal/min	6,700
Total flow rate, 10^6 lb/hr	8.85
Total flow rate at pump temperature, gal/min	20,000
Heat-exchanger inlet temperature, °F	517
Heat-exchanger outlet temperature, °F	767
Heat-exchanger inlet pressure, psig	13
Heat-exchanger outlet pressure, psig	11
Steam-generator inlet pressure, psig	5
Pump inlet pressure, psig	4
Total sodium volume, cu ft	4000
Total sodium weight, lb	225,000
Approximate sodium cycle time at full flow, sec	85
Piping system:	
Pipe size	12 and 18 in., wall thickness $\frac{3}{8}$ in.
Average fluid velocity in pipe, ft/sec	9
Pipe material	$2\frac{1}{4}$ wt.% Cr–1 wt.% Mo
Design pressure, psig	175
Design temperature, °F	900
Pressure drop, total, psi	14
Pumping equipment:	
Number of pumps	3
Type	Double-volute centrifugal vertical with oil-lubricated mechanical seal
Pump design:	
Capacity (each), gal/min	13,000
Temperature (max.), °F	1000
Total dynamic head, ft	100
Efficiency, %	82
Pumping power, kw	115

Steam-generator Design and Performance Data (200-Mw Operation)

Steam-generator equipment:	
Number of units	3
Type	Once-through cross and counterflow
Material	
Tubes and headers	$2\frac{1}{4}$ wt.% Cr–1 wt.% Mo
Shell	$2\frac{1}{4}$ wt.% Cr–1 wt.% Mo
Fluid in tubes	Water and steam
Pressure loss, psi	5
Shell-side fluid	Sodium
Pressure loss, psi	2
Operating data (each unit):	
Steam-generating capacity, lb/hr	211,560
Steam conditions:	
Pressure, psia	600
Temperature, °F	764
Feedwater temperature entering, °F	340
Secondary sodium data (shell side):	
Flow, 10^6 lb/hr	2.95
Temperature	
Entering, °F	767
Leaving, °F	517
Heat transferred	
Feed-heating section, 10^6 Btu/hr	33.7
Evaporating section:	
First section, 0-50% quality, 10^6 Btu/hr	77.4
Second section, 50-75% quality, 10^6 Btu/hr	38.7
Third section, 75-100% quality, 10^6 Btu/hr	38.7
Superheating section, 10^6 Btu/hr	39.0
Total heat transfer, 10^6 Btu/hr	227.5

Table 11.8—Fermi Design Data (continued)

Heat-transfer area (based on tube OD):	
Feedwater section, sq ft	965
Evaporating section:	
First section, 0-50% quality, sq ft	1250
Second section, 50-75% quality, sq ft	360
Third section, 75-100% quality, sq ft	555
Superheating section, sq ft	7,670
Total area, sq ft	10,800
Overall heat-transfer coefficient:	
Feed heating section, Btu/hr/sq ft/$^\circ$F	310
Evaporating section:	
First section, 0-50% quality, Btu/hr/sq ft/$^\circ$F	605
Second section, 50-75% quality, Btu/hr/sq ft/$^\circ$F	630
Third section, 75-100% quality, Btu/hr/sq ft/$^\circ$F	330
Superheating section, Btu/hr/sq ft/$^\circ$F	96
Logarithmic mean temperature difference:	
Feed-heating section, $^\circ$F	113
Evaporating section	
First section, 0-50% quality, $^\circ$F	103
Second section, 50-75% quality, $^\circ$F	171
Third section, 75-100% quality, $^\circ$F	214
Superheating section, $^\circ$F	53

These positions, identical in design to those in the core, may be used for additional fuel subassemblies if needed. The orifice design in each type subassembly, however, controls the amount of coolant received.

The fuel region of each core subassembly consists of 140 round pins, each having a nominal length of 32 25/32 in. and an outer diameter of 0.158 in., consisting of uranium—10 wt. % molybdenum alloy with a uranium enrichment of 25% U^{235}. Each pin is clad with 0.005 in. of reactor-grade zirconium metallurgically bonded to the fuel alloy. Zirconium end caps serve as closures at the top and bottom. The lower end of each pin is fastened to the support structure by anchor bars inserted through slots in the bottom end caps. The upper ends are free to accommodate changes in length resulting from temperature changes and radiation effects. As shown in Figs. 11.56 and 11.57, the core subassembly is enclosed in an outer stainless-steel tube of square cross section, measuring 2.646 in. on a side and having a nominal wall thickness of 0.096 in. The square subassembly shape permits a plate type fuel to be used in a subsequent core, if found desirable. At the top of the outer tube is a combination handling head and hold-down contact. A lower support section, the nozzle, consisting of two concentric round tubes, is attached at the bottom. The spring (Fig. 11.56) permits thermal expansion of the subassembly structure. A strainer is also provided at the inlet of each core subassembly. The core section of the subassembly is shown in Fig. 11.58. The upper and lower axial-blanket regions of the core subassemblies contain sixteen 0.395-in.-diameter rods of uranium—3 wt. % molybdenum alloy, with the uranium depleted to 0.35% U^{235}. A 0.010-in.-thick stainless-steel cladding is used for these rods. Both the inner and outer blanket subassemblies utilize a lattice of 25 rods, each having the same diametral dimensions as the axial-blanket rods. In the case of the inner blanket subassemblies, the support structure includes a thermal-expansion spring arrangement identical to that used in the core units; details are shown in Fig. 11.59. Outer radial-blanket subassemblies

may fill the remaining 500 positions shown in Fig. 11.55. These have a simple support structure as indicated in Fig. 11.59.

11.7.4 CONTROL ELEMENTS

In this reactor poison control is used rather than fuel or reflector control. Chapter 9 has details on the control rods. Available excess reactivity is intentionally kept rather small. Furthermore, the fuel-management scheme minimizes the reactivity changes caused by fuel burnup. The eight safety rods and two operating control rods utilize B^{10} in boron carbide as the absorber. One of the operating control rods, used for regulating purposes, has a maximum reactivity insertion rate of 2/3 cent/sec; the other, used for shim control, is designed for a 1 cent/min insertion. The eight safety rods, spaced uniformly as shown in Fig. 11.55, provide a shutdown reactivity of over 8 dollars, and the two operating control rods have a total worth of 92 cents.

Each of the control elements is housed in a cylindrical guide tube, which, in turn, is mounted inside a square tube having the same outside dimensions as a core subassembly (Fig. 9.21 of Chap. 9). Heat generated by a control rod is removed by sodium flowing from the core inlet plenum through pressure breakdown orifices inserted in the section between the two support plates. Flow is directed upward through the control-rod assembly and then through the annulus formed by the control-rod assembly and the inner round guide tube.

During reactor operation the safety rods are held just above the upper axial blanket by a latch on each safety-rod drive unit. Reactivity adjustments for start-up, power-level changes, and burnup compensation are made by means of the two operating control rods. These two rods are raised and lowered at different rates, as mentioned above.

11.7.5 HEAT-TRANSPORT SYSTEM

In the primary coolant system, shown in schematic form in Figs. 11.60 and 4.16 of Chap. 4, three

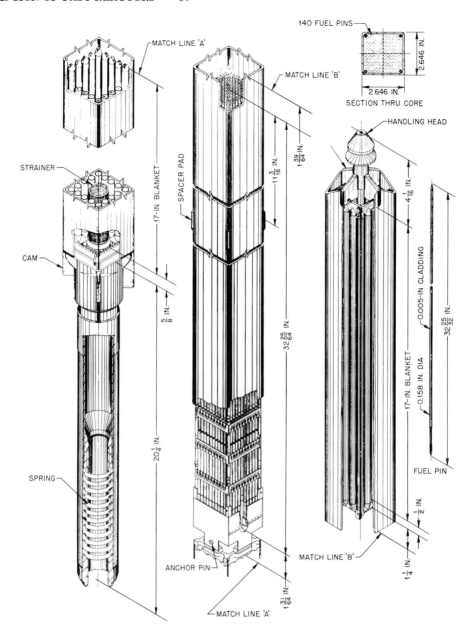

FIG. 11.56—Isometric view of Fermi fuel subassembly [66].

coolant loops are utilized. Each contains a pump and intermediate heat exchanger. The pump, a vertical-shaft single-stage centrifugal type, rated at 11,800 gal/min and driven by a 1000-hp motor, circulates sodium to the core through a 14-in.-diameter pipe. About 13% of the total flow is pumped through a 6-in. pipe to the radial blanket, shown in Fig. 11.60 and Fig. 4.34 of Chap. 4. Core coolant flows upward from the lower inlet plenum of the core, through the reactor core itself, and then to the upper reactor vessel, which serves as an exit plenum, as shown in Fig. 4.32 of Chap. 4. The hot sodium then flows by gravity from this "pool" to the shell side of the intermediate heat exchanger through a 30-in.

line. The intermediate heat exchangers are counter-flow shell-and-tube units, constructed of type 304 stainless steel. The primary sodium stream, now at lower temperature, returns to the primary pump. Additional details on the primary cooling system are given in Chap. 4. A summary of design conditions for several reactor power levels is given in Table 11.9. A system of secondary containment for the primary system consists of a welded, leaktight enclosure for the reactor vessel, the primary system, the pump tanks, and the inter-mediate heat-exchanger shells. This structure, which protects against loss of sodium, is described in Chap. 4.

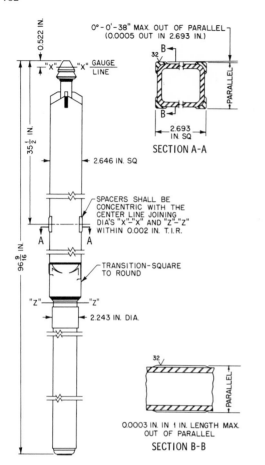

FIG. 11.57—Fermi fuel subassembly (external side view) [66].

Three secondary coolant loops are provided, each corresponding to a primary loop. Heat is transferred from the intermediate heat exchanger to the shell side of a steam generator by sodium circulated by a 13,000 gal/min pump driven by a 350-hp motor. The steam generators are vertical shell-and-tube exchangers of a single-wall tube construction, arranged for a combination of cross and counter flow. A number of design features provide protection against any leaks within the units. The tube-to-tube sheet joints, for example, are located in an inert-gas space above the sodium to reduce thermal shocks.

11.7.6 SHIELDING, STRUCTURES, AND COMPONENTS

The reactor vessel and internal components are shown in Figs. 11.52 and 4.34 of Chap. 4. Core

Table 11.9—Heat-removal System Design Conditions, Fermi

Power, Mw(t)	Primary sodium temperature, °F		Secondary sodium temperature, °F		Steam at turbine	
	Inlet	Outlet	Inlet	Outlet	Pressure, psia	Temp., °F
200	550	800	517	767	576	760
300	550	800	500	750	590	742
430	600	900	520	820	865	780

and blanket subassemblies are contained within the lower reactor vessel; the upper reactor-vessel section, at approximately atmospheric pressure, serves as a mixing pool for the hot sodium. The upper section contains a core hold-down device and offset fuel-handling mechanism. The hold-down device maintains radial alignment of the upper ends of the core assembly and prevents subassembly movement induced by the uplift force of the sodium flow.

Spent fuel and blanket subassemblies are removed from the reactor vessel and deposited in a transfer-rotor container by the offset handling mechanism. Each subassembly in a finned transfer pot can be transported by the transfer rotor container to the exit port; then the subassemblies are raised vertically into a cask car by the cask-car gripper. Spent fuel is unloaded from the cask car in the fuel and repair building, where the fuel is placed in decay storage prior to shipping operations. Both the hold-down device and offset handling mechanism are mounted eccentrically on the rotating plug so that the hold-down device will be swung away when the handling mechanism is swung over the core.

The lower reactor vessel includes provision for safe containment of molten fuel in case of core meltdown. This section, located in the inlet plenum, is arranged so the thickness of the molten material in the region will be about 1 1/4 in. A conical flow guide is installed to prevent a buildup of fuel in the center of the meltdown section by dispersing the molten fuel as it enters the plenum.

A detailed description of the shield system is given in Chap. 8. The reactor vessel is surrounded by a graphite neutron shield located in a nitrogen atmosphere inside the primary shield tank, as indicated in Fig. 4.34 of Chap. 4. The shield system also includes a 12-in.-thick laminated steel thermal shield inside the reactor-vessel wall. A secondary shield, consisting of a 30-in. thickness of concrete, surrounds the primary shield tank and prevents neutron activation of the secondary sodium system. A 5-ft-thick biological shield outside the containment vessel completes the radial shielding system.

The containment vessel (Fig. 11.61) is a vertical cylinder with hemispherical top head and semi-ellipsoidal bottom head. It houses the reactor and the primary system. The inside diameter is 72 ft, and the overall height is 120 ft, of which 51 ft is below grade. Design specifications, based on the containment of the sodium—air reaction, provide for the possibility of an internal pressure of 32 psig.

11.7.7 OPERATING EXPERIENCE

Starting in July 1959 and terminating on May 31, 1961, a series of nonnuclear tests was performed at Fermi on components in the reactor portion of the plant. The so-called test facility included the reactor vessel, primary shield tank, rotating-shield plug, fuel-handling mechanisms, safety-rod drives, and one primary-system sodium loop. These components, together with sodium purification, were used in conducting a full scale mechanical and hydraulic test of the reactor. The tests were isothermal up to temperatures of 1000°F. The overall

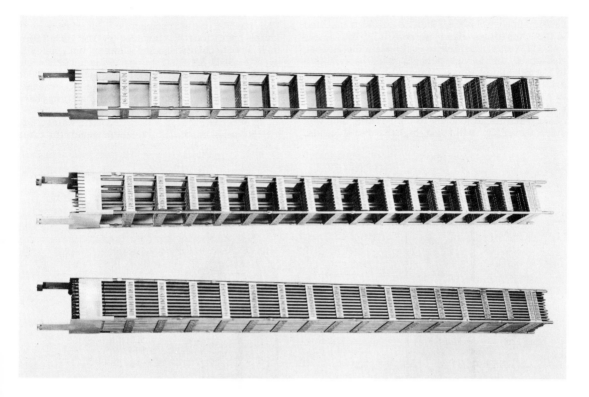

FIG. 11.58—Fermi fuel subassembly core section [66].

results of the nonnuclear tests were satisfactory although modifications were necessary, as shown in Fig. 11.62. Experience with the use of sodium was excellent. The operation of equipment in sodium and other environments presented no major difficulties and indicated the high purity of large amounts of sodium (up to 400,000 lb) in the system can be maintained without difficulty. The test indicated that the construction materials used in the system are compatible with sodium. Figure 11.62 shows the schedule of larger construction modifications and test operations and succinctly describes the test operations.

Starting July 1, 1961, the Fermi plant was incorporated around the test facility and pre-operational tests began preparatory to nuclear testing. Testing to 1000°F for a period of approximately one week checked out the operation of safety rods, fuel-handling mechanisms, and sodium pumps. The systems, in general, performed satisfactorily. Following the 1000°F test, tests of graphite directly around the reactor vessel (inside the insulation) indicated that the material failed to withstand the high-temperature test. Tests indicated that the borated graphite did not conform to design specifications and would have to be replaced. Tests on the remainder of the material outside the insulation in the primary shield tank indicated that this graphitic material also needed replacement. It was apparent that moisture and oxygen control is a must in the use of high-temperature graphite. All the graphite in the primary shield tank was replaced with high-density high-temperature reactor-grade graphite. Any

boron used was in the form of boron carbide. The reinstallation of the graphite shield was a primary factor in delaying completion of the reactor.

During the test of the offset fuel-handling mechanism (OHM), it became jammed due to malfunction and maloperation. The OHM was bent when an inadvertent attempt was made to move it laterally before it was fully delatched from a partially raised dummy subassembly. An interlock had been disconnected for the purpose of carrying out the test. The OHM was removed with a light-weight removal container in such a manner as not to violate the inert-gas integrity of the reactor. After disassembly it was found that the gripper and the stabilizer foot were not in the proper positions. After removal of the OHM and reduction of the sodium level, observation of the core and blanket subassemblies indicated a number of displaced subassemblies. Investigation showed that the subassembly heads had stuck to the hold-down plate fingers when the hold-down was raised. When the plug was rotated with the heads engaged to the fingers, the result was bending of the fingers and of the subassemblies. Subsequent lowering of the hold-down resulted in further damage and in non-seating of some of the subassemblies in the support plate, which further resulted in flow erosion of the support-plate holes. For repairs the reactor vessel was drained of sodium, and personnel in protective suits entered the reactor. They removed the center support plate and the hold-down plate with its fingers. The hold-down finger sockets were redesigned. Other modifications were made to the control- and safety-rod guide tubes. The center support plate had Stellite bushings inserted in the holes to prevent further possibility of erosion. The OHM was modified to strengthen the gripper linkage so that enough strength would be available to permit application of impact loads to force the gripper open. The stabilizer foot was redesigned to assure that the OHM would not be locked over a partially raised subassembly. The stabilizer assembly and its attachment to the rotating tube was strengthened to withstand higher lateral loads.

The possibility of obstructions interfering with future operations was avoided by the installation of a new mechanism called a sweep arm, which is used to check for obstructions in the upper plenum above the core and blanket. Approximately 2000 man-hours were expended in the vessel by personnel using protective suits within the argon atmosphere to accomplish repairs.

In July 1961 a series of hydrostatic water tests at 850 psig on the No. 2 steam generator tubes

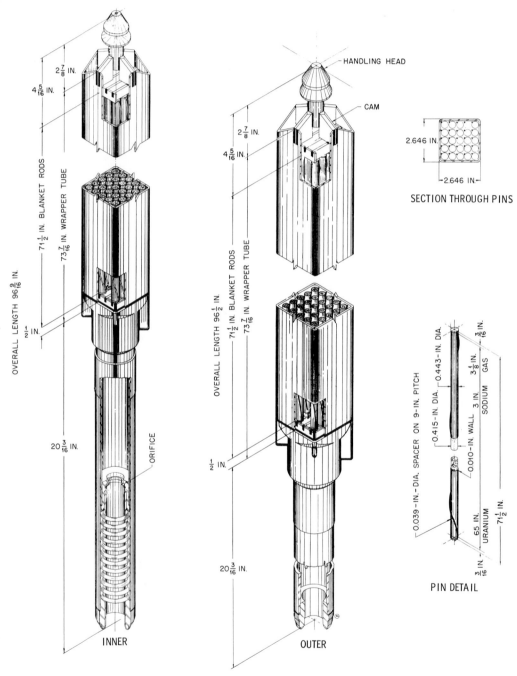

FIG. 11.59—Fermi radial-blanket subassemblies [66].

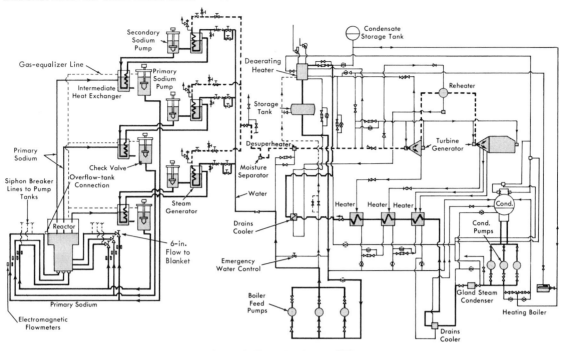

FIG. 11.60—Fermi flow diagram [67].

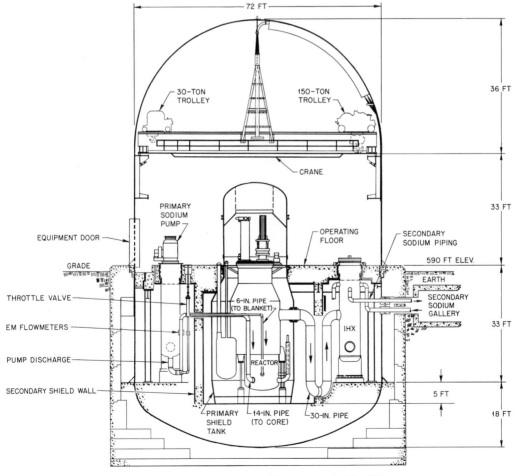

FIG. 11.61—Vertical cross section of Fermi reactor building [66].

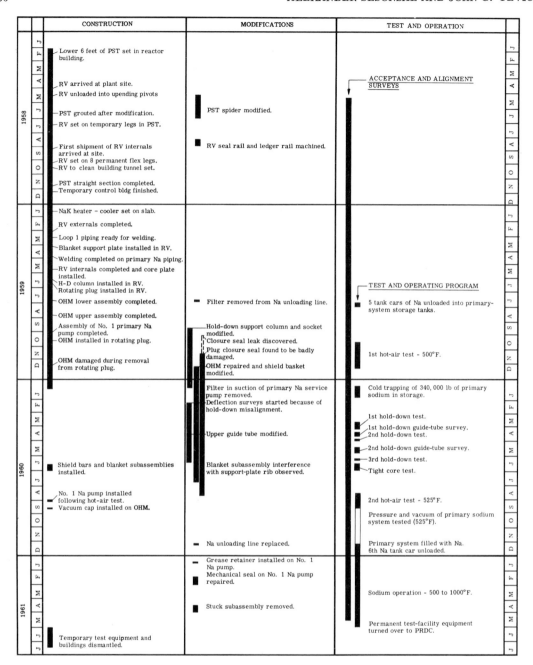

	CONSTRUCTION	MODIFICATIONS	TEST AND OPERATION	
1958	Lower 6 feet of PST set in reactor building.			J F M A M J J A S O N D
	RV arrived at plant site.		ACCEPTANCE AND ALIGNMENT SURVEYS	
	RV unloaded into upending pivots			
	PST grouted after modification.	PST spider modified.		
	RV set on temporary legs in PST.			
	First shipment of RV internals arrived at site.	RV seal rail and ledger rail machined.		
	RV set on 8 permanent flex legs.			
	RV to clean building tunnel set.			
	PST straight section completed.			
	Temporary control bldg finished.			
1959	NaK heater – cooler set on slab.		TEST AND OPERATING PROGRAM	J F M A M J J A S O N D
	RV externals completed.			
	Loop 1 piping ready for welding.			
	Blanket support plate installed in RV.			
	Welding completed on primary Na piping.			
	RV internals completed and core plate installed.	Filter removed from Na unloading line.	5 tank cars of Na unloaded into primary-system storage tanks.	
	H-D column installed in RV.			
	Rotating plug installed in RV.			
	OHM lower assembly completed.			
	OHM upper assembly completed.	Hold-down support column and socket modified.		
	Assembly of No. 1 primary Na pump completed.	Closure seal leak discovered.	1st hot-air test – 500°F.	
	OHM installed in rotating plug.	Plug closure seal found to be badly damaged.		
	OHM damaged during removal from rotating plug.	OHM repaired and shield basket modified.		
1960	Shield bars and blanket subassemblies installed.	Filter in suction of primary Na service pump removed.	Cold trapping of 340,000 lb of primary sodium in storage.	J F M A M J J A S O N D
		Deflection surveys started because of hold-down misalignment.	1st hold-down test.	
			1st hold-down guide-tube survey.	
		Upper guide tube modified.	2nd hold-down test.	
			2nd hold-down guide-tube survey.	
			3rd hold-down test.	
		Blanket subassembly interference with support-plate rib observed.	Tight core test.	
	No. 1 Na pump installed following hot-air test.			
	Vacuum cap installed on OHM.		2nd hot-air test – 525°F.	
			Pressure and vacuum of primary sodium system tested (525°F).	
		Na unloading line replaced.	Primary system filled with Na.	
			6th Na tank car unloaded.	
1961		Grease retainer installed on No. 1 Na pump.		J F M A M J J
		Mechanical seal on No. 1 Na pump repaired.	Sodium operation – 500 to 1000°F.	
		Stuck subassembly removed.		
	Temporary test equipment and buildings dismantled.		Permanent test-facility equipment turned over to PRDC.	

FIG. 11.62. Schedule of major construction, modifications, and test operations for Fermi test facility [70].

indicated leaks. Subsequent checks indicated 71 tubes were cracked through the tube wall. All these were located opposite one of the two sodium inlets. The tests of the tubes indicated that residual stresses, corrosion effects, and elevated temperatures induced stress corrosion cracking. The entire tube bundle of No. 2 steam generator was retubed at the fabricator. All three units were stress relieved and inspected prior to reassembly.

In December 1962 a sodium—water reaction took place in the No. 1 steam generator blowing the rupture disk installed for just such a possibility.

The water was dumped manually by an operator to prevent further introduction of water. The No. 1 secondary loop was drained, and the tube bundle was removed and cleaned in approximately 800 gal of alcohol. The largest cleaning operation up to 1963 to remove sodium from one component was performed without incident. Examination showed extensive tube damage due to the vibration of the tubes against the support structures as well as erosion caused by the sodium—water reaction during the period between a reaction and the rupture disk blowout. Small- and full-scale models in water of the tube bundle and its baffle indicated that the vibration of the tubes at the sodium inlet had been as high as 0.250 in. Baffling and lacing of the tubes has been carried out to reduce this vibration to a negligible quantity.

A program was initiated to modify the check valves in the primary system. The 16-in. check valves induced high-pressure surges when one of the loops was shut down with either one or two of the loops operating. A program has been carried out to install new check valves, modified to include dashpots and springs to reduce the surge pressure to negligible valves.

Each of the more than 3000 cans in the rotating plug containing graphite is vented by three 1/16 in. holes to the argon cover gas above the sodium in the reactor. The primary system tests at 1000°F, and at lower temperatures, released material in the graphite binder to the primary system. This release resulted in carbon and other contamination of the primary system. Extensive programs of sodium sampling, analysis, and filtration have been carried out to determine what contaminants are present and how they affect the system. Tests of the materials in the primary system indicated some degree of carburization but not sufficient to affect operation of the reactor.

Preoperational tests prior to criticality on Aug. 23, 1963, were successfully completed; only minor modifications of the control and safety rods and control drives were required.

The approach to criticality started July 24, 1963. The fuel subassemblies were loaded as follows:

Date (1963)	No.	Cumulative	Inverse count 1/(counts/min)* arbitrary units
July 24	11	11	0.26
August 1	11	22	0.14
August 2	11	33	0.08
August 4	17	50	0.04
August 6	16	66	0.02
August 10	6	72	0.016
August 11	5	77	0.0125
August 15	6	83	0.0094
August 16	4	87	0.007
August 17	3	90	0.0064
August 17	3	93	0.0056
August 18	2	95	0.005
August 19	1	96	0.0047
August 21	1	97	0.0045
August 22	1	98	0.0043
August 23	1	99	0.0042

* Counts per minute with all safety rods down. Criticality was reached with 99 subassemblies. The estimated critical mass is 465.55 kg of U^{235} at 400°F isothermal operation.

11.8 Rapsodie Reactor

11.8.1 INTRODUCTION

In France, the Commissariat a l'Energie Atomique (CEA) has included the development of fast breeder reactors in its program to utilize plutonium fuel that will be made available from other reactors. The long-term advantages of efficient fuel utilization and a low cost potential are also recognized.

Rapsodie, with planning begun in 1958, is an experimental reactor designed for a maximum power of 20 Mw(t) [5, 6, 71, 72]. Operating parameters, however, are similar to those which would be used in a full-scale reactor. Furthermore, a relatively high flux, 10^{15} neutron/cm^2/sec, will provide the means for irradiating fuel for future reactors. The use of plutonium for the first loading of the reactor, in the form of a mixed plutonium—uranium oxide element, is an example of the advanced philosophy utilized. A power density of 700 kw/liter at the center of the core is planned.

This reactor is to be located at the Cadarache Center in southeastern France; completion is scheduled for mid-1965. Criticality may be obtained in 1966.

11.8.2 REACTOR FEATURES

Rapsodie will consist of six buildings and will occupy approximately 5 acres (Figs. 11.63 and 11.64). At the center is the cylindrical reactor containment building, which houses the reactor and the primary coolant circuit. Around this building are (1) a conventional type building housing the control room, laboratories, and offices, (2) a fuel-storage and component-repair building, which also houses decontamination facilities, (3) a secondary-system heat-exchanger building, (4) an inert-gas building, and (5) an auxiliary building for electrical supply and diesel generators. Only the conventional building and the fuel-storage and -repair building are connected to the reactor containment building by airlocks.

A summary of design data is given in Table 11.10. The reference system is based on the mixed oxide (PuO$_2$—UO$_2$) fuel.

A view of the reactor assembly is shown in Fig. 11.65. The fuel subassemblies, which contain both a fuel section and an axial blanket section, are in a central region surrounded by radial blanket subassemblies. Removable subassemblies outside this region serve as reflectors. The concentric steel cylinder assembly, as shown in Fig. 11.66, is used for both a nonremovable reflector and thermal shield.

A jacket located outside the reactor vessel serves as a means for circulating gas for preheating.

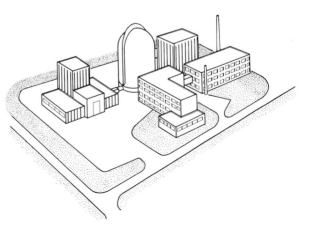

FIG. 11.63—Perspective view of Rapsodie plant [71].

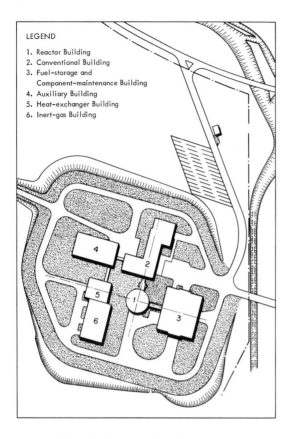

LEGEND

1. Reactor Building
2. Conventional Building
3. Fuel-storage and
   Component-maintenance Building
4. Auxiliary Building
5. Heat-exchanger Building
6. Inert-gas Building

FIG. 11.64—Plan view of Rapsodie plant [71].

Eventually this space may serve for cooling the reactor during shutdown. Steel containers filled with thermal insulation are located outside the pre-heating jacket. Additional structures consist of the containment tank and the biological shield. An outer blast shield consists of three concentric layers, borated graphite, light-weight cellular concrete, and reinforced concrete. Additional features are shown in Fig. 11.67. A single sodium inlet pipe is shown with two sodium outlet pipes located in a vertical plane perpendicular to the plane of the inlet pipe.

11.8.3 CORE ARRANGEMENT

An extensive program of fuel evaluation and development has been carried out on a UO_2—PuO_2 mixed oxide fuel and on various uranium—plutonium—molybdenum ternary alloys. Although the metal fuel is attractive because of its good heat conductivity at the high power densities, irradiation experiments have indicated excessive swelling. An additional disadvantage of the alloys is their poor compatability with stainless steel. A double-clad design would be necessary, consisting of an interior layer of niobium and an exterior layer of stainless steel with sodium bonding. The French CEA has chosen the oxide because it presents fewer fabrication problems than the alloy and because there is a greater background of irradiation and production experience with the oxide.

The fuel subassemblies are illustrated in Fig. 11.68; dimensions are given in Table 11.10. In the core region of the subassembly, 37 fuel rods are assembled in a stainless-steel container with a

Table 11.10—Rapsodie Design Data Applicable to PuO_2–UO_2

Reactor Data

Core volume, liters/cu ft	40.7/1.44
Core height, cm/in.	34/13.4
Core diameter, cm/in.	38.8/15.3
Core composition, vol.%:	
Fuel	42.85
Sodium	33.25
Stainless steel	23.00
Helium	0.90
Fuel composition (tentative):	
UO_2, vol.%	75
PuO_2, vol.%	25
Uranium enrichment, %	40
Critical mass:	
Pu, kg	39
U^{235}, kg	61
Thermal power:	
Core, Mw(t)	16.6
Axial blanket, Mw(t)	0.2
Radial blanket, Mw(t)	3.2
Total, Mw(t)	20.0
Average power density:	
Kw(t)/liter	407
Kw(t)/cu ft	11,500

Core Characteristics at $20°C$

Fuel pin:	
Length, cm/in.	34/13.39
Fuel diameter, cm/in.	0.572/0.226
OD stainless cladding, cm/in.	0.67/0.264
Cladding thickness, cm/in.	0.049/0.019
Diameter of spiral wire, cm/in.	0.125/0.049
Length of gas space, cm/in.	11.9/4.685

Table 11.10—Rapsodie Design Data Applicable to PuO$_2$–UO$_2$ (continued)

Subassembly can:
Across flats, cm/in.	4.98/1.96	
Thickness of can wall, cm/in.	0.1/0.039	
Overall subassembly length, cm/in.	166.5/65.6	

	Radial with spiral wire	Axial
Blanket rods:		
Length of blanket material, cm/in.	99.00/39	23.50/9.26
Diameter of blanket material, cm/in.	1.51/0.60	1.31/0.516
ID of rod cladding, cm/in.	1.55/0.61	1.35/0.532
OD of rod cladding, cm/in.	1.65/0.65	1.45/0.571
Diameter of spiral wire, cm/in.	0.0365/0.0144	0.08/0.032
Gas-chamber length, cm/in.	11.00/4.33	2.50/0.985
Hex. can dimensions same as for fuel		

Number of Subassemblies in Each Zone (Fig. 11.66)

Zone:
I (high pressure)	19
II (high pressure)	18
III (high pressure)	18 + 6 control rods
IV (high pressure)	30
V (low pressure)	36
VI (low pressure)	42
VII (low pressure)	390
VII (steel reflectors; low pressure)	186

Control-Rod Data

	Regulating control rod	Safety and compensation
Number of rods	2	4
Length of borated rods, cm/in.	45/17.7	45/17.7
Diameter of borated rod:		
ID, cm/in.	31.4/12.4	31.4/12.4
OD, cm/in.	43.5/17.1	43.5/17.1
B^{10}, kg/lb	0.1/0.22	1.0/2.2
B^{10} in boron, %	18.8	90
Total travel, cm/in.	45/17.7	45/17.7
Velocity:		
Raise, (cm/sec)/(in./min)	0.5/11.8	36.0/850
Lower, (cm/sec)/(in./min)	0.5/11.8	360.0/8500
Scram		0.4 sec for 90% of travel

Heat-Transport System Characteristics (Per Loop; Primary Sodium Loops)

Power, Mw(t)	10
Flow, (kg/hr)/(lb/hr)	225,000/496,000
Reactor inlet temperature, °C/°F	450/842
Reactor outlet temperature, °C/°F	540/1004
Na volume external to reactor, m^3/cu ft	5.4/190
Na volume in reactor, m^3/cu ft	10/353
Piping system:	
Material	316 or 321 SS
Inner diameter reactor to pump, cm/in.	30/11.8
Inner diameter pump to reactor, cm/in.	20/7.9
Maximum velocity in reactor, (m/sec)/(ft/sec)	1.95/6.4

hexagonal cross section. Each individual element consists of a number of sintered pellets of mixed uranium and plutonium oxide (25 wt. % PuO$_2$) contained in the stainless-steel tube. A spring arrangement maintains contact between the various pellets in the column, and provision is made in the upper region of the element to collect fission gases. Separation between pins is maintained by a wire spiral.

The ternary alloy under consideration as an alternate consists of 75 wt. % uranium, 15 wt. % plutonium, and 10 wt. % molybdenum. A double-cladding design prevents the formation of a plutonium—iron eutectic, and the space between layers is filled with sodium to assure heat transmission. The wire-spiral separation of pins is used in this case as well.

Both the upper and lower blanket sections consist of a cluster of seven large-diameter elements of depleted uranium. A lower base plate is provided to distribute the coolant. The lower end of the subassemblies, shaped in the form of a nozzle with an internal venturi section, reduces upward forces induced by the coolant flow and aids in positioning. The upper end of the subassembly is provided with a handling lug pierced with three holes for the sodium coolant outlet.

The radial-blanket subassemblies are similar to the fuel subassemblies, but they contain a continuous seven-rod internal structure of large-diameter depleted-uranium elements. Removable stainless-steel reflector subassemblies are available to provide flexibility of operation and fuel movement.

11.8.4 CONTROL RODS

A poison type control system is utilized which has four safety rods, each containing about 100 g of B^{10} in boron carbide. In addition, two regulating rods are provided, each containing about 100 g of B^{10}.

Each of the six rods located on the boundary between the core and the radial blanket in the high-pressure coolant zone moves in a hexa-

gonal guide tube similar to the hexagonal fuel-subassembly cans for a distance of 45 cm (17.7 in.). The rod boron carbide is enclosed in a cylindrical can, which is attached to a Stellite nozzle and handling head for the drive-shaft gripper. Control-rod drive mechanisms are located in six sections around the cover-plate equipment. Removal of the control rods is accomplished by means similar to those used for refueling a cask car.

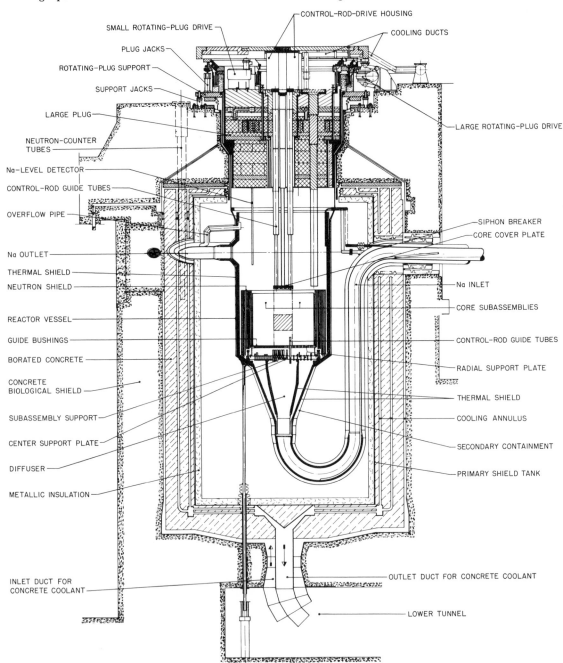

FIG. 11.65—Vertical cross section of Rapsodie reactor [71].

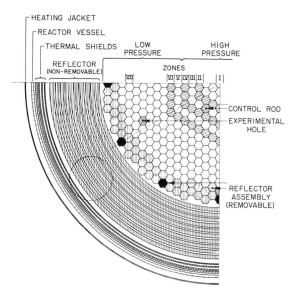

FIG. 11.66—Horizontal cross section of Rapsodie reactor [71].

11.8.5 HEAT-TRANSPORT SYSTEM

The primary coolant flow is shown in schematic form in Fig. 11.69. Sodium is used as the coolant in both the primary and secondary systems. In the first operational phase, heat rejection to air is planned for the secondary system, rather than a steam generator—turbogenerator installation.

Two coolant loops are provided, each designed for a 10-Mw(t) load, utilizing centrifugal pumps.

Sodium is pumped by a vertical centrifugal pump rated at 1540 gal/min (Fig. 11.70). Discharge from the pump tank enters the lower section of the reactor vessel and then flows to the flow divider—diffuser assembly shown in Fig. 4.45 of Chap. 4. The flow baffle separates the coolant into a high-pressure zone, providing a coolant for the core and inner radial blanket, and a low-pressure zone for the outer radial blanket. There is a possibility that the diffuser assembly has been eliminated in the late stages of design. The diffuser assembly provides a noncritical geometry for the collection of fuel in the event of a melt-down accident. The coolant passes from the reactor outlet to the intermediate heat exchanger shown in Fig. 4.84 of Chap. 4. Primary sodium circulates through the shell of this vertical stainless-steel tube exchanger, and secondary sodium circulates through the tubes. In the design the upper tube sheet is fixed, and the lower tube sheet is floating to permit thermal expansion of the tube bundle. The tubes themselves are located in 12 concentric sections.

As in the case of other sodium-cooled reactors, the thermal-transport system is provided with auxiliary components and equipment, i. e., necessary expansion tanks, purification loops, and a variety of instrumentation, as described in Chap. 4.

11.8.6 SHIELDING, STRUCTURES, AND COMPONENTS

Within the reactor vessel both the removable and nonremovable reflector regions tend to reduce

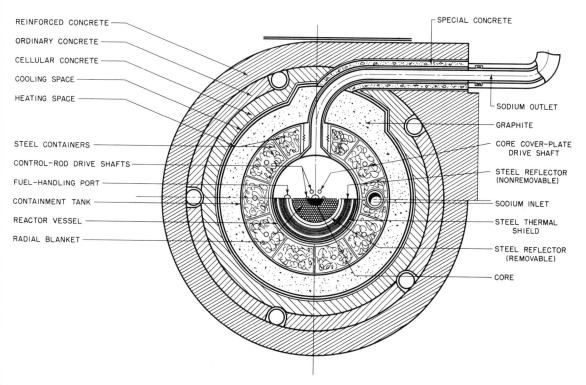

FIG. 11.67—Horizontal cross section of Rapsodie reactor and shield [71].

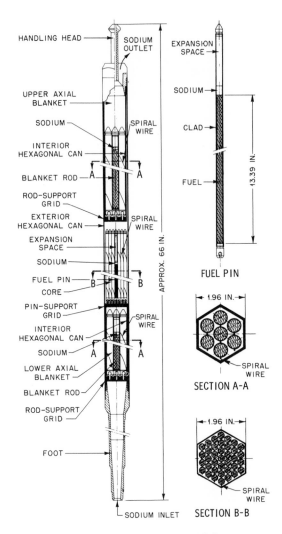

FIG. 11.68—Rapsodie fuel subassembly [71].

Illustrated in Fig. 11.67 are steel containers filled with thermal insulation or steel plates located between the reactor vessel itself and a cylindrical containment tank to prevent heat transfer by radiation. The tank acts as a second barrier in the event of vessel rupture. The containment tank is of plain carbon steel 15 mm (0.6 in.) thick. Additional containment is provided by a radial biological shield consisting of a 600-mm (23.5-in.) thickness of borated graphite (3% boron) which will be maintained at a minimum temperature of 220°C (428°F) by cooling gas.

Additional shielding includes a 400-mm-thick (16-in.) wall of cellular concrete which protects the columns supporting the rotating plugs. Also included is a 400-mm (16-in.) thickness of ordinary concrete, and, finally, a 650-mm (25.6-in.) thickness of heavily reinforced concrete maintained below 50°C (140°F). Thermal insulation is provided between the inner graphite and cellular concrete. A fixed plug is located between the containment tank and the reactor vessel shown in Fig. 11.65. Internal to the reactor vessel are two rotating plugs, a large concentric rotating plug and a small eccentric rotating plug. Penetrations through the rotating plugs are (1) a fuel-handling port, (2) control-rod drive-shaft ports, (3) core cover-plate drive-shaft ports, (4) two ports for introducing experimental apparatus (experimental ports), and (5) two ports for liquid-level indicators. Two sets of ball bearings are used for rotating the plugs. Two liquid-metal seals of tin—bismuth provide a gastight seal between the exterior atmosphere and the reactor cover gas. Details of the plug construction are shown in Fig. 4.46 of Chap. 4.

Provision is made in the design for a number of mechanical handling operations, i. e., the removal of fuel subassemblies, control rods, and their guide tubes, and the introduction of such items. A handling port located in the small eccentric rotating plug provides access for a gripper arrangement attached to a cask car (see Fig. 7.65, Chap. 7) which may reach any subassembly in the reactor. The cask car includes provision for cooling two irradiated subassemblies.

Transfer of subassemblies and other equipment from the containment building is by means of a secondary handling system since the primary cask car is at all times within the building. A transfer compartment, shown in Fig. 11.71, is provided for the movement of such subassemblies from one cask car to the other. Various other facilities are provided for necessary fuel-handling operations.

A view of the outer containment building for the reactor is given in Fig. 11.72. The container is in the form of a cylinder, 82 ft in diameter and 144 ft high. About half the height is below grade. This building houses the reactor, the primary coolant loops, part of the secondary coolant system, and necessary fuel-handling and auxiliary components. The reactor installation also includes a conventional building, shown in Fig. 11.73, and a fuel-storage and component-maintenance building shown in Fig. 7.71 of Chap. 7. A heat-exchanger building, a gas-system component building, and an auxiliary-equipment building, as indicated in Fig. 11.64, complete the installation.

the neutron energy as well as attenuate the flux. The nonremovable portion of the reflector consists of 10 concentric cylindrical shields made of stainless steel, 24 mm (0.95 in.) thick, and separated by an 8-mm (0.32-in.) space. Outside this assembly is a thermal shield consisting of four concentric cylinders having thicknesses of 4 mm (0.16 in.), 7 mm (0.28 in.), 10 mm (0.39 in.), 10 mm (0.39 in.), respectively. The reactor vessel, shown in Fig. 11.65, of type 316 stainless steel, consists of a lower 12-mm-thick (0.47-in.) elliptical cylinder, a main 15-mm-thick (0.59-in.) plate section, and an upper section located between the fixed plug and a large rotating plug.

Preheating of the reactor vessel is made possible by a 4-mm-thick (0.16 in.) jacket which permits circulation of an inert gas at 150°C (302°F). This preheating prior to the introduction of sodium will minimize thermal shock as well as provide for the heating of sodium in the event of freezing.

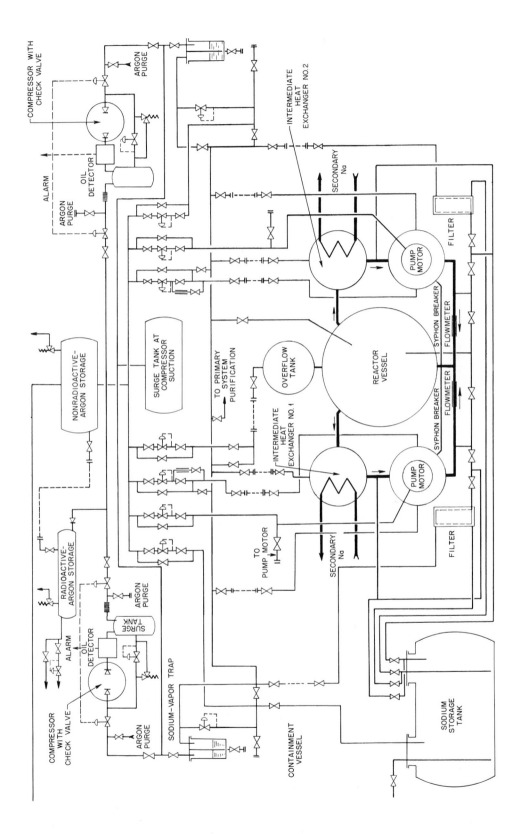

FIG. 11.69—Rapsodie primary and inert-gas system [71].

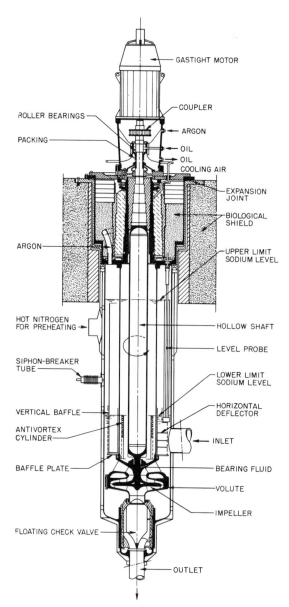

GASTIGHT MOTOR

COUPLER

ROLLER BEARINGS

ARGON

PACKING

OIL

OIL

COOLING AIR

EXPANSION JOINT

BIOLOGICAL SHIELD

ARGON

UPPER LIMIT SODIUM LEVEL

HOT NITROGEN FOR PREHEATING

HOLLOW SHAFT

LEVEL PROBE

SIPHON-BREAKER TUBE

LOWER LIMIT SODIUM LEVEL

HORIZONTAL DEFLECTOR

VERTICAL BAFFLE

ANTIVORTEX CYLINDER

INLET

BAFFLE PLATE

BEARING FLUID

VOLUTE

IMPELLER

FLOATING CHECK VALVE

OUTLET

FIG. 11.70—Rapsodie primary pump [71].

References

GENERAL

1. L. J. Koch and H. C. Paxton, Ann. Rev. Nucl. Sci., 9:437 (1959).
2. G. Fischer et al. (Eds.), Proceedings of the Conference on the Physics of Breeding, USAEC Report ANL-6122, Argonne National Laboratory, 1959.
3. Civilian Power Reactor Program. Part III. Book 1. Status Report on Fast Reactors as of 1959, USAEC Report TID-8518 (Bk-1), Superintendent of Documents, U. S. Government Printing Office, Washington, 1960.
4. Power Reactor Experiments, Vols. I and II, Proceedings of a Symposium, Vienna, October 1961, Proceedings Series, STI/PUB-51, International Atomic Energy Agency, Vienna, 1962.
5. F. G. Dawson (Comp.), Plutonium as a Power Reactor Fuel, USAEC Report HW-75007, (Proceedings of American Nuclear Society Topical Meeting, Richland, Washington, Sept. 13–14, 1962), General Electric Co., 1962.
6. Physics of Fast and Intermediate Reactors, Vol. III, Proceedings of a Seminar held in Vienna, Aug. 3–11, 1961, Proceedings Series, STI/PUB-49 (Vol. III), International Atomic Energy Agency, Vienna, 1962.

CLEMENTINE

7. E. T. Jurney et al. (Eds.), The Los Alamos Fast Plutonium Reactor, USAEC Report TID-10048, Los Alamos Scientific Laboratory, May 1954.
8. G. P. Arnold et al., Disassembly of the Los Alamos Fast Reactor, USAEC Report LA-1575, Los Alamos Scientific Laboratory, July 1953.

EBR-I

9. R. R. Smith et al., Instability Studies with EBR-I, Mark-III, USAEC Report ANL-6266, Argonne National Laboratory, December 1960.
10. R. R. Smith et al., A Mechanism Explaining the Instability of EBR-I, Mark-III, USAEC Report ANL-6354, Argonne National Laboratory, September 1961.
11. R. E. Rice et al., EBR-I, Mark-III –Design Report, USAEC Report ANL-5836, Argonne National Laboratory, March 1958.
12. Experimental Power and Test Reactors, A Technical and Pictorial Summary, USAEC Report TID-4562, November 1956.
13. S. Lawroski et al., Reactor Development Program Progress Report, USAEC Report ANL-6233, Argonne National Laboratory, October 1960.
14. S. Lawroski et al., Reactor Development Program Progress Report, USAEC Report ANL-6269, Argonne National Laboratory, 1960.
15. S. Lawroski et al., Reactor Development Program Progress Report, USAEC Report ANL-6328, Argonne National Laboratory, February 1961.
16. S. Lawroski et al., Reactor Development Program Progress Report, USAEC Report ANL-6343, Argonne National Laboratory, March 1961.
17. S. Lawroski et al., Reactor Development Program Progress Report, USAEC Report ANL-6355, Argonne National Laboratory, April 1961.
18. S. Lawroski et al., Reactor Development Progress Report, USAEC Report ANL-6433, Argonne National Laboratory, September 1961.
19. H. V. Lichtenberger et al., Operating Experience and Experimental Results Obtained from a NaK-cooled Fast Reactor, in Proceedings of the First United Nations International Conference on The Peaceful Uses of Atomic Energy, Geneva, 1955, Vol. 3, pp. 345–360, United Nations, New York, 1956.
20. EBR-I Operating Experience, Nucl. Safety, 3(2):68–71 (December 1961).
21. M. Grotenhuis, EBR-I Shield Design-Notes, International School of Nuclear Science and Engineering, Argonne National Laboratory, 1961.
22. R. O. Haroldsen et al., Safety Analysis Report, EBR-I, Mark-IV, USAEC Report ANL-6411, Argonne National Laboratory, February 1963.

BR-5

23. R. R. Matthews, Soviet Fast Reactor—BR-5, Nucl. Eng., 4(41):359–360 (October 1959) and Fast Reactors: A Soviet Outlook, Nucl. Eng., 7(71): 137–141 (April 1962).
24. A. I. Leipunsky et al., Experimental Fast Reactors in the Soviet Union, in Proceedings of the Second United Nations International Conference on the Peaceful Uses of Atomic Energy, Geneva, 1958, Vol. 9, p. 348, United Nations, New York, 1959.
25. A. I. Leipunsky et al., Experimental Fast Reactors in the Soviet Union, in Physics of Fast and Intermediate Reactors, Vol. III, Proceedings of a Seminar held in Vienna Aug. 3–11, 1961, Proceedings Series, STI/PUB-49 (Vol. III), International Atomic Energy Agency, Vienna, 1962.
26. M. C. Pinchasik et al., Operating Experience with the BR-5 Reactor, in Power Reactor Experiments, Vol. I, Proceedings of a Symposium, Vienna, Oct. 23–27, 1961, p. 375, Proceedings Series, STI/PUB-51, International Atomic Energy Agency, Vienna, 1962.

LAMPRE-I

27. H. G. Barkman et al., Los Alamos Molten Plutonium Reactor Experiment, LAMPRE Hazard Report, USAEC Report LA-2327, Los Alamos Scientific Laboratory, June 1959.
28. S. Glasstone (Ed.), Quarterly Status Report on LAMPRE Program for Period Ending May 20, 1960, USAEC Report LAMS-2438, Los Alamos Scientific Laboratory, June 1960.

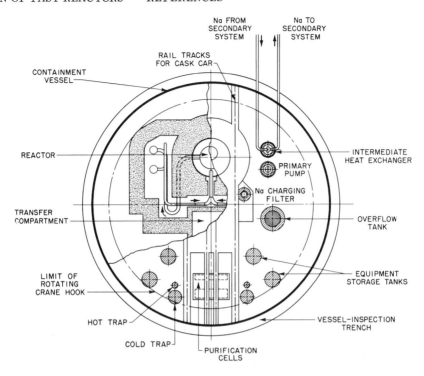

FIG. 11.71—Plan view Rapsodie reactor building [71].

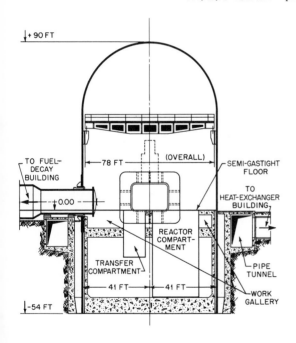

FIG. 11.72—Rapsodie reactor containment building, vertical view [71].

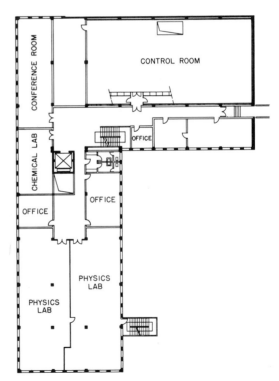

FIG. 11.73—Rapsodie conventional building (control room, offices, and laboratories) plan view first floor [71].

29. S. Glasstone (Ed.), Quarterly Status Report on LAMPRE Program for Period Ending August 20, 1960, USAEC Report LAMS-2462, Los Alamos Scientific Laboratory, September 1960.
30. Staff, Quarterly Status Report on LAMPRE Program for Period Ending November 20, 1960, USAEC Report LAMS-2487, Los Alamos Scientific Laboratory, December 1960.
31. Staff, Quarterly Status Report on LAMPRE Program for Period Ending February 20, 1961, USAEC Report LAMS-2531, Los Alamos Scientific Laboratory, March 1961.
32. Staff, Quarterly Status Report on LAMPRE Program for Period Ending May 20, 1961, USAEC Report LAMS-2564, Los Alamos Scientific Laboratory, June 1961.

33. Staff, Quarterly Status Report on LAMPRE Program for Period Ending August 20, 1961, USAEC Report LAMS–2620, Los Alamos Scientific Laboratory, September 1961.
34. Staff, Quarterly Status Report on LAMPRE Program for Period Ending November 20, 1961, USAEC Report LAMS–2647, Los Alamos Scientific Laboratory, December 1961.
35. B. M. Carmichael and G. L. Ragan, The Startup of the First Molten Plutonium Reactor, Trans. Am. Nucl. Soc., 4(2):364 (November 1961).
36. B. M. Carmichael and G. L. Ragan, Some Effects Peculiar to the Liquid Metal Fuel of LAMPRE–I, Trans. Am. Nucl. Soc., 4(2):365 (November 1961).
37. Staff, Quarterly Status Report on LAMPRE Program for Period Ending May 20, 1962, USAEC Report LAMS–2681, Los Alamos Scientific Laboratory, March 1962.
38. Staff, Quarterly Status Report on LAMPRE Program for Period Ending May 20, 1962, USAEC Report LAMS–2720, Los Alamos Scientific Laboratory, June 1962.
39. LAMPRE–I Final Design Status Report, USAEC Report LA–2833, Los Alamos Scientific Laboratory, January 1962.

DOUNREAY

40. H. Cartwright et al., The Dounreay Fast Reactor–Basic Problems in Design, in Proceedings of The Second United Nations International Conference on the Peaceful Uses of Atomic Energy, Geneva, 1958, Vol. 9, p. 316, United Nations, New York, 1959.
41. Proceedings of the Symposium on the Dounreay Fast Reactor, London, Dec. 7 1960, arranged by The Institution of Mechanical Engineers under the aegis of the British Nuclear Energy Conference, Institution of Mechanical Engineers, London, 1961.
42. J. Allen, Coolant Clean-up in DFR, Nuclear Engineering, 7(76):352 September 1962.
43. D. C. G. Smith and K. W. Brindley, Physics Experience on DFR, Nuclear Engineering, 7(76):347 (September 1962).
44. J. L. Phillips, Operating Experience with the Dounreay Fast Reactor–1, Nuclear Power, 7(75):46–52 (July 1962).
45. J. L. Phillips, Operating Experience with the Dounreay Fast Reactor–2, Nuclear Power, 7(76):50–54 (August 1962).

EBR–II
(Also see Refs. 13 through 18)

46. L. J. Koch et al., Experimental Breeder Reactor II (EBR–II) Hazard Summary Report, USAEC Report ANL–5719, 1957, and Addendum to Hazard Summary Report Experimental Breeder Reactor–II (EBR–II), USAEC Report ANL–5719 (Add.), Argonne National Laboratory, 1964.
47. J. R. Dietrich and W. H. Zinn, Solid Fuel Reactors, Addison-Wesley Publishing Company, Inc., Cambridge, Mass., 1958.
48. Power Reactor Technology, 4(4):84 (September 1961).
49. M. Grotenhuis, A. E. McArthy, and A. D. Rossin, Experimental Breeder Reactor–II (EBR–II) Shield Design, USAEC Report ANL–6614, Argonne National Laboratory, September 1962.
50. W. B. Lowenstein, The Physics Design of EBR–II, in Physics of Fast and Intermediate Reactors, Vol. III, Proceedings of a Seminar held in Vienna, Aug. 3–11, 1961, Proceedings Series, STI/PUB–49 (Vol. III), International Atomic Energy Agency, Vienna, 1962.

EBR–II PROCESSING

51. Pyrometallurgical Fuel Processing, all references found in the journals, Reactor Fuel Processing, A Quarterly Technical Progress Review, 3(1):25 (January 1960); 3(2):27 (April 1960); 3(3):24 (July 1960); 4(1):25 (January 1961); 4(2):38 (April 1961); 4(3):30 (July 1961); 4(4):37 (October 1961); 5(1):38 (January 1962); 5(2):27–33 (April 1962).
52. L. Burris et al., Recent Advances in Pyrometallurgical Process, Trans. Am. Nucl. Soc., 4(2):192 (November 1961).
53. V. G. Trice and N. R. Chellew, The Melt Refining of Irradiated Uranium: Application to EBR–II Fast Reactor. VI. The Behavior

of Plutonium in the Melt-Refining Process, Nucl. Sci. Eng., 9(1):55 (January 1961).
54. A. Schneider and N. R. Chellew, The Melt Refining of Irradiated Uranium: Application to EBR–II Fast Reactor Fuel. IX. The Evolution of Xenon and Krypton, Nucl. Sci. Eng., 9(1):59 (January 1961).
55. N. R. Chellew, G. A. Bennett, and V. G. Trice, The Melt Refining of Irradiated Uranium: Application to EBR–II Fast Reactor Fuel. VIII. The Behavior of Rare Earths, Yttrium, Barium, Strontium, and Cesium, Nucl. Sci. Eng., 9(1):64 (January 1961).
56. J. Wolkoff and A. A. Chilenskas, The Melt Refining of Irradiated Uranium: Application to EBR–II Fast Reactor Fuel. XI. Sorption and Retention of Sodium and Cesium Vapor on Stationary Beds at Elevated Temperature, Nucl. Sci. Eng., 9(1):71 (January 1961).
57. N. R. Chellew and V. G. Trice, The Melt Refining of Irradiated Uranium: Application to EBR–II Fast Reactor Fuel. X. The Behavior of Zirconium, Nucl. Sci. Eng., 9(1):78 (January 1961).
58. N. R. Chellew and M. Ader, The Melt Refining of Irradiated Uranium: Application to EBR–II Fast Reactor Fuel. XI. Behavior of Iodine in Melt Refining, Nucl. Sci. Eng., 9(1):82 (January 1961).
59. N. R. Chellew and G. A. Bennett, The Melt Refining of Irradiated Uranium: Application to EBR–II Fast Reactor Fuel. XII. The Behavior of Ruthenium, Molybdenum, Palladium, Technetium, Antimony, Cadmium, Rhodium, and Tellurium, Nucl. Sci. Eng., 9(1):87 (January 1961).
60. L. Burris et al., The Melt Refining of Irradiated Uranium: Application to EBR–II Fast Reactor Fuel. I. Introduction, Nucl. Sci. Eng., 6(6):493 (December 1959).
61. G. J. Bernstein et al., The Melt Refining of Irradiated Uranium: Application to EBR–II Fast Reactor Fuel. II. Experimental Furnaces, Nucl. Sci. Eng., 6(6):496 (December 1959).
62. D. C. Hampton et al., The Melt Refining of Irradiated Uranium: Application to EBR–II Fast Reactor Fuel. III. Preparation of Experimental Alloys, Nucl. Sci. Eng., 6(6):501 (December 1959).
63. C. L. Rosen et al., The Melt Refining of Irradiated Uranium: Application to EBR–II Fast Reactor Fuel. IV. Interraction of Uranium and Its Alloys with Refractory Oxides, Nucl. Sci. Eng., 6(6):504 (December 1959).
64. G. A. Bennet et al., The Melt Refining of Irradiated Uranium: Application to EBR–II Fast Reactor Fuel. V. Yield of Fissionable Material Upon Pouring, Nucl. Sci. Eng., 6(6):511 (December 1959).
65. M. Gazith, Literature Survey in Pyrometallurgical Purification of Metals, Israel Atomic Energy Commission, Israeli Report LS–93, January 1961.

FERMI

66. Enrico Fermi Atomic Power Plant Technical Information and Hazards Summary Report, Power Development Company, Vols. 1, 2, and 3, October 1962.
67. Enrico Fermi Atomic Power Plant, USAEC Report APDA-124, Atomic Power Development Associates, January 1959.
68. A. Amorosi and J. G. Yevick, An Appraisal of the Enrico Fermi Reactor, in Proceedings of the Second United Nations International Conference on the Peaceful Uses of Atomic Energy, Geneva, 1958, Vol. 9, p. 358, United Nations, New York, 1959.
69. J. R. Dietrich and W. H. Zinn, Solid Fuel Reactors, Addison-Wesley Publishing Company, Inc., Cambridge, Mass., 1958.
70. R. H. Costello et al., APDA Reactor Components Test, Report APDA-147, November 1962.

RAPSODIE

71. C. P. Zaleski and L. Vautrey, Le Reacteur Rapide Surregenerateur, Vols. 1 and 2, Commissariat a l'Energie Atomique, France, Oct. 23, 1961.
72. F. Sebilleau and C. P. Zaleski, Plutonium as a Fuel for the Fast Reactor Rapsodie, Paper 15 in Plutonium as a Power Reactor Fuel, USAEC Report HW-75007 (Proceedings of American Nuclear Society Topical Meeting, Richland, Washington, Sept. 13–14, 1962), General Electric Co., 1962.

Index